MATHEMATICS:

APPLICATIONS AND INTERPRETATION

 ENHANCED ONLINE

HIGHER LEVEL
COURSE COMPANION

Paul Belcher
Jennifer Chang Wathall
Suzanne Doering
Phil Duxbury
Panayiotis Economopoulos
Jane Forrest

Peter Gray
Tony Halsey
David Harris
Lorraine Heinrichs
Ed Kemp
Paul La Rondie

Palmira Mariz Seiler
Michael Ortman
Nuriye Sirinoglu Singh
Nadia Stoyanova Kennedy
Paula Waldman

OXFORD
UNIVERSITY PRESS

OXFORD
UNIVERSITY PRESS

Great Clarendon Street, Oxford, OX2 6DP, United Kingdom

Oxford University Press is a department of the University of Oxford. It furthers the University's objective of excellence in research, scholarship, and education by publishing worldwide. Oxford is a registered trade mark of Oxford University Press in the UK and in certain other countries

British Library Cataloguing in Publication Data

Data available

978-0-19-842705-6

3 5 7 9 10 8 6 4

Paper used in the production of this book is a natural, recyclable product made from wood grown in sustainable forests. The manufacturing process conforms to the environmental regulations of the country of origin.

Printed in Italy by L.E.G.O.SpA

Acknowledgements

The author would like to thank the following authors for contributions to digital resources:

Paul Belcher	David Harris
Ingrid Delange	Georgios Ioannadis
Suzanne Doering	Blas Kolic
Ben Donaldson	Julija Markeviciute
Panayiotis Economopoulos	Vilda Markeviciute
Tom Edinburgh	Martin Noon
Jim Fensom	Dane Rogers
Jane Forrest	Daniel Wilson-Nunn
Peter Gray	Tom Wolstenholme
Tony Halsey	

The publisher and authors would like to thank the following for permission to use photographs and other copyright material:

Cover image: iStock
p650: ARUN SANKAR/AFP/Getty Images.
All other photos by Shutterstock.

Course Companion definition

The IB Diploma Programme Course Companions are designed to support students throughout their two-year Diploma Programme. They will help students gain an understanding of what is expected from their subject studies while presenting content in a way that illustrates the purpose and aims of the IB. They reflect the philosophy and approach of the IB and encourage a deep understanding of each subject by making connections to wider issues and providing opportunities for critical thinking.

The books mirror the IB philosophy of viewing the curriculum in terms of a whole-course approach and include support for international mindedness, the IB learner profile and the IB Diploma Programme core requirements, theory of knowledge, the extended essay and creativity, activity, service (CAS).

IB mission statement

The International Baccalaureate aims to develop inquiring, knowledgable and caring young people who help to create a better and more peaceful world through intercultural understanding and respect.

To this end the IB works with schools, governments and international organisations to develop challenging programmes of international education and rigorous assessment.

These programmes encourage students across the world to become active, compassionate, and lifelong learners who understand that other people, with their differences, can also be right.

The IB learner profile

The aim of all IB programmes is to develop internationally minded people who, recognising their common humanity and shared guardianship of the planet, help to create a better and more peaceful world. IB learners strive to be:

Inquirers They develop their natural curiosity. They acquire the skills necessary to conduct inquiry and research and show independence in learning. They actively enjoy learning and this love of learning will be sustained throughout their lives.

Knowledgeable They explore concepts, ideas, and issues that have local and global significance. In so doing, they acquire in-depth knowledge and develop understanding across a broad and balanced range of disciplines.

Thinkers They exercise initiative in applying thinking skills critically and creatively to recognise and approach complex problems, and make reasoned, ethical decisions.

Communicators They understand and express ideas and information confidently and creatively in more than one language and in a variety of modes of communication. They work effectively and willingly in collaboration with others.

Principled They act with integrity and honesty, with a strong sense of fairness, justice, and respect for the dignity of the individual, groups, and communities. They take responsibility for their own actions and the consequences that accompany them.

Open-minded They understand and appreciate their own cultures and personal histories, and are open to the perspectives, values, and traditions of other individuals and communities. They are accustomed to seeking and evaluating a range of points of view, and are willing to grow from the experience.

Caring They show empathy, compassion, and respect towards the needs and feelings of others. They have a personal commitment to service, and act to make a positive difference to the lives of others and to the environment.

Risk-takers They approach unfamiliar situations and uncertainty with courage and forethought, and have the independence of spirit to explore new roles, ideas, and strategies. They are brave and articulate in defending their beliefs.

Balanced They understand the importance of intellectual, physical, and emotional balance to achieve personal well-being for themselves and others.

Reflective They give thoughtful consideration to their own learning and experience. They are able to assess and understand their strengths and limitations in order to support their learning and professional development.

Contents

Number and algebra

Functions

Geometry and trigonometry

Statistics and probability

Calculus

Exploration

Digital contents

Digital content overview

Click on this icon here to see a list of all the digital resources in your enhanced online course book. To learn more about the different digital resource types included in each of the chapters and how to get the most out of your enhanced online course book, go to page ix.

Syllabus coverage

This book covers all the content of the Mathematics: applications and interpretation HL course. Click on this icon here for a document showing you the syllabus statements covered in each chapter.

Practice exam papers

Click on this icon here for an additional set of practice exam papers.

Worked solutions

Click on this icon here for worked solutions for all the questions in the book.

Introduction

The new IB diploma mathematics courses have been designed to support the evolution in mathematics pedagogy and encourage teachers to develop students' conceptual understanding using the content and skills of mathematics, in order to promote deep learning. The new syllabus provides suggestions of conceptual understandings for teachers to use when designing unit plans and overall, the goal is to foster more depth, as opposed to breadth, of understanding of mathematics.

What is teaching for conceptual understanding in mathematics?

Traditional mathematics learning has often focused on rote memorization of facts and algorithms, with little attention paid to understanding the underlying concepts in mathematics. As a consequence, many learners have not been exposed to the beauty and creativity of mathematics which, inherently, is a network of interconnected conceptual relationships.

Teaching for conceptual understanding is a framework for learning mathematics that frames the factual content and skills; lower order thinking, with disciplinary and non-disciplinary concepts and statements of conceptual understanding promoting higher order thinking. Concepts represent powerful, organizing ideas that are not locked in a particular place, time or situation. In this model, the development of intellect is achieved by creating a synergy between the factual, lower levels of thinking and the conceptual higher levels of thinking. Facts and skills are used as a foundation to build deep conceptual understanding through inquiry.

The IB Approaches to Teaching and Learning (ATLs) include teaching focused on conceptual understanding and using inquiry-based approaches. These books provide a structured inquiry-based approach in which learners can develop an understanding of the purpose of what they are learning by asking the questions: why or how? Due to this sense of purpose, which is always situated within a context, research shows that learners are more motivated and supported to construct their own conceptual understandings and develop higher levels of thinking as they relate facts, skills and topics.

The DP mathematics courses identify twelve possible fundamental concepts which relate to the five mathematical topic areas, and that teachers can use to develop connections across the mathematics and wider curriculum:

Approximation	Modelling	Representation
Change	Patterns	Space
Equivalence	Quantity	Systems
Generalization	Relationships	Validity

Each chapter explores two of these concepts, which are reflected in the chapter titles and also listed at the start of the chapter.

The DP syllabus states the essential understandings for each topic, and suggests some concept-specific conceptual understandings relevant to the topic content. For this series of books, we have identified important topical understandings that link to these and underpin the syllabus, and created investigations that enable students to develop this understanding. These investigations, which are a key element of every chapter, include factual and conceptual questions to prompt students to develop and articulate these topical conceptual understandings for themselves.

A tenet of teaching for conceptual understanding in mathematics is that the teacher does not **tell** the student what the topical understandings are at any stage of the learning process, but provides investigations that guide students to discover these for themselves. The teacher notes on the ebook provide additional support for teachers new to this approach.

A concept-based mathematics framework gives students opportunities to think more deeply and critically, and develop skills necessary for the 21st century and future success.

Jennifer Chang Wathall

Investigation 1

A   Measuring a potato

1   Make a list of all the physical properties of a potato. Which of these properties can you measure? How could you measure them? Are there any properties that you cannot measure? How do we determine what we can measure?

2   **Factual**   What does it mean to measure a property of an object? How do we measure?

3   **Factual**   Which properties of an object can we measure?

4   **Conceptual**   Why do we use measurements and how do we use measuring to define properties of an object?

In every chapter, investigations provide inquiry activities and factual and conceptual questions that enable students to construct and communicate their own conceptual understanding in their own words. The key to concept-based teaching and learning, the investigations allow students to develop a deep conceptual understanding. Each investigation has full supporting teacher notes on the enhanced online course book.

Gives students the opportunity to reflect on what they have learned and deepen their understanding.

Reflect   Why might extrapolation be risky?

Developing inquiry skills

Apply what you have learned in this section to represent the first opening problem with a tree diagram.

Hence find the probability that a cab is **identified** as yellow.

Apply the formula for conditional probability to find the probability that the cab was yellow **given that** it was identified as yellow.

How does your answer compare to your original subjective judgment?

Every chapter starts with a question that students can begin to think about from the start, and answer more fully as the chapter progresses. The developing inquiry skills boxes prompt them to think of their own inquiry topics and use the mathematics they are learning to investigate them further.

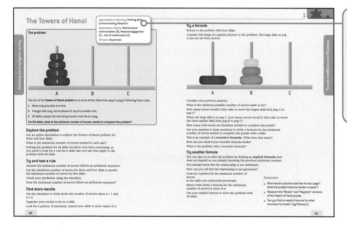

The modelling and investigation activities are open-ended activities that use mathematics in a range of engaging contexts and to develop students' mathematical toolkit and build the skills they need for the IA. They appear at the end of each chapter.

The chapters in this book have been written to provide logical progression through the content, but you may prefer to use them in a different order, to match your own scheme of work. The Mathematics: applications and interpretation Standard and Higher Level books follow a similar chapter order, to make teaching easier when you have SL and HL students in the same class. Moreover, where possible, SL and HL chapters start with the same inquiry questions, contain similar investigations and share some questions in the chapter reviews and mixed reviews — just as the HL exams will include some of the same questions as the SL paper.

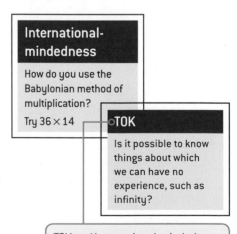

International-mindedness

How do you use the Babylonian method of multiplication?

Try 36×14

TOK

Is it possible to know things about which we can have no experience, such as infinity?

TOK and International-mindedness are integrated into all the chapters.

How to use your enhanced online course book

Throughout the book you will find the following icons. By clicking on these in your enhanced online course book you can access the associated activity or document.

 Prior learning

Clicking on the icon next to the "Before you start" section in each chapter takes you to one or more worksheets containing short explanations, examples and practice exercises on topics that you should know before starting, or links to other chapters in the book to revise the prior learning you need.

 Additional exercises

The icon by the last exercise at the end of each section of a chapter takes you to additional exercises for more practice, with questions at the same difficulty levels as those in the book.

 Animated worked examples

This icon leads you to an animated worked example, explaining how the solution is derived step-by-step, while also pointing out common errors and how to avoid them.

> Click on the icon on the page to launch the animation. The animated worked example will appear in a second screen.

> Click here for a transcript of the audio track.

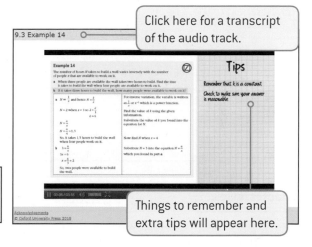

> Things to remember and extra tips will appear here.

Example 14

The distance, d metres, that a rock falls varies directly with the square of the time taken, t seconds.

a If the rock falls 6 metres in 2 seconds, write an equation for d in terms of t.

b Find the distance the rock has fallen after 5 seconds.

 Graphical display calculator support

Supporting you to make the most of your TI-Nspire CX, TI-84+ C Silver Edition or Casio fx-CG50 graphical display calculator (GDC), this icon takes you to step-by-step instructions for using technology to solve specific examples in the book.

> Click on the icon for the menu and then select your GDC model.

 **Data sets**

Access a spreadsheet containing a data set relevant to the text associated with this icon.

 Teacher notes

This icon appears at the beginning of each chapter and opens a set of comprehensive teaching notes for the investigations, reflection questions, TOK items, and the modelling and investigation activities in the chapter.

Assessment opportunities

This Mathematics: applications and interpretation enhanced online course book is designed to prepare you for your assessments by giving you a wide range of practice. In addition to the activities you will find in this book, further practice and support are available on the enhanced online course book.

End of chapter tests and mixed review exercises

This icon appears twice in each chapter: first, next to the "Chapter summary" section and then next to the "Chapter review" heading.

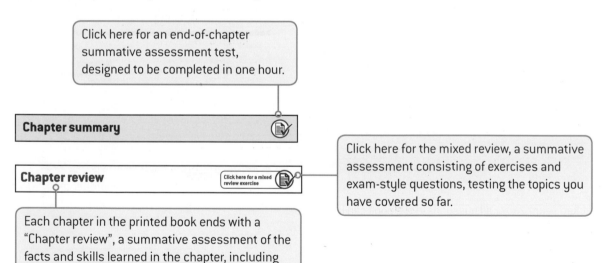

Click here for an end-of-chapter summative assessment test, designed to be completed in one hour.

Chapter summary

Chapter review   Click here for a mixed review exercise

Click here for the mixed review, a summative assessment consisting of exercises and exam-style questions, testing the topics you have covered so far.

Each chapter in the printed book ends with a "Chapter review", a summative assessment of the facts and skills learned in the chapter, including problem-solving and exam-style questions.

Exam-style questions

Exam-style questions

21 P1: a Find the binomial expansion of $\left(1 - \dfrac{x}{4}\right)^3$ in ascending powers of x.

(3 marks)

Plenty of exam practice questions, in Paper 1 (P1) or Paper 2 (P2) style. Each question in this section has a mark scheme in the worked solutions document found on the enhanced online course book, which will help you see how marks are awarded.

The number of darker bars shows the difficulty of the question (one dark bar = easy; three dark bars = difficult).

Click here for further exam practice

Exam practice exercises provide exam style questions for Papers 1, 2, and 3 on topics from all the preceding chapters. Click on the icon for the exam practice found at the end of chapters 3, 7, 11, and 15 in this book.

Introduction to Paper 3

The new HL exams will have three papers, and Paper 3 will have just two extended response problem-solving questions. This introduction, on page 136, explains the new Paper 3 format, and gives an example of a Paper 3 question, with notes and guidance on how to interpret and answer it.

There are more Paper 3 questions in the exam practice exercises on the Enhanced Online Course Book, at the end of Chapters 3, 7, 11, and 15.

Answers and worked solutions

Answers to the book questions

Concise answer to all the questions in this book can be found on page 765.

Worked solutions

Worked solutions for **all** questions in the book can be accessed by clicking the icon found on the Contents page or the first page of the Answers section.

Answers and worked solutions for the digital resources

Answers, worked solutions and mark schemes (where applicable) for the additional exercises, end-of-chapter tests and mixed reviews are included with the questions themselves.

1 Measuring space: accuracy and geometry

In this chapter you will approximate and calculate measures of angles, distances, areas and volumes in two and three dimensions. You will determine how these tools are used in astronomy to measure the distance to nearby stars, in cartography to measure distances between landmarks, and in navigation to determine the course of ships and aircrafts. In addition, you will explore other applications in surveying, architecture, disaster assessment and biology.

Concepts
- Space
- Quantity

Microconcepts
- Rounding
- Percentage error
- Standard form
- Operations with rational exponents
- Right triangles: Sine, cosine, tangent ratios
- Angles of elevation and depression
- Bearings
- Non-right triangles: Sine rule and cosine rule
- Circles: Length of arc, area of sector
- Volume and surface area of 3D figures
- Angle between line and plane

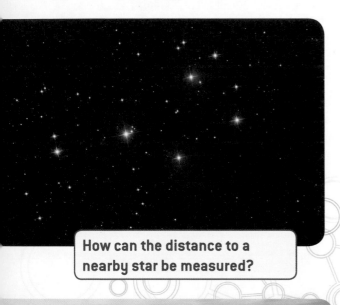

How can the distance to a nearby star be measured?

How does a sailor calculate the distance to the coast?

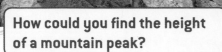

How could you find the height of a mountain peak?

How would you decide which shape and size make a cell more efficient in passing materials in and out of its membrane?

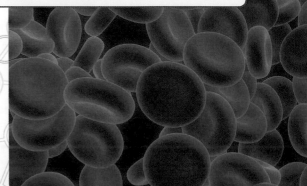

In 1856 The Great Trigonometric Survey of India measured the height of Mount Everest, known in Napali as Sagarmatha and in Tibetan as Chomolungma. The surveyors measured the distance between two points at sea level and then measured the angles between the top of the mountain and each point.

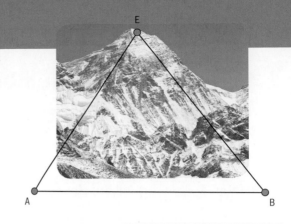

The summit of Mount Everest is labeled E, the two points A and B are roughly at sea level and are 33 km apart.

If $\hat{E} = 90°$, what would be the maximum possible height of Mount Everest?

Think about and then **write down** your own intuitive answer to each question. **Discuss** your answer with a friend then **share** your ideas with your class.

- Why do you think it took so long to determine the elevation of Mount Everest?
- Why do you think surveyors prefer to measure angles, but not lengths of sides?
- What assumptions are made?

Developing inquiry skills

Write down any similar inquiry questions you might ask if you were asked to find the height of tree, the distance between two towns or the distance between two stars.

What questions might you need to ask in these scenarios which differ from the scenario where you are estimating the height of Mount Everest?

Think about the questions in this opening problem and answer any you can. As you work through the chapter, you will gain mathematical knowledge and skills that will help you to answer them all.

Before you start

Click here for help with this skills check

You should know how to:

1 Round to significant figures and decimal places.
eg Write the number 80.426579 to:
  a 2 decimal places
  b 3 significant figures.
  a 80.43 **b** 80.4

2 Evaluate integer and rational exponents.
eg $3^{-4} = \dfrac{1}{3^4} = \dfrac{1}{81}$, $16^{\frac{1}{2}} = \sqrt{16} = 4$

3 Use properties of triangles, including Pythagoras' theorem.

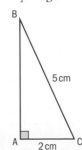

eg Find the length of AB in this triangle.
$AB^2 = BC^2 - AC^2$
$AB^2 = 5^2 - 2^2$
$AB^2 = 21$
$AB = \sqrt{21} = 4.58$ cm (3 s.f.)

Skills check

1 Write down each number rounded to:
  a 2 decimal places
  b 3 significant figures.
  i 0.6942 **ii** 28.706
  iii 77.984561

2 Evaluate
  a 2^{-3} **b** $27^{\frac{1}{3}}$

3 In each of these right triangles, find the length of side x.

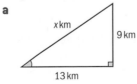

a [triangle with x km, 9 km, 13 km]
b [triangle with 7 km, x km, 5 km]

1.1 Representing numbers exactly and approximately

In mathematics and in everyday life, we frequently encounter numbers that have been measured or estimated. In this section you will investigate how we can quantify uncertainty in the numbers and calculations we use throughout this course.

Investigation 1

Margaret Hamilton worked for NASA as the lead developer for Apollo flight software. The photo here shows her in 1969, standing next to the books of navigation software code that she and her team produced for the Apollo mission that first sent humans to the Moon.

1 Estimate the height of the books of code stacked together, as shown in the image. What assumptions are you making?

2 Estimate the number of pages of code for the Apollo mission. How would you go about making this estimation? What assumptions are you making?

3 **Factual** What is an estimate? What is estimation? How would you go about estimating? How can comparing measures help you estimate?

4 **Conceptual** Why are estimations useful?

Recall that we can specify accuracy using **significant figures** (**digits**). The digits that can be determined accurately are called **significant figures**. Thus, a scale that could only register up to the hundredths of a gram mass until 99.99 g, could only measure up to 4 figures of accuracy (4 significant figures).

In your IA or on specific exam questions, you may need to choose an appropriate degree of accuracy. When performing operations on measurements, round answers to the same number of significant figures as the least accurate measurement. This is illustrated in the example below.

> **EXAM HINT**
>
> Write your final answers as exact values or rounded to at least 3 s.f., unless otherwise instructed. Round only your final answer and not any intermediate calculations.

Example 1

A component of an aircraft wing is being designed in the shape of a right triangle. One of the legs must measure 17 cm and the hypotenuse must measure 97.1 cm, as shown in the diagram.

a Find the height of the triangle, rounding your answer **to the given degree of accuracy**.

   i To 4 d.p. (decimal places)   ii To 2 s.f.

b Find the area of the material (in cm^2) necessary to manufacture the component to an appropriate degree of accuracy.

c Show that intermediate rounding to 2 s.f. leads to an inaccurate answer.

a i 95.6003 cm ii 96 cm	Use Pythagoras to find the height of the triangle: $\sqrt{97.1^2 - 17^2} = 95.60026151\ldots$ If the question did not specify a level of accuracy, we would round to 3 s.f.: 95.6 cm.
b $A = \frac{1}{2}bh = \frac{1}{2} \times 17 \times 95.60026151\ldots$ $= 812.602\ldots$ $= 810 \text{ cm}^2 \, (2 \text{ s.f.})$	Use the most accurate value (store or copy/paste with technology) when calculating. You could also write down your work as $A = \frac{1}{2} \times 17 \times 95.6$. Do not use this to calculate! Round area to 2 s.f. because the least accurate measurement, 17 cm, has 2 s.f.
c $A = \frac{1}{2} \times 17 \times 96 = 816$ $= 820 \text{ cm}^2 \, (2 \text{ s.f.})$ $\neq 810 \text{ cm}^2$	This shows why rounding intermediate answers should be avoided in all calculations.

Exercise 1A

1 A restaurant is remodelling and replacing its circular tables with square tables. They want the new tables to have the same area as the old ones. The circumference of the circular tables is measured to be 4.1 m. Find the side length of the new square tables

  i to an appropriate degree of accuracy

  ii to 3 s.f.

2 The heights of 10 koalas, measured to the nearest cm, are: 81, 73, 71, 80, 76, 84, 73, 88, 91, 75.

Find the mean (average) height of the koalas to an appropriate degree of accuracy.

Bounds and error

Suppose you find the weight of a bag of coffee as 541.5 g, accurate to the nearest 0.1 g. Then the exact weight w of the bag could be anywhere in the interval $541.45 \text{ g} \leq w < 541.55 \text{ g}$, as all of these values would round to 514.5 g.

If a measurement M is accurate to a particular unit u, then its exact value V lies in the interval
$$M - 0.5u \leq V < M + 0.5u$$
The endpoints of this interval are called the **lower** and **upper bounds**. Upper and lower bounds provide one way to quantify the **uncertainty** of a measurement when the exact value is unknown.

TOK

How does the perception of the language being used distort our understanding?

Example 2

A state park is created on a triangular area between roads. The triangular area is measured to have a base length of 3.1 km and corresponding height of 4.2 km. The measurement tool is accurate to the nearest tenth of a kilometre. Find the upper bound to the area of the park.

$3.1 + 0.05 = 3.15$ km $4.2 + 0.05 = 4.25$ km	The upper and lower bounds for the base length will be $3.1 - 0.05 \leq b < 3.1 + 0.05$ $3.05 \leq b < 3.15$ and for the height $4.2 - 0.05 \leq h < 4.2 + 0.05$ $4.15 \leq h < 4.25$
Area of park $< \dfrac{1}{2} \times 3.15 \times 4.25$ Area of park < 6.69 km² (3 s.f.)	Using the area of triangle and upper bounds. Area of a triangle $= \dfrac{1}{2} \times$ base $\times$ height

Since measurements are approximate there is always error in the measurement results. A measurement error is the difference between the exact value (V_E) and the approximate value (V_A), ie:

$$\text{Measurement error} = V_A - V_E$$

Investigation 2

Tomi and Massimo measured the length of a yardstick and the length of a foot and obtained 92.44 cm for the length of a yard and 31.48 cm for the length of a foot.

1   Given that the exact values of 1 yard is 91.44 cm and 1 foot is 30.48 cm, find the measurement error in the two measurements obtained by Tomi and Massimo.

Tomi thinks that the two measurements were equally inaccurate. Massimo thinks that one of the two measurements is more accurate than the other.

2   Who do you agree with: Tomi or Massimo? Explain why.

Massimo decides to find the magnitude of the error as a percentage of the measured length.

3 Write down the measuring error in the length of one yard as a fraction of the exact length of the yard. Give your answer as percentage.

4 Write down the measuring error in the length of one foot as a fraction of the exact length of one foot. Give your answer as percentage.

5 [Conceptual] In what ways is expressing measuring errors as a percentage of the measured length helpful?

6 [Conceptual] How can measurement errors be compared?

When the exact value of a quantity is known, the error of a measured (approximate) value can be found as a percentage of the exact value:

Percentage error formula

Percentage error $= \left| \dfrac{V_A - V_E}{V_E} \right| \times 100\%$, where V_A is the approximate

(or measurement) value and V_E is the exact value.

Example 3

The fraction $\dfrac{22}{7}$ is often used as an approximation of π.

a Find the percentage error of this approximation.

b Find the least accurate decimal approximation of π needed to approximate π within 0.001% of the true value.

a Percentage error $= \left\| \dfrac{\frac{22}{7} - \pi}{\pi} \right\| \times 100\%$ $= 0.0402\%$ (3 s.f.)	Note the absolute value creates a positive value.
b $\left\| \dfrac{V_A - \pi}{\pi} \right\| \leq 0.00001$	Translating 0.001% to a decimal
$-0.00001 \leq \dfrac{V_A - \pi}{\pi} \leq 0.00001$ $\pi - 0.00001\pi \leq V_A \leq \pi + 0.00001\pi$	$\|x\| \leq C$ means $-C \leq x \leq C$ Keep values exact until the last step, then evaluate π with technology. Write enough digits of the upper and lower bounds to see where they differ.
$3.14156 \leq V_A \leq 3.14162$ So $V_A = 3.1416$ will approximate π to within 0.001%	

Exercise 1B

1 Find the range of possible values for the following measurements, which were rounded to the indicated degrees of accuracy:

  a 24 mm (nearest mm)

  b 3.2 m (tenth of a metre)

  c 1.75 kg (0.01 kg)

  d 1400 g (3 s.f.)

2 In 1856, Andrew Waugh announced Mount Everest as 8840 m high, after several years of calculations based on observations made by the Great Trigonometric Survey. More recent surveys confirmed the height at 8848 m.

  a Assuming the more recent survey is an exact value, calculate the percentage error made in the earlier survey.

  b If the more recent survey was accurate to the nearest metre, find the range of possible values for the exact height of Mount Everest.

3 Two lab groups in a Physics class measure the times for a ball to fall 1 metre and record the times in the following tables.

Group 1	
Trial	Time (s)
1	0.45
2	0.53
3	0.47
4	0.55
5	0.43
6	0.67

Group 2	
Trial	Time (s)
1	0.48
2	0.56
3	0.34
4	0.49
5	0.30
6	0.45

  a Find the average of all the measurements for each group.

  Using the laws of Physics the true value for the time of the fall is 0.452 seconds given air resistance can be ignored.

  b Calculate the percentage error for each set of data.

  c Based on your calculations, comment on the uncertainty of the results of each group.

4 With 72 million bicycles, correct to the nearest million, Japan is at the top of the list of countries with most bicycles per capita. On average, Japanese people travel about 2 km, correct to the nearest km, on their bicycles each day. Calculate the upper bound for total distance travelled by all the bicycles in Japan per year.

5 To determine if a business is making enough profit the following formula is used $P = \dfrac{s - c}{s}$ where P is relative profit, S is sales income and C is costs. If a company has \$340 000 worth of sales and \$230 000 as costs, each correct to 2 significant figures, calculate the maximum and minimum relative profit to an appropriate degree of accuracy.

6 The temperature today in Chicago is 50 °F. Being used to Celsius, Tommaso wants to convert the °F to °C to know what to wear outside. But instead of using the standard conversion formula $°C = \dfrac{5}{9} \times (°F - 32)$ he uses his grandmother's rule that is easier, but gives an approximate value: "Subtract 32° from the value in °F and multiply the result by 0.5".

a Calculate the actual and an approximate temperature value in °C using the standard formula and Tommaso's grandmother's rule.

b Calculate the percentage error of the approximate temperature value, in °C.

7 A factory produces circular slabs for use in construction. They guarantee that all slabs produced will have an area within 0.2% of the "target" of 163 m².

a Find the range of values for the radius that will ensure all slabs produced are within this range.

b Determine how accurately the radius must be measured during production to ensure that it will fall within this range.

Exponents and standard form

Exponents can make representing numbers and performing calculations easier and more exact. In particular, when dealing with very large of very small numbers, such as in astronomy, macroeconomics, or chemistry, **standard form** (or **scientific notation**) can be more efficient.

International-mindedness

Where did numbers come from?

Geometry and trigonometry

> Recall that a number can be written in the **standard form**
> $$a \times 10^k$$ with **coefficient** $1 \leq a < 10$ and **exponent** $k \in \mathbb{Z}$.

Investigation 3

1 The three countries with the largest populations in 2017 were:

India: 1.34 billion

USA: 3.24×10^8

China: 1 409 517 397

a Convert all numbers to standard form. Round to 3 s.f. as needed.

b Explain how you can easily order these numbers from smallest to largest when they are converted to standard form.

Gross Domestic Product (GDP) measures the total value of goods and services produced by a country and is one way to measure the wealth of countries. The GDP per capita (per person) of three countries for 2017 is given in the table below.

Country	GDP per capita ($/person)
India	1983
USA	59 501
China	8643

To find the total GDP of each country, multiply GDP per capita by population. First you will investigate how to multiply numbers in standard form by hand.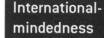

Continued on next page

2 Complete the examples below using technology:

	x	y	xy
(a)	3×10^5	2×10^9	
(b)	8×10^1	1×10^4	
(c)	2×10^{-3}	4×10^{17}	
(d)	5×10^6	3×10^{12}	
(e)	4×10^5	9×10^{-7}	

3 How can you find the product $(b \times 10^m)(c \times 10^n)$ in the form $a \times 10^k$ where $1 \le a < 10$ and k is an integer? Make sure your process is consistent with all five examples above.

4 How does your process for multiplication relate to the law of exponents, $x^p \times x^q = x^{p+q}$?

5 Now estimate and calculate the GDP of each country.

   a Write each GDP per capita in standard form.

   b Estimate the GDP of each country, without use of technology. Round your numbers as needed.

   c Use your GDC to calculate the GDP of each country.

   d Compare your estimates with the calculations. Was the magnitude (power of 10) of your estimate correct?

6 **Conceptual** How does standard form help with calculations?

> Numbers in standard form can be multiplied or divided following rules for exponents:
>
> $$(b \times 10^m)(c \times 10^n) = bc \times 10^{m+n} \text{ and } \frac{b \times 10^m}{c \times 10^n} = \frac{b}{c} \times 10^{m-n}$$
>
> After performing the operation, ensure your answer is given in the form $a \times 10^p$, where $0 \le a < 10$ by adjusting the exponent as needed.

HINT

Recall that you can enter numbers on your GDC in standard form: 3.4×10^7 is usually entered as 3.4 E 7. Make sure that you translate this calculator notation back to proper standard form when transferring answers from technology.

TOK

What might be the ethical implications of rounding numbers?

Example 4

Light travels at a speed of 3×10^8 m/s. The Earth is approximately 150 million kilometres from the Sun. Estimate the time, in seconds, that light takes to travel from the Sun to the Earth.

Since distance = speed × time, $$\text{time} = \frac{1.50 \times 10^{11} \text{ m}}{3 \times 10^8 \text{ m/s}}$$ $$= 0.5 \times 10^3 \text{ s}$$ $$= 500 \text{ s}$$	Convert the distance to metres in standard form: $$150 \text{ million km} = 1.50 \times 10^8 \text{ km}$$ $$= 1.50 \times 10^{11} \text{ m}$$ Divide coefficients and subtract exponents. Note that technology could also be used to divide.

A **negative exponent** represents a reciprocal power:

$$x^{-n} = \frac{1}{x^n}$$

A **rational exponent** represents a power of a root:

$$x^{\frac{p}{q}} = \sqrt[q]{x^p} = \left(\sqrt[q]{x}\right)^p, p, q \in \mathbb{Z}$$

In particular, $x^{\frac{1}{2}} = \sqrt{x}$.

The following rules of exponents hold for $a > 0$ and $m, n \in \mathbb{Q}$

$$a^m \times a^n = a^{m+n}$$
$$(a^m)^n = a^{mn}$$
$$\frac{a^m}{a^n} = a^{m-n}$$

HINT

You should be able to evaluate exponents and roots by hand or with technology, such as:

$$\sqrt[3]{50} = 50^{\frac{1}{3}} \approx 3.68$$

$$2^{-4} = \frac{1}{2^4} = \frac{1}{16}$$

While we will frequently use technology to approximate values for rational exponents in this course, exact values allow us to calculate more precisely and to use rules of exponents.

Example 5

a Find the surface area of a cube with volume $50\,\text{cm}^3$

  i exactly

  ii approximately.

b **i** Find a general formula for the surface area of a cube with volume $V\,\text{cm}^3$.

  ii Hence, determine the volume needed for a surface area of $1000\,\text{cm}^2$.

a $V = 50 = s^3$, so $s = 50^{\frac{1}{3}}$. $$SA = 6s^2 = 6\left(50^{\frac{1}{3}}\right)^2$$	Solve for the side length (s). Substitute into the surface area formula.
i $= 6 \times 50^{\frac{2}{3}}\,\text{cm}^2$	Apply the rule $(a^m)^n = a^{mn}$.
ii $81.4\,\text{cm}^2$	Evaluate with technology.
b **i** $SA = 6V^{\frac{2}{3}}$	Generalizing 50 to V.
ii $1000 = 6V^{\frac{2}{3}}$ $$\left(V^{\frac{2}{3}}\right)^{\frac{3}{2}} = \left(\frac{1000}{6}\right)^{\frac{3}{2}}$$ $$V = 2150\,\text{cm}^3 \,(3\text{ s.f.})$$	Isolate V by dividing by six and then raising both sides to the reciprocal power. The exponent on V becomes $\frac{2}{3} \times \frac{3}{2} = 1$

Example 6

A stuffed animal company finds that each store can sell stuffed bears for a price of $p = \dfrac{240}{\sqrt{x}}$,

where x represents the population of the city in which the store operates, in thousands. Research also shows that the weekly quantity q of stuffed bears that will be sold can be found

with the formula $q = 0.9x^{\frac{3}{4}}$. The total weekly revenue of a store is the product of its price and quantity sold.

a Determine an expression for the price in the form ax^m, where $a \in \mathbb{R}$ and $m \in \mathbb{Q}$.

b Determine store revenue in the form ax^m, where $a \in \mathbb{R}$ and $m \in \mathbb{Q}$.

c If the company wants to open a store that will make at least \$1500 per week, determine the smallest population of city they should consider.

a $\quad p = \dfrac{240}{\sqrt{x}} = 240x^{-\frac{1}{2}}$	
b $\quad r = 240x^{-\frac{1}{2}} \times 0.9x^{\frac{3}{4}} = 216x^{\frac{1}{4}}$	Multiply price by quantity. Multiply coefficients and add the exponents.
c $\quad 1500 = 216x^{\frac{1}{4}}$	Isolate x.
$\qquad x = \left(\dfrac{1500}{216}\right)^4 = 2330$ (3 s.f.)	"Undo" the $\dfrac{1}{4}$ exponent by raising both sides to the 4th power.
The city should have a population of at least $2\,330\,000$.	Interpret the solution; x is measured in thousands.

Exercise 1C

1 For each operation, **i** estimate a value for the answer without technology, **ii** find the exact value using technology. Express all answers in the form $a \times 10^k$ where $1 \le a < 10$ and $k \in \mathbb{Z}$.

  a $(1.08 \times 10^{-3})(9.2 \times 10^7)$ **b** $\dfrac{7 \times 10^4}{7.24 \times 10^{-6}}$

2 Calculate each expression using technology to 3 s.f. Express all answers in the form $a \times 10^n$ where $1 \le a < 10$ and $k \in \mathbb{Z}$.

  a $(2.35 \times 10^{-6})(4 \times 10^1)$

  b $\dfrac{7.1 \times 10^6}{8.5 \times 10^2}$

  c $\dfrac{4}{3}\pi \, (5 \times 10^{-7})^3$

  d $\dfrac{50}{\left(8.8 \times 10^{-5}\right)^{-2}}$

> **HINT**
>
> Remember to put brackets around numbers in standard form when you perform operations on them.

3 Simplify each expression and write your solution

  i without negative exponents

  ii in the form ab^c, where a, b, and c are values or variables.

  a $\dfrac{15x^{\frac{1}{2}}}{x}$ **b** $7^{-\frac{1}{3}} \times 7^{\frac{4}{3}}$

  c $\dfrac{5 \times 2^{-3t}}{40}$ **d** $\left(\dfrac{5}{3^x}\right)^2$

4 There are initially 120 bacteria in a Petri dish and the population doubles approximately every hour, which can be represented by the formula $B = 120 \times 2^t$ where B is the number of bacteria and t is the time in hours since the bacteria began growing.

  a Find B when $t = 1$, $t = \dfrac{3}{2}$, and $t = 2$.

b Comment on what your answers tell you about the growth of the bacteria. What is the meaning of the value obtained when $t = \dfrac{3}{2}$.

5 The half-life of iodine-131 is approximately 8 days, which means the mass of a sample of iodine decays by half every 8 days. The amount remaining can be calculated using the formula $I = 1600 \times 2^{-\frac{t}{8}}$, where t is the time in days since the beginning of the sample.

a Write down this formula without negative exponents.

b Find the amount of material remaining after 4 days as an exact and approximate value.

6 The image of a speck of dust in an electron microscope is 1.2×10^2 mm wide. The image is 5×10^2 times larger than the actual size. Determine the width of the actual speck of dust.

7 The Earth's mass is 5.97×10^{24} kg and Mercury's mass is 3.29×10^{23} kg. How many times more massive is the Earth than Mercury?

8 The Earth's surface area is approximately 5.1×10^8 km² (2 s.f.) and its population is 7.6×10^9 (2 s.f.). **Population density** is the number of people per square kilometre. Determine the population density of the Earth assuming all the surface area is habitable by humans.

About 30% of the Earth's surface is land, including Antarctica. Determine the population density of the earth assuming that all the land is habitable, but not the oceans.

1.2 Angles and triangles

Trigonometric ratios in a right triangle

The ratios of the sides of a right-angled triangle are called **trigonometric ratios**. The three most common trigonometric ratios are the **sine (sin)**, **cosine (cos)**, and **tangent (tan)**. These are defined for acute angle A in the right-angled triangle below:

$$\sin(\hat{A}) = \frac{\text{Opposite}}{\text{Hypotenuse}}$$

$$\cos(\hat{A}) = \frac{\text{Adjacent}}{\text{Hypotenuse}}$$

$$\tan(\hat{A}) = \frac{\text{Opposite}}{\text{Adjacent}}$$

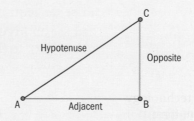

In the definitions above, "opposite" refers to the length of the side opposite angle $\hat{A}$, "adjacent" refers to the length of the side adjacent to angle $\hat{A}$, and "hypotenuse" refers to the length of the hypotenuse (the side opposite the right angle).

HINT

Some people use the mnemonic **SOH-CAH-TOA**, pronounced "soh-kuh-toh-uh", to help them remember the definitions of sine, cosine, and tangent.

International-mindedness

Diagrams of Pythagoras' theorem occur in early Chinese and Indian manuscripts. The earliest references to trigonometry are in Indian mathematics.

Reflect What are trigonometric ratios?

Example 7

For each triangle, solve for the unknown angles and sides.

a

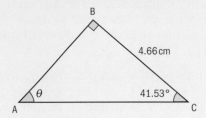

b

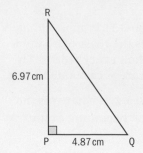

a In △ABC: $\theta = 90° - 41.53° = 48.47°$ $\cos(41.53°) = \dfrac{BC}{AC}$ $AC = \dfrac{4.66}{\cos(41.53°)} \Rightarrow AC = 6.22\,(3\text{ s.f.})$ $AB = \sqrt{AC^2 - BC^2} = 4.13\text{ cm }(3\text{ s.f.})$	[BC] is adjacent to angle $\hat{C}$, use the cosine ratio to find hypotenuse AC. Ensure technology is set to degree mode. Round answers to 3 s.f. Use Pythagoras' theorem to find AB. Use the exact value of AC stored in your calculator (not the rounded value) when performing your calculations.
b In △PQR: $RQ = \sqrt{PR^2 + PQ^2} = 8.50\,(3\text{ s.f.})$ $\tan(P\hat{Q}R) = \dfrac{PR}{PQ} = \dfrac{6.97}{4.87}$ $P\hat{Q}R = \tan^{-1}\left(\dfrac{6.97}{4.87}\right) = 55.1°\,(3\text{ s.f.})$ $P\hat{R}Q = 90 - 55.1 = 34.9°$	Use Pythagoras' theorem to find RQ. When solving for an unknown angle, determine a trig ratio with two known sides (use exact lengths when possible). PR is opposite side to $P\hat{Q}R$ and PQ is adjacent, so choose tangent. Then use an **inverse trig function**, in this case $\tan^{-1}(x)$, to find the angle.

Angles of elevation and depression

Suppose an observer is standing in front of a tree, with their eyes at point A as shown in the diagram. Angle BÂC is formed when the observer looks up at the top of the tree. This angle is called an **angle of elevation** above the horizontal line at eye level (AB).

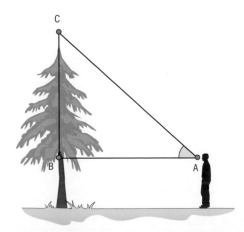

Similarly, when the object of sight falls below the horizontal at the eye level, an **angle of depression** is formed, as shown in the diagram.

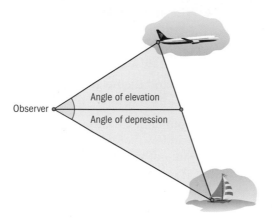

Example 8

Emma stands 15 m away from a tree. She measures the angle of elevation to the top of the tree as 40° and her height to eye level as 142 cm.

a Find the height of the tree.

b Frank, whose height is 1.8 m to eye level, is standing on the other side of the tree. His kite is stuck at the very top of the tree. He knows the length of the kite string is 16 m. What is the angle of elevation as Frank looks up at his kite?

a $\tan 40° = \dfrac{h}{15}$

$h = 15\tan 40°$

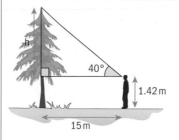

Height of tree = 15 tan 40° + 1.42
$= 14.0\,\text{m (3 s.f.)}$

Add Emma's height to eye level.

b $\sin\theta = \dfrac{15\tan 40° + 1.42 - 1.8}{16} = \dfrac{12.206\ldots}{16}$

Subtract Frank's height from the height of the tree to find the opposite side length. Use the sine ratio as opposite and hypotenuse lengths are known.

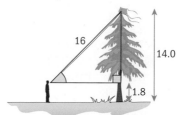

$\theta = \sin^{-1}\left(\dfrac{12.206}{16}\right) = 49.7°\,(3\ \text{s.f.})$

Use inverse sine (sin⁻¹) to find the angle.

Exercise 1D

1 Determine all unknown sides and angles for each of the right triangles below:

a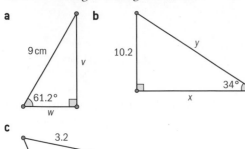

9 cm, 61.2°, v, w

b 10.2, y, x, 34°

c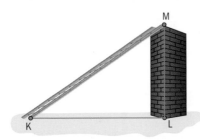

3.2, z, 4.7

2 A ladder [KM] is 8.5 m long. It currently leans against a vertical wall so that LK̂M = 30°.

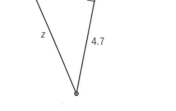

M, K, L

i Find the distance KL.

ii Find how far up the wall the ladder reaches.

iii The instructions for use of the ladder state that the angle it makes with the ground should not exceed 55°. Find the maximum height that the ladder can reach up the wall.

3 A hiker, whose eye is 1.6 m above ground level, stands 50 m from the base of a vertical cliff. The angle between the line connecting her eye and the top of the cliff and a horizontal line is 58°.

a Draw a diagram representing the situation.

b Find the height of the cliff.

4 The angle of depression from the top of a vertical cliff to a boat in the sea is 17°. The boat is 450 m from the shore.

a Draw a diagram.

b Find the height of the cliff. Give your answer rounded to the nearest metre.

5 Your family wants to buy an awning for a window that will be long enough to keep the sun out when it is at its highest point in the sky. The awning is attached to the wall at the top of the window and extends horizontally. The height of the window is 2.80 m. The angle of elevation of the sun at this point is 70°. Find how long the awning should be. Write your answer correct to 2 d.p.

6 Scientists measure the depths of lunar craters by measuring the shadow length cast by the edge of the crater on photographs. The length of the shadow cast by the edge of the Moltke crater is about 606 m, given to the nearest metre. The sun's angle of elevation "at the time the photograph was taken" is 65°. Find the depth of the crater. State your answer rounded to the nearest metre.

7 Maatsuyker Island Lighthouse is the last Australian lighthouse still being officially operated by lightkeepers. The lighthouse is 15 m high from its base to the balcony, and located 140 m above sea level.

The caretaker is standing at the balcony and notices a ship at the horizon.

Find the straight line distance from the lighthouse balcony to the ship.

You may find it useful to draw a diagram like this

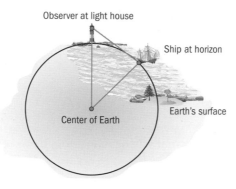

Observer at light house
Ship at horizon
Earth's surface
Center of Earth

8 Hans is constructing an accessibility ramp for a library that should reach a height of 27 cm with an angle no greater than 13°.

a Find the shortest possible length of ramp to achieve this.

b Hans cuts a length of wood to make the ramp. He cuts it to the length calculated in part **a** but can only cut it with an accuracy to the nearest centimetre. If the actual height required by the ramp is 27.43 cm, find the maximum possible percentage error between the desired 13° and the actual angle of the ramp.

Non-right triangles and the sine rule

The trigonometric ratios we have used so far require a right triangle. If we have a non-right triangle, can we still find missing sides and angles?

Investigation 4

Part 1

Draw a scalene **obtuse** triangle △ABC (without a right angle) using dynamic geometry software, and label the vertices.

• Measure all the angles and side lengths of the triangle.

• Find the following **ratios** correct to 3 significant figures.

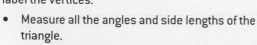

$$\frac{\sin \hat{A}}{a} = \underline{\hspace{2cm}} \qquad \frac{\sin \hat{B}}{b} = \underline{\hspace{2cm}} \qquad \frac{\sin \hat{C}}{c} = \underline{\hspace{2cm}}$$

What do you notice?

Part 2

Draw a scalene **acute** triangle △DEF (without a right angle) and label the vertices. Measure all the angles and side lengths

Find the following **ratios** correct to 3 significant figures

$$\frac{DE}{\sin \hat{F}} = \underline{\hspace{2cm}} \qquad \frac{EF}{\sin \hat{D}} = \underline{\hspace{2cm}} \qquad \frac{DF}{\sin \hat{E}} = \underline{\hspace{2cm}}$$

What do you notice?

Part 3

Repeat parts 1 and 2 for a right angled triangle. What do you notice?

Part 4

Are there any other types of triangle you could draw? Repeat Parts 1 and 2 for any other types of triangle you draw.

Conceptual What can you say about the ratio of the sine of an angle to the length of the side opposite the angle, in any triangle?

When is it most useful to use the sine rule with the angles "on top"? With the side lengths "on top"?

Sine Rule: In any non-right triangle, the ratio of each side to its opposite angle is the same for all three sides.

$$\frac{\sin \hat{A}}{a} = \frac{\sin \hat{B}}{b} = \frac{\sin \hat{C}}{c} \quad \text{or} \quad \frac{a}{\sin \hat{A}} = \frac{b}{\sin \hat{B}} = \frac{c}{\sin \hat{C}}$$

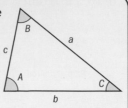

When solving a problem you will use just two of the three sides to set up an equation. When you are solving for a side length, it is easier to use the version with side lengths in the numerator, and similarly for angles.

Example 9

In a triangle $\triangle DEF$, DE = 12 cm, EF = 14 cm and $D\hat{E}F = 45°$.

Draw a labelled diagram and find the size of the angle $E\hat{F}D$ to the nearest degree.

Let $E\hat{F}D = \theta$

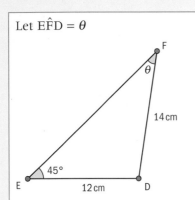

Use the Sine Rule with angles on top to solve for a missing angle more easily.

Solve this equation for θ using inverse sine.

$$\frac{\sin 45°}{14} = \frac{\sin \theta}{12}$$

$$\sin \theta = \frac{12 \sin 45°}{14}$$

$$\theta = \sin^{-1}\left(\frac{12 \sin 45°}{14}\right)$$

$\theta = 37.30742828°$

$\theta \approx 37°$ (to the nearest degree)

Keep answers exact until the last step to avoid rounding errors.

Bearings

A bearing is an angle measured clockwise from North. The diagram on the left shows a bearing of 127° and the diagram on the right shows the bearings of the major compass directions.

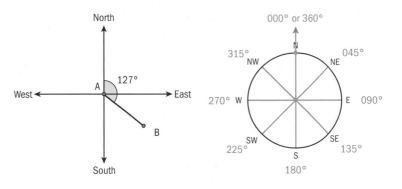

International-mindedness

The word "sine" started out as a totally different word and passed through Indian, Arabic and Latin before becoming the word that we use today. Research on the Internet what the original word was.

Number and algebra

Example 10

A ship S is located on a bearing of 120° from port A, and 042° from port B. The port A is directly North of the port B.

The distance between ports A and B is 15.2 miles.

Find the distance from the ship to each port.

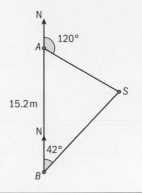

Geometry and trigonometry

$\hat{A} = 180° - 120° = 60°$	Use angle rules to find $\hat{A}$ and $\hat{S}$.
$\hat{S} = 180° - (42° + 60°) = 78°$	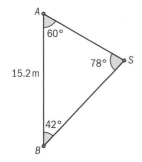
$\dfrac{AS}{\sin 42°} = \dfrac{BS}{\sin 60°} = \dfrac{15.2}{\sin 78°}$	
$AS = \sin 42° \times \dfrac{15.2}{\sin 78°} = 10.4$ miles (3 s.f.)	
$BS = \sin 60° \times \dfrac{15.2}{\sin 78°} = 13.5$ miles (3 s.f.)	

Use the sine rule to find the lengths.

Triangulation

Surveyors extensively use **triangulation** to indirectly calculate large distances. By measuring the distance between two landmarks and the angles between those landmarks and a third point, the surveyor can calculate the other two distances in the triangle formed by those points. This process can then be repeated to form a chain of triangles and is illustrated in the following example.

TOK

What does it mean to say that mathematics is an axiomatic system?

Example 11

The diagram shows a lake with three docks at points B, C and D. The distance AB along a highway is known to be 870 m. Surveyors measure the angles as given in the diagram.

a Use triangulation to find the distances BC and BD.

b Nils, who rows at a speed of 1.5 m/s, starts from dock B. Calculate how much longer will it take him to cross the lake if he rows to the further of the two docks.

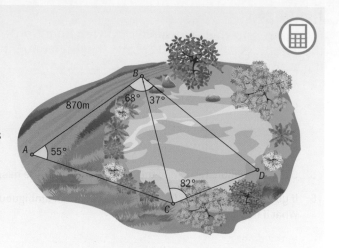

a $\hat{C} = 180 - 55 - 68 = 57°$	Find the angle opposite the known side,
$\dfrac{BC}{\sin 55°} = \dfrac{870}{\sin 57°}$	$\hat{C} = 180 - \hat{A} - A\hat{B}C$
	Substitute into the Sine Rule to find BC.
$BC = \dfrac{870 \times \sin 55°}{\sin 57°} = 950\,m$ (3 s.f.)	
$\dfrac{BC}{\sin 61°} = \dfrac{BD}{\sin 82°}$	Repeat the process with angles B$\hat{C}$D and $\hat{D}$. Remember to use the "exact" value of BC from your calculator.
$BD = \dfrac{BC \times \sin 82°}{\sin 61°} = 962\,m$ (3 s.f.)	
b $\dfrac{BD - BC}{1.5} = \dfrac{112\,m}{1.5} = 74.9\,s$	Using time $= \dfrac{\text{distance}}{\text{speed}}$.

Investigation 5

1 Use the Sine Rule to find $\hat{D}$ in the diagram on the right:

2 Explain why the solution you've obtained is not consistent with the diagram.

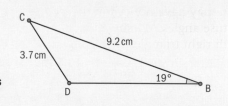

The issue you have just encountered is known as the **Ambiguous Case** of the Sine Rule. When **two sides and the non-included angle** are known, and the **unknown angle** is **opposite the longer of the two sides**, then two triangles are possible:

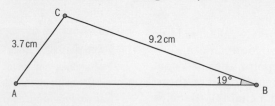

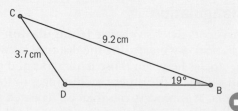

Overlaying these two diagrams shows how the triangles are related:

If you draw a circle with centre C and radius 3.7 cm then the circle will intersect the line at points A and B.

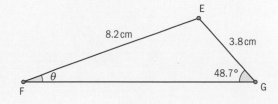

3 Check that $\hat{A}$ matches what you calculated in Question 1.

4 Use the diagram above to explain:

  a why $\hat{A} = C\hat{D}A$ **b** and hence how angles $\hat{A}$ and $C\hat{D}B$ are related.

5 Use this relationship to find the correct solution to the missing angle in Question 1.

6 If you find one solution for a missing angle in an ambiguous case is 39°, what will be the other solution? What if the angle is $x°$?

7 In the diagram on the right, the unknown angle is opposite the shorter of the two sides; the angle at G is fixed. Is it possible in this case to draw two different triangles? Draw them or explain why it's not possible.

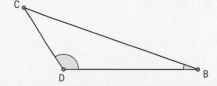

8 [Conceptual] Why does the Sine Rule not always have just one solution?

Sine Rule – Ambiguous Case

When **two sides and one angle** are known, and the **unknown angle** is **opposite the longer of the two sides**, then two triangles are possible:

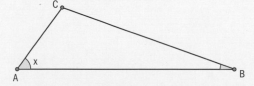

The two possible solutions for the angle opposite the longer side are supplementary (sum to 180°).

Depending on additional information, you may be able to rule out one of the two possible solutions.

You may have noticed in the example above that we encountered obtuse angles. When we defined sine, cosine, and tangent, we did so with right triangles, so all angles were acute. In Chapter 8 you will explore further how we define trig ratios for angles outside this range. For this chapter, it is sufficient to evaluate with technology.

Exercise 1E

1 For each triangle given below,

  i sketch a diagram, labelling known sides and angles

  ii state, with a reason, the number of possible triangles that satisfy the given information.

  iii For each possible triangle, find all missing lengths and angles.

  a In $\triangle ABC$, $AC = 8\,cm$, $A\hat{C}B = 101°$, and $A\hat{B}C = 32°$.

  b In $\triangle DEF$, $DF = 14.7\,cm$, $EF = 6.2\,cm$, $\hat{D} = 22°$

  c In $\triangle GHI$, $GH = GI = 209\,cm$, $\hat{H} = 52°$

2 A surveyor must determine the distance between points A and B that lie on opposite banks of a river. A point C is 450 m from A, on the same side of the river as A. The size of angle BÂC is 45° and the size of angle AĈB is 55°. Approximate the distance from A to B to the nearest metre.

3 A portion of a power line support tower is to be constructed as congruent triangles, as shown in the diagram. The crossing beams will each be 11 m long and will intersect at an acute angle of 50°, and $\hat{S} = 37°$. Find the lengths of all sides of the triangle QPT.

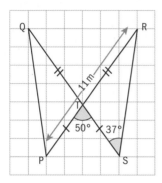

4 A ship leaves a port and travels along a bearing of 165° for 270 km. To avoid an incoming storm, it then changes course to a bearing of 203° for another 130 km and anchors. Find its bearing and distance from port.

5 Karl and Shayne are located at point A along a beach and wish to swim to an island, represented by point P. Karl swims directly from point A to point P, a distance of 1750 m at a bearing of 297°. Shayne wants to swim no further than 1000 m, so he walks along the shoreline at a bearing of 270 degrees to get closer to the island. Determine the shortest distance he must walk, and the bearing he should follow as he swims, so that his swim from B to P is 1000 m.

Area of a Triangle

Investigation 6

Consider a plot of land in the shape of triangle △ABC with sides of lengths a, b and c.

The height h is drawn from C towards [AB], so that h is perpendicular to [AB].

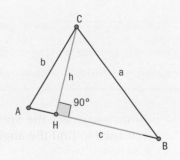

1 Write an expression for the area of the triangle in terms of c and h.

2 Consider △BHC. Write an expression for the height h in terms of a and angle $\hat{B}$.

3 Substitute your expression for h from question **2** into your expression for the area from question **1**.

4 **Factual** What is the formula for the area of any triangle?

5 **Conceptual** How can you find the area of any triangle?

The area of any triangle ABC can be calculated given two sides and the angle between them:

$$\text{area} = \frac{1}{2}ac\sin B$$

International-mindedness

In the 17th century, triangulation was used in an argument between England and France over the curvature of the Earth. Research how the curvature of the Earth was first measured in the 18th century.

Example 12

A surveyor triangulating a region uses a tree at the opposite side of the river as reference point. He measures $\hat{ADC} = 34°$. He walks along the bank of the river on a straight line and measures the distance he walked as DC = 47 m, to the nearest metre. From point C, he measures angle $\hat{C} = 27°$.

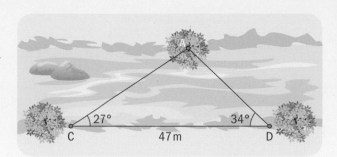

Calculate the area covered.

	To find the area we need to find one additional side length; choosing AD.
$\hat{A} = 180° - 34° - 27°$ $\hat{A} = 119°$	Determine the angle opposite the known side.
$\dfrac{AD}{\sin 27°} = \dfrac{47}{\sin 119°}$ $AD = \dfrac{47\sin 27°}{\sin 119°} \dots (1)$	When applying the Sine Rule note the ambiguous case does not apply as a length (not an angle) is being found.
$\text{Area} = \dfrac{1}{2} \times \dfrac{47\sin 27°}{\sin 119°} \times 47 \sin 34°$ $\text{Area} = 321 \, \text{m}^2 \ (3 \text{ s.f.})$	Do not round the answer at this stage. Area $\triangle ACD = \dfrac{1}{2} AD \times DC \times \sin D$; substitute AD from (1).

Cosine rule

Suppose we know all three side lengths a, b, c of a triangle, but no angles:

Then we do not have enough information to use the Sine Rule, so a different method must be used to find the angles.

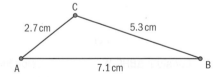

The **Cosine Rule** for $\triangle ABC$ can be used to find an angle given three sides:

$$\cos A = \frac{b^2 + c^2 - a^2}{2bc}, \text{ where } a$$

is the side opposite $\hat{A}$.

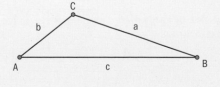

It can also be rearranged to solve for a side given two sides and the included angle:
$$a^2 = b^2 + c^2 - 2bc \cos A$$

In the case of the triangle above, you would find angle $\hat{A}$ as follows:

$$A = \cos^{-1}\left(\frac{2.7^2 + 7.1^2 - 5.3^2}{2 \cdot 2.7 \cdot 7.1}\right) = 39.4°$$

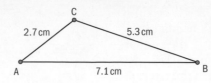

C

2.7 cm   5.3 cm

A   7.1 cm   B

HINT

When entering this into technology, ensure the numerator and denominator are in brackets to correctly represent the fraction:

$$\cos^{-1}\left(\frac{(2.7^2 + 7.1^2 - 5.3^2)}{(2 \cdot 2.7 \times 7.1)}\right)$$

Example 13

A surveyor of a lake measures
AC = 225 m, and AB = 290 m, and
$B\hat{A}C = 72°$ as shown in the diagram.

a Find BC.

b Find $\hat{C}$.

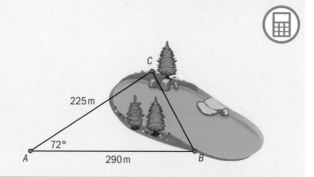

225 m

72°

A   290 m   B

a $a^2 = b^2 + c^2 - 2bc\cos A$; $CB^2 = 290^2 + 225^2 - 2 \times 225 \times 290 \times \cos 72°$ $CB = \sqrt{94398.2\ldots}$ $CB = 307\,\text{m}\ (3\ \text{s.f.})$	Use the Cosine Rule as two sides and an included angle are given. Substitute the given values for b, c, and angle $\hat{A}$ in the standard form of the rule.
b $\dfrac{\sin C}{290} = \dfrac{\sin 72°}{BC}$ $C = \sin^{-1}\left(\dfrac{290\sin 72°}{307}\right)$ $= 63.9°$	Either Sine or Cosine Rule can be used as we now have 3 sides and 1 angle. Since the unknown angle is opposite the shorter side, you do not need to consider the Ambiguous Case.

Exercise 1F

1   Find the lengths of the missing sides and angles for the following triangles.

a

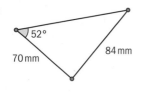

52°

70 mm

84 mm

b

14 cm

66°

48°

c

53°   13.9 cm

8.8 cm

d

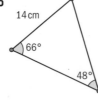

4x

2x

3x

25 m

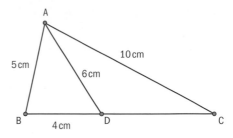

2 To find the third side of ΔABC with AB = 40 cm, BC = 25 cm and BÂC = 35°, Velina and Kristian offered the following suggestions:

Kristian suggested: "Use the cosine rule as you are given two sides and one angle."

Velina suggested: "Use the sine rule as you are given two sides and an angle opposite to one of them."

State whose method is correct and justify your statement. Use the correct method to solve the triangle.

3 A straight air route between two cities A and B is of distance 223 km. Due to bad weather, the pilot had to fly first from city A to city C which was at a distance of 152 km and then turned and flew to city B. The distance between the cities B and C is 285 km. Find the angles between the three cities.

4 Given point A and collinear points B, D and C as arranged in the diagram shown, find:

a the measure of angle B

b the area of triangle ACD.

5 The area of ΔABC is 29.6 cm², $\hat{B}$ = 25° and BC = 7 cm. Find the length of side AB.

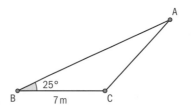

6 Calculate the area of the quadrilateral ABDC.

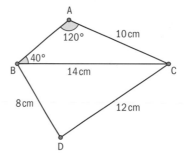

Arc length and area of sector

Sometimes we are interested in only a piece of a circle, either an **arc** of the circumference, or a **sector** of its area, as show in the diagram. The length of an arc will be a fraction of the circumference proportional to its **central angle** θ, and similarly for the area of a sector.

Length of arc formula
The length of the arc of a circle with radius r and with central angle θ (in degrees) is:

$$\frac{\theta}{360°} \times 2\pi r$$

Area of sector formula
The area of a sector with central angle θ is:

$$\frac{\theta}{360°} \times \pi r^2$$

TOK

To what extent do instinct and reason create knowledge? Do different geometries (Euclidean and non-Euclidean) refer to or describe different worlds? Is a triangle always made up of straight lines? Is the angle sum of a triangle always 180°?

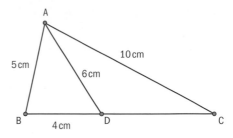

Example 14

A city park with a circular perimeter contains several sidewalks represented by the sides of triangle ABC. The length of sidewalk [AC] = 85 m and $B\hat{A}C = 75°$.

a Find how much longer the circular arc $\overset{\frown}{BC}$ is than the straight path [BC].

b Find the area of the segment that is between the chord [BC] and the arc $\overset{\frown}{BC}$

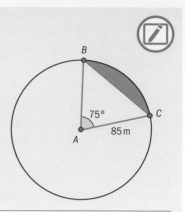

a $\overset{\frown}{BC} = \dfrac{75°}{360°} \times 2\pi(85) = 111.265$ m	Using length of arc formula.
	Since AB = AC = 85 m, ΔABC is isosceles, so $\hat{B} = \hat{C} = \dfrac{180 - 75}{2} = 52.5°$. 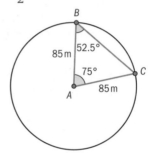
$\dfrac{BC}{\sin 75°} = \dfrac{85}{\sin 52.5°}$ BC = 103.489 m 111.265 − 103.489 = 7.78 m longer	Now there is sufficient information to use the Sine Rule.
b $A_{\text{sector}} - A_{\text{triangle}}$ $= \dfrac{75}{360} \times \pi \times 85^2 - \dfrac{1}{2}(85)(85)\sin 75°$ $= 1240$ m²	Find the difference between the length of the arc and the length of the chord. Use formula $A = \dfrac{1}{2}ab \sin C$ for the area of the triangle.

Exercise 1G

1 Determine **i** the length of the each arc **ii** the area of each sector for the radius r and central angle α given below. Give your answer correct to 2 d.p.

a $r = 5$ cm; $\alpha = 70°$

b $r = 4$ cm; $\alpha = 45°$

c $r = 10.5$ cm, $\alpha = 130°$

2 A clock is circular in shape with diameter 25 cm. Find the length of the arc between the markings 12 and 5 rounded to the nearest tenth of cm.

3 The London Eye is a giant Ferris wheel in London with a diameter of 120 m. The wheel passenger capsules are attached to the circumference of the wheel, and the wheel rotates at 26 cm per second.

Find:

a the length that a passenger capsule would travel if the wheel makes a rotation of 200°

b the time, in minutes, that it would take for passenger capsule to makes a rotation of 200°

c the time, in minutes, that it would take for passenger capsule to makes a full revolution.

Give your answers to the nearest integer.

4 a A sector with radius 10 cm and central angle $x°$ has area $48\pi\,\text{cm}^2$.

Find the size of the angle $x°$.

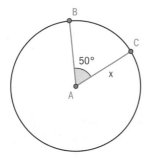

b A sector with radius x cm and central angle 50° has area $8\pi\,\text{cm}^2$.

Find the length of the radius x cm.

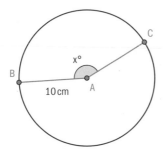

5 Determine the area of the shaded region of wooded patch in a circular park if the radius of the circle is

a 8 cm   **b** 12 cm.

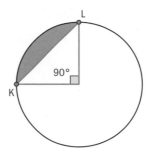

6 Find the area of the region shaded below if the circle has radius 4 cm and the central angle of sector BAC is 55 degrees.

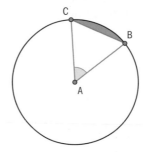

7 A landscaper builds a regular hexagonal patio in a circular garden. The area not covered by the patio will be covered in grass.

The radius of the garden is 10.5 m.

Find the area of grass in the garden.

Developing inquiry skills

Look again at the opening problem. The Great Trigonometric Survey used an instrument called a theodolite to measure the angles from points A and B to the summit E.

$\hat{BAE} = 30.5°$ and $\hat{ABE} = 26.2°$.

Points A and B are 33 km apart.

Find the height of Mount Everest to the nearest metre.

1.3 Three dimensional geometry

In this section, you will use the tools of trigonometry to solve problems in three dimensions, including finding lengths, angles, surface areas and volumes.

Shapes with three dimensions (length, width and height) are called **solids**.

A **polyhedron** is a solid composed of polygonal **faces** that connect along line segments called **edges**. Edges meet at a point, called a **vertex** (plural **vertices**).

You are likely to be familiar with the 3D solids we will encounter:

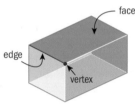

Volumes of 3D solids

You have already learned how to find the volume of cuboids, prisms and cylinders:

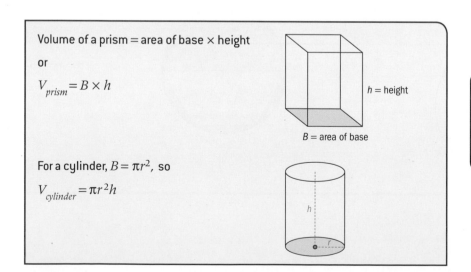

Volume of a prism = area of base × height

or

$V_{prism} = B \times h$

h = height

B = area of base

For a cylinder, $B = \pi r^2$, so

$V_{cylinder} = \pi r^2 h$

> **HINT**
>
> The bases are the parallel faces. They are not necessarily the "bottom" of the shape.

Example 15

Find the volume of triangular prism whose base is an isosceles triangle with two equal sides of 12 cm. The angle between them is 130°. The height of the prism is 15 cm.

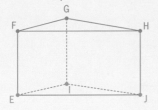

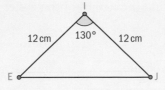

$V = \dfrac{12 \times 12 \times \sin 130°}{2} \times 15$ $= 827 \text{ cm}^3 \text{ (3 s.f.)}$	To find the volume you need to find the area of the triangular base for which you can use the area formula. Remember that the volume is measured in cubic units.

TOK

What are the platonic solids and why are they an important part of the language of mathematics?

Geometry and trigonometry

Volume of pyramids, cones and spheres

Shape	Pyramid	Cone	Sphere
Volume	$V = \dfrac{1}{3}(\text{base area} \times \text{height})$	$V = \dfrac{1}{3}\pi r^2 h$	$V = \dfrac{4}{3}\pi r^3$

Example 16

Calculate the volume of each solid.

a

b

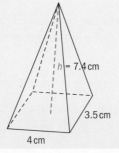

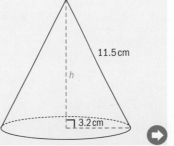

Continued on next page

HINT

Note that the volume of a pyramid or cone is the one third the volume of a prism or cylinder with the same base area and height.

a $V = \dfrac{1}{3}(4 \times 3.5 \times 7.4)$ Use $V = \dfrac{1}{3}(\text{base area} \times \text{height})$

        $= 34.5 \, \text{cm}^3 \, (3 \text{ s.f.})$

b $\text{height} = \sqrt{11.5^2 - 3.2^2}$ Use Pythagoras' theorem to find the height of the cone.

        $= 11.0458\ldots \, \text{cm}$

   $V = \dfrac{1}{3}\pi \times 3.2^2 \times 11.0458\ldots$ Use $V = \dfrac{1}{3}\pi r^2 h$ to find the

        $= 118 \, \text{cm}^3 \, (3 \text{ s.f.})$ volume.

Example 17

A cylindrical can holds three tennis balls. Each ball has a diameter of 6 cm, which is the same diameter as the cylinder, and the cylinder is filled to the top. Calculate the volume of space in the cylinder not taken up by the tennis balls.

Volume of cylinder $= \pi \times 3^2 \times 18 = 508.9 \, \text{cm}^3$ The cylinder has radius = 3 cm, height = 18 cm

Volume of 3 balls $= 3 \times \dfrac{4}{3}\pi \times 3^3$ Each ball has radius 3 cm

        $= 339.3 \, \text{cm}^3$

Space $= 508.9 - 339.3 = 169.6 \, \text{cm}^3$

Exercise 1H

1   Find the volume of each object:

   a   A cone with a base radius of 22 cm and a height that is half of the base's circumference.

   b   A regular hexagonal prism with base side lengths 5 cm and height 23 cm.

   c   A hemisphere whose circular face has a surface area of 412 cm².

2   The grain stored inside a cylindrical silo is transferred to a transport container in the shape of a triangular prism. The container's triangular base has side lengths 5.8 m, 5.8 m and 8.1 m and height 7.2 m. The silo has a radius of 5.83 m.

   a   Find the volume of grain that will be removed from the silo if the container is completely filled.

   b   Find the amount by which the height of grain inside the silo will decrease. Give your answers to an appropriate degree of accuracy.

3   **a**   Estimate the volume in m³ of each of the following (approximately) spherical objects.

     i   A lithium atom, radius 0.15 nm ($1 \, \text{nm} = 1 \times 10^{-9} \, \text{m}$)

     ii   The Earth, which has equatorial circumference = 40 075 km

iii UY Scuti, one of the largest known stars, with diameter equal to 1700 solar radii (radius of Sun = 6.957×10^5 km)

b Hence, determine which is relatively larger: the Earth compared to an atom, or UY Scuti compared to the Earth.

4 a Find the volume of material used to construct the Red Pyramid in Cairo, given that it has a height of 105 m, a base length of 220 m, and is estimated to be 96% solid.

b Given that the average block of stone used to construct the pyramid had dimensions $130 \times 130 \times 30$ cm and weighed approximately 2250 kg, find the total weight of the pyramid.

5 A family is replacing the hot water cylindrical tank of the house. They cannot change the height of the boiler but they can double its width. If the previous tank could hold 100 l, predict the volume of the new tank. State the volume of the tank if its width has tripled.

Surface area

The **surface area** of a solid is the sum of the area of all its faces. Because the faces are two-dimensional, it is often convenient to deconstruct the 3D shape into a 2D net:

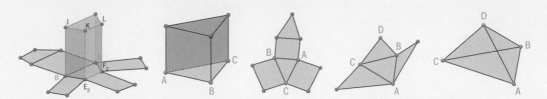

Surface area of prisms and cylinders

Recall that for a prism or cylinder, the surface area (SA) is the sum of both bases and the **lateral area** (LA, area of the non-base sides).

$$SA = LA + 2B$$

The lateral area of a prism or cylinder is rectangular when drawn as a net, as shown in the diagrams below:

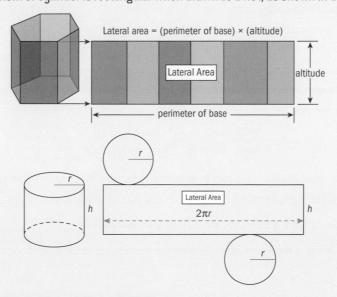

Hence $LA = ph$, where p is the perimeter of the base.

For a cylinder, the surface area formula can be written more specifically as:
$SA = 2\pi r h + 2\pi r^2$

Investigation 7

Surface area of a regular pyramid

1 Draw a net for each regular pyramid:

   a A square pyramid

   b A triangular-based pyramid

   c A hexagonal pyramid

2 The lateral area is the sum of the sides that are not the base. Describe a process for calculating this area that is consistent with all three pyramids. On your net, label (and draw, if needed) any dimensions necessary for these calculations.

3 Explain how this formula corresponds to the process you described in question 2.

4 If the pyramid is not regular, will this formula still work? Investigate the net of the rectangular pyramid at right to decide.

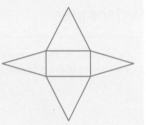

Surface area of a cone

A cone also has a **slant height** l from its vertex to the edge of the base, as shown on the left. If the cone is cut along its slant height and round the edge of the base, the net on the right is created.

 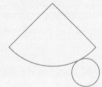

5 The lateral area of the cone is a sector of a larger circle.

   a Sketch this larger circle on the net.

   b In terms of the cone's radius r and slant height l,

      i What is the radius of the circle, of which the lateral area is a sector?

      ii What is the circumference of this circle?

      iii What is the length of the arc corresponding to this sector?

   c The length of an arc and the area of a sector are proportional:

$$\frac{\text{area of sector}}{\text{area of circle}} = \frac{\text{length of arc}}{\text{circumference}}$$

   Combining this with what you found in part **b**, determine the area of the sector (lateral area).

6 a **Factual** What are the formulae for finding surface area for these solids?

   b **Conceptual** How are the formulae for surface area derived?

   c **Conceptual** What is the same about finding the surface area of various solids? What is different?

One formula for calculating the **lateral area of a regular pyramid** is:

$$LA = \frac{1}{2}pl$$

Where p is the perimeter of the base, and l is the **slant height** of the pyramid, or altitude of one of the triangular faces.

The **surface area of a pyramid** is the sum of the lateral area and the area of the base:

$$SA = LA + B$$

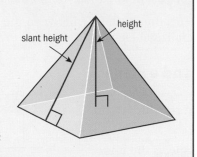

The **lateral area of a cone** is

$$LA = \pi r l$$

Where r is the radius of the base and l is the slant height. The **surface area of a cone** is

$$SA = LA + B = \pi r l + \pi r^2$$

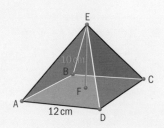

The **surface area of sphere** with radius r is $SA = 4\pi r^2$.

Example 18

Find the surface area of a right square-based pyramid with base side length $12\,$cm and height $10\,$cm:

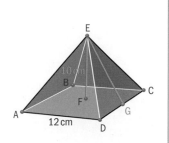

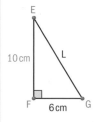

$$l = \sqrt{10^2 + 6^2} = \sqrt{136}$$

$$SA = \frac{1}{2}\left(4 \times 12\right)\sqrt{136} + 12^2$$

$$= 424\,\text{cm}^2$$

For a regular pyramid,

$$SA = LA + B \text{ and } LA = \frac{1}{2}pl$$

Since lateral area requires slant height, we draw the slant height EG and recognize that it forms a right triangle EFG with the height.

FG = 6 as it is half the side length

Using Pythagoras' theorem, solve for the slant height and substitute.

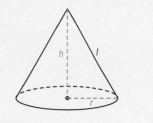

Note that in the example above, we identified a right triangle that was useful in relating different lengths or angles in the 3D diagram.

The triangle EFG also indicates the angle EĜF between the slant height and the base, which is generalized below..

Angle between a line and a plane

To draw the angle between the line AG and the plane ABCD:

- Draw a line from G that meets the plane ABCD at 90°. Here that line is [GC]
- Then connect A to point C to form a right angled triangle. Angle GÂC is the angle between line [AG] and plane ABCD.

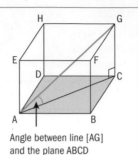

Angle between line [AG] and the plane ABCD

Example 19

A right cone has a radius 5 cm and a total surface area of 300 cm², rounded to the nearest integer.

Find:

a the slant height, l, of the cone   **b** the height, h, of the cone

c the volume of the cone   **d** the angle that the slant height makes with the base of the cone.

a $300 = \pi \times 5 \times l + \pi \times 5^2$ $l = 14.0985... = 14.1$ cm (3 s.f.)	Draw a diagram and label known information. Total surface area $= \pi r l + \pi r^2$ Substitute the given values in order to find the slant height, l. 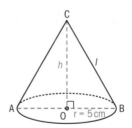
b $h^2 = l^2 - r^2$ $h = \sqrt{14.0985...^2 - 5^2} = 13.2$ cm (3 s.f.)	Use triangle OBC and Pythagoras' theorem to find the height from the slant height.
c $V = \dfrac{1}{3} \times \pi \times 5^2 \times 13.1821...$ $= 345$ cm³	

d $\cos \hat{C}BO = \dfrac{r}{l} = \dfrac{5}{14.0985...}$

$\hat{C}BO = \cos^{-1}\left(\dfrac{5}{14.0985...}\right) = 69.2°$ (3 s.f.)

To find the angle between [BC] and the base, draw a segment from C perpendicular to the base – this is [CO]. Connect to point B to create triangle CBO. Angle CBO is the angle between the line and the plane.

Exercise 1I

1 Find the surface area of the following solids.

a A cylinder with radius 2.5 cm and height 7.3 cm.

b A right cone with radius 3.5 cm and height 12 cm.

c A regular triangular pyramid with base side length and slant height 17 mm.

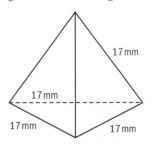

d A regular pentagonal pyramid with base side length 2.4 cm and vertical height 4.2 cm.

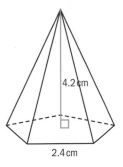

2 Find the missing dimension for the objects below given that each has a surface area of 525 cm².

i The radius of a sphere.

ii The height of cylinder, given that its radius is half of its height.

iii The height of a cone with base circumference 25 cm.

3 Cells must exchange different molecules across their boundaries in order to survive. The amount of material that can be taken in or released is limited by the surface area of the cell.

a If the ratio of surface area to volume is too low, then the cell is unable to exchange enough material.

i Find, in terms of its radius r, the ratio of surface area to volume of a spherical cell.

ii Find the largest possible radius of the cell, in metres, if the ratio of surface area to volume must be greater than 955 000 (with the radius measured in metres).

b Find an expression in terms of radius r for the ratio of surface area to volume for each of the following objects, given that their volume is equal to that of the sphere of radius r:

i A cube.

ii A cylinder with two half-spheres attached at its bases, and height of cylinder equal to five times the radius of its base.

iii Hence, if the sphere has unit volume, find how many times more surface area each object will have than the sphere.

4 A polyhedron whose faces are congruent regular polygons is known as a **Platonic solid**. A cube is one familiar example; another is a **tetrahedron** – a triangular pyramid with all faces equilateral triangles. A company produces tetrahedral dice for games with a side length of 1.2 cm. They sell approximately 3.5 million dice per year.

a Find the total surface area that will be painted on the dice.

b The paint is sold in cylindrical cans with a height of 25.4 cm and diameter 6.5 cm. Determine how many cans must be bought if the average thickness of the paint is 25.4 microns (1 micron = 1×10^{-6} m).

c Shipment costs $16 per kg. Determine the total shipping cost of the paint.

5

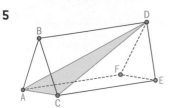

The triangular prism given above has the following side lengths.

AB = BC = 6 cm

AC = 4 cm

BD = 8 cm

Calculate the area of $\triangle$ACD correct to 2 decimal places.

6 Find the volume and surface area of the following composite solids:

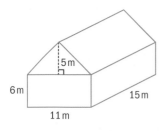
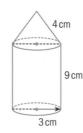

7

A silo consists of a cylinder with a hemispherical roof attached to its top base. The radius of the cylinder is 3 m and its height is 12 m.

a Find the volume of the silo.

b The entire silo is to be painted. Find how much paint is needed if 1 l of paint covers 8.5 m² of surface.

8 ABCDEFGH is a cube with edge length 6 cm. I, J and K are midpoints of the respective edges.

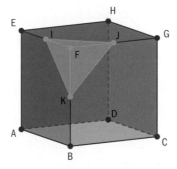

The corner of the cube is cut off as shown in the diagram. Find the remaining volume and surface area.

Chapter summary

- If a measurement M is accurate to a particular unit u, then its exact value V lies in the interval:
$M - 0.5u \leq V < M + 0.5u$

  The endpoints of this interval are called the **lower** and **upper bounds**. **Measurement error** $= V_A - V_E$

- **Percentage error formula**

  Percentage error $= \left| \dfrac{V_A - V_E}{V_E} \right| \times 100\%$, where V_A is the approximate (or measured) value

  and V_E is the exact value.

- The following rules of exponents hold for $a > 0$ and $m, n \in \mathbb{Q}$

  ○ $a^m \times a^n = a^{m+n}$ ○ $(a^m)^n = a^{mn}$ ○ $\dfrac{a^m}{a^n} = a^{m-n}$

- The general form for **standard form** is $a \times 10^k$ with coefficient $1 \le a < 10$ and exponent $k \in \mathbb{Z}$.

- Numbers in standard form can be multiplied or divided following rules for exponents:

$$(b \times 10^m)(c \times 10^n) = bc \times 10^{m+n} \quad \text{and} \quad \frac{b \times 10^m}{c \times 10^n} = \frac{b}{c} \times 10^{m-n}$$

- A **negative exponent** represents a reciprocal power: $x^{-n} = \dfrac{1}{x^n}$

- A **rational exponent** represents a power of a root: $x^{\frac{p}{q}} = \sqrt[q]{x^p} = \left(\sqrt[q]{x}\right)^p$, $p, q \in \mathbb{Z}$

- In a right triangle ABC:

  ○ $\sin(A) = \dfrac{\text{Opposite}}{\text{Hypotenuse}}$

  ○ $\cos(A) = \dfrac{\text{Adjacent}}{\text{Hypotenuse}}$

  ○ $\tan(A) = \dfrac{\text{Opposite}}{\text{Adjacent}}$

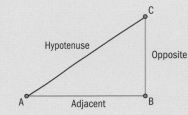

- The **Sine Rule** for triangle ABC can be used to find missing sides and angles in right or non-right triangles:

$$\frac{\sin A}{a} = \frac{\sin B}{b} = \frac{\sin C}{c} \quad \text{or} \quad \frac{a}{\sin A} = \frac{b}{\sin B} = \frac{c}{\sin C}$$

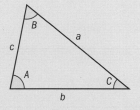

- **Sine Rule – Ambiguous Case**

  When **two sides and one angle** are known, and the **unknown angle** is **opposite the longer of the two sides**, then two triangles are possible:

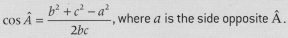

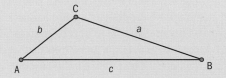

- The area of any triangle ABC is given the formula:

$$\text{area} = \frac{1}{2} bc \sin A$$

- The **Cosine Rule** for $\triangle \mathrm{ABC}$ can be used to find an angle given three sides:

$$\cos \hat{A} = \frac{b^2 + c^2 - a^2}{2bc}, \text{ where } a \text{ is the side opposite } \hat{A}.$$

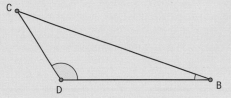

Or to find a side:

$$a^2 = b^2 + c^2 - 2bc \cos \hat{A}$$

Continued on next page

- **Length of Arc Formula**

  The length of the arc of a circle with radius r and with central angle θ (in degrees) is:

  $$\frac{\theta}{360°} \times 2\pi r$$

- **Area of Sector Formula**

  The area of a sector with central angle θ is: $\dfrac{\theta}{360°} \times \pi r^2$

Shape	Pyramid	Cone	Sphere	Prism	Cylinder
Volume	$V = \dfrac{1}{3}\left(\text{base area} \times \text{height}\right)$	$V = \dfrac{1}{3}\pi r^2 h$	$V = \dfrac{4}{3}\pi r^3$	$V = \text{base area} \times \text{height}$	$V = \pi r^2 h$

- **Surface Area**

  For prisms:

  $$SA = LA + 2B$$

  For cylinders:
  $$SA = 2\pi r h + 2\pi r^2$$

- For a pyramid or cone:
  $$SA = LA + B$$

  For a regular pyramid:

  $$LA = \frac{1}{2}pl, \text{ where } p = \text{perimeter of base, } l = \text{slant height}$$

- For a cone,
  $$SA = LA + B = \pi r l + \pi r^2$$

- The **surface area of sphere** with radius r is $SA = 4\pi r^2$.

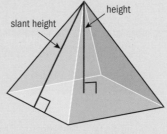

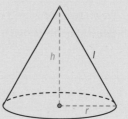

Developing inquiry skills

Look back at the opening problem. Mount Everest can be modelled as a right cone with base radius equal to approximately 16 km, and the average snow depth is approximately 4 m. Estimate the amount of snow at Mount Everest.

Chapter review

1 Calculate each of the following, giving the answers **i** to one decimal place **ii** to three significant figures.

a $\dfrac{5^{\frac{1}{3}}+8-\sqrt{6}}{47}$ b $(5+8)^{\frac{1}{3}}-\dfrac{\sqrt{6}}{47}$

c $(5+8)^{\frac{1}{3}}-\sqrt{\dfrac{6}{47}}$ d $5^{\frac{1}{3}}+\dfrac{8-\sqrt{6}}{47}$

e $\dfrac{\left(5+8-\sqrt{6}^{\frac{1}{3}}\right)}{47}$

2 **a** An estimate of the number of settings on the WWII Enigma code machine is estimated at 1.5×10^{19}. Given that the exact value is $15\,896\,255\,521\,782\,636\,000$, determine the percentage error of this estimate.

b Assuming that the age of the universe is 13.82 billion years, and that each of the Enigma machine settings is written down every second, determine whether the 13.82 billion years would be enough time to write down all the settings.

3 Cardano published this formula in 1545 to find one solution of the equation $x^3 + px = q$:

$$x = \sqrt[3]{\sqrt{\left(\frac{p}{3}\right)^3+\left(\frac{q}{2}\right)^2}+\frac{q}{2}} - \sqrt[3]{\sqrt{\left(\frac{p}{3}\right)^3+\left(\frac{q}{2}\right)^2}-\frac{q}{2}}$$

Use this formula to find a solution of $x^3 + 3x = 5$ and find the percentage error when compared to the answer you get using technology.

4 In a triangle $\triangle PQR$, $PQ = 13.4\,cm$, $QR = 15\,cm$ and angle $\hat{P} = 31°$. Find PR by
a one application of the cosine rule
b two applications of the sine rule.

5 In New York City, the heights of the observatories of the One World Trade Centre, the Empire State Building and the Rockefeller Center are 382.2 m, 320 m and 259 m, respectively. The horizontal direct distance between the Empire State Building and the Rockefeller Center is 1310 m and the direct distance between the One World Trade Center and the Empire State Building is 4600 m.

Find the angle of elevation from the observation decks of the Rockefeller Centre to the Empire State and the angle of depression from the One World Trade Center to the Empire State.

6 Sophie learns that the Cheops pyramid on the Giza plateau in Egypt is constructed on a vast scale. She wants to know more.

a Given that the base of the pyramid is approximately square in shape with sides of length 230 m to the nearest metre, calculate the upper and lower bounds of the exact area A of the base.

You are given that a football pitch which meets the requirements for an international football fixture must have width at least 64 metres and no more than 75 m, and that the length must be between 100 m and 110 m inclusive.

b Find the upper and lower bounds for the number of football pitches that fit into the base area of the Cheops pyramid **i** as a ratio R **ii** as a number P of complete pitches.

7 The speed of light is approximately $3 \times 10^8\,m/s$.

Determine the radius of a circular clock if the tip of its second hand is to move at the speed of light. Express your answer in km using standard form correct to 4 significant figures.

8 A cone has base radius r and height h. Let θ be the angle that the slant height of the cone makes with its base. A cylinder has the same height and radius as the cone.

The cylinder is modified so that the section of the cylinder corresponding to a sector of the base with central angle α is removed:

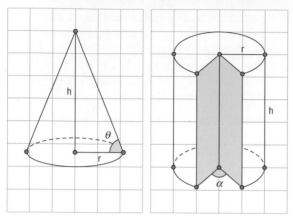

a Find the value of α so that the volume of the cone and the volume of the cylinder are equal.

b For this value of α, find the value of θ so that the lateral areas of the cone and the modified cylinder are equal.

9 The diagrams represent the pyramid of Cheops. You are given that the vertical height VB = 146.64954 and the side of the square base EF = 230.35655 m. M is the midpoint of [EF].

a Find all the sides and angles of the △VBM.

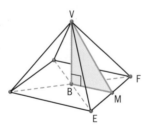

b Find all the sides and angles of △VBF.

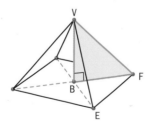

c Find all the sides and angles of △VEF and its area.

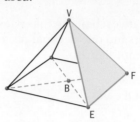

d The Ancient Greek historian Herodotus claimed that the Cheops pyramid was designed so that the square of its height was equal to the area of each of its faces. Find the percentage error in the claim of Herodotus.

10 A highway is to be built in a desert. The highway forms a straight line in the locality of a town Alphaville which is 5 km from the highway. The highway is planned to pass through Betatown which is situated 13 km from Alphaville. The planners need to build a straight access road from Alphaville to the highway to meet the highway at a junction J. The speed limit on the access road will be 70 km/h and on the highway 110km/h.

a Determine the time taken for the journey from Alphaville to Betatown via J in terms of the distance from J to Betatown.

b Determine the time taken for the journey from Alphaville (A) to Betatown (B) via J in terms of the angle between AJ and JB.

Exam-style questions

11 **P1:** In an electric circuit, the resistance (R ohms) of a component may be calculated using the formula $R = \dfrac{V}{I}$, where V is the potential difference across the component and I is the current through the component.

The potential difference is measured as 6 V (to the nearest volt), and the current is measured as 0.2 Amps, to the nearest tenth of an Amp.

a Calculate lower and upper bounds for the resistance. (3 marks)

b The actual value of the resistor is 30 Ω. Calculate the maximum possible percentage error that could be obtained. (2 marks)

12 P2: Simplify the following algebraic expressions.

a $\sqrt{3x^3 \times 12x^0 \times 4x^5}$ (3 marks)

b $\dfrac{\left(x^{-2}\right)^5}{\left(x^3\right)^{-4}}$ (3 marks)

c $\left(\dfrac{343x^9}{27y^6}\right)^{-\frac{2}{3}}$ (5 marks)

13 P1: The following table gives the masses (in kg) of the various particles which make up an atom.

Particle	Mass (kg)
Neutron	1.675×10^{-27}
Proton	1.673×10^{-27}
Electron	9.109×10^{-31}

a Find the average (mean) mass of all three particles, giving your answer in standard form to 3 s.f. (2 marks)

A helium atom consists of two protons, two neutrons, and two electrons.

b Determine the ratio of electron mass to neutron mass, giving your answer in the form $1 : x$ where x is accurate to 3 s.f. (2 marks)

c Calculate the percentage error in mass when taking the mass of an electron to be 1×10^{-30} kg. (2 marks)

14 P2: A cylindrical block of metal has base radius 12 cm and height 50 cm. The block is to be melted down and used to produce a number of metal ball bearings, each of radius 2 cm. Calculate the number of ball bearings that can be produced from this block. (6 marks)

15 P1: The following diagram shows a semi-circle, centre O. AO = 15 cm and arc AB = 10 cm.

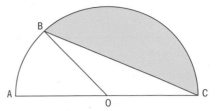

a Find the area of the shaded region, giving your answer to 3 significant figures. (4 marks)

b Find the perimeter of the shaded region, giving your answer to 3 significant figures. (5 marks)

16 P1: In a triangle ABC, AB = x, AC = $x + 1$ and BÂC = 60°.

The area of the triangle is $14\sqrt{3}$ cm².

Find the perimeter of the triangle. (8 marks)

17 P2: ABCDE is a square-based pyramid.

The vertex E is situated directly above the centre of the face ABCD. AB = 16 cm and AE = 20 cm

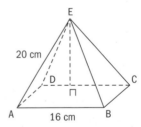

a Calculate the angle between the line AE and the plane face ABCD. (4 marks)

b Calculate the angle between the plane face BCE and the face ABCD. (4 marks)

c Calculate the angle between the line AE and the line EC. (2 marks)

d Find the volume of the pyramid. (2 marks)

e Find the total surface area of the pyramid. (3 marks)

Three squares

Approaches to learning: Research, Critical thinking

Exploration criteria: Personal engagement (C), Use of mathematics (E)

IB topic: Proof, Geometry, Trigonometry

The problem

Three identical squares with length of 1 are adjacent to one another. A line is connected from one corner of the first square to the opposite corner of the same square, another to the opposite corner of the second square and another to the opposite corner of the third square:

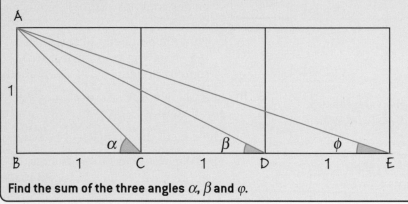

Find the sum of the three angles α, β and φ.

Exploring the problem

Look at the diagram

What do you think the answer may be?

Use a protractor if that helps.

How did you come to this conjecture?

Is it convincing?

This is not an accepted mathematical truth. It is a conjecture, based on observation.

You now have the conjecture $\alpha + \beta + \varphi = 90°$ to be proved mathematically.

Direct proof

What is the value of α?

Given that $\alpha + \beta + \varphi = 90°$, what does this tell you about α and $\beta + \varphi$?

What are the lengths of the three hypotenuses of $\triangle ABC$, $\triangle ABD$ and $\triangle ABE$?

Hence explain how you know that $\triangle ACD$ and $\triangle ACE$ are similar.

What can you therefore conclude about $C\hat{A}D$ and $C\hat{E}A$?

Hence determine why $A\hat{C}B = C\hat{A}D + A\hat{D}C$ and conclude the proof.

Proof using an auxiliary line

An additional diagonal line, CF, is drawn in the second square and the intersection point between CF and AE is labelled G:

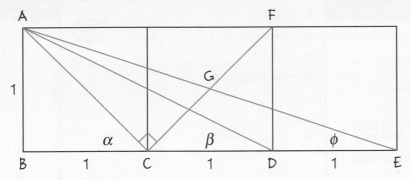

Explain why BÂC = α.

Explain why EÂF = φ.

If you show that GÂC = β, how will this complete the proof?

Explain how you know that $\triangle$GAC and $\triangle$ABD are similar.

Hence explain how you know that GÂC = $\angle$BD̂A = β.

Hence complete the proof.

Proof using the cosine rule

The diagram is extended and the additional vertices of the large rectangle are labelled X and Y and the angle is labelled θ:

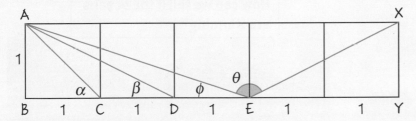

Explain why XÊY = β.

Calculate the lengths of AE and AY.

Now calculate AÊY (θ) using the cosine rule.

Hence explain how you know that $\beta + \varphi = 45°$.

Hence complete the proof.

Extension

Research other proofs on the Internet.

You could also try to produce a proof yourself.

You do not have to stop working when you have the proof.

What could you do next?

2 Representing and describing data: descriptive statistics

Statistics is concerned with the collection, analysis and interpretation of quantitative data. Statistical representations and measures allow us to represent data in many different forms to aid interpretation. Both statistics and probability provide important representations which enable us to make predictions, valid comparisons and informed decisions.

Concepts
- Representation
- Validity

Microconcepts
- Population
- Bias
- Samples, random samples, sampling methods
- Outliers
- Discrete and continuous data
- Histograms
- Box-and-whisker plots
- Cumulative frequency graph
- Measures of central tendency and dispersion
- Skewness
- Scatter graphs
- Correlation

How can scientists determine whether a new drug is likely to be a successful cure?

How can we tell if the oceans are warming?

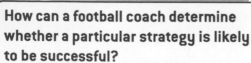

How can a football coach determine whether a particular strategy is likely to be successful?

How can you persuade a potential customer that your product is better than the competition?

The picture shows a graph of GDP per capita (gross domestic product per person) and life expectancy taken from Gapminder (www.gapminder.org). Click the icon for a spreadsheet of the complete data for this graph.

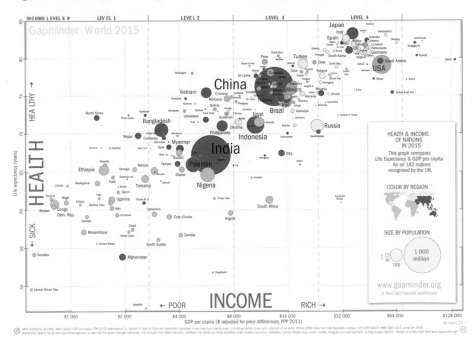

- Name four pieces of information represented in this graph.
- How do you think this data could have been collected? How exact do you think it might be?
- Can you identify any relationships from the graph?
- Do you need to use all the data for analysis or can you just use a sample of the data?
- Do you find anything surprising in the graph?
- Describe the scale on the *x*-axis. Why do you think it has been done like that?

Developing inquiry skills

Write down any similar inquiry questions you might ask to investigate the relationship between two different quantities, for example, GDP per capita and infant mortality or life expectancy and population.

What questions might you need to ask in these scenarios which differ from the scenario where you are investigating. How are these questions different from those used to investigate the relationship between GDP and life expectancy?

Think about the questions in this opening problem and answer any you can. As you work through the chapter, you will gain mathematical knowledge and skills that will help you to answer them all.

Before you start

Click here for help with this skills check

You should know how to:

1 Find the mean, median or mode of a set of numbers by hand, and the mean and median using statistical summaries on the GDC.

2 Find the mean, median or mode from a frequency table by hand or using statistical summaries on the GDC.

Skills check

1 Find the mean, median and mode of these numbers by hand:
14, 15, 17, 22, 26, 22, 21, 16, 17, 22

2 Find the mean and median of the numbers above using your GDC.

2.1 Collecting and organizing data

Qualitative data is non-numerical, eg "it was fun", "blue".

Quantitative data is numerical. Quantitative data can be **discrete** or **continuous**.

Discrete data is data which takes specific (discrete) values, eg "number of accidents", "points in the IB diploma".

Continuous data is data which can take a full range of values, eg "height", "speed".

International-mindedness

Ronald Fisher (1890–1962) lived in the UK and Australia and has been described as "a genius who almost single-handedly created the foundations for modern statistical science". He used statistics to analyse problems in medicine, agriculture and social sciences.

Investigation 1

1   In a certain school, grades in the final IB HL Mathematics exam are given:

4, 3, 6, 7, 5, 7, 4, 4, 5, 7, 6, 7, 6, 6, 4, 6, 6, 4

   Factual   Is the data discrete or continuous?

2   A frequency table can be created for the data in question 1.

   Copy and complete the frequency table:

Grade, g	3	4	5	6	7
Frequency	1	5			

3   Heights, to the nearest centimetre, of primroses in the garden are measured and given:

4, 3, 6, 7, 5, 7, 4, 4, 5, 7, 6, 7, 6, 6, 4, 6, 6, 4

   Factual   Is the data continuous or discrete?

4   A frequency table can be created for this data.

   Copy and complete the grouped frequency table:

Height, h, in cm	$2.5 \leq h < 3.5$	$3.5 \leq h < 4.5$	$4.5 \leq h < 5.5$	$5.5 \leq h < 6.5$	$6.5 \leq h < 7.5$
Frequency	1	5			

   Explain why the two cases are different.

5   **Conceptual**   When would discrete or continuous data occur? Think about how you would obtain the data and whether you would need any particular tools.

6   Ages, in years, of children in a nursery class are given:

4, 3, 6, 7, 5, 7, 4, 4, 5, 7, 6, 7, 6, 6, 4, 6, 6, 4

   Factual   Is the data continuous or discrete?

7   Explain why the frequency table would again be different and create the table.

Note: Age is a special case of data as it can also be regarded as discrete when you are considering only completed years.

HINT

Think about when you become 3 and when you stop being 3.

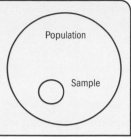

A **population** includes all members of a defined group.

A **sample** is a subset of the population, a selection of individuals from the population.

Biased sampling is where the method may cause you to draw misleading conclusions about the population.

Population

Sample

For example, drawing conclusions about people's use of public transport from a survey conducted in a train station.

The sampling methods below can be used if you can list every member of the population.

Simple random sampling: every member of the population is equally likely to be chosen. For example, allocate each member of the population a number. Then use random numbers to choose a sample.

Systematic sampling: find a sample of size n from a population of size N by selecting every k th member where $k = \dfrac{N}{n}$ to the nearest whole number.

For example, choosing every 15th student from the school register to find a sample of 100 from a population of 1500.

Stratified sampling: is selecting a random sample where numbers in certain categories are proportional to the numbers in the population.

For example, if 20% of students in a school were in Grade 7, then you would choose 20% of your sample from Grade 7.

Example 1

An educational psychologist recorded the IQs of 200 people. The 200 people are sorted in order of age and a sample of 40 is selected from the list and the mean of the sample is found, which will be used as an estimate for the mean of the whole population.

Identify the type of sample used in each case. Give any advantages and/or disadvantages in using this method to estimate the population mean.

a Take the first 20 numbers and the last 20 numbers.

b Take every fifth IQ.

c Generate 40 random numbers between 1 and 200 and use them to select the sample.

Continued on next page

a This is a biased sample since it is not random. It is easy to use but it is unreliable. Only the youngest and oldest will be selected.

b This is systematic sampling since every fifth entry is selected. It is easy to use and is not time consuming.

You can start at any number and choose every fifth number until you have 40 numbers in total.

It is possible to have different answer for this depending on the starting place. The fact you can start with any number means that each person has an equal chance of being selected.

c This is a random sample. Each time a random sample is chosen, different numbers will be generated. The advantage is that it is truly random. The dis-advantage is that it will produce different numbers each time and it can be time-consuming.

If you are not able to list every member of the population then you have to generate a sample to represent the population in the best way you can.

> **Quota sampling**: decide how many members of each group you want to sample and take samples from the population until you have a large enough sample for each group.

For example, the school canteen is considering introducing a new lunch menu and would like feedback from the students. The school has 250 boys and 300 girls and so the canteen manager decides to interview 25 boys and 30 girls to find out their opinion of the new menu. He stands at the entrance to the canteen and interviews the first 25 boys and 30 girls that come into the canteen.

Quota sampling is not random. It can be biased and unreliable. The advantage is that it is inexpensive, easy to perform and saves time.

However, it is more reliable than convenience sampling where people are selected based on availability and are not representative of the population. This type of sampling is also a non-probability sample and can also be biased and unreliable.

> **Convenience sampling**: take samples from the members of the population that you have access to until you have a sample of the desired size.

For example, asking people at a shopping centre to fill out a survey until you have 50 responses.

Investigation 2

All of the students at Valley High School must join either the Robotics Club or the Astronomy Club. The Headteacher at Valley High School wants to know if the Robotics Club members are performing better in Mathematics than the Astronomy Club members. He finds the scores of all students in the school in their University entrance exam for the last five years.

1 Give reasons why the Headteacher would have removed the names of the students.

2 Give reasons why you may prefer to do further analysis of the data using a sample, rather than all the data available.

3 **Conceptual** Why do we need to take a sample from the population?

Five suggestions are made as to how a sample of size 30 could be taken to see if Robotics club members are performing better than Astronomy Club members in Mathematics.

- Randomly select 30 students from all the results.
- Randomly select 30 students from the 2017 cohort.
- Randomly select 15 Robotics Club members and 15 Astronomy Club members from all the results.
- Use stratified sampling to randomly select students from each year according to the numbers in that year.
- Randomly choose a student and then choose every 18th student from there (upon reaching the end of the data, return to the beginning).

4 For the first suggestion, a GDC can generate 30 random integers from 1 to 545. Use this method to create a sample of 30 students' Mathematics result, along with their club. Consider what you will do if a number is repeated, or if the number points to a missing data item.

5 **Factual** Does your sample have an equal number of Robotics Club and Astronomy Club members?

6 **Factual** Does your sample have representative numbers from the different years?

7 **Conceptual** Can you identify any bias created when you have used this method of sampling?

8 **Conceptual** Can you think of different occasions where this type of sampling could have created extreme bias?

> **HINT**
>
> Make sure you can generate random numbers on your GDC.

Continued on next page

9 Use similar methods to collect a sample of 30 students' results using suggestion 2 and suggestion 3.

For each suggestion consider the guiding questions above and state the advantages of that particular method of sampling in this example.

Conceptual Can you identify any additional bias that might have been created by the sampling method or a bias that has been eliminated?

10 For suggestion 4, explain why you need to select four students from 2013, six from 2014, five from 2015, seven from 2016 and eight from 2017. Collect the sample for suggestion 4.

11 For suggestion 5, explain why you would take every 18th student.

   i What if you took every 10th student?

   ii Collect the sample for suggestion 5.

   iii Explain why this method also selects students according to the number in a particular year.

12 Discuss the pros and cons of each suggestion.

Which suggestion do you think will be the most representative of the population – that is all Robotics Club and Astronomy Club members in Valley High School?

13 **Conceptual** What are the different sampling methods and how do they provide meaningful insight into the general population?

Keep your results – you will be using them in sections 2.2 and 2.3.

Exercise 2A

1 It is suggested that the English results at Valley High School have been improving in the last five years. Choose a suitable sampling method to collect data that might be used to give evidence as to whether this is true or not.

Collect the sample and save it for use in sections 2.2 and 2.3.

---

2 A dog kennel has 120 dogs. The ages of the dogs, in order, are shown below.

1, 1, 1, 1, 1, 1, 1, 1, 1, 1, 2, 2, 2, 2, 2, 2, 2, 2, 3, 3, 3, 3, 3, 3, 3, 3, 3, 3, 3, 3, 3, 3, 3, 3, 4, 4, 4, 4, 4, 4, 4, 4, 4, 4, 4, 4, 5, 5, 5, 5, 5, 5, 5, 5, 5, 5, 5, 5, 5, 5, 5, 5, 5, 5, 6, 6, 6, 6, 6, 6, 6, 6, 6, 7, 7, 7, 7, 7, 7, 7, 7, 7, 7, 8, 8, 8, 8, 8, 8, 8, 8, 8, 9, 9, 9, 9, 9, 10, 10, 10, 10, 11, 11, 11, 11, 12, 12, 12, 13, 13, 13, 14, 14, 15, 16, 16.

   a Construct a table of values to represent the ages of the dogs and the frequency of their ages.

   b A sample of the population was taken to check the health of the dogs in the kennel. A systematic sample of every 5 dogs was used. How many dogs were taken for the sample?

   c In order to take a sample of 50 dogs, stratified by their age, state the number of dogs of each age you need to select.

---

3 In a poll to predict the results in an election, a sample from the population is taken with the intention of providing an accurate forecast. Explain why the sample would be stratified, and suggest different strata that might be important.

Developing inquiry skills

In the opening section you saw data from different countries regarding life expectancy, GDP, population and region. If you were to take a sample from all those countries to draw conclusions, how might you stratify your sample in order to reduce bias?

2.2 Statistical measures

Measures of central tendency (or averages)

- The most common measures of central tendency are the mean, median and mode.
- The **mode** of a data set is the value that occurs most frequently. There can be no mode, one mode, or several modes.
- The **median** of a data set is the value that lies in the middle when the data are arranged in size. When there are two middle values then the median is the midpoint between the two values.
- The **mean** of a data set is the sum of all the values divided by the number of values. For a discrete data set of n values the formula is $\bar{x} = \dfrac{1}{n} \sum_{i=1}^{n} x_i$

  where $\sum_{i=1}^{n} x_i = x_1 + x_2 + x_3 + \cdots + x_n$. Σ means "the sum of". For example, the mean of the numbers 3, 4, 8, 12, 16 is the sum (Σ) of the numbers divided by 5.
- When there is a frequency table, you need to use the data values and the corresponding frequencies to calculate the mean.

TOK

Do different measures of central tendency express different properties of the data?

How reliable are mathematical measures?

HINT

Make sure you know how to find the statistical summaries on your technology – for both lists of data and for frequency tables.

Statistics and probability

Example 2

The number of days of sunshine in Helsinki in January was recorded for a period of 35 years and the data is given in the frequency table:

a   State the modal number of days of sunshine in January in Helsinki for the period.

b   Calculate the mean number of days of sunshine in January in Helsinki for the period.

c   Determine the median number of days of sunshine in January in Helsinki for the period.

d   Comment on how a "day of sunshine" might be defined.

Number of days of sunshine	Number of years
3	1
4	2
5	1
6	2
7	7
8	5
9	9
10	8

Continued on next page

a 9 days	There are 9 years where there were 9 days of sunshine.
b 7.94 days	Remember that the frequency table represents the data set
	{3, 4, 4, 5, 6, 6, 7, 7, 7, 7, 7, 7, 7, 7, 8, 8, 8, 8, 8, 9, 9, 9, 9, 9, 9, 9, 9, 9, 10, 10, 10, 10, 10, 10, 10, 10}.
	$$\frac{3+(2\times4)+5+(2\times6)+(7\times7)+(5\times8)+(9\times9)+(8\times10)}{35}$$
	$$=\frac{278}{35}=7.94\ (3\ \text{s.f.})$$
	Or the answer can be obtained directly from the statistical summaries on the GDC.
c 8 days	For 35 data items, the median will be the 18th.
	The 14th to 18th data items are all 8 so the median is 8 days.
	Or the answer can be obtained directly from the statistical summaries on the GDC.
d Days with more than 3 hours where you can see the sun.	Many interpretations possible.

Measures of dispersion

- Measures of dispersion measure how spread out a data set is.
- The most common measure of dispersion is the **range**, which is found by subtracting the smallest number from the largest number.
- The standard deviation, σ_n, gives an idea of how the data values are related to the mean. The standard deviation is also known as the root-mean-squared deviation; its formula is:

$$\sigma_n = \sqrt{\frac{1}{n}\sum_{i=1}^{n}(x_i - \overline{x})^2} = \sqrt{\frac{1}{n}\sum_{i=1}^{n}x_i^2 - \overline{x}^2}$$

EXAM HINT

In examinations you will use your technology to find the standard deviation.

From the first formula it can be seen that the standard deviation is found by considering the distance of each point from the sample mean. If the differences are larger then the value of σ will also be greater.

The **variance** is the standard deviation squared: σ_n^2.

TOK

Why are there different formulae for the same statistical measures like mean and standard deviation?

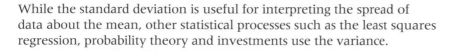

While the standard deviation is useful for interpreting the spread of data about the mean, other statistical processes such as the least squares regression, probability theory and investments use the variance.

> If the data is arranged in ascending order the nth percentile is the piece of data that is $n\%$ along the list. Hence the median is also the 50th percentile. The **interquartile range** (IQR) is the **upper quartile**, Q_3, minus the **lower quartile**, Q_1.
>
> When the data are arranged in order, the lower quartile is the median data point of the lower half of the data (at the 25th percentile) and the upper quartile is the median data point of the upper half of the data (at the 75th percentile).

> * Outliers are extreme data values, or the result of errors in reading data, that can distort the results of statistical processes.
> * Outliers can affect the mean by making it larger or smaller, but most likely will not affect the median or the mode.
> * Outliers can affect the standard deviation by making it larger, but they most likely will not affect the interquartile range.

> An **outlier** is defined as a data item that is more than $1.5 \times$ IQR below Q_1 or above Q_2.

Example 3

The number of days of precipitation in January in London for 2008–2017 is given in the table:

Year	2008	2009	2010	2011	2012	2013	2014	2015	2016	2017
Days of precipitation	19	16	21	21	13	21	30	26	21	15

(data from weatheronline.co.uk)

a Write down the range of the number of days of precipitation in January in London for these years.

b Calculate the interquartile range of the number of days of precipitation in January in London for these years.

c Find the standard deviation of the number of days of precipitation in January in London for these years.

d Find whether the 30 cm precipitation in January 2014 is an outlier.

a 17 days	The maximum value is 30 and the minimum value is 13. $30 - 13 = 17$.
b 5 days	Upper half of the data is $21, 21, 21, 26, 30$. The median of those is the middle term which is 21.

Continued on next page

Statistics and probability

	Lower half of the data is $13, 15, 16, 19, 21$.
	The median of those is 16.
	Interquartile range is $Q_3 - Q_1 = 21 - 16 = 5$
	Or the answer can be obtained directly from the statistical summaries on the GDC.
c 4.80 days	This value should be obtained directly from the GDC.
d $Q_3 = 21$ and IQR $= 5$ so it is true that $30 > 21 + 1.5 \times 5$ so the data item for 2014 is, as expected, an outlier.	

Investigation 3

1   In section 2.1, you collected five samples from the Mathematics results from Valley High School. Use each of the samples obtained to find an estimate of the mean and standard deviation of the Mathematics results all Robotics and Astronomy Club members in Valley High School over the period 2013–2017.

The mean and standard deviation of the population is in fact:

	Mean	Standard deviation
Robotics Club	75.3	12.5
Astronomy Club	78.5	9.74

Compare your answers with the actual values. Which seemed to be the best sampling method?

2   **Conceptual** Explain why you would have used technology for all those calculations.

Investigation 4

Complete the table for the following sets of numbers:

A: Find the mean and standard deviation of the numbers 3, 4, 6, 8, 9, 10, 15, 17.

B: Add 3 to each of the numbers in A and then find the mean and standard deviation.

C: Subtract 2 from each of the numbers in A and then find the mean and standard deviation.

D: Add 5 to each of the numbers in A and then find the mean and standard deviation.

E: Multiply the numbers in A by 3 and then find the mean and standard deviation.

F: Multiply the numbers in A by −2 and then find the mean and standard deviation.

G: Multiply the numbers in A by 0.5 and then find the mean and standard deviation.

	Mean	Standard deviation
A		
B		
C		
D		
E		
F		
G		

1 **Factual** What happens to the mean when you add or subtract a number from each term?

2 **Factual** What happens to the standard deviation when you add or subtract a number from each term?

3 **Factual** What happens to the mean when you multiply each number by a constant?

4 **Factual** What happens to the standard deviation when you multiply each number by a constant?

5 **Conceptual** Why does adding a constant to every value in a data set result in no change in the standard deviation?

6 The mean of a set of numbers is 10 and the standard deviation is 1.5.

   a If you add 3 to each term, write down the new mean and standard deviation.

   b If you multiply each term by 4, write down the new mean and standard deviation.

International-mindedness

The 19th century German psychologist Gustav Fechner popularized the median as a measure of central tendency although French mathematician Pierre Laplace had used it earlier.

The mean of a set of numbers is $\bar{x}$ and the standard deviation is σ_x.

If you add k to or subtract k from each of the numbers then the mean is $\bar{x} \pm k$ and the standard deviation is σ_x.

If you multiply each number by k then the mean is $k \times \bar{x}$ and the standard deviation is $|k| \times \sigma_x$.

Statistics and probability

Exercise 2B

1 Find the mean, median and mode for the following data sets and comment on any pieces of data that you think may be outliers.

   a The times of 25 telephone calls in minutes:

   1.0, 1.5, 2.3, 2.6, 2.8, 3.0, 3.4, 3.8, 4.1, 4.5, 4.6, 4.8, 5.2, 5.3, 5.5, 5.8, 6.0, 6.3, 6.6, 7.3, 7.5, 7.5, 7.5, 17.8, 25.0

   b The heights, in metres, of 15 sunflowers:

   1.1, 2.2, 2.5, 2.5, 2.5, 3.1, 3.5, 3.6, 3.9, 4.0, 4.1, 4.4, 4.6, 4.9, 6.1

   c The results of a Geography test:

   22, 39, 45, 46, 46, 52, 54, 58, 62, 62, 62, 67, 70, 75, 78, 82, 89, 91, 95, 98

2 In a survey, 25 people were asked how many times they visited the cinema in the last two weeks. The results are given in the frequency table:

Number of visits	0	1	2	3	5	8
Number of people	5	5	6	2	1	1

   a Find the mean, median and modal number of visits.

   b Find the standard deviation and the variance of the number of visits.

3 The table shows the number of orthodontist visits per year made by the students in Grade 10.

Number of visits	0	4	6	8	10	12	14
Frequency	3	2	8	4	2	12	5

a Find the mode, the median and the mean, and comment on which is the most appropriate to use.

b Find the standard deviation and comment on the result.

c Find the range and interquartile range, and comment on the spread of the data.

4 The heights in centimetres of 15 basketball players are:

> 175, 183, 191, 196, 198, 201, 203, 203, 204, 206, 207, 209, 211, 212, 213

The heights of 15 randomly chosen males are:

> 154, 158, 158, 162, 165, 168, 171, 176, 178, 180, 181, 182, 182, 183, 186

a Find the mean and standard deviation for each group.

b Compare your answers and comment on any similarities or differences.

5 Mr Jones, a teacher in Valley High School, collects the following data from his class and suggests that it provides evidence that Robotics Club members are better at Maths than Astronomy Club members.

Name	Club	Result	Name	Club	Result
Abdullah L	R	72	Justine H	R	83
Angela W	R	96	Kara F	A	70
Arthur B	R	84	Kay H	A	60
Brad S	A	61	Lia S	A	70
Dalia V	A	83	Marcus C	A	64
Eddie R	A	77	Marina B	R	89
Elsie D	A	78	Mattias L	R	52
Emma M	A	60	Natalya A	A	60
Ernesto H	R	65	Preston H	A	68
Hadassah H	R	79	Thalia C	A	69
Jenny E	A	83	Vance T	R	83
Joanna S	R	81	Waylon D	R	57
Jonathan S	A	69			

Calculate the mean, median, standard deviation and quartiles for the Robotics and Astronomy Clubs' Maths results in Mr Jones' class. State whether or not your calculations support Mr Jones' claim.

6 For the sample collected in Exercise 2A question 1, find the mean and standard deviation for the English results of each year. Comment on any changes in the distribution of English results over the five years that are indicated by these values.

7 The number of sweets in 25 bags has a mean of 30 and standard deviation of 3. In a special promotion, the manufacturer doubles the number of sweets in each bag. Write down the new mean and the new standard deviation of the number of sweets in a bag.

8 Mrs Ginger's Grade 8 class sat an English test. The test was out of 40 marks. The mean score was 32 marks and the standard deviation was 8 marks.

In order to change this to a mark out of 100, Mrs Ginger thinks that it would be all right to multiply all the scores by 2 and then add 20 to each one.

Mr Ginger thinks that it would be fairer to multiply all the scores by 2.5.

Miss Ginger suggests multiplying by 3 and subtracting 20 from each score.

a Write down the new mean and the new standard deviation for each suggestion.

Matty had an original score of 12, Zoe had an original score of 25 and Ans had an original score of 36.

b Find their new scores under all three suggested changes.

c Comment on how each of these three suggestions would affect students with low, middling and high marks out of 40.

Statistical measures of continuous data

Until now we have been looking at finding summary measures for discrete data.

For continuous data we can only consider estimations as we never know the exact value of any data item.

> If data is continuous you find **estimates** for the mean, variance or standard deviation by assuming that all of the data values are equally spread around the midpoint.
>
> You can find a **modal class** if the data are arranged in intervals of equal width.

Example 4

Heights of 200 fir trees are measured and the results recorded:

Height, h (m)	$0 < h \leq 1$	$1 < h \leq 2$	$2 < h \leq 3$	$3 < h \leq 4$	$4 < h \leq 6$	$6 < h \leq 10$
Frequency	17	35	69	51	22	6

a Find estimates for the mean and standard deviation of the height of these fir trees.

b State why your calculations are estimates.

a Estimate of mean = 2.85 Estimate of SD = 4.36 (3 s.f.)	First enter the data into your GDC using mid-points as the data points then find values as normal.
b They are only estimates because mid-points have been entered as estimates of what the data points might actually have been.	Having entered the data all the summary values, for example the median or quartiles can be found directly from the GDC.

Statistics and probability

Exercise 2C

1 For the following sets of data, find

  i the modal class

  ii an estimate for the mean

  iii an estimate for the median.

  Comment on the meaning of these values and state which one is most appropriate to use in each case, giving a reason for your answer.

a

Number of cars, n	Frequency
$0 \le n < 30$	12
$30 \le n < 60$	28
$60 \le n < 90$	39
$90 \le n < 120$	42
$120 \le n < 150$	54
$150 \le n < 180$	65

b

Speed of cars, s (mph)	Frequency
$40 \le s < 45$	4
$45 \le s < 50$	8
$50 \le s < 55$	23
$55 \le s < 60$	15
$60 \le s < 65$	6
$65 \le s < 70$	4

c

Time to complete a puzzle, t (minutes)	Frequency
$2 \le t < 3$	2
$3 \le t < 4$	5
$4 \le t < 5$	3
$5 \le t < 6$	7
$6 \le t < 7$	4
$7 \le t < 8$	9
$8 \le t < 9$	3

2 Gal asked 60 people how much money they had spent the last time they had eaten in a restaurant. The table shows his results.

Cost of dinner, c (GBP)	Frequency
$10 \le c < 20$	6
$20 \le c < 30$	12
$30 \le c < 40$	28
$40 \le c < 50$	10
$50 \le c < 60$	4

a Write down the modal class.

b Find an estimate for the mean and the median.

c Find an estimate for the standard deviation and comment on the result.

d Find an estimate for the variance, the range and the interquartile range and explain why these are all estimates.

3 The table shows the heights of 50 wallabies.

Height, x cm	Frequency
$150 \le x < 160$	3
$160 \le x < 170$	5
$170 \le x < 180$	13
$180 \le x < 190$	23
$190 \le x < 200$	4
$200 \le x < 210$	2

a Write down the modal class.

b Find an estimate for the mean and standard deviation; comment on your answer.

4 The table shows the monthly salaries of all the staff at Mount High College.

Monthly salary, $x	Number of males	Number of females
$1000 < x \le 1500$	4	9
$1500 < x \le 2000$	8	14
$2000 < x \le 2500$	14	11
$2500 < x \le 3000$	16	10
$3000 < x \le 3500$	7	3
$3500 < x \le 4000$	2	1
$4000 < x \le 4500$	3	0

a Find the mean and standard deviation for each group.

b Compare your answers and comment on any similarities or differences.

Developing inquiry skills

Take a sample from the data in the opening section and use it to calculate statistical summaries, to determine whether different regions have different life expectancies.

2.3 Ways in which you can present data

Frequency histograms

A **histogram** is very similar to a **bar chart**. However, in a histogram there are no spaces between the bars.

Bar charts are useful for graphing **qualitative** data such as colour preference, whereas histograms are used to graph **quantitative** data.

Frequency histograms, like bar charts, have the vertical axis representing frequency.

To draw a frequency histogram, you need to find the lower and upper boundaries of the classes and draw the bars between these boundaries.

Example 5

The data shown in the table was collected for Hawkmoth caterpillars, measured to the nearest cm.

Length, l (cm)	4	5	6	7	8	9
Frequency	19	56	74	45	5	1

Use the data to draw a frequency histogram.

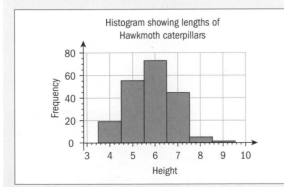

As data goes from 3.5–9.5, our horizontal axes needs to include at least that. Choose 3–10.

The maximum frequency is 74 so have the vertical axis up to say 80.

First bar has height of 19 and width from 3.5 to 4.5 etc.

Box-and-whisker diagrams

Box-and-whisker diagrams (often just called box diagrams) are another convenient way to present data to allow us to easily visualize characteristics of the data. They can be drawn for discrete or continuous data and are often very convenient for comparing sets of data.

> To draw a box diagram, you first need to calculate the median, the quartiles, and the minimum and maximum values of the data. You then draw the box diagram as shown.
>
>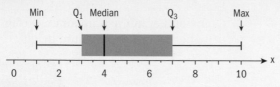

Example 6

The box-and-whisker diagrams below show the heights of all prominent peaks in different regions of central Asia.

a State which region has the tallest mountain.

b State the region with the lowest standard deviation.

c Estimate the median height of peaks in the Karakoram.

d Estimate the interquartile range of heights of peaks in the Himalaya.

e Estimate the range of heights of peaks in the Karakoram.

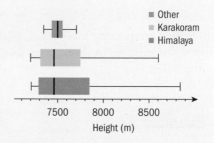

a Himalaya	The maximum value is over 8800 which is higher than any other region (in fact Mount Everest which is 8848 m).
b Other	The data is less spread than the other regions.
c 7450 m	Somewhere between 7400 and 7500, about the same as for the Himalaya
d 550 m	About 7850 – 7300 = 550
e 1400 m	About 8600 – 7200 = 1400

> The outliers are represented on a box-and-whisker diagram as separate crosses.

Example 7

The box-and-whisker diagrams from Example 6 are
shown along with outliers.

a State in which region you would find the second
highest mountain.

b Estimate the height of the second highest mountain
in the Himalaya.

c Estimate the difference between the highest peak
and the second highest peak in the Karakoram.

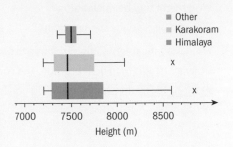

a The Karakoram	The outlier in the Karakoram is (slightly) higher than the maximum height in the Himalaya, apart from Everest (in fact it is K2).
b 8600 m	The maximum height inside the outlier is about 8600 m.
c 500 m	About $8600 - 8100 = 500$ m

Investigation 5

Five investment companies, Altrucorp, Betterinvest, Cityshares, Dependshare and Eversafe each wish for
you to invest your money through their company.

Eversafe promotes itself by saying that "over half its clients get a return of over 9.35% – more than 0.17%
better than its nearest rival".

The summary data for the five companies is given here. Explain why Eversafe is justified in its claim.

Company	Number of investors	Mean % return	Median % return	Standard Deviation	Minimum % return	Maximum % return	Q_1	Q_3
A	106	9.12651	9.0063	0.522407	8.50703	11.5461	8.7799	9.35084
B	259	9.11148	9.17521	0.356837	7.46087	9.72693	8.91512	9.36484
C	978	9.09267	9.09045	0.195937	8.43358	9.63638	8.96163	9.22571
D	1222	9.09522	9.08718	0.491454	7.34769	11.0731	8.76	9.42048
E	312	9.08224	9.35156	0.794434	5.58167	9.59996	8.95071	9.53696

1 Draw a box-and-whisker diagram to illustrate the five companies. Explain how that would help to decide
on which company you would use to invest your money.

2 The box-and-whisker diagram for Altrucorp is shown with outliers.

Why might this change your perception
of the company?

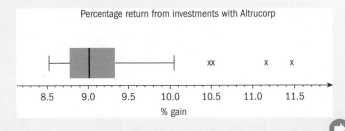

Percentage return from investments with Altrucorp

Continued on next page

3 Altrucorp uses this graph to promote itself.

Why might this be misleading?

Would it be dishonest advertising?

4 What statistic might Cityshares use to promote itself?

Draw a histogram to best promote the company.

Conceptual In what ways could you use graphics to mislead?

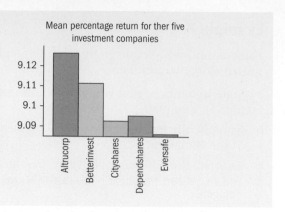

Mean percentage return for ther five investment companies

Exercise 2D

1 The number of days of precipitation in January in London for 2008–2017 is given in the table:

Year	2008	2009	2010	2011	2012	2013	2014	2015	2016	2017
Days of precipitation	19	16	21	21	13	21	30	26	21	15

(data from weatheronline.co.uk)

Draw a box-and-whisker diagram for the number of days of precipitation in London for the given years, marking the outlier.

2 The time, in minutes, to complete 200 games of chess is shown in the table.

Time, x minutes	Frequency
$20 \leq x < 30$	36
$30 \leq x < 40$	67
$40 \leq x < 50$	48
$50 \leq x < 60$	27
$60 \leq x < 70$	10
$70 \leq x < 80$	7
$80 \leq x < 90$	5

a Draw a histogram to represent this data.

b Find the mean, median, Q_1, Q_3 and range, and determine if there are any outliers.

c Given that the quickest time was 26 minutes and the longest time was 84 minutes, draw a box-and-whisker plot to represent this data.

3 a Use the data from example 3 in section 2.2 to draw a histogram for the number of days of sunshine in Helsinki. You

should regard the discrete data as continuous to draw a histogram (ie treat 1 day as an interval from 0.5 to 1.5).

b Comment on the symmetry of the data.

4 For each of the five samples you collected from the Mathematics results from Valley High School in section 2.1, draw separate box-and-whisker diagrams for the Robotics Club and Astronomy Club, clearly showing any outliers. The box-and-whisker diagram for the entire student population is shown.

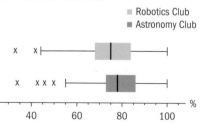

State which of your samples best represents the school population over the period 2013–2017.

Cumulative frequency

The **cumulative frequency** is the sum of all the frequencies up to and including the new value. To draw a cumulative frequency curve, you need to construct a cumulative frequency table, with the upper boundary of each class interval in one column and the corresponding cumulative frequency in another. Then plot the upper class boundary on the x-axis and the cumulative frequency on the y-axis.

- If data is continuous we find **estimates** for the median or interquartile range from a cumulative frequency curve or cumulative frequency polygon.
- To find any **percentile**, $p\%$, you read the value on the curve corresponding to $p\%$ of the total frequency.

Investigation 6

1   A sample of 200 Hawkmoth caterpillars were measured and their lengths to the nearest cm are given in the table:

Length, l (cm)	4	5	6	7	8	9
Frequency	19	56	74	45	5	1

Explain why 75 of the caterpillars are less than 5.5 cm.

2   Use your answer from above to complete the cumulative frequency table:

Length, l (cm)	$l < 3.5$	$l < 4.5$	$l < 5.5$	$l < 6.5$	$l < 7.5$	$l < 8.5$	$l < 9.5$
Cumulative frequency			75				

Factual   How are all the values for the cumulative frequency calculated?

The points can be plotted and joined with a curve to create a cumulative frequency curve or joined with straight lines to create a cumulative frequency polygon. Unfortunately, that is not normally a task that can be completed on the GDC.

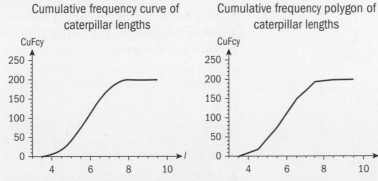

Cumulative frequency curve of caterpillar lengths

Cumulative frequency polygon of caterpillar lengths

The curve shows how many caterpillars are less than a given length. Since half of the caterpillars are less than the median length, we can read off from the graph that 100 caterpillars are less than 5.8 cm. So the median is 5.8 cm.

> **EXAM HINT**
>
> If you are asked to draw a cumulative frequency curve, do **not** draw a cumulative frequency polygon.

Continued on next page

Statistics and probability

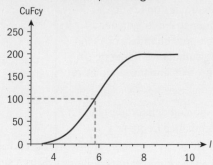

Cumulative frequency curve
of caterpillar lengths

When using the GDC, there were 74 data points entered as 6 cm. The actual lengths of all these caterpillars was somewhere between 5.5 cm and 6.5 cm. When calculating the statistical summaries on the GDC, it gives the median as 6, whereas it appears as 5.8 from the graph.

3 Why should this be different?

25% of caterpillars will be less than the value of Q_1. Use the graph to read off the approximate value of Q_1.

4 **Factual** How would you use the cumulative frequency graph to find an estimate for the upper quartile of the data?

Similarly use the graph to find the value of Q_3 and of the interquartile range.

5 How could you use the graph to find how many caterpillars were more than 7 cm?

6 **Conceptual** What is the purpose of using cumulative frequency graphs?

7 Use the cumulative frequency curve to find the 95th and the 90th percentiles.

> **EXAM HINT**
>
> Always show lines on the graph to show how you have found the required value.

> **TOK**
>
> Why have mathematics and statistics sometimes been treated as separate subjects?

Exercise 2E

1 The table shows the average times, in minutes, that 100 people waited for a train.

Time, x minutes	Frequency
$0 \leq x < 2$	5
$2 \leq x < 4$	11
$4 \leq x < 6$	23
$6 \leq x < 8$	31
$8 \leq x < 10$	19
$10 \leq x < 12$	8
$12 \leq x < 14$	3

a Draw a cumulative frequency table for this data.

b Sketch the cumulative frequency curve.

c Use your graph to find an estimate for the median and interquartile range.

d Find the 10th percentile.

The train company will refund the fare if their customers have to wait 11 minutes or more for a train.

e Determine the number of customers who can claim for a refund of their fare.

2 Nuria recorded the number of words in a sentence in one chapter of her favourite book. The results are shown in the table.

Number of words, x	Frequency
$0 \le x < 4$	5
$4 \le x < 8$	32
$8 \le x < 12$	41
$12 \le x < 16$	28
$16 \le x < 20$	22
$20 \le x < 24$	12
$24 \le x < 28$	7
$28 \le x < 32$	3

a Construct a cumulative frequency table for this data.

b Sketch the cumulative frequency curve.

c Use your graph to find an estimate for the median and interquartile range.

d Determine if there are any outliers.

e Find the 90th percentile.

f The smallest sentence had 1 word and the longest sentence had 31 words. Draw a box-and-whisker plot to represent this information.

g A children's book has, on average, 8 words in a sentence and an adult book has, on average, 15 words in a sentence. State the type of book you think Nuria is reading. Explain your answer.

---

3 In example 6, the heights of 200 fir trees were given as:

Height, h (m)	$0 < h \le 1$	$1 < h \le 2$	$2 < h \le 3$	$3 < h \le 4$	$4 < h \le 6$	$6 < h \le 10$
Frequency	17	35	69	51	22	6

a Construct a cumulative frequency table for the heights of fir trees.

b Draw a cumulative frequency curve for the heights of fir trees.

c Estimate the median height of the 200 fir trees.

d Estimate the interquartile range of the heights.

e Estimate the 10th percentile of the heights.

f If the tallest 12 trees are to be felled, estimate the height of the smallest tree felled.

---

4 Use the data in Section 2.3, investigation 6, to draw a box-and-whisker diagram to illustrate the lengths of the 200 Hawkmoth caterpillars.

5 A tourist attraction is open 350 days in the year. The number of visitors each day for the 350 days was recorded and the results are shown in the table.

Number of visitors, n	Frequency
$100 \le n < 200$	24
$200 \le n < 300$	36
$300 \le n < 400$	68
$400 \le n < 500$	95
$500 \le n < 600$	73
$600 \le n < 700$	38
$700 \le n < 800$	16

a Draw a suitable graph to represent this data.

b Use your graph or the data to find an estimate for the median and interquartile range.

c State whether or not there are any outliers.

d The smallest number of visitors was 185 and the largest number was 792. Draw a box-and-whisker plot to represent this data.

If the number of tourists is less than 350, then the attraction loses revenue.

e Determine the number of days that the attraction loses revenue.

Developing inquiry skills

Would you have a better understanding of a set of data after looking at either:

a the raw data

b summary statistics

c statistical charts

d a combination of two or more of the above.

At the end of section 2.2, you collected a sample from the data in the opening section. Use that data to draw statistical charts to illustrate your findings.

International-mindedness

Hans Rosling (1948–2017) was a professor of international health at Sweden's Karolinska Institute. He co-founded the Swedish chapter of Medécins Sans Frontières, and was able to clearly show the importance of collecting and understanding real data in order to understand situations and plan for the future.

2.4 Bivariate data

- Are students who are good at Mathematics also good at Physics?
- Is smoking linked to lung cancer?
- Is the re-election of a government influenced by the state of the economy?
- Is a good breakfast essential to success in school?

In the previous sections we have been looking at ways to analyse a set of data in one variable. Frequently it is necessary to look at ways in which one variable interacts with another.

> **Bivariate** data has **two** variables; **univariate** data has only **one** variable.
>
> With bivariate data you have **two sets of data** that you want to compare to see if there is any **correlation** between the two sets.

Mr Price was interested to find out if the number of past papers that his students completed had an effect on the grade they obtained in their final examination. The data he collected is shown below.

Number of past papers	2	6	5	1	4	8	3	12	7	4	2	8	10	9
Examination grade (%)	48	70	61	45	58	85	55	96	80	56	43	88	92	89

He plots all these points on a graph to see if there is any correlation between the two sets of data. The number of past papers is the **independent** variable and this is plotted on the *x*-axis. The examination grade is the **dependent** variable and this is plotted on the *y*-axis.

The pattern of dots or crosses will give him an indication of how closely the variables are related.

Do you think that the two sets of data are related?

How closely do you think they are related?

What advice would you give to students who have to take examinations?

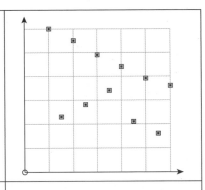

Types of correlation

If you have date items x_1, x_2, ..., x_n with associated data items y_1, y_2, ..., y_n then we can draw a **scatter diagram** by plotting the data pairs (x_1, y_1), (x_2, y_2), ..., (x_n, y_n).

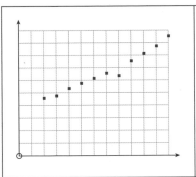 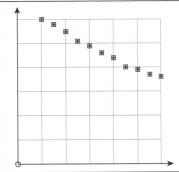

Correlation can be **positive**. When the independent variable increases, so does the dependent variable.	Correlation can be **negative**. When the independent variable increases, the dependent variable decreases.	There can also be **no correlation**. This occurs when the points are scattered randomly.

Correlation can also be described as strong, moderate or weak.

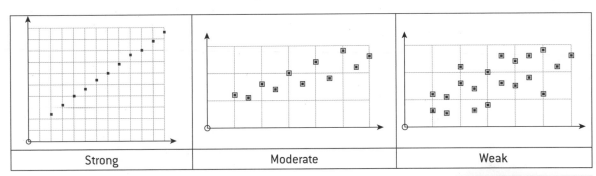

Strong	Moderate	Weak

Correlation does not imply **causation**. Two quantities may have very strong correlation but that may be due to an underlying cause in common, or simply coincidence.

TOK

To what extent can we rely on technology to produce our results?

Statistics and probability

Example 8

1 The table shows the number of schools and the number of restaurants in a town over a 40-year period.

Year	1980	1985	1990	1995	2000	2005	2010	2015	2020
Number of schools	12	13	15	15	16	17	17	18	19
Number of restaurants	28	30	33	34	36	36	38	39	40

Continued on next page

a Draw a scatter graph of the number of schools and the number of restaurants.

  b Describe the correlation between the two sets of data.

  c State whether or not you think that one set of data "causes" the other set.

  d State another reason why the number of schools and the number of restaurants increased over the 40-year period.

1 a

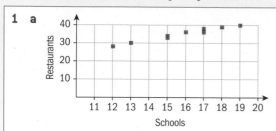

  b There is a strong, positive correlation.

  c Not directly.

  d The population in the town could be increasing every year, which could require more schools and more restaurants.

- A **line of best fit** can be drawn on a scatter diagram, by plotting the point $(\bar{x}, \bar{y})$ and drawing a line through that point that best follows the trend of the data.

- If the gradient of that line is positive then we say that the data has **positive correlation**.

- If the gradient of the line is negative then it has **negative correlation**.

- The strength of correlation is determined by how close the data points are from the line.

Example 9

The results of ten students in their final Mathematics and Physics exams are given.

Student	1	2	3	4	5	6	7	8	9	10
Mathematics result (%)	78	56	88	93	44	76	33	59	82	99
Physics result (%)	84	62	84	100	51	90	42	74	80	89

  a Plot the information on a scatter diagram.

  b Plot the point $(\bar{x}, \bar{y})$ and draw the line of best fit.

  c Predict the Physics result for a student who scored 65% on their Mathematics exam.

  d State whether or not the results indicate that students who are good at Mathematics are also good at Physics.

a

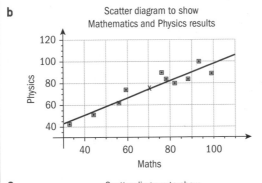

Plot the points $(78, 84)$, $(56, 62)$ etc on a set of axes.

b

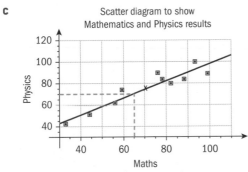

The mean of x_1, x_2, ..., x_{10} is $\bar{x} = 70.8$.

The mean of y_1, y_2, ..., y_{10} is $\bar{y} = 75.6$.

Mark $(70.8, 75.6)$.

Draw line so that is best matches.

c

Scatter diagram to show
Mathematics and Physics results

Use the line of best fit to predict the score.

Using the line of best fit to predict a data value within the range of the given data is called interpolation.

The predicted score is 70%

d There is some indication that high results in Mathematics correspond to high results in Physics

The line of best fit has a positive gradient and the data are closely clustered around the line of best fit.

The example above shows what appears to be quite a strong correlation.

We have a measure of the strength of linear correlation, called Pearson's product-moment correlation coefficient (PMCC), which is denoted by r.

PMCC can be calculated using technology and takes values between -1 and 1. $r = 1$ indicates perfect positive correlation, whereas $r = -1$ indicates perfect negative correlation. $r = 0$ indicates no correlation

Statistics and probability

Make sure you know how to calculate the value of r using your technology.

Example 10

Year	2000	2001	2002	2003	2004	2005	2006	2007	2008	2009
x	227	456	509	497	596	573	661	741	809	717
y	29.8	30.1	30.5	30.6	31.3	31.7	32.6	33.1	32.7	32.8

a For the data shown, calculate r, Pearson's product-moment correlation coefficient.

b Comment on the strength of correlation.

a 0.918	$r = 0.918$
b The data shows strong positive correlation.	r is close to 1 so there is strong positive correlation

In example 10, you found a strong positive correlation. This might be surprising if you consider that the data items for x were the number of people who died by becoming entangled in their bedsheets in the US and the data values for y were the amount of cheese per capita consumed in the US (in lb). (Data from http://www.tylervigen.com/spurious-correlations.)

Investigation 7

A drug is developed for treating a skin condition. A trial was undertaken to discover the effects of different daily dosages. The table gives effects on the decrease in the area of skin affected and the amount of fever the patient is showing.

Dosage (mg)	4	5	6	7	8	9	10	11	12
Percentage decrease in area of skin affected per year	5.9	8.2	12.7	20.6	18.7	8.4	24.9	34.2	35
Patient temperature (°C)	39.3	39.2	38.8	38.8	38.4	38.4	38	38.3	37.7

1 With a horizontal axis from 0 to 20 and a vertical axis from 0 to 40, plot the percentage decrease against the dosage.

2 Does your scatter diagram indicate that a higher dosage of the drug is likely to produce a greater percentage decrease in the skin affected?

3 Explain why we would consider dosage to be the independent variable and the percentage decrease in infected skin to be the dependent variable.

4 A researcher believes that one of the data points was recorded incorrectly during the trial.

• Which data point could be classified as an outlier?

• If the data was recorded correctly, give another explanation why the outlier does not fit the pattern of the other results.

5 Exclude the outlier to calculate the PMCC. Comment on the correlation.

6 Draw another scatter diagram with a horizontal axis from 0 to 20 and a vertical axis from 37 to 40. Plot the patient temperature against the dosage.

7 Continue to exclude the outlier to calculate the PMCC in this case. Comment on the correlation.

8 Do your results indicate that the dosage given influences the patient temperature?

9 Again in each case, excluding the outlier, calculate the coordinates of $(\bar{x}, \bar{y})$ and draw the line of best fit onto your graph.

10 The trial continued with increased dosages and the results are given.

Dosage (mg)	13	14	15	16	17	18	19
Percentage decrease in area of skin affected per year	36.3	35.2	36.6	33.1	36.6	25.8	21
Patient temperature (°C)	38.3	37.2	38	38.3	37.6	37.3	37.8

Plot the extra data points onto your scatter diagrams.

11 Do the data points maintain the same trend?

Give possible reasons why.

12 If you were to calculate the value of r for the whole data set explain what you would expect to find.

13 **Conceptual** Can we use extrapolation to predict beyond the data points? Why or why not?

> Extrapolation means estimating a value at a point that is larger than (or smaller than) the data you have.
>
> Trends in data are only valid for the range of study. We cannot **extrapolate** to draw conclusions outside of that range.

Exercise 2F

1 The table shows the size, in inches, of 10 laptop screens and the cost, in euros, of the laptop.

Size, inches	11.6	11.6	13.3	14	14	14	15	15.6	15.6	15.6
Cost, euros	145	170	700	450	370	175	320	500	420	615

a Plot the points on a scatter diagram.

b Describe and interpret the correlation.

c Comment on whether the size has an influence on the cost.

2 The table gives the heights, in cm, and weights, in kg, of 11 football players selected at random.

Height, h cm	161	173	154	181	172	184	176	169	165	180	173
Weight, w kg	74	76	61	80	76	88	79	76	75	83	75

a Plot the points on a scatter diagram.

b Calculate the coordinates of the point $(\bar{h}, \bar{w})$ and mark it on your graph.

c Draw a line of best fit.

d Predict the weight of a football player with height 170 cm.

e Calculate Pearson's Product-Moment Correlation Coefficient for the data.

f Describe the correlation. Interpret what this means in terms of the football players.

g Comment on whether the correlation might indicate a causation in this instance. Justify your answer.

3 A sample of 15 people were taken and given a vocabulary test. Their test results, v (%), were compared against their heights, h (cm), and the results given in the table:

h	1.18	1.26	1.32	1.50	1.63	1.70	1.69	1.45	1.56	1.23	1.44	1.53	1.60	1.38	1.30
v	51	64	59	67	80	82	77	75	67	54	66	81	75	69	54

a Draw a scatter diagram to show the data, with height as the independent variable.

b Calculate the coordinates of the point $(\bar{h}, \bar{v})$ and mark it on your graph.

c Draw a line of best fit.

d Klaus is 1.92 m tall, predict his vocabulary test result and comment on your prediction.

e Calculate Pearson's Product-Moment Correlation Coefficient for the data.

f Comment on the correlation of the data.

g Comment on whether this shows that taller people have better vocabularies.

4 Prices of unleaded fuel and diesel (in euros) in December 2017 are recorded across 28 EU countries.

Unleaded	1.168	1.403	1.064	1.259	1.203	1.156	1.597	1.229	1.416	1.421	1.369	1.558	1.151	1.389
Diesel	1.068	1.392	1.069	1.207	1.215	1.094	1.395	1.229	1.3	1.303	1.209	1.359	1.18	1.279
Unleaded	1.581	1.117	1.143	1.18	1.31	1.678	1.065	1.544	1.07	1.172	1.26	1.236	1.459	1.361
Diesel	1.444	1.037	1.039	1.043	1.18	1.37	1.041	1.354	1.083	1.035	1.217	1.157	1.467	1.394

http://www.fuel-prices-europe.info/

a Draw a scatter plot of the data, with the cost of unleaded fuel as the independent variable.

b Calculate the value of r and comment on the correlation between the cost of unleaded fuel and the cost of diesel.

Developing inquiry skills

For the country data given in the opening of this chapter, take a suitable sample to determine whether GDP and income have any correlation.

Chapter summary

- **Qualitative data** is non-numerical, eg "it was fun", "blue".
- **Quantitative data** is numerical. Quantitative data can be **discrete** or **continuous**.
- **Discrete data** is data which takes specific (discrete) values, eg "number of accidents", "points in the IB diploma".
- **Continuous data** is data which can take a full range of values, eg "height", "speed".
- A **population** includes all members of a defined group.
- A **sample** is a subset of the population, a selection of individuals from the population.
- **Biased sampling:** The sampling method is not random so not all members of the population are equally likely to be selected. Biased sampling may cause you to draw misleading conclusions about the population.

- **Simple random sampling:** every member of the population is equally likely to be chosen. For example, allocate each member of the population a number. Then use random numbers to choose a sample.
- **Systematic sampling:** find a sample of size n from a population of size N by selecting every k th member where $k = \dfrac{N}{n}$ rounded to the nearest whole number.
- **Stratified sampling:** is selecting a random sample where numbers in certain categories are proportional to the numbers in the population.
- **Quota sampling:** decide how many members of each group you want to sample and take samples from the population until you have a large enough sample for each group.
- **Convenience sampling:** take samples from the members of the population that you have access to until you have a sample of the desired size.
- The most common measures of central tendency are the mean, median and mode.
- The **mode** of a data set is the value that occurs most frequently. There can be no mode, one mode, or several modes.
- The **median** of a data set is the value that lies in the middle when the data are arranged in size. When there are two middle values then the median is the midpoint between the two values.
- The **mean** of a data set is the sum of all the values divided by the number of values. For a discrete data set of n values the formula is $\bar{x} = \dfrac{1}{n}\displaystyle\sum_{i=1}^{n} x_i$, where $\displaystyle\sum_{i=1}^{n} x_i = x_1 + x_2 + x_3 + \cdots + x_n$. Σ means "the sum of".
- When there is a frequency table, you need to use the data values and the corresponding frequencies to calculate the mean.
- Measures of dispersion measure how spread out a data set is.
- The most common measure of dispersion is the **range**, which is found by subtracting the smallest number from the largest number.
- The standard deviation, σ_n, gives an idea of how the data values are related to the mean. The greater the standard deviation, the more spread out the data.
- In examinations you will use your GDC to find the standard deviation.
- The **variance** is the standard deviation squared: $(\sigma_n)^2$.
- The **interquartile range** (IQR) is the **upper quartile**, Q_3, minus the **lower quartile**, Q_1.
- When the data are arranged in order, the lower quartile is the data point at the 25th percentile and the upper quartile is the data point at the 75th percentile.
- An **outlier** is defined as a data item that is more than $1.5 \times$ IQR below Q_1 or above Q_3.
- Outliers are extreme data values, or the result of errors in reading data, that can distort the results of statistical processes.
- Outliers can affect the mean by making it larger or smaller, but most likely will not affect the median or the mode.
- Outliers can affect the standard deviation by making it larger or smaller, but they most likely will not affect the interquartile range.
- Given the mean of a set of numbers is $\bar{x}$ and the standard deviation is σ_x.
  If you add k to or subtract k from each of the numbers then the mean is $\bar{x} \pm k$ and the standard deviation is σ_x.
  If you multiply each number by k then the mean is $k \times \bar{x}$ and the standard deviation is $|k| \times \sigma_x$.

Statistics and probability

Continued on next page

- If data is continuous we find **estimates** for the mean, variance or standard deviation by assuming that all of the data values are equally spread around the midpoint.
- We can find a **modal class** if the data are arranged in intervals of equal width.
- Frequency histograms, like bar charts, have the vertical axis representing frequency.
- To draw a frequency histogram, you need to find the lower and upper boundaries of the classes and draw the bars between these boundaries.
- To draw a box-and-whisker plot you need five pieces of information: the smallest value, the lower quartile, the median, the upper quartile and the largest value.
- The outliers are represented on the box-and-whisker diagram as separate crosses.
- The **cumulative frequency** is the sum of all the frequencies up to and including the new value. To draw a cumulative frequency curve, you need to construct a cumulative frequency table, with the upper boundary of each class interval in one column and the corresponding cumulative frequency in another. Then plot the upper class boundary on the x-axis and the cumulative frequency on the y-axis.
- If data is continuous we find **estimates** for the median or interquartile range from a cumulative frequency curve or cumulative frequency polygon.
- To find any **percentile**, $p\%$, you read the value on the curve corresponding to $p\%$ of the total frequency.
- **Bivariate** data has **two** variables; **univariate** data has only **one** variable.
- With bivariate data you have **two sets of data** that you want to compare to see if there is any **correlation** between the two sets.
- A **line of best fit** can be drawn on a scatter diagram, by plotting the point $(\overline{x}, \overline{y})$ and drawing a line through that point that best follows the trend of the data.
- If the gradient of that line is positive then we say that the data has **positive correlation**.
- If the gradient of the line is negative then it has **negative correlation**.
- The strength of correlation is determined by how close the data points are from the line.
- PMCC can be calculated using the GDC and takes values between -1 and 1. $r = 1$ indicates perfect positive correlation, whereas $r = -1$ indicates perfect negative correlation. $r = 0$ indicates no correlation.
- Extrapolation means estimating a value at a point that is larger than (or smaller than) the data you have.
- Trends in data are only valid for the range of study. We cannot **extrapolate** to draw conclusions outside of that range.

Developing inquiry skills

Thinking about the opening problem:

- Has what you have learned in this chapter helped you to answer the questions?
- What information did you manage to find?
- What assumptions did you make?
- How will you be able to construct a model?
- What other things did you wonder about?

Thinking about the inquiry questions from the beginning of this chapter:

- Has what you have learned in this chapter helped you to think about an answer to most of these questions?
- Are there any that you are interested in and would like to explore further, perhaps for your internal assessment topic?

Chapter review

Click here for a mixed review exercise
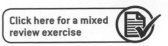

1 The times, in minutes, it takes for 60 males and 40 females to swim 500 metres are:

Males:

16	14	17	8	12	11	13	15	12
10	10	9	13	16	15	8	9	10
11	10	9	13	18	15	15	13	14
14	10	20	9	7	20	18	13	14
15	15	12	11	15	10	10	11	11
17	18	19	21	9	18	16	15	15
18	12	12	13	15	10			

Females:

10	9	9	16	18	22	10	21	14
15	18	19	19	15	15	12	10	22
24	16	18	19	21	10	17	18	14
12	12	11	10	10	16	18	19	21
22	19	15	18					

a Find the mean and standard deviation for the males and the females and compare them.

b Find the mean and standard deviation for the 100 swimmers.

c Using a random sampling method to select 40 swimmers from the 100 swimmers and find the mean and standard deviation of the sample.

d Using a systematic sampling method, find the mean and standard deviation of 40 swimmers.

e Using a stratified sample, find the mean and standard deviation of 40 swimmers.

f In each case, compare your answers to the mean and standard deviation of the population.

2 Find the mean, median and mode for the following data sets. State which measure of central tendency is best to use in each case.

a The heights of 15 dogs, in cm:

7	23	32	41	32	56	64	67
88	91	110	78	56	45	32	

b The price of a pair of shoes in dollars:

46	54	58	62	62	79
96	120	135	185	270	300

c The hours Grade 12 students sleep:

4	7	6	6	8	6	9	8	6	5
4	5	5	6	8	8	8	6	7	

3 The data in the table show the lengths of 120 pike fish.

Length of pike, l cm	Frequency
$20 \le l < 30$	2
$30 \le l < 40$	12
$40 \le l < 50$	23
$50 \le l < 60$	46
$60 \le l < 70$	28
$70 \le l < 80$	9

a Write down the modal class.

b Find estimates for the median, mean and standard deviation.

c Draw a histogram to represent the data.

4 A company records its profits for the years 2000 to 2005. The results (to the nearest $500) are shown in the table.

Year	2000	2001	2002	2003	2004
Profit ($)	12 000	13 000	15 000	17 500	21 000

a Calculate the mean profit for the five years.

b Calculate the standard deviation of the profits over these five years.

c Calculate the percentage increase in profits from 2000 to 2001.

d The company illustrates its profits in its brochure using the bar chart shown:

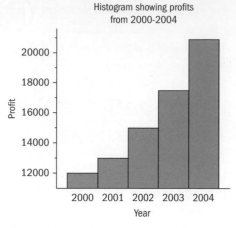

Histogram showing profits from 2000-2004

i Explain why this diagram may give a misleading picture.

ii State reasons why the bar chart might be drawn in this way.

5 Ursula measures the heights of 35 tulips in her garden. The data she gathered is:

20	20	21	22	22	22	24
25	27	28	28	29	30	31
32	33	33	34	34	34	35
35	36	37	39	39	39	40
41	41	42	43	43	44	45

a Find the mean and standard deviation and comment on your answer.

b Find the range and interquartile range.

c Find the median and check whether there are any outliers.

d Draw a box-and-whisker plot to represent the data.

6 The number of push-ups that the Grade 11 students can perform is:

Girls:

2	4	5	5	7	8	8
10	10	13	15	15	15	18
20	21	22	23	24	25	25
26	27	28	30			

Boys:

5	8	10	12	12	12	15
18	18	20	21	22	22	25
25	28	30	31	31	35	35
38	45	46	48			

a Find the mean, median, Q_1, Q_3 and range for the girls and for the boys, and check whether there are any outliers.

b Draw box-and-whisker plots to represent the data.

c Compare the two plots.

7 The grouped frequency table shows the number of hours of voluntary service completed by the 200 students at a community high school.

Number of hours, x	Frequency
$0 \leq x < 10$	8
$10 \leq x < 20$	16
$20 \leq x < 30$	41
$30 \leq x < 40$	54
$40 \leq x < 50$	36
$50 \leq x < 60$	22
$60 \leq x < 70$	17
$70 \leq x < 80$	6

a Construct a cumulative frequency table for this data.

b Plot the points and draw the cumulative frequency curve.

c Use your curve to find an approximate value for the median and the interquartile range.

The lowest number of hours completed was 8 and the greatest number was 76.

d Draw a box-and-whisker plot to represent the data.

8 Waiting times in a busy post office are recorded over the course of a day. The times are recorded in the frequency table:

Time (m)	3.5–4	4–4.5	4.5–5	5–5.5	5.5–6	6–6.5	6.5–7	7–7.5	7.5–8	8–8.5	8.5–9
Frequency	6	14	48	89	121	129	103	70	30	10	2

a Calculate estimates of the mean and standard deviation of the waiting time.

b Construct a cumulative frequency table for the data, and use it to draw a cumulative frequency curve.

c Use your graph to estimate:

  i the median waiting time

  ii the lower and upper quartile of the waiting times

  iii the interquartile range

  iv the 85th percentile of waiting times.

d Draw a box-and-whisker plot of the data.

e Determine, with reasons, whether any customers could be considered outliers.

9 Mr Farmer has 50 chickens. He collects data on the temperature and the average number of eggs that the chickens lay.

Temperature, °C	Number of eggs
14	43
15	44
16	48
17	46
18	50
19	48
20	50
21	52
22	53
23	55

a Draw a scatter graph to represent this information.

b Describe the correlation.

c State whether you think the temperature has an effect on the number of eggs laid. Give a reason for your answer.

10 Ten people were included in a survey to measure reaction time against age, and the data is shown in the table.

Age (years)	13	18	22	26	28	42	55	66	78	84
Reaction time (s)	0.45	0.44	0.54	0.55	0.61	1.02	0.77	0.93	0.88	1.11

a Draw a scatter diagram to illustrate the data.

b Identify an outlier in the data set.

c Remove the outlier and calculate the mean point for the rest of the data.

d Draw the line of best fit onto your scatter diagram.

e Calculate r, the PMCC for the data (excluding the outlier).

f Comment on the correlation of reaction time according to age.

Exam-style questions

11 **P1:** Eight primary school children were given a spelling test which was marked out of 20.

Their results were: 15, 20, 18, 4, 12, 17, 12, 9

Find:

a the range of the data (1 mark)

b the mean mark (2 marks)

c the median mark (1 mark)

d the modal mark (1 mark)

e the variance of the data. (2 marks)

Statistics and probability

12 P2: The following tables show the mean daily temperatures, by month, in both Tenerife and Malta.

Tenerife		Malta	
Month	**Mean daily temperature (°C)**	**Month**	**Mean daily temperature (°C)**
January	19	January	16
February	20	February	16
March	21	March	17
April	21	April	20
May	23	May	24
June	25	June	28
July	28	July	31
August	29	August	31
September	28	September	28
October	26	October	25
November	23	November	21
December	20	December	17

a Find the mean temperature over the course of the year for Tenerife. (2 marks)

b Find the standard deviation of temperatures in Tenerife. (2 marks)

c Find the mean temperature over the course of the year for Malta. (2 marks)

d Find the standard deviation of temperatures in Malta. (2 marks)

e By referring directly to your answers from parts **a**–**d**), make contextual comparisons about the temperatures in Tenerife and Malta throughout the year. (4 marks)

---

13 P2: Ben practises playing the Oboe daily. The time (in minutes) he spends on daily practice over 28 days is as follows.

10, 15, 30, 35, 40, 40, 45, 55, 60, 62, 64, 64, 66, 68, 70, 70, 72, 75, 75, 80, 82, 84, 90, 90, 105, 110, 120, 180

a Find the median time. (2 marks)

b Find the lower quartile. (2 marks)

c Find the upper quartile. (2 marks)

d Find the range. (2 marks)

e Determine whether there are any outliers in the data. (4 marks)

f Draw a box-and-whisker diagram for the above data, marking any outliers as required. (3 marks)

14 P2: The following raw data is a list of the height of flowers (in cm) in Eve's garden.

26.5, 53.2, 27.5, 33.6, 44.6, 39.5, 24.9, 45.1, 47.8, 39.3, 33.1, 38.7, 44.1, 22.3, 44.1, 30.5, 25.5, 35.9, 37.1, 40.2, 23.3, 36.2, 34.8, 37.3

a Copy and complete the following grouped frequency table.

Height, (x cm)	Frequency
$20 \leq x < 25$	
$25 \leq x < 30$	
$30 \leq x < 35$	
$35 \leq x < 40$	
$40 \leq x < 45$	
$45 \leq x < 50$	
$50 \leq x < 55$	

(3 marks)

b Find an estimate for the mean height, using the frequency table. (2 marks)

c Find an estimate for the variance, using the frequency table. (2 marks)

d Find an estimate for the standard deviation, using the frequency table. (2 marks)

e Eve's neighbour's garden was also surveyed. It was found that the flowers in the neighbour's garden had a mean height of 32.1 cm and standard deviation 7.83 cm. Compare the heights of the flowers in both gardens, drawing specific conclusions. (3 marks)

15 P1: Icicles creamery decided to analyse their ice cream sales to see if there was any correlation between sales and the average outdoor temperature for that particular month.

The following data was collected:

Month	Mean temp-erature ($T°C$)	Sales ($\$$)
January	3	350
February	4	650
March	9	900
April	11	920
May	17	1080
June	22	1200
July	25	1260
August	29	1390
September	19	1220
October	11	880
November	8	770
December	6	500

a Plot the given points on a scatter diagram. (2 marks)

b Calculate the coordinates of the point $\left(\overline{T}, \overline{P}\right)$ and hence draw a line of best fit. (3 marks)

c Calculate Pearson's Product Moment Correlation Coefficient for this data, and interpret your result. (2 marks)

d Comment on whether you can conclude, from this data, that outdoor temperature affects ice cream sales. (2 marks)

16 P1: An analysis was undertaken of the weight of new cars sold during one particular month. To aid in the calculation, 5000 kg was subtracted from every data value, and each result divided by 200. The mean of these new values was 9.6 and the standard deviation 2.15.

a Find the actual mean weight of the new cars sold. (2 marks)

b Find the standard deviation of the new cars sold. (2 marks)

17 P1: An analysis was undertaken in Sydney to determine if there was any correlation between an employee's salary ($\$s$ Australian dollars, AUD) and the distance they lived from the centre of Sydney (d km). The data from ten employees was collected, and the results were as follows.

Salary (s AUD)	Distance from centre (d km)
155000	0.3
92000	3.0
66000	2.5
72000	4.8
116000	1.2
153000	1.9
48000	4.0
118000	2.2
106000	4.1
140000	0.9

a Calculate Pearson's product-moment correction coefficient for this data, and interpret your result. (3 marks)

b Plot a scatter diagram to represent this data. Calculate values for $\overline{s}$ and $\overline{d}$, and hence draw a line of best fit on your scatter diagram. (5 marks)

c It is suggested that the scatter diagram could be used to determine the average salary of an employee living 7 km from the city centre.

Suggest two reasons why this may not be accurate. (3 marks)

What's the difference?

Approaches to learning: Thinking skills, Communicating, Collaborating, Research

Exploration criteria: Presentation (A), Mathematical communication (B), Personal engagement (C), Reflection (D), Use of mathematics (E)

IB topic: Statistics, Mean, Median, Mode, Range, Standard deviation, Box plots, Histograms

Example experiment

Raghu does an experiment with a group of 25 students.

Each member of the group does a reaction test and Raghu records their times.

Raghu wants to repeat the experiment, but with some change.

He then wants to compare the reaction times in the two experiments.

Discuss:

How could Raghu change his experiment when he does it again?

With each change, is the performance in the group likely to improve/stay the same/get worse?

Alternatively, Raghu could use a different group when he repeats the experiment.

What different group could he use?

With each different group, is the performance likely to improve/stay the same/get worse?

2

Modelling and investigation activity

Your experiment

Your task is to devise an experiment to test your own hypothesis.

You will need to do your experiment two times and compare your results.

Step 1: What are you going to test? State your aim and hypothesis

Write down the aim of your experiment and your hypothesis about the result.

Why do you think this is important?

What are the implications of the results that you may find?

Make sure it is clear what you are testing for.

Step 3: Do the experiment and collect the data.

Construct a results sheet to collect the data.

Give clear, consistent instructions.

Step 4: Present the data for comparison and analysis.

How are you going to present the data so that the two sets can be easily compared?

How are you going to organize the summary statistics of the two data sets so that you can compare them?

Do you need to find all of the summary statistics covered in this chapter?

Step 6: Conclusions and implications.

What are the conclusions from the experiment?

Are they different to or the same as your hypothesis? To what extent? Why?

How confident are you in your results? How could you be more certain?

What is the scope of your conclusions?

How have your ideas changed since your original hypothesis?

Step 2: How are you going to collect the data? Write a plan

- What resources/sites will you need to use?
- How many people/students will you be able to/ need to collect data from to give statistically valid results?
- Exactly what data do you need to collect? How are you going to organize your data? Have you done a trial experiment?
- Are there any biases in the way you present the experiment? How can you ensure that everyone gets the same instructions?
- Is your experiment a justifiable way of testing your hypothesis? Justify this. What are the possible criticisms? Can you do anything about these?
- Is the experiment reliable? Is it likely that someone else would reach a similar conclusion to you if they used the same method?

Step 5: Compare and analyse.

Describe the differences between your two sets of data.

Make sure that your conclusion is relevant to your aim and hypothesis stated at the beginning.

Extension

- How could you test whether the spread of the data has changed significantly, rather than the average?
- In what way could you incorporate the work you have done so far on bivariate data?
- It is possible to test data using a more "mathematical" test. Investigate, for example, the "difference in means test".

3 Dividing up space: coordinate geometry, Voronoi diagrams, vectors, lines

This chapter explores two- and three-dimensional space and the relationship between points and lines in space. In two-dimensional space the world we live can be represented by a map and our position given by our coordinates as defined on the map. We can use these coordinates to see where objects are in relation to each other, and calculate their distance apart. In three dimensional space we need a third coordinate for height. Straight line motion through this space can be defined using a vector equation of the line, and with this equation we can see if objects will collide, or how long they would take to travel a given distance.

Concepts
- Space
- Relationships

Microconcepts
- Gradient
- Equations of straight lines
- Perpendicular lines
- Parallel lines
- Perpendicular bisectors
- Points of intersections of lines
- Coordinates of mid-point in 3D
- Distance in 3D
- Voronoi diagrams
- Area of Voronoi diagrams
- Vectors
- Displacement vectors
- Parallel and perpendicular vectors
- Normalising a vector
- Scalar product
- Application of scalar product to finding the angle between two vectors/lines
- Vector product
- Applications of vector product to areas
- Vector equation of a line
- Motion with constant velocity in 2D and 3D

How could you determine the distance between stars?

How can you find out whether two aircraft will collide if they maintain their current flight paths?

How could a town with four fire stations be divided into regions so that the nearest fire truck is dispatched to the fire location?

How can you find the surface area of a crystal when given the coordinates of its vertices.

An island has control of all economic resources within its territorial waters. These resources may include fishing, mining, or offshore oil exploration.

The positions of three small islands are shown.

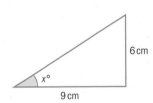

- How could you model the positions of the three islands?
- How could you use your model to decide how to divide the territorial waters between the islands?
- What information do you need to be able to answer this question?
- What assumptions would you need to make?
- What factors might influence how to divide the waters between the islands?

Developing inquiry skills

Write down any similar inquiry questions you might ask if you were asked to divide the area between different landmarks; for example, deciding which fire station should assume responsibility for different areas of a town or deciding which hospital is closer to your home.

How are these questions different from those used to investigate how territorial waters are being divided between three islands?

Think about the questions in this opening problem and answer any you can. As you work through the chapter, you will gain mathematical knowledge and skills that will help you to answer them all.

Before you start

Click here for help with this skills check

You should know how to:

1 Find the distance between two points.
   eg Find the distance between A(2, 3) and B(6, 2).

   $d = \sqrt{(6-2)^2 + (2-3)^2} = \sqrt{17}$

2 Find the midpoint of the line segment joining two points.

   eg The midpoint of A(2, 3) and B(6, 2) is

   $\left(\dfrac{2+6}{2}, \dfrac{1+2}{2}\right) = (4, 1.5)$

3 Find angles and sides in right-angled triangles.
   eg

   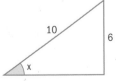

   $\sin x = \dfrac{6}{10}$

   $x = \arcsin\left(\dfrac{6}{10}\right)$

   $= 36.9°$ (3 s.f.)

4 Use bearings.

Skills check

1 Find the length of the line segment joining A(1, 2) and B(5, 4).

2 Find the midpoint of the line segment joining A(1, 2) and B(5, 4).

3 **a** Find the values of x and y.
   b Find the value of the angle x.

   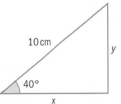

4 Town A and B are 50 km apart and the bearing of B from A is 060°
   a Find the distance B is
      i east of A   **ii** north of A.
   b Find the bearing of A from B.

3.1 Coordinate geometry in 2 and 3 dimensions

Coordinates in 3 dimensions

The position of a point in 3-dimensional space is given by three coordinates along three mutually perpendicular axes.

For example, suppose that your classroom is a cuboid with width 7 m, length 8 m and height is 3 m. If one corner of the room is chosen as the origin, then a light in the centre of the ceiling will have coordinates (3.5, 4, 3).

> **TOK**
>
> Is it ethical that Pythagoras gave his name to a theorem that may not have been his own creation?

Investigation 1

A cuboid with sides of length 5, 4 and 3 is shown in the diagram. The origin is at the point O and the coordinates of the point A are (5, 4, 3).

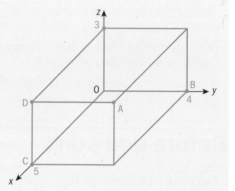

1 Write down the coordinates of B, C and D.

  If A and B are two points [AB] should be read as "the line segment with A and B as end points".

2 Write down the coordinates of the midpoint of [OA] and [BC].

3 Hence conjecture a formula for finding the mid-point of the line segment joining (x_1, y_1, z_1) and (x_2, y_2, z_2).

4 **a** Use your formula to find the midpoint of [BD].

  b How can you use a previous answer to verify the formula works?

If A and B are two points AB should be read as "the length of the line segment with A and B as end points" or "the length of [AB]".

5 **a** Use Pythagoras' theorem to find BC.

  b Hence find BD.

A cuboid with sides of length p, q and r is shown in the diagram below. The origin is at the point O and the coordinates of the point A are (p, q, r).

6 Use Pythagoras' theorem to find an expression for the length BC.

7 Hence write down an expression for the length BD in terms of p, q and r.

8 Use your answer to **5** to verify your formula.

9 Hence conjecture a formula for finding the length of the line segment joining (x_1, y_1, z_1) and (x_2, y_2, z_2). Justify your answer.

Factual What is the formula for finding the midpoint of the line segment joining two points in 3D?

Factual What is the formula for finding the distance between 2 points in 3D?

Conceptual How are the formulae for distance between two points and midpoint of a line segment in 3 dimensions related to the same formulae in 2 dimensions?

Both the formula for the midpoint of a line segment and the length of a line segment between two points in 2 dimensions can be extended to 3 dimensions.

Given the two points $A(x_1, y_1, z_1)$ and $B(x_2, y_2, z_2)$:

- the midpoint of [AB] is $\left(\dfrac{x_1 + x_2}{2}, \dfrac{y_1 + y_2}{2}, \dfrac{z_1 + z_2}{2} \right)$

- the length $AB = \sqrt{\left(x_2 - x_1\right)^2 + \left(y_2 - y_1\right)^2 + \left(z_2 - z_1\right)^2}$.

Exercise 3A

1 A and B are two points with coordinates as given below. Find:

   a the distance between A and B

   b the midpoint of the line segment joining A and B.

     i (2, 1), (1, −4)

     ii (2, 4, −3), (0, 3, −2)

2 A and B are two points with coordinates as given below. Find:

   a AB

   b the midpoint of [AB]

     i (21, −13), (−3, 14)

     ii (−17, 11, 0), (−2, 8, −12)

3 A tracking station lies at the origin of a coordinate system with the x-axis due east, the y-axis due north and the z-axis vertical with units in kilometers. At a particular time two aircraft have coordinates (20, 25, 11) and (26, 31, 12) relative to the tracking station.

   a Find the distance the two aircraft are apart at this time.

   b The radar at the tracking station has a range of 40 km. Determine whether it would be able to detect both aircraft at this time.

4 The side of a hill can be regarded as a right angled triangular prism as shown. A path goes in a straight line from the point A to the midpoint of [BC], M, and then to D. Distances are all given in metres.

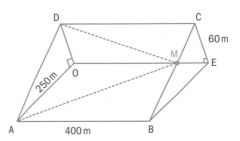

Take O as the origin of a coordinate system. With [OA] lying along the x-axis and [OE] lying along the y-axis and with the z-axis vertical.

   a Write down the coordinates of A, B, C and D.

   b Find the coordinates of M.

   c Find the total length of the path from A to D.

5 A surveyor records the coordinates of all the vertices of the base of the Great Pyramid at Giza. Unfortunately he loses two of them so he only has values for A and B at diagonally opposite corners.

The origin for the coordinate system is some distance away from the pyramid and is on land 21 m higher than the base of the pyramid.

The coordinates he has are A(97,77,−21), B(340,−139,−21). The base of the pyramid forms a square.

a Find the area of the base of the pyramid.

The surveyor knows from other sources that the height of the pyramid is 138 m.

b Find the volume of the pyramid.

c Find the coordinates of the vertex of the pyramid.

d Find the shortest distance from one of the corners of the base to the vertex of the pyramid.

Developing inquiry skills

Look back at the opening problem for the chapter. You were trying to divide the territorial waters between three islands.

The positions of the islands can be modelled as shown:

The lines $x=0$, $x=100$, $y=0$ and $y=80$ mark the boundary of international waters and distances are given in kilometres. The islands are given exclusive fishing rights within these boundaries with the island closest to a point having the rights at that point.

How can you find the distances between each of the islands?

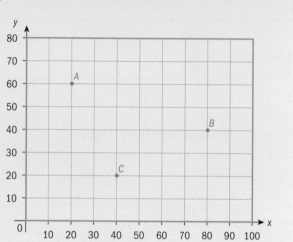

3.2 The equation of a straight line in 2 dimensions

Vertical and horizontal lines

The vertical line on which the value of each x-coordinate is 2 has equation $x = 2$. The horizontal line on which the value of each y-coordinate is 3 has equation $y = 3$.

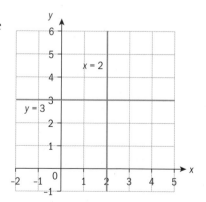

Reflect What is the form of an equation of a vertical/horizontal line?

The gradient of the line segment joining two points

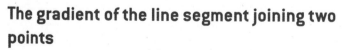

The gradient of the line segment joining two point can be calculated by finding how far the line segment goes "up" divided by how far it goes across.

The gradient (m) of the line segment joining (x_1, y_1) and (x_2, y_2) is given by:

$$m = \frac{y_2 - y_1}{x_2 - x_1}$$

International-mindedness

Cartesian coordinates are named after Frenchman René Descartes.

The gradient intercept form for the equation of a straight line

The equation of the line passing through (x_1, y_1) and (x_2, y_2) can be given in **gradient-intercept** form as $y = mx + c$ where c is the value of the y-intercept.

The gradient can be found as above and the value of c can be found by substituting one of the points.

This is the form that is usually used when entering the equation of a straight line into a graphical display calculator.

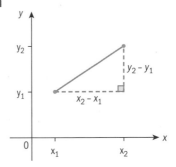

For two points A and B (AB) should be read as "the line containing the points A and B".

Example 1

For the two points A(2, 2) and B(6, 1)

a Find the gradient m of (AB) (the line passing through A and B).

b Find the equation of (AB) in the form $y = mx + c$.

c Sketch the line for $-2 \leq x \leq 12$.

d Find:

   i the value of y when x is 4.7   **ii** the y-intercept.

a $m = \dfrac{1-2}{6-2} = \dfrac{-1}{4}$

a It is important you are careful to subtract both coordinates in the same order. The gradient can also be found from a sketch:

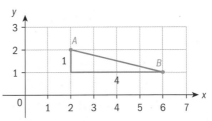

From the diagram $m = \dfrac{-1}{4}$

Because the line goes down as you look from left to right the gradient is negative.

Continued on next page

Functions

Geometry and trigonometry

b $y = -\dfrac{1}{4}x + c$

Substitute one of the points on the line; for example, (2, 2).

$2 = -\dfrac{1}{4} \times 2 + c$

$c = 2.5$

Equation is $y = -\dfrac{1}{4}x + 2.5$

b The same result would have been obtained if (6, 1) had been substituted.

c

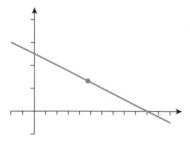

c The question will often specify the domain and hence the required range on the x-axis. The required range for the y-axis can, if necessary, be found from the "table" function on the GDC.

d i When $x = 4.7$ $y = 1.325$
ii 2.5

d These are easy to calculate without the graph but make sure you know how to get these values from your GDC.

Reflect What is the formula for calculating the gradient of a line?

Exercise 3B

1 Write down:

  a the equation of the vertical line passing through (2, 7)

  b the equation of the horizontal line passing through (4, 6)

  c the point of intersection of the two lines.

2 Find the equation of the following lines.

  a gradient = 3, y-intercept 5

  b gradient = −2, y-intercept 0.4

  c gradient = 4.5, passing through (0, 5)

  d gradient = 2, passing through (3, 5).

3 Find the equation of the line passing through the two points given.

  a (3, 5) and (5, −3)

  b (2, −1) and (3, 4)

  c (−3, 2) and (3, 4)

4 A Cartesian grid is superimposed on a map of a city. The y-axis lies in the direction of North and the x-axis due East. The North-South boundaries of the city lie along the lines $x = 0$, $x = 22$ and the distances are in kilometres.

A straight road passes through the city. The road passes through the points with coordinates (6, 8) and (12, −4) and stays within the city boundaries for $0 \le x \le 22$.

  a Find the equation of the road.

  b Find the coordinates of the road as it crosses:

    i the western boundary of the city

    ii the eastern boundary of the city.

  c Find the length of the road within the city boundary.

Investigation 2

Consider the straight line passing through the point $(1, 3)$, shown below

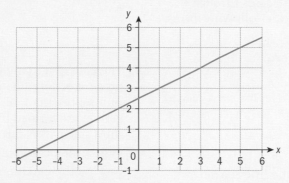

1 Take any point on the line and show that the gradient of the line joining it to $(1, 3)$ is equal to 0.5.

2 Let (x, y) be a point on the line. Explain why $0.5 = \dfrac{y-3}{x-1}$

3 Generalise the result from question 2 to give an expression for the gradient in terms of x and y for a straight line with gradient m that passes through a known point (x_1, y_1).

4 Show that the expression derived in question 3 can be written as $y - y_1 = m(x - x_1)$.

$y - y_1 = m(x - x_1)$ is the **point gradient** form of the equation of a line.

5 Use your answer to question 2 to write the equation of the line given in point-gradient form.

6 Write the equation found in questions 5 in the form $y = mx + c$ by expanding the brackets and simplifying.

7 Write the equation derived in question 6 in the form $ax + by + d = 0$ where $a, b, d \in \mathbb{Z}$

$ax = by + d = 0$ is the **general** form of the equation of a straight line.

Conceptual What are the three forms of the equation that give the relation between the x-coordinates and the y-coordinates of all points on a straight line?

Reflect How do you find the x- and the y-intercepts from the equation of a line? In which form of a line are intercepts easier to find?

> The **point-gradient** form for the equation of a line with gradient equal to m, which passes through the point (x_1, y_1) is $y - y_1 = m(x - x_1)$.
>
> The **general** form of the equation of a straight line is written as $ax + by + d = 0$ where a, b and d are all integers.

The point-gradient form is the easiest to find if given two points or one point and the gradient.

The general form is the easiest for finding intercepts and is often the form used when solving systems of linear equations (simultaneous equations).

EXAM HINT

Point-gradient form can be easily rearranged to give the equation in gradient-intercept form, but if an exam question does not ask for a particular form it is perfectly acceptable not to rearrange.

Functions

Geometry and trigonometry

Exercise 3C

1 Write down the equation of a line with gradient, m, and which passes through the given point, in each of the following forms:

i point-gradient form

ii gradient-intercept form

iii general form.

    a $m = 2$, $(3, 9)$ **b** $m = \dfrac{1}{2}$, $(6, 5)$

    c $m = -\dfrac{1}{3}$, $(6, -7)$

2 Find the equations of the lines passing through the points given in

i point-gradient form

ii gradient-intercept form

iii general form.

    a $(2, 5)$ and $(5, 11)$

    b $(0, 4)$ and $(2, 2)$

    c $(2, 6)$ and $(3, 9)$

    d $(-2, -6)$ and $(1, -8)$

3 Find the gradient of each of the lines

    a $2x - 3y - 7 = 0$

    b $4x + 7y - 6 = 0$

    c $ax + by + d = 0$

4 The plan of a triangular garden is drawn on a set of coordinate axes in which one unit represents 1 m. Two of the sides of the garden are formed by the x- and y-axes. The third side passes through the points $(1, 5)$ and $(3, 2)$.

    a Find the equation of the line which includes the third side.

    b Write this equation in general form.

The owner of the garden wishes to cover it completely in grass.

    c Find the area of turf (grass) he will need to buy.

Intersections of Lines

You need to be able to solve systems of two linear equations "by hand" but also by using applications on your GDC or by plotting their graphs.

If using graphs, the solution to the system will be given by the coordinates of the intersection of the two lines.

For example, if given the starting positions and the directions of two straight railway tracks, it would be possible to find the equations of the lines that the tracks follow and hence find where they will meet.

Example 2

a Find the coordinates of the x- and y-intercepts for the graph of $2x + 3y - 6 = 0$.

b Write the following equation in general form, $y = x - \dfrac{1}{2}$

c Find the point of intersection of the two lines **i** analytically **ii** using an appropriate application on your technology.

a When $x = 0$, $3y = 6$

so $y = 2$

When $y = 0$, $2x = 6$

so $x = 3$

Coordinates are $(0, 2)$ and $(3, 0)$

b $2x - 2y - 1 = 0$

c **i** $2x + 3y = 6$

$2x - 2y = 1$

subtract the two equations to get

$5y = 5 \Rightarrow y = 1$

substitute this value into either equation to get $x = 1.5$

ii $2x + 3y = 6$

$2x - 2y = 1$

$x = 1.5$, $y = 1$

a x-intercepts occur when $y = 0$ and y-intercepts occur when $x = 0$.

The intercepts are the values of x or y so you need to check whether the question is asking for the intercepts or the coordinates of the intercepts.

b It is usual to avoid beginning the equation with a negative coefficient but $-2x + 2y + 1 = 0$ is an equally valid answer.

c **i** The solution can be found using elimination or substitution, for example by replacing y in

$2x + 3y - 6 = 0$ with $y = x - \dfrac{1}{2}$ to get

$2x + 3\left(x - \dfrac{1}{2}\right) - 6 = 0$

$\Rightarrow 5x - 1.5 - 6 = 0 \Rightarrow x = 1.5$

ii When solving a system of equations using your technology, there is no need to write down details of the method.

Some calculators have an inbuilt simultaneous equation solver. If not the solution can be found by drawing both lines and finding the point of intersection, $(1.5, 1)$.

Functions

Geometry and trigonometry

Reflect How do you find the point of intersection of two non-parallel lines?

Exercise 3D

1 **a** Find the solutions to

i $2x + y = 8$
$3x - 2y = 33$

ii $2x + 10y = 3$
$3x + 15y = 4.5$

iii $y = 2x + 1$
$4x - y = 5$

iv $y - 2 = 3(x - 4)$
$y = 2x - 9$

b Solve

i $x + 3y = 1$
$5x + 16y = 8$

ii $3x + 2y = 4$
$5x - 4y = 20.6$

2 Two friends, Alison and Bernard are walking along two different roads. The roads can be represented in the Cartesian plane by the lines with equations

$$y = -x + 410 \text{ and } y = \frac{1}{2}x - 100.$$

At 2:00 pm Alison is on the first road at the point with coordinates (0, 410) and Bernard is at the point with coordinates (50, −75), where the units are in meters.

a Verify that Bernard is on the road with equation $y = \frac{1}{2}x - 100$ at 2:00 pm.

b Find the coordinates of the point of intersection of the two roads.

At 2:00 pm the two friends begin walking at 4 kmh⁻¹ towards the intersection.

c i Show that Bernard arrives at the intersection first.

ii Find the length of time he needs to wait before Alison arrives.

3 Road signs showing the steepness of hills are often given as percentages where the figure is derived using the following formula

$$\frac{\text{vertical height gained or lost}}{\text{horizontal distance covered}} \times 100$$

a A road gains 5 m while covering 20 m horizontally. State the percentage that would be written on the road sign.

There is a triangular hill directly outside my house. On the way up the hill from my house I pass a sign indicating the slope is 10%. On the way down the other side of the hill, I pass one indicating the slope is 15%.

b State which road is steeper.

I decide to take my house to be the origin for a coordinate system and one day I go over the hill to the other side and reach my local shop. My GPS tells me the horizontal distance of the shop from my home is 2.45 km and I am at the same level as my house.

c Assuming the roads up and down the hill are straight lines and lie in the plane of the coordinate system find

i the equation of the road going up from my house

ii the equation of the road going down from the top of the hill to the shop.

d Find the height of the hill

e Find the total distance of my journey from my house to the shop.

4 A straight line makes an angle α with the x-axis where $0 \le \alpha < 90°$.

a Explain why the gradient of the line is equal to tan α.

The air traffic control tower at an airport is taken as the origin of a coordinate system. An aircraft begins its descent 7500 m from the control tower and from a height of 580 m. Let x be the horizontal distance from the control tower and y the height of the aircraft. The angle of descent of the aircraft is 4° to the horizontal and its path will take it directly above the control tower.

The runway begins 700 m from the control tower and in the same direction as the aircraft's approach.

b Find the equation for the line of descent for the aircraft in the form $y = mx + c$.

c Find the height of the aircraft as it passes over the control tower.

d Find the distance of the aircraft from the start of the runway when it lands.

International-mindedness

Road steepness is often given as a ratio or percentage. What is it in your country? What others can you find?

Parallel and perpendicular lines

Parallel lines will have the same gradient as each other but a different intercept on the y-axis.

For example $y = 1.5x + 4$ is parallel to $y = 1.5x - 1$.

Lines which are perpendicular intersect at 90°.

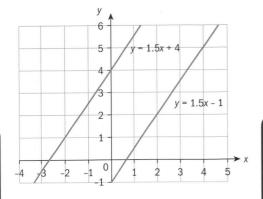

In general $y = mx + c_1$ is parallel to $y = mx + c_2$

If $y = m_1 x + c_1$ and $y = m_2 x + c_2$ are perpendicular (and neither m_1 or m_2 are equal to 0) then $m_1 m_2 = -1$ or

$m_2 = -\dfrac{1}{m_1}$ (the negative reciprocal of m_1)

For example, if a line has a gradient of $\dfrac{2}{3}$ the line

perpendicular to it will have gradient $-\dfrac{1}{\left(\dfrac{2}{3}\right)} = -\dfrac{3}{2}$

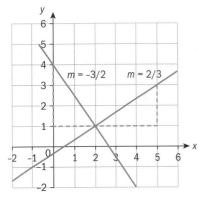

The perpendicular bisector

The perpendicular bisector of the line segment joining two points is the line that passes through the midpoint of the line segment and is perpendicular to it.

The perpendicular bisector of the line segment joining A(2, 2) and B(4, 6) is shown below.

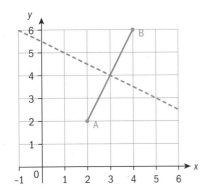

Example 3

Find the equation of the perpendicular bisector of the line segment joining A(2, 2) and B(4, 6).

Midpoint of [AB] is (3, 4)	Using the formula for midpoint.
Gradient of [AB] is $\dfrac{4}{2} = \dfrac{1}{2}$	Using the formula for gradient.
Equation of perpendicular bisector is $y - 4 = -2(x - 3)$	Find the negative reciprocal to get the gradient of the perpendicular line and use point-gradient form to get the equation.
$y = -2x + 10$	This last stage was not necessary as a particular form was not specified but it does give the equation in a simpler form.

Reflect What is the gradient of a line parallel to a line with gradient m?

What is the gradient of a line perpendicular to a line with gradient m?

How do you find the equations of perpendicular bisectors given either two points, or the equation of a line segment and its midpoint?

Investigation 3

A ship is sailing along the line forming the perpendicular bisector of the line segment between two lighthouses (A and B), as shown.

The coordinates of A are (0, 8) and the coordinates of B are (6, 0). At 1 pm the ship is at (7, 7). All units are kilometres.

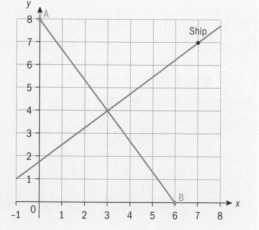

1 Find the equation of the perpendicular bisector of [AB].

2 Verify that the ship is on the perpendicular bisector of [AB].

3 Find the distance of the ship from

   a A **b** B.

   Comment on your results.

4 From the definition of the perpendicular bisector use the above diagram to prove that the ship will always be equidistant from the two lighthouses so long as it stays on this course.

Conceptual What is the relation between all points on the perpendicular bisector of the line segment joining two points and those two points?

Exercise 3E

1   Write down the gradients of the lines which are perpendicular to the lines given.

   a $y = -2x + 7$ **b** $y - 3 = \dfrac{1}{3}(x - 21)$

   c $2x - 4y - 5 = 0$ **d** $6x + 7y + 12 = 0$

2   **a**   Verify that $bx - ay = d_1$ is perpendicular to $ax + by = d_2$.

   b   Hence find the equation of the line perpendicular to $x + 2y - 10 = 0$ which passes through (2, 5).

   c   Find the equation of the line perpendicular to $3x - 2y = 7$ which passes through (6, 5).

3   **a**   Explain why the shortest distance from a point A to a line lies on the line through A, perpendicular to the line.

   The line l has equation $3x - 4y + 7 = 0$ and the point A has coordinates (5, −7).

   b   Find the equation of the line perpendicular to l which passes through A.

   c   Find the point of intersection of the line found in part **b** and l.

   d   Hence find the shortest distance of A from l.

4   Find the shortest distance from

   a   (2, 4) to $3x + 5y + 8 = 0$

   b   (5, −1) to $y = 3x - 2$.

5   Let A and B be two lighthouses with coordinates (12, 18) and (17, 16). A ship S is travelling on the line that keeps it an equal distance from the two lighthouses.

   Find the position of S when it is north-east of the lighthouse A.

6   Two towns have coordinates (5, 18) and (17, 24). A rail track is laid along the line with equation $y = x + 10$ and a station is to be built to serve the two towns. Distances are in kilometres.

   a   Find the position the station should be built to minimize the total distance between the station and the two towns and state this distance.

   b   It is decided that the station will be built so it is an equal distance from both towns. Find the position the station should be built and state the distance between the two towns.

Developing inquiry skills

Look back at the opening problem for the chapter. You were trying to divide the territorial waters between three islands.

1   Find the equations of the perpendicular bisectors between the islands.

2   Find the coordinates of the point where the perpendicular bisectors between A and B and A and C meet.

Verify that the perpendicular bisector between B and C also passes through this point. Do you think these lines divide the waters in a fair way? Justify your answer.

TOK

How does the variation in language and symbols affect the knowledge gained and communicated in mathematics?

3.3 Voronoi diagrams

There are five airports in a state, shown as dots on the diagram. The coloured regions on the diagram indicate which of the airports is closest to a given position. This means if there is an emergency and the position of the plane is known the information about the nearest airport is very easily obtained.

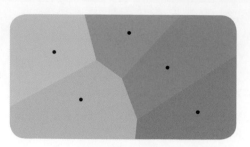

This is an example of a Voronoi diagram, named after Georgy Voronoy (1868–1908). It shows the sets of points that are closer to a chosen point (a **site**) than to any other sites on the plane. The regions formed are known as **cells**.

> **Reflect** What does a Voronoi diagram show?

Investigation 4

Three points A, B and C lie inside a square of side length 10 units whose sides are formed by the lines $x = 0$, $x = 10$, $y = 0$ and $y = 10$.

The points A, B and C have coordinates (1, 8), (8, 8) and (3, 2).

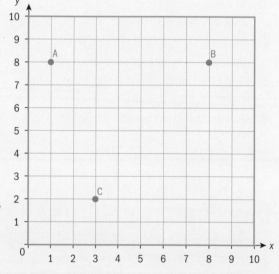

1   Construct a copy of the diagram either by using online software (for example Geogebra or Desmos) or by copying onto graph paper.

2   State the equation of the line which contains all points equidistant from A and B and show this on the diagram.

3   Add the lines to the diagram which contain all those points equidistant from

    a   A and C   **b**   B and C.

4   By inspection shade all those points which are closest to each of A, B or C.

> **Conceptual** What can be said about the boundaries of a Voronoi diagram?

> **Reflect** How do you find the equation of the boundary of a cell on a Voronoi diagram?

> The boundaries of the **cells** in a Voronoi diagram are formed by perpendicular bisectors of the line segments joining the sites.

International-mindedness

Georgy Voronoy was a Russian mathematician who studied at St Petersburg University.

The best approach is rarely to draw all the perpendicular bisectors at the same time and then create the diagram.

This diagram shows that even with just 4 points there are difficulties in deciding which of them form boundaries to the cells, and with more points it would become even more difficult. The incremental algorithm described below avoids this problem by adding each of the sites one at a time.

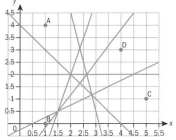

Investigation 5

There are four fire stations (A, B, C and D) in a town. The coordinates of the fire stations are A(1, 4), B(1, 0), C(5, 1) and D(4, 3).

In order to improve response time the town has installed a new centralized fire response system, which allows a dispatcher to send a fire truck from the nearest fire station to the location of fire. How should the town be divided into areas so that there is one fire station in each area and this fire station is the closest one for each house in the section?

The solution will be found through constructing a Voronoi diagram using an **incremental algorithm.**

> **HINT**
>
> Many software packages allow you to draw and obtain the equation of perpendicular bisectors directly. If not using software a perpendicular bisector can be constructed using a compass or by finding its equation and drawing it.

Method

1 Plot the fire stations A and B on coordinate axes, either by hand or using a software package. Draw the perpendicular bisector between A and B and gently shade those points nearest to A.

2 Add fire station C to the diagram and find the equations of the perpendicular bisectors of [AC] and [BC] and add these to the diagram. What do you notice?

3 The incremental Algorithm:

  i Begin with the perpendicular bisector which lies between the new site (C) and the site in whose cell this site currently lies (B).

  ii Move along this line until you reach an intersection with another of the perpendicular bisectors between the new site and an existing one (this will also be on a boundary of the previous Voronoi diagram).

  iii Leave the intersection along the other new perpendicular bisector in the direction that lies entirely in the cell surrounding another of the sites (this will be the direction that creates a convex polygon around the new site).

  Hence you should trace out the edge of the new cell in the order U, V and W shown in the diagram.

  iv The algorithm stops either when you return to your starting point (if the cell is bounded) or if there are no more intersections (if the cell is unbounded). In this case you may need to reverse the direction of the algorithm to ensure all sides have been found.

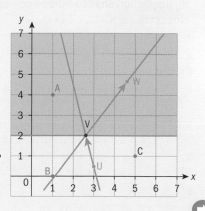

4 Shade the region containing the new site.

5 Having completed the diagram for the first three sites the final site, D, is now added and the process described in stages 2 and 3 is repeated. This time there will be two intersection points with the perpendicular bisectors of [BD] and [AD].

Continued on next page

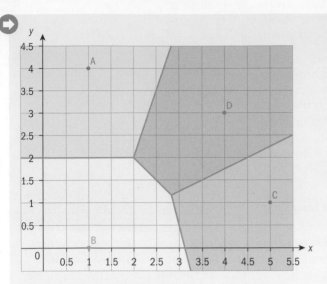

HINT

Normally a final version of the Voronoi diagram will have the perpendicular bisectors removed so only the edges of the regions remain as in the diagram shown.

A few years later a new fire station is built in the town at the point with coordinates $(2, 1)$.

6 Use the incremental algorithm to construct the new Voronoi diagram showing the areas served by each of the fire stations.

7 Place the fifth fire station on the diagram given just before the start of the investigation which shows the positions of A,B,C and D and their perpendicular bisectors. How easy would it have been to draw a Voronoi diagram without using the incremental algorithm?

8 [Conceptual] Why is the incremental algorithm used in the construction of a Voronoi diagram?

[Reflect] What is the incremental algorithm?
How many edges meet at a vertex of a Voronoi diagram?

International-mindedness

Voronoi diagrams are used in computer graphics, epidemiology, geophysics, and meteorology.

Nearest neighbour interpolation

If each site is assigned a numerical value (such as the amount of rain that fell on a particular day or a level of pollutant) then the value of all points in each site's cell is assumed to equal that value.

Exercise 3F

In the questions below unless told to calculate the equations of the perpendicular bisectors you can construct the lines using a pair of compasses, by eye or by using software.

1 By finding the perpendicular bisectors between each of the points, use the incremental algorithm to complete the Voronoi diagrams for the given sites.

  a $(1, 1)$, $(3, 1)$, $(2, 3)$

  b $(1, 1)$, $(5, 1)$, $(5, 5)$, $(3, 5)$

2 An Internet weather website uses readings taken at three different stations. A visitor to the website will be told the temperature of the station nearest to their location (nearest neighbour interpolation). The weather stations are at the points with coordinates

  A $(1, 1)$ **B** $(3, 1)$ **C** $(3, 5)$.

  a Use the incremental algorithm to construct a Voronoi diagram showing the regions that would be assigned to each of the weather stations.

At a particular time a visitor to the website is at point (1, 4) and the readings at the different stations are A: 22°C, B: 24°C and C: 21°C.

b Write down the temperature that would be given to the visitor to the site.

3 A company that collects meteorological data has many rainfall collection points. In two of their areas (I and II) in which they had four collection points they decide to add a fifth.

The original points are shown as A to D in the following diagrams and the new point is labelled E.

a The point E and some of the perpendicular bisectors between E and the other points are shown. For each area find the equation of the missing perpendicular bisector(s), add it to the diagram, and indicate the new cells.

I

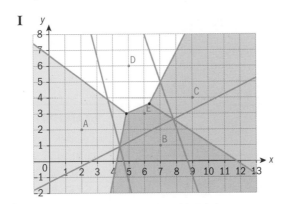

II

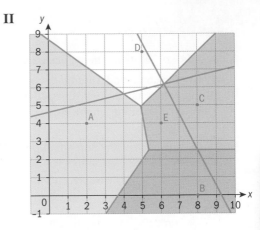

b It is given that on a particular day the rainfall in area I is recorded as

A: 22 mm   B: 31 mm   C: 24 mm
D: 19 mm   E: 21 mm

Use nearest neighbour interpolation to give an estimate for the amount of rain that fell at a point with coordinates (5, 4)

i before point E was added

ii after point E was added.

c It is given that on a particular day the rainfall in area II is recorded as

A: 9 mm   B: 11 mm   C: 14 mm
D: 8 mm   E: 12 mm.

Use nearest neighbour interpolation to give an estimate for the amount of rain that fell at a point with coordinates (4.5, 1)

i before point E was added

ii after point E was added.

The toxic waste dump problem

This problem is to find the point on the Voronoi diagram that is as far as possible from any of the sites. It is called **the toxic waste dump problem** because one application might be to find where waste can be dumped so that it is as far as possible from habitation.

However, it is more frequently used in consideration of where to place businesses or shops.

Another way of thinking about the problem is to say it is at the centre of the largest circle that can be drawn on the diagram that does not contain any of the sites.

Functions

Geometry and trigonometry

Investigation 6

1 a Add five points randomly placed on a Geogebra worksheet.

b Use the command, *Voronoi*, to construct a Voronoi diagram with these five points as the sites. Check that you have three distinct points at which three edges meet. If you do not, move one of the original points until you do.

c Use the *Circle with Centre through Point* command to consruct the largest possible circle that contains no sites within it, centred on each of the three points where the vertices intersect.

d What do you notice?

2 a Explain using the diagram why there will always be three sites equidistant from a vertex of a Voronoi diagram which has three edges incident to it.

b Explain why the circle with V as a center which passes through A will also pass through B and C.

3 Explain why another site D cannot be inside this circle with centre V.

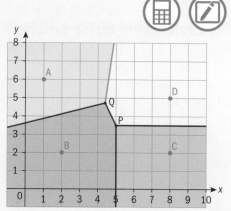

This circle is known as the largest empty circle because it does not contain sites and to extend it further would mean it would be no longer be empty.

4 **Conceptual** Where on a Voronoi diagram would you look for the solution to the toxic waste dump problem?

> Within a Voronoi diagram the solution to the toxic waste dump problem will be at an intersection of cell boundaries or on the boundary of the diagram.

EXAM HINT

In exams the solution will always be one of the internal vertices rather than a boundary edge.

Example 4

A town has four coffee shops, A, B, C and D. An entrepreneur wishes to open a new shop in the town but would like it to be as far as possible from all the other four coffee shops.

Consider the Voronoi diagram showing the positions of the 4 coffee shops on a set of coordinate axes. A(1, 6), B (2, 2), C(8, 2) D(8, 5) where one unit represents 1 km.

a Find the coordinates of the vertices P and Q in the Voronoi diagram.

b Determine the best position for the new shop so as to be as far as possible from any other shop.

a P is the point where $x = 5$ and $y = 3.5$ meet: (5, 3.5)

The perpendicular bisector of [AB] is $-x + 4y = 14.5$

The perpendicular bisector of [AD] is $7x - y = 26$

The perpendicular bisector of [BD] is $2x + y = 13.5$

The coordinates of Q are (4.39, 4.72)

b Centred at P:

$PD = \sqrt{(5 - 3.5)^2 + (8 - 5)^2} = 3.35$

Centred at Q:

$QA = \sqrt{(6 - 4.72)^2 + (4.39 - 1)^2} = 3.62$

The new coffee shop should therefore be built as close as possible to the point Q.

Three perpendicular bisectors meet at the vertices, finding the intersection of any two will be sufficient to find the point.

Any two of these equations need to be calculated by first finding the midpoint and gradient.

The coordinates can then be found algebraically or by using a GDC.

The solution will be at whichever of the points P and Q is furthest from the three sites nearest to them.

Only one length for each needs to be checked as each of the other two points will be an equal distance from the vertex.

Reflect How do you find the distance from an intersection point to a site if given both coordinates?

How do you decide which intersection point is the solution to the toxic waste dump problem?

Exercise 3G

1 A town is divided into a coordinate system with distances measured in kilometres north and east of a fixed origin. Within this town three schools A, B and C are at the points with coordinates A(1, 3), B(6, 4) and C (6, 1).

It is decided that a new school should be built as close as possible to the point which is furthest from all three existing schools.

a Explain why this point will be at the intersection of the perpendicular bisectors of [AB], [BC] and [AC].

b Find the equations of the perpendicular bisectors of [AB] and [BC]

c Hence find the coordinates of the point where the new school should be built.

d Determine the distance between the new school and each of the other schools.

2 At a fair there are three hamburger stands, A, B and C. The fairground is in the shape of a rectangle with dimensions 100 m by 50 m. The bottom left-hand side of the field can be regarded as the origin of a coordinate system, with the diagonally opposite corner as (100, 50). The hamburger stands are at the points A(20, 30), B(80, 30) and C (40, 10) as shown on the diagram below.

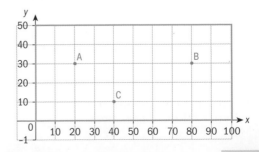

a Find the equation of the perpendicular bisector of

   i A and C   **ii** B and C.

People will always go to the hamburger stand that is closest to them.

b Draw the Voronoi diagram that represents this situation.

c Find the proportion of the fair ground in which people would go to

   i Stand C   **ii** Stand A.

d A fourth hamburger stand is to be added to the fairground at a point as far away as possible from the other three stands.

   i State the coordinates of the position at which it should be built.

   ii Determine how far it will be from the other hamburger stands.

3 A town can be considered as a rectangle which runs 10 km east to west and 8 km north to south. A coordinate grid is placed on a map of the town with the origin in the south-west corner. There are four schools in the town, A, B, C and D whose coordinates are: A (2, 5), B (3, 3), C (8, 6), D (8, 1).

Children go to the school that is closest to their home when measured by a direct line.

An estate agent wishes to construct a diagram which easily shows in which school's catchment area a house lies.

   a Find the perpendicular bisector of [AB].

   b Show the positions of A and B and the perpendicular bisector on a diagram of the town.

The perpendicular bisectors of [AC] and [BC]

are $y = -6x + 35.5$ and $y = -\dfrac{5}{3}x + \dfrac{41}{3}$

   c Use the incremental algorithm to construct the Voronoi diagram for the three schools.

   d **i** Find the perpendicular bisectors of [BD] and [CD] and show these on the diagram.

      ii Explain why there is no need to calculate the perpendicular bisector of [AD].

      iii Construct the diagram required by the estate agent.

   e Find the coordinates of the two vertices where three edges meet.

f Hence find the percentage area of the town covered by school C to 2 significant figures.

g A fifth school is to be built in the town as far as possible from the other schools. Find the coordinates of the point at which it would be built if it was to meet this requirement.

h On the diagram already drawn plot the fifth school at the position found in **g** and **sketch** the new Voronoi diagram. There is no need to find equations for the new perpendicular bisectors.

4 The map of a rectangular province is shown with the positions of the bases for the flying doctors shown on a coordinate grid centred at one of the corners in the province (units are in 100s of miles).

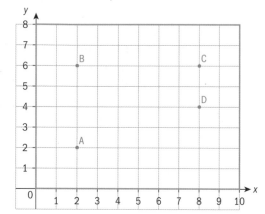

When an emergency occurs the doctor that is based closest to the location of the emergency will fly out to the scene.

   a Construct a Voronoi diagram for the four sites.

A neighbouring province asks if the doctor based at point A (2, 6) can also help out in their province. The director replies it would be possible if he is currently covering a smaller area than at least two of the other doctors.

   b Find where the perpendicular bisector of AD meets the line $y = 4$.

   c Find the area of the cells surrounding

      i A   **ii** B   **iii** C   **iv** D.

   d Hence state whether or not the doctor based at A will be able to support the other province?

5 The diagram below shows the Voronoi diagram for the points A(0,2), B(6,2), C(6, 5), and D(2,5).

The four points represent stations at which environmental readings are taken. The axes are measured in 10 km sections, east and north of a town which is situated at the origin. Hence B is 60 km east and 20 km north of this town.

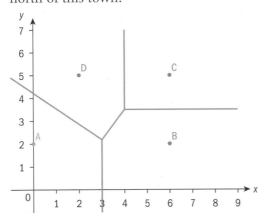

Each of the towns are connected by straight roads.

An environmental officer decides to drive from A to B, B to C, C to D and back to A.

a i Show the total distance driven is 166 km to the nearest km.

ii Find the proportion of the journey during which he is closest to the station at A.

The environmental officer receives a call from the owner of a home at N, whose coordinates are (4, 3.5). The owner is concerned at the level of pollution he

is experiencing, due to road congestion caused by construction.

The officer decides that he will work out what level of pollution would be expected in this location under normal conditions based on the data he has and will compare it with what the home owner is experiencing.

The pollution readings from each of the stations are (based on Air Quality Health Index):

A 4.5   B 2.1   C 2.6   D 2.8

b The officer decides to use as an expected value the average pollution recorded at 3 of the stations.

i Explain why this is reasonable and which three stations he should use.

ii Find the value he will use.

Readings of the air quality health index at N are taken over a period of 15 days and are shown below

3.0, 2.8, 2.1, 3.4, 3.1, 2.9, 3.0, 3.2, 2.8, 2.7, 2.6, 3.1, 3.0, 3.2, 2.7

c i Find the median, lower quartile, upper quartile and inter-quartile range for this data.

ii Show the data on a box-and-whisker plot, indicating the position of any outliers.

d Using the results from parts **b** and **c** comment on the house owner's claim that traffic congestion is causing greater than expected pollution near his home.

Developing inquiry skills

Look back at the opening problem for the chapter. You were trying to divide the territorial waters between three islands.

1 Draw the Voronoi diagram showing the regions in which each of the three islands have exclusive fishing rights.

2 Find the area of each of these regions.

3.4 Displacement vectors

A boat sails 4 km on a bearing of 30°, followed 3 km south-east, then 4 km due east and 2 km on a bearing of 080° as shown. How far is it from its starting point and what bearing would it have to travel on to return directly to the starting point?

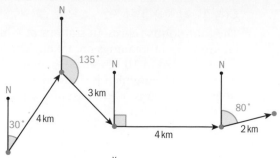

Consider how you might solve this using trigonometry.

Vectors provide a straightforward way to answer questions like this as well as many others.

If you move from the point A at (1, 1) to the point B at (4, 6) your movement can be represented by the directed line segment, or **vector**, as shown. A vector has both a magnitude (length) and direction.

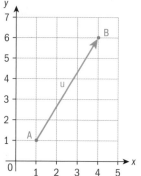

Because the vector goes from A to B we can write it as $\overrightarrow{AB}$. Alternatively, we can give it a name such as $\boldsymbol{u}$. In print a vector is named using bold font, when handwritten it is written as $\underset{\sim}{u}$ or $\vec{u}$.

Vectors are normally described in **component** form. The vector shown can be written as a column vector $\overrightarrow{AB} = \begin{pmatrix} 3 \\ 5 \end{pmatrix}$ or, using the **base** vectors $\boldsymbol{i}$ and $\boldsymbol{j}$ as $\overrightarrow{AB} = 3\boldsymbol{i} + 5\boldsymbol{j}$. In each case the first number, or component, indicates movement in the x-direction and the second movement in the y-direction.

The vector $\overrightarrow{BA} = \begin{pmatrix} -3 \\ -5 \end{pmatrix}$ because to move from B to A you need to go 3 units to the left and 5 down.

It will always be the case that the vector $\overrightarrow{AB} = -\overrightarrow{BA}$

Addition of vectors

Two vectors are added by adding the corresponding components.

$\begin{pmatrix} 1 \\ 2 \end{pmatrix} + \begin{pmatrix} 3 \\ -1 \end{pmatrix} = \begin{pmatrix} 4 \\ 1 \end{pmatrix}$ or $(3\boldsymbol{i} + 5\boldsymbol{j}) + (\boldsymbol{i} + 2\boldsymbol{j}) = (4\boldsymbol{i} + 7\boldsymbol{j})$

> **EXAM HINT**
>
> The choice of which notation to use may depend on the context but in an exam, both are equally valid.

Exercise 3H

1 Write the following vectors as column vectors and using $\boldsymbol{i}$ and $\boldsymbol{j}$ notation.

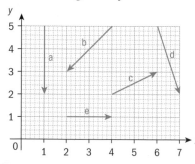

2 Find:

a $\begin{pmatrix} 2 \\ 1 \end{pmatrix} + \begin{pmatrix} -5 \\ 3 \end{pmatrix}$

b $(3\boldsymbol{i} - \boldsymbol{j}) + (4\boldsymbol{i} + 5\boldsymbol{j})$

c $\begin{pmatrix} -2 \\ 5 \end{pmatrix} + \begin{pmatrix} -4 \\ -3 \end{pmatrix}$

d $(\boldsymbol{i} - 2\boldsymbol{j}) + 4\boldsymbol{i}$

3 Find

a $\begin{pmatrix} 2 \\ 3 \end{pmatrix} + \begin{pmatrix} 2 \\ 3 \end{pmatrix}$ **b** $\begin{pmatrix} 2 \\ 3 \end{pmatrix} + \begin{pmatrix} 2 \\ 3 \end{pmatrix} + \begin{pmatrix} 2 \\ 3 \end{pmatrix}$

c Explain how you multiply a vector by a scalar.

d $\boldsymbol{i}$ and $\boldsymbol{j}$ can also be written as $\begin{pmatrix} 1 \\ 0 \end{pmatrix}$ and $\begin{pmatrix} 0 \\ 1 \end{pmatrix}$

Hence verify $3\boldsymbol{i} + 4\boldsymbol{j} = \begin{pmatrix} 3 \\ 4 \end{pmatrix}$

4 Let $\overrightarrow{AB} = \begin{pmatrix} 1 \\ 2 \end{pmatrix}$ as shown.

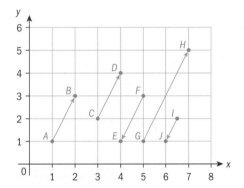

a Write the following vectors in component form and in terms of the vector $\overrightarrow{AB}$.

   i $\overrightarrow{CD}$ **ii** $\overrightarrow{FE}$

   iii $\overrightarrow{GH}$ **iv** $\overrightarrow{IJ}$

b Comment on what can be deduced about parallel vectors.

5 State which of the following vectors are parallel to $5\boldsymbol{i} + 2\boldsymbol{j}$.

a $-5\boldsymbol{i} - 2\boldsymbol{j}$ **b** $25\boldsymbol{i} - 10\boldsymbol{j}$

c $-\boldsymbol{i} - 0.4\boldsymbol{j}$ **d** $\begin{pmatrix} 20 \\ 50 \end{pmatrix}$

e $\begin{pmatrix} 4 \\ 6 \end{pmatrix} + \begin{pmatrix} 6 \\ -2 \end{pmatrix}$ **f** $2\begin{pmatrix} -10 \\ 4 \end{pmatrix}$

g $2\begin{pmatrix} 3 \\ 3 \end{pmatrix} - 3\begin{pmatrix} -3 \\ 0 \end{pmatrix}$

6 a Find p and q if

   i $\begin{pmatrix} 4p \\ 6 \end{pmatrix} + \begin{pmatrix} 6 \\ -2q \end{pmatrix} = \begin{pmatrix} -2p \\ 2 \end{pmatrix}$

   ii $\begin{pmatrix} 3p \\ -2q \end{pmatrix} + \begin{pmatrix} 2q \\ p \end{pmatrix} = \begin{pmatrix} 7 \\ 1 \end{pmatrix}$

b i Find p if $\begin{pmatrix} p+1 \\ 2p \end{pmatrix}$ is parallel to $\begin{pmatrix} 4 \\ 1 \end{pmatrix}$

   ii Find q if $\begin{pmatrix} 2q-3 \\ q+6 \end{pmatrix}$ is parallel to $\begin{pmatrix} -3 \\ 1 \end{pmatrix}$

Reflect How can you demonstrate that two vectors have the same direction?

$\boldsymbol{a}$ and $\boldsymbol{b}$ are parallel if and only if $\boldsymbol{b} = k\boldsymbol{a}$, where k is a scalar.

Investigation 7

1 a Plot on graph paper the points $P(1, 4)$ and $Q(8, 10)$ and write down the vector $\overrightarrow{PQ}$.

b Pick another point, A, anywhere on the coordinate grid and add it to your graph.

c Write down the vectors $\overrightarrow{PA}$ and $\overrightarrow{AQ}$ and calculate $\overrightarrow{PA} + \overrightarrow{AQ}$.

Continued on next page

Functions

Geometry and trigonometry

d Pick another point B anywhere on the coordinate grid and add it to your graph.

   e Write down the vectors $\overrightarrow{PB}$ and $\overrightarrow{BQ}$ and calculate $\overrightarrow{PB} + \overrightarrow{BQ}$.

   f Comment on your results.

2 **a** Add points C and D anywhere on your graph.

   b On your graph draw the vectors $\overrightarrow{PA}$, $\overrightarrow{AB}$, $\overrightarrow{BC}$ and $\overrightarrow{CQ}$.

   c Find the values of $\overrightarrow{PA}$, $\overrightarrow{AB}$, $\overrightarrow{BC}$ and $\overrightarrow{CQ}$ and calculate the sum of these four vectors.

   d Conjecture a general property of the addition of vectors.

   Conceptual What is the geometric meaning of a vector sum?

From the above we can derive the **triangle law of vector addition.**

$$\overrightarrow{AC} = \overrightarrow{AB} + \overrightarrow{BC}$$

This can be extended to any number of vectors. A consequence of the law is that the sum of two of more displacement vectors is always equal to the final displacement and is independent of the route taken.

Position vectors

A position vector gives a point's displacement from the origin.

The point A with coordinates $(4, 2)$ has position vector $\overrightarrow{OA} = \boldsymbol{a} = \begin{pmatrix} 4 \\ 2 \end{pmatrix}$

The point B with coordinates $(-2, 3)$ has position vector $\overrightarrow{OB} = \boldsymbol{b} = \begin{pmatrix} -2 \\ 3 \end{pmatrix}$

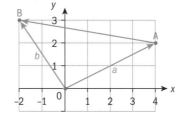

TOK

When is it ethically correct to provide a person's location?

It can be seen from the diagram and using the triangle law of vector addition that $\overrightarrow{AB} = \overrightarrow{AO} + \overrightarrow{OB} = -\overrightarrow{OA} + \overrightarrow{OB}$

This is normally written as $\overrightarrow{AB} = \overrightarrow{OB} - \overrightarrow{OA}$ or $\overrightarrow{AB} = \boldsymbol{b} - \boldsymbol{a}$.

Example 5

A is the point with coordinates $(6, 1)$ and B is the point with coordinates $(-2, 5)$.

a Find the vector $\overrightarrow{AB}$.

A ship moves from the point A to a point C which has coordinates $(7, 4)$ and then onto point B.

b Find the vectors $\overrightarrow{AC}$ and $\overrightarrow{CB}$.

c Write down an equation linking $\overrightarrow{AB}$, $\overrightarrow{AC}$ and $\overrightarrow{CB}$.

d Verify your answer is true for the values obtained in parts **a** and **b**.

From point B the ship moves on to the point D where $\overrightarrow{BD} = \begin{pmatrix} 5 \\ 2 \end{pmatrix}$

e Find the vector $\overrightarrow{AD}$.

f Find the coordinates of D.

a $\overrightarrow{AB} = \begin{pmatrix} -2 \\ 5 \end{pmatrix} - \begin{pmatrix} 6 \\ 1 \end{pmatrix} = \begin{pmatrix} -8 \\ 4 \end{pmatrix}$

Using $\overrightarrow{AB} = \boldsymbol{b} - \boldsymbol{a}$

b $\overrightarrow{AC} = \begin{pmatrix} 7 \\ 4 \end{pmatrix} - \begin{pmatrix} 6 \\ 1 \end{pmatrix} = \begin{pmatrix} 1 \\ 3 \end{pmatrix}$

Using $\overrightarrow{AC} = \boldsymbol{c} - \boldsymbol{a}$ and $\overrightarrow{CB} = \boldsymbol{b} - \boldsymbol{c}$

$\overrightarrow{CB} = \begin{pmatrix} -2 \\ 5 \end{pmatrix} - \begin{pmatrix} 7 \\ 4 \end{pmatrix} = \begin{pmatrix} -9 \\ 1 \end{pmatrix}$

c $\overrightarrow{AB} = \overrightarrow{AC} + \overrightarrow{CB}$

Care needs to be taken as the triangle law for vector addition requires the vectors to follow on from each other. The endpoint of the first vector must be the first point of the second.

The sketch below indicates the order required.

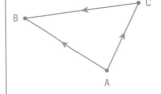

d $\begin{pmatrix} -8 \\ 4 \end{pmatrix} = \begin{pmatrix} 1 \\ 3 \end{pmatrix} + \begin{pmatrix} -9 \\ 1 \end{pmatrix}$

e $\overrightarrow{AD} = \overrightarrow{AB} + \overrightarrow{BD}$

$\begin{pmatrix} -8 \\ 4 \end{pmatrix} + \begin{pmatrix} 5 \\ 2 \end{pmatrix} = \begin{pmatrix} -3 \\ 6 \end{pmatrix}$

f $\overrightarrow{OD} = \overrightarrow{OA} + \overrightarrow{AD}$

Remember the coordinates of D are obtained from its position vector $\overrightarrow{OD}$.

$\overrightarrow{OD} = \begin{pmatrix} 6 \\ 1 \end{pmatrix} + \begin{pmatrix} -3 \\ 6 \end{pmatrix} = \begin{pmatrix} 3 \\ 7 \end{pmatrix}$

Hence coordinates are (3, 7).

Give the answer as coordinates rather than a position vector if this is what is asked for.

Reflect How do you find the displacement vector between two points A and B?

Exercise 3I

1 The points A, B and C have coordinates $(1, 4)$, $(2, 5)$ and $(-1, 6)$ respectively.

   a Find the vectors

     i $\overrightarrow{OA}$ **ii** $\overrightarrow{AB}$ **iii** $\overrightarrow{AC}$ **iv** $\overrightarrow{CA}$.

The point D is such that $\overrightarrow{CD}$ is equal to $\begin{pmatrix} 4 \\ 1 \end{pmatrix}$.

   b **i** Write down an equation that gives $\overrightarrow{BD}$ in terms of $\overrightarrow{BA}$, $\overrightarrow{AC}$ and $\overrightarrow{CD}$.

     ii Hence write down an equation that gives $\overrightarrow{BD}$ in terms of $\overrightarrow{AB}$, $\overrightarrow{AC}$ and $\overrightarrow{CD}$.

     iii Hence find $\overrightarrow{BD}$.

     iv Find the coordinates of D.

2 **a** $\overrightarrow{AB} = \begin{pmatrix} 1 \\ 4 \end{pmatrix}$ and $\overrightarrow{BC} = \begin{pmatrix} -1 \\ 2 \end{pmatrix}$

    find **i** $\overrightarrow{AC}$ and **ii** $\overrightarrow{CA}$.

   b $\overrightarrow{AB} = \begin{pmatrix} 2 \\ 4 \end{pmatrix}$ and $\overrightarrow{BC} = \begin{pmatrix} -1 \\ 3 \end{pmatrix}$

    and $\overrightarrow{AD} = \begin{pmatrix} 2 \\ 3 \end{pmatrix}$ find $\overrightarrow{DC}$.

3 The points A, B, C and D have coordinates $(1, 0)$, $(2, 3)$, $(7, 5)$ and $(6, 2)$ respectively.

   a Find the vectors $\overrightarrow{AB}$ and $\overrightarrow{DC}$.

   b State which type of quadrilateral is formed by ABCD. Justify your answer.

   c State two other vectors which must be equal.

4 An aircraft flies from an airport at A to one at B and then on to C. The routes taken can be given by the vectors $\overrightarrow{AB} = \begin{pmatrix} 75 \\ 90 \end{pmatrix}$ and $\overrightarrow{BC} = \begin{pmatrix} -35 \\ -100 \end{pmatrix}$ km.

   a Find the vector $\overrightarrow{AC}$.

   b The aircraft then flies directly back to A. Write down the vector that describes this flight.

   c Calculate the direct distance from C to A.

5 A surveyor is putting flags out in a large field. His movements between the flags can be described by the vectors $(5\boldsymbol{i} + \boldsymbol{j})$, $(-2\boldsymbol{i} + 4\boldsymbol{j})$, $(4\boldsymbol{i} + 2\boldsymbol{j})$, $(6\boldsymbol{i} + 4\boldsymbol{j})$.

   a Find his displacement from his starting position when he puts out the last flag.

   b Write down the displacement vector that will take him back to his starting position.

The magnitude and direction of a vector

The magnitude of a vector $\boldsymbol{v}$ is its length. It is written as $|\boldsymbol{v}|$ and can be found using Pythagoras' theorem.

The magnitude of $\begin{pmatrix} 3 \\ 4 \end{pmatrix} = \left| \begin{matrix} 3 \\ 4 \end{matrix} \right| = \sqrt{3^2 + 4^2} = 5$

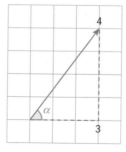

TOK

How certain is the shared knowledge of mathematics?

The direction of a vector is normally given as an angle. Within a Cartesian coordinate system the angle is normally measured anti-clockwise from the positive x-axis.

The direction of the vector $\begin{pmatrix} 3 \\ 4 \end{pmatrix}$ is the angle α where $\tan \alpha = \dfrac{4}{3}$ hence $\alpha = 53.1°$.

In many contexts it is more natural to describe a vector by giving its magnitude and direction, but because manipulation of vectors is much easier when given in component form it is important to be able to switch between forms.

Example 6

Write the following displacement as a column vector and in *i, j* form: 15 m on a bearing of 130°.

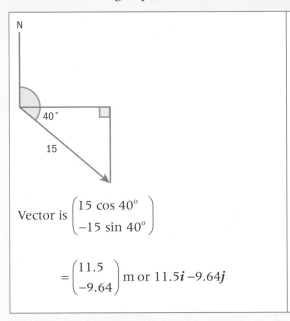

Vector is $\begin{pmatrix} 15 \cos 40° \\ -15 \sin 40° \end{pmatrix}$

$= \begin{pmatrix} 11.5 \\ -9.64 \end{pmatrix}$ m or $11.5i - 9.64j$

In order to find the entries for the column vector first create a right-angled triangle and then use trigonometry.

From the direction of the vector you will be able to see which entries should be positive and which negative.

Reflect How do you find the magnitude and direction of a vector in 2 dimensions?

How do you write a vector given as a magnitude and direction in component form?

Investigation 8

1 A boy walks 5 km on a bearing of 045° and then 8 km on a bearing of 120°.

   a Show this information on a diagram.

   b Use the cosine and sine rules to find his distance and bearing from his starting point at the end of the walk.

   c i Write the displacements 5 km on a bearing of 045° and 8 km on a bearing of 120° as column vectors where the first component indicates displacement east and the second displacement north.

   ii Use your answer to part **c i** to find how far east and how far north from his starting point the boy is at the end of his walk.

   iii Hence give his **resultant** (final) displacement as a column vector.

   iv Use your answer to part **c iii** to find his distance and bearing from his starting point at the end of the walk.

Continued on next page

Functions

Geometry and trigonometry

➡ **2** A boat sails 60 m on a bearing of 030°, followed by 90 m on a bearing of 160° and 40 m on a bearing of 280° where it touches a buoy.

   a By writing each of the displacement vectors in component form find how far the buoy is from the boat's starting position?

   b Think about how you would you attempt this question if asked to do it using sine and cosine rules.

Factual How can you represent vectors?

Conceptual Which representation is easier to use to find a resultant?

Reflect How do you find a particle's displacement from its starting point if given its successive individual displacements?

> The sum of two or more vectors is called the **resultant** vector.

Exercise 3J

1 For the resultant of each of the vector sums below, find the

   i magnitude

   ii direction (as an angle anti-clockwise from the direction of i).

  a $\begin{pmatrix} 1 \\ 3 \end{pmatrix} + \begin{pmatrix} -1 \\ 2 \end{pmatrix} + \begin{pmatrix} 4 \\ -1 \end{pmatrix}$

  b $(5i + 2j) + (-6i - 4j)$

  c $2\begin{pmatrix} 3 \\ 2 \end{pmatrix} - 3\begin{pmatrix} -4 \\ -1 \end{pmatrix}$

  d $5(i + 2j) + 3(i - 3j)$

2 The magnitude of a vector $\begin{pmatrix} a \\ b \end{pmatrix}$ can be written as $\left| \begin{matrix} a \\ b \end{matrix} \right|$.

  a Verify that $\left| \begin{matrix} 48 \\ 20 \end{matrix} \right|$ is equal to $4\left| \begin{matrix} 12 \\ 5 \end{matrix} \right|$.

  b By first taking out a factor and without using a GDC, find the magnitude of

    i $\begin{pmatrix} 18 \\ 24 \end{pmatrix}$ **ii** $\begin{pmatrix} -30 \\ 40 \end{pmatrix}$ **iii** $\begin{pmatrix} 28 \\ -21 \end{pmatrix}$

3 A designer needs to construct a line segment of a given length in a given direction. His software requires him to enter the line segment as a single column vector.

Find the column vector he needs to input in the following situations, using the fact that a vector which is in the same direction as a vector u can be written as ku. $k > 0$

  a A vector that is in the same direction as $\begin{pmatrix} 3 \\ 4 \end{pmatrix}$ but with a magnitude of 8.

  b A single vector which is equivalent to the resultant of a vector in the same direction as $\begin{pmatrix} 0 \\ 1 \end{pmatrix}$ followed by the vector $\begin{pmatrix} 5 \\ 0 \end{pmatrix}$ and has magnitude $\sqrt{74}$.

  c A vector which is equivalent to the resultant of a vector in the same direction as $\begin{pmatrix} 1 \\ 1 \end{pmatrix}$, followed by the vector $\begin{pmatrix} 1 \\ -5 \end{pmatrix}$ and has magnitude $\sqrt{50}$.

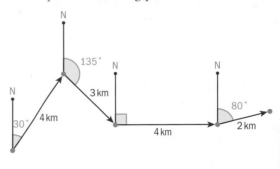

4 A man walking in a large field walks 200 m north-east and 175 m west.

   a Write each of the displacements as a column vector.

   b Hence find his final distance from his starting point.

5 A boat sails 4 km on a bearing of 030°, followed 3 km south-east, then 4 km due east and 2 km on a bearing of 080° as shown on the right. Determine its final distance from the starting point. Find also the bearing it would have to travel on to return directly to the starting point.

Vectors in 3 dimensions

The work done on vectors so far can be extended to three dimensions.

Example 7

Let A be the point with coordinates $(1, 5, 8)$ and B be the point with coordinates $(2, -1, 5)$ and let O be the origin.

   a Show on a sketch the points A, B and O and the vectors $\overrightarrow{OA}$, $\overrightarrow{OB}$ and $\overrightarrow{AB}$.

   b Write down the position vector of A.

   c Find the distance of A from the origin O.

   d Find the vector $\overrightarrow{AB}$.

   e Find $\left|\overrightarrow{AB}\right|$.

   f Find the vector that is parallel to $\overrightarrow{AB}$ but with twice the magnitude.

a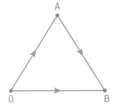

b $\overrightarrow{OA} = \begin{pmatrix} 1 \\ 5 \\ 8 \end{pmatrix}$

c $\left|\overrightarrow{OA}\right| = \sqrt{1^2 + 5^2 + 8^2} \approx 9.49$

d $\overrightarrow{AB} = \begin{pmatrix} 2 \\ -1 \\ 5 \end{pmatrix} - \begin{pmatrix} 1 \\ 5 \\ 8 \end{pmatrix} = \begin{pmatrix} 1 \\ -6 \\ -3 \end{pmatrix}$

It is rarely necessary to draw accurate diagrams. A two-dimensional sketch of a three-dimensional situation is normally sufficient.

This can also be written as $i + 5j + 8k$ where i, j and k are the base vectors $\begin{pmatrix} 1 \\ 0 \\ 0 \end{pmatrix}, \begin{pmatrix} 0 \\ 1 \\ 0 \end{pmatrix}$ and $\begin{pmatrix} 0 \\ 0 \\ 1 \end{pmatrix}$.

Pythagoras' theorem can be extended to give the magnitude of vectors in three dimensions.

The triangle law of vector addition also holds and in particular $\overrightarrow{AB} = b - a$

Continued on next page

Functions

Geometry and trigonometry

e $\left|\overrightarrow{AB}\right| = \sqrt{1^2 + 6^2 + 3^2} = \sqrt{46} = 6.78$

f $2\overrightarrow{AB} = \begin{pmatrix} 2 \\ -12 \\ -6 \end{pmatrix}$

Note that this is equivalent to finding the length AB using the formula

$$\sqrt{(x_2 - x_1)^2 + (y_2 - y_1)^2 + (z_2 - z_1)^2}$$

Reflect How do you find the magnitude of a vector in 3 dimensions?

Exercise 3K

1 Find the magnitude of each of the following vectors without using a calculator.

a $8i - 4j + k$ **b** $\begin{pmatrix} 2 \\ 1 \\ 2 \end{pmatrix}$

c $3\begin{pmatrix} 4 \\ -3 \\ 0 \end{pmatrix}$

d $5(2i - 3j + 6k)$

2 A small plane travels along the three vectors $\begin{pmatrix} 3 \\ 1 \\ 2 \end{pmatrix}$, $\begin{pmatrix} 2 \\ 4 \\ 1 \end{pmatrix}$ and $\begin{pmatrix} 7 \\ 4 \\ 3 \end{pmatrix}$ in succession.

State the vector it will have to travel along to return to its starting point

3 a If A and B have position vectors a and b and if M is the midpoint of [AB] show that $\overrightarrow{OM} = \dfrac{1}{2}(a + b)$.

Three points P, Q and R have coordinates (1, 3, 6), (−1, 0 5) and (2, 4, −1).

b Find the vectors $\overrightarrow{PQ}$ and $\overrightarrow{QR}$.

c Hence or otherwise find the vector $\overrightarrow{PR}$.

The quadrilateral PQRS is a parallelogram.

d Find the coordinate of S.

e Find the midpoint of the vector $\overrightarrow{PR}$.

f Find the midpoint of the vector $\overrightarrow{QS}$.

g What do the answers for parts **e** and **f** tell you about the diagonals of a parallelogram?

3.5 The scalar and vector product

How might you use trigonometry to find the angle between the diagonals of a cube, or the area of a triangular forest if given its coordinates in three dimensions?

This section will demonstrate vector techniques that allow both these questions to be easily solved.

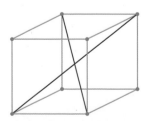

Investigation 9

Let A and B be two points in a plane with position vectors a and b.

1 Let A have coordinates $(1, 2, 3)$ and B have coordinates $(2, 5, -2)$.

    a Find the vector $\overrightarrow{AB}$.

    b Find the value of $|a|^2$, $|b|^2$ and AB^2.

    c Hence calculate $\frac{1}{2}\left(|a|^2 + |b|^2 - AB^2\right)$.

The scalar product of two vectors a and b is written as $a \cdot b$ and is calculated by finding the sum of the product of corresponding components. Hence in 2 dimensions for $a = \begin{pmatrix} a_1 \\ a_2 \end{pmatrix}$ and $b = \begin{pmatrix} b_1 \\ b_2 \end{pmatrix}$.

$a \cdot b = a_1 b_1 + a_2 b_2$ and in 3 dimensions for $a = \begin{pmatrix} a_1 \\ a_2 \\ a_3 \end{pmatrix}$ and $b = \begin{pmatrix} b_1 \\ b_2 \\ b_3 \end{pmatrix}$ $a \cdot b = a_1 b_1 + a_2 b_2 + a_3 b_3$

    d Evaluate $a \cdot b$ for the values of A and B given above.

    e Conjecture an alternative expression for $a \cdot b$.

2 For $a = \begin{pmatrix} a_1 \\ a_2 \end{pmatrix}$ and $b = \begin{pmatrix} b_1 \\ b_2 \end{pmatrix}$ find expressions for $|a|^2$, $|b|^2$ and AB^2 and hence prove your conjecture in part **1e** for vectors in 2 dimensions.

3 Use $a = \begin{pmatrix} a_1 \\ a_2 \\ a_3 \end{pmatrix}$ and $b = \begin{pmatrix} b_1 \\ b_2 \\ b_3 \end{pmatrix}$ to show that your conjecture also works in 3 dimensions.

4 Consider the diagram.

    a Use the cosine law to prove that

$$|a||b|\cos\theta = \frac{1}{2}\left(|a|^2 + |b|^2 - AB^2\right)$$

    b Hence write down an expression which gives $\cos\theta$ in terms of the magnitudes of a and b and the scalar product of a and b.

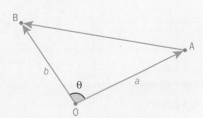

5 Find the scalar product of the two vectors given and hence find the angle between them.

    i $\begin{pmatrix} 1 \\ 2 \end{pmatrix}$ and $\begin{pmatrix} -2 \\ 3 \end{pmatrix}$ **ii** $\begin{pmatrix} 2 \\ 0 \\ -4 \end{pmatrix}$ and $\begin{pmatrix} -3 \\ 2 \\ 2 \end{pmatrix}$

6 **a** Find the scalar product of $\begin{pmatrix} 2 \\ 1 \\ -3 \end{pmatrix}$ and $\begin{pmatrix} -2 \\ 10 \\ 2 \end{pmatrix}$

    b What does this tell you about the angle between the two vectors?

7 **Conceptual** What can the scalar product be used to find?

Reflect   How can you calculate the scalar product of two vectors?

> The **scalar** or dot product is written as $a \cdot b = a_1 b_1 + a_2 b_2$ for 2 dimensional vectors and $a \cdot b = a_1 b_1 + a_2 b_2 + a_3 b_3$ for 3 dimensional vectors.
> In addition $a \cdot b = = |a||b| \cos \theta$
> This allows us to find the angle between any two vectors, $\cos \theta = \dfrac{a \cdot b}{|a||b|}$
> If $a \cdot b = 0$ then a and b are perpendicular.

Example 8

Find p if $2p\boldsymbol{i} + \boldsymbol{j} - 3\boldsymbol{k}$ and $2\boldsymbol{i} + 3\boldsymbol{j} + p\boldsymbol{k}$ are perpendicular.

$a \cdot b = 4p + 3 - 3p = 0$ $p = -3$	When two vectors are perpendicular $\cos \theta = 0$ and so $a \cdot b = 0$.

Reflect   How can you use the scalar product to show two vectors are perpendicular?

Exercise 3L

1 Calculate the angle between the following pairs of vectors.

   a $\begin{pmatrix} 2 \\ -1 \\ 4 \end{pmatrix}$ and $\begin{pmatrix} 3 \\ 1 \\ 2 \end{pmatrix}$ **b** $\begin{pmatrix} 2 \\ 0 \\ 1 \end{pmatrix}$ and $\begin{pmatrix} -2 \\ 1 \\ -1 \end{pmatrix}$

   c $2\boldsymbol{i} + \boldsymbol{j} - \boldsymbol{k}$ and $3\boldsymbol{i} + 2\boldsymbol{j}$

   d $2\boldsymbol{i} - \boldsymbol{j} - 2\boldsymbol{k}$ and $3\boldsymbol{i} + 2\boldsymbol{j} - 5\boldsymbol{k}$

   e $\begin{pmatrix} 2 \\ 3 \end{pmatrix}$ and $\begin{pmatrix} 4 \\ 6 \end{pmatrix}$ **f** $\begin{pmatrix} 2 \\ 0 \\ 1 \end{pmatrix}$ and $\begin{pmatrix} -4 \\ 0 \\ -2 \end{pmatrix}$

2 A triangle has vertices at the points A(1, 2, 3), B(0, 2, 5) and C(1, 3, −2).

   a State which two vectors you could use to find the angle at **i** A   **ii** B.

   b Find all the angles of the triangle.

   c Find the length of the longest side.

3 Find p if the two vectors given are perpendicular.

   a $\begin{pmatrix} 2 \\ 1 \\ p \end{pmatrix}$ and $\begin{pmatrix} -3p \\ 2 \\ -2 \end{pmatrix}$ **b** $\begin{pmatrix} p \\ -2 \\ 4 \end{pmatrix}$ and $\begin{pmatrix} p-1 \\ p \\ -1 \end{pmatrix}$

4 Triangle ABC has vertices A(1, 3, 2), B(2, 4, −1) and C(2, 3, k).

   a Find the possible value of k if the triangle has a right angle at C.

   b For these values of k find the CA and CB and hence the area of the triangles.

5 Find the acute angle between the diagonals of a cube.

The vector product

A second way of multiplying vectors is to form the **vector product**. As its name suggests the result of this multiplication will be a third vector.

In three dimensions the vector product can be calculated as follows:

For $\boldsymbol{a} = \begin{pmatrix} a_1 \\ a_2 \\ a_3 \end{pmatrix}$ and $\boldsymbol{b} = \begin{pmatrix} b_1 \\ b_2 \\ b_3 \end{pmatrix}$ the vector product $\boldsymbol{a} \times \boldsymbol{b}$ is given by

$$\boldsymbol{a} \times \boldsymbol{b} = \begin{pmatrix} a_2 b_3 - b_2 a_3 \\ a_3 b_1 - b_3 a_1 \\ a_1 b_2 - b_1 a_2 \end{pmatrix}$$

Investigation 10

This investigation leads to a key property of the vector product.

1 Use the formula given above to find the vector product of $\boldsymbol{a} = \begin{pmatrix} 2 \\ 2 \\ 1 \end{pmatrix}$ and $\boldsymbol{b} = \begin{pmatrix} 3 \\ 1 \\ -2 \end{pmatrix}$

2 Find the scalar product of your answer to 1 with $\begin{pmatrix} 2 \\ 2 \\ 1 \end{pmatrix}$ and $\begin{pmatrix} 3 \\ 1 \\ -2 \end{pmatrix}$

Write down what you notice and what this means about $\boldsymbol{a} \times \boldsymbol{b}$.

3 Verify your result by repeating 1 and 2 with two vectors of your choosing.

4 Use the formula for $\boldsymbol{a} \times \boldsymbol{b} = \begin{pmatrix} a_2 b_3 - b_2 a_3 \\ a_3 b_1 - b_3 a_1 \\ a_1 b_2 - b_1 a_2 \end{pmatrix}$ to find the result of $(\boldsymbol{a} \times \boldsymbol{b}) \bullet \boldsymbol{a}$.

5 [Conceptual] What can you say about the direction of the vector product of two vectors?

The vector product of two non-parallel vectors is perpendicular to both vectors.

Geometrically two vectors that are not in the same line will define a plane and the vector product will be a vector perpendicular to that plane.

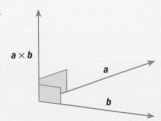

The area of a triangle

Consider the triangle shown.

We know from chapter 1 that the area of a triangle can be found from the formula

$$\text{Area} = \frac{1}{2}ab\sin C$$

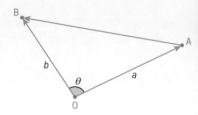

For the triangle above this could be written as $\frac{1}{2}|a||b|\sin\theta$.

To find the area of the triangle a value for θ could be calculated using the scalar product. It is possible though to find the area directly using the **vector product**.

The magnitude of the vector obtained when calculating the vector product is $|a \times b| = |a||b|\sin\theta$

Hence the area of the triangle with vectors a and b as two of its sides will have area $\frac{1}{2}|a \times b|$.

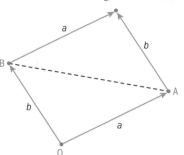

The area of the parallelogram with vectors a and b as two of its sides will have area $|a \times b|$.

> The vector product can also be found for two dimensional vectors by taking the third component as equal to 0.

International-mindedness

Area can be measured in square units like m^2, but also "packets" like hectares or acres.

Which countries use bigha, mou, feddan rai, tsubo?

Example 9

a Find the vector product of the vectors $\begin{pmatrix} 2 \\ 0 \\ 1 \end{pmatrix}$ and $\begin{pmatrix} 4 \\ 1 \\ -2 \end{pmatrix}$. Show it is perpendicular to both of these vectors.

b Find the area of the triangle which has these vectors as two of its sides.

a $\begin{pmatrix} 2 \\ 0 \\ 1 \end{pmatrix} \times \begin{pmatrix} 4 \\ 1 \\ -2 \end{pmatrix} = \begin{pmatrix} -1 \\ 8 \\ 2 \end{pmatrix}$	The calculations can be done by excluding the row you are trying to find and with the remaining four numbers finding the product of top left and bottom right and subtracting the product of top right and bottom left.
	For the first entry you have $0 \times -2 - 1 \times 1 = -1$
	For the second row you repeat this process and make the answer negative or multiply and subtract in the opposite order. $-(2 \times -2 - 4 \times 1) = 8$ or $4 \times 1 - 2 \times -2 = 8$
	Final entry is $2 \times 1 - 4 \times 0 = 2$

$$\begin{pmatrix} 2 \\ 0 \\ 1 \end{pmatrix} \cdot \begin{pmatrix} -1 \\ 8 \\ 2 \end{pmatrix} = -2 + 0 + 2 = 0$$

To show two vectors are perpendicular you need to demonstrate that their scalar product is 0.

$$\begin{pmatrix} 4 \\ 1 \\ -2 \end{pmatrix} \cdot \begin{pmatrix} -1 \\ 8 \\ 2 \end{pmatrix} = -4 + 8 - 4 = 0$$

Hence perpendicular.

b Area $= \dfrac{1}{2}|a \times b|$

$= \dfrac{1}{2}\sqrt{1^2 + 8^2 + 2^2} = 4.15$

Reflect How do you calculate the vector product of two vectors?

How do you find the area of a triangle defined by two vectors?

What does the magnitude of a vector product represent?

Example 10

Find the area of the parallelogram with vertices A $(1, 1, 0)$ B $(2, 3, 1)$, C $(4, 2, 4)$ and D $(3, 0, 3)$.

$$\overrightarrow{AB} = \begin{pmatrix} 1 \\ 2 \\ 1 \end{pmatrix}$$

You can take any two of the non-parallel sides to find the area. A sketch makes it clear which ones are possible.

$$\overrightarrow{AD} = \begin{pmatrix} 2 \\ -1 \\ 3 \end{pmatrix}$$

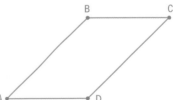

$$\overrightarrow{AB} \times \overrightarrow{AD} = \begin{pmatrix} 5 \\ -1 \\ -5 \end{pmatrix}$$

The area of the parallelogram is given by the formula, area $= |a \times b|$.

Area $= \sqrt{51} = 7.14$

Reflect How do you find the area of a parallelogram defined by two vectors?

Functions

Geometry and trigonometry

Exercise 3M

1 a Find the vector product of the following vectors.

$$a = \begin{pmatrix} 2 \\ 1 \\ 3 \end{pmatrix} \text{ and } b = \begin{pmatrix} 1 \\ -1 \\ 2 \end{pmatrix}$$

b Verify that the vector product is perpendicular to both **a** and **b**.

2 Find the vector products of the following pairs of vectors.

a $\begin{pmatrix} 2 \\ -1 \\ 4 \end{pmatrix}$ and $\begin{pmatrix} 3 \\ -1 \\ 2 \end{pmatrix}$ **b** $\begin{pmatrix} 2 \\ 0 \\ 1 \end{pmatrix}$ and $\begin{pmatrix} -2 \\ 3 \\ -1 \end{pmatrix}$

c $2i + j - k$ and $3i + 2j$

d $2i - j - 2k$ and $3i + 2j - 5k$

3 Two sides of a triangle ABC are formed by

the vectors $\overrightarrow{AB} = \begin{pmatrix} 2 \\ 0 \\ 1 \end{pmatrix}$ and $\overrightarrow{AC} = \begin{pmatrix} -2 \\ 1 \\ -1 \end{pmatrix}$

a Find the vector forming the third side.

b Find the area of the triangle.

4 A triangle has vertices at the points A(1, 2, 3), B(0, 2, 5) and C(1, 3, −2).

Find the area of triangle ABC.

5 A parallelogram ABCD has vertices at A(1, 2, −3), B(1, 2, 5) and C(4, 3, 5).

a Find the coordinates of D.

b Find the area of the parallelogram.

c Verify that ABCD is a rectangle.

6 A surveyor is measuring the area of a rectangular roof. His instruments give the coordinates of the corners of the roof as (−2, 4, 2), (−3, 1, 3), (3, −1, 3) and (4, 2, 2) where the coordinates are in metres from a fixed origin. Find the area of the roof.

7 A crystal is in the shape of a square-based pyramid as shown. All the sides are made up of isosceles triangles. The coordinates of the vertex are (1, 3, 2) and the coordinates of two adjacent vertices on the base are (2, 3, −1) and (−1, 3, 1).

Find the surface area of the crystal.

3.6 Vector equations of lines

An air-traffic controller sees that the paths of two planes are about to cross. He knows the regulations state that when the planes cross the vertical height between them must be greater than 300 m and if it is not their distance apart has to be always greater than 10 km. He knows the position and velocities of each aircraft. Does he need to instruct one of them to change their direction?

This section will consider what we can deduce about the future paths of objects travelling with constant velocities.

> **TOK**
>
> Do you think that there are times when analytical reasoning is easier to use than sense perception when working in three dimensions?

Investigation 11

Consider the line which passes through a point $A(1, 3)$ and is

parallel to the vector $b = \begin{pmatrix} 2 \\ 1 \end{pmatrix}$

1   Explain why the position vector of C can be written as

$$\begin{pmatrix} 1 \\ 3 \end{pmatrix} + 2 \begin{pmatrix} 2 \\ 1 \end{pmatrix}$$

2   Write down similar expressions in the form $a + tb$ for the position vectors of A, B and D.

3   What can you deduce about the position vector of any point on the line?

4   Why will this not be true for any point not on the line?

5   Show that A, B, C and D can also be written in the form $\begin{pmatrix} 3 \\ 4 \end{pmatrix} + s \begin{pmatrix} -2 \\ -1 \end{pmatrix}$, stating the value of s in each case.

6   **Factual**   What is the vector equation of a line in symbols?

7   **Conceptual**   How do we express the vector equation of a line in word?

The vector equation of a line is normally written as $r = a + tb$ where r is the

vector $\begin{pmatrix} x \\ y \end{pmatrix}$ in two dimensions, and $\begin{pmatrix} x \\ y \\ z \end{pmatrix}$ in three dimensions, a is the

position vector of a point on the line and b is a vector parallel to the line – a **direction vector**.

The vector equation of a line is not unique as any point on the line and any vector parallel to the direction of the line could be used.

Every point on the line will have a particular value of the parameter t, where t is a measure of how far the point is away from A as a multiple of the vector b.

TOK

Why might it be argued that vector equations are superior to Cartesian equations?

Different forms for the equation of a line

A line passing through $A(1, 2, 1)$ in the direction of the vector

$\begin{pmatrix} 1 \\ 8 \\ -2 \end{pmatrix}$ can be given in **vector form** as $r = \begin{pmatrix} x \\ y \\ z \end{pmatrix} = \begin{pmatrix} 1 \\ 2 \\ 1 \end{pmatrix} + t \begin{pmatrix} 1 \\ 8 \\ -2 \end{pmatrix}$ or

$$r = \begin{pmatrix} x \\ y \\ z \end{pmatrix} = \begin{pmatrix} 1+t \\ 2+8t \\ 1-2t \end{pmatrix}$$

Functions

Geometry and trigonometry

This equation can also be split up to give the **parametric form of the equation of a line** as three separate equations:

$x = 1 + t$

$y = 2 + 8t$

$z = 1 - 2t$

or even as a general set of coordinates

$(1 + t, \ 2 + 8t, \ 1 - 2t)$

> **Reflect** How do you convert the vector equation of a line to a parametric equation?

Example 11

a Find the equation of the line which passes through the points A(1, 0, 2) and B(2, 3, −1).

b Determine whether or not the point (3, 6, −4) is on the line.

c Find the angle between the line through A and B and the line $r = \begin{pmatrix} 3 \\ 6 \\ -4 \end{pmatrix} + t \begin{pmatrix} -1 \\ -2 \\ 1 \end{pmatrix}$

a Direction of line is $\overrightarrow{AB} = \begin{pmatrix} 1 \\ 3 \\ -3 \end{pmatrix}$ $r = \begin{pmatrix} 1 \\ 0 \\ 2 \end{pmatrix} + t \begin{pmatrix} 1 \\ 3 \\ -3 \end{pmatrix}$	The vector equation of a line is not unique. Any vector in the same direction as the line can be used and any point. The following would also be correct. $r = \begin{pmatrix} 2 \\ 3 \\ -1 \end{pmatrix} + t \begin{pmatrix} -1 \\ -3 \\ 3 \end{pmatrix}$
b $\begin{pmatrix} 3 \\ 6 \\ -4 \end{pmatrix} = \begin{pmatrix} 1 \\ 0 \\ 2 \end{pmatrix} + t \begin{pmatrix} 1 \\ 3 \\ -3 \end{pmatrix}$ $3 = 1 + t \Rightarrow t = 2$ $\begin{pmatrix} 1 \\ 0 \\ 2 \end{pmatrix} + 2 \begin{pmatrix} 1 \\ 3 \\ -3 \end{pmatrix} = \begin{pmatrix} 3 \\ 6 \\ -4 \end{pmatrix}$ Therefore (3, 6, −4) is on the line.	If a point is on the line there must be a value for t that gives all three coordinates. An alternative method is to solve the equation for each coordinate and see if the same value of t is obtained each time.
c $\begin{pmatrix} 1 \\ 3 \\ -3 \end{pmatrix} \cdot \begin{pmatrix} -1 \\ -2 \\ 1 \end{pmatrix} = -1 - 6 - 3 = -10$ $\cos\theta = \dfrac{-10}{\sqrt{19}\sqrt{6}} \Rightarrow \theta = 159°$ or $\theta = 21°$	The lines clearly intersect at (3, 6, −4), so it is meaningful to talk about the angle between the lines. The angle between the lines will be the angle between the direction vectors. The angle between two lines can either be given as an obtuse or an acute angle unless a specific direction is specified.

Reflect How do you find the vector equation of a line if you are given its direction and the coordinates of a point it passes through?

How do you test whether or not a point lies on a given line?

The angle between two intersecting lines is the angle between their **direction vectors**.

Exercise 3N

1 Find a vector equation of the line passing through the following two points

   a (2, 4) and (3, 1)

   b (2, 1, −1) and (4, 2, 0)

2 a The point $(a, -2, b)$ lies on the line

$$r = \begin{pmatrix} x \\ y \\ z \end{pmatrix} = \begin{pmatrix} 1 \\ 2 \\ 1 \end{pmatrix} + t\begin{pmatrix} 1 \\ 8 \\ -2 \end{pmatrix}.$$

   Find a and b.

   b Find the coordinates of the point on the line with x-coordinate equal to 0.

3 a Find the value of s and p if the point $(2, s, p-1)$ lies on the line

$$r = \begin{pmatrix} 1 \\ 0 \\ 2 \end{pmatrix} + t\begin{pmatrix} 1 \\ 3 \\ 1 \end{pmatrix}$$

   b i Verify the point A $(1, -3, 8)$ lies on the

      line $r = \begin{pmatrix} 3 \\ 1 \\ 2 \end{pmatrix} + t\begin{pmatrix} 1 \\ 2 \\ -3 \end{pmatrix}$ and state the value

      of t for this point.

   The point B is also on the line and has parameter $t = 5$.

     ii Write down the vector $\overrightarrow{AB}$.

4 a Verify that the point (2, 1, 3) lies on both of the lines

$$r = \begin{pmatrix} 4 \\ -5 \\ 1 \end{pmatrix} + t\begin{pmatrix} -1 \\ 3 \\ 1 \end{pmatrix} \text{ and } r = \begin{pmatrix} 4 \\ 2 \\ 0 \end{pmatrix} + s\begin{pmatrix} 2 \\ 1 \\ -3 \end{pmatrix}$$

   b Find the acute angle between the two lines.

5 Two lines l_1 and l_2 have equations

$$r = \begin{pmatrix} 3 \\ 5 \\ 2 \end{pmatrix} + t\begin{pmatrix} -1 \\ 2 \\ 1 \end{pmatrix} \text{ and } r = \begin{pmatrix} 3 \\ 5 \\ 2 \end{pmatrix} + s\begin{pmatrix} 2 \\ -4 \\ -2 \end{pmatrix}$$

   a Explain why l_1 and l_2 are parallel.

   b Verify that (1, 9, 4) lies on both lines.

   c Explain what this tells you about the two lines.

6 The points A and B have coordinates $(1, -5, 6)$ and $(5, -3, 11)$ respectively.

   The line l_1 has equation $r = \begin{pmatrix} 3 \\ 1 \\ 2 \end{pmatrix} + s\begin{pmatrix} 1 \\ 3 \\ -2 \end{pmatrix}$

   a Show A lies on l_1.

   b Show $\overrightarrow{AB}$ is perpendicular to l_1.

7 The line l_1 has equation $r = \begin{pmatrix} 2 \\ 0 \\ 1 \end{pmatrix} + t\begin{pmatrix} 1 \\ 3 \\ 2 \end{pmatrix}$

   a Write down the coordinates of the point P which lies on the line and has parameter t.

   b The point A has coordinates (1, 2, −2). Find the vector $\overrightarrow{AP}$.

   c Find the value of t for which the vector $\overrightarrow{AP}$ is perpendicular to l_1.

   d Find the point on l_1 that is closest to A.

   e Hence find the shortest distance from A to the line l_1.

Reflect Which vectors are used to find the angle between two intersecting lines?

How do you test to see if two parallel lines are coincident?

Velocity equations

The **velocity** of an object is a vector quantity which needs both a magnitude and a direction to define it.

A velocity of $10\,\text{ms}^{-1}$ north is different to a velocity of $10\,\text{ms}^{-1}$ east.

Velocity represents the change in displacement of the object during one unit of time.

An object's **speed** is a measure of **distance** covered in one unit of time, so speed is the magnitude of the velocity vector, $|v|$.

Investigation 12

Consider a boat which is initially at the point A with coordinates $(5, 1)$ and is moving with a velocity of $(-2i + j)\,\text{km h}^{-1}$, where i and j are unit vectors east and north respectively, measured from a port O.

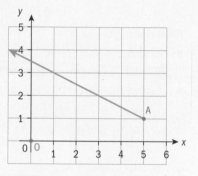

1 a Write down the position vector of the boat after it has been travelling for one hour.

b Write down the position vector of the boat after it has been travelling for 2 hours.

c Write down the position vector of the boat after it has been travelling for t hours.

2 a What can be said about the x-coordinate of the displacement vector when the boat is directly north of O?

b Find the value of t when the boat is directly north of O.

3 a What can be said about the x- and y-coordinate of the displacement vector when the boat is north-west of O (on a bearing of $315°$ from O)?

a Find the value of t at which the boat is north-west of O.

4 **Conceptual** How can the motion of a particle travelling with constant velocity be expressed and what do the variables and parameter stand for in this representation?

Reflect What is the displacement equation for an object travelling with velocity v if it is initially at a point with position vector a?

HINT

Initially means at the point when $t = 0$.

The position of a particle moving with velocity v and whose position vector at $t = 0$ is r_0 can be given by the equation $r = r_0 + vt$.

Example 12

A ship A has position vector $3i + 4j$ at 13:00 hours where i and j represent 1 km east and north of a harbour, respectively. Two hours later the position of A is $2i + 8j$.

a Find the velocity of A.

b Find the speed of A.

c Write down an expression for the position of A t hours after 13:00 as a single vector.

d Find the time at which A is directly north of the harbour.

a $\begin{pmatrix} 2 \\ 8 \end{pmatrix} = \begin{pmatrix} 3 \\ 4 \end{pmatrix} + 2v$ $2v = \begin{pmatrix} -1 \\ 4 \end{pmatrix}$ $\Rightarrow v = \begin{pmatrix} -0.5 \\ 2 \end{pmatrix} \text{kmh}^{-1}$	The velocity can be found by substituting the given values into $r = r_0 + vt$
b $\text{Speed} = \sqrt{2^2 + 0.5^2}$ $= 2.06\,\text{kmh}^{-1}$	Speed is the magnitude of the velocity vector.
c $r = \begin{pmatrix} 3 \\ 4 \end{pmatrix} + \begin{pmatrix} -0.5 \\ 2 \end{pmatrix} t$ $r = \begin{pmatrix} 3 - 0.5t \\ 4 + 2t \end{pmatrix}$	Writing an expression for displacement as a single vector can make subsequent calculations easier.
d $\begin{pmatrix} x \\ y \end{pmatrix} = \begin{pmatrix} 3 - 0.5t \\ 4 + 2t \end{pmatrix}$ $x = 0 \Rightarrow 0.5t = 3 \Rightarrow t = 6$ At $t = 6$ $y = 16\,\text{km}$ Hence A is 16 km north of the harbour.	When the boat is north of the harbour its x-coordinate will be zero.

Unit vectors

Unit vectors are vectors with a length of 1 unit. The unit vector in the same direction as b is written as $\dfrac{b}{|b|}$

If a particle has speed $v\,\text{ms}^{-1}$ in the direction of b its velocity will be $v\dfrac{b}{|b|}$

Changing the magnitude of a vector while keeping its direction constant is referred to as **rescaling** the vector. Rescaling to form a vector with a magnitude of one is referred to as **normalising** the vector.

Example 13

A boat is travelling with a speed of $7.5\,\text{ms}^{-1}$ in a direction parallel to the vector $3\mathbf{i} + 4\mathbf{j}$.

Write the velocity vector of the boat in component form.

Magnitude of $3\mathbf{i} + 4\mathbf{j}$ is 5 Velocity is $\dfrac{7.5}{5}\begin{pmatrix}3\\4\end{pmatrix} = 1.5\begin{pmatrix}3\\4\end{pmatrix}$ $\qquad = \begin{pmatrix}4.5\\6\end{pmatrix}$	The magnitude of the vector is found using Pythagoras. A unit vector in the same direction would therefore be $\dfrac{1}{5}\begin{pmatrix}3\\4\end{pmatrix}$ and a vector with magnitude 7.5 will be 7.5 times this vector.

Relative position

> If A has a position vector $\mathbf{r}_A$ and B has position vector $\mathbf{r}_B$ then the **relative position** of B from A is the vector $\overrightarrow{AB} = \mathbf{r}_B - \mathbf{r}_A$

This is useful for finding when one object is in a particular position relative to the other, for example when one is north of the other, and also for finding the distance between the objects at a given time.

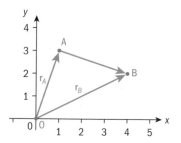

Example 14

At time $t = 0$ a model boat A is at $(2, 5)$ and is travelling with a speed of $4\,\text{ms}^{-1}$ in the direction of $\begin{pmatrix}3\\-4\end{pmatrix}$. The x component is the displacement due east from an origin and the y component due north. All distances are in metres.

a Find an expression for the position vector of A ($\mathbf{r}_A$) at time t.

A boat B has position vector given by $\mathbf{r}_B = \begin{pmatrix}3\\-2\end{pmatrix} + \begin{pmatrix}2\\1\end{pmatrix}t$

b Show that the two boats do not collide.

c Find the shortest distance between the two boats and the value of t at which this occurs.

d Find the value of t at which B is due east of A.

a Magnitude of $\begin{pmatrix} 3 \\ -4 \end{pmatrix}$ is $\sqrt{3^2 + 4^2} = 5$

Velocity of A is $\dfrac{4}{5}\begin{pmatrix} 3 \\ -4 \end{pmatrix} = \begin{pmatrix} 2.4 \\ -3.2 \end{pmatrix}$

Displacement of A is given by

$$r_A = \begin{pmatrix} 2 \\ 5 \end{pmatrix} + \begin{pmatrix} 2.4 \\ -3.2 \end{pmatrix} t$$

a Dividing a vector by its magnitude creates a vector in the same direction with a magnitude of 1 (a unit vector). Multiplying this by 4 will give a vector of magnitude (speed) equal to 4.

b Equating x-coordinates

$2 + 2.4t = 3 + 2t$

$t = \dfrac{1}{0.4} = 2.5$

When $t = 2.5$ the y-coordinate of A is -3.2 and the y-coordinate of B is 0.5.
So the two boats do not collide.

b If the boats collide there will be a value of t at which both the x- and y-coordinates are equal.

An alternative method is to equate the y-coordinates and see if the solution gives the same value of t.

c The distance between the two boats is $\left|\overrightarrow{AB}\right|$

$$r_A = \begin{pmatrix} 2 + 2.4t \\ 5 - 3.2t \end{pmatrix}, \quad r_B = \begin{pmatrix} 3 + 2t \\ -2 + t \end{pmatrix}$$

$$r_B - r_A = \begin{pmatrix} 1 - 0.4t \\ -7 + 4.2t \end{pmatrix}$$

$$\left|r_B - r_A\right| = \sqrt{\left(1 - 0.4t\right)^2 + \left(-7 + 4.2t\right)^2}$$

Minimum distance is $0.332\,\text{m}$ when $t = 1.67\,\text{s}$

c Writing the two displacement vectors as single vectors makes the subtraction easier.

This is a variation of $\left|\overrightarrow{AB}\right| = \boldsymbol{b} - \boldsymbol{a}$ met in section 3.4.

The minimum of the function is found using a GDC.

d B is due east of A when $-7 + 4.2t = 0$
Hence $t = 0.6$

d Using $r_B - r_A = \begin{pmatrix} 1 - 0.4t \\ -7 + 4.2t \end{pmatrix}$

An alternative approach is just to equate the two y components, so

$5 - 3.2t = -2 + t$ without finding the vector for relative position.

Functions

Geometry and trigonometry

Reflect How do you find the relative position of point A from point B if given the position of each?

How might you find the least distance between two objects each moving with constant velocity?

How might you find the time when the bearing of one object to another is in a given direction?

Exercise 30

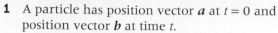

1 A particle has position vector a at $t = 0$ and position vector b at time t.

Find **i** the velocity **ii** the speed of the particle if

a $a = 2i + j$, $b = 4i + 5j$, $t = 2$

b $a = \begin{pmatrix} 2 \\ -1 \end{pmatrix}$, $b = \begin{pmatrix} 1 \\ 1 \end{pmatrix}$, $t = 4$

c $a = 3i + j - k$, $b = i + 5j + k$, $t = 2$

d $a = \begin{pmatrix} 1 \\ 0 \\ 1 \end{pmatrix}$, $b = \begin{pmatrix} 1 \\ 4 \\ -3 \end{pmatrix}$, $t = 4$

2 Write the following velocities as column vectors taking the base vectors as due east and north.

a $10\,kmh^{-1}$ due west

b $7.5\,kmh^{-1}$ in the direction $\begin{pmatrix} -3 \\ 4 \end{pmatrix}$

c $18\,kmh^{-1}$ in the direction $\begin{pmatrix} -1 \\ -4 \\ 8 \end{pmatrix}$

d $5\,kmh^{-1}$ south-west

e $15\,kmh^{-1}$ on a bearing of $040°$

f $12\,kmh^{-1}$ on a bearing of $120°$.

3 A buoy is set as the origin of a coordinate system. At 13.00 a boat is 20 m east and 30 m north of a buoy and has position vector $\begin{pmatrix} 20 \\ 30 \end{pmatrix}$.

a Find the distance of the boat from the buoy at 13:00.

The boat is moving with velocity $\begin{pmatrix} -3 \\ -5 \end{pmatrix}$ ms^{-1}.

b Find the position of the boat t seconds after 13:00.

c Hence find the shortest distance from the boat to the buoy.

4 A particle has position vector $3i + j$ when t = 0 and is moving with a velocity of $10\,ms^{-1}$ in the direction of $3i - 4j$. Find

a the position vector at time t

b its position when $t = 4$

c its distance from the origin at $t = 4$

d the distance travelled in the first four seconds.

5 A particle's displacement from an origin O is given by $r = \begin{pmatrix} 1 \\ 0 \\ 2 \end{pmatrix} + \begin{pmatrix} -1 \\ 3 \\ 1 \end{pmatrix} t$.

a Find the particle's position at $t = 3$.

At $t = 3$ the particle changes its velocity to $\begin{pmatrix} 1 \\ 4 \\ 0 \end{pmatrix}$

b Find an equation for the particle's displacement from O at time

i t $(t \geq 3)$

ii t', the time from the change of velocity.

c Find **i** the displacement **ii** the distance of the particle from O when $t = 5$.

6 Let i be the unit vector directed east and j the unit vector directed north and let a harbour H be situated at the origin.

At 10:00 ship A is at the point with position vector $-5i + 10j$ km relative to H and is travelling with velocity $2i + 2j$ km/h. Ship B is at the point $3i + 4j$ km and has velocity $-2i + 5j$ km/h.

a Show the two ships would collide if they maintained these velocities.

In order to avoid a collision A changes its velocity to $(i + 2j)$km/h.

b Find the vector $\overrightarrow{AB}$ at time t hours after 10:00.

c Find the distances between the two ships when A is north of B and give the time at which this occurs.

d Find the shortest distance they are apart and the time at which this occurs.

7 A hot air balloon is flying over level ground with a speed of $3.5\,ms^{-1}$ in the direction $\begin{pmatrix} 6 \\ 2 \\ 3 \end{pmatrix}$ where the first component is due east, the second due north and the third is perpendicular to the ground.

a i Find the velocity of the balloon.

  ii Write down the speed at which it is ascending.

The balloon passes over a tracking station at time $t = 0$ and its position relative to the tracking station at this time is $\begin{pmatrix} 0 \\ 0 \\ 30 \end{pmatrix}$

b Find the balloon's displacement relative to the tracking station one minute later.

At this point the balloon begins to descend at $0.6\,ms^{-1}$ while still travelling on the same bearing.

c Write down the displacement of the balloon from the tracking centre at time t' where t' is the time from the point when the descent begins.

d Find the time it takes for the balloon to reach the ground from the moment it begins its descent.

e Find the distance of the balloon from the tracking station when it reaches the ground.

8 A ship, S, is travelling south with a speed of $9\,kmh^{-1}$.

a Write down its velocity as a column vector in which the two components are due east and north.

At 10:00, S has displacement $\begin{pmatrix} 20 \\ 15 \end{pmatrix}$ relative to a lighthouse, O. At the same time a speedboat, B, is traveling with velocity $\begin{pmatrix} 9 \\ 12 \end{pmatrix}$ and its displacement from O is $\begin{pmatrix} 0 \\ 5 \end{pmatrix}$

b Find the distance between S and B at 10:00.

c Find the relative position of S from B t hours after 10:00.

At the point where S is south-east of B the boat changes direction while maintaining the same speed.

d Find the time at which B changes direction and its displacement from O at which this occurs.

e Write down the displacement of S from O at this point.

f Find the bearing at which B needs to travel in order to intercept S.

Functions

Geometry and trigonometry

Chapter summary

- Given the two points $A(x_1, y_1, z_1)$ and $B(x_2, y_2, z_2)$:

  - the midpoint of [AB] is $\left(\dfrac{x_1 + x_2}{2}, \dfrac{y_1 + y_2}{2}, \dfrac{z_1 + z_2}{2} \right)$

  - the length $AB = \sqrt{(x_2 - x_1)^2 + (y_2 - y_1)^2 + (z_2 - z_1)^2}$

- The gradient (m) of the line segment joining (x_1, y_1) and (x_2, y_2) is given by: $m = \dfrac{y_2 - y_1}{x_2 - x_1}$

Continued on next page

- For two points A and B (AB) should be read as "the line containing the points A and B".
- The **point-gradient** form for the equation of a line with gradient equal to m, which passes through the point (x_1, y_1) is $y - y_1 = m(x - y_1)$.
- The **general** form of the equation of a straight line is written as $ax + by + c = 0$ where a, b and c are all integers.
- $y = mx + c_1$ is parallel to $y = mx + c_2$
- If $y = m_1x + c_1$ and $y = m_2x + c_2$ are perpendicular (and neither m_1 or m_2 are equal to 0) then

  $m_1m_2 = -1$ or $m_2 = -\dfrac{1}{m_1}$ (the negative reciprocal of m_1).

- The boundaries of the **cells** in a Voronoi diagram are formed by perpendicular bisectors of the line segments joining the sites.
- **Nearest neighbour interpolation:** Each site is assigned a numerical value and the value of all points in each site's cell is assumed to equal that value.
- Within a Voronoi diagram the solution to the toxic waste dump problem will be at an intersection of cell boundaries or on the boundary of the diagram.
- a and b are parallel if and only if $b = ka$.
- From the above you can derive the **triangle law of vector addition.**

  $\overrightarrow{AC} = \overrightarrow{AB} + \overrightarrow{BC}$

- A consequence of the law is that the sum of two of more displacement vectors is always equal to the final displacement and is independent of the route taken.
- The sum of two or more vectors is called **resultant** vector.
- The **scalar** or dot product is written as $\boldsymbol{a} \cdot \boldsymbol{b} = a_1b_1 + a_2b_2$ for 2 dimensional vectors and $\boldsymbol{a} \cdot \boldsymbol{b} = a_1b_1 + a_2b_2 + a_3b_3$ for 3 dimensional vectors.
- In addition $\boldsymbol{a} \cdot \boldsymbol{b} = = |\boldsymbol{a}||\boldsymbol{b}| \cos\theta$.
- This allows us to find the angle between any two vectors, $\cos\theta = \dfrac{\boldsymbol{a} \cdot \boldsymbol{b}}{|\boldsymbol{a}||\boldsymbol{b}|}$
- If $\boldsymbol{a} \cdot \boldsymbol{b} = 0$ then $\boldsymbol{a}$ and $\boldsymbol{b}$ are perpendicular.
- The vector product of two vectors is perpendicular to both vectors.
- Geometrically two vectors that are not in the same line will define a plane and the vector product will be a vector perpendicular to that plane.
- The vector product can also be found for two dimensional vectors by taking the third component as equal to 0.

- The vector equation of a line is normally written as $\boldsymbol{r} = \boldsymbol{a} + t\boldsymbol{b}$ where $\boldsymbol{r}$ is the vector $\begin{pmatrix} x \\ y \end{pmatrix}$ in two

  dimensions, and $\begin{pmatrix} x \\ y \\ z \end{pmatrix}$ in three dimensions where $\boldsymbol{a}$ is the position vector of a point on the line and

  $\boldsymbol{b}$ is a vector parallel to the line – a **direction vector.**
- The vector equation of a line is not unique as any point and any direction vector could be used.

  Every point on the line will have a particular value of the parameter t, where t is a measure of how far the point is away from A as a multiple of the vector $\boldsymbol{b}$.

- The angle between two intersecting lines is the angle between their **direction vectors.**
- The **velocity** of an object is a vector quantity which needs both a magnitude and a direction to define it.
- An object's **speed** is a measure of **distance** covered in one unit of time, so speed is the magnitude of the velocity vector, $|v|$.
- The position of a particle moving with velocity v and whose displacement at $t = 0$ is r_0 can be given by the equation $r = r_0 + vt$.
- **Unit vectors** are vectors with a length of 1 unit. The unit vector in the same direction as b is written as $\dfrac{b}{|b|}$
- If a particle has speed v ms^{-1} in the direction of b its velocity will be $v\dfrac{b}{|b|}$
- Changing the magnitude of a vector while keeping its direction constant is referred to as **rescaling** the vector. Rescaling to form a vector with a magnitude of one is referred to as **normalising** the vector.
- If A has a position vector r_A and B has position vector r_B then the relative position of B from A is the vector $\overrightarrow{AB} = r_B - r_A$

Developing inquiry skills

Look back at the opening problem for the chapter. You were trying to divide the territorial waters between three islands.

Island A feels it is not getting a fair allocation of the area. An alternative is proposed whereby instead of the previous area it can have exclusive fishing rights for all of the region within 35 km of the centre of the island, including the international waters, except where this would overlap with an area closer to one of the other islands.

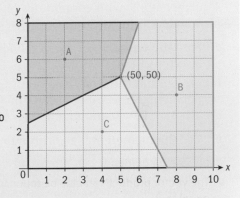

Vector methods will be used to find the area of this region.

a Use the diagram to write down the **vector** equations of the three perpendicular bisectors from the opening problem.

Let P and Q be the points on the perpendicular bisectors of [AB] and [AC] which are 35 km from A and on the edges of the Voronoi diagram.

b Find the vectors $\overrightarrow{AP}$ and $\overrightarrow{AQ}$.

c Show the new region in which A has exclusive fishing rights on the diagram.

d Use the scalar product to find $Q\hat{A}P$.

e Find the area of the region in which island A has exclusive fishing rights.

Chapter review

Click here for a mixed review exercise

1 Relative to a radar station on the ground two aircraft, A and B have positions (1.2, 8.5, 3.1) and (−0.2, 9.4, 2.6) respectively, where the units of measurement are kilometres.

  a Find the distance the aircraft are from each other.

  b Determine which of the aircraft is farthest from the radar station.

2 **a** Find the equation of the line passing through the two points (1, 5) and (6, 3).

  b Find the coordinates of the point where this line meets the line with equation $5x − 2y + 5 = 0$.

3 A, B and C have coordinates (2, 4) , (2, 6) and (8, 6) respectively.

  a Write down the equations for the perpendicular bisectors of [AB] and [BC].

  b Find the equation of the perpendicular bisector of [BC].

  c Construct a Voronoi diagram with A, B and C as the three sites.

A further site D with coordinates (4, 3) is now added to the diagram.

  d Find the equation of the perpendicular bisector of [AD].

It is given that the equations of the perpendicular bisectors of [BD] and [CD] are $4x − 6y + 15 = 0$ and $4x + 3y − 3 = 0$.

  e Use the incremental algorithm to add site D to your Voronoi diagram.

4 The positions of three hamburger outlets in a town can be given on a Cartesian coordinate system as A(2, 4) , B(6, 5) and C(3, 2) where the units are in kilometres.

  a Find the equations of the perpendicular bisectors of [BC] and [AC].

A rival firm wishes to set up its own outlet in the town but as far as possible from the outlets already in place.

  b Find the coordinates of the position where the new outlet should be built to satisfy this requirement.

  c Determine its distance from the other three outlets.

5 The displacement of a toy boat at time t minutes is given by the equation

$$r = \begin{pmatrix} 5 \\ 6 \end{pmatrix} + t \begin{pmatrix} -4 \\ -3 \end{pmatrix}$$ where distances are

measured in metres.

  a Write down the position of the boat when $t = 0$ and $t = 2$.

  b Find the speed of the boat.

  c Find an expression for the distance of the boat from the origin at time t.

  d Hence find the minimum distance of the boat from the origin and the time at which it occurs.

6 Let $a = \begin{pmatrix} 1 \\ 2 \\ p \end{pmatrix}$ and $b = \begin{pmatrix} 2 \\ q-1 \\ 1 \end{pmatrix}$

  a If a and b are perpendicular find a relationship between p and q.

  b Find the values of p and q for which a and b are parallel.

  c Find the angle between a and b when $p = 3$ and $q = 2$.

7 A tetrahedron is resting on a flat surface. The coordinates of the vertices are (4.5, 1.5, 0), (2.0, 3.5, 0), (3.5, 3.0, 0) and (2.5, 2.5, 2.0).

Find the volume of the tetrahedron.

8 The line l_1 has equation $r = \begin{pmatrix} 3 \\ 1 \\ 2 \end{pmatrix} + t \begin{pmatrix} -1 \\ 3 \\ 2 \end{pmatrix}$

  a The point A(−8, 34, n) lies on l_1, find the value of n

The line $r = \begin{pmatrix} 1 \\ -2 \\ u \end{pmatrix} + s \begin{pmatrix} -1 \\ p \\ q \end{pmatrix}$ intersects l_1 at

A and is perpendicular to l_1.

  b Find the values of p, q and u.

9 A plane A is flying north-east at $750\,\text{kmh}^{-1}$ and is climbing at a rate of $2\,\text{kmh}^{-1}$. At 15:00 it is directly over a tracking station and is at a height of 8.2 km.

a Find an expression for the displacement of the plane from the tracking station at time t hours after 15:00.

At 15:30 a second plane B is 13.1 km directly above the tracking station flying on a bearing of 030° at 800 kmh^{-1} and descending at a rate of 1 kmh^{-1}.

b Find an expression for the displacement of B from the tracking station t hours after 15:00.

c Find the distance the two planes are apart when they have the same height.

Exam-style questions

10 P1: The coordinates of point P are $(-3, 8)$ and the coordinates of point Q are $(5, 3)$. Point M is the midpoint of PQ.

a Find the coordinates of M. (2 marks)

L_1 is the line through P and Q.

b Find the gradient of L_1. (2 marks)

The line L_2 is perpendicular to L_1 and passes through M.

c i Write down the gradient of L_2.

ii Find the equation of L_2. Give your answer in the form $y = mx + c$.

(3 marks)

11 P2: The line, L, has equation $y = 3x - 5$. For the lines given below, state with reasons if they are parallel to L, perpendicular to L, or neither.

(6 marks)

i $y = \dfrac{1}{3}x - 7$

ii $-6x + 2y + 8 = 0$

iii $y - 5 = 2(x - 7)$

iv $y = -\dfrac{1}{3}x + 4$

v $x + 3y + 9 = 0$

12 P1: A ski resort is designing two new ski lifts. One lift connects station B (at the base of a mountain) and station P at the top of a ski run. The other lift connects station P with station Q, which is at the top of another ski run.

The three stations are placed on a three-dimensional coordinate system (measured in metres). The coordinates of each station are $B = (0, 0, 0)$, $P = (500, 400, 300)$, $Q = (900, 600, 700)$.

A skier wishes to reach the top of the run located at P from the base of the mountain.

a Determine the distance covered by the skier on the ski lift from the base of the mountain to P. (2 marks)

In order for a skier to reach the top of the ski run at Q they must take the lift from the base of the mountain to P, and then take a separate lift from P to Q.

b Determine the total distance covered by a skier on the ski lifts from the base of the mountain to Q.

(3 marks)

13 P1: A triangle ABC is defined by the position vectors $\overrightarrow{OA} = \begin{pmatrix} 1 \\ 2 \\ 1 \end{pmatrix}$, $\overrightarrow{OB} = \begin{pmatrix} 2 \\ 3 \\ 1 \end{pmatrix}$ and $\overrightarrow{OC} = \begin{pmatrix} 4 \\ 5 \\ 2 \end{pmatrix}$.

a Calculate $\overrightarrow{AB} \times \overrightarrow{AC}$. (3 marks)

b Hence find the area of triangle ABC. (2 marks)

14 P1: Lines L_1 and L_2 are given by the equations

L_1: $ax - 3y = 9$ L_2: $y = \dfrac{2}{3}x + 4$

The two lines are perpendicular.

a Find the value of a. (3 marks)

b Hence, determine the coordinates of the intersection point of the lines.

(2 marks)

15 P2: The cuboid ABCOFPDE has vertices with coordinates shown in the diagram.

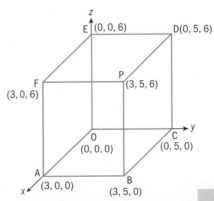

a   Find the surface area of the cuboid.

(2 marks)

b   Find the length of the diagonal BE.

(2 marks)

Diagonals AD and BE intersect at the point M.

c   **i**   Find the coordinates of M.

     ii   Find angle $\widehat{AMB}$, in degrees, using a vector method. You must show all your working. (7 marks)

16 P1: A new airport, S, is to be constructed at some point along a straight road, R, such that its distance from a nearby town, T, is a minimum.

The town, T, and the road, R, are placed on a plane where town, T, has coordinates (80, 140) and the road, R, has equation $y = x - 80$. All coordinates are given in kilometres.

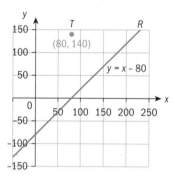

a   Determine the coordinates of S, the new airport. (6 marks)

b   Find the distance between T and the new airport. (2 marks)

17 P1: Four mathematicians live on the bottom floor of a circular tower of radius 10 m. They sit 5 m from the centre of the circle equally spaced around it as shown in the diagram below.

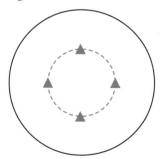

Each mathematician scatters papers, with equations written on them, on the floor around them but always ensures that his papers are nearer to him than to another mathematician.

a   Copy the above diagram and sketch a Voronoi diagram on it, showing where each mathematician's papers can be situated. (2 marks)

b   Calculate the area of the floor that each mathematician uses. (2 marks)

Another mathematician joins the group and sits in the centre of the circle. All of the other mathematicians rearrange their papers according to the same rule as before.

c   Make another copy of the original diagram and sketch on it a new Voronoi diagram, to represent the new situation. (4 marks)

d   Find the area of floor that the 5th mathematician ends up using. (2 marks)

e   Calculate the area of floor that each of the original four mathematicians now uses. (2 marks)

f   State how many points on the floor there are that are equidistant from any three mathematicians. (1 mark)

18 P2: An aircraft takes off from an airfield. The position of the aircraft at time t hours after takeoff is given by the vector

$$\mathbf{r} = \begin{pmatrix} 0 \\ 0 \\ 1 \end{pmatrix} + t \begin{pmatrix} 50 \\ 60 \\ 1 \end{pmatrix}.$$

Distances are measured in kilometres.

a   Find the position vector of the aircraft 4 hours after takeoff. (7 marks)

A second aircraft takes off from a different airfield. The position vector of this aircraft is given by the vector

$$\mathbf{s} = \begin{pmatrix} -90 \\ -100 \\ 0 \end{pmatrix} + \lambda \begin{pmatrix} 60 \\ 70 \\ 1 \end{pmatrix}.$$

b Determine if the two flight paths intersect and, if so, state the point of intersection. (6 marks)

The two aircraft took off at the same time, so $\lambda = t$.

c State, with a reason, whether the two aircraft actually collide. (2 marks)

d Calculate the distance between the two airfields. (2 marks)

e Calculate the shortest distance that ever exists between the two aircraft and the time when this occurs. (5 marks)

Click here for further exam practice

Real-life Voronoi

Approaches to learning: Thinking skills: Evaluate, Critiquing, Applying

Exploration criteria: Presentation (A), Personal engagement (C), Use of mathematics (E)

IB topic: Voronoi diagrams

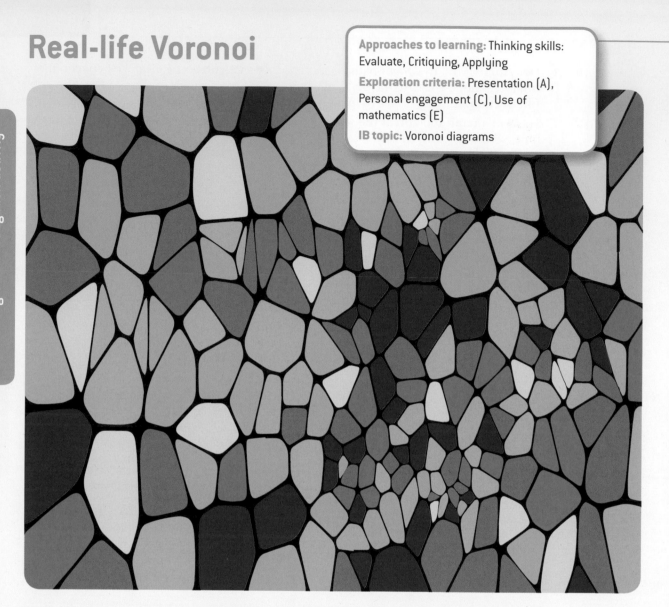

Voronoi diagrams

In this chapter you have been introduced to Voronoi diagrams.

Voronoi Diagrams have been used here to answer questions about **distance** and **area**:

1 Distance

Finding points that are equidistant to several sites or a path that stays far away from sites or where something can be located so that it is as far as possible from existing sites.

Which questions from the chapter could be listed in this group?

2 Area

Considering the territories and regions of influence of animals or retail or food places.

Which questions from the chapter could be listed in this group?

You can use Voronoi diagrams to answer similar questions that you create for yourself in explorations.

Exploration

As part of your exploration you will need to provide an aim and a context for your choice of topic.

First write down **all** potentially interesting areas for you to consider for an exploration.

You are now going to try to create an exploration that you could use Voronoi diagrams to answer.

Consider the type of questions that are possible and combine this with something(s) from your list of ideas.

Write the aim and context for your choice.

It may be helpful to think about how you would write the problem as a textbook question for someone else to answer.

Think about:

- Can you give a clear rationale for your choice of topic?
- Is the aim clearly stated?
- Do you have clearly articulated parameters for the problem?
- Is the aim manageable and completable within a sensible page limit and timeframe?
- Are you going to be able to find the relevant information?

You could now solve the problem you have created using the incremental algorithm introduced in the chapter.

Which method is best for answering your question given the available information and the form that this information is given in?

Could a computer software program (such as Geogebra) be used?

Or could the question be answered by hand using a compass and ruler for construction or by superimposing on a grid and using the equation of a perpendicular bisector?

Extension

Find out about "Nearest neighbour interpolation".

This is an important application of Voronoi diagrams where the aim is to interpolate values of a function at points near to sites, given the value at those sites.

This could be used, for example, to estimate or predict pollution or precipitation levels when you know the pollution or precipitation readings only at particular sites in a region.

Paper 3 question and comments

Paper 3 in the IBDP Mathematics Higher Level course consists of two extended, closed questions, each of which should take approximately 30 minutes to complete.

Usually the questions will provide an opportunity for you to apply the mathematics you have learned to solve a "real-life problem".

Often you will be using mathematics in situations you have not encountered before, and certainly some of the later parts of the questions will have a "problem solving" aspect where you have to choose the best method – out of possibly several different approaches – available to you.

But because paper 3 questions are "closed" problems, there will always be a solution for you to find.

The question will be structured so that the easier parts will normally be at the beginning of the question and, as the question progresses, less and less direction will be provided by the questions.

Paper 3 questions do require a particular set of skills. It is important to make use of the five-minute reading time so you can best assess all that the question is asking of you: You need to be familiar with the overall shape of the question. You need to look at which parts you are confident you can do, and which will require more thought.

In these questions, not being able to do an earlier part should not prevent you answering some of the later parts. Always read through the question carefully and check which parts you can do even if you have not completed all the previous parts. A question part which asks you to "show that..." is often an indicator that the result will be needed in a later part of the question.

The question that follows is typical of the style of a paper 3 question. The notes given are general exam hints, and do not contain any instructions with regard to how to do this particular question.

Give yourself 30 minutes and see how much you can do in that time. If you are not used to extended questions you might struggle to complete it, but with practice you will quickly be able to maximize the marks you can attain.

HINT

Most paper 3 questions will begin with a statement of the task.

1 [Maximum marks: 27]

The aim of the question is to find the shortest distance between Lima in Peru and Tokyo in Japan, to an appropriate degree of accuracy.

A point on the surface of the Earth can be described using two angles. Its longitude measures how far east the point is from the prime meridian, $0°$. Its latitude measures how far north the point is from the equator. A negative longitude indicates the point is west of the prime meridian and a negative latitude indicates it is south of the equator.

Let the Earth be modelled as a sphere of radius 6370 km. Let the centre of the Earth be the origin (O) of a coordinate system in which the z-axis passes through the two poles, and the x- and y-axis lie in the plane containing the equator with the x-axis passing through the point on the equator with longitude $0°$.

HINT

Because this information is given in a "stem" rather than within a question part, the information applies to the whole question.

a The diagram shows the equator set in the given coordinate system. You are looking at the *x*- and *y*-axis from above.

> **HINT**
>
> This is setting up the information for part **a**. Because it is given within the part you will not need to use this information for the later parts.

HINT

This part is not directly related to solving the main problem but it develops some of the insights needed as well as providing a straight forward introduction to the question.

Paper 3 question and comments

Two towns A and B lie on the equator. A has coordinates $(6370, 0, 0)$. The longitude of town B is given by the angle α.

α is positive for counter clockwise rotations and negative for clockwise rotations.

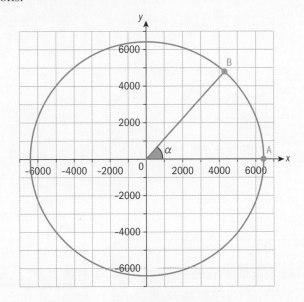

i When $\alpha = 50°$ show that the coordinates of B, to three significant figures, are $(4090, 4880, 0)$.

> **HINT**
>
> The command term is "show that". It is likely this answer will be required in a later part.
>
> Because it is "show that", you must make sure you show all your working.

> **HINT**
>
> All IB exam papers will have the instruction on the cover sheet to give answers "exactly or to 3 significant figures". Often the best policy is to write down a long answer and then round it to 3 sf for your final answer. If using an intermediate answer in a later calculation make sure you use the full result from your GDC rather than a rounded answer.

ii Find the shortest distance around the surface of the Earth from A to B.

iii Find the shortest straight-line distance between A and B.

iv Find the percentage error in using the straight-line distance as an approximation for the distance along the surface of the Earth.

(9 marks)

Consider the point P, which lies on the surface of the sphere at the point with latitude θ and longitude ϕ, as shown in the diagram below. Let the radius of the Earth be R.

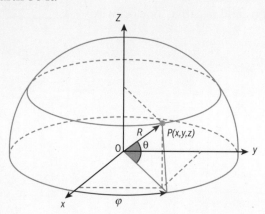

b i Write down the z-coordinate of P in terms of R and θ.

ii Find the coordinates of P in terms of R, θ and ϕ. (4 marks)

In this model, Lima in Peru lies at the point with latitude −12.05 and longitude −77.04.

c Show that the coordinates of Lima are $(1397, -6071, -1329)$.

(2 marks)

In this same model, Tokyo lies at the point with latitude 35.69 and longitude 139.70. This point has coordinates $(-3945, 3346, 3717)$.

Let Lima be at the point L and Tokyo be at the point T.

d **i** Write down $\left| \overrightarrow{OL} \right|$

> **HINT**
>
> The command term is "write down" so do not be tempted to try and do lots of working out. Pause and consider whether or not there is a quick route to the answer.
>
> Also there has been a switch from cartesian coordinates to vector notation here. This could be a hint for the best way to approach later parts of the question.

> **HINT**
>
> As the question moves on, there is more of a problem solving element to it.
>
> There is more than one way to solve part **d (ii)**, and some ways are quicker than others.

ii Find the angle LÔT.

iii Hence find the shortest distance around the surface of the earth between Lima and Tokyo. (8 marks)

> **HINT**
>
> "Hence" tells you that you have to use the earlier part. If you could not find the angle but know how to find the shortest distance, write down a sensible value for part **ii** and you may get follow through marks.

In reality, the Earth is not a perfect sphere and the distance from the centre of the Earth to the surface is between 6353 km and 6384 km.

> **HINT**
>
> Often when looking at real-life situations, mathematical models are necessarily simplifications and so consideration of limitations of the model, or error bounds to your solutions, become important.

e **i** Find upper and lower bounds for the distance between Lima and Tokyo along the shortest route, assuming that both are the same distance from the centre of the Earth.

> **HINT**
>
> The command term is "find", so there is some work to be done, but part **e** only has 4 marks to it and requires you to give two bounds and an approximation in part **ii**. This appears to be quite a lot of work for relatively few marks, so there must be an easy solution. Try to think of a simple approach to this problem before working through the whole process for a second and then a third time.

ii Hence give the distance between the two cities to an appropriate degree of accuracy. (4 marks)

4 Modelling constant rates of change: linear functions and regressions

All of these questions are about situations that can be represented by a mathematical model. These models will allow you to study relationships between the variables and to make predictions.

A rental car costs a fixed amount plus $\$t$ per kilometre. How can I find the maximum number of kilometres that can be paid with $\$A$?

It's a hot summer's day – how long will it take to fill your swimming pool?

How much do you have to invest in your bank account to grow your savings so you can buy that yacht? And how much does the interest rate matter?

In general, is there a relationship between the number of children in a family and the family's income?

Stefan drives taxis part-time, usually driving between 10 and 40 km per day. Currently, on each day that he drives he earns a fixed amount of $20 plus $2.50 for every kilometre that the taxi's meter is on. Stefan wants to increase his annual income so that it is equal to the annual average salary of $44 000. He is thinking of increasing the income per kilometre by $0.30 per month every month for the next year.

What will his daily income be if he drives 10, 20, 30 or 40 km?

How will his income change if he increases the income per kilometre by $0.30 each month?

How can you model the daily income for different values of income per kilometre?

Will he reach the annual average salary in one year's time? If not, how long will it take?

What assumptions do you need to make to answer these questions?

Developing inquiry skills

Write down any similar inquiry questions you could ask and investigate for another business or charging structure. What information would you need to find? Think about the questions in this opening problem and answer any you can. As you work through the chapter, you will gain mathematical knowledge and skills that will help you to answer them all.

Before you start

Click here for help with this skills check

You should know how to:

1 Find the equation of a line given a graph or information about the line.

eg

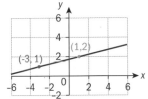

Calculate the gradient: $m = \dfrac{5 - 1.5}{3 - 2} = 0.7$

Substitute in point-gradient form:

$y - 5 = 0.7(x - 3)$

Convert to gradient-intercept form:

$y - 5 = 0.7x - 2.1$

$y = 0.7x + 2.9$

2 Given an equation, substitute a value for one variable and solve for the other.

eg $y = 7 - 5x$

a Find y when $x = 3$.

$y = 7 - 5(3) = -8$

b Find x when $y = 3$.

$3 = 7 - 5x$

$-4 = -5x$

$x = \dfrac{4}{5}$

Skills check

1 Find the equation of each line:

a

b

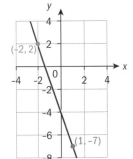

2 Given that $y = 1.5x - 4$,

a find y when $x = 18$.

b find x when $y = 2$.

4.1 Functions

Functions help us to model situations with predictable relationships between two variables. In the following investigation you will investigate what a function is and the different ways that you can represent it.

International-mindedness

One of the first mathematicians to study the concept of functions was Frenchman Nicole Oresme in the 14th century.

Investigation 1

Amir loves running. Here are the **contexts** of six of his recent runs, 1–6, and some graphs, A–G, that might describe the runs.

Run 1: Amir runs on flat ground for 10 minutes.

Run 2: He runs downhill.

Run 3: He runs 10 km.

Run 4: He runs up a mountain and back.

Run 5: He stops to chat with a friend midway through his run.

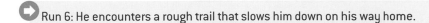

Run 6: He encounters a rough trail that slows him down on his way home.

A

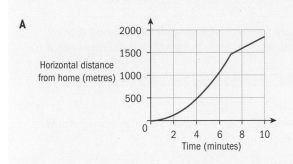

B

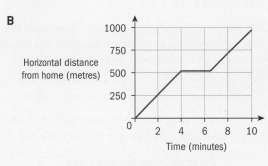

C

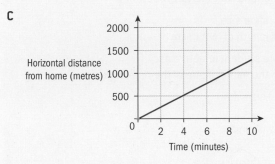

D

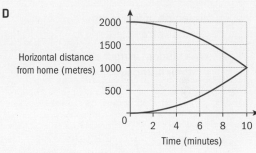

E

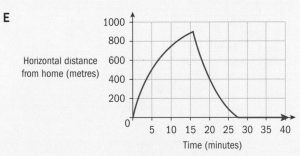

F

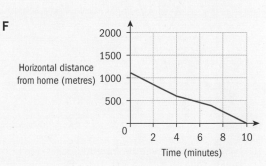

G

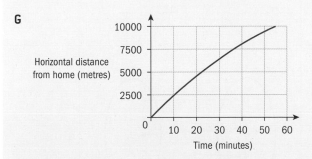

1   Match each run to a graph, giving two specific reasons why you know they match.

2   One graph does not match any of the runs. Explain why it is not possible for this graph to represent a person running over time.

A **relation** is a set of ordered pairs (x, y) that specifies corresponding values of the **independent** (x) and **dependent** (y) variables. A graph is one way to represent a relation between two variables.

Investigation 2

The graphs in Investigation 1 corresponding to the different contexts are examples of representations of **functions**. They show Amir's distance from home as a function of time. The graph that did not match a context is an example of a **non-function**.

Here are some more examples of functions and non-functions and different ways that you can represent them, as equations, tables or mapping diagrams.

1   For each pair of examples, describe how the relationship between the **inputs** (x-values) and **outputs** (y-values) differs between the function and the non-function.

	Relations that are functions	Relations that are not functions
a	$x =$ length of foot in cm $y =$ shoe size	$x =$ shoe size $y =$ length of foot in cm
b	$x =$ a student in your class $y =$ their birthday	$x =$ a student in your class $y =$ the name of one of their siblings
c	$y = x^2$ 	$x^2 + y^2 = 1$
d		

x	y
-7	-22
-2	15
0	8
7	15

x	y
-2	3
0	0
7	-14
7	11

e   This representation is a **mapping diagram**:

2 Based on your descriptions, what generally is the difference between a relation that is a function and a relation that isn't? Make sure that your generalisation is consistent with all of the examples.

3 **Factual** What types of relations are functions?

4 **Factual** What are the different ways that a function can be represented?

5 **Conceptual** How can you identify that a relation is a function from a graph, table, mapping diagram or context?

> A **function** is a relation between two sets in which every element of the first set (input, independent variable) is mapped onto **one and only one** element of the second set (output, dependent variable).
>
> That is, y is a function of x if, for each x-value, there is exactly one corresponding value of y.

Example 1

For each relation, determine, with a reason, whether y is a function of x.

a In an annual survey of panda populations, x = time (in years since 1977), y = number of pandas.

b The relation $x \to 2x^2 - 1$ with the set of inputs $A = \{-3, -2, 0, 2\}$. Note that the **mapping** notation $x \to 2x^2 - 1$ represents the same relation as $y = 2x^2 - 1$.

c The relation $x = y^2$.

---

a Yes, because each year will have exactly one measurement of the panda population.

b Yes, because each input has exactly one corresponding output:

x	$y = 2x^2 - 1$
−3	17
−2	7
0	−1
2	7

Substitute each x-value into the formula to find the corresponding y-value. For example, when $x = -3$:

$$y = 2(-3)^2 - 1$$
$$= 2(9) - 1$$
$$= 18 - 1$$
$$= 17$$

Note that two inputs can have the same output.

c No, because an x-value can have two corresponding y-values. For example, $x = 9$ corresponds to $y = 3$ and $y = -3$.

One method for determining whether a graph represents a function is the **vertical line test**: if you can draw a vertical line that intersects the graph more than once, then the graph fails the test and represents a non-function. Otherwise, the graph is a function.

For example, the relation in the graph is not a function, because the vertical line $x = 1$ intersects the graph at $(1, 2)$ and $(1, -2)$.

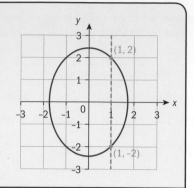

Reflect Why is the vertical line test consistent with the definition of function?

Exercise 4A

1 Determine, with reasons, whether y is a function of x in each context.

  a In a group of 500 people, $x = \{1, 2, 3, 4, \ldots, 10, 11, 12\}$ and $y =$ a person born in month x.

  b In the same group of people, $x = \{1, 2, 3, 4, \ldots, 10, 11, 12\}$ and $y =$ the number of people in the group born in month x.

2 For each mapping diagram or graph, decide with a reason whether it represents a function.

  a

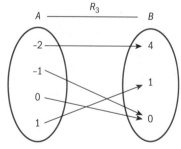

  b

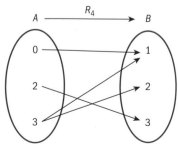

  c

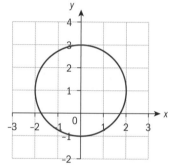

  d

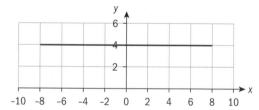

  e

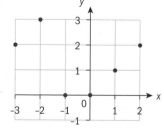

f

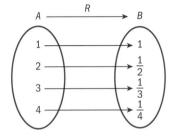

3 a Write down the mapping R in the form $x \to \dots$

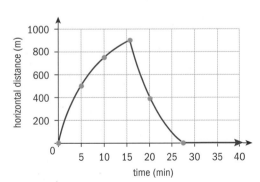

b State whether or not R is a function.

c Write down the output of $x = 2$ under R.

d The set A is extended to $\{1, 2, 3, 4, a\}$, and a is mapped onto 3. State the value of a.

4 Consider the mapping $y = x^3$.

a State the output when the input is $x = -1$.

b State the input when $y = -64$.

c Let the set of inputs be $A = \{-1, 0, 1, 2, 3, 4\}$. Find B, the set of outputs.

d State, with a reason, whether or not the mapping $y = x^3$ from A to B is a function.

Function notation

> You can use **function notation** to concisely communicate a function's output for a given input by writing $y = f(x)$ or $f(x) = y$. You also say that y is the **image** of x under the function f.

For example, here is Run 4 from Investigation 1 in both graph and table form.

x	y
0	0
5	520
10	790
15	945
20	390
25	45

From the table you can see that the time $x = 5$ minutes corresponds to a distance of $y = 520$ meters; You could write $f(5) = 520$. This is read "f of 5 is 520" – it does not mean "f times 5".

In this context, it means that after 5 minutes, Amir is 520 meters from home. How can you see this from the graph?

Investigation 3

In this investigation you'll explore what information you can gather from different function representations, including function notation.

Explore function notation by using the graph and table we've just looked at to answer these questions as accurately as possible.

1 What y-value solves $y = f(10)$? What does this mean in context?

2 What two x-values solve $f(x) = 600$? What does this mean in context?

3 What is the furthest distance from home that Amir reaches, and when does he reach it? Express your answer in function notation in the form $f(x) = y$.

4 When does Amir reach home? Express your answer in function notation.

5 **Conceptual** What useful information does function notation communicate?

Example 2

Raquel invests $1200 in a savings account whose value increases over time. The future value, V, of the account is a function of the time t (in years) invested, represented by the equation $V(t) = 1200 \times (1.03)^t$ for $0 \le t \le 50$.

a Find

   i $V(0)$ ii $V(50)$

   Interpret each of these in context.

b If Raquel keeps her money invested for 50 years, determine how much she will earn on her initial $1200.

c Sketch a graph of the function V for $0 \le t \le 50$.

d If Raquel invests her money in 2015, determine the year when the value of her account will reach $2500.

a i $V(0) = \$1200$ This shows that Raquel invested $1200 initially.	Substitute the given inputs ($t = 0$ and $t = 50$) into the function. $V(0) = 1200 \times (1.03)^0 = 1200$
ii $V(50) = \$5260$ (3 s.f.) This shows that Raquel will have $5260 in the account after 50 years.	$V(50) = 1200 \times (1.03)^{50} = 5260.687\ldots$ Alternatively, graph $y = 1200 \times (1.03)^x$ and use the TRACE or TABLE function of your GDC to find the y-values corresponding to $x = 0$ and $x = 50$.
b $4060	Find $V(50) - V(0)$.

c

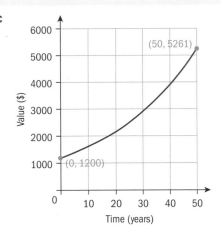

Graph the function $y = 1200 \times (1.03)^x$ with technology.

Choose an appropriate graphing window: since the given set of input values is $0 \leq t \leq 50$, set the x-axis to display from 0 to 50. From part **a**, the output grows to approximately \$5300, so set the y-axis to display from 0 to 6000.

d $V(t) = 2500$

As you want to find the time when the value is \$2500, you are solving $V(t) = 2500$.

Graph $y = 2500$ on the same screen as $y = 1200 \times (1.03)^x$. Use technology to find the intersection of these two graphs.

$t = 24.8$

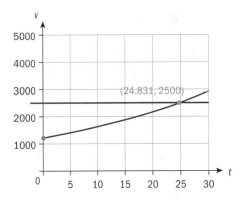

Raquel's account will reach a value of \$2500 during the year 2039.

Since $t = 0$ corresponds to the year 2015, Raquel's account value will reach \$2500 during the 24th year after 2015, or 2039.

The graphical method used to solve $V(t) = 2500$ in Example 2 can be generalized to solve any equation of a single variable.

> To solve the equation $f(x) = g(x)$, graph both $f(x)$ and $g(x)$ and find their point(s) of intersection. $f(x)$ and $g(x)$ are equal at such points, so the x-value(s) of the coordinate(s) solve the equation.

For example, to solve $x^2 + 1 = 5 - 2x$, graph $y = x^2 + 1$ and $y = 5 - 2x$ and find their intersection point(s).

The solutions to the equation $x^2 + 1 = 5 - 2x$ are $x = -3.24$ and $x = 1.24$ (3 sf).

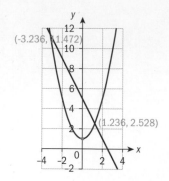

Exercise 4B

1 The function f is shown in the graph.

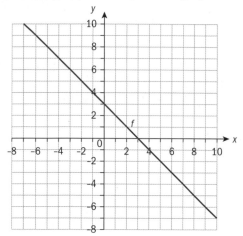

a Write down the values of

i $f(-2)$

ii $f(6)$.

b Find the value(s) of x that solve each of these equations:

i $f(x) = 3$

ii $f(x) = 0$.

c Find the set of values of x for which $f(x) < 0$.

2 Consider the function f defined by $f(x) = 10 - 4x$.

a Calculate

i $f(2)$

ii $f\left(-\dfrac{1}{2}\right)$

b Show that $f(2.5) = 0$.

c There is a value of x for which $f(x) = -6$. Find this value of x.

3 Gravity decreases the further you are from the centre of the Earth. The force of gravity F, measured in Newtons (N), on Jaime, who weighs 70 kg at home, is a function of his height above sea level h, measured in kilometres. The function $F(h)$ is shown in the graph. Hence estimate answers to the following questions.

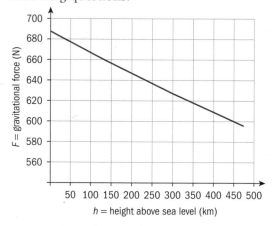

a i Find $F(0)$. Interpret its meaning in context.

ii If Jaime is currently an astronaut on the International Space Station, 410 km above sea level, find the gravitational force on him.

iii State your answer to part ii as a percentage of the force at sea level. State how much lighter Jaime is on the space station.

b Solve $F(h) = 625$ and interpret its meaning in context.

c Find the height at which the force of gravity is 5% less than at sea level. Write down your answer in function notation.

Domain and range

> The **domain** of a function is the set of all possible input values x.

Recall Run 3 from Investigation 1, in which Amir ran a 10 km from his house.

This can be modeled by the equation $g(x) = -1.336x^2 + 255x$. If you graph this function with technology you will see that the graph extends beyond the portion shown in the investigation.

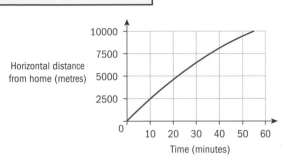

For the function $g(x)$, any value can be input as x, so you say that its **domain** is the set of all real numbers, $x \in \mathbb{R}$. (Recall that $x \in S$ means that x is a member of the set S.) $\mathbb{R}$ is the default domain if one is not specified.

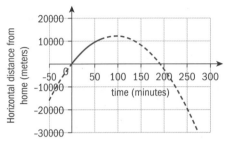

> The **range** of a function $f(x)$ is the set of y-values (or outputs, or images) corresponding to all the inputs in the domain.

For example, $f(x) = x^2$ has domain $x \in \mathbb{R}$ and range $f(x) \geq 0$ or $y \geq 0$, because squaring all numbers results in a non-negative number. You can see this on the graph of $f(x)$.

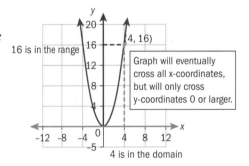

Graph will eventually cross all x-coordinates, but will only cross y-coordinates 0 or larger.

16 is in the range

4 is in the domain

Investigation 4

The domain of a function is sometimes **restricted** to a smaller set that makes sense for the real-world context that the function represents. This is the **reasonable domain**.

Consider again the context of Amir's 10 km run. The first graph shows $g(x)$ graphed with domain $x \in \mathbb{R}$ and the second shows $g(x)$ graphed with the domain restricted to only the portion relevant to the 10 km run.

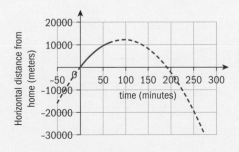
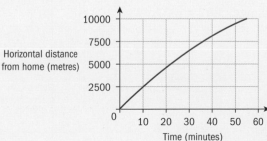

Continued on next page

Functions

1 **Factual** How can you see from the graph of $g(x)$ that the domain is $x \in \mathbb{R}$?

2 Estimate a **reasonable domain** for $g(x)$ in the context of the 10 km run.

3 Use the graph of $g(x)$ with domain $x \in \mathbb{R}$ to describe its approximate range.

4 The **reasonable range** is the range associated to the reasonable domain; that is, the set of outputs corresponding to the set of inputs in the reasonable domain. What is the **reasonable range** of $g(x)$ in the context of the 10 km run?

5 **Conceptual** How does the real-world context of a function influence its reasonable domain and range?

Example 3

For each of the following functions, find its domain and range.

a The function $f(x)$ is defined by the graph. Note that, like a number line diagram, if a graph has a solid dot ● then this means that the point is included in the graph. If there is a hollow dot ○ then this means that the point is not included in the graph.

b The function $f(x) = 7 - \dfrac{1}{3}x$, $-2 \le x < 4$.

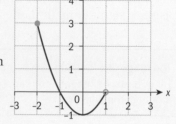

a Domain: $-2 \le x < 1$

  Range: $-1 \le y \le 3$

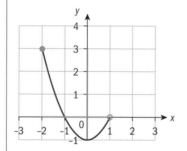

Project the graph onto the x-axis to see that the domain (the green line) is $-2 \le x < 1$. Observe that $x = 1$ is not included in the domain.

Project the graph onto the y-axis to see that the range (the blue line) is $-1 \le y \le 3$.

b Domain: $-2 \le x < 4$

  Range: $5.67 < y \le 7.67$

Graph $f(x) = 7 - \dfrac{1}{3}x$ on the given domain:

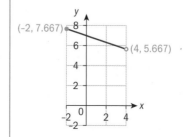

The endpoints of the domain will in this case also be the endpoints of the range. Find these coordinates with technology or by substitution:

$f(-2) = 7.67, f(4) = 5.67$

Note that the graph contains the upper endpoint but not the lower one.

Exercise 4C

1 A function $T(d)$ gives the average daily temperature T, in °C, of a certain city during last January, where $d = 1$ corresponds to January 1st.

  a Explain the meaning of $T(2) = 25$.

  b State the domain of the function T.

  c Write down the greatest possible number of values in the range of T.

d	2	8	15	18	22	29
T	25	22	26	20	21	28

2 Consider the function $f(x) = -2x + 3$, $-1 \le x \le 3$

  a Find

    i $f(-1)$ ii $f(3)$

  b Find the value of x such that $f(x) = 2$.

  c Sketch the graph of this function. Label clearly the end points of the graph.

  d Hence, find the range of this function.

3 Find the domain and range of each of these functions whose graphs are as follows.

  a

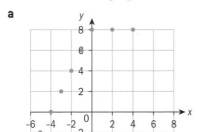

  b

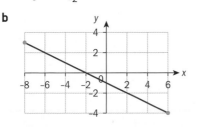

c

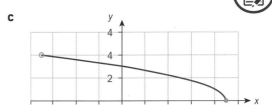

d

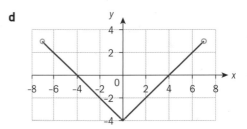

4 Robbin is a mountain guide planning a two-week camping trip that will serve between three and eight clients. She knows that the total weight per person, w kg, of food that must be carried for p people (not including Robbin) can be calculated by the function $w(p) = 9 + \dfrac{15}{p+1}$.

  a Write down the reasonable domain for $w(p)$.

  b Find and interpret $w(3)$ and $w(8)$.

  c Find the associated reasonable range for $w(p)$.

  d The company Robbin works for advertises that clients can expect to carry 11–12 kg of food each. Find the number of people Robbin can take on the trip in order to meet this requirement.

5 The cost of solar-powered energy has become cheaper over time as technology has improved and more solar power is installed. The table shows the cost of solar energy (measured in dollars per watt of energy) at several recent dates.

Year	Jan 2014	Jun 2014	Jan 2015	Jun 2015	Jan 2016
Cost of solar energy ($ per W)	3.82	3.75	3.65	3.53	3.31

Based on this data, researchers found that the cost of solar energy, S, as a function of time, t (in years since 2014), can be represented as $S(t) = -0.09t^2 - 0.0651t + 3.81$. They expect their model to be valid until 2019. The equation and the points from the table are shown in the graph.

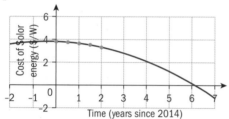

a State the reasonable domain for $S(t)$.

b Estimate the reasonable range for $S(t)$.

c Estimate what the cost of solar was in June of 2016.

d Find the year in which the researchers predict the cost of solar energy will fall below $1.50 per watt.

e Explain why the function may not lead to reasonable predictions for years beyond 2019.

6 A company produces water bottles at a cost of $C(q) = 27\,000 - \dfrac{60\,000\,000}{q + 5000}$ euros, where q represents the number of bottles produced, $0 \le q \le 30\,000$. Assuming all bottles are sold, its revenue, or earnings, can be modelled by $R(q) = \dfrac{1.75}{10\,000} q(30\,000 - q)$. In the following questions, round all monetary values to the nearest euro.

a Find the revenue earned when 2500 water bottles are sold. Express your answer in function notation.

b Calculate how much more revenue the company will earn selling 5000 water bottles than selling 2500.

c Solve $C(q) = 20\,000$ and interpret your answer in context.

d Sketch both functions on the same graph using technology. Find the **break-even point(s)**: the number of bottles the company must sell so that its costs and revenues are equal.

e The company makes a profit if its revenue is greater than its cost. Determine the values of q for which the company will make a profit.

7 The value of Renee's car, in UK£, is changing as a function of time. This relationship can be expressed by the equation $V(t) = \dfrac{8500}{t+1} + 5(t-15)^2$, where t is the time in years since she purchased the car in 2008, $0 \le t \le 60$.

a Using the equation or a graphical representation of the function, find the values of a and b in the table. If more than one value is possible, list all possible values.

t	$V(t)$
0	a
1	b
3	2845
c	4000

b Find the year in which the car's value will drop below UK£1000.

c If Renee keeps her car long enough, it will become an antique and will begin to increase in value. Find the year in which her car's value will be as high as when she bought it.

4.2 Linear models

In this section you will explore several specific types of linear functions and the real-world situations that they model.

TOK

What is the relationship between real-world problems and mathematical models?

Functions

Investigation 5

Use the graphs of Amir's Runs 1 and 2 from Investigation 1 to answer the questions as precisely as possible.

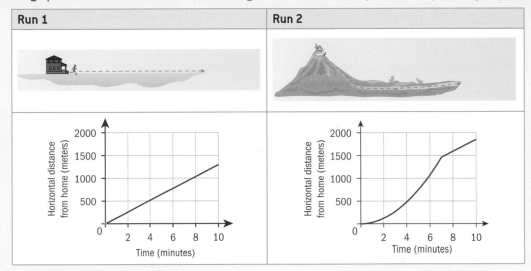

1 What is Amir's total distance travelled and total time taken in each run?

2 Average speed can be calculated by

$$\text{average speed} = \frac{\text{total distance}}{\text{total time}}.$$

What is Amir's average speed in each run?

3 Is Amir travelling at this average speed for the whole of Run 1? For Run 2? How can you tell?

4 The **rate of change** between two variables is the amount of change in the dependent variable per unit change in the independent variable. For Run 1, how far does Amir run in one minute? Use this to calculate the rate of change of his distance per unit time.

5 What does the rate of change tell you about Amir's run?

6 Find the equation of the line that represents Run 1 in the form $y = mx + c$.

7 How do the gradient and y-intercept parameters in your equation correspond to the context?

8 **Factual** What do the letters m and c stand for in $y = mx + c$.

9 **Conceptual** What does the constant rate of change represent in a linear function and what does the y intercept represent in terms of the dependent and independent variables?

> A **linear function** $f(x) = mx + c$, where m and c are constants, represents a context with a **constant rate of change**. The constants in an equation are called **parameters**. A linear function has the parameters gradient (m) and y-intercept (c).

Example 4

If you have travelled between lower and higher altitudes, you may have noticed that the air pressure changes. Air pressure at sea level (0 km) is defined as 1 atmosphere (atm). At an altitude of 5000 feet, or 1.524 km, above sea level, air pressure is 83.7% of the pressure at sea level, or 0.837 atm. Assume that the relationship between air pressure and altitude is linear.

a Find an equation to express air pressure P (in atm) as a function of altitude a (in km).

b Interpret the gradient and y-intercept of $P(a)$ in context.

c If $(k, 0.5)$ is a point on the graph of $P(a)$, find the value of k and interpret its meaning in context.

a $P(a) = 1 - 0.107a$	Use the given pairs of independent and dependent variables to calculate the gradient of the linear function: $(0, 1)$ and $(1.524, 0.837)$.
	The y-intercept in this case is given as one of the coordinates.
	So, $c = 1$ and $m = \dfrac{0.837 - 1}{1.524 - 0} = -0.107$.
b As the altitude increases, the air pressure reduces at a rate of 0.107 atm per kilometre.	The gradient is the rate of change between the dependent variable (pressure in atm) and independent variable (altitude in km).
The atmospheric pressure at ground level (0 km) is 1 atm.	The y-intercept occurs at $a = 0$.
c $k = 4.67$	Method 1:
The air pressure will be 50% of the pressure at sea level at an altitude of 4.67 km.	Use technology to find the intersection of the function with the line $y = 0.5$:
	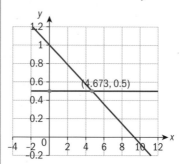
	Method 2:
	Substitute $P(a) = 0.5$ in the equation and solve for a:
	$0.5 = -0.107a + 1$
	$a = \dfrac{-0.5}{-0.107} = 4.67$

Recall that there are three common ways to represent a linear equation:

- Gradient-intercept form: $y = mx + c$
- Point-gradient form: $y - y_1 = m(x - x_1)$, where (x_1, y_1) is any point on the graph.
- Standard or general form: $ax + by + d = 0$, where a, b and d are constants.

The gradient-intercept form translates directly to the linear function $f(x) = mx + c$, but the other two forms can be useful starting points depending on the information given in the problem.

> **International-mindedness**
>
> The word "modeling" is derived from the Latin word "modellus", which means a human way of dealing with reality

Functions

Example 5

A water tank drains at a constant rate. It contains 930 litres of water 3.5 minutes after it starts to drain. It takes 50 minutes for the tank to empty. Let W be the amount of water in the tank (in litres) t minutes after it started to drain.

a Find a gradient–intercept model for $W(t)$, the amount of water in the tank with respect to time.

b Write down the amount of water in the tank when it starts to drain.

c Write down the rate at which the water tank is emptying.

d Use your model to find the amount of water after 30 minutes.

a $W(t) = -20t + 1000$	If the tank drains at a constant rate then it is a linear function: $W(t) = mt + c$ From the information given you can create the ordered pairs (3.5, 930) and (50,0). Method 1: As you have two points, use these to calculate the gradient: $m = \dfrac{0 - 930}{50 - 3.5} = -20$ Substitute the gradient and one point into the point-gradient form: $y - 0 = -20(x - 50)$ Convert to gradient-intercept form. Method 2: Substituting each point into the equation $W(t) = mt + c$ gives: $\begin{aligned} 3.5m + c &= 930 \\ 50m + c &= 0 \end{aligned}$ Use technology to solve these simultaneous equations. $m = -20$, $c = 1000$

Continued on next page

b 1000 litres	When it starts to drain, $t = 0$. This is the y-intercept of the function.
c The tank drains at 20 litres per minute.	The rate at which the tank drains (the rate of change) is given by the gradient, m.
d 400 litres	Substitute $t = 30$ into the formula: $W(30) = -20 \times 30 + 1000 = 400$

Exercise 4D

1   State which of the following are linear functions. If the function is linear, state its gradient.

   a $f(x) = 3$ **b** $g(x) = 5 - 2x$

   c $h(x) = \dfrac{2}{x} + 3$ **d** $t(x) = 5(x - 2)$

2   For each context

   i   identify the independent and dependent variables and their units

   ii   determine whether a linear function can be used to model the relationship between the two variables, and if so, state the rate of change.

   a   Parking at an airport is charged at $18 for the first hour parked and $12.50 for each subsequent hour.

   b   The population of fish in a lake declines by 7% each year.

   c   Italy charges a value-added tax (VAT) of 22% on all purchases. The amount of tax you pay depends on the amount of your purchase (in euros).

   d   Sal's Ski Resort notices the following trend in sales of daily passes:

Daily high temperature, °C	−4	−1	3	7
Number of daily passes sold	430	406	374	342

3   The table shows values for a function $y = f(x)$.

x	1	3	5	8
y	3	7	11	15

Determine whether $y = f(x)$ is a linear function or not.

4   An online shipping company charges a fixed cost plus US$100 per kilogram of shipment. The total price of shipping is given by the function $P(x) = 100x + 30$, where x is the weight of the shipment.

   a   Write down the fixed cost.

   b   Find the price when the shipment weighs 1.5 kg.

Daniel pays US$310 for a shipment.

   c   Find the weight of this shipment.

5   Ewout is 13 km from home and is walking at a velocity of 65 metres per minute. Velocity is the rate of change of distance over time.

   a   Find an equation to represent Ewout's distance from home, d (in kilometres), as a function of time, t (in minutes).

   b   Determine the distance from home Ewout will be after one hour.

   c   Find the x-intercept of the graph of $d(t)$ and interpret its meaning in the context of the problem.

6   In 2018, Sneakies was the largest shoe company in the industry: their sales represented 64% of all shoe sales by all companies. However, analysts projected that in 2019 they would sell only 62.65% of all shoes, and that without any changes, their percentage share of shoe sales would decline at the same steady rate for the foreseeable future.

   a   Find an equation in gradient-intercept form for the function $S(t)$ that represents Sneakies' shoe sales (as a percentage of all shoe sales) t years after 2018.

   b   Find the year when Sneakies is predicted to no longer sell the majority (over 50%) of shoes.

The graph represents the projected sales of rival company Foot Talker.

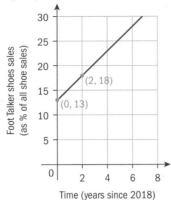

c Show that Foot Talker is growing faster than Sneakies is declining, in terms of their percentage of total shoe sales.

d Find an equation for $F(t)$, the function representing Foot Talker's sales over time.

e Find the year when Foot Talker will sell more shoes than Sneakies.

7 The straight line graph shows the velocity v of a moving body, in metres per second, at time t seconds.

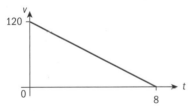

a Write down the initial velocity of the moving body.

b Determine the number of seconds it will take for the body to stop moving.

c Find the rate of change of the velocity with respect to time.

d Find a model for v.

8 A spring is stretched by suspending different weights from it. The length of the spring, L, in centimetres can be modelled by a linear function $L = mW + c$, where W is the weight suspended in grams.

When the weight suspended is 50 g, the length of the spring is 20 cm.

a Write down an equation that shows this information.

When the weight suspended is 80 g, the length of the spring is 35 cm.

b Write down an equation that shows this second piece of information.

c Find the values of m and c.

d Hence, find the length of the spring when a weight of 90 g is suspended.

Functions

Direct variation

Investigation 6

This investigation will help you to determine what direct variation is.

1 For each of the following functions:

  i find an equation that expresses the dependent variable in terms of the independent variable

  ii sketch its graph on an appropriate domain.

  a The circumference C of a circle in terms of its radius r.

  b The currency conversion between US$ d and euros e. One euro is worth US$1.32.

Continued on next page

TOK

Around the world you will often encounter different words for the same item, like gradient and slope, trapezium and trapezoid or root and surd.

Sometimes more than one type of symbol might have the same meaning, such as interval and set notation.

To what extent does the language we use shape the way we think?

c The price P you pay in Happy Shop in terms of the regular price R if there is a sign that says "Today you pay 15% less for every single item".

d The volume of a certain type of wood in terms of the weight:

Volume V (dm³)	1	2	3
Weight W (kg)	0.9	1.8	2.7

2 Describe any similarities in the equations of the four functions.

3 Describe any similarities in the graphs of the four functions.

4 **Conceptual** How can you identify a direct variation relationship from a graph, equation or context?

> A particular type of linear function known as **direct variation** is when the dependent variable is **directly proportional** to the independent variable.
>
> This can be represented as $f(x) = mx$, where $m = \dfrac{y}{x}$ is the **constant of proportionality**.

Exercise 4E

1 You are given that the conversion rate from Chinese yuan to Australian dollars is CNY1 = AUD0.21.

   a Find an equation that will convert AUD to CNY.

   b Interpret the gradient of your equation in context.

   c Grace has AUD75 and wants to buy a souvenir on her trip to China worth 599 yuan. Determine how much more in AUD (to the nearest dollar) she will need to withdraw from her bank to make the purchase (assuming that her bank uses this conversion rate and charges no extra fees).

2 Hooke's law, $F = kx$, states that the force F (in Newtons or N) required to stretch a spring is directly proportional to the displacement, which is the length x (in metres) that the spring is stretched beyond its natural length. Andrew adds a mass corresponding to a force of 15 N to the bottom of a hanging spring and finds that his spring stretches 0.64 m.

   a Find an equation to express the force as a function of the displacement.

   b Use your function to predict the length of the spring when a force of 80 N is applied.

If instead the spring is compressed (shortened), then both a negative force and negative displacement occur.

   c Find the force needed to compress the spring by 1.5 m from its natural length.

The modelling process

When you describe a real-world situation with a linear function, you say that the function is a **model** of the situation. An appropriate model represents essential features of the situation in a way that can be used to analyse the situation and make predictions and decisions about it. The **modelling process** consists of some or all of the steps illustrated in the diagram and in the following example.

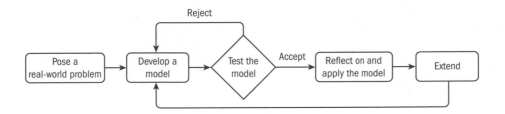

Example 6

Lucy is researching shipping companies for her business to use. She ships between 200 and 500 kg of products each week. Ted's Transport charges a rate of $15.99 per kg, plus a flat fee. She knows her friend used Ted's Transport and paid about $2800 to ship 170 kg of belongings.

a State a real-world problem:

List some relevant questions you might ask here.

b Develop a model:

  i State the independent and dependent variables in this situation.

  ii Explain why a linear model is appropriate for this situation.

  iii Find an equation for your linear model in gradient-intercept form.

c Test the model:

The following week, Lucy makes her first shipment of 310 kg and pays $5031.90. Comment on whether this is consistent with your model. If not, find an alternative model, giving reasons for how you choose to revise it.

d Apply your model:

The following week, Lucy budgets $4500 for shipping. State the maximum weight she can ship, to the nearest kilogram.

e Reflect on the model:

  i Find $C(0)$, and comment on its meaning in the context of the problem.

  ii State a reasonable domain and associated range if Lucy uses it to predict weekly shopping costs.

a One possible question could be: How can you calculate the cost of a shipment from its weight?	
b **i** The dependent variable cost (C in $) is a function of the independent variable weight (w in kg).	Use the coordinate pair $(170, 2800)$ and the known gradient, 15.99, to create an equation in point-gradient form:
ii A linear model is appropriate because a constant rate of change between the two variables is specified: $15.99 per kg.	$C - 2800 = 15.99(w - 170)$ Convert to gradient-intercept: $C = 15.99w - 15.99 \times 170 + 2800$
iii $C(w) = 15.99w + 81.70$	$= 15.99w + 81.70$

Continued on next page

c $C(310) = 5038.60$

The model's prediction is close, but too high by $6.70.

Because the gradient must be 15.99, you adjust the y-intercept by subtracting 6.70:

$C(w) = 15.99w + 75$

d 276 kg

Since $C \leq 4500$, you solve

$4500 \leq 15.99w + 75$

$w \leq 276.7$

e **i** $C(0) = 75$.

This shows that the flat fee is $75.

ii Domain: $200 \leq w \leq 500$

Range: $3272 \leq C \leq 8070$

The problem specifies that she will ship between 200 and 500 kg.

Because the model is linear, the lowest and highest costs will occur at the endpoints: $C(200) = 3273$, $C(500) = 8070$.

Reflect What does it mean to make a mathematical prediction?

How do you use the modelling process to represent and make predictions about real-world contexts?

International-mindedness

The development of functions bridged many countries including France (René Descartes), Germany (Gottfried Wilhelm Leibniz), and Switzerland (Leonhard Euler).

The following example illustrates why the standard form of the equation of a straight line can be a useful representation.

Example 7

Siria reads her English textbook at a pace of 2 minutes per page and her Biology textbook at 3 minutes per page. She has two hours available to read.

a Write an equation that shows the relationship between the number of pages of English (x) and of Biology (y) that Siria can read in this time. Define all the variables.

b **i** Find the x- and y-intercepts of the graph of your equation.

ii Use these to sketch a graph of the equation.

iii Interpret each intercept in the context of the problem.

c Siria ends up reading 45 pages in total. Determine how many pages of English and of Biology she read.

a x = pages of English read

y = pages of Biology read

$2x + 3y = 120$

b **i** y-intercept: $(0, 40)$

x-intercept: $(60, 0)$

Siria will take $2x$ minutes to read x pages of English and $3y$ minutes to read y pages of Biology. These two times will add up to 2 hours (120 minutes).

To find the y-intercept, substitute $x = 0$ and solve for y. Similarly, for the x-intercept substitute $y = 0$ and solve for x.

Note: The equation can also be converted to gradient-intercept form:

$$2x + 3y = 120$$
$$3y = 120 - 2x$$
$$y = 40 - \frac{2}{3}x$$

ii

Label bvoth axes.

Plot both intercepts and connect them with a line.

iii If Siria reads only English then she can read 60 pages in two hours. If she reads only Biology, she can read 40 pages.

c Siria read 15 pages of English and 30 pages of Biology.

Because the total number of pages must be 45, you have a second equation:

$x + y = 45$

Solving with technology,

$$\begin{cases} 2x + 3y = 120 \\ x + y = 45 \end{cases}$$

has the solution $(15, 30)$

Exercise 4F

1 UK£1 is worth approximately US$1.33.

a Find a formula for $u(x)$, where u is the amount in US$ corresponding to UK£x.

b Find the amount in UK£ equivalent to US$100.

c Your bank charges you a fixed fee to exchange currency. You exchange UK£500 and receive US$661.72.

i Find the amount of the fixed fee in US$.

ii Write down the amount in US$ you receive from the bank, B, as a function of the amount in UK£, x.

iii Determine the amount you must exchange to have at least US$1000

2 Economists often use a **demand function** to express the relationship between the price of something and the number of people willing to buy it at that price. Seong Woo performs market research and determines that the number of people, N, who are willing to buy a concert ticket for price p (in euros) can be modelled by the equation $N(p) = 5000 - 36p$.

a State the meaning of the gradient parameter in this context. Explain the meaning of the y-intercept.

b Find the number of people willing to buy a concert ticket if it costs 75 euros.

c Solve $N(p) = 0$ and interpret the meaning of your answer.

d State the reasonable domain and associated range of this model.

e A **supply function** shows the relationship between the price of something and the quantity of it that a company is willing to sell. If the company putting on the concert has a supply function of $S(p) = 28p - 504$, find the price at which the supply and demand for tickets will be equal (This price is called the **equilibrium price**.)

3 The air pressure P (in atm) and the boiling point of water B (in degrees Celsius) can be found as functions of altitude (in kilometres above sea level) using the following functions:

$P(a) = -0.107a + 1$

$B(a) = -11.7a + 100$

As the boiling point of water decreases, food takes longer to cook. The United States Department of Agriculture recommends altering cooking procedures for raw meat at heights above 3000 feet, or 918 m.

a **i** Find the percentage of the sea-level atmospheric pressure at this altitude.

ii Find water's boiling point at this altitude.

A recipe book lists its cooking times for sea level and suggests adding 2 minutes of cooking time for every 5 °C that the boiling point lowers.

b Explain why a linear model is an appropriate choice to model the relationship between boiling point and cooking time.

c Find an equation to express the cooking time T (in minutes) as a function of boiling point B (in Celsius) for a recipe that takes 15 minutes to cook at sea level.

d Calculate how much longer a 15-minute recipe will take to cook in the world's highest city, La Rinconada, Peru, located at an altitude of 5130 m above sea level.

e State the reasonable domain and associated range of the model $T(B)$.

4 Alfie is buying some meat for pizza toppings, Pepperoni costs €3.50 per 100 g and Parma ham costs €6.50 per 100 g. He wants to spend €25 in total.

a Write an equation that represents the relationship between the amount of pepperoni and the amount of ham Alfie can order. Define all the variables.

b Find the intercepts of the graph that represents your equation and interpret their meaning in context.

c Alfie decided that he would like to order 200 g more pepperoni than ham. Determine the amount of each topping he should buy.

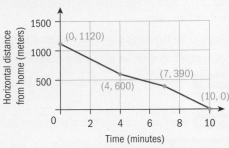

Piecewise functions

Investigation 7

Amir's Run 6 from Investigation 1 is shown, along with a more detailed graph.

Graph axes: Horizontal distance from home (meters) vs Time (minutes). Points: (0, 1120), (4, 600), (7, 390), (10, 0).

1 What does the graph tell you about the rate of change of each section of Amir's run? Explain how this relates to the context.

2 Why can this particular context not be modelled accurately by a single linear function?

3 Describe how you could model sections of Amir's run accurately with linear functions.

4 Find a linear equation in point-gradient form to model each section separately, filling in the table.

	Starting point	Ending point	Gradient	Point-gradient equation
Section 1				
Section 2				
Section 3				

5 Convert each equation to gradient-intercept form. In the "domain" column, write the domain of x-values to which the equation applies.

	Equation	Domain
Section 1		
Section 2		
Section 3		

6 How fast is Amir running on each piece of his run, and for how long does he run at that speed?

The set of equations you have created can be used to form a piecewise function:

$$f(x) = \begin{cases} -130x + 1120 & 0 \leq x < 4 \\ -70x + 880 & 4 \leq x < 7 \\ -130x + 1300 & 7 \leq x \leq 10 \end{cases}$$

To find the value of a piecewise function for a given value of x, use the formula corresponding to the domain in which x lies. For example, if $x = 5$, since $4 \leq 5 < 7$ you use the second piece and find that $f(5) = -70(5) + 880 = 530$.

7 a If $x = 7$, would you use the second or third piece to evaluate $f(7)$? Justify your answer.

b Based on this, why is it important that the pieces of the function do not overlap on their domains?

Continued on next page

Functions

8 Use your piecewise model to find each of the following and interpret it in the context of the problem:

a $f(3)$ **b** $f(8)$ **c** x if $f(x) = 500$

A piecewise function is **continuous** if one piece connects to the next with no breaks or jumps.

9 Check that your piecewise function is continuous with the following steps:

a Verify using the equations that the endpoint of the first section matches the beginning point of the second section.

b Repeat for the endpoint of the second section and the beginning point of the third section.

c Why can there not be any other breaks or jumps elsewhere in the function?

10 **Factual** What is a piecewise function and how do you evaluate a piecewise function for a specific value?

11 **Factual** How do you check that a piecewise function is continuous?

12 **Conceptual** When is a piecewise linear function a useful model?

Example 8

Consider the piecewise function

$$h(t) = \begin{cases} \dfrac{1}{30}t & 0 \le t < 315 \\ 15 - \dfrac{1}{70}t & t \ge 315 \end{cases}$$

a Sketch the graph of the function.

Suppose that $h(t)$ is modelling the height h (in centimetres) of water in a bathtub as a function of time t (in seconds).

b Give a possible explanation for what happens at $t = 315$.

c Find the number of minutes until the bathtub is empty.

d Hence, write down a practical domain for $h(t)$.

a

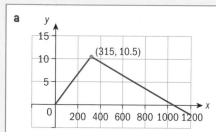

Graph both lines completely using technology or by hand. Then remove the portions of the lines that do not fall within the domain of each piece.

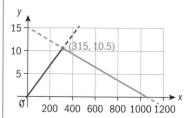

b The bathtub begins to drain at this time, as the height of the water changes from increasing to decreasing.

Use technology or substitution to find the point where the pieces connect, at $t = 315$.

c $t = 1050$ seconds or 17.5 minutes	The bathtub will empty when $h = 0$. Find the t-intercept with technology or by substitution.
d $0 \le t \le 17.5$	

Exercise 4G

1 Consider $f(x) = \begin{cases} 2x - 1 & -5 \le x < 2 \\ 4 - \dfrac{1}{2}x & 2 \le x < 7 \end{cases}$

a Sketch a graph of $f(x)$.

b Find

   i $f(5.7)$ **ii** $f(-3.2)$

c Find the value(s) of x for which $f(x) = 2$.

d Verify that $f(x)$ is continuous.

e State the domain and range of $f(x)$.

---

2 a Construct a piecewise function for Amir's Run 5 from Investigation 1.

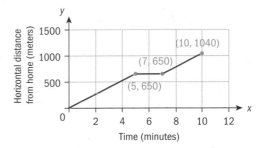

b Verify from the formulas that the function is continuous.

c Determine how long it took Amir to run from 300 m to 800 m away from home.

---

3 A cell phone company offers a plan with a flat rate of \$35 per month for up to one gigabyte (GB) of data. Any data used beyond 1 GB costs 6 cents per megabyte (MB), and 1000 MB = 1 GB.

a Find a piecewise linear model for the monthly cost C (in \$) of the phone as a function of the amount of data d (in GB) used.

b Determine the monthly cost if

   i 500 MB is used   **ii** 2 GB is used.

c The cell phone company offers an alternative plan that costs \$59/month for unlimited data. Determine when this plan is the better deal.

d It is January 3rd, and Yaqeen has used 172 MB of data. She is currently on the original \$35/month plan but is considering switching. Assume that her data usage will continue at the same constant rate.

   i Estimate her data usage for the month of January.

   ii Determine which plan is cheaper for Yaqeen, and how much cheaper it will be than the other plan.

Developing inquiry skills

Looking back at the opening problem, will the taxi driver reach his desired annual salary if he keeps his profit per kilometer at $2.50?

How can you model the taxi driver's daily profit for different values of profit per kilometer? What about monthly profit? State any assumptions that you make in your model.

TOK

"The object of mathematical rigour is to sanction and legitimize the conquests of intuition"

—Jacques Hadamard

Do you think that studying the graph of a function contains the same level of mathematical rigour as studying the function algebraically?

4.3 Inverse functions

Investigation 8

Jamie moves from the United States to Thailand. She would like to convert Celsius temperatures back to the Fahrenheit scale as it is more familiar to her. Jamie knows that water freezes at 0 degrees Celsius or 32 degrees Fahrenheit, and that it boils at 100 degrees Celsius or 212 degrees Fahrenheit. She also knows that both scales have a constant rate of change.

1 Use this information to plot two points representing equivalent temperatures on a graph with temperatures in Celsius as the independent variable and temperatures in Fahrenheit as the dependent variable.

2 Use these two points to create a linear model $F(x) = mx + c$ that converts a Celsius temperature of x degrees to its equivalent temperature in Fahrenheit.

3 Normal human body temperature is 98.6°F, or 37°C. Test the accuracy of your model by checking that it predicts this temperature correctly.

After ten years, Jamie moves back to the US from Thailand. Now she's more familiar with the Celsius scale and would like a way to convert Fahrenheit temperatures to Celsius.

4 Explain why the independent and dependent variables will be reversed.

5 Plot the two points representing the boiling and freezing points of water on a graph with axes corresponding to your independent and dependent variables.

6 As you did before, create a linear model $C(x)$ in gradient-intercept form that converts a Fahrenheit temperature of x degrees to its equivalent temperature C in Celsius. Then test the accuracy of your model.

7 Absolute zero, the coldest possible temperature, is −459.67°F. Find this temperature in Celsius.

8 **a** Summarize the points that you've found on the graphs of your two functions in the table.

	$(x, C(x))$	$(x, F(x))$
Freezing		
Boiling		
Body temperature		
Absolute zero		

b Generalise your results. What point on the graph of $F(x)$ corresponds to the point (a, b) on the graph of $C(x)$? Explain why this makes sense in the context of temperature conversion.

c Considering that absolute zero is the coldest possible temperature and that there is no upper limit on temperatures, find the practical domain and associated range of each model.

	$C(x)$	$F(x)$
Domain		
Range		

d What is the relationship between the domain and range of C and F? Explain why this makes sense in context.

9 **Conceptual** How are the inputs and outputs of inverse functions related? How are the practical domain and range of a linear model related to the domain and range of its inverse?

In Investigation 8 you created an example of two **inverse functions.** You say that $C(x)$ and $F(x)$ are inverses because if $C(a) = b$ then $F(b) = a$ for any a in the domain of $C(x)$.

- You use the notation $f^{-1}(x)$ to denote the inverse function of $f(x)$. If $f(a) = b$, then $f^{-1}(b) = a$. Informally, you think of the inverse function $f^{-1}(x)$ as "reversing" or "undoing" the function $f(x)$.

- If $C(x)$ is a function that maps the domain A onto the range B, written $C: A \rightarrow B$, then $C^{-1}: B \rightarrow A$, as illustrated.

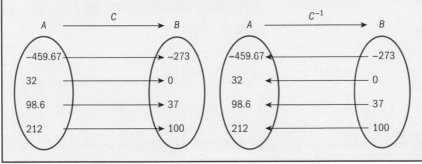

For the functions in Investigation 8, you could also write the Fahrenheit function, $F(x)$, as the inverse of the Celsius function: $F(x) = C^{-1}(x)$.

Example 9

The function $f(x) = 7 - \dfrac{1}{2}x$ is defined on the domain $-5 \le x \le 5$.

a Find $f^{-1}(6)$.

b Determine whether $f^{-1}(11)$ exists. If it does, find it.

c Find the range of $f(x)$.

d State the domain and range of $f^{-1}(x)$.

e Solve $f^{-1}(x) = 0$.

Continued on next page

a $f^{-1}(6) = 2$	Since $f(a) = b$ means $f^{-1}(b) = a$, $f^{-1}(6) = a$ means $f(a) = 6$. Solve $6 = 7 - \dfrac{1}{2}x$ algebraically or with technology.
b $f^{-1}(11)$ is not defined.	$11 = 7 - \dfrac{1}{2}x$ means that $x = -8$, which is outside the domain of f.
c Range: $4.5 \leq y \leq 9.5$	You know that $f(x)$ is linear, so you can find its values at the endpoints of the domain to find the range. $f(-5) = 9.5$, $f(5) = 4.5$
d Domain: $4.5 \leq x \leq 9.5$ Range: $-5 \leq y \leq 5$	The domain of $f^{-1}(x)$ is the range of $f(x)$ and vice versa.
e $x = 7$	$f^{-1}(x) = 0$ means $f(0) = x$.

Exercise 4H

1 For each function, find (or estimate) $f^{-1}(4)$. Justify your answer.

a $f(x) = 3x + 5$ **b** $x \rightarrow \dfrac{1}{2}x$

c
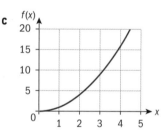

d
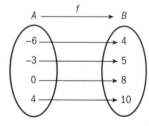

2 The graph of $g(x)$ is shown.

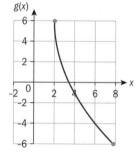

a Find the domain and range of the inverse, $g^{-1}(x)$.

b Estimate the solution to $g^{-1}(x) = 4$.

3 The circumference of a circle is a function of its radius: $C(r) = 2\pi r$. Find $C^{-1}(8)$ and interpret its meaning in context.

4 For the function $f(x) = 2x + c$, find the value of c such that $f^{-1}(21) = -5$.

Equations and graphs of inverse functions

Because the inverse function $f^{-1}(x)$ reverses the input and output of $f(x)$, you can find its equation by switching the variables x and y in the equation for $f(x)$.

For example, to find the inverse of the °C to °F function $F(x) = \frac{9}{5}x + 32$:

Write $F(x)$ as y: $y = \frac{9}{5}x + 32$

Swap x and y: $x = \frac{9}{5}y + 32$

Solve for y: $x - 32 = \frac{9}{5}y$

$$y = \frac{5}{9}(x - 32)$$

$$y = \frac{5}{9}x - 17.8 \text{ (3 s.f.)}$$

So $F^{-1}(x) = \frac{5}{9}x - 17.8$.

Investigation 9

1 Verify that the equation for F^{-1} found above agrees with your equation for $F^{-1}(x)$ from Investigation 8.

2 Use graphing technology to plot both $F(x)$ and $F^{-1}(x)$ on the same coordinate plane. Remember to use the domain and range of each function to estimate a reasonable graphing window the equation for F^{-1} found above.

3 Find the inverse of each of the following functions using the algebraic process demonstrated above. Then add both the function and its inverse to your graphing screen. Graph each function and its inverse in the same colour, if possible.

   a $f(x) = 3x$ b $g(x) = 5x - 100$ c $h(x) = -\frac{1}{2}x - 25$

4 a Use your graphs and/or equations to complete the table.

Function	y-intercept	x-intercept	Point of intersection with inverse
$F(x)$			
$F^{-1}(x)$			
$f(x)$			
$f^{-1}(x)$			
$g(x)$			
$g^{-1}(x)$			
$h(x)$			
$h^{-1}(x)$			

   b Describe any patterns you notice in the table.

5 Graph the **identity line** $y = x$ on your coordinate plane. What relationship do you notice between the graph of a function, the graph of its inverse, and the line $y = x$? Can you explain how this relates to the fact that $f(a) = b$ means $f^{-1}(b) = a$?

6 **Conceptual** How can the relationship between inverse functions be seen in their graphs and their equations?

Example 10

Laura is planning to construct a pool consisting of a rectangle joined to a semicircle of radius x, as shown in the diagram. The sides of the rectangle perpendicular to this side will be of length 6 m. The pool must fit within an 18 m by 18 m square.

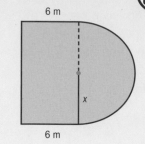

a Find a model for the perimeter P (in meters) of this pool as a function of its radius x.

b Find the reasonable domain and associated range of this model.

c Find an equation for the inverse function $P^{-1}(x)$ in gradient–intercept form.

d State the independent and dependent variables of the function $P^{-1}(x)$.

e Edging for the pool comes in three lengths: 15, 30 or 45 metres. Determine which length will give Laura a rectangle that is closest to a square.

a $P(x) = \pi x + 2x + 12$	The rectangle has side lengths 6 and $2x$. The semicircle has circumference $\dfrac{2\pi x}{2} = \pi x$.
b Domain: $0 < x \le 9$ Range: $12 < P \le 58.3$	x represents the radius, which must be positive. As the pool must fit within an 18×18 square, $x + 6 \le 18$ and $2x \le 18$, so $x \le 9$. $P(0) = 12$ and $P(9) = 58.3$.
c $P^{-1}(x) = 0.194x - 2.33$	$\begin{aligned} x &= \pi y + 2y + 12 & &\text{Swap } x \text{ and } y. \\ x - 12 &= (\pi + 2)y & &\text{Factorise.} \\ \frac{x-12}{\pi+2} &= y & &\text{Divide by the } y \text{ coefficient to isolate } y \\ & & &\text{and convert numbers to decimal} \\ & & &\text{approximations.} \end{aligned}$
d Independent variable x is the perimeter. Dependent variable y is the radius associated with that perimeter.	
e Laura should choose the 30 m edging because it results in the rectangle whose dimensions are most similar.	Find the radius for each perimeter by evaluating P^{-1}, then double the result to find one side of the rectangle. The length of the other side is 6 m: $P^{-1}(15) = 0.583\,\text{m}$: $6\,\text{m} \times 1.166\,\text{m}$ $P^{-1}(30) = 3.50\,\text{m}$: $6\,\text{m} \times 7\,\text{m}$ $P^{-1}(45) = 6.62\,\text{m}$: $6\,\text{m} \times 12.8\,\text{m}$

Exercise 4I

1 For each of the following functions:
   i Sketch a graph of the inverse function.
   ii State the domain and range of $f^{-1}(x)$.
   iii Estimate the solution of $f(x) = f^{-1}(x)$.

a

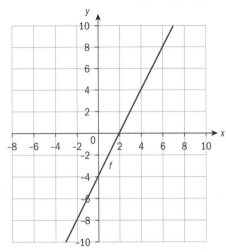

b

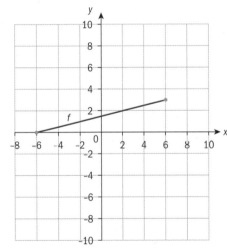

c

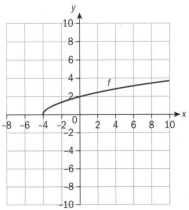

2 Consider $f(x) = -2.5x + 5$ for $0 \leq x \leq 3$.
   a Draw the graph of f on a pair of axes. Use the same scale on both axes.
   b Point A lies on the graph of f^{-1} and has coordinates $(b, 3)$. Find the value of b.
   c Determine the missing entries in the table.

Function	Domain	Range
f	$0 \leq x \leq 3$	
f^{-1}		

   d Draw the graph of f^{-1} on the same set of axes used in part **a**.
   e Find the coordinates of the point that lies on the graph of f, the graph of f^{-1} and the graph of $y = x$.

3 Dieneke travels from Amsterdam to Budapest, a distance of 1400 km. On the first day she covers 630 km. She notes that her average speed is 90 km hr^{-1} on day 1. Assume that she continues at the same average speed on the second day without any breaks.

   a Supposing that she begins driving at 8 am on day 2. Find an equation that expresses her total distance travelled from Amsterdam, d (in kilometres), as a function of time, x (in hours since 8 am of day 2).

   b Find an equation for the inverse function $d^{-1}(x)$.

   c Use the inverse function to predict the time (to the nearest minute) at which Dieneke will arrive at the following points:
      i halfway between Amsterdam and Budapest
      ii in Prague, 880 km from Amsterdam
      iii in Budapest.

   d Comment on which of the three places Dieneke should plan to stop for a midday meal.

Composition and the formal definition of inverse

You think of an inverse function as reversing or undoing a function. To formalise this in a definition, you need a way to show that you are performing more than one function in a row.

For example, at a restaurant in Rome, you notice that a €2 per table charge has been added to your bill for x euros. You also plan to add a 10% tip. If you calculate the tip and then add the table charge, you would perform the calculations

$$x \to 1.1x \to 1.1x + 2$$

If you add the table charge and then the tip, your process would be

$$x \to x + 2 \to 1.1(x + 2)$$

Let $c(x) = x + 2$ represent the table charge function and $t(x) = 1.1x$ represent the tip function. Then the first case above can be represented as

$$x \to t(x) \to c(t(x))$$

The mapping diagram shows the final charge that would result for several different bills.

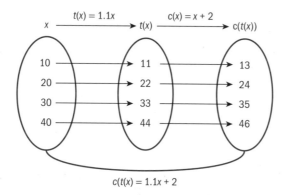

$$c(t(x)) = 1.1x + 2$$

> You call the inputting of one function into another a **composition of functions**, and denote it as $c \circ t(x)$ or $c(t(x))$.

Note that a composition is also a function; in the example above, it is given by the formula $c(t(x)) = 1.1x + 2$.

Example 11

If $f(x) = 5 - \dfrac{1}{6}x$ and $g(x) = \dfrac{3}{2}x + 12$, find a simplified expression for

a $f \circ g(8)$

b $f \circ g(x)$

a $\quad f \circ g(8) = f(g(8))$

$\qquad = f\left(\dfrac{3}{2}(8) + 12\right)$

$\qquad = f(24)$

$\qquad = 5 - \dfrac{1}{6}(24)$

$\qquad = 1$

Note that in the composition $f(g(x))$, the x-value is input first into g. The output of g (in this case, 24) is the input of f.

b $\quad f \circ g(x) = f\left(\dfrac{3}{2}x + 12\right)$

$\qquad = 5 - \dfrac{1}{6}\left(\dfrac{3}{2}x + 12\right)$

$\qquad = 5 - \dfrac{1}{4}x - 2$

$\qquad = -\dfrac{1}{4}x + 3$

Here you replace the x in $f(x)$ with the expression for $g(x)$.

Functions

Example 12

In the Earth's atmosphere, as altitude increases the average temperature decreases, as shown by the graph of the function $T(x)$ on the left. On the right, the function $C(x)$ converting Fahrenheit to Celsius temperatures is graphed.

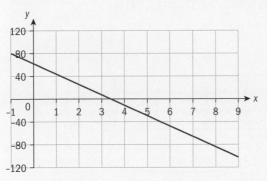
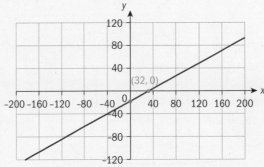

a Use the graphs to estimate $C(T(2))$ and interpret your answer in context.

b Predict the temperature in Celsius at the top of Mount Everest (8848 m).

c Solve $C(T(x)) = 0$ and interpret your answer in context.

Continued on next page

a $C(T(2)) \approx C(20) \approx -5$

This means that at an altitude of 2 km above sea level, the average temperature is −5°C.

b $C(T(8.848)) \approx C(-100) \approx -75°C$

c $C(T(x)) = 0$ when $T(x) = 32$.

This happens when $x \approx 1.5$.

At an altitude of 1.5 km above sea level, the average temperature is 0°C.

From the graphs, $T(2) \approx 20$ and $C(20) \approx -5$.

Work backwards: first find the zeroes or x-intercepts of $C(x)$ from the graph. There is one at (32, 0):

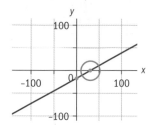

So the function $T(x)$ must give an output of 32. Estimate the intersection of $y = 32$ and $T(x)$.

Investigation 10

In this investigation you will determine how to use compositions to prove that two functions are inverses.

In Investigation 9 you found that the inverse of the function $f(x) = 5x - 100$ is $f^{-1}(x) = \dfrac{1}{5}x + 20$.

1 Find the following values, and comment on how your results relate to the concept of an inverse function.

   a $f(10)$ **b** $f^{-1}(-50)$

2 Complete the following mapping diagrams for the compositions $f^{-1}\circ f(x)$ and $f\circ f^{-1}(x)$.

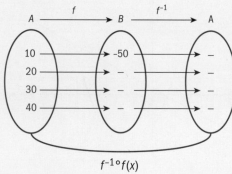

  b What do you notice about the compositions $f^{-1}\circ f(x)$ and $f \circ f^{-1}(x)$?

3 Based on this, what is true about the composition of inverses? Why does this make sense?

4 Test your conjecture on the function $f(x) = 3x + 2$ by finding its inverse function and composing the function with its inverse.

5 **Conceptual** How do you prove that two functions are inverses?

You call the function $i(x) = x$ that "does nothing" to x the **identity function**. The composition of a function and its inverse, in either order, will result in the identity: $f \circ f^{-1}(x) = f^{-1}(x) \circ f(x) = x$.

Exercise 4J

1 If $f(x) = 8x - 25$, $g(x) = 4 - x$ and $h(x) = \dfrac{3}{2}x$, find:

a $f \circ g(1)$

b $h \circ f(4)$

c $g \circ f(x)$

d $h \circ h \circ h(x)$

2 Returning to the example of the bill at the restaurant, recall that $c(x) = x + 2$ represents the table charge function and $t(x) = 1.1x$ represents the tip function.

a Show that $c(t(x)) \neq t(c(x))$ by finding a simplified function for each.

b Determine which order of composition will provide the waiter with the larger tip, and state, in terms of x, how much larger.

3 Find two functions $f(x)$ and $g(x)$ such that $h(x) = f(g(x))$ if:

a $h(x) = \dfrac{7}{3}x - 5$

b $h(x) = 4(x - 2)$

c $h(x)$ is shown in the graph.

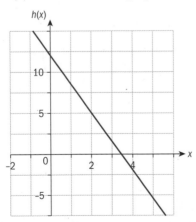

4 The number of window panes a company can produce is a function of time t, measured in hours of operation per day, and is given by $w(t) = 7t - 3$. The company's profit $P is a function of the number of windows sold, given by $P(w) = 50w - 2000$.

a Find the company's profit (or loss) if it operates for 4 hours a day.

b Find the company's profit as a function of time, expressed in the form $P(t) = mt + c$ where $m, c \in \mathbb{R}$.

c Determine the number of hours (to the nearest hour) that the factory must operate in order to earn a (positive) profit.

5 Show that the temperature conversion functions $C(x) = \dfrac{5}{9}x - 17.8$ and $F(x) = \dfrac{9}{5}x + 32$ are approximate inverses of each other.

6 Use the graph to solve $f \circ g(x) = 0$.

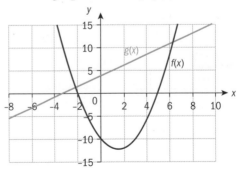

Functions

4.4 Arithmetic sequences and series

Investigation 11

Pablo starts his first full-time job at the age of 24. In his first year he earns $3250 per month after taxes, or $39 000 per year. He is given a salary schedule that shows how his salary will increase over time:

Years in job	1	2	3	4	5
Annual salary	39 000	39 900	40 800	41 700	42 600

The salaries can also be written as an ordered list of numbers or **sequence:**

39 000, 39 900, 40 800, 41 700, 42 600

Each number is a **term**. To identify a specific term in the sequence, for example, the 4th, you write u_4. So, in the sequence above,

$u_1 = 39\,000$ (also called the **first term**)
$u_2 = 39\,900$ (the second term)
$u_3 = 40\,800$

and so on.

In general, u_n is the nth term. The entire sequence is denoted by $\{u_n\}$.

1   Complete the table by calculating the difference between every two terms. The first is done as an example. What do you notice?

Years in job (term number)	1	2	3	4	5
Annual salary	39 000	39 900	40 800	41 700	42 600
Difference between terms	—	39 900 – 39 000 = 900			

2   **a**   Plot the first five terms of the sequence from the table above and verify they form a straight line. A sequence that creates a linear graph is called **arithmetic**. What is the gradient of this line?

How can it be predicted from the terms of the sequence?

   b   What is the y-intercept of the line associated with the sequence?

How can it be predicted from the terms of the sequence?

3   **Factual** How do you determine whether a sequence is arithmetic without graphing it?

4   **Factual** If a sequence is arithmetic, how are the parameters of the corresponding linear function related to the first term and difference between terms of the sequence?

5   Use the pattern in the sequence $\{u_n\}$ to predict Pablo's annual salary if he stays in the same job and retires at the age of 65. You may find it helpful to complete the table:

Age	24	25	26	27	...	64	65
Number of term (n)	1	2	3	4	...		
Number of differences added (d = $900)	0	1	2		...		
Term (u_n)	39 000	39 000 + 900 = 39 900	39 000 + 2 × 900 = 40 800		...		

6   **Conceptual** How can you describe the nth term of an arithmetic sequence?

A sequence is **arithmetic** if the difference between consecutive terms is constant. This difference is called the **common difference**.

To calculate the **nth term** of an arithmetic sequence $\{u_n\}$ with first term a_1 and common difference d:

$$u_n = u_1 + (n-1)d$$

Verify that this formula is consistent with the method you described in Investigation 11.

Example 13

For each of the following arithmetic sequences:

    i State its first term and common difference.

    ii Find the 10th term of the sequence.

    iii Determine, giving your reasons, whether 49 is an element of the sequence.

a $u_n = 3n + 1$, $n \in \mathbb{Z}^+$. Remember that $\mathbb{Z}^+$ is the set of positive integers: $\{1, 2, 3, \ldots\}$.

b 206, 199, 192, …

a **i** Arithmetic. $u_1 = 4$, $d = 3$	The formula for calculating u_n is linear, so the sequence is arithmetic. The gradient or common difference is 3 and $u_1 = 3(1) + 1 = 4$.
ii $u_{10} = 31$	Using the formula $u_n = u_1 + (n-1)d$: $u_{10} = 4 + (10 - 1) \times 3 = 31$
iii Yes, 49 is the 16th term.	You wish to determine whether any whole-number value of n results in $u_n = 49$. Use algebra or technology to solve the following: $49 = 4 + (n - 1) \times 3$ This gives $n = 16$.
b **i** Arithmetic. $u_1 = 206$, $d = -7$	The sequence decreases by 7.
ii $u_{10} = 143$	As d is negative, you subtract $7(n-1)$: $u_{10} = 206 - 7(10 - 1) = 143$
iii No, 49 lies between u_{23} and u_{24}.	You solve as in part **b**: $49 = 206 - 7(n - 1)$ Solving yields $n = 23.4$ (3 s.f.), a non-integer.

Example 14

A piledriver is a machine used in construction to drive support poles into the ground by repeatedly striking them. Acme construction company uses a piledriver that drives support poles 0.12 m deeper into the ground with each strike. The current support pole has already been driven 13.6 m into the ground.

a If the sequence $\{u_n\}$ represents the depth of the support pole after n strikes, find the first three terms of the sequence.

b Write down an expression for the nth term of the sequence.

c The support poles must be driven to a depth of at least 38 m below ground. Determine

  i the number of strikes needed to reach this depth

  ii the exact depth it will then have reached.

a $u_1 = 13.6$, $u_2 = 13.72$, $u_3 = 13.84$	The pole is at an initial depth of 13.6 m, so $u_1 = 13.6$.
	The piledriver adds an additional depth of 0.12 m per strike, so $d = 0.12$.
b $u_n = 13.6 + 0.12(n - 1)$	Using $a_n = a_1 + (n - 1)d$.
c **i** 205 strikes	u_n represents the depth after n strikes, so you need to solve $u_n \geq 38$.
	Solve directly or using graphing technology, choosing an appropriate window:
	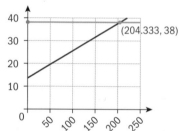
	This gives $n = 204.33$. As n must be a whole number and the depth must be 38 m or more, you choose the next largest whole number, so $n = 205$.
ii $u_{205} = 38.08$ m	Using the formula, $u_{205} = 13.6 + 0.12(205 - 1)$.

Exercise 4K

1 For each of the following sequences:

  i Predict the next three terms of the sequence.

  ii Determine whether the sequence is arithmetic, stating the common difference if it is.

  a 7.3, 15.9, 24.5, 33.1, ...

  b 5, −17, −39, −61, ...

  c 61, 70, 88, 95, ...

  d 10, 5, 2.5, ...

2 For each of the sequences below, use the formula to write down the first three terms if $n \in \mathbb{Z}^+$. Then determine whether the sequence is arithmetic; state the first term and the common difference if it is.

  a $a_n = 2.5n + 7$

  b $b_n = 5000 - 2350n$

  c $c_n = n(2n + 1)$

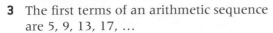

3 The first terms of an arithmetic sequence are 5, 9, 13, 17, …

  a Write an expression for the general (nth) term of this sequence.

  b Determine whether 116 is a term of this sequence.

4 When a company opened up it had 85 employees. It decided to increase the number of employees by 10 at the beginning of each year.

  a Find the number of employees during the second year and during the third year.

  b Determine the number of employees this company will have during the 10th year.

  c Determine after how many years the company will have 285 employees.

5 A sequoia tree that was 2.6 m tall when it was planted in 1998 grows at a rate of 1.22 meters per year.

  a Write down a formula to represent the height of the tree in years, with a_1 representing the height in 1998.

  b Find the height of the tree in 2025.

  c The tallest living sequoia tree, the General Sherman tree in the US Sequoia National Park, has a height of 84 m. Determine in what year the tree planted in 1998 would reach that height if it continues with the same rate of growth.

Sometimes you will need to find missing parameters (first term, common difference or number of terms) by interpreting information about your sequence.

Example 15

Julie swims each day in a 25 m pool. Today, she notes that she swims her first warm-up lap in 1 minute and 6 seconds. She then swims the remainder of her laps at a constant speed. After her fifth lap, she checks the clock and sees that 4 minutes 18 seconds have passed. Her entire swim takes 19 minutes 30 seconds.

a If the sequence $\{u_n\}$ represents Julie's total swim time after each lap in minutes, write down u_1 and u_5.

b Find the common difference, d, of this sequence. Explain its meaning in the context of the problem.

c Determine the number of laps that Julie swims.

a $u_1 = 1.1$, $u_5 = 4.3$	You convert minutes and seconds to minutes: 6 seconds = $\dfrac{6}{60}$ minutes = 0.1 minutes.
b $d = 0.8$ Julie takes 0.8 minutes, or 48 seconds, to swim one lap.	Four differences are added between the first and fifth terms, so $\dfrac{(4.3-1.1)}{4} = 0.8$. This can also be solved by substituting into the equation $u_5 = u_1 + 4d$: $4.3 = 1.1 + 4d$ $d = \dfrac{4.3-1.1}{4}$

Continued on next page

Functions

c Julie swam 24 laps.	The last (nth) term of the sequence is 19.5:
	$1.1, u_2, u_3, u_4, 4.3, \ldots, 19.5$
	Substitute into the nth-term equation:
	$1.1 + (n - 1) \times 0.8 = 19.5$
	Solving using algebra or technology gives $n = 24$.

Exercise 4L

1   The first term of an arithmetic sequence is −10 and the seventh term is 1.

   a   Find the value of the common difference.

   b   Find the 15th term of this sequence.

2   Consider the arithmetic sequence $0, u_2, u_3, u_4, 10, \ldots$

   a   Find the common difference.

   b   Find u_3.

3   You enter your pet frog in a 1000 cm jumping contest. He hops the full race and beyond! His distance from the finish line is represented by the sequence $975, 950, \ldots, -225$. Here, u_n represents the distance from the finish line after n hops.

   a   Write down the common difference and interpret its meaning in context.

   b   Find the 10th term. Interpret its meaning in context.

   c   Determine the number of hops it takes your frog to finish the race.

   d   Determine the number of terms in the sequence. Interpret this number in the context of the problem.

4   In an arithmetic sequence, $u_3 = 12$ and $u_{10} = 43.5$. The common difference is d.

   a   Write down two equations in u_1 and d to show this information.

   b   Find the value of u_1 and of d.

   c   Find the 100th term.

5   The first row of a theatre has 22 seats. The tenth row has 49. The last row has 106. The number of seats per row follows an arithmetic progression.

   a   Find an expression for the number of seats in the nth row.

   b   Determine the number of rows in the theatre.

6   A trebuchet is a medieval weapon that hurls a heavy object through the air, similar to a catapult. The distance that the object flies depends linearly on its weight. Tyler builds a trebuchet and collects a set of objects each weighing an an integer value of kilograms. He finds that a 1 kg object travels 12 m. He also notes that an object weighing 9 kg travels twice as far as one weighing 3 kg.

Let $\{u_n\}$ represents the distance travelled (in metres) by an object with a weight of n kg.

   a   Write down u_1.

   b   Write down expressions for u_3 and u_9 in terms of u_1 and d.

   c   Write an equation relating u_3 and u_9.

   d   Solve this equation to find d.

   e   If Tyler wants to hurl an object 100 m, calculate how heavy this object should be.

Simple interest

The **principal** or **capital** is the money that you initially put in a savings institution or a bank. The **account balance** is the total amount of money either saved or owed at given point in time.

Interest is a percentage of the principal or account balance paid to you (for a savings account) or paid by you (for a loan). **Simple interest** is calculated as a fixed percentage of the principal and hence is a type of arithmetic sequence.

Functions

The total amount of simple interest I earned on a principal P over n years at an interest rate of $r\%$ per year can be calculated using the formula

$I = P \times r \times n$

The total savings account balance is given by

$A = P + (P \times r \times n)$

Example 16

An amount of $5000 is invested at a simple interest rate of 3% per annum (p.a., meaning each year) for a period of 8 years.

a Calculate the interest received after 8 years.

b Find the account balance after the 8 years.

c Find the time it will take for the account balance to double.

a $1200	Substituting in the formula $I = P \times r \times n$: $I = 5000 \times 0.03 \times 8 = 1200$
b $6200	The account balance is found by adding the interest to the capital: $5000 + 1200 = 6200$
c 34 years	The account balance must be double its initial principal: $2 \times 5000 = 10\,000$. Substituting and solving with technology: $10\,000 = 5000 + 5000 \times 0.03 \times n$ $n = 33.3$ (3 s.f.) As the interest is calculated at the end of the year, the principal will not exceed double until the 34th year.

Example 17

Gabe pays a total of $1500 in simple interest on a car loan over 5 years with a 2.3% interest rate p.a. Find, to the nearest dollar, the original value of the car.

$P = \$13\,043$	Using $I = P \times r \times n$: $$1500 = P \times 0.023 \times 5$$ $$P = 13\,043$$ Note that for a loan, simple interest is paid to the bank. It is not added to the account balance as savings interest is.

Exercise 4M

1 Calculate the total simple interest and final account balance of a savings account in which $9000 is invested at a rate of 5.9% p.a. for 3 years.

2 Find the amount of money borrowed if after 7 years the interest charged is UK£9000 at a rate of 7.5% per annum.

3 Find the annual interest rate if €1840 in interest is earned after 5 years on a principal of €8000.

4 Stephen deposits $8600 in a bank account that pays simple interest at a rate of 6.5% per annum. Determine the year in which Stephen's money doubles.

Arithmetic series

In Investigation 11 you modelled Pablo's annual salary as an arithmetic sequence with first term $39 000, common difference $d = \$900$, and 42 terms:

$$a_n = 39\,000 + 900(n - 1)$$

What if Pablo would like to know how much money he will earn in total over the course of his career? You can represent this total as a **series**, or the sum of a sequence:

$$S_{42} = 39\,000 + 39\,900 + 40\,800 + \ldots + 75\,900$$

Here, S_{42} stands for the sum of the first 42 terms of the sequence.

You can also represent this series with the **sigma notation** introduced in Chapter 2:

$$\sum_{i=1}^{n} a_i = \sum_{i=1}^{42} (39\,000 + 900(i - 1))$$

n = number of terms (and ending value of i)

Index variable and starting value

Term i (general formula for a term)

How do you evaluate this sum? You will investigate a simpler series to look for a pattern that you can generalise.

Investigation 12

According to mathematical legend, Karl Gauss was asked as a boy to add the numbers 1 to 100 in order to keep him busy during class. He found the sum almost instantly. So will you.

1 The sum of the numbers 1 to 100 is written below. Instead of adding them in order, you will add them up in the indicated pairs. What is the sum of each pair?

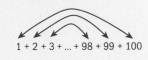

$1 + 2 + 3 + ... + 98 + 99 + 100$

2 How many pairs would you have to total, if you continued this process?

3 Use your answers above to determine the sum of the series.

4 Try the same method on this smaller series, and confirm that your method gives you the same sum as if you add it in order:

$5 + 8 + 11 + 14 + 17 + 20$

5 **Factual** Generalise your method to a formula for finding the sum of any arithmetic series:

If $S_n = u_1 + u_2 + u_3 + ... + u_n$, then $S_n = \sum_{i=1}^{n} u_i = ?$

6 Use your formula to find Pablo's lifetime earnings.

7 **Factual** When is it more useful to represent a context as an arithmetic series than as a linear function?

8 **Conceptual** How is an arithmetic series represented and calculated?

The sum of n terms of an arithmetic series with first term u_1 and common difference d is given by

$$S_n = \sum_{i=1}^{n} u_i = \frac{n}{2}(u_1 + u_n)$$

or

$$(2u_1 + (n-1)d) \times \frac{n}{2}$$

Example 18

a Find the sum of the arithmetic series $-10 + (-6) + (-2) + ... + 90$.

b Write down this series in sigma notation.

c Find the least number of terms from this series needed to obtain a sum greater than 100.

Continued on next page

a $S_{26} = 1040$	This is an arithmetic series with common difference 4.
	To find n, solve $u_n = 90$:
	$90 = -10 + (n-1) \times 4$
	Solving with technology or algebraically, $n = 26$.
	Then:
	$$S_{26} = \frac{26}{2}(-10 + 90) = 1040$$
b $\displaystyle\sum_{i=1}^{26}(-10 + (i-1) \times 4)$	Since $u_1 = -10$ and $d = 4$, you can write the general term u_i. From part **a** the number of terms $n = 26$. so you represent the series in the sigma notation: $$\sum_{i=1}^{n} u_i$$
c 11 terms	To find n so that the sum is greater than 100, you set up the inequality:
	$$S_n = \frac{n}{2}(2 \times (-10) + (n-1) \times 4) > 100$$
	$$= \frac{n}{2}(-20 + (n-1) \times 4)$$
	Solve with technology by graphing or using a table.

n	Sum
9	54
10	80
11	110

The sum is smaller than 100 when $n = 10$, and larger when $n = 11$.

Example 19

A skydiver jumping from a plane 4200 m above the ground falls 9.5 metres in the first second. In each succeeding second she falls 7.8 metres more than in the previous one. This continues until she opens her parachute.

a Find the distance that she falls during the 20th second.

b Find the total distance she has fallen after 20 seconds.

c The skydiver should open her parachute at or before 600 m above ground level. Determine the latest time, to the nearest second, that she can open her parachute.

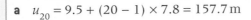A second skydiver leaving the same plane also falls 9.5 metres in the first second, but falls *d* metres more each second than the previous one. After 5 seconds she has fallen approximately 120 metres.

d Find *d* to the nearest tenth of a metre.

e Explain, with a reason, which skydiver is falling faster.

Functions

a $u_{20} = 9.5 + (20 - 1) \times 7.8 = 157.7\,\text{m}$

The distance the skydiver has travelled after each second is an arithmetic sequence with first term 9.5 and common difference 7.8.

b $S_{20} = (9.5 + 157.7) \times \dfrac{20}{2} = 1672\,\text{m}$

Because the sequence represents the additional distance she falls with each second, her total distance will be the sum of these second-by-second distances.

c $3700 = (2 \times 9.5 + (n - 1) \times 7.8) \times \dfrac{n}{2}$

At a height of 600 m above ground level the skydiver will have fallen a total of $4200 - 600 = 3700\,\text{m}$

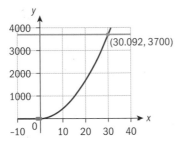

The sum must therefore be less than 3700. You use this to set up an inequality and solve with technology:

At 30 seconds she will be above 600 m; at 31 seconds she will be below.

$n \leq 30.092$

The latest the skydiver can safely open her parachute is after 30 seconds.

d $d = 7.3\,\text{m}$

For the second skydiver the first term is still 9.5 but the common difference is unknown.

You know that $S_5 = 120$.

Substitute the known information into the sum formula and use technology to solve for the unknown, *d*:

$120 = (2 \times 9.5 + (5 - 1)d) \times \dfrac{5}{2}$

$d = 7.25 = 7.3\,\text{m}$ to the nearest tenth of a metre.

e The first skydiver is faster, as her distances are increasing by 7.8 m each second rather than 7.3 m.

1 Find the sum of the first 20 terms of the arithmetic series $6 + 3 + 0 - 3 - 6 - \ldots$

2 Find the sum of the first 30 multiples of 8.

3 Consider the series $52 + 62 + 72 + \ldots + 462$.

   a Find the number of terms.

   b Find the sum of the terms.

4 Janet begins farming on 1 acre of land. Each year, as her business grows, she buys more land to farm. She buys an additional 5 acres in the second year and 9 acres in the third year.

   a Assuming that the amount of land she buys each year continues in the same pattern, write down a sum that represents the total land she owns after ten years.

   b Write down this sum in sigma notation.

   c Calculate S_{10} and find S_n in terms of n.

   d Find the value of n for which $S_n = 2000$, and interpret the meaning of n in context.

5 An arithmetic series has $S_1 = 4$ and $d = -3$.

   a Write down an expression for S_n in terms of n.

   b Find S_{10}.

   c Find the smallest n for which $S_n < -250$.

6 Montserrat is training for her first race. In her first training week she runs 3 km, and in the second training week she runs 3.5 km. Every week she runs 0.5 km more than the previous one.

   a Determine the number of kilometres Montserrat runs in her 10th training week?

   b Calculate the total number of kilometres that Montserrat will have run by her 15th training week.

7 In Exercise 4L question **5**, you found the number of rows of seats in a theatre that has 22 seats in the first row, 49 in the tenth row, and 106 in the last row. Recall that the number of seats in each row increases by a constant amount.

   a Find the total number of seats in the theatre.

   b An architect is designing another theatre for a university that wants to have 25 rows, a total of at least 6000 seats, and a first row of 16 seats. The number of seats per row will increase by a constant amount. Determine the least possible value for the increase and the total number of seats it will provide.

Approximately arithmetic sequences

Sometimes arithmetic sequences can be used to model a context even if it is not perfectly arithmetic.

An **approximately arithmetic sequence** has approximately equal differences between terms and its graph is nearly linear.

When a sequence of real-world data is approximately arithmetic, find a common difference for your model by averaging the common differences of the data.

TOK

Do you think that mathematics is just the manipulation of symbols under a set of rules?

Exercise 40

1 Scientists use tree rings to determine the age of trees. Each ring corresponds to one year of the tree's growth (see the picture).

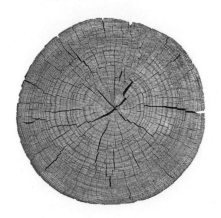

Abby examines a tree stump and measures the radius of each of the first five rings. She records the results in a table.

Ring	1	2	3	4	5
Radius (mm)	27	31	34	38	40

She notes that the radii of the rings continue to increase approximately linearly. The radius of the entire tree stump is 1.8 m. Approximately how old was the tree?

2 Dionissi is an economist who has been tasked with modelling the trade deficit between his country and Australia. (A trade deficit means that his country buys more products from Australia than Australia buys from his country. A trade surplus is the opposite. The relation is measured as a percentage of the country's gross domestic product, or GDP.) Dionissi finds that the deficit has been growing in the following pattern over ten recent years:

Year	2007	2008	2009	2010	2011	2012	2013	2014	2015	2016
Surplus/deficit (% of GDP)	2.28	1.95	1.57	1.21	0.82	0.45	0.12	−0.24	−0.59	−0.96

Using this data, construct an approximate arithmetic sequence and use it to predict the trade deficit in 2025

Developing inquiry skills

Looking back at the opening problem, how will the taxi driver's income change if he increases the income per kilometre by $0.30 after one month?

How can you model the daily income for different values of income per kilometre?

How have you used the modelling process discussed in this section to investigate this problem?

4.5 Linear regression

In the previous section you developed a method to model approximately arithmetic sequences. In this section, we'll investigate how you can model approximately linear situations with linear models. In this investigation you will improve on the method developed in Chapter 2 for creating a line of best fit.

Investigation 13

1 The scatter graph shows a set of eight data points and also two lines of best fit, L_1 $(f_1(x) = 0.81x + 2.36)$ and L_2 $(f_2(x) = 0.65x + 3.08)$. One of these lines models this set of points better than the other. Which line do you think best fits this data? Why?

One way to measure the fit of a line to a data set is to calculate **residuals**. A residual is the difference between the actual y-value and the predicted y-value. Therefore, residuals are the errors made when using best-fit lines to make predictions.

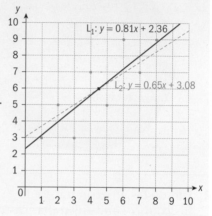

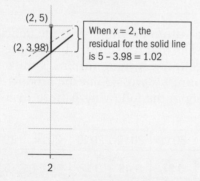

When $x = 2$, the residual for the solid line is $5 - 3.98 = 1.02$

2 a What does a positive residual tell you about the predicted y-value compared with the actual y-value?

   b Will the line that better fits the data have residuals with generally smaller or larger values? Why?

3 Calculate the residuals for each line by completing the table. (You can leave the square of residuals columns blank for now.) The first point has been done as an example. You may wish to use spreadsheet technology to make your calculations more efficient.

Point	x	y	Predicted y using L_1	Residual using L_1	Square of residual using L_1	Predicted y using L_2	Residual using L_2	Square of residual using L_2
(1, 3)	1	3	$0.81×1 +$ $2.36 = 3.17$	$3 - 3.17 =$ -0.17	0.0289	$0.65×1 +$ $3.08 = 3.73$	$3 - 3.73 =$ -0.73	0.5329
(2, 5)	2							
(3, 3)	3							
(4, 7)	4							
(5, 5)	5							
(6, 9)	6							
(7, 7)	7							
(8, 9)	8							
				$SS_{res} =$			$SS_{res} =$	

4 To get a total of the residuals for a line, you could simply add them all. Try adding all the residuals of L_1. What happens? Is this a good measure of the overall "error" of the line?

So that positive and negative residuals do not cancel each other, you will square each residual before adding them together. You call this the sum of square residuals, or SS_{res}.

5 Find the squares of the residuals for each line, then add them to find the sum of square residuals.

Point	Residual using L_1	Square of residual using L_1	Residual using L_2	Square of residual using L_2
(1, 3)	−0.17	0.0289	−0.73	0.5329
(2, 5)				
(3, 3)				
(4, 7)				
(5, 5)				
(6, 9)				
(7, 7)				
(8, 9)				
		$SS_{res} =$		$SS_{res} =$

6 Based on the values of SS_{res}, which line has the better fit? Does this support your conjecture from step **1**? You only chose two lines to compare, but there are many other possible choices.

7 To see where the least squares regression line gets its name from, open the least squares regression app on your GDC.

   a What happens to the size of the squares as you make the line a worse fit for the data? A better fit?

   b How are the areas of the squares connected to the sum of square residuals calculation?

   c What parameters can you change about the line?

8 **Conceptual** How do we use sum of square residuals to define the parameters in the least squares regression line and why does this lead to a line of best fit?

- The residual for a point (x_i, y_i) in a data set modelled by the linear function $f(x)$ is given by
  residual of $x_i = y_i - f(x_i)$.

- For a set of n data points $\{(x_i, y_i)\}$ and approximating linear function $f(x)$,
  $$SS_{res} = \sum_{i=1}^{n} \left(y_i - f(x_i) \right)^2.$$

- The line that minimizes the sum of square residuals, that is, the line that has the smallest possible SS_{res}, is called the **least squares regression line** or **linear regression equation.** If the vertical (y) residuals are minimised the regression line is said to be "y on x". This line is used for predicting y-values from given x-values.

Continued on next page

TOK

When students see a familiar equation with a transformation, they will often get a "gut feeling" about what the function looks like.

Respond to this question:

"Is intuition helpful or harmful in mathematics?"

- In examinations and most applications, it is sufficient (and more efficient) to calculate the linear regression equation $f(x) = mx + c$ using technology. However, it is possible to calculate the parameters using for a given data set $\{(x_i, y_i)\}$ using the formulas:

$$m = \frac{\sum(x_i - \bar{x})(y_i - \bar{y})}{\sum(x_i - x)^2}, \quad c = \bar{y} - m\bar{x}$$

Recall that $\bar{x}$ represents the mean or average of the data set $\{x_i\}$.

You can now calculate the linear regression equation and use it to predict y-values from known x-values, as the following example shows.

Example 20

At a coach station, the maximum temperature in °C (x) and the number of bottles of water sold (y) were recorded over 10 consecutive days. The collected data are summarized in the table.

Day	1	2	3	4	5	6	7	8	9	10
x	20	19	21	21.3	20.7	20.5	21	19.3	18.5	18
y	140	130	140	145	143	145	145	125	120	123

a Use a graph of the data to justify why a linear regression is appropriate.

b Find the regression line of y on x.

c Interpret the gradient and y-intercept of the regression equation in context.

d Use the regression equation to predict the number of bottles that will be sold at a temperature of 19.5°C.

a Because the data is approximately linear, linear regression is appropriate.

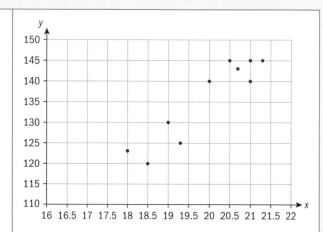

b $y = 8.05x - 24.7$

The GDC shows the general form of the equation as $y = ax + b$ with $a = 8.05$ (3 s.f.) and $b = -24.7$ (3 s.f.).

c The gradient of 8.05 indicates that an increase of 1°C corresponds to an increase of about 8 bottles sold.

The y-intercept is outside the range of the data set and is negative, so it does not have meaning in the context.

d 132

Substitute $x = 19.5$ in the regression equation, and solve either with technology or algebraically:

$y = 8.05(19.5) - 24.7 = 132.2$

Exercise 4P

1 The travel time in minutes (x) and the price in euros (y) of ten different train journeys between various places in Spain are shown in the table.

x	128	150	102	140	140	98	75	130	80	132
y	25.95	40	24.85	31.8	30.2	28.95	21.85	34.5	23.25	26

a Plot the data points on a scatter diagram. Use your diagram to justify why a linear regression is appropriate.

b Write down the equation of the regression line of y on x.

c Predict the price of a train journey of 2 hours.

d Comment on whether the regression equation be more reliable in predicting the price for a journey of 10 minutes or 100 minutes. Justify your answer.

2 The heights in metres (x) and weights in kilograms (y) of ten male gorillas are shown in the table.

x	1.9	1.83	1.81	1.79	1.74	1.91	1.93	1.86	1.81	1.95
y	275	267	260	257	258	272	273	268	261	273

a Plot the data points on a scatter diagram. Use your diagram to justify why a linear regression is appropriate.

b Write down the equation of the least squares regression line for this data.

c Predict the weight of a gorilla that is 1.8 m tall.

d Interpret the meaning of the gradient in context.

3 Two potential lines of fit for the data set shown in the table are $f_1(x) = -0.861x + 8.11$ and $f_2(x) = -0.913x + 8.30$. One of these is the linear regression equation.

x	1.2	6.5	3.7
y	7.4	2.8	4.3

a Match each equation to its graph, with reasons.

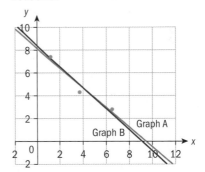

b Calculate the sum of square residuals for each equation and hence determine which is the linear regression equation.

Validity of predictions

In previous investigations, and in Chapter 2, you found that you cannot always make valid predictions from a linear regression. In the next investigations, you will explore the conditions under which more valid predictions can be made.

International-mindedness

In 1956, Australian statistician, Oliver Lancaster made the first convincing case for a link between exposure to sunlight and skin cancer using statistical tools including correlation and regression.

Investigation 14

In Chapter 2 you learned how to calculate Pearson's correlation coefficient to measure the strength and direction of a linear correlation. The four sets of data in the table are known as Anscombe's Quartet after their inventor, statistician Francis Anscombe.

I		II		III		IV	
x	y	x	y	x	y	x	y
10.0	8.04	10.0	9.14	10.0	7.46	8.0	6.58
8.0	6.95	8.0	8.14	8.0	6.77	8.0	5.76
13.0	7.58	13.0	8.74	13.0	12.74	8.0	7.71
9.0	8.81	9.0	8.77	9.0	7.11	8.0	8.84
11.0	8.33	11.0	9.26	11.0	7.81	8.0	8.47
14.0	9.96	14.0	8.10	14.0	8.84	8.0	7.04
6.0	7.24	6.0	6.13	6.0	6.08	8.0	5.25
4.0	4.26	4.0	3.10	4.0	5.39	19.0	12.50
12.0	10.84	12.0	9.13	12.0	8.15	8.0	5.56
7.0	4.82	7.0	7.26	7.0	6.42	8.0	7.91
5.0	5.68	5.0	4.74	5.0	5.73	8.0	6.89

1   Find the correlation coefficient of each data set. What does this suggest about the strength of the correlation?

2   Graph each data set using technology.

3   What additional information do the graphs give you that the correlation coefficient did not? What does this tell you about relying solely on the correlation coefficient to measure the appropriateness of a linear regression?

4   For each data set, decide whether it is appropriate to model it with a linear regression, giving reasons.

5   **Conceptual** How does the graph help us to decide whether a linear regression and Pearson's correlation coefficient are appropriate to model a data set?

International-mindedness

Karl Pearson (1857–1936) was an English lawyer and mathematician. His contributions to statistics include the product-moment correlation coefficient and the chi-squared test.

He founded the world's first university statistics department at the University College of London in 1911

Investigation 15

A random sample of 12 students is taken to see if there is any linear relationship between height (in cm) and shoe size or height and age (in years). The data is shown in the table.

Height (cm)	160	187	175	180	186	170	185	172	174	180	165	170
Shoe size	37	42	39	38	40	38	41	39	38	40	37	39
Age (years)	13.7	16.2	16.5	15.8	15.5	14.3	15.2	13.8	14.3	14.7	14.4	15.3

1   Plot shoe size and age against height on two scatter diagrams. Is a linear regression appropriate for each?

2   Calculate Pearson's correlation coefficient for both data sets. Which correlation is stronger?

3 a Find the regression equation for each pair of variables.

  b For a student who is 163 cm tall, use your regression equations to predict

  i the shoe size of that student   **ii** the age of the student.

  c Which prediction do you think is more accurate, and why?

4 ⟨Conceptual⟩ How does the strength of Pearson's correlation coefficient of a data set impact the accuracy of predictions made from its linear regression?

We'll focus now only on the shoe size regression.

5 So far you have only predicted values of y. Can you also predict values of x? You will explore this in what follows.

  a Use the regression equation of y on x (or S on h) to predict the height of a student with shoe size 38.

  b Now create the regression of x on y (or h on S) by switching the independent and dependent variables and re-running the regression. Compare its correlation coefficient to that of the y on x regression.

  c Use the regression of x on y to predict the height of a student with shoe size 38. Compare with your prediction from part **a**. What do you notice?

  d Can you think of a reason why predictions of shoe size from height would be more accurate than predictions of height from shoe size?

6 Why can the regression of y on x not always be used to reliably predict x from a given y?

7 ⟨Conceptual⟩ Summarise: When is it appropriate to use a linear regression for prediction?

> Predictions from linear regression are more accurate when the correlation coefficient is stronger. At least a moderate correlation and linear relationship should be established before making predictions from a linear regression.

TOK

What is the difference between correlation and causation?

To what extent do these different processes affect the validity of the knowledge obtained?

Exercise 4Q

1 Kiernan wonders whether there is a correlation between how sunny a city is and how happy its inhabitants are. Suppose that each of the graphs below represent the data he collects. For each data set, state one or more reasons why the prediction made may not be valid.

a

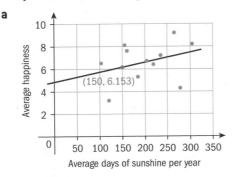

$r = 0.319$

Prediction: A city with 150 days of sunshine per year will have an average happiness of 6.15.

b

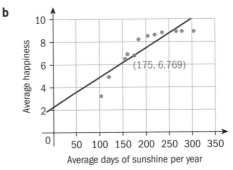

$r = 0.880$

Prediction: A city with 175 days of sunshine per year will have an average happiness of 6.80.

c

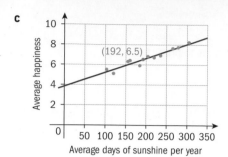

$r = 0.955$

Prediction: A city with an average happiness of 6.5 will have 192 sunny days.

d

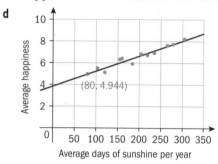

$r = 0.955$

Prediction: A city with 80 days of sunshine per year will have an average happiness of 4.94.

2 The rate at which crickets chirp can be used to predict the temperature. In the table, data has been collected on the number of chirps in a 15-second period and the surrounding temperature in degrees Fahrenheit.

Chirps	44	35	20.4	33	31	35	18.5	37	26
Temperature (°F)	80.5	70.5	57	66	68	72	52	73.5	53

a Determine whether the data follow a linear trend.

b Find the correlation coefficient and interpret its meaning.

c Based on the above, explain whether it is appropriate to model and make predictions about this data with a linear regression.

d **i** Find the regression equation of the temperature T on the number of chirps c.

   ii If the temperature is 75°F, predict the number of chirps or explain why it is not valid to do so.

   iii You count 40 chirps a minute. Predict the temperature and explain whether your prediction is valid.

e The *Old Farmer's Almanac* suggests the following rule for predicting temperature from chirps: count the number of chirps in 14 seconds, then add 40. Explain how consistent your regression equation is with this rule.

3 Lee is interested in the cryptocurrency Bitcoin. He knows that computer graphics cards can be used to "mine" Bitcoins and wonders whether there is a relationship between the value of a Bitcoin and the current price of a graphics card. He collects the data shown in the table on different days between August and December 2017.

Bitcoin value ($)	4204	3686	4394	5697	7118	7279	10859	17601	13412	16178	13585	10035
Graphics card price ($)	690	660	680	650	550	650	750	1500	1000	1300	1250	1200

a Determine whether the data follows a linear trend.

b Find the correlation coefficient and interpret its meaning.

c Based on the above, explain whether it is appropriate to model and make predictions about this data with a linear regression.

d **i** Find the regression equation of graphics card price G on Bitcoin value b.

   ii On December 8th the value of a Bitcoin was $12320. Predict the price of a graphics card on this day.

e Interpret the gradient of the regression equation in the context of Bitcoin value and graphics card price.

Chapter summary

- A **function** is a relation between two sets in which every element of the first set is mapped onto **one and only one** element of the second set.

- The **domain** of a function is the set of all input values. The **reasonable domain** of a function modelling a real-world context is the set of input values that are relevant in that context.

- A **linear function** $f(x) = mx + c$, where m and c are constants, represents a context with a **constant rate of change**. It has a **gradient parameter** (m) and a y-**intercept parameter** (c).

- A linear model with formula $y = mx$ relates two variables, x and y, that are in **direct variation** (proportion).

- A **piecewise function** is a function that is defined by a different formula on each piece of is domain.

- You use the notation $f^{-1}(x)$ to denote the **inverse function** of $f(x)$. If $f(a) = b$, then $f^{-1}(b) = a$.

- The graphs of inverse functions are symmetric about the **identity line** $y = x$. The equation of an inverse function can be found by exchanging x and y in the equation for the function.

- You call the inputting of one function into another a **composition of functions**, and denote it $f \circ g(x)$ or $f(g(x))$. Here the function g is performed first and its result input into f.

- By definition, two functions are inverses if their composition is the **identity function** $i(x) = x$: $f \circ f^{-1}(x) = f^{-1} \circ f(x) = x$.

- A sequence in which the **difference** between consecutive terms remains constant is called an **arithmetic sequence**. This constant value is called **common difference** of the sequence.

- The general term (or n**th term**) of an arithmetic sequence with first term u_1 and common difference d is $u_n = u_1 + (n-1)d$, where $n \in \mathbb{Z}^+$.

- The total amount of **simple interest** I earned on a principal P over n years at an interest rate of $r\%$ per year can be calculated using the formula $I = P \times r \times n$. The total savings account balance A is given by $A = P + P \times r \times n$.

- The sum, S_n, of the first n terms of an arithmetic sequence $u_1, u_2, u_3, \ldots$ can be calculated using the formula $S_n = \dfrac{n}{2}(2u_1 + (n-1)d)$. The sum of a sequence is a **series**.

- The **sum of square residuals** for a set of n data points $\{(x_i, y_i)\}$ and approximating linear function $f(x)$ is given by $SS_{res} = \sum_{i=1}^{n}(y_i - f(x_i))^2$.

- The linear function $f(x) = mx + c$ that minimises SS_{res} for a given data set is the **least squares regression line** or the **linear regression equation**. It is calculated using technology in examinations.

- Predictions from a linear regression are only appropriate when the data displays a clear linear trend in its scatter plot, the correlation coefficient r is at least moderate, and you predict values of the dependent variable. Predictions are more valid when using **interpolation** to predict within the data set, rather than **extrapolation** that predicts for values outside the data set.

Developing inquiry skills

Has what you have learned in this chapter helped you to answer the questions from the beginning of the chapter about the taxi driver's income?

How could you apply your knowledge to investigate other business charging structures? What information would you need to find?

Thinking about the inquiry questions from the beginning of this chapter:

- Discuss if what you have learned in this chapter has helped you to think about an answer to these questions.

- Consider whether there are any that you are interested in and would like to explore further, perhaps for your internal assessment topic.

Chapter review

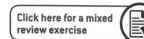
Click here for a mixed review exercise

1 Takumi is supervising the cleanup of an oil spill. The surface area A of ocean remaining to be cleaned (in m²) is a function of the time t worked (in hours), modelled by the equation $A(t) = 1350 - 2.7t$.

  a Find the time it will take to clean the spill.

  b Find a reasonable domain and range for this model.

  c Sketch a graph of $A(t)$ for this domain.

  d Find $A(5)$ and interpret its meaning in context.

2 For each of the following relations, determine whether it is a function, and if so, whether it is a one-to-one function.

  a

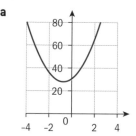

  b $3x - 5y = 30$

  c x = volume of a cylinder, y = radius of the cylinder

3 Damir is researching a potential link between family size and life expectancy in Asian and Middle Eastern countries. He collects the data shown in the table.

Country	Life expectancy (years)	Babies per woman	Country	Life expectancy (years)	Babies per woman
Japan	84.2	1.48	Jordan	76.7	3.24
China	76.9	1.64	Tajikistan	72.2	3.27
Vietnam	74.9	1.95	Pakistan	68	3.35
Myanmar	70.3	2.17	Papua New Guinea	61.1	3.56
Indonesia	72	2.31	Yemen	67.1	3.79
Saudi Arabia	77.6	2.45	Australia	82.9	1.83
Kazakhstan	72	2.57	Turkmenistan	70.5	2.79
Philippines	70.5	2.86	Nepal	71.5	2.05

Source: Gapminder (http://bit.ly/2Kax5Z6)

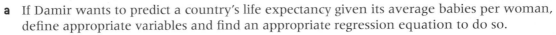

a If Damir wants to predict a country's life expectancy given its average babies per woman, define appropriate variables and find an appropriate regression equation to do so.

b Write down two reasons why it is valid to make predictions from this regression line.

c Predict the life expectancy of Malaysia, which has an average of 2 babies per woman. Explain whether your prediction is valid.

d Interpret the gradient of the regression line in context.

4 The two graphs show the relationship between the distance an aircraft travels (in kilometres), the time it takes to fly that distance (in hours) and the fuel used (in litres).

Graph 1

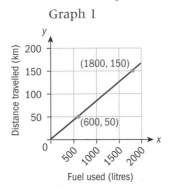

Graph 2

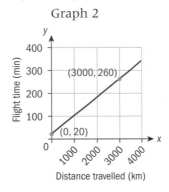

a Write down which graph represents direct variation, with a reason.

b Find and interpret the gradient of each graph in context.

c Find an equation for the travel time T of the aircraft as a function of litres used, x, and use it to predict how long a flight will be that uses 150 000 litres of fuel.

5 Tiffany is working part-time while she attends college. She is saving money each month for a car costing $6500, as well as $3000 in her savings account for unexpected expenses. As of this month, she has $400 saved and is saving $150 per month.

a At this rate, determine how many more months it will take Tiffany to save for her goal.

Tiffany decides that she will increase her savings by a fixed amount of k each month (starting from $150) so that she can reach her savings goal within one year.

b Find the smallest value of k (rounded to the nearest dollar) so that Tiffany can achieve her goal.

c If Tiffany continues to increase her monthly savings at this rate and spends none of it, determine after how many more months she will have at least $20 000 saved.

6 Lydia lives in Amsterdam and is budgeting for three upcoming weekend trips. For each, she can either fly or drive. The car rental company is offering a special deal of €49 for a weekend plus €0.06 per kilometre driven.

a Write a linear function of the rental car's cost €C as a function of distance travelled, d (km).

b Lydia prefers flying to driving, but she will only pay up to €50 more to fly than to drive. Given the information in the table, determine

i whether she should fly or drive for each trip, with reasons

ii how much she should budget for all three trips.

Destination	One-way distance from Amsterdam (km)	Cost of round-trip flight (€)
Brussels	210	130
Hamburg	470	150
Paris	515	240

7 Nadia remembers that the balance of her savings account, which pays simple interest, was 8% greater 5 years after she first invested it, and that she had €3200 more in 2018 than in 2013. Determine Nadia's initial investment and interest rate.

8 Several countries use a progressive tax system in which additional income is taxed at a higher marginal rate. The table shows Canada's marginal tax rates in 2018.

Income	Marginal tax rate
First CA$46 605	15.0%
Over CA$46 605 up to CA$93 208	20.5%
Over CA$93 208 up to CA$144 489	26.0%
Over CA$144 489 up to CA$205 842	29.0%
Over CA$205 842	33.0%

Source: https://www.taxtips.ca/taxrates/canada.htm

For example, a person earning CA$50 000 will be taxed at 15% on the first CA$46 605 and 20.5% on the remaining CA$3395.

a Ian made CA$122 000 this year. Find how much he will pay in taxes.

b Construct a piecewise function and corresponding reasonable domain to model the tax owed, T, as a function of total income earned, x.

c Ian wins a major prize for excellence in neuroscience and has two options: one payment of CA$40 000, or two equal payments of CA$20 000 over two years.

   i Determine the amount of tax he will pay over these two years in each scenario, assuming his other earnings remain the same.

   ii Based on this, state the better option if Ian wishes to minimise his tax payment.

9 **a** Find the inverse of the following piecewise function. State its domain and range.

$$f(x) = \begin{cases} 5 - \dfrac{1}{3}x & -6 \le x \le 3 \\ -2x + 10 & x > 3 \end{cases}$$

b Show that the function

$$f(x) = \begin{cases} 5 - \dfrac{1}{3}x & -6 \le x \le 3 \\ 2x - 2 & x > 3 \end{cases}$$

is not invertible.

Exam-style questions

10 **P1:** Paired, bivariate data (x, y) that is strongly correlated has a y on x line of best fit given by $y = mx + c$.

The data represents students' test scores in Geography, x, and test scores in Environmental Systems, y.

When $x = 70$ an estimate for y is 100. When $x = 100$ an estimate for y is 140.

a Find the value of

   i m **ii** c (3 marks)

b State whether the correlation is positive or negative.   (1 mark)

c Given that the value of $\bar{x}$ is 90, find the value of $\bar{y}$.   (3 marks)

d When $x = 60$ find an estimate for the value of y.   (2 marks)

11 **P1:** The price of renting a car (£C) from "Cars-R-Us" for d days is given by the formula $C = 30 + 12.5d$.

The price of renting a car (£C) from "Car-nage" for d days is given by the formula $C = 70 + 8.35d$.

Abel wishes to rent a car for the duration of his holiday.

He decides to rent from "Car-nage" as it will be cheaper for him.

a What is the minimum length of Abel's holiday?   (3 marks)

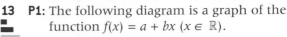

b If Abel's holiday is between 14 and 21 days, find an inequality which shows the range in which Abel's car hire bill will lie. (4 marks)

12 P2: Paired bivariate data (x, y) is given in the table below.

The data represents the heights (x metres) and lengths (y metres) of a rare type of animal found on a small island.

x	2.4	3.6	2.8	1.8	2.0	2.2	3.0	3.4
y	3.0	4.0	3.0	1.7	2.0	2.3	3.1	2.7

  a **i** Calculate the Pearson product moment correlation coefficient for this data.

    ii In two words, describe the linear correlation that is exhibited by this data.

    iii Calculate the y on x line of best fit. (6 marks)

Another four examples of this rare animal are found on a nearby smaller island.

This extra data is given in the table below.

x	2.3	2.7	3.0	3.5
y	4.1	1.5	4.2	1.5

  b **i** Calculate the Pearson product moment correlation coefficient for the combined data of all 12 animals.

    ii In two words, describe the linear correlation that is exhibited by the combined data.

    iii Suggest a reason why it may not be valid to calculate the y on x line of best fit for the combined data. (5 marks)

13 P1: The following diagram is a graph of the function $f(x) = a + bx$ ($x \in \mathbb{R}$).

  a Determine the value of a and the value of b. (2 marks)

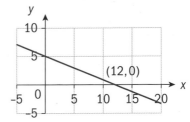

  b Find an expression for $f^{-1}(x)$. (4 marks)

  c Solve the equation $f(x) = f^{-1}(x)$, giving your answer in an exact form. (3 marks)

  d Explain why, for any function $h(x)$, the equation $h(x) = h^{-1}(x)$ will have the same solution(s) as the equation $h(x) = x$. (1 mark)

14 P1: The first four terms of an arithmetic sequence are given by 7, $3a + b$, $5a - 6b$, $2a + 9b + 4$.

  a Find the value of a and the value of b. (5 marks)

  b Find the least number of terms required so that the sum of the series exceeds 1000. (5 marks)

15 P2: Functions f and g are given such that $f(x) = x - 24$ ($x \in \mathbb{R}$) and $gf(x) = 2x^2 + 18$ ($x \in \mathbb{R}$).

  a State the range of $f(x)$. (1 mark)

  b State the range of $gf(x)$. (1 mark)

  c Solve the equation $fgf(x) = 0$. (3 marks)

  d Determine the function $g(x)$. (6 marks)

Functions

Graphs of functions: describing the "what" and researching the "why"

Approaches to learning: Thinking skills, Communicating, Research

Exploration criteria: Presentation (A), Mathematical communication (B), Personal engagement (C)

IB topic: Graphs, Functions, Domain

Bulgaria population data

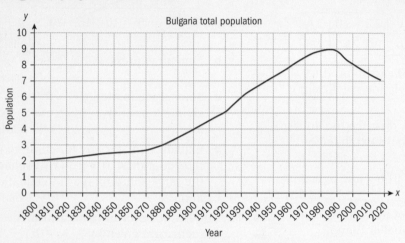

This graph includes two essential elements:

- A title.
- *x*- and *y*-axes labels with units.

Using sources

You can use your general knowledge, printed sources and Internet sources to research data. Different sources can often give different explanations, and not all sources are valid, useful or accurate.

How do you know if a source is reliable?

Use Internet research to find out more precisely what happened at the key dates shown on the Bulgaria population graph.

Keep a record of any sources that you use.

Could you use the graph to predict what might happen to the population of Bulgaria in the future? Explain your answer.

> Without any research, write a paragraph to describe this graph.
>
> Do not just describe the graph, but also explain why it might have this shape. Include any interesting points and regions on the graph "where things happen".

Worldwide Wii console sales

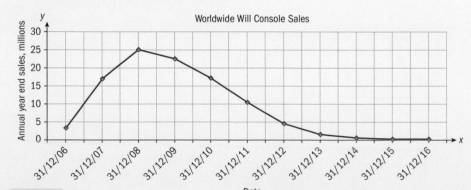

Initially **without research** write a paragraph about this graph, then research the reasons for the shape of this graph.

Global mean temperature anomaly

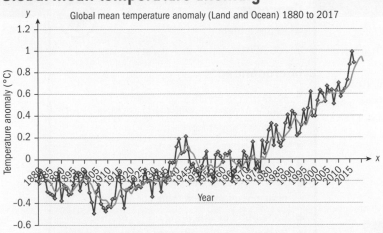

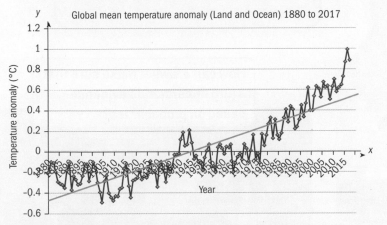

What is the domain?

When is the graph rising (increasing)?

When is the graph falling (decreasing)?

What is the shape of the graph?

Describe and explain.

Research what is meant by Global Mean Temperature Anomaly.

This data is based on deviations from the base average for 1951 to 1980.

On the graph in red the 5-year moving average trend line is included. What is a 5-year moving average?

On the second graph is a linear trend line. What is a linear trend line?

What are the advantages and disadvantages of each of the representations of the data shown?

Describe the data, note any interesting points or trends and to try to explain and investigate why the trends may be as they are.

TOK

This is a potentially controversial topic with many opinions and theories. How can you protect against your own biases?

Extension

Find and research a graph from the news or an academic journal from one of your subjects or another source.

Describe and explain the trends and the reason for the shape of the graph.

Now display or print out the graph.

Write a series of questions for other students to answer that encourage them to describe and explain the graph.

5 Quantifying uncertainty: probability

Probability enables us to quantify the likelihood of events occurring and evaluate risk. This chapter looks at the language of probability, how to quantify probability and the basic tools you need to solve problems involving probability.

Concepts
- Representation
- Quantity

Microconcepts
- Uncertainty and random behaviour
- Trial, outcome, equally likely outcomes and relative frequency
- Sample space and event
- Theoretical probability
- Venn diagrams, tree diagrams, sample space diagrams and tables of outcome
- Compound events
- Exclusive, independent and dependent events

How can a geneticist quantify the chance that a child may inherit the same colour of eyes as his father?

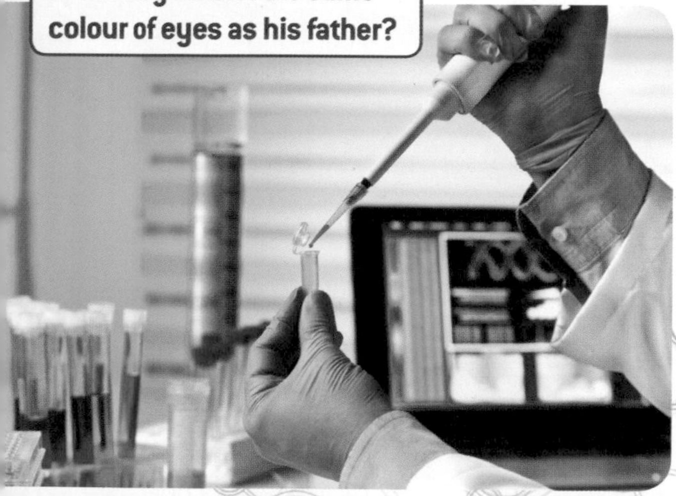

How can a lawyer make sure that a jury understands evidence based on probabilities?

"37% chance of rain tomorrow." How can you reach a common agreement on how to interpret and apply statements like this?

Daniel Kahneman (Nobel Prize winner in economic science) and Amos Tversky (cognitive and mathematical psychologist) spent decades collaborating and researching together. Below is an adaptation of one of the questions they set to students:

Two taxi companies operate in Mathcity: Blackcabs and Yellowrides.

85% of the cabs in the city work for Blackcabs and are coloured black.

The rest of the cabs in the city work for Yellowrides and are coloured yellow.

A taxi was involved in a hit and run accident at night. A witness told police that the taxi involved was yellow. The court carried out a series of tests on the reliability of the witness, asking her to identify the colour of a random sequence of taxis. The witness correctly identified each one of the two colours 80% of the time and failed 20% of the time.

1 What is the probability that the taxi involved in the accident was yellow?

2 Karolina carries out a traffic survey in Mathcity. She sits at an interchange and notes the colour of the first six cabs that pass her. What number of yellow cabs is she most likely to observe?

- What types of diagram can help represent the problem?

- What assumptions did you make?

Developing inquiry skills

Write down any similar inquiry questions you might ask if you were asked to predict the reliability of the witness if 50% of the cars in the city were Yellowrides or if another taxi company Blue Taxis also operated in Mathcity.

What questions might you need to ask in these scenarios?

Think about the questions in this opening problem and answer any you can. As you work through the chapter, you will gain mathematical knowledge and skills that will help you to answer them all.

Before you start

Click here for help with this skills check

You should know how to:

1 Find simple probabilities.

eg A number is chosen at random from the set of natural numbers {1, 2, 3, …, 100}.

Find the probability of choosing a cube number.

The cube numbers in the set are 1, 8, 27 and 64. Probability of a cube number

$$= \frac{4}{100} = 0.04$$

Skills check

1 A number is chosen at random from the set {1, 2, 4, 5, 9, 10, 11, 16, 17, 25, 26, 27}

Find the probability that the number is:

a prime　b odd　c a square number.

2 A student collects this data:

	Smoker	Non-smoker
Male	12	47
Female	6	51

A person is chosen at random from the survey. Find the probability that they are:

a female　b a male smoker

c a non-smoker.

5.1 Reflecting on experiences in the world of chance. First steps in the quantification of probabilities

Probability is synonymous with uncertainty, likelihood, chance and possibility. You can quantify probability through three main approaches: subjective, experimental and theoretical.

You may judge that you are more likely to get to school on time if you take a particular route, based on your experience with traffic. Subjective probabilities are based on past experiences and opinions rather than formal calculations.

TOK

Do you rely on intuition to help you make decisions?

Investigation 1

We use subjective probability in everyday life every time we make a judgement of how likely something is to occur. For example, you may judge that you are more likely to get to school on time if you take a particular route, based on your experience with traffic. We justify subjective probabilities to ourselves through a mixture of past experiences, opinions and intuition.

How likely do you judge these outcomes to be?

A: There will be a financial crisis in Europe during the next 10 years.	B: It will rain tomorrow.	C: There will be a financial crisis in Asia during the next 10 years.
D: Choosing one digit at random from the decimal expansion of $\frac{1}{6}$, you get 6.	E: The world will be free of all dictators within the next 10 years.	F: The sequence 999999 is found somewhere in the first 1000 digits of pi.
G: The team winning the FIFA World Cup in 2030 will be from the Americas.	H: Humans will land on Mars by 2050.	I: If you cut a strip of paper into three lengths at random, they can form a triangle.

Display your answers by plotting them on this probability scale:

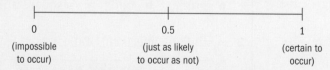

0	0.5	1
(impossible to occur)	(just as likely to occur as not)	(certain to occur)

Compare, contrast, discuss and **justify** your answers within a small group.

You may find disagreements with others, based on your opinions, experience or beliefs.

When is it easier to reach a common agreement on the value of a subjective probability?

Experimental probability

You should use these terms when discussing and quantifying probabilities:

> **Experiment:** A process by which you obtain an observation.
>
> **Trials:** Repeating an experiment a number of times.
>
> **Outcome:** A possible result of an experiment.
>
> **Event:** An outcome or set of outcomes.
>
> **Sample space:** The set of all possible outcomes of an experiment, always denoted by U.

These terms are illustrated in the following example:

Erin wants to explore the probability of throwing a prime number with an octahedral die. She designs an **experiment** that she feels is efficient and bias-free. Erin places the die in a cup, shakes it, turns the cup upside down, then reads and records the number thrown.

Erin repeats her experiment until she has completed 50 **trials**. She knows that the **outcome** of each trial can be any number from $U = \{1, 2, 3, 4, 5, 6, 7, 8\}$ and that the **event** she is exploring can be described as a statement: "throw a prime with an octahedral die" or a set of outcomes that make the statement true: $\{2, 3, 5, 7\}$.

Erin can either write **P(throw a prime)** to represent the probability of her event occurring or **P(A)** if A denotes the set $\{2, 3, 5, 7\}$.

Statistics and probability

> **HINT**
>
> A crucial assumption in many problems is that of **equally likely outcomes**.
>
> A consequence of the geometry of the shapes shown here is that they form *fair dice*. Each outcome on a fair die is equally likely as any other.

One way to quantify probability is with relative frequency, also known as experimental probability. The general formula for the relative frequency of an event A after n trials is:

$$\text{Relative frequency of } A = \frac{\text{Frequency of occurrence of event } A \text{ in } n \text{ trials}}{n}$$

This is also known as the experimental probability of the event A.

Theoretical probability gives you a way to quantify probability that does not require carrying out a large number of trials.

The formula for the theoretical probability $P(A)$ of an event A is:

$P(A) = \dfrac{n(A)}{n(U)}$ where $n(A)$ is the number of outcomes that make A happen

and $n(U)$ is the number of outcomes in the sample space.

Whenever $P(A)$ represents a subjective, experimental or theoretical probability, then $0 \leq P(A) \leq 1$.

Investigation 2

1 Imagine throwing a fair 12-sided die 15 times. Let A be the event "throw a prime number".

2 Use technology to show the sequence of experimental probabilities of A after 1, 2, 3, …, 100 throws. You should be able to create a graph like one of these:

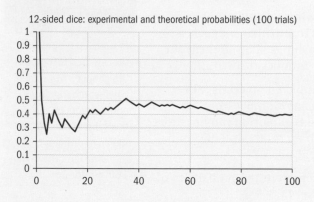

12-sided dice: experimental and theoretical probabilities (100 trials)

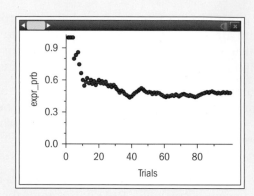

Number of trial (n)	Outcome	Event	Frequency of occurrence in n trials	Relative frequency in n trials
1	2	Prime	1	1
2	11	Prime	2	1
3	5	Prime	3	1
4	9	Not prime	3	0.75
5	4	Not prime	3	0.6
6	2	Prime	4	0.666667
7	4	Not prime	4	0.571429
8	8	Not prime	4	0.5
9	2	Prime	5	0.555556
10	12	Not prime	5	0.5
11	6	Not prime	5	0.454545
12	1	Not prime	5	0.416667
12	1	Not prime	5	0.416667
14	3	Prime	6	0.428571
15	11	Prime	7	0.466667

3 Show that for this experiment, $P(A) = \dfrac{5}{12} \approx 0.417$. Add a horizontal line with equation $y = 0.417$ to your graph. Press F9 (spreadsheet) or Ctrl+R (TiNspire) to carry out another 100 trials.

4 Repeat until you have seen each of these three scenarios:
 • The experimental probability is always greater than the theoretical probability.
 • The experimental probability is always less than the theoretical probability.
 • The experimental probability is often equal to the theoretical probability.

You may wish to adapt your spreadsheet so that it carries out 1000 trials. Examine the columns in your spreadsheet and the features on your graph.

5 **Factual** What is the set of *all* possible values of theoretical probabilities?

6 What relationship does your graph have with the line $y = \dfrac{5}{12}$?

7 **Factual** What is the relationship between relative frequency and theoretical probability in the short term?

8 **Factual** What is the relationship between relative frequency and theoretical probability in the long term?

9 **Conceptual** In the short term, does random behaviour involve predictability or unpredictability?

10 **Conceptual** In the long term, does random behaviour involve predictability or unpredictability?

11 **Conceptual** How may we interpret and apply the number quantified by the formula for the theoretical probability of an event?

Example 1

Find the probability of each event and determine which event is least likely.

 T: throw a factor of 24 on a four-sided die.

 O: throw a prime on an eight-sided die.

 D: throw at least 11 on a 12-sided die.

 C: throw at most 3 on a three-sided die.

 I: throw a multiple of 5 on a 20-sided die.

All the dice are fair and are numbered from 1 up to the number of sides on the die.

$n(T) = n(\{1, 2, 3, 4\}) = 4 = n(U)$ so $P(T) = 1$	Every element of $\{1, 2, 3, 4\}$ is a factor of 24. $P(T) = \dfrac{n(T)}{n(U)} = \dfrac{4}{4} = 1$, so T is certain to happen.
$n(O) = n(\{2, 3, 5, 7\}) = 4$, $n(U) = 8$ so $P(O) = \dfrac{4}{8} = 0.5$	
$n(D) = n(\{11, 12\}) = 2$, $n(U) = 12$	"at least 11" means "11 or more"

Continued on next page

so $P(D) = \dfrac{2}{12} = \dfrac{1}{6} = 0.1\dot{6}$

$n(C) = n(\{1, 2, 3\}) = 3$, $n(U) = 6$

so $P(C) = \dfrac{3}{6} = 0.5$

$n(I) = n(\{5, 10, 15, 20\}) = 4$, $n(I) = 20$

so $P(I) = \dfrac{4}{20} = 0.25$

Hence, D is the least likely event.

| "at most 3" means "3 or less" |

Just as theoretical probability gives you a way to predict long-term behaviour of relative frequency, a simple rearrangement gives you a way to predict how many times an event is likely to occur in a given number of trials.

Example 2

a A fair coin is flipped 14 times. Predict the average number of times you expect a head to be face up.

b Statistical data built up over 5 years shows that the probability of a student being absent at a school is 0.05. There are 531 students in the school.

    Predict the number of students that you expect to be absent on any given day and interpret your answer.

c State the assumptions supporting your answer for part **b**.

a $14 \times 0.5 = 7$. Seven heads are expected.	The expected number of occurrences is $n\,P(A)$.
b $531 \times 0.05 = 26.55$. So, around 26 or 27 students are expected to be absent.	Note that 26.55 students cannot actually be absent.
c This assumes that absences on all days of the year are equally likely.	

Exercise 5A

1 A letter is picked at random from the letters of RANDOM. Calculate the probability that it is a letter from MATHS.

2 This dartboard has 20 sectors each of equal area.

If a dart lands in a numbered sector at random, find the probability that the number is:

a at least 4   **b** more than 6

c less than 30   **d** no more than 14

e prime   **f** square

g a solution to the equation $x^2 = 3$.

3 A survey was carried out in a small city centre street one Saturday afternoon. Shoppers were asked about how they travelled that day. The results are shown in the table below.

Mode of transport	Car	Bus	Foot
Male	40	59	37
Female	33	41	29

One shopper is randomly selected.

a Find the probability that this shopper travelled by car.

One male shopper is randomly selected.

b Find the probability that this male shopper travelled by foot.

c 1300 shoppers visit the town in one week. Estimate the number of shoppers who travelled by bus.

4 A personal identification number (PIN) consists of four digits. Consider the PIN 0005 equal to the number 5, etc. Find the probability that a PIN number is:

a equal to 0000

b less than 8000 and more than 7900

c divisible by 10

d at least 13.

5 Take a narrow strip of paper 20 cm long. Use your calculator to generate a random decimal length between 0 and 20 and cut the strip into two strips at this length. Label the two strips H and T. Toss a coin. If the coin shows heads choose strip H. Measure its length and use your calculator to find a place to cut it at random into two strips.

Can you make a triangle with your three pieces?

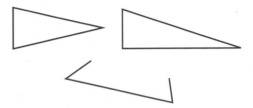

Make a guess on the probability scale as to how likely it is that a triangle can be formed following this process. Use your classmates' results to quantify the experimental probability.

6 A health professional is investigating the theoretical probability that a randomly chosen female smokes is 0.17. She organizes a survey and asks 11 278 females if they smoke or not. Using her theoretical probability, determine the number of females she would predict to be smokers.

7 A multiple-choice test consists of 10 questions. Each question has five answers. Only one of the answers is correct. For each question, Jose randomly chooses one of the five answers. Predict the expected number of questions Jose answers correctly.

Developing inquiry skills

There are four outcomes in the first opening scenario:

- A taxi is yellow and is identified as yellow.
- A taxi is yellow and is identified as black.
- A taxi is black and is identified as yellow.
- A taxi is black and is identified as black.

Are these equally likely outcomes?

In 1000 trials, how many occurrences of each outcome would you expect?

5.2 Representing combined probabilities with diagrams

You have taken the first steps in the quantification of probabilities, experienced random experiments and investigated how to make predictions in the world of chance by application of formulae.

Probability situations themselves have a structure that you can represent in different ways, for example in problems where two or more sets are combined in some way.

Investigation 3

1   For each situation, think about how best to represent the situation with a diagram.

Compare and contrast your diagrams with others in your class **then** solve the problems.

Situation 1

In a class survey on subject choices, Isabel, Clara, Coco, Anastasiia and Fangyu all state that they study biology. Isabel, Clara, Fangyu and Tomas all study chemistry whereas Barbora, Coco and Achille study neither biology nor chemistry.

2   Find the probability that a student chosen randomly from this class studies both biology and chemistry.

3   Create your own probability question using your representation of the situation and have another student answer it.

4   **Situation 2**

One example of a Sicherman die is a fair cubical die with this net:

It is thrown together with a fair octahedral die whose faces are numbered 1, 2, 3, 4, 5, 6, 7 and 8.

	6		
8	4	1	5
	3		

5   Find the probability that the number obtained by adding the two numbers thrown on each die is prime.

6   Find and describe a pattern in your representation of this situation and acquire some knowledge from your pattern.

7   **Conceptual**   What advantages are there in using a diagram in problem-solving with combined probabilities?

Two frequently used representations of probability problems are Venn diagrams and sample space diagrams.

A **Venn diagram** represents the sample space with a rectangle. Within the rectangle, each event is represented by a set of outcomes in a circle or an oval shape and is labelled accordingly.

A **sample space diagram** is a useful way to represent the whole sample space and often takes the form of a table.

International-mindedness

A well-known French gambler, Chevalier de Méré, consulted Blaise Pascal in Paris in 1650 with questions about some games of chance. Pascal began to correspond with his friend Pierre de Fermat about these problems, which began their study of probability.

Example 3

In a class survey, Rikardo, Malena, Daniel, Maria, India and James reported that they study environmental systems and societies *(ESS)*. India, Pietro, Mathea and Haneen said that they study geography *(G)*. Rikardo and James were the only ones who reported that they studied Spanish *(S)* whereas Sofia and Yulia studied none of the subjects mentioned in the survey. Draw the data in a Venn diagram.

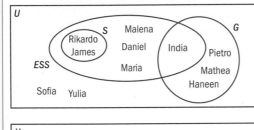

Each set is represented by a italic capital letter.

U represents the entire sample space. In set terminology, this is called the universal set.

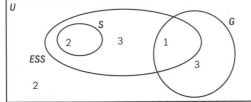

This diagram can be simplified to show the number of students in each region.

Example 4

Use the Venn diagram in Example 3 to find the probabilities that a student chosen randomly from this class:

a studies ESS

b studies ESS but not Spanish

c studies all three subjects

d studies exactly two of the subjects.

a $P(ESS) = \dfrac{n(ESS)}{n(U)} = \dfrac{2+3+1}{11} = \dfrac{6}{11}$

P(ESS) represents the "Probability of choosing a student at random from the set *ESS*".

b $\dfrac{4}{11}$

There are a total of four students within the *ESS* oval but outside the Spanish oval.

c 0

The diagram clearly shows that there are no students who study all three subjects.

d $\dfrac{3}{11}$

The diagram clearly shows that two students Rikardo and James study Spanish and ESS, whereas one student India – studies both geography and ESS. These are the only three students who study exactly two of the subjects surveyed.

Example 5

It is claimed that when this pair of Sicherman dice is thrown and the two numbers obtained added together, the probability of each total is just the same as if the two dice were numbered with 1, 2, 3, 4, 5 and 6. Verify this claim.

	2				6	
4	2	1	3	8 4	1	5
	3				3	

Sample space diagram for the total of two die numbered 1, 2, 3, 4, 5 and 6:	Form a sample space diagram for each experiment. Enter each total in the table as shown.

	1	**2**	**3**	**4**	**5**	**6**
1	2	3	4	5	6	7
2	3	4	5	6	7	8
3	4	5	6	7	8	9
4	5	6	7	8	9	10
5	6	7	8	9	10	11
6	7	8	9	10	11	12

Sample space diagram for the two Sicherman dice:

	1	**2**	**2**	**3**	**3**	**4**
1	2	3	3	4	4	5
3	4	5	5	6	6	7
4	5	6	6	7	7	8
5	6	7	7	8	8	9
6	7	8	8	9	9	10
8	9	10	10	11	11	12

In both tables, $P(T = 2) = P(T = 12) = \dfrac{1}{36}$

$P(T = 3) = P(T = 11) = \dfrac{2}{36} = \dfrac{1}{18}$

$P(T = 4) = P(T = 10) = \dfrac{3}{36} = \dfrac{1}{12}$

$P(T = 5) = P(T = 9) = \dfrac{4}{36} = \dfrac{1}{9}$

$P(T = 6) = P(T = 8) = \dfrac{5}{36}$

and $P(T = 7) = \dfrac{6}{36} = \dfrac{1}{6}$

The probability of each total is the same for each pair of dice, so the claim is true.

Then find the probability of each outcome in the sample space, representing the total as T.

State your conclusion.

Once time has been invested in drawing a diagram, it can be used to quantify many different probabilities.

TOK

Do ethics play a role in the use of mathematics?

Exercise 5B

1 Alex throws a fair tetrahedral (four-sided) dice and a fair octahedral (eight-sided) dice. He defines M as the product of his two numbers. Find:

  a P(M is odd)   **b** P(M is prime)

  c P(M is both odd and prime)

Bethany has two fair six-sided dice, which she throws. She defines N as the product of her numbers. Find:

  d P(N is odd)   **e** P(N is more than 13)

  f P(N is a factor of 36)

Bethany and Alex can see that the probability that M is odd equals the probability that N is odd. Try to find more events that have the same probabilities for each of their experiments. Find at least one such event.

2 A survey of 127 consumers found that 81 had a tablet computer, 70 had a smartphone and 29 had both a smartphone and a tablet computer.

  a Find the number of consumers surveyed who had neither a smartphone nor a tablet.

  b Find the probability that when choosing one of the consumers surveyed at random, a consumer who has only a smartphone is chosen.

  c In a population of 10 000 consumers, predict how many would have only a tablet computer.

3 In a class of 20 students, 12 study biology, 15 study history and 2 students study neither biology nor history.

  a Find the probability that a student selected at random from this class studies both biology and history.

  b Given that a randomly selected student studies biology, find the probability that this student also studies history.

4 These dice compete in the "Dice World Cup". A pair of dice is thrown and the highest number wins. The semi-finals are A vs B and C vs D. The winners of each semi-final go in to the final.

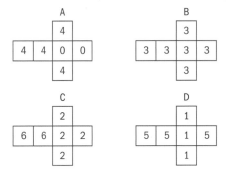

Construct sample space diagrams to find the probabilities of the outcomes of each semi-final.

5 The dice in the previous question are called non-transitive dice. Show that A is likely to beat B, that B is likely to beat C and that C is likely to beat A. You may wish to explore the meaning of the term *transitive* and try to design your own non-transitive dice.

6 Two cubical dice are rolled in a game. The score is the greater of the two numbers. If the same number appears on both dice, then the score is that number. Find the probability that the score is at most 4.

Developing inquiry skills

In the first opening scenario, imagine 100 trials. How many outcomes would you expect in each area shown on this diagram?

		Cab yellow?	
		Yes	No
Witness correct?	Yes	??	??
	No	??	??

5.3 Representing combined probabilities with diagrams and formulae

In Section 5.2, you found probabilities by representing combined events in a sample space diagram or a Venn diagram. There are other ways to find probabilities of combined events, which can add to your problem-solving skills.

In this section, you will use Venn diagrams to investigate and represent laws of probability and you will use these symbols, language and definitions:

Name	Symbol applied to events	Informal language	Formal definition
Intersection	$A \cap B$	A and B	Events A and B **both** occur
Union	$A \cup B$	A or B	Events A **or** B **or both** occur
Complement	A'	Not A	Event A **does not** occur
Conditional	$A|B$	A given B	Event A **given that** event B **has** occurred

Example 6

A student is chosen at random from this class. If E is the event "the student takes ESS" and G is the event "the student takes geography", then find these probabilities and interpret what they mean:

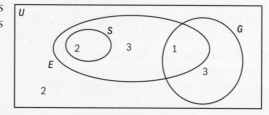

a $P(E \cap G)$ and $P(G \cap E)$ **b** $P(E \cup G)$ and $P(G \cup E)$

c $P(E')$

d $P(E|G)$ and $P(G|E)$

---

a $P(E \cap G) = P(G \cap E) = \dfrac{1}{11}$ is the probability that a randomly chosen student studies **both** ESS and geography.

Only one student takes both ESS and geography. This example illustrates that $E \cap G$ means exactly the same as $G \cap E$. In fact this is always true.

b $P(E \cup G) = \dfrac{2+3+1+3}{11} = \dfrac{9}{11}$ is the probability that a randomly chosen student studies ESS **or** geography **or both**.

Similarly, $E \cup G$ means the same as $G \cup E$ hence $P(E \cup G) = P(G \cup E)$ is always true.

c $P(E') = \dfrac{5}{11}$ is the probability that a randomly chosen student **does not** study ESS

There are 5 students outside the ESS oval. $P(E') = 1 - \dfrac{6}{11} = \dfrac{5}{11}$ is another way to find the probability required.

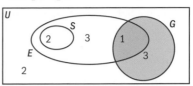

d $P(E\,|\,G) = \dfrac{1}{1+3} = \dfrac{1}{4}$, the probability that a randomly chosen student studies ESS **given** that he/she studies geography.

However, $P(G\,|\,E) = \dfrac{1}{2+3+1} = \dfrac{1}{6}$.

These are not equal since the information **given** changes the sample space. This example shows that $P(E|G) = P(G|E)$ is not generally true.

Since it is **given** that G has occurred, the sample space is now G, not U.

Only 1 student studies ESS and geography, hence $P(E\,|\,G) = \dfrac{1}{4}$. Notice how this contrasts with $P(E) = \dfrac{6}{11}$.

International-mindedness

The Dutch scientist Christiaan Huygens, a teacher of Leibniz, published the first book on probability in 1657.

Just as areas of mathematics like trigonometry or sequences have formulae, so does probability. In this investigation, you will consider some relationships that you can generalize as laws of probability.

Investigation 4

The following Venn diagrams represent how many students study art or biology in four different classes, using the sets A and B.

Fill in the probabilities for each Venn diagram and investigate your answers.

Venn Diagram	1	2	3	4	5	6	7	8	9	10
	$P(A)$	$P(A')$	$P(B)$	$P(A\cap B)$	$P(A\cup B)$	$P(A|B)$	$P(A)+P(B)$	$P(A)\times P(B)$	$P(A)+P(B)$ $-P(A\cap B)$	$\dfrac{P(A\cap B)}{P(B)}$
Class of 2019										
Class of 2018										
Class of 2017										
Class of 2016										

Continued on next page

Statistics and probability

➡ Examine your results.

Answer these questions and discuss your answers in a group.

1   What relationship exists between the probabilities in columns 1 and 2?

2   This relationship is true in general. Why?

3   What relationship exists between the probabilities in columns 5 and 9?

4   This relationship is true in general. Why?

5   What relationship exists between the probabilities in columns 6 and 10?

6   **Factual** Which Venn diagram shows "mutually exclusive events", ie ones that cannot occur together?

7   **Factual** Which Venn diagram shows "independent events", ie events for which the outcome of one is unaffected by the outcome of the other?

8   **Conceptual** What is the difference between mutually exclusive and independent events? Can mutually exclusive events be independent? Why or why not?

For events A and B, the following laws apply:

- $P(A \cup B) = P(A) + P(A) - P(A \cap B)$

- $P(A|B) = \dfrac{P(A \cap B)}{P(B)}$

- This can be rearranged to give the multiplicative law of probabilities:
  $P(A \cap B) = P(A|B)P(B)$.

Two events A and B are **mutually exclusive** if they cannot **both** occur. Hence:

- Knowing that A has occurred means you know that B cannot, and that knowing that B occurs means you know that A cannot.

- $P(A \cap B) = P(B \cap A) = 0$

- $P(A \cup B) = P(A) + P(B)$

Two events A and B are **independent** if the occurrence of each event does **not affect in any way** the occurrence of the other. Hence:

- Knowing that A has occurred does not affect the probability that B does, and knowing that B occurs does not affect that probability that A does.

- $P(A|B) = P(A)$ and $P(B|A) = P(B)$

- $P(A \cap B) = P(A) \times P(B)$

- If A and B are not independent, they are **dependent**.

If events A and A' are **complementary** then A' is the set of outcomes that are not in the event A:

- A and A' are mutually exclusive.

- $P(A) + P(A') = 1$.

Reflect Are complementary events independent events?

Are complementary events mutually exclusive?

Can mutually exclusive events be independent?

Can non-mutually exclusive events be independent?

You can use the laws of probability to justify other statements.

Example 7

Marcelo is playing in a cricket match and a game of hockey at the weekend.

The probability that his team will win the cricket match is 0.2, and the probability of winning the hockey match is 0.6. Assume that the results in the matches are independent.

a Find the probability that Marcelo's team wins both matches.

b Find the probability that Marcelo's team wins the cricket match or the hockey match.

c Determine if winning the cricket match and winning the hockey match are mutually exclusive. Justify your answer.

a $P(C \cap H) = 0.2 \times 0.6 = 0.12$	Let C be the event "wins the cricket match" and H be "wins the hockey match". Since you are given that C and H are independent, you can use $P(C \cap H) = P(C) \times P(H)$.
b $P(C \cup H) = 0.2 + 0.6 - 0.12 = 0.68$	Apply the formula.
c C and H are not mutually exclusive because $P(C \cap H) \neq 0$.	Write a complete and clear reason.

Example 8

Let H and G be events such that $P(H) = \frac{1}{3}$, $P(G) = \frac{3}{7}$ and $P(H \cup G) = \frac{13}{21}$.

Find $P(H \cap G)$ and $P(H|G)$ and hence, determine if H and G are independent.

$P(H \cup G) = P(H) + P(G) - P(H \cap G)$ So $\frac{13}{21} = \frac{1}{3} + \frac{3}{7} - P(H \cap G)$, hence $P(H \cap G) = \frac{1}{7}$	Write down the appropriate formula.
$P(H\|G) = \dfrac{P(H \cap G)}{P(G)} = \dfrac{\frac{1}{7}}{\frac{3}{7}} = \dfrac{1}{3}$	Write down the appropriate formula.
Since $P(H\|G) = P(H)$, H and G are independent.	Write a complete and clear reason.

Statistics and probability

Exercise 5C

1 For these pairs of events, state if they are mutually exclusive, independent or neither.

a A = throw a head on a fair coin
B = throw a prime number on a fair die numbered 1, 2, 3, 4, 5, 6.

b C = it rains tomorrow, D = it rains today

c D = throw a prime number on a fair die numbered 1, 2, 3, 4, 5, 6, E = throw an even number on the same die.

d F = throw a prime number on a fair die numbered 1, 2, 3, 4, 5, 6, G = throw an even number on another die.

e G = choose a number at random from {1, 2, 3, 4, 5, 6, 7, 8, 9, 10} that is at most 6, H = choose a number from the same set that is at least 7.

f M = choose a number at random from {1, 2, 3, 4, 5, 6, 7, 8, 9, 10} that is no more than 5, H = choose a number from the same set that is 4 or more.

g S = choose a Spanish speaker at random from a set of students represented by this set, T = choose a Turkish speaker at random from this set.

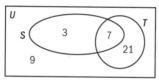

2 Use a Venn diagram to confirm that

a $A = (A \cap B) \cup (A \cap B')$ and that $(A \cap B)$ and $(A \cap B')$ are mutually exclusive events.

b $P(A) = P((A \cap B) \cup (A \cap B'))$

c $P(A) = P(A)\, P(B) + P(A \cap B')$

d Hence, $P(A \cap B') = P(A)(1 - P(B))$ so A and B' are independent.

3 Daniel throws a fair dice numbered with {1, 2, 3, 4, 5, 6} five times.

a Write down the probability that Daniel throws the sequence

  i 4, 1, 3, 5, 2   **ii** 1, 1, 1, 1, 1

  iii 6, 5, 4, 3, 2

b Find the probability that he throws at least one 3.

c Daniel simulates this experiment with a spreadsheet. Predict how many times in 10 000 trials he would expect to throw the sequence 1, 1, 1, 1, 1.

d Find the probability that he throws a Yahtzee (all five numbers are equal).

e After how many throws would he expect to have thrown 3 Yahtzees?

4 Events G and H are such that $P(G) = 0.3$ and $P(H) = 0.6$.

a Find $P(G \cup H)$ when G and H are mutually exclusive;

b Find $P(G \cup H)$ when G and H are independent.

c Given that $P(G \cup H) = 0.63$, find $P(H \mid G)$.

5 Achille and Barbora throw a fair octahedral die until one of them throws an eight.

a Find the probability Barbara wins on one of her first two throws, if she throws first.

b Investigate if throwing first gives Barbora an advantage in this game.

6 $P(A) = 0.35$, $P(A \cup B) = 0.75$ and $P(A|B) = 0.35$. Find $P(B)$.

Developing inquiry skills

Which of the events in the first opening scenario are independent? Which are mutually exclusive?

5.4 Complete, concise and consistent representations

You can use diagrams as a rich source of information when solving problems. Choosing the correct way to represent a problem is a skill worth developing. For example, consider the following problem:

In a class of 15 students, 3 study art and 6 study biology of which 1 studies art. A student is chosen at random. How many simple probabilities can you find? How many combined probabilities can you find?

Let A represent the event "An art student is chosen at random from this group" and B "A biology student is chosen at random from this group".

> **HINT**
>
> If you represent the problem only as **text**, the simple probabilities $P(A) = \dfrac{1}{5}$
>
> and $P(B) = \dfrac{2}{5}$ can be found easily, but calculating these do not show you the
>
> whole picture of how the sets relate to each other.

Represent this information as follows in a **Venn diagram** to see more detail:

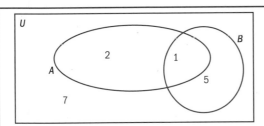	The rectangle represents the sample space U for which $P(U) = 1$, the total probability. The diagram allows us to find $P(B\|A) = \dfrac{1}{3}$, $P(B'\|A) = \dfrac{2}{3}$ etc easily.
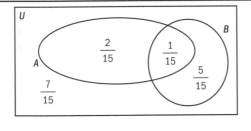	The Venn diagram can be adapted to show the distribution of the total probability in **four** regions that represent mutually exclusive events: $P(A \cap B) = \dfrac{1}{15}$, $P(A' \cap B) = \dfrac{5}{15}$, $P(A \cap B') = \dfrac{2}{15}$ and $P(A' \cap B') = \dfrac{7}{15}$.

Hence, the probability that a randomly chosen student studies neither biology nor art is $P(A' \cap B') = \dfrac{7}{15}$. The simple probability

$P(B) = P(A \cap B) + P(A' \cap B) = \dfrac{1}{15} + \dfrac{1}{3} = \dfrac{2}{5}$ is represented as a union of two mutually exclusive events in the Venn diagram.

The Venn diagram can be used to find all the simple, combined and conditional probabilities.

A tree diagram representation of this problem is as follows:

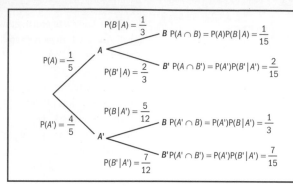

	The total probability of 1 is distributed along the branches of the tree using the multiplication law of probability.
	The probability at the end of a branch is found by applying the multiplication law of probability. For example, $$P(A \cap B) = P(A)P(B|A) = \frac{1}{5} \times \frac{1}{3} = \frac{1}{15}.$$

Notice that the simple probability $P(B) = P(A \cap B) + P(A' \cap B) = \frac{1}{15} + \frac{1}{3} = \frac{2}{5}$

can be found from summing the probabilities at the end of two branches of the tree diagram.

> A tree diagram is another way to represent all the possible outcomes of an event. The end of each branch represents a combined event.

Choosing an appropriate diagram to represent a probability problem is an important stage in the problem-solving process.

Investigation 5

Maria considers an experiment in which a bag contains n_1 dice of colour c_1 and n_2 dice of colour c_2. Two dice are chosen with replacement.

Maria works out the probability of choosing two dice of different colour in two ways after drawing a tree diagram.

Method one: $P(\text{two dice have different colours}) = \dfrac{n_1}{n_1 + n_2} \times \dfrac{n_2}{n_1 + n_2} + \dfrac{n_2}{n_1 + n_2} \times \dfrac{n_1}{n_1 + n_2}$

Method two: $P(\text{two dice have different colours}) = 1 - P(\text{two dice have same colour}) =$

$$1 - \left(\dfrac{n_1}{n_1 + n_2} \times \dfrac{n_1}{n_1 + n_2} + \dfrac{n_2}{n_1 + n_2} \times \dfrac{n_2}{n_1 + n_2} \right)$$

Maria reflects on the methods and decides that there is not a significant difference in terms of efficiency because in the first method she finds and adds two probabilities whereas in the second she finds two probabilities and subtracts their sum from 1 using complementary events.

Maria explores the same situation and methods but for n_1, n_2 and n_3 dice with distinct colours c_1, c_2 and c_3, respectively.

1 How many probabilities would be found and added using method one? A tree diagram may be useful to count the number of ways.

2 How many probabilities would be found, added and their total subtracted from 1 using method two?

⮕ Repeat for n_1, n_2, n_3 and n_4 dice with distinct colours c_1, c_2, c_3 and c_4, respectively.

3 **Factual** Hence, fill in the table:

Number of dice	How many probabilities would be found and added from the tree diagram representation	How many probabilities would be found, added and their total subtracted from 1 using a complementary events representation.
2	2	2
3		
4		
5		
k		

4 **Factual** Can you generalize for $n_1, n_2, \ldots, n_k$ dice with distinct colours $c_1, c_2, \ldots, c_k$?

5 **Conceptual** Why is it useful to calculate probabilities for the complementary event in some situations?

The complementary probability law $P(A) = 1 - P(A')$ may be more efficient in some situations.

Exercise 5D

1 A bag contains 12 green socks, 8 yellow socks and 7 red socks. Two socks are drawn at random without replacement. Find the probability that the two socks have the same colour.

2 A jewellery box contains 13 gold earrings, 10 silver earrings and 12 titanium earrings. Two earrings are drawn at random with replacement. Find the probability that they are made of different metals.

3 A supermarket uses two suppliers of strawberries, C and D. Supplier C provides 70% of the supermarket's strawberries. The strawberries are examined in a quality control inspection (QCI). It is found that 90% of the strawberries supplied by C pass QCI and 95% of the strawberries from D pass QCI.

A strawberry is selected at random.

a Find the probability that the strawberry passes QCI.

b Given that a strawberry passes QCI, find the probability that it came from supplier D.

c In a sample of 2000 strawberries, find the expected number of strawberries that would fail QCI.

d The supermarket wants the probability that a strawberry passes QCI to be 0.93. Find the percentage of strawberries that should be supplied by D to achieve this.

4 Chevy plays a game in which she throws a pair of fair cubical dice numbered {1, 2, 3, 4, 5, 6} 24 times. Find the probability that she throws at least one double six.

Statistics and probability

5   A factory produces a large number of electric cars. A car is chosen at random from the production line as a prize in a competition. The probability that the car is blue is 0.5. The probability that the car has five doors is 0.3. The probability that the car is blue or has five doors is 0.6. Find the probability that the car chosen is not a blue car with five doors.

Pietro solves this problem with a Venn diagram but Maria solves it with a tree diagram. They both get the correct answer. Solve the problem both ways, discuss and then state who used the most efficient method.

6   **a**   In a five-a-side football match, there are 10 players on the pitch plus the referee. Find the probability that they all have different birthdays. (Assume all birthdays are equally likely.)

      b   Find the smallest number of people needed on the football pitch so that the probability of at least two of them sharing a birthday is greater than 0.5.

Chapter summary

Three perspectives on probability:

- Subjective probability is derived from an individual's personal judgment about whether a specific outcome is likely to occur.

- For experimental and theoretical probability, you use the following terminology:

  - Experiment: A process by which you obtain an observation
  - Trials: Repeating an experiment a number of times
  - Outcome: A possible result of an experiment
  - Event: An outcome or set of outcomes
  - Sample space: The set of all possible outcomes of an experiment, always denoted by U

- We write $P(A)$ to represent the probability of event A occurring.

- Experimental probability is given by

  $$\text{Relative frequency of } A = \frac{\text{Frequency of occurrence of event } A \text{ in } n \text{ trials}}{n}$$

- The theoretical probability of an event A is $P(A) = \dfrac{n(A)}{n(U)}$ where $n(A)$ is the number of outcomes that make A happen and $n(U)$ is the number of outcomes in the sample space.

- Whenever $P(A)$ represents a subjective, experimental or theoretical probability, then $0 \leq P(A) \leq 1$.
- The expected number of occurrences of $A = nP(A)$.

Three probability diagrams:

- A Venn diagram represents the sample space with a rectangle. Within the rectangle, each event is represented by a set of outcomes in a circle or an oval shape and is labelled accordingly.

- A sample space diagram is a useful way to represent the whole sample space and often takes the form of a table. It is especially useful when the situation involves combining two sets in some way to form a sample space.

- A tree diagram is a useful way to represent two or more combined events, often involving choices and conditional probabilities.

- Notation used to represent probabilities of combined events:

Name	Symbol applied to events	Meaning
Intersection	$A \cap B$	Events A and B both occur
Union	$A \cup B$	Events A or B or both occur
Complement	A'	Event A does not occur
Conditional	$A|B$	Event A given that event B has occurred

Probability laws which are always true:

$$P(A \cup B) = P(A) + P(B) - P(A \cap B)$$

$$P(A|B) = \frac{P(A \cap B)}{P(B)}$$

$$P(A) + P(A') = 1$$

Types of combined events and the special cases of probability laws that follow:

Type of event	Consequences
Events A and B are mutually exclusive if they cannot both occur.	$P(A \cap B) = P(B \cap A) = 0$ $P(A \cup B) = P(A) + P(B)$
Events A and B are independent if the occurrence of each event does not affect in any way the occurrence of the other.	$P(A|B) = P(A)$ $P(B|A) = P(B)$ $P(A \cap B) = P(B \cap A) =$ $P(A)P(B)$
The events A and A' are complementary. Hence, A and A' are mutually exclusive.	$P(A) + P(A') = 1$

- The complementary probability law $P(A) = 1 - P(A')$ can give you a quick way to solve problems.

Developing inquiry skills

Apply what you have learned in this section to represent the first opening problem with a tree diagram.

Hence, find the probability that a cab is **identified** as yellow.

Apply the formula for conditional probability to find the probability that the cab was yellow **given that** it was identified as yellow.

How does your answer compare to your original subjective judgement?

Chapter review

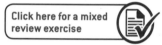

Click here for a mixed review exercise

1 B and C are independent events. $P(B \cap C) = 0.1$ and $P(B \cap C') = 0.4$. Find $P(B' \cup C)$.

2 $P(X) = \dfrac{2}{3}$, $P(X|Y') = \dfrac{7}{12}$, $P(X|Y) = 0.8$

   a   Find $P(Y)$.

   b   Determine if X and Y are independent events.

3   **a**   Find the probability of the outcome "throw at least one six" when a fair cubical die is thrown 1, 2, 3, 4, 5, ..., n times.

   b   Hence, find the least value of n for which P(throw at least one six in n throws) is 99.5%

4   A packet of seeds contains 65% green and 35% red seeds. The probability that a green seed grows is 0.85 and that a red seed grows is 0.74. A seed is chosen at random from the packet.

   a   Calculate the probability that the seed grows.

   b   Calculate the probability that the seed is green and grows.

   c   Calculate the probability that the seed is red or it grows.

5   Each **odd** number from 1 to $5n$ where n is odd is written on a piece of paper and placed in a box.

   a   Calculate how many pieces of paper there are in the box.

   b   Find the probability in terms of n that a paper selected at random from the box shows a number that is divisible by 5.

6   A company fleet has six blue and n white cars. Two cars are chosen without replacement. The probability that two blue cars are chosen is $\dfrac{1}{7}$. Find the value of n.

7   The genes in human chromosome pairs determine if a child is male or female. Males have an X and Y chromosome pair and females an X and X pair. Inheriting the XY combination causes male characteristics to develop and XX causes female characteristics to develop. Sperm contain an X or Y with equal probability and an egg always contains only an X. An infant inherits one chromosome determining gender from each parent.

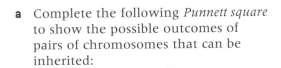

a Complete the following *Punnett square* to show the possible outcomes of pairs of chromosomes that can be inherited:

		Chromosome inherited from mother	
		X	**X**
Chromosome inherited from father	X	X**X**	
	Y	**X**Y	

b Hence, show that the probability that a child is born female is 0.5.

Exam-style questions

8 **P1:** A box contains 16 chocolates, of which 3 are known to contain nuts.

Two chocolates are selected at random.

Find the probability that

a exactly one chocolate contains nuts (3 marks)

b at least one chocolate contains nuts. (3 marks)

9 **P2:** Hamid must drive through three sets of traffic lights in order to reach his place of work. The probability that the first set of lights is green is 0.7.

The probability that the second set of lights is green is 0.4.

The probability that the third set of lights is green is 0.8.

It may be assumed that the probability of any set of lights being green is independent of the others.

a Find the probability that all three sets of lights are green. (2 marks)

b Find the probability that only one set of lights is green. (3 marks)

c Given that the first set of lights is red (ie not green), find the probability that the following two pairs of lights will be green. (2 marks)

d Find the probability that at least one set of lights will be green (3 marks)

10 **P1:** Jake and Elisa are given the same mathematics problem.

The probability that Jake can solve it is 0.35.

If Jake has solved it, the probability that Elisa can solve it is 0.6, otherwise it is 0.45.

a Draw a tree diagram to illustrate the above situation, showing clearly the probabilities on each branch. (3 marks)

b Find the probability that at least one of the students can solve the problem. (2 marks)

c Find the probability that Jake solves the problem, given than Elisa has. (4 marks)

11 **P1:** A and B are events such that $P(A) = 0.3$, $P(B) = 0.65$ and $P(A \cup B) = 0.7$

By drawing a Venn diagram to illustrate these probabilities, find:

a $P(A' \cap B)$ (2 marks)

b $P(A \cup B')$ (2 marks)

c $P(A \cap B)'$ (2 marks)

12 **P1:** In a survey, 48 people were asked about their holidays over the past year. It was found that 32 people had taken a holiday in Europe, and 25 people had taken a holiday in the USA.

Everyone surveyed had been to at least Europe or the USA.

a Determine how many people had taken a holiday in both Europe and the USA. (2 marks)

b Find the probability that a randomly selected person had been to Europe, but not the USA. (3 marks)

c Explain why the events "taking a holiday in Europe" and "taking a holiday in the USA" are not independent events. (3 marks)

13 P2: The Venn diagram illustrates the number of students taking each of the three sciences: Physics, Chemistry and Biology.

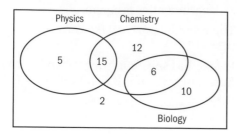

A student is randomly chosen from the group.

Find the probability that

a the student studies Chemistry or Biology (2 marks)

b the student studies neither Physics nor Biology (2 marks)

c the student studies Physics, given that they study Chemistry (2 marks)

d the student studies Biology, given that they study Physics (2 marks)

e the student studies Physics, given that they do not study Biology. (2 marks)

14 P1: A and B are independent events, such that $P(A) = 0.3$ and $P(B) = 0.5$.

Find the following probabilities.

a $P(A \cap B)$ (2 marks)

b $P(A \cup B)$ (2 marks)

c $P(B' \cap A)$ (2 marks)

d $P(B|A')$ (3 marks)

15 P2: The Venn diagram below shows the probabilities for three events A, B and C.

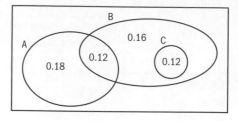

a Justify that events B and C are not independent. (2 marks)

b Explain why events A and C are mutually exclusive. (2 marks)

c Determine whether events A and B are independent. (4 marks)

d Determine whether events A' and C' are mutually exclusive. (2 marks)

e Find $P(A \cap C')$. (2 marks)

16 P2: At a local sports centre, members can either play tennis or squash.

The probability that a member plays tennis is 0.8.

Given that a member plays squash, the probability that they play tennis is 0.8.

The probability that a member does not play squash is 0.1.

The information is illustrated by the following Venn diagram, where a, b, c and d are probabilities:

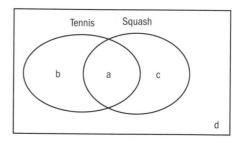

a Find the value of *a* and the value of *c*. (5 marks)

b Find the value of *b* and the value of *d*. (3 marks)

c Find the probability that a randomly chosen member plays only one sport. (2 marks)

d Find the probability that a randomly chosen member plays tennis given that they do not play squash. (2 marks)

e Find the probability that a randomly chosen member does not play squash, given that they do not play tennis. (2 marks)

f Let *S* be the event that a member plays squash, and let *T* be the event that a member plays tennis. Determine whether:

  i events *S* and *T* are mutually exclusive (1 mark)

  ii events *S* and *T* are independent. (2 marks)

Random walking!

Approaches to learning: Critical thinking

Exploration criteria: Mathematical communication (B), Personal engagement (C), Use of mathematics (E)

IB topic: Probability, Discrete distributions

The problem

A man walks down a long, straight road. With each step he either moves left or right with equal probability. He starts in the middle of the road. If he moves three steps to the left or three steps to the right, he will fall into a ditch on either side of the road. The aim is to find probabilities related to the man falling into the ditch, and in particular to **find the average number of steps he takes before inevitably falling into the ditch**.

Explore the problem

Use a counter to represent the man and a "board" to represent the scenario:

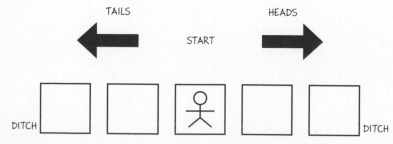

Toss a coin.

Let a tail (T) represent a left step and a head (H) represent a right step.

Write down the number of tosses/steps it takes for the man to fall into the ditch.

Do this a total of 10 times.

Calculate the average number of steps taken.

Construct a spreadsheet with the results from the whole class.

Calculate the average number of steps taken from these results.

How has this changed the result?

Do you know the actual average number of steps required?

How could you be certain what the average is?

Calculate probabilities

Construct a tree diagram that illustrates the probabilities of falling into the ditch within five steps.

Use your tree diagram to answer these questions:

What is the probability associated with each sequence in which the man falls into the ditch after a total of exactly five steps?

What is the probability that the man falls into the ditch after a total of exactly five steps?

What is the minimum number of steps to fall into the ditch?

What is the maximum number?

What is the probability that the man falls into the ditch after a total of exactly three steps?

Explain why all the paths have an odd number of steps.

Let x be the number of the steps taken to fall into the ditch.

Copy and complete this table of probabilities:

x	1	2	3	4	5	6	7	8	9	10	11	12	....
$P(X=x)$													

Look at the numbers in your table.

Can you see a pattern?

Could you predict the next few entries?

Simulation

Since there is an infinite number of values of x, calculating the expected number of steps to fall into the ditch would be very complicated.

An alternative approach is to run a computer simulation to generate more results, and to calculate an average from these results.

You can write a code in any computer language available that will run this simulation as many times as needed.

This will allow you to improve on the average calculated individually and as a class.

Although this would not be a proof, it is convincing if enough simulations are recorded.

Extension

Once you have a code written you could easily vary the problem.

What variations of the problem can you think of?

You may also be able to devise your own probability question which you could answer using simulation.

6 Modelling relationships with functions: power and polynomial functions

If for example you are trying to use mathematics to model the path of a javelin, the shape of bridge or the maximum volume of a container, you will need to study equations of curves. This chapter looks at ways of modelling real-life scenarios with curves, and fitting equations to curves in order to predict the height of the curve (which would tell you, for example, the height of the javelin below) and the distance spanned by a curve (telling you the distance the javelin travels).

Concepts
- Modelling
- Relationships

Microconcepts
- Quadratic, cubic, inverse proportional and power functions
- One-to-one and many-to-one functions
- Axis intercepts, zeros, roots, vertex and symmetry of graphs
- Increasing and decreasing functions and concavity
- Vertical and horizontal asymptotes
- Composite functions
- Inverse functions including domain restriction
- Transformations of graphs
- Modelling and regression

How can you predict where a javelin will land? How can you find out when its speed is fastest?

What is the maximum volume of a box made from a piece of card with squares cut from each corner?

How long does it take an object to fall, given that the distance varies directly with the square of the time taken?

How can you find the price of a car, given that the price varies inversely with the age of the car?

Oliver is practising his basketball skills.

- What shape is the path of the ball? Sketch a path for the ball from Oliver's hands to the basketball hoop.
- Sketch a path for the ball from Oliver's hands to the hoop when he is
  - standing further away from the hoop
  - standing closer to the hoop
  - standing on a platform
  - sitting on the floor.
- What do you notice about the shape of the ball's path when Oliver is in different positions? What changes and what is the same?

How can you model a path of a basketball from Oliver's hands to the hoop from any point on the court?

How can the model help you to predict whether the ball will go into the hoop or not?

- What information do you need to know to build this model?
- What assumptions would you need to make in your model?

Developing inquiry skills

Write down any similar inquiry questions you might ask to model the path of something in a different sport, for example determining where an archer's arrow would land, deciding whether a tennis ball would land within the baseline, or considering whether a high-jumper would clear the bar successfully.

Think about the questions in this opening problem and answer any you can. As you work through the chapter, you will gain mathematical knowledge and skills that will help you to answer them all.

Before you start

Click here for help with this skills check

You should know how to:	Skills check
1 Substitute coordinates into an equation. eg Substitute $(1, 3)$ into $y = 2x^2 + 4x + c$, in order to find the value of parameter c. $3 = 2 \times 1^2 + 4 \times 1 + c \Rightarrow c = -3$	**1** If $y = 2x^2 - 3x + c$, find the value of c at the point $(2, -1)$.
2 Solve quadratic equations using the quadratic formula. eg $2x^2 + 5x - 3 = 0$ $x_{1,2} = \dfrac{-5 \pm \sqrt{5^2 - 4 \times 2 \times (-3)}}{2 \times 2}$ $\Rightarrow x_1 = \dfrac{1}{2}, x_2 = -3$	**2** Solve the following quadratic equations using the quadratic formula: **a** $x^2 - x - 6 = 0$ **b** $3x^2 + x - 2 = 0$
3 Solve quadratic equations by factorising. eg $x^2 - 6x + 5 = 0$ $(x - 5)(x - 6) = 0$ $x = 5$ and $x = 6$	**3** Solve the following quadratic equations by factorising: **a** $x^2 + 2x - 8 = 0$ **b** $x^2 - 6x + 8 = 0$

6.1 Quadratic models

A dolphin jumps above the surface of the ocean. The path of the jump can be modelled by the function $f(x) = -0.09375x^2 + 1.875x - 3.375$, in which:

- x represents the horizontal distance, in metres, which the dolphin has travelled from the point where it left the water
- $f(x)$ represents the vertical height, in metres, of the dolphin above the surface of the water.

How can you find out how far the dolphin jumped and how high it jumped?

When a dolphin jumps out of the water, what does the path of its jump look like?

To investigate the dolphin's jump, you could use your GDC to plot a graph of the equation that is used to model the path of the jump. By finding the coordinates of certain points on the graph, you could tell how far and how high the dolphin jumped.

This section shows you how to do this.

Quadratic functions are polynomial functions where the highest power of the independent variable (x) is 2.

For example, $f(x) = ax^2 + bx + c$, $a \neq 0$ and $a, b, c \in \mathbb{R}$ is a quadratic function.

The fundamental (simplest) quadratic function is $f(x) = x^2$.

The shape of the graph of a quadratic function is called a **parabola**.

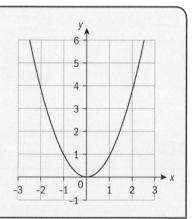

Reflect State what type of function $f(x) = ax^2 + bx + c$ would be if $a = 0$.

How are quadratic graphs different from linear graphs?

How are they the same?

The maximum or minimum turning point on the graph of a quadratic function is called the **vertex**.

The graph of a quadratic function is symmetric about a vertical line called the **axis of symmetry**, going through its **vertex**.

> **Reflect** Describe how to find the domain of a function from its graph.
>
> Describe how to find the range of a function from its graph.

TOK

We have seen the involvement of several nationalities in the development of quadratics.

To what extent do you believe that mathematics is a product of human social collaboration?

Functions

> The y-intercept is the value of $f(0)$.

Transferring a graph from screen to paper

When you "**sketch**" a graph, you do not need to be as accurate as when you have to "**draw**" a graph on graph paper, but your sketch should:

- show the general shape of the graph accurately
- label the coordinates of any axes intercepts
- label the coordinates of any vertices.

You can sketch (or draw) the graph of a quadratic function by hand with the help of your GDC. In many cases the **domain** of the function that you need to sketch or draw will be explicitly given. In such cases you should only sketch (or draw) the part of the function that is in the given domain.

Example 1

a Sketch the graph of the function $f(x) = 7 - 2x - x^2$, for $-5 \le x \le 3$, and hence determine the range.

b State the range if the domain were unrestricted.

a

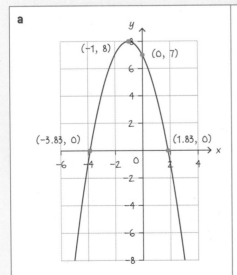

Use your GDC to sketch a graph within a given domain.

The end points, the y-intercept, the x-intercepts and the vertex (maximum) can all be obtained from the graph on your GDC. Make sure you clearly show these points on your diagram.

The range of the function is $-8 \le y \le 8$.

Continued on next page

EXAM HINT

Draw and label your axes. You must draw the shape of the graph correctly and label the points where the graph cuts the axes, as well as the vertex. Since you are asked for a sketch, you do not need to put a full scale on the axes, but you should have at least one number on each axis. In an exam the points that need to be shown on the sketch will be given in the question. These are likely to include the points where the graph cuts the axes as well as any maximum or minimum points.

b The range of the function is $y \leq 8$.	You can evaluate the function f at any real value of x, so the domain is the set of all real numbers. There is still a maximum value of the function, at $(-1, 8)$.

In a model of a real-life situation you might need to consider the domain and the range without them being explicitly given.

Example 2

Sketch the graph of the function $h(t) = -0.846t^2 + 22.2t + 478$, representing the height h, in metres above the ground, of a projectile at time t minutes after it was launched. Find the maximum height that the projectile will reach.

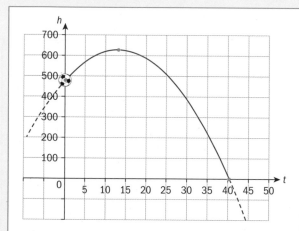 The maximum height above the ground of the projectile is $h = 624$.	You first need to decide on a reasonable domain and range in the context of the question. Here the input variable is time, so the domain cannot contain negative values, meaning that $t \geq 0$. Similarly, since the output variable is the height in metres above the ground, the range cannot contain negative values. The starting point should be at $(0, 478)$ and the ending point at approximately $(40.3, 0)$. The vertex should be placed at approximately $(13.1, 624)$. This will further restrict the domain. The resulting graph should only appear within the first quadrant.

> **HINT**
>
> When the **domain** of the function is **not explicitly given**, you might need to do some working in order to choose an appropriate view window in your GDC. The most important point of a parabola that should be in your view window is the vertex. This means that finding the vertex analytically or by using the table function in the GDC might prove to be very helpful.

Exercise 6A

1 Find the equation of the axis of symmetry of the following functions.

 a $f(x) = x^2 + x + 1$

 b $f(x) = -2x^2 + 4x - 3$

 c $f(x) = \frac{1}{2}x^2 + 4x + 5$

 d $f(x) = x^2 - 6x$

 e $f(x) = -5x^2 + 1000x - 49945$

2 Sketch the graph of the following functions, within the specified domains and hence determine their range. On your graph show clearly any intersections with the coordinate axes, the axis of symmetry and the vertex and state the range.

 a $f(x) = -x^2$, for $-3 \leq x \leq 4$

 b $f(x) = -2x^2 + 4x - 3$, for $0 \leq x \leq 2$

 c $f(x) = \frac{1}{2}x^2 - 4x + 5$, for $0 \leq x \leq 4$

 d $f(x) = \frac{1}{2}x^2 - 4x + 5$, for $0 \leq x \leq 8$

 e $f(x) = -5x^2 + 1000x - 49945$, for $95 \leq x \leq 105$

 f $P(q) = 75 - 0.000186q^2$, where P is the price at which q units of a certain good can be sold and where $q \leq 500$

3 Consider the curve defined by the equation $y = 0.4x^2 - 2x - 8$.

 a Find the coordinates where the curve crosses the x-axis.

 b Find the coordinates of the intercept with the y-axis.

 c Find the equation of the axis of symmetry of the curve.

 d Find the point of intersection of this curve with the curve given by the equation $y = -5x^3$.

4 Zander is playing a game of baseball. He hits the ball and the height of the ball is modelled by the formula $y = -0.018x^2 + 0.54x + 1.0$, where y is the height of the ball, in metres, and $x > 0$ is the horizontal distance in metres.

 a Find the maximum height that the ball reaches.

 b Find the positive value for x when the graph crosses the x-axis and explain what this value represents in context.

 c Find the y-intercept and explain what this represents in context.

5 Omar is on the school shot-put team. The path of the shot-put is modelled by a quadratic function with equation $y = 1.5 + 0.75x - 0.05x^2$, where y is the height of the shot-put in metres and $x > 0$ is the horizontal distance travelled in metres.

 a Find the maximum height that the shot-put reaches.

 b Write down the equation of the axis of symmetry.

 c Find the positive value for x when the graph crosses the x-axis and explain what this value represents in context.

 d Find the y-intercept and explain what this value represents in context.

6 Ziyue is the goalkeeper in his football team. He takes a free kick from the goal and the vertical path of the ball is modelled by the function $f(x) = -0.06x^2 + 1.2x$, where $f(x)$ is the height of the ball, in metres, and x is the horizontal distance travelled by the ball, in metres.

 a Find the maximum height that the ball reaches.

 b Write down the equation of the axis of symmetry.

 c Find the x-intercepts and explain what these values represent.

7 The vertical cross-section of a ramp in a skateboard park is modelled by the function $f(x) = 10.67 - 1.6x + 0.0417x^2$, where x is the horizontal distance in metres from the start and $f(x)$ is the vertical distance above the ground in metres. The ramp has been constructed in such a way that part of its base lies below the level of the ground around the ramp.

 a Find the minimum depth of the run.

 b Find the x-intercepts and explain what these values represent.

8 Jin throws a stone into the air. The height of the stone above the ground can be modelled by the function $f(t) = 1 + 7.25t - 1.875t^2$, where t is the time, in seconds, that has passed since the stone was thrown, and $f(t)$ is the height of the stone, in metres.

   a Find the maximum height that the stone reaches.

   b Determine how long it takes for the stone to land on the ground.

9 A bullet is fired from the top of a cliff. The path of the bullet may be modelled by the equation $y = -0.0147x^2 + 2x + 96$ $(x \geq 0)$, where x is the horizontal distance from the foot of the cliff and y is the vertical distance above the sea which meets the foot of the cliff.

   a State the height of the cliff.

   b Find the maximum height reached by the bullet.

   c Find the distance the bullet is from the foot of the cliff, when it hits the sea.

10 Consider an arithmetic sequence with first three terms 13, 9 and 5.

   a Show that the sum of the first n terms of the arithmetic sequence is given by the quadratic expression $S_n = 15n - 2n^2$, $n \in \mathbb{Z}^+$.

   b Use the table function on the GDC to plot the values of S_n for $1 \leq n \leq 8$.

   c Hence, find the maximum possible value of the sequence.

   d Determine the greatest value of n for which the sum is positive.

11 The equation of motion when throwing something vertically upwards is given by the formula $h(t) = h_0 + v_0 \times t - \frac{1}{2}g \times t^2$, where h_0 is the initial height above the ground, v_0 is the initial upward speed and g (= $9.81\,\text{m s}^{-2}$) is the acceleration due to gravity. Consider someone standing on the roof of a building 21 m tall, who throws a ball vertically upwards with an initial speed of $15\,\text{m s}^{-1}$.

   a Sketch the graph of the height of the ball against time.

   b Determine the maximum height that the ball will reach.

   c Determine how long the ball will need in order to fall to the ground.

Problems involving quadratics

Example 3

A rectangular mirror has perimeter 260 cm.

a If the length of the mirror is x cm, find the height of the mirror in terms of x.

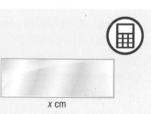

x cm

b Find an equation for the area of the mirror, $A\,\text{cm}^2$, in terms of x.

c Use your GDC to plot a graph of your equation for the area of the mirror, showing area A on the y-axis and length x on the x-axis. Choose a suitable domain and range.

d Find the coordinates of the points where the graph intersects the x-axis.

e State what these two values of x represent.

f Find the equation of the graph's line of symmetry.

g State what the equation of the line of symmetry represents in this context.

a   Let the height of the rectangle be y cm.

$$2x + 2y = 260$$
$$x + y = 130$$
$$y = 130 - x$$

Label the height y cm and form an equation in x and y for the perimeter of the rectangle.

b   Area = length × height

$$A = xy$$
$$A = x(130 - x)$$

Substitute $y = 130 - x$, which you found in part **a.**

c

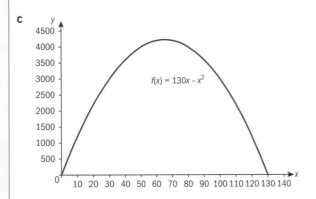

$f(x) = 130x - x^2$

Use your GDC to locate the turning point. A reasonable domain would be from 0 to 150, and range from 0 to 4500.

d   The x-intercepts are $(0,0)$ and $(130,0)$.

e   The x-coordinates 0 and 130 are the upper and lower limits between which the value of x must lie.

Use your GDC to find the zeros of the function.

f   The line of symmetry is $x = 65$

You can find the line of symmetry by finding the coordinates of the vertex on your GDC or by finding the midpoint of the two x-intercepts.

g   This is the value of x which gives the largest area of the mirror.

The axis of symmetry passes through the vertex of the graph, which is a maximum in this case.

Functions

Exercise 6B

1   A rectangular picture frame has perimeter 100 cm.

   a   The width of the frame is x cm. Find an expression, in terms of x, for the height of the frame.

   b   Find an expression for the area, A cm², in terms of x.

   c   Sketch the graph of A against x.

   d   Find the x-intercepts.

   e   Find the y-intercept.

   f   Find the equation of the axis of symmetry.

   g   Find the coordinates of the vertex.

   h   Write down the maximum area of the picture frame, and the dimensions of the picture frame that give this maximum area.

2 A rectangular picture frame has perimeter 70 cm.

   a The width of the frame is x cm. Find an expression, in terms of x, for the height of the frame.

   b Find an expression for the area of the frame, A cm², in terms of x.

   c Sketch the graph which shows how A varies with x. Use a suitable domain and range.

   d Find the x-intercepts of the graph in part **c**.

   e State what these two values of x represent.

   f Use the x-intercepts to find the equation of the graph's line of symmetry, and state what this tells you in the context of the problem.

3 A company produces and sells books.

The weekly cost, in euros, for producing x books is €$(0.1x^2 + 400)$.

The weekly income from selling x books is €$(-0.12x^2 + 30x)$.

   a Show that the weekly profit, $P(x)$, can be written as $P(x) = -0.22x^2 + 30x - 400$.

   b Sketch the graph of the profit function showing the coordinates of the vertex and axes intercepts.

   c State what the x-intercepts represent in the context of the problem.

   d Find the equation of the axis of symmetry of the graph, and state what this tells you in the context of the problem.

4 The first four terms of an arithmetic sequence are:

6 10 14 18

   a Show that the sum to n terms can be written as $2n^2 + 4n$.

   b If the sum to n terms is 880, write a quadratic equation to represent this information.

   c Find the set of values of n for which the sum to n terms is greater than 880.

5 A dolphin is jumping out of the water and its motion follows the shape of a parabola. If the dolphin reaches the maximum height at 1.3 seconds after it started jumping out of the water, determine when it will fall back in the water.

6 Marina bought 12 metres of fencing to construct a small playground for her daughter in her rectangular 10 m by 8 m backyard. She wants to decide how to place the fencing in order to construct the largest rectangular playground. Three sides of her backyard are enclosed by walls of adjacent houses and one side is connected to her house through a sliding door.

   a The first design that she wanted to analyse was that of a rectangular playground in the middle of the backyard.

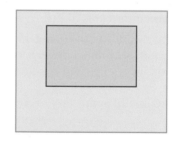

   i If the length of one side of the playground is x, find the length of the other side in terms of x.

   ii Find an expression for the area of the playground in terms of x.

   iii Using an appropriate domain for the area function, sketch its graph.

   iv Hence determine the maximum possible area that the playground can have.

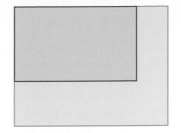

b The second design that she wanted to analyse was that of a rectangular playground with one side being the adjacent wall of her backyard.

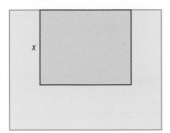

i If the length of one side of the playground is x as shown in the diagram, find the length of the other side in terms of x.

ii Find an expression for the area of the playground in terms of x.

iii Using an appropriate domain for the area function, sketch its graph.

iv Hence determine the maximum possible area that the playground can have.

i If the length of one side of the playground is x, find the length of the other side in terms of x.

ii Find an expression for the area of the playground in terms of x.

iii Using an appropriate domain for the area function, sketch its graph.

iv Hence determine the maximum possible area that the playground can have.

v State the dimensions that produce the maximum area from all the possible designs.

c A third design that she wanted to analyse was that of a rectangular playground with two sides being on the walls of one of the corners of her backyard.

Restricted domains and the inverse of a function

From chapter 4 you will recall the following facts about the inverse function f^{-1}:

- $f^{-1} \circ f(x) = f \circ f^{-1}(x) = x$.

- The graph of $y = f^{-1}(x)$ can be obtained by reflecting the graph of $y = f(x)$ in the line $y = x$.

- To find the inverse function write as $y = f(x)$, interchange x and y and rearrange to make y the subject of the expression.

This section will explore a particular requirement for inverse functions to exist.

Investigation 1

A pyrotechnician has developed a model function for the trajectory of the fireworks that he launches: $h(t) = 180 - 5(t-6)^2$. This is a function of height against time. In this way he can predict the height h of the fireworks, t seconds after launch.

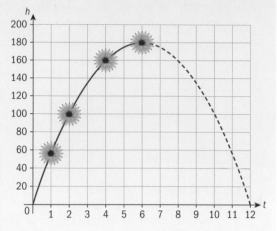

He is planning a show with a large number of fireworks. To create the most amazing spectacle, he wants the fireworks to burst at different heights so that they do not overlap, as shown on the graph. Knowing the desired height of burst of each firework, he needs to work out the corresponding time. What he has realized is that, instead of knowing the input of the function, he now knows the output and is looking for the input, which leads to a time-consuming solution of quadratic equations each time.

So, he has decided to reverse the variables of the function and make the height h the input and the time t the output. To do this he needs to make t the subject of the equation.

After reaching the maximum height, the fireworks will start falling back to the ground. This means that they will be at a certain desired height at two different times. It is required, though, that the fireworks burst while they are ascending.

1   How should the domain of the model function be restricted so that each height corresponds to a single time?

2   Rearrange the model function $h(t) = 180 - 5 (t-6)^2$ so that it becomes a function of time t with respect to height h.

3   What do you notice? How can the restricted domain from question **1** help?

The function $h(t)$ is an example of a **many-to-one** function: two (or more) different inputs map to the same output. When each output corresponds to exactly one input, we say a function is **one-to-one**. Here is an example of each function type:

One-to-one: $y = 3x - 5$ Many-to-one: $y = x^2$

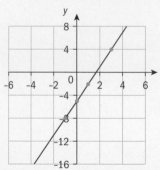   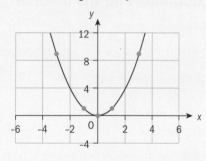

4   You can create the inverse relation of any function by reflecting it across the line $y = x$, as you did for inverse functions.

   a   Sketch the graph of the inverse relation of each of the example functions above.

   b   Use your graphs to explain why the one-to-one function's inverse relation is a function, but the many-to-one's inverse relation is **not** a function.

5   **Conceptual**   Why is a function not always invertible (invertible means that its inverse function exists), and when is it possible for a function to be invertible?

An easy way to test whether or not a function has an inverse is to use the horizontal line test. This test says, if any horizontal line cuts the curve more than once then an inverse function does not exist.

> If a function is many-to-one, we can sometimes **restrict its domain** so that it is one-to-one.

Example 4

Consider the function $f(x) = (x - 2)^2$.

a State reasons why f^{-1} does not exist if the domain of f is $x \in \mathbb{R}$.

b The domain is now restricted to $x \geq k$. Find the smallest possible value of k such that the function is invertible.

c Restricting $f(x)$ to this domain, sketch the graph of $f^{-1}(x)$.

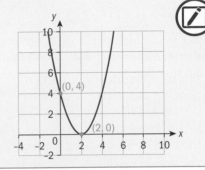

a f^{-1} does not exist because f is many-to-one. For example, $f(0) = 4$ and $f(4) = 4$.

Note that a many-to-one function will not pass the **horizontal line test**: A horizontal line can be drawn that intersects the function more than once.

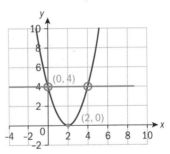

b $\{x \mid x \geq 2\}$

The function is symmetric around $x = 2$, so there are two x-values corresponding to each positive y-value. Eliminating the left "half" of the function will remove one of these x-values.

c The graph of f^{-1} is in orange.

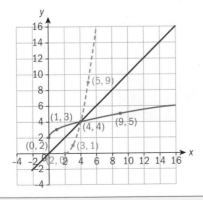

Sketch the line $y = x$ to see where the function will be reflected.

Use the table or point-plotting feature of your graphing technology to find several coordinates on the graph of $f(x)$. Invert these to find the corresponding coordinates of $f^{-1}(x)$.

Functions

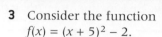

Exercise 6C

1 Restrict the domain of the following quadratic functions so that they can have an inverse and then find their inverse, stating its range.

a $f(x) = x^3 + 4$

b $f(x) = (x - 1)^3 - 2$

c $f(x) = 2(x + 3)^3$

d $f(x) = 1 - 3(x - 2)^3$

2 The model function linking the price €p of a can of soda to its demanded quantity Q, is given by the model function $Q(p) = 175 - 3.5p$.

The cost of producing one can is €5 and the company has a fixed cost of €875 in making these cans.

a Find the modelling function for the revenue of the company.

b Find the modelling function for the costs of the company.

c Hence find the modelling function for the profit of the company.

3 Consider the function $f(x) = (x + 5)^2 - 2$.

a Use technology to sketch the graph.

b Explain why f^{-1} does not exist if the domain of f is $x \in \mathbb{R}$.

c Find the largest positive domain such that the function is invertible.

d Sketch the graph of $f^{-1}(x)$ on this restricted domain.

4 Construct a piecewise linear function that meets the following requirements:

a The function has three pieces, two with different positive gradients and one with a negative gradient.

b The function is continuous.

c The function is invertible when the domain is restricted to $x \geq 3$, but is not invertible on the domain $x \geq k$ for k smaller than 3.

TOK

How can you deal with the ethical dilemma of using mathematics to cause harm, such as plotting the course of a missile?

Developing inquiry skills

Look back at the opening problem for this chapter. Oliver was trying to throw a basketball through a hoop.

What type of function could you use to model the path of the basketball?

6.2 Problems involving quadratics

The equation of a linear function has the general form $f(x) = mx + c$, with two parameters (m and c) defining a unique line. To determine the value of these two parameters, you need the coordinates of two points, since there is a single line going through two given points. This will create two linear equations with two unknowns, which you will be able to solve through your GDC.

The equation of a quadratic function has the general form $f(x) = ax^2 + bx + c$, with three parameters (a, b and c) defining a unique parabola. To determine the value of these three parameters, you now need the coordinates of three points, since there is a single parabola going through three given points. This will create three linear equations with three unknowns, which you will be able to solve through your GDC.

Example 5

A student wants to model the path of a rock with respect to time.

He is standing at the top of a vertical cliff at a height of 20 m and throws a rock upwards as shown in the diagram.

He starts counting time at the instant he throws the rock, at point A.

He measures that the time at which the rock is again at eye level, at point B, is $t = 3.26$ s.

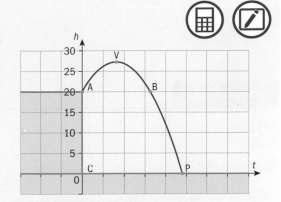

He finally measures that the time at which the rock falls into the sea, at point P, is $t = 4.8$ s.

The simplest function that will model the height of the rock with respect to time is a quadratic of the form $h(t) = at^2 + bt + c$.

Determine this function.

There are two methods you can use to do this.	
Method 1: Using **Quadratic regression** on your GDC.	
You need to identify three clear points on the curve.	You can take any three points on the graph as long as they are exact.
Known points are A(0, 20), B(3.26, 20) and P(4.8, 0).	Use the information from the question. At A, $t = 0$ and $h = 20$. At B the height is the same as at A, 20. At P the rock is at ground level, where $h = 0$.
	In your GDC, put the t values in List 1 and the h values in List 2.
The parabola is given by the equation $h(t) = -2.71t^2 + 8.82t + 20$	Then go to Statistics Quadratic regression. Here you see the values of the parameters a, b and c.

Continued on next page

Method 2: Using **Simultaneous equation solver** on your GDC.

Curve passes through A(0, 20), B(3.26, 20) and P(4.8, 0).

Substituting these points into the given function:

Using point A: $a(0)^2 + b(0) + c = 20 \Rightarrow c = 20$

Using point B: $a(3.26)^2 + b(3.26) + 20 = 20$
$\Rightarrow a(3.26)^2 + b(3.26) = 0$

Using point P: $a(4.8)^2 + b(4.8) + 20 = 0$
$\Rightarrow a(4.8)^2 + b(4.8) = -20$

$h(t) = -2.71t^2 + 8.82t + 20$

First, find the three points on the curve as in Method 1.

For each of the three points, substitute the coordinates of t and h into the general equation of a parabola, $h = at^2 + bt + c$.

This gives you three simultaneous equations in a, b and c.

Solve these equations on your GDC to give the solution.

Exercise 6D

Find the quadratic functions represented by the following graphs.

1

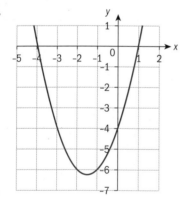

2

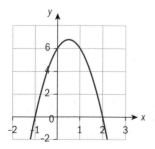

3

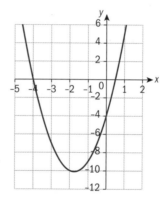

4

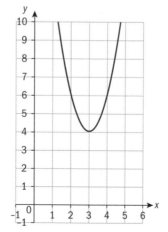

Find approximate quadratic functions represented by the following graphs.

5 a

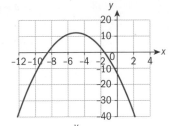

b

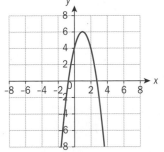

6 The graph of the quadratic function $f(x) = ax^2 + bx + c$ passess through point P(3, −4).

   a Show that $9a + 3b + c = -4$.

   The graph also passess through points Q(−2, 9) and R(5, −30).

   b Find two more equations for a, b and c.

   c Solve the system of equations to determine the values of a, b and c.

   d Sketch the graph of this function clearly showing points P, Q and R.

7 A mathematics student wants to create a model function for the Gateway Arch in St. Louis in the US state of Missouri. The arch is both 192 m wide and high. Find a suitable modelling function.

8 In a football game, if a player is fouled outside the penalty area, they are awarded a free kick.

In a free kick, the player sets the ball at the point where they were fouled, and the opponents can make a "wall" at a distance of 9.1 metres. The goal at which the player taking the free kick is aiming, has a height of 2.4 metres. Assuming that the player was fouled about 20 metres from the goal and that the tallest football players who will make the wall have a height of about 2 metres, we are faced with the problem of creating the trajectory to describe the optimum path of the ball towards the net.

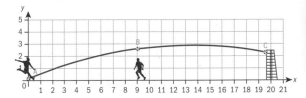

Assume the path of the ball can be modelled as a parabola.

Find the equation of the path of the ball which passes just over the head of the tallest players in the wall and then passes just under the crossbar of the goal, as shown in the diagram.

9 The arched truss for an outdoor concert has the following shape:

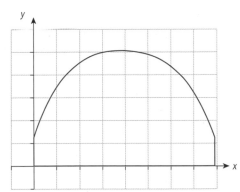

The function that models this arch is known to be $f(x) = -0.12x^2 + 1.92x + 3$, where x is the horizontal distance from the bottom left corner and y is the height. The curved part of the arch rests on 3m vertical sides.

Because of the wind expected during the concert, the organizers decided to bring the arched part of the stage down by 1 metre while keeping the vertical section at 3 m. Find the new function that will model the arched part of the stage.

Quadratic regression

In order to choose a quadratic model to describe a certain set of data, the data need to have some specific features. These include:

- the data having a single maximum or a single minimum point (corresponding to the vertex of a parabola)
- the data being symmetric about a certain vertical line (corresponding to the axis of symmetry of a parabola)
- the data having a variable rate of change, creating a curve (corresponding to the shape of a parabola).

The more data you have, the more certain you are about the choice of curve to model them. As you saw before, you need at least three points in order to create a quadratic model.

- If you have exactly three points, there is a single parabola going through them, but not enough evidence that it is the correct curve to use. In such a case, you need to know in advance that you are indeed looking for a parabola in order to go on and find one.

  If you have more than three points from a data collection process, it is almost certain that they will not lie exactly on the graph of a certain quadratic function. This means that you need to determine the parabola of best fit through these given points. Your GDC can easily and quickly perform this operation through quadratic regression.

  The difference from the previous example is that now you need to check whether the parabola fits the data well or not. The measure for this is the **coefficient of determination**, which your GDC calculates. It takes values between 0 and 1 where 1 would indicate that all the points in the data set lie on the curve. The coefficient of determination can be used for any curve. If used to test for a linear function its value will be the same as the square of the PMCC which you met in Chapters 2 and 4.

International-mindedness

The Sulba Sutras (around 500 BCE) and the Bakhshali manuscripts (around 300 AD), both from India, contained an algebraic formula for solving quadratic equations.

You always need to keep in mind the following diagram when finding the best fit curve for messy data.

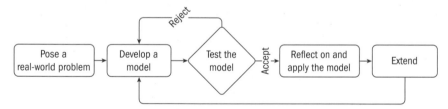

Example 6

A patient takes a specific drug in the form of a pill. Data is collected for the amount of the drug found in the bloodstream of the patient as soon as he has taken the medication. Time (t) is measured in hours and the concentration of the medication (C) is measured in milligrams of the medication found per litre of blood.

t	0	1	2	3	4	5	6	7	8	9	10
$C(t)$	0	4.87	7.17	10.27	12.81	13.05	15.03	13.3	12.22	11.29	8.26

a Plot a scatter plot of the given data.

b State a suitable type of function that would model this set of data points.

c Use your GDC to determine the model function for this set of data.

d Comment on the choice of model by determining the coefficient of determination.

e Sketch the model function over the scatter plot and comment on the closeness of fit to the original data.

f Hence, determine the time at which the medication is at its maximum effect.

g Using the model function, determine the time at which the medication will have been fully absorbed by the patient.

h Use the model to determine the concentration of the medication after 24 hours?

a

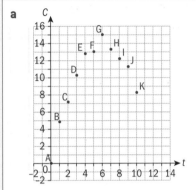

b There is strong evidence that the data depicts quadratic behaviour. There is a maximum point, there seems to be some kind of symmetry and the data follows a parabolic shape.

c $C(t) = -0.3741375t^2 + 4.56328438t + 0.12111888$

d The coefficient of determination is $R^2 = 0.98617438$, which shows very strong quadratic association.

e

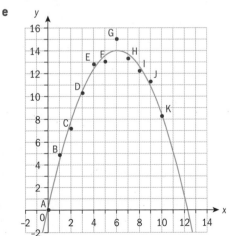

Sketching the graph over the data points you get the graph shown.

It is now evident that the regression curve fits the data very closely.

Continued on next page

Functions

f The maximum amount of medication occurs around 6.1 hours after it was taken by the patient.	Using the graph of the model function on your GDC.
g It will take about 12.2 hours for the whole of the medication to be fully absorbed and not be present any more in the bloodstream.	
h No, as the value would be negative. $C(24) < 0$	After the time that the concentration of the medication becomes zero, the model cannot be used anymore as the value would become negative.

Exercise 6E

1 A company's weekly profit, in euros, in relation to the number of units sold each week, is given in the table below.

Number of units sold	200	300	400	500	600	700	800	900	1000	1100
Profit (euros)	4900	8000	10 000	12 000	12 600	13 200	13 000	10 000	8000	6000

a Plot these points on your GDC or other graphing software.
Put the number of units sold on the x-axis and the profit on the y-axis.

b Using your GDC or technology, find the best fit quadratic function through these points.

c State whether the function you found in part **b** is a good fit for this data. Justify your answer.

d Explain whether you could use this function to predict the value of the profit at a particular time during the year.

2 A company's weekly profit, in GBP in relation to the number of units sold each week, is given in the table below.

Number of units sold	0	5	10	15	20	25	30	35	40	45
Profit (GBP)	−350	−100	50	200	300	400	450	350	320	150

a Plot these points on your GDC or other graphing software.
Put the number of units sold on the x-axis and the profit on the y-axis.

b Using your GDC or technology, find the best fit quadratic function through these points.

c State whether the function you found in part **b** is a good fit for this data. Justify your answer.

d The company uses this function to predict what the profit would be in week 52. Explain whether this prediction would be reliable.

3 Mees measures the outside temperature, in °C, every 2 hours over a 24-hour period. His measurements are given in the table below.

Time (hours)	4:00	6:00	8:00	10:00	12:00	14:00	16:00	18:00	20:00	22:00	24:00	2:00
Temperature (°C)	4	5	10	15	18	21	19	14	11	8	7	4

a Use your GDC to plot these points.

b Find the best fit quadratic function through these points.

c Hence, find an estimate of the outside temperature at 17.00. State whether this is likely to be a reasonable estimate, and justify your answer.

4 Cindy tries to make a model of a suspension bridge. To do so, she estimates the distance of various points on the bridge from where she is standing across the harbour, and the height of each point of the suspension cable above the ground. Her data is shown in the table below.

Distance from Cindy (m)	0	100	150	200	300	400	450	500	550	600	700	750
Height of bridge (m)	250	220	180	175	100	50	168	172	150	200	205	210

a Plot these points on your GDC or other graphing software. Put the distance on the x-axis and the height on the y-axis.

b Using your GDC or technology, find the best fit quadratic function through these points.

c Deduce whether Cindy's data will allow her to model the bridge. Justify your answer.

d Using your answer to part **c**, explain whether your best fit quadratic function could be used to find the height of the bridge at 410 metres from Cindy.

5 A shot-put athlete is training for a major competition. He wants to improve his technique. For this he recorded on video a great number of his tries at putting the shot at various release angles. He then analysed the video in order to create pairs of data between the angle of release and the distance at which the shot landed. The data are the following:

Angle	0	7.4	16.6	28.6	36.7	41.8	47.0	51.0	55.0	57.3	63.6
Distance	12.4	13.6	14.9	15.9	15.9	15.6	14.9	14.2	13.4	12.7	10.8
Angle	66.5	68.2	71.0	72.2	75.1	77.9	80.8	82.5	85.9	87.1	88.0
Distance	9.9	9.2	8.2	7.6	6.6	5.3	4.2	3.5	1.8	1.2	0.0

a Use quadratic regression to find the equation of the parabola that best describes the above set of data.

b Determine the optimal angle at which the athlete should put the shot in order to achieve the best results.

c Comment on the appropriateness of using the model function.

Transformations of graphs

Investigation 2

Consider the function $f(x) = x^2$.

1 Let $g(x) = f(x) + 3 = x^2 + 3$.

a Fill in the following table of values.

x	-3	-2	-1	0	1	2	3
$f(x)$							
$g(x)$							

b Plot both graphs on your GDC.

c How does adding a positive number affect the graph? How does it affect the coordinates?

d How would subtracting a positive number from a function affect its graph?

Continued on next page

Functions

2 Let $h(x) = 2 \times f(x) = 2x^2$.

    a Fill in the following table of values.

x	−3	−2	−1	0	1	2	3
$f(x)$							
$h(x)$							

    b Plot both graphs on your GDC.

    c How does multiplying a function by a number greater than 1 affect the graph? How does it affect the coordinates?

    d Which points remain invariant under this transformation?

    e How would multiplying a function by a number between 0 and 1 affect its graph?

3 Let $k(x) = -f(x) = -x^2$.

    a Fill in the following table of values.

x	−3	−2	−1	0	1	2	3
$f(x)$							
$k(x)$							

    b Plot both graphs on your GDC.

    c How does changing the sign of a function affect the graph? How does it affect the coordinates?

    d Which points remain invariant under this transformation?

4 Let $p(x) = f(x + 1) = (x + 1)^2$.

    a Fill in the following table of values.

x	−4	−3	−2	0	1	2	3
$f(x)$							
$p(x)$							

    b Plot both graphs on your GDC.

    c How does adding a positive number to the independent variable x of a function affect the graph? How does it affect the coordinates?

    d How would subtracting a positive number from the independent variable affect its graph?

5 Let $q(x) = p(2x) = (2x + 1)^2$.

    a Fill in the following tables of values.

x	−4	−3	−2	−1.5	−1	−0.5	0	0.5	1	2
$p(x)$										
$q(x)$										

    b Plot both graphs on your GDC.

    c How does multiplying the independent variable x of a function affect the graph? How does it affect the coordinates?

    d Which points remain invariant under this transformation?

    e How would dividing the independent variable by a number affect its graph?

6 Let $r(x) = p(-x) = (-x+1)^2$.

    a Fill in the following table of values.

x	−4	−3	−2	−1	0	1	2	3	4
$p(x)$									
$r(x)$									

    b Plot both graphs on your GDC.

    c How does changing the sign of the independent variable of x a function affect the graph? How does it affect the coordinates?

    d Which points remain invariant under this transformation?

7 **Conceptual** What is the effect of changing the parameters of the quadratic function $y = a(bx + c)^2 + d$ on its graph?

You can express transformations of functions in three different ways: using mathematical notation, using a geometric description or using a graphical representation.

Mathematical notation	Geometric description	Graphical representation
$y = f(x) + k$	Vertical translation k units up, with vector $\begin{pmatrix} 0 \\ k \end{pmatrix}$	
$y = f(x) - k$	Vertical translation k units down, with vector $\begin{pmatrix} 0 \\ -k \end{pmatrix}$	

Continued on next page

Functions

Mathematical notation	Geometric description	Graphical representation
$y = k \times f(x)$	Vertical stretch with scale factor k	
$y = \dfrac{f(x)}{k} = \dfrac{1}{k} \times f(x)$	Vertical stretch with scale factor $\dfrac{1}{k}$	
$y = -f(x)$	Vertical reflection in the x-axis	
$y = f(x + k)$	Horizontal translation k units left, with vector $\begin{pmatrix} -k \\ 0 \end{pmatrix}$	

Mathematical notation	Geometric description	Graphical representation
$y = f(x - k)$	Horizontal translation k units right, with vector $\begin{pmatrix} k \\ 0 \end{pmatrix}$	
$y = f(kx)$	Horizontal stretch with scale factor $\dfrac{1}{k}$	
$y = f\left(\dfrac{x}{k}\right) = f\left(\dfrac{1}{k} \times x\right)$	Horizontal stretch with scale factor k	
$y = f(-x)$	Horizontal reflection in the y-axis	

You can also combine transformations within the same function.
Changing the order of transformations can change the result.

Example 7

Write down a full geometric description of a sequence of transformations required to transform the function $f(x) = x^2$ to the function $g(x) = 5 - 2(x + 3)^2$.

	You need to think about the transformations in sequential steps.
	It is better to work with the algebraic notation first and then give the geometric description.
Horizontal translation 3 units to the left.	$y = x^2 \rightarrow y = (x + 3)^2$
Vertical stretch with scale factor 2.	$y = (x + 3)^2 \rightarrow y = 2(x + 3)^2$
Vertical reflection in the x-axis.	$y = 2(x + 3)^2 \rightarrow y = -2(x + 3)^2$
Vertical translation 5 units up.	$y = -2(x + 3)^2 \rightarrow y = 5 - 2(x + 3)^2$

HINT

When giving a geometric description of a transformation you should include the variable it affects using the terms *vertical* or *horizontal* for transformations on the y- or x-axis respectively, the type of transformation using the terms *translation, stretch* or *reflection,* and the "value" of the specific transformations, which will be units and direction for translations, scale factor for stretches, and the mirror line for reflections.

Example 8

The graph of $g(x) = 5 - 2(x + 3)^2$ is transformed into the graph of $f(x)$ by the following sequence of transformations:

- a vertical stretch with scale factor 2 followed by
- a horizontal translation of 4 units to the left followed by
- a vertical translation of 3 units down.

Find an expression for $f(x)$.

	If an order is specified, you need to use the transformations in the order they are given.
Let $p(x)$ represent a vertical stretch with scale factor 2.	When working with a composition of functions, you should work "from the inside out".
$(p \circ g)(x) = 2g(x) = 2(5 - 2(x + 3)^2)$ $= 10 - 4(x + 3)^2$	
Let $q(x)$ represent a horizontal translation of 4 units to the left.	You can either perform a transformation to the whole of the function or you can perform a transformation only on the input variable.

TOK

How accurate is a visual representation of a mathematical concept?

$$(q \circ p \circ g)(x) = q(10 - 4(x + 3)^2)$$
$$= 10 - 4(x + 3 + 4)^2$$
$$= 10 - 4(x + 7)^2$$

Let $r(x)$ represent a vertical translation of 3 units down.

$$(r \circ q \circ p \circ g)(x) = r(10 - 4(x + 7)^2)$$
$$= 10 - 4(x + 7)^2 - 3$$
$$= 7 - 4(x + 7)^2$$

Exercise 6F

1 Determine a full geometric description of the following transformations:

a from $f(x) = x^2$ to $g(x) = \left(\dfrac{x}{2}\right)^2 - 3$

b from $f(x) = 2(x - 3)^2 + 4$ to $g(x) = x^2$

c from $f(x) = x^2$ to $g(x) = 4(x - 1)^2 + 2$

d from $f(x) = 2(x - 3)^2 + 4$ to $g(x) = 2 - (2 - x)^2$.

2 Determine the function resulting from the following transformations starting from $f(x) = x^2$:

a translation 3 units to the left, followed by a reflection about the x-axis, followed by a vertical stretch with scale factor 2

b translation 2 units to the left, followed by a horizontal stretch with scale factor 2

c horizontal stretch with scale factor 2, followed by translation 2 units to the left

d translation 1 unit up followed by a translation 2 units left followed by a reflection in the y-axis

3 Consider the curve $y = 2(x - 1)^2 + 5$.

a State the vertex of the graph.

b Show that the point (3, 13) lies on the curve.

The curve undergoes the following transformations. A reflection in the y-axis, a horizontal translation of 3 units to the right and a vertical stretch scale factor 2.

c Find the new position of:

i the vertex

ii the point (3, 13).

d Use your answer to part **c** to find the equation of the transformed curve.

e Verify your answer by transforming the equation.

4 Consider the functions $f(x) = x^2$ and $g(x) = 5 - (x - 2)^2$.

a Write down a **full geometric description** of the sequence of transformations required to obtain the function $g(x)$ from the function $f(x)$.

b If $g(x)$ is stretched vertically with a scale factor of 2 and then translated by the vector $\begin{pmatrix} -1 \\ 3 \end{pmatrix}$ to become $h(x)$, determine an expression for $h(x)$.

5 Given the function $f(x) = 11 - (x - 2)^2$ in the domain $2 \le x \le 5$.

a i Sketch the graph of $f(x)$ in the given domain.

ii Determine the range of $f(x)$ in the given domain.

iii The graph of $f(x)$ can be obtained from the graph of $y = x^2$ using a sequence of transformations. Write down a full geometric description of the transformations.

b The function $f(x)$ undergoes the following sequence of transformations in order to become the function $g(x)$: first a translation 3 units to the right and 1 unit down followed by a stretch by scale factor $\dfrac{1}{2}$ parallel to the y-axis.

Determine an expression for the function $g(x)$.

6 The function $f(x) = x^2$ becomes the function $g(x) = 2(x + 2)^2 - 15$ under a sequence of transformations. The function $g(x)$, is furthermore translated by the vector $\begin{pmatrix} 2 \\ 5 \end{pmatrix}$ to become the function $h(x)$. Determine the full geometric description of the transformations required to take function $h(x)$ **back** to the function $f(x)$.

7 Consider the functions $f(x) = x^2$ and $g(x) = 3(x - 1)^2 + 2$.

  a The graph of g can be obtained from the graph of f using a sequence of transformations. Write down a full geometric description of each of these transformations.

  b The graph of g is translated 3 units down and reflected about the x-axis to become the graph of the function $h(x)$. Determine an expression for $h(x)$.

8 Consider the function $f(x) = x^2$ and the transformation functions $t(x) = x + 1$, $s(x) = 2x$ and $r(x) = -x$.

  Find expressions for the following composite functions giving a full geometric description of the transformations they represent (noting the order).

  a $(t \circ f \circ r)(x)$

  b $(s \circ f \circ t)(x)$

  c $(t \circ s \circ f)(x)$

  d $(f \circ s \circ r)(x)$

  e For each of the four functions above, determine the coordinates of their vertex using the concepts of transformations.

9 The curve $y = x^2$ is transformed by two sets of transformations:

  i a translation of 3 units to the right followed by horizontal stretch of a scale factor of 2.

  ii a horizontal stretch scale factor 2, followed by a translation of 6 units to the right.

  a Find the image of $(1, 1)$ after each of these sets of transformations.

  b Find the image of the curve $y = x^2$ after each set of transformations and explain from the equations why the two sets of transformations result in the same image.

Developing inquiry skills

Return to the chapter opening problem where Oliver throws a basketball through a hoop.

Which three points are you able to find in the path of the basketball?

How could you use these points to model its path?

6.3 Cubic functions and models

Here is a picture of part of a roller coaster.

It is in the shape of the graph of a cubic function.

> **Reflect** How are graphs of cubic functions different from graphs of quadratic functions? Are there any similarities between the graphs of quadratic and cubic functions?

Functions

Cubic models

> **Cubic functions** are polynomial functions where the highest power of x is 3.
> For example, $f(x) = ax^3 + bx^2 + cx + d, a \neq 0$ and $a, b, c, d \in \mathbb{R}$ is a cubic function.
> The fundamental (simplest) cubic function is $f(x) = x^3$.

> **Reflect** State what type of function $f(x) = ax^3 + bx^2 + cx + d$ would be if $a = 0$.

TOK

Descartes showed that geometric problems could be solved algebraically and vice versa.

What does this tell us about mathematical representation and mathematical knowledge?

You can sketch (or draw) the graph of a cubic function by hand with the help of your GDC. In many cases the **domain** of the function that you need to sketch or draw will be explicitly given. In such cases you should only sketch (or draw) the part of the function that is in the given domain.

Make sure that any x- and y-intercepts are in the correct place on the graph. Also, the local maximum and minimum values need to be in the correct place.

You can also use the table of values on the GDC to plot the coordinates of some more points that lie on the curve if necessary.

HINT

A point where the gradient of the curve changes from positive to negative or vice versa is called a local maximum or minimum point. The word local is used because often in the case of cubics there is no actual maximum or minimum.

Example 9

Sketch the graphs of $y = f(x)$ for the following functions.

a $f(x) = (x-2)^3, 0 \leq x \leq 4$ **b** $f(x) = x^3 - 7x^2 + 4x - 12, -2 \leq x \leq 8$

On your sketch, label the coordinates of points where the graphs intersect the axes, and any local maximum or minimum points.

Continued on next page

a

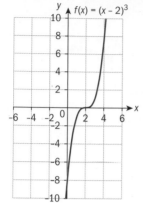

You can see from your GDC that this curve:

- does not have any local maximum or minimum points
- cuts the y-axis at the point $(0, -8)$
- cuts the x-axis at $(2, 0)$.

Draw suitable axes and mark these points on them.

You can take a few more points from the table of values to help you complete the graph, eg $(1, -1)$, $(3, 1)$ and $(4, 8)$.

Plot your points and draw a smooth line through the points.

b

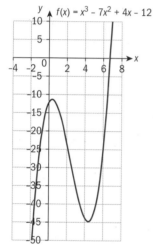

You can see from your GDC that this curve:

- has a local maximum point at $(0.306, -11.4)$
- has a local minimum point at $(4.36, -44.7)$
- cuts the y-axis at $(0, -12)$
- cuts the x-axis at $(6.67, 0)$.

These four points are probably enough to help you sketch the curve, but you can look at other points from the table of values if you need to.

Draw suitable axes and mark these points on them. Then sketch the curve.

Investigation 3

An open box is made from a piece of card measuring 12 cm by 10 cm, with squares of side x cm cut from each corner.

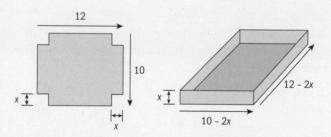

1 Explain why the width of the box is $(10 - 2x)$ cm, the length is $(12 - 2x)$ cm and the height is x cm.

2 Find an equation for the volume, V, of the open box in terms of x.

3 Use technology to plot a graph of V against x, $0 \leq x \leq 8$.

4 Explain why the function describing the volume of the open box cannot have an inverse under the maximum possible domain and restrict the domain accordingly in order to make the function invertible.

5 What is the difference between a quadratic and a cubic function in trying to isolate the input variable x?

6 Why will it be difficult to find the inverse of the function representing the volume of the box?

7 Find the x-intercepts.

8 What are the upper and lower limits for the value of x in the context of this problem? Explain why.

9 What are the coordinates of the local maximum and local minimum points of the graph?

10 Which of these is not a possible value for the volume of the box? Justify your answer.

11 Given a certain value of x, could you use this model to predict what the volume of the box would be? What limitations would you have?

12 **Conceptual** Using your answer to question **11**, do you think that, in general, cubic models could be used to predict information about real-life situations?

> Not all cubic functions have a maximum and a minimum turning point. Some have neither. Also, cubic functions can have one, two or three real roots and have rotational symmetry about a point called the **point of inflexion.**

Exercise 6G

Sketch the graphs of $y = f(x)$ for the following functions.

Write down the coordinates of points where the graphs intersect the axes, and any local maximum and minimum points.

1 $f(x) = (x + 3)^3$

2 $f(x) = x^3 - 2x^2 - x + 3$

3 $f(x) = 2x^3 - 2x^2 - 12x$

4 $f(x) = 3(x + 2)^3 - 4$

5 $f(x) = 3x(x - 4)(x + 1)$

6 Sketch each function and reflect it in the line $y = x$ to find the inverse function. Write down the equation of the inverse function in each case.

  a $f(x) = x^3 + 3$

  b $f(x) = 4x^3$

  c $f(x) = 2x^3 + 1$

7 Sketch the graph of $y = x^3 - 6x^2 + 3x + 10$.

  a Using your GDC, find the coordinates of the x-intercepts and the y-intercept.

  b Find the coordinates of the vertices.

  c The graph is reflected in the y-axis. Write down the equation of the reflected graph.

8 The temperature (T °C) over a 24-hour period beginning at 19:00 on Monday evening is represented by the function $T(x) = 23.5 - 1.72t + 0.2t^2 - 0.0056t^3$, where t is the number of hours that have passed since 19:00.

  a State the highest and lowest temperatures in this 24-hour period.

  b Find the temperature at 05:00 on Tuesday morning.

Regulations state that a hospital should be at a maximum temperature of 22 °C. If the temperature rises above this, the air conditioning system should be switched on.

  c Assuming that the temperature in the hospital is the same as the outside temperature when the air conditioning system is off, find the number of hours over the 24-hour period during which the air conditioner must be switched on. Give your answer in hours, correct to 1 dp.

  d Comment on whether this model would be useful to predict the outside temperature of the hospital at 01:00 on Wednesday morning. Justify your answer.

9 Sketch the graph of the following functions, within the specified domains and hence determine their range.

  a $f(x) = -x^3$, for $-3 \leq x \leq 3$

  b $f(x) = x^3 - 2x^2 + 4x - 3$, for $-4 \leq x \leq 4$

  c $f(x) = x^3 - 7x^2 + 11x - 5$, for $0 \leq x \leq 5$

10 Deana wants to construct an open box from a square piece of cardboard. The cardboard has side length 50 cm. To create the box, she cuts from each corner a smaller square of side length x cm.

  a Determine expressions for the dimensions of the box in terms of x.

  b Determine an expression for the volume of the box in terms of x.

  c State the domain for the expression of the volume of the box.

  d Sketch the graph representing the volume of the box.

  e Determine the dimensions of the box that has the maximum volume and state the corresponding maximum volume.

11 The maximum monthly temperature in a certain city during the course of one year (from January to December) can be modelled by the equation

  $T(t) = 0.162t^3 - 3.36t^2 + 18.2t + 1.74$, where t is the month number and $t = 1$ corresponds to January.

  a Find the maximum temperature in April.

  b Find the month during which the greatest and lowest maximum temperatures occur.

  c Find the mean of the two temperatures in part **b**.

  d State the month whose maximum temperature is approximately equal to the average you found in part **c**.

  e Comment on your findings.

12 A graphic designer has created a function from which to make a tilde symbol (~). The function that produces the tilde is
$f(x) = 0.0867x^3 - 0.828x^2 + 2.01x + 1.27$
in the domain $0 \leq x \leq 6$.

  a Sketch the graph representing the tilde.

  b Determine the range of values of the function in the given domain.

  c Determine the dimensions of the smallest rectangle (in mm) in which the tilde can fit.

13 Violet is designing the roof for a new building. In order to finalize her design, she created a model using a 3D printer.

The function that describes the vertical cross-section of the model roof is

$$f(x) = \frac{1}{81}x^3 - \frac{7}{27}x^2 + \frac{49}{36}x \text{ for } 0 \leq x \leq 13,$$

where x is the horizontal distance in cm from the leftmost end of the model roof and y is the vertical distance in cm from the bottom of the model roof. The model is made at a scale ratio of 1:200, meaning that a length of 1 cm on the model corresponds to a length of 200 cm on the actual roof.

  a Sketch the graph representing the model roof.

  b Determine the total horizontal length of the actual roof.

  c Determine the maximum height of the model roof above its base at $y = 0$.

Since the roof will be built on top of a building, the function needs to be adjusted so that y represents the distance from the bottom of the building. The building on which the roof is going to be built will be 24 m tall.

  d Determine the function that will represent the actual roof on top of the building, and describe a transformation which maps the previous function onto this one.

14 The logo of a GDC manufacturing company is given by $y = x^3 - 6x^2 + 9x$, in the domain $0 \leq x \leq 4$, where x and y are the coordinates from the centre of the frame enclosing the logo measured in cm. The frame is a square of side length 5 cm.

a Sketch the graph of the function representing the logo on your GDC.

b Determine the coordinates of the y-intercept.

c Determine the coordinates of the maximum and minimum points of the logo.

d Determine the range of the logo.

In order to make the logo more appealing, it was suggested that the design should be altered under a series of transformations. First to reflect the logo about the x-axis, then to stretch it vertically by a scale factor of $\frac{1}{2}$ and finally to translate it 4 units down.

e Write the function representing each of the transformations.

f Use the notation of composite functions to express all the transformations in the appropriate order.

g Write down the function of the new transformed logo in the form $f(x) = ax^3 + bx^2 + cx + d$, stating its domain.

h Sketch the graph of the logo, showing clearly the maximum and minimum points as well as the y-intercept.

i Comparing the two graphs and their corresponding functions, determine the significance of the sign of the coefficient of the x^3 term.

j Comparing the two graphs and their corresponding functions, determine the significance of the value of the constant term.

15 By restricting the domain of the following functions (where necessary), determine the domain on which each function is invertible.

a $f(x) = x^3 - 6x^2 + 9x - 1$

b $f(x) = 2x^3 - 3x^2 - 6x + 5$

c $f(x) = x^3 - 3x^2 + 3x + 2$

d $f(x) = 2x^3 - 3x^2 + 6x + 1$

16 An IB student wants to create some open boxes from pieces of cardboard to use them as flower pots for a biology experiment. The piece of cardboard has dimensions 40 cm by 60 cm. In order to turn it into a box, she cuts squares on each one of the corners of the cardboard and then folds the sides in. After making the first few at random, she realized that she could fill them with different amounts of soil. Determine the dimensions of the squares she cuts out in order to be able to put as much soil as possible in the flower pots?

Cubic regression

As with linear and quadratic regression, you can also model data using cubic regression.

The data in this case needs to depict the features of the graph of a cubic function. In order to choose a cubic model to describe a certain set of data, the data need to have some specific features. These include:

- the data having two vertices: one maximum and one minimum point
- the data being rotationally symmetric about a certain point
- the data having a variable concavity (both concave up and concave down).

The more data you have, the more certain you are about the choice of curve to model them. You need at least four points in order to create a cubic model.

Example 10

The path of a ski jumper is illustrated on the diagram on the right.

In order to determine a function to model this jump, the diagram was processed with graphing software to determine a set of points that the path of the ski jumper goes through, x being the horizontal distance from the starting point and y being the vertical displacement from the starting point. The points are listed in the table on the next page.

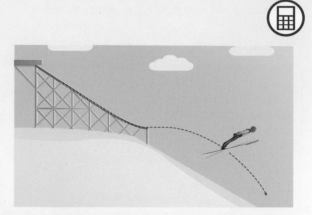

| x | 34.8 | 58.2 | 83.1 | 105.9 | 120.3 | 141.9 | 161.4 | 180 | 195 | 206.1 | 218.4 | 228.9 | 239.4 |
| y | −19.5 | −34.2 | −49.5 | −61.8 | −64.8 | −64.8 | −68.1 | −74.4 | −82.5 | −90.6 | −101.1 | −112.5 | −125.7 |

a Enter the data into your GDC.

b State the type of function suitable for modelling this set of data points.

c Use your GDC to determine the model function for this set of data.

d Determine the coefficient of determination. Interpret your result in context.

e Plot the model function over the scatter plot and comment on the closeness of fit to the original data.

The straight line that represents the slope of the mountain on which the skier will land passes through the points $(0, 0)$ and $(360, −210)$.

f Determine the equation of the line going through these two points.

g Find the point at which the ski jumper will land on the slope.

From that point on and up to the point where $x = 400$, the skier moves along the straight line describing the slope of the mountain.

h Write in piecewise form the function describing the whole path of the skier.

> **b** A cubic function would be suitable to model the ski jumper's path as it is first concave upwards and then concave downwards.
>
> **c** $f(x) = −0.0000346x^3 + 0.0136x^2 − 1.94x + 35.4$
>
> **d** $R^2 = 0.995$
>
> The coefficient of determination shows an almost perfect fit, implying a good choice of model.

e

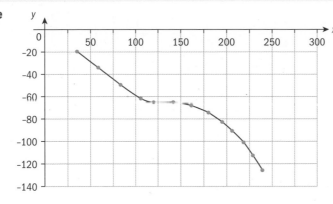

f The slope of the line is $m = \dfrac{-210 - 0}{360 - 0} = -\dfrac{7}{12}$

$\Rightarrow y - 0 = -\dfrac{7}{12}(x - 0) \Rightarrow y = -\dfrac{7}{12}x \approx -0.583x$

g $-0.0000346x^3 + 0.0136x^2 - 1.94x + 35.4 = -0.583x$

$\Rightarrow x = 254 \Rightarrow y = -148$

Equating the two functions or finding their point of inter-section graphically.

Notice that we are looking for the point which is further down the slope.

h $f(x) = \begin{cases} -0.0000346x^3 + 0.0136x^2 - 1.94x + 35.4, & 0 \le x \le 254 \\ -0.583x, & 254 < x \le 400 \end{cases}$

Functions

Exercise 6H

1 The table below shows the height, h metres, of the tide at time t hours after midnight.

Time (t)	0	1	2	3	4	5	6	7	8
Height (h)	6	5	4	2.5	2	3	3.5	5	6.5

a Using technology, find the equation of the best fit cubic function which models this data.

b Hence, find an estimate for the minimum height of the tide.

c Find a quadratic function that could also be used to model this data.

d State whether a cubic or a quadratic function would best model this data. Justify your answer by considering the coefficient of determination.

2 The temperature, in °C, for 1 day was recorded every 3 hours from 18.00.

Time	0	3	6	9	12	15	18	21	24
Temperature (°C)	12	9	5	4	8	13	17	16	13

a Using technology, plot these points and find the best fit function to model this data.

b Justify your choice of best fit function.

c Explain why it would be appropriate to use your model to give approximations for the times between the recorded hours on the day but not for predicting the temperature for the next day.

3 The number of cases of an infection in a city was recorded each week for 12 weeks.

Week	1	2	3	4	5	6	7	8	9	10	11	12
Number	24	62	103	152	209	245	232	191	146	123	96	58

a Using technology, plot these points and find the best fit function to model this data.

b Justify your choice of best fit function.

c Comment on the problems of your model in predicting the number of future cases.

4 a Using technology, plot these points and find the best fit function to model this data.

Month	1	2	3	4	5	6	7	8	9	10	11	12
Number of fish	63	82	104	91	83	68	52	41	35	45	56	71

b Justify your choice of best fit function.

c Comment on the appropriateness of the model.

---

5 Consider the following values:

x	1	2	3	4	5	6
y	7	21	27	20	18	8

a For this data find (giving all parameters to 3sf)

  i the least squares quadratic regression function

  ii the corresponding value for the coefficient of determination

  iii the least squares cubic regression function

  iv the corresponding value for the coefficient of determination.

b Comment on the better model to estimate non-integer values in the range $0 \le x \le 6$.

It is now given that the values give the path of a particle moving under gravity, where x represents the horizontal displacement from a given point and y the height.

c State one reason why you might prefer the quadratic over the cubic model

6 a Find the maximum value for:

  i $y = x^2 - x$

  ii $y = x - x^3$ between $x = 0$ and $x = 1$.

7 Eliana is modeling the path of a ball for her IA. She plots its path using software and this is shown on the diagram below.

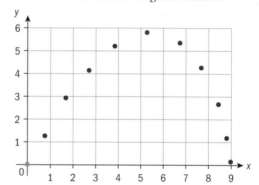

She was expecting to demonstrate that the path of the ball could be modelled by a quadratic equation.

a From the diagram state one reason why a quadratic might be a good model and one reason why it might not.

b Eliana decides that a cubic model might be better. Explain using your answer to part **a** and the diagram above why this might be more appropriate than a quadratic.

8 Violins have specific holes on their top surface called F-holes. These holes plays a very important role in the quality of the sound of the violin.

A violin maker wants to create a function modeling the contour of the F-holes on a violin to be able to carve them with the use of a computer numerical control (CNC) machine.

To do so he put a certain number of points depicting the contour of the bottom side of the F-hole on a graph paper and marked down their coordinates.

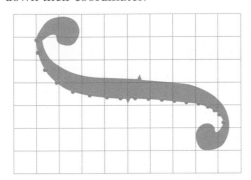

The points are the following:

x	0	0.126	0.750	1.80	3.21	4.69	6.22	7.50	8.66
y	9.14	8.62	7.91	6.28	5.26	4.91	4.57	4.13	4.25
x	9.85	11.0	12.1	13.2	14.3	15.1	15.7	16.1	16.5
y	4.73	4.82	4.75	4.36	4.41	3.70	3.54	2.87	2.66

a Explain why a cubic curve would be a good model for the lower side of the F-hole.

b Use cubic regression to find the function that best describes the above set of data stating the domain for which it is valid.

c Comment on the appropriateness of using the model function.

d Determine whether the function modelling the F-holes of the violin has local maximum and minimum points.

9 At Roller Coaster Mania Park, they claim to have the longest vertical roller coaster drop in the world. The previous longest roller coaster drop was 130 m. Part of the sideview of a rollercoaster has roughly the following shape.

This shape can be modelled by the function

$$f(x) = \frac{139x^3 - 14595x^2 + 250200x + 7818500}{62500}$$

$0 \le x \le 75$, where x is the horizontal distance in metres from the start and y is the vertical distance in metres.

a Find the maximum height of the roller coaster in this section.

b Find the minimum height of the roller coaster in this section.

c Calculate the vertical drop of this roller coaster, and comment on your answer

10 The amount of water in the Caniapiscau water reservoir in Quebec, can be modelled by the cubic function $V(t) = 0.1t^3 - 1.8t^2 + 7.2t + 54.3$, where t is time in months after the 1st of January and V is the volume of water in km³. When the water supplies fall below 48 km³, a warning is sent out asking people to be more careful in their use of water.

a Sketch the graph representing the volume of water in the reservoir for the course of one year by choosing an appropriate domain.

b Find the value of t at which there is the maximum amount of water in the water reservoir.

c Find the value of t at which there is the minimum amount of water in the water reservoir.

d State the months of the year when the warning about water consumption is active.

Functions

Developing inquiry skills

Now that you have learned different ways to model data from real-life situations, what type of function do you think would be the best way to model the path of Oliver's basketball?

Can you find sufficient data points to model the path of the ball?

Can you use the official height of a basket to help find points?

Is it possible to find a general equation that will fit all possibilities?

6.4 Power functions, direct and inverse variation and models

Let d be the diameter, A the circumference and V the volume of a sphere of radius r.

You can write the following equations:

$d = k_1 r$, $A = k_2 r^2$ and $V = k_3 r^3$.

What are the values of k_1, k_2 and k_3 assuming the units of each are the same.

> **Reflect** Can you think of two features common to the graphs of d, A and V for $r \geq 0$.

A **power function** is a function of the form $f(x) = ax^n$, where a and n are the parameters of the function and n is a member of $\mathbb{R}$.

Parameter $a \neq 0$, since $a = 0$ would make the function zero.

- If $n = 0$, the function is constant.
- If $n = 1$, the function is linear.
- If $n = 2$, the function is quadratic.
- If $n = 3$, the function is cubic.

The fundamental (simplest) power function is $f(x) = x^n$.

HINT

When n is not a positive integer the domain might be restricted. For example $f(x) = ax^{0.5}$ has a domain $x > 0$.

Investigation 4

1 Sketch the graphs of the following power functions.

   a $f(x) = x^2$ **b** $f(x) = x^3$ **c** $f(x) = x^4$

   d $f(x) = x^5$ **e** $f(x) = x^6$ **f** $f(x) = x^7$

2 Can you group power functions in smaller categories?

3 How are they the same and how are they different from a parabola?

4 How are they the same and how are they different from a cubic graph?

5 How many maximum and minimum points can a power function have?

6 Are power functions symmetric? If yes, what type of symmetry do they possess?

7 What happens to the graph of power functions as the value of the power increases?

8 **Conceptual** What are the distinguishing geometrical features of positive and negative power functions?

> **HINT**
>
> Use a view window of $-3 \leq x \leq 3$ and $-6 \leq y \leq 6$.

Functions

The graphs of all **even positive** power functions have a shape similar to a parabola and are symmetric about the y-axis.

The graphs of all **odd positive** power functions have a shape similar to a cubic function and are rotationally symmetric about the origin.

As the index of positive power functions increases, the graphs tend to become flatter around the origin.

Example 11

A designer wants to create a model function for a bowl that she sketched by hand in order to be able to process it digitally. To do so, she put the sketch over a grid and marked some data points, with the centre of the bottom of the bowl being the origin.

The data points are the following:

Point	A	B	C	D	E	F	G	H	I
x	−16.5	−15.1	−14	−12.8	−11.3	−9.3	−7.5	−5.3	0
y	7	4.9	3.62	2.53	1.54	0.7	0.3	0.07	0

Point	J	K	L	M	N	O	P	Q
x	5.3	7.5	9.3	11.3	12.8	14	15.1	16.5
y	0.07	0.3	0.7	1.54	2.53	3.62	4.9	7

Continued on next page

a Plot the given data on your GDC or other technology.

She first thought of using a quadratic function to model the shape.

b Explain why a quadratic function could be suitable to model this shape.

c Use your GDC to determine the quadratic model function for this set of data.

d Find the coefficient of determination, and comment on your answer.

e Sketch the model function over the scatter plot and comment on the closeness of fit to the original data.

Not being satisfied with the model function she created, she decided to determine a new quartic model function.

f Explain why the designer might have not been satisfied with the model function she created and why a quartic function could be a suitable alternative model.

g Use your GDC to determine the quartic model function for this set of data.

h Find the coefficient of determination, and comment on its significance in relation to the previous model.

i Sketch the model function over the scatter plot and comment on the closeness of fit to the original data and compare it to the previous model.

Using the quartic model, the designer want to create a model for another bowl whose dimensions are double in size to the original.

j Determine the equation of the model function for the larger bowl.

a

b A quadratic formula would be suitable to model this shape since the data points seem to have vertical symmetry and also because of their constant concavity.

c The best fit parabola is: $f(x) = 0.0263x^2 - 1.15$ Using quadratic regression in the GDC.

d $R^2 = 0.933$

The coefficient of determination shows that the model function describes the data set very closely.

e

Although the model function goes through (or close to) most points, it still misses the bottom point by a significant amount.

f The quadratic model had some major problems in describing the shape of the bowl, the most important being at the bottom of the bowl.

A quartic function can be a better fit, since in addition to depicting symmetry and constant concavity, it also is flatter close to the origin.

g The best fit quartic function is:
$$f(x) = 0.0000946x^4 - 0.0000649x^2 + 0.000214$$

| | Using quartic regression in the GDC. |

h $R^2 = 0.999$

The coefficient of determination shows almost perfect fit and is of course significantly better than the quadratic.

i

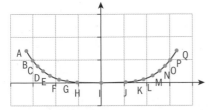

The model function goes perfectly through all the data points and describes the shape of the bowl in a much better way than the quadratic.

j $g(x) = 2f\left(\dfrac{x}{2}\right) = 0.0000942x^4 = 0.0000118x^4$

| | The enlarged bowl is double the size both in the x and in the y directions. |

Direct Variation

Two quantities that are related by a power law of the form
$y = ax^n$, $a, n \in \mathbb{R}^+$ are said to be **vary directly** with each other, or to be **directly proportional** to each other.

Because there is only one unknown parameter just one pair of values is required in order to find the relationship, assuming the value of n is known.

Example 12

The rate of the spread of fungus on a petri disk (x) varies directly with the square of the perimeter of the area covered by the fungus (p). If the rate is 2cm²s⁻¹ when the perimeter is 3.2 cm.

a Find the equation relating the rate of spread to the perimeter.

b Find the perimeter when the rate is $6 \, cm^2 s^{-1}$.

Continued on next page

a $x = ap^2$

$2 = a \times 3.2^2$

$\Rightarrow a \approx 0.195 \Rightarrow x = 0.195p^2$

b $6 = 0.195p^2$

$p^2 = 30.72 \Rightarrow p = 5.54$ cm

| The general equation for the power function. |
| Substituting the values. |

Power Regression

The power regression function on a GDC will find the best fit curve of the form $y = ax^n$, $a, n \in \mathbb{R}$.

> **HINT**
>
> On most calculators power regression can only be used if all the data points are greater than 0.

Exercise 6I

1 It is known that the resistance to motion of an object falling through a liquid is sometimes best modelled as varying directly with the object's velocity and sometimes as with the square of the velocity.

Emily wishes to test these theories and so releases a weight in a tube of thick liquid. By measuring how quickly it falls, she calculates that when it is travelling at $2 \, \text{cm s}^{-1}$ the resistance is $4.2 \, \text{N}$.

a Write down an equation linking resistance R with velocity v for each of the two possible models.

To test the models further she collects the following data:

v	3.2	4.0
R	7.1	11.1

b Find the value of R predicted by each of the models for $v = 3.2$ and $v = 4.0$.

c By considering the sum of the square residuals say which model is most likely to best fit the situation.

d Use the power regression function on your GDC and all three data points to find another possible model.

e By considering the sum of squares of residuals for the power function, comment on which model best fits Emily's data.

2 The distance, d metres, that a ball rolls down a slope varies directly with the square of the time, t seconds, it has been rolling. In 2 seconds the ball rolls 9 metres.

a Find an equation connecting d and t.

b Find how far the ball rolls in 5 seconds.

c Find the time it takes for the ball to roll 26.01 metres.

3 The mass of a uniform sphere varies directly with the cube of its radius. A certain sphere has radius 3 cm and mass 113.1 g.

Find the mass of another sphere with radius 5 cm.

4 Sketch the graph of the following functions, within the specified domains and hence determine their range.

a $f(x) = -x^5$, for $-3 \le x \le 3$

b $g(x) = \dfrac{x^4}{4}$, for $-4 \le x \le 4$

c $h(x) = 2x^{12}$, for $-2 \le x \le 2$

5 Viola is conducting an experiment to demonstrate the relation between the radius and the volume of a sphere. She gathered the following data.

r (cm)	1	2	3	4	5	6	7	8
V (cm³)	4.19	33.5	113	268	524	905	1440	2140

a Plot the given data on your GDC.

b Use your GDC to determine the power function model for this set of data.

c Comment on the choice of model by determining the coefficient of determination.

d Sketch the model function over the scatter plot and comment on the closeness of fit to the original data.

e Use the model function to determine the volume of a sphere with radius 10 cm.

f Comment on how the value found in part **e** compares with the actual value of the volume of a sphere of radius 10 cm found using the appropriate formula.

6 According to building specifications and physical measurements, the maximum weight that foundation columns of tall buildings can carry varies directly with the fourth power of their perimeter.

In a specific sample check, it was found that a column with a perimeter of 6 m could hold a weight of 55 000 kg.

a Find the formula that relates the perimeter of the column to the weight it can carry.

b Estimate the weight that another column of the same make with a perimeter of 8 m can hold.

c Calculate the perimeter that a column should have in order to be able to hold 200 000 kg?

7 Find the inverse of the following one-to-one functions:

a $f(x) = x^2$ for $x \le 0$

b $f(x) = -x^3$

c $f(x) = 2x^5$

Inverse variation

Investigation 5

A mathematician drives along the same route to school every day.

1 How is the time that he takes to get to school affected by his driving speed?

2 One day when he was very early there was no traffic so he traveled at twice his normal average speed. How did the time taken to complete the journey change from normal?

3 On the way home he was caught in heavy traffic so he only managed half his normal average speed. How did the time taken to complete the journey change from normal?

4 **Factual** How could you describe the variation between speed and time?

5 **Conceptual** How would you describe real situations that model asymptotic behavior?

When n is negative and $x > 0$, the function $f(x) = ax^n$ represents inverse variation.

Investigation 6

1 Sketch the graphs of the following inverse variation functions:

a $f(x) = \dfrac{1}{x^2}$ b $f(x) = \dfrac{1}{x^3}$ c $f(x) = \dfrac{1}{x^4}$

d $f(x) = \dfrac{1}{x^5}$ e $f(x) = \dfrac{1}{x^6}$ f $f(x) = \dfrac{1}{x^7}$

2 How can you describe the shape of a inverse variation function?

3 Can you group inverse variation functions in smaller categories?

4 Are inverse variation functions symmetric? If yes, what type of symmetry do they possess?

5 **Factual** Describe what happens to the y-value of the function as

a x becomes very large

b as x approaches 0 from the positive side

c as x approaches 0 from the negative side.

6 What happens to the graph of inverse variation functions as the value of the power becomes more negative?

7 **Conceptual** What are the distinguishing geometrical features of inverse variation functions?

HINT

Use a view window of $-3 \le x \le 3$ and $-6 \le y \le 6$.

TOK

Aliens might not be able to speak an Earth language but would they still describe the equation of a straight line in similar terms? Is mathematics a formal language?

An **asymptote** is a line that a graph approaches but never crosses or touches.

International-mindedness

Asymptote comes from the Greek word "ασύμπτωτη", meaning "to not fall on top of each other".

If a quantity y **varies inversely** with x^n for $x > 0$ then $y = kx^{-n}$ or $y = \dfrac{k}{x^n}$. In these situations y will decrease as x increases and vice versa.

As with direct variation a single point is needed to find the value of the parameter k.

Example 13

The number of hours N taken to build a wall varies inversely with the number of people x who are available to work on it.

a When three people are available the wall takes two hours to build. Find the time it takes to build the wall when four people are available to work on it.

b Given it takes three hours to build the wall, state how many people worked on it.

a $N = \dfrac{k}{x}$

$N = 2$ when $x = 3$ so $2 = \dfrac{k}{3}$

$k = 6$

$N = \dfrac{6}{x}$

$N = \dfrac{6}{4} = 1.5$

So, it takes 1.5 hours to build the wall when four people work on it.

b $3 = \dfrac{6}{x}$

$3x = 6$

$x = \dfrac{6}{3} = 2$

So, two people were available to build the wall.

For inverse variation, the variable is written as $\dfrac{1}{x}$ or x^{-1} which is a power function.

Find the value of k using the given information.

Substitute the value of k you found into the equation for N.

Now find N when $x = 4$.

Substitute $N = 3$ into the equation $N = \dfrac{6}{x}$ which you found in part **a**.

Sometimes the terms direct or inverse variation might not be used but the context will make it clear how to form the required equations.

Investigation 7

1 A local authority pays its workers depending on the number of hours that they work each week. If the workers are paid €22 per hour, complete the following table:

Number of hours	20	25	30	35	40
Pay (€)					

Plot a graph of this information on your GDC.

Describe how a worker's pay varies with the number of hours worked.

2 The local authority has decided to put artificial grass tiles on a football field.

If four people are available to lay the grass tiles, it takes them two hours to complete the work.

Fill in this table showing the number of people available and the number of hours it takes to complete the work.

Number of people	1	2	4	6	8	12
Number of hours			2			

Plot a graph of this information on your GDC.

Factual How do the number of hours to complete the work vary with the number of men available?

3 **Conceptual** For problems which involve direct and inverse variation, how does understanding the physical problem help you to choose the correct mathematical function to model the problem with?

> Any value of x that makes the denominator of a function equal to zero is excluded from the domain of the function. The vertical line represented by this x-value is called a **vertical asymptote** on the graph of the function.

Investigation 8

Consider the function $f(x) = \dfrac{1}{x}$.

1 Which value of x makes the denominator equal to zero?

2 Which vertical line is the vertical asymptote of the graph of $f(x)$?

Now consider the function $g(x) = f(x-2)$.

3 Which value of x makes the denominator equal to zero?

4 Which vertical line is the vertical asymptote of the graph of $g(x)$?

5 Give a full geometric description of the transformation represented by $g(x)$.

6 What do you notice? How does this transformation affect the vertical asymptote?

Now consider the function $h(x) = f(x) + 3$.

7 To which value does the function tend as x becomes infinitely positive or negative?

8 Which horizontal line is the horizontal asymptote of the graph of $h(x)$?

9 Give a full geometric description of the transformation represented by $h(x)$.

10 What do you notice? How does this transformation affect the horizontal asymptote?

Finally consider the function $j(x) = f(x-h) + k$.

11 Give a full geometric description of the transformation represented by $j(x)$.

12 Hence write down the equations of the asymptotes of $j(x)$.

13 Conceptual How do you identify an asymptote?

> The function $f(x) = \dfrac{1}{x-h} + k$ has a vertical asymptote $x = h$ and a horizontal asymptote $y = k$.

Example 14

Consider the function $f(x) = \dfrac{1}{x}$ when $x \neq 0$. The graph of $y = f(x)$ is transformed to become the following functions. Give a description of the transformations they represent and hence write down the equations of the asymptotes of the transformed function.

a $g(x) = f(x) - 3$

b $h(x) = f(x - 3)$

c $j(x) = f(x + 1) - 2$

a $g(x)$ represents a translation 3 units down. Vertical asymptote $x = 0$. Horizontal asymptote $y = -3$.	The vertical asymptote will remain unaffected. The horizontal asymptote will be translated 3 units down.
b $g(x)$ represents a translation 3 units to the right. Vertical asymptote $x = 3$. Horizontal asymptote $y = 0$.	The vertical asymptote will be translated 3 units to the right. The horizontal asymptote will remain unaffected.
c $g(x)$ represents a translation 1 units to the left and 2 units down. Vertical asymptote $x = -1$. Horizontal asymptote $y = -2$.	The vertical asymptote will be translated 1 units to the left. The horizontal asymptote will be translated 2 units down.

Exercise 6J

1 The volume V of a gas varies inversely with the pressure p of the gas. The pressure is 20 Pa when its volume is $180\,m^3$. Find the volume when the pressure is 90 Pa.

2 A group of children attend a birthday party. The number of pieces of candy c that each child receives varies inversely with the number of children n.

When there are 16 children, each one receives 10 pieces of candy. Find the number of pieces of candy each child receives when there are 20 children.

3 Sketch the graph of the following functions, within the specified domains and hence determine their range.

a $f(x) = \dfrac{1}{x^5}$, for $-3 \leq x \leq 3$ $x \neq 0$.

b $g(x) = \dfrac{4}{x^4}$, for $-4 \leq x \leq 4$ $x \neq 0$

c $h(x) = \dfrac{1}{2x^{12}}$, for $-2 \leq x \leq 2$ $x \neq 0$

4 The density of a sphere of **fixed** mass varies inversely as the cube of its radius.

A sphere with radius 10 cm has a density of 500 kg/m³.

a Find the density of a sphere with radius 5 cm.

b If we require a sphere to have a density of 100 kg/m³, find its radius.

5 Timothy had to choose a topic for his Mathematical Exploration. Being a prospective engineering student, he decided to investigate the inverse-square law. The law states that light intensity from a specific light source is inversely proportional to the square of the distance from the source. To validate the physical law, he performed an experiment where he positioned a light source at various distances to a receiver measuring its intensity. The data he collected appear in the following table.

d (cm)	10	15	20	25	30	35	40	45
I (lux)	3232	1434	805	513	353	259	201	159

a Plot this data on your GDC.

b Explain why an inverse variation function could be suitable to model this set of data.

c Use your GDC to determine the power function model for this set of data.

d Find the coefficient of determination, and comment on your answer.

e Sketch the model function over the plot of the points and comment on the closeness of fit to the original data.

f Use your model to estimate the light intensity if the light source moves to 50 cm from the receiver.

6 A company selling used cars wants to create mathematical models for the value of cars as a function of their age. Taking as reference one of its biggest selling models, it collected data relating the selling price to the number of years since the car was produced.

The data are shown in the table:

Age (years)	1	2	3	4	5	6	7	8	9	10
Price (€)	21641	17890	14709	12613	12239	10223	10501	9744	8257	6772

a Plot this data on your GDC.

b Explain why a linear function would not be suitable to model this set of data.

c Explain why an inverse variation function could be suitable to model this set of data.

d Use your GDC to determine the power function model for this set of data.

e Find the coefficient of determination, and comment on your answer.

f Sketch the model function over the points and comment on the closeness of fit to the original data.

g According to this model, find the age of the car when its value falls below €4000?

7 Restrict the domain of the following functions (where it is needed) in order to make them invertible.

a $f(x) = \dfrac{1}{x^4}$, for $x \neq 0$

b $f(x) = \dfrac{2}{x^3}$, for $x \neq 0$

c $f(x) = -\dfrac{1}{x^2}$, for $x \neq 0$

8 Find the inverse of the following one-to-one functions.

a $f(x) = \dfrac{1}{x^4}$, for $x < 0$

b $f(x) = \dfrac{2}{x^3}$, for $x \neq 0$

c $f(x) = \dfrac{1}{x^2}$, for $x > 0$

9 a Describe the transformations required to convert the function $f(x) = \dfrac{1}{x}$ to the function $g(x) = 3 - \dfrac{2}{x-1}$.

b Determine the asymptotes of both $f(x)$ and $g(x)$.

c State the transformations described in part **a** relate to the relative positions of the asymptotes of the two functions

10 The graph of $g(x) = 1 - \dfrac{2}{x-2}$ can be obtained from the graph of $f(x) = \dfrac{1}{x}$ using a sequence of transformations. Give a full geometric description of each of the transformations required in order for $g(x)$ **to go back** to $f(x)$.

11 The following diagram shows a demand curve for a product. The horizontal axis shows the price (p) a company could sell a product for and the vertical axis shows the percentage (N) of the market who would buy the product at this price.

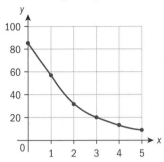

a i Explain why a power function of the form $N = kp^n$ might be a good model for the demand curve, stating a necessary restriction on the possible values of n.

ii State one reason why a function of this form is not a good model for the demand curve.

Two of the points have coordinates $(1, 57)$ and $(4, 13)$.

b Use these points to find possible values for k and n.

Chapter summary

• The standard form of a quadratic function is $f(x) = ax^2 + bx + c$.

• The fundamental (simplest) quadratic function is $f(x) = x^2$.

• The shape of the graph of all quadratic functions is called a **parabola** and is symmetric about a vertical line called the **axis of symmetry**, going through its **vertex**.

• Parabolas have **constant** concavity, either being constantly concave upwards or constantly concave downwards.

• The quadratic equation $ax^2 + bx + c = 0$ has the solution

$$x_{1,2} = \frac{-b \pm \sqrt{\Delta}}{2a}, \text{ where } \Delta = b^2 - 4ac.$$

• In order for any function to have an inverse, its domain has to be restricted in such a way as to make sure that it is a **one-to-one** function.

• Transformations of functions can be expressed in three different ways. One is their mathematical notation, the second is the geometric description and the third is the graphical representation.

  ○ $y = f(x) + k$: vertical translation k units up, with vector $\begin{pmatrix} 0 \\ k \end{pmatrix}$

  ○ $y = f(x) - k$: vertical translation k units down, with vector $\begin{pmatrix} 0 \\ -k \end{pmatrix}$

Continued on next page

- $y = k \times f(x)$: vertical stretch with scale factor k

- $y = \dfrac{f(x)}{k} = \dfrac{1}{k} \times f(x)$: vertical stretch with scale factor $\dfrac{1}{k}$

- $y = -f(x)$: vertical reflection in the x-axis

- $y = f(x + k)$: horizontal translation k units left, with vector $\begin{pmatrix} -k \\ 0 \end{pmatrix}$

- $y = f(x - k)$: horizontal translation k units right, with vector $\begin{pmatrix} k \\ 0 \end{pmatrix}$

- $y = f(kx)$: horizontal stretch with scale factor $\dfrac{1}{k}$

- $y = f\left(\dfrac{x}{k}\right) = f\left(\dfrac{1}{k} \times x\right)$: horizontal stretch with scale factor k

- $y = f(-x)$: horizontal reflection in the y-axis

- The standard form of a cubic function is $f(x) = ax^3 + bx^2 + cx + d$.
- The fundamental (simplest) cubic function is $f(x) = x^3$.
- The graphs of all cubic functions are symmetric about a point called the **point of inflexion**.
- The standard form of a power function is $f(x) = ax^n$.
- The fundamental (simplest) power function is $f(x) = x^n$.
- The graph of all even direct variation functions have a shape similar to a parabola and are symmetric about the y-axis. The graph of all odd direct variation functions have a shape similar to a cubic function and are symmetric about the origin.
- The graph of all inverse variation functions have the coordinate axes as asymptotes.
- Any value of x that makes the denominator of a function equal to zero is excluded from the domain of the function. The vertical line represented by this x-value is called a **vertical asymptote** on the graph of $f(x)$.
- If a function tends towards a constant value as the independent variable (x) tends towards positive and/or negative infinity, this constant value represents a horizontal asymptote on the graph of the function.

Developing inquiry skills

How many different trajectories would there be if the ball were to follow a straight line from the hands of the player to the hoop?

How many different trajectories are there in the case that the ball follows a curved line from the hands of the player to the hoop, as in the drawing here?

How would the initial angle at which the ball leaves the hands of the player affect the angle at which it arrives at the hoop?

How would this angle increase the chance of the player making the basket?

Knowing the maximum height of the ball, could we determine a unique model for the trajectory it follows?

How does the height up to which the ball goes increase the chance of the player making the basket?

How can we determine the optimum path for a basketball player to score a basket?

What else would we need to know to answer this question?

What assumptions have you made in the process?

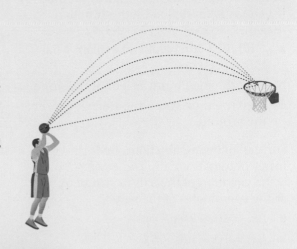

Chapter review

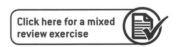
Click here for a mixed review exercise

1 Sketch the graph of:
 a $f(x) = x^2 - 2$
 b $f(x) = x^2 - 5x + 4$.

2 The perimeter of a picture is 400 cm.
 a If the length of the picture is x cm, find the height in terms of x.
 b Find an expression for the area, A cm², of the picture in terms of x.
 c Sketch this graph using a suitable domain and range.

 d Find the x-intercepts and and interpret your results in context.

3 For the graph of the function $f(x) = x^2 + 6x - 7$ find:
 a the coordinates of the y-intercept
 b the coordinates of the x-intercepts
 c the equation of the axis of symmetry
 d the coordinates of the vertex.

4 Anmol throws a stone in the air. The height of the stone, $h(t)$ metres, at time t seconds is modelled by the function $h(t) = -2.2625x^2 + 8.575x + 1.9$.

   a Find the y-intercept and explain what this represents.

   b Find the maximum height of the stone.

   c Find the time when the stone lands on the ground.

5 For the following functions, find
   i the coordinates of the x-intercepts
   ii the equation of the axis of symmetry
   iii the coordinates of the vertex.

   a $f(x) = 3(x - 2)(x - 4)$

   b $f(x) = 4(x + 1)(x - 5)$

6 Sketch the following cubic functions.

   a $f(x) = 2x^3 - 1$

   b $f(x) = (x - 1)(x + 1)(x - 3)$

7 The number of lilies, N, in a pond from 2004 until 2020 can be modelled using the function $N(x) = -0.04x^3 + 0.9x^2 - 7x + 70$, where x is the number of years after 2004.

   a Sketch the graph of $N(x) = -0.04x^3 + 0.9x^2 - 7x + 70$ for $0 \le x \le 20$.

   b Find the number of lilies after 5 years.

   c Find the number of lilies after 12 years.

   d Find the maximum number of lilies and the year in which this occurs.

   e Find the minimum number of lilies and the year in which this occurs.

   f Find when there are 60 lilies in the pond.

8 The number of miles, m, travelled varies directly with the time, t, for which the train has been travelling.

   a If the train travels 100 miles in 1.25 hours, find a relationship connecting m and s.

   b Find the number of miles travelled after 2 hours.

   c Find how long it takes to travel 300 miles.

9 The line $2y = x + 3$ intersects the curve $f(x) = x^2 + 2x - 5$ at the points A and B. Find the coordinates of A and B.

10 Sketch the graph of the function $f(x) = x^2 - 2x - 3$ for the domain $0 \le x \le 4$.

   Find the range of $y = f(x)$ in the given domain.

11 The acceleration a of a rocket is inversely proportional to the square root of the time since take off t.

   Its acceleration is $6.2 \, \text{m s}^{-2}$ when $t = 5.76 \, \text{m s}^{-2}$.

   a Find the acceleration of the rocket as a function of time.

   b Find the value of t at which the acceleration is equal to $0.5 \, \text{m s}^{-2}$.

12 A quadratic curve has x-intercepts at $(0, 0)$ and $(6, 0)$, and the vertex is at $(h, 8)$.

   a Find the value of h.

   b Find the equation of the curve in the form $y = ax^2 + bx + c$.

13 The curve $y = kx^n$ passes through the points $(2, 32)$ and $(4, 2)$. Find the values of k and n:

   a without using a GDC

   b using the power regression on a GDC.

> To do this without a GDC is beyond the scope of the syllabus. This is a good extension exercise. If you are having trouble, the worked solution found in the digital resources may help.

14 The dimensions of a rectangular swimming pool are shown in the diagram.

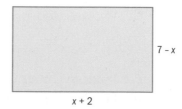

Determine the set of value(s) that the variable x should take, such that the area of the swimming pool is greater than 16.

15 A farmer wants to make a rectangular pen for his sheep. He needs to put fencing on three sides, with the other side being a brick wall as shown in the diagram.

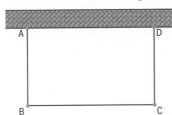

The total length of fencing that he can use is 60 m.

a Given that the length of side AB is x, determine an expression in terms of x for the length of the side BC.

b Hence determine an expression for the total area of the pen.

c With the aid of a graph, or otherwise, determine the length of side AB (ie the value of x) which makes the area take its maximum value.

16 A ball is thrown vertically upwards into the air. The height, h metres, of the ball above the ground after t seconds is given by $h = -t^2 + 6t + 12$.

a Write down the **initial** height above the ground of the ball (that is, its height at the instant when it is released).

b Show that the height of the ball after one second is 17 metres.

c At a later time the ball is **again** at a height of 17 metres.

  i Write down an equation that t must satisfy when the ball is at a height of 17 metres.

  ii Solve the equation **algebraically**.

d i Find **when** the ball reaches its maximum height.

  ii Find the maximum height of the ball.

17 Draw the graph of the function $f(x) = 2x^3 - x^2 - x + 1$, for $-1 \le x \le 1$, and hence determine the range.

18 The monthly precipitation in Oxford in mm during the course of one year (from January to December) can be modelled by the function $P(t) = 0.11t^3 + 1.87t^2 - 6.91t + 45$, where t is the number of the month, and $0 \le t \le 1$ corresponds to January.

a Find the precipitation in Oxford in mm in July.

b Find the months during which the greatest and lowest precipitation occur.

c Find the mean of the two precipitations in part **b**.

d Find the month during which the mean from part **c** occurs.

e Use your results from **a** – **d** to comment on what the position of the month with the mean rainfall tells you about when the majority of the rain falls in Oxford.

19 Sketch the graph of the following functions within the specified domains and hence determine their range.

a $f(x) = -x^4$, for $-3 \le x \le 3$

b $g(x) = \dfrac{x^5}{4}$, for $-4 \le x \le 4$

c $h(x) = 3x^9$, for $-2 \le x \le 2$

20 The average price of a litre of gasoline in France in each year from 2006 to 2017 is given in the following table.

Year	2006	2007	2008	2009	2010	2011	2012	2013	2014	2015	2016	2017
Price (€)	29.66	29.39	28.84	28.57	28.51	28.62	28.69	29.52	29.79	30.16	30.31	30.96

a Find a cubic model for this data.

b Comment on the suitability of using this model to predict future gasoline prices.

c Estimate the price in 2021.

21 Sketch the graph of the following functions, within the specified domains and hence determine their range.

a $f(x) = -\dfrac{1}{x^3}$, for $-3 \leq x \leq 3$, when $x \neq 0$.

b $g(x) = \dfrac{1}{x^4}$, for $-4 \leq x \leq 4$, when $x \neq 0$.

c $h(x) = \dfrac{1}{2x^5}$, for $-2 \leq x \leq 2$, when $x \neq 0$.

Exam-style questions

22 P1: The height (s m) of an object which moves freely under gravity is given by $s = c + ut - 5t^2$, where c m is the initial height of the object, u m s^{-1} is the initial velocity in the upward direction, and ts is time the object has been moving for.

Peter releases a model rocket from a platform 1.7 m above the ground. The rocket's initial velocity is 50 m s^{-1}.

a Find the time between the rocket setting off and returning to strike the platform. (2 marks)

b Hence write down how long it takes for the rocket to reach its maximum height. (2 marks)

c Calculate the maximum height of the rocket. (2 marks)

Peter's friend Paul does exactly the same thing, but the height of his platform is 1.8 m.

d By considering the difference in the two displacement-time graphs for the two model rockets, write down the answers to parts **a**, **b** and **c** for Paul's rocket. (4 marks)

23 P2: a Determine the set of values of k for which the quadratic equation $x^2 + kx + 9 = 0$, $x \in \mathbb{R}$ has
i one repeated root
ii no real roots
iii two distinct roots. (8 marks)

b For $k \in \mathbb{R}$, determine how many roots the equation $-x^2 + kx + 9 = 0$, $x \in \mathbb{R}$ has. (3 marks)

24 P2: Consider the quadratic function $f(x) = (x - 3)^2 + 7$.

a Write down the coordinates of the minimum point of this quadratic. (2 marks)

b Find the largest possible domain and range of $f(x)$ which include the point $(4, 8)$ such that the inverse function $f^{-1}(x)$ exists. (3 marks)

c Find the inverse function $f^{-1}(x)$, and state its domain and range. (5 marks)

25 P1: The cubic function
$$h(x) = \frac{\left(x^3 - 105x^2 + 3000x\right)}{1000}, \quad 0 \leq x \leq 80$$
models the height of a roller coaster ride, in metres, over the first 80 m of its circuit. x represents the horizontal distance from the start of the ride, and is also measured in metres.

a Find the coordinates of the local minimum point. (3 marks)

b Find the coordinates of the local maximum point. (3 marks)

c Find the set of values of x for which the roller coaster is above 50 m. (3 marks)

26 P1: When a coin is dropped down into an ancient well, the time (t seconds) it takes the coin to fall a distance of d metres can be modelled by $t = \sqrt{5}d^{\frac{1}{2}}$.

a Find how long it takes a coin to fall 10 m. (2 marks)

A coin is dropped into the well, and a splash is heard 8 seconds later as it hits the water at the bottom.

b Find the depth of the well down to the waterline. (2 marks)

If a frog can catch the coin at a depth equal to the time it takes to fall that depth, he changes into a handsome prince.

c Find how far, below the top of the well, a frog should be hanging on, waiting if he wants to become a handsome prince. (2 marks)

27 P1: James has forgotten his 4-digit passcode *abcd*, where *a, b, c, d* are digits between 0–9. To help him remember it, he has written down a mathematical puzzle which will allow him to work it out without giving it away easily to others:

If he splits the password into two 2-digit integers $x = ab$ and $y = cd$ (for example, if $a = 4$ and $b = 5$ then $x = 45$), then $x + y = 24$ and $xy = 143$.

Find the two possibilities that James' passcode could be. (6 marks)

28 P2: Consider the function $f(x) = x^2$.

The graph of the function is translated vertically to define a new function $g(x) = f(x) + k$.

a Find the value of k such that the graph of $g(x)$ passes through the point $(3, 4)$. (2 marks)

The graph of the function is translated horizontally to define a new function $h(x) = f(x - l)$.

b Find the values of l such that the graph of $h(x)$ passes through the point $(3, 4)$. (3 marks)

The graph of the function is translated to define a new function $m(x) = f(x - r) + s$.

c Find the values of r and s such that the minimum point of $m(x)$ is $(3, 4)$. (3 marks)

The graph of the function is transformed to define a new function $n(x) = af(x - b) + c$.

d Find the values of a, b and c such that the maximum point of $m(x)$ is $(3, 4)$. (4 marks)

29 P2: In an archaeological dig three small red squares are found on the ruin of a mosaic. It is believed that they were part of a red curve. A coordinate system is introduced and the three points have coordinates of $(1, 10)$, $(2, 27)$ and $(4, 115)$.

a Find the equation of a quadratic curve that passes through these three points. (4 marks)

Later a fourth red square is discovered with coordinates of $(5, 198)$.

b Determine if this new point lies on the quadratic curve found in part **a**. (2 marks)

c Find the equation of a cubic function that does pass through all four points. (5 marks)

30 P2: A horizontal suspension bridge has a cable above it. The shape of the cable can be modelled by a quadratic curve. The height of the cable is 10 m above the bridge at each of the two ends of the bridge. The cable is 2 m above the bridge in the middle of the bridge.

Find how far above the bridge the cable is at one quarter of the way along the bridge, from one end. (8 marks)

Hanging around!

Approaches to learning: Thinking skills: Create, Generating, Planning, Producing
Exploration criteria: Presentation (A), Personal engagement (C), Reflection (D)
IB topic: Quadratic Modelling, Using technology

Investigate

Hang a piece of rope or chain by its two ends. It must be free hanging under its own weight. It doesn't matter how long it is or how far apart the ends are.

What shape curve does the hanging chain resemble?

How could you test this?

Import the curve into a graphing package

A graphing package can fit an equation of a curve to a photograph.

Take a photograph of your hanging rope/chain.

What do you need to consider when taking this photo?

Import the image into a graphing package.

Carefully follow the instructions for the graphing package you are using.

The image should appear in the graphing screen.

Fit an equation to three points on the curve

Select three points that lie on the curve.

Does it matter which three points you select?

Would two points be enough?

In your graphing package, enter your three points as *x*- and *y*-coordinates.

Now use the graphing package to find the best fit quadratic model to your three chosen points.

Carefully follow the instructions for the graphing package you are using.

Test the fit of your curve

Did you find a curve which fits the shape of your image exactly?

What reasons are there that may mean that you did not get a perfect fit?

The shape that a free-hanging chain or rope makes is actually a **catenary** and not a parabola at all. This is why you did not get a perfect fit.

Research the difference between the shape of a catenary and a parabola.

> **International-mindedness**
>
> The word "catenary" comes from the Latin word for "chain".

> **Did you know?**
>
> A football field is often curved to allow water to run off to the sides.

Modelling and investigation activity

Extension

Explore one or more of the following – are they quadratic?

> The curve of a banana.

> The cross section of a football field.

> The path of a football when kicked in the air – here you would need to be able to use available software to trace the path of the ball as it moves.

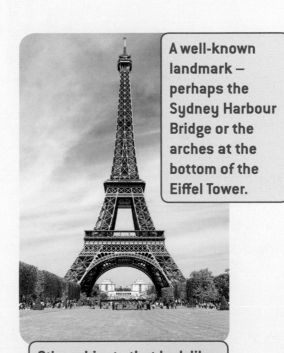

> A well-known landmark – perhaps the Sydney Harbour Bridge or the arches at the bottom of the Eiffel Tower.

> Other objects that look like a parabola – for example, the arch of a rainbow, water coming from a fountain, the arc of a Satellite dish.

Modelling rates of change: exponential and logarithmic functions

The reduction in temperature, the curve of a skateboard ramp, the value of an investment under compound interest, and radioactive decay can all be modelled by certain families of curves. This chapter looks at the characteristics of some of these families of curves, and considers how they can be used to model and predict outcomes in real-life situations.

Concepts
- Change
- Modelling

Microconcepts
- Common ratio, geometric sequences, geometric series and infinite geometric sequences
- Convergence and divergence
- Percentage, interest rate, compound interest, compounding periods, present value, future value, annuity and amortization
- Exponents, exponential growth/decay, inverse functions, logarithms, exponential functions and half-life
- Horizontal asymptotes
- Logistic functions and log-log graphs

How long will it take you to become a millionaire if you receive US\$1 the first month, US\$2 the second month, US\$4 the third month, US\$8 the fourth month and so on?

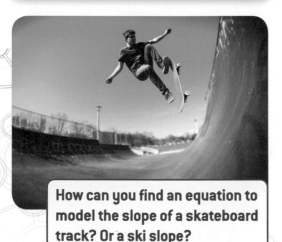

If the temperature of a cup of tea reduces at a given rate, will it ever reach 0°C?

How can you find an equation to model the slope of a skateboard track? Or a ski slope?

Does the same amount of money have the same value today, yesterday and tomorrow?

Look back at the Gapminder graph on p. 45.

1 Describe how the scale on the *x*-axis increases.

2 Would the *x*-axis ever reach zero?

3 Describe how the scale on the *y*-axis increases.

4 What would be the problem in using the same scale on both axes?

5 What type of function could you use to model the general trend of the data points?

Before you start

Developing inquiry skills

Think about the questions in this opening problem and answer any you can. As you work through the chapter, you will gain mathematical knowledge and skills that will help you to answer them all.

Click here for help with this skills check

You should know how to:

1 Apply the laws of exponents.
eg $x^2 \times x^3 = x^5$

2 Find a specific percentage of a quantity.

eg 6% of $24 = \dfrac{6}{100} \times 24 = 1.44$

3 Mappings of the elements of one set to another. Illustration by means of sets of ordered pairs, tables, diagrams and graphs.

eg given the function $f(x) = 2x + 1$ when $x = 3 \Rightarrow f(3) = 2 \times 3 + 1 = 7$

This means that number 3 from the set of the domain is mapped onto number 7 on the set of the range.

Similarly using more *x* values:

x	1	2	3	4
y	3	5	7	9

Graphically:

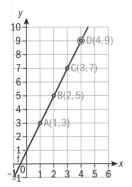

4 Sigma notation.

$$S_n = \sum_{i=1}^{n} u_i = u_1 + u_2 + u_3 + u_4 + \ldots + u_n$$

eg $\displaystyle\sum_{i=1}^{5} i^2 = 1^2 + 2^2 + 3^2 + 4^2 + 5^2 = 55$

Skills check

1 Find the value of:

a $(x^2)^3$ b $\left(\dfrac{a}{b}\right)^{-1}$ c $x^{-2} \times \sqrt{x}$

d $\dfrac{\sqrt{x}}{\sqrt[3]{x}}$ e $\left(\sqrt{x}\right)^5$

2 Find the value of:

a 3% of 24   b 15% of 72

c 28% of 150

3 Consider the function $f(x) = 1 - 3x$.

a Copy and complete the following table based on $f(x)$.

x	−1	0	1	2
y				

b Find the value of $f(12)$.

c Graph the function $f(x)$.

4 Find the value of the following:

a $\displaystyle\sum_{i=1}^{10} 2i + 1$ b $\displaystyle\sum_{i=5}^{10} 2i + 1$ c $\displaystyle\sum_{i=1}^{4} i^3$

7.1 Geometric sequences and series

The Australian Open Men's Singles competition is part of the Grand Slam tennis tournaments. In this competition, 128 players start competing in straight elimination matches until the final, where the champion is declared.

a How many matches are played in the first three rounds of the tournament?

b What do you notice?

c How many matches are be played in the last round (the final round) of the tournament?

d How many matches will be played in total during the complete course of the tournament?

> The nth term of a geometric sequence is given by the formula:
> $$u_n = u_1 \times r^{n-1}, r \neq 1$$

Investigation 1

1 a One common counting method is decimal counting. This uses units, tens, hundreds, thousands, etc. ie multiples of 1, 10, 100, ... Determine the rule for going from one category to the next.

b In a single elimination (or knockout) tournament, the number of remaining participants follows the pattern 64, 32, 16, ... Determine the rule for going from one number to the next.

c The value of a car depreciates because of age. A certain car has the following value at the end of each year after purchase. €40 000, €32 000, €25 600, ... Determine the rule for going from one value to the next.

d A pendulum consists of a hanging weight that can swing freely. When moving from side to side, it gets displaced from its rest position. For a certain pendulum the displacements at each end of its oscillation were recorded to be 40, −20, 10, −5, ... Determine the rule for going from one value to the next.

What do you notice in the pattern of the terms in all these examples?

Why aren't these sequences arithmetic?

2 Complete the table for each geometric sequence.

	1st term	2nd term	3rd term	4th term	5th term	6th term
a	1	10	100			
b	64	32	16			
c	40 000	32 000	25 600			
d	40	−20	10			

➡️ **Factual** For each sequence, determine whether it is increasing, decreasing or oscillating.

Conceptual When do the terms of a geometric sequence increase? When do they decrease? When do they oscillate?

3 **a** To get from the first term of a geometric sequence to the second you need to multiply by the common ratio. $u_2 = u_1 \times r = u_1 r$

How many terms after the first term is the second term?

How does this relate to the expression above?

b To get from the second term of a geometric sequence to the third you need to multiply again by the common ratio. $u_3 = u_2 \times r = u_1 r \times r = u_1 r^2$

How many terms after the first term is the third term?

How does this relate to the expression above?

c How many terms after the first term is the eighth term?

How does this relate to an expression for the eighth term u_8 in terms of the first term u_1 and the common ratio r?

d How many terms after the fifth term is the eighth term?

How does this relate to an expression for the eighth term u_8 in terms of the fifth term u_5 and the common ratio r?

e How many terms after the first term is the nth term of the sequence?

How does this relate to an expression for the nth term u_n in terms of the first term u_1 and the common ratio r?

Conceptual How can you find the general term of a geometric sequence?

> **International-mindedness**
>
> The *Elements*, Euclid's book from 300BC, contained geometric sequences and series.

> **HINT**
>
> A sequence of terms that has a common ratio equal to 1 (a sequence of constant terms) is not a geometric sequence.

> A sequence of numbers in which each term can be found by multiplying the preceding term by a **common ratio**, r, is called a geometric sequence.
>
> For a sequence to be geometric, $r \neq 1$.

Example 1

For each of the following geometric sequences, find the common ratio, the value of the specified term, and an expression for the nth term.

a $4, 12, 36, \ldots, u_8, \ldots$

b $2, -6, 18, \ldots, u_5, \ldots$

c $2, 2.2, 2.42, \ldots, u_6, \ldots$

d $\dfrac{1}{3}, \dfrac{2}{3}, \dfrac{4}{3}, \ldots, u_7, \ldots$

a $r = \dfrac{12}{4} = 3$ $u_8 = u_1 \times r^7 = 4 \times 3^7 = 8748$ $u_n = u_1 \times r^{n-1} = 4 \times 3^{n-1}$	In order to determine the common ratio of a geometric sequence you need to divide any term of the sequence by the preceding term.

Continued on next page ➡️

b $r = \dfrac{-6}{2} = -3$

$u_5 = u_3 \times r \times r = 18 \times (-3) \times (-3) = 162$

$u_n = u_1 \times r^{n-1} = 2 \times (-3)^{n-1}$

c $r = \dfrac{2.2}{2} = 1.1$

$\begin{aligned} u_6 = u_1 \times r^5 = 2 \times 1.1^5 &= 3.22102 \\ &= 3.22 \text{ (3 s.f.)} \end{aligned}$

$u_n = u_1 \times r^{n-1} = 2 \times 1.1^{n-1}$

d $r = \dfrac{\left(\dfrac{2}{3}\right)}{\left(\dfrac{1}{3}\right)} = 2$

$u_7 = u_1 \times r^6 = \dfrac{1}{3} \times 2^6 = \dfrac{64}{3}$

$u_n = u_1 \times r^{n-1} = \dfrac{1}{3} \times 2^{n-1} = \dfrac{2^{n-1}}{3}$

Sometimes when the term you are trying to find is a term very close to the ones you already have, instead of using the formula you can just multiply by the common ratio as many times as is necessary until you reach the required term.

Exercise 7A

1 For each one of the following geometric sequences, find the common ratio, the value of the specified term and an expression for the nth term.

   a $5, 10, 20, \ldots, u_7, \ldots$

   b $-3, 15, -75, \ldots, u_8, \ldots$

   c $\sqrt{2}, \sqrt{6}, 3\sqrt{2}, \ldots, u_6, \ldots$

   d $\dfrac{3}{2}, 1, \dfrac{2}{3}, \ldots, u_4, \ldots$

   e $2, 20, 200, \ldots, u_{10}, \ldots$

2 For each one of the following geometric sequences, find the common ratio and an expression for the nth term.

   a $u_1 = 3$ and $u_4 = 24$

   b $u_1 = 32$ and $u_6 = 243$

   c $u_1 = 1$, $u_5 = 81$ and all terms are positive.

   d $u_1 = \dfrac{1}{2}$ and $u_4 = \dfrac{4}{27}$

   e $u_1 = -2$, $u_7 = -1458$ and the sequence has both positive and negative terms.

   f $u_3 = 13.5$ and $u_6 = 367.5$

3 There is a flu epidemic in Cozytown. On the first day, 2 people have the flu. On the second day, 10 people have the flu. On the third day, 50 people have the flu.

   a   Show that the number of people with the flu forms the first of three terms in a geometric sequence.

   b   Calculate how many people have the flu after 1 week (7 days).

   c   Use your model to calculate how many people will have the flu after 1 year. Comment on the reasonableness of your answer.

Investigation 2

Censuses have taken place in the United Kingdom every ten years since 1801. Studies of the findings on the population have shown that it is increasing by 0.6% each year. The population in the last census at the beginning of 2011 was found to be 63.2 million.

Assuming the population continues to increase at the same rate:

1   Explain why the population at the beginning of 2012 can be found by multiplying 63.2 million by 1.006.

2   The population (in millions) at the beginning of 2017 can be given by $1.006^n \times 63.2$. State the value of n.

3   If a population increases at a rate $p\%$ per year write down an expression for the population after n years (P_n) in terms of the original population (P_0).

4   Explain how this formula is different from the usual formula for a geometric series.

The population of Japan is decreasing on average by 0.2% per year. Its population in 2018 is 127 million.

Assuming the rate of decrease remains the same:

5   Write down an expression for the population of Japan in 2025 and calculate this value.

6   In which year would the population drop below 120 million?

7   If a population decreases at a rate $p\%$ per year write down an expression for the population after n years (P_n) in terms of the original population (P_0).

8   **Conceptual** What type of sequence models a situation with constant percentage change?

9   **Conceptual** How do geometric sequences model real-life situations?

Percentage change is a form of a geometric sequence.

When terms **increase** by $p\%$ from the preceding term, their common ratio corresponds to $r = 1 + \dfrac{p}{100}$.

When terms **decrease** by $p\%$ from the preceding term, their common ratio corresponds to $r = 1 - \dfrac{p}{100}$.

TOK

Why is proof important in mathematics?

Example 2

Costis bought a car for €16 000. The value of the car depreciates by 10% each year.

a   Find the value of the car at the end of the first year.

b   Find the value of the car after 5 years.

c   Calculate after how many years the value of the car fall below half its original value.

Continued on next page

a 10% of €16 000 is $\dfrac{10}{100} \times 16000 = €1600$

$V_1 = 16000 - 1600 = €14400$

or $r = \dfrac{100 - 10}{100} = 0.9$ and

$V_1 = 16\,000 \times 0.9$
$\quad = €14\,400$

A decrease of 10% is found by multiplying by 0.9.

b $V_5 = 16\,000 \times 0.9^5 = €9447.84$

c Half of the original value is €8000

$16\,000 \times 0.9^n < 8000$

This equation can be solved directly using the table or graphing function on a GDC.

$n > 6.58 \Rightarrow n \geq 7$

After 7 years the value of the car will first drop below half of its original value and become $V_7 = 16\,000 \times 0.9^7 = €7652.75$

Example 3

The number of Snapchat daily users is found to be increasing by 2.5% per month. In May of 2018, the number of Snapchat daily users is 187 million.

a Determine the number of daily users in December 2018.

b Find the month of which year when the number of daily users first exceeds 300 million.

c The company aims to reach 300 million daily users during May of 2019. Determine the monthly percentage increase required to achieve this goal.

a $V_{Dec} = V_{May} \times r^7 \Rightarrow$

$V_{Dec} = 187 \times 1.025^7 = 222$ million daily users.

From May (5th month) to December (12th month) the number of months that will pass is $12 - 5 = 7$ months and so the power to which the common ratio is raised is 7.

b $V = V_{May} \times r^n \Rightarrow 187 \times 1.025^n > 300$

$\Rightarrow n > 19.1 \Rightarrow n \geq 20 \Rightarrow n_{min} = 20 \Rightarrow$ after 20 months the number of daily users will exceed 300 million, ie in November of 2020.

The common ratio is $r = \dfrac{100 + 2.5}{100} = 1.025$

c $V_{May2019} = V_{May2018} \times r^{12} \Rightarrow 300 = 187 \times r^{12}$

$\Rightarrow r = 1.040 \Rightarrow \dfrac{100 + p}{100} = 1.040$

$\Rightarrow p = 4.0\%$

From May of 2018 until May of 2019, the number of months that will pass is 12 and so the power to which the common ratio is raised is 12.

> The exponent n to which the common ratio r is raised will always be the number of time periods that have elapsed since the growth or decay begins.

Exercise 7B

1 At the end of 2016 the population of a city was 200 000. At the end of 2018 the population was 264 500.

   a Assuming that these end of year figures follow a geometric sequence, find the population at the end of 2017.

   b Calculate the population at the end of 2020.

   c Comment on whether this increase will continue.

2 One kilogram of tomatoes costs $2.20 at the end of 2015. Prices rise at 2.65% per year. Find the cost of a kilogram of tomatoes at the end of 2019.

3 Petra buys a camper van for €45 000. Each year the camper van decreases in value by 5%. Find the value of the camper van at the end of six years.

4 Beau spends €15 000 buying computer materials for his office. Each year the materials depreciate by 12%.

   a Find the value of the materials after three years.

   b Find how many years it takes for the materials to be worth €5000.

5 Find the common ratio for the geometric sequence representing the following percentage changes:

   a increase by 12.5%   **b** decrease by 7.3%

   c becomes 89%   **d** increase by 0.1%

6 Determine the number of times that the % change is applied in the following cases and determine their value.

The diameter of sequoia trees increases by 5% each year.

   a If the diameter of a sequoia tree today is 1.2 m, find what it will be in 7 years.

   b If the diameter of the first annual measurement made was 1.2 m, determine the 7th measurement.

   c If the diameter at the beginning of 2010 was 1.2 metres, find the diameter at the **end** of 2017.

7 The world population at the beginning of 2019 is 7.7 billion people. Assume the annual rate of increase throughout the time periods considered in the question is 1.72%.

   a Find the world population after one decade.

   b Determine the world population 7 years ago.

   c Determine the world population at the **end** of 2040.

   d Determine when the world population has doubled compared to the beginning of 2019?

   e Calculate the annual percentage increase in order for the world population to become 10 billion in 2090.

Investigation 3

Let S_n denote the sum of the first n terms of a geometric series, so

$$S_5 = \sum_{i=1}^{5} u_i = u_1 + u_1 r + u_1 r^2 + u_1 r^3 + u_1 r^4$$

1 Write down an expression for rS_5.

2 Hence find an expression in terms of u_1 and r for:

   a $rS_5 - S_5$ **b** S_5.

The result obtained in part **b** can be generalized to $S_n = \dfrac{u_1 \left(r^n - 1 \right)}{r - 1}$.

Continued on next page

3 Explain why the formula can also be written as $S_n = \dfrac{u_1\left(1 - r^n\right)}{1-r}$ and why this form might be easier to use when $r < 1$.

According to a story, Sissa ibn Dahir, invented the game of chess for King Shihram to play. The king was so pleased with the game that he asked Sissa what reward he wanted for this great invention. Sissa said that he would take this reward: the king should put one grain of wheat on the first square of a chessboard, two grains of wheat on the second square, four grains on the third square, eight grains on the fourth square, and so on, doubling the number of grains of wheat

4 Find how many grains of wheat the King would have to give Sissa.

5 How does this compare with the annual world production of wheat consisting of approximately 1.2×10^{16} grains?

The sum of the first n terms of a geometric sequence is called a geometric series and is given by the formula:

$$S_n = \sum_{k=1}^{n} u_k = \frac{u_1 \times \left(r^n - 1\right)}{r - 1} = \frac{u_1 \times \left(1 - r^n\right)}{1 - r}, \quad r \neq 1$$

Example 4

The first term of a geometric sequence is equal to 3 and the common ratio is equal to 2.

a Find the sum of the first 10 terms of the sequence.

b Find the sum of the next 10 terms of the sequence.

a $S_{10} = \dfrac{3 \times \left(2^{10} - 1\right)}{2 - 1} = 3069$

b $S_{20} = \dfrac{3 \times \left(2^{20} - 1\right)}{2 - 1} = 3\,145\,725$

Thus the sum of the next 10 terms of the sequence is

$S_{20} - S_{10} = 3\,145\,725 - 3069 = 3\,142\,656$

The sum of the next ten terms of the geometric series is actually the sum $u_{11} + u_{12} + u_{13} + \ldots + u_{20}$. You can think of this as the sum of the first 20 terms minus the sum of the first 10 terms.

$S_{20} = u_1 + u_2 + u_3 + \ldots + u_{10} + u_{11} + \ldots + u_{20}$

$S_{10} = u_1 + u_2 + u_3 + \ldots + u_{10}$

$\Rightarrow S_{20} - S_{10} = u_{11} + u_{12} + \ldots + u_{20}$

Example 5

The students in a school decided to raise money in order to install hammocks in the campus. They have 10 days to raise the required money of €300.
The money raised on the first day was €50. The money that they raise on each subsequent day is 15% less than the previous.

a Calculate the amount of money they expect to raise in total. Comment on whether this will be enough to purchase the hammocks.

b Calculate the number of full days they would need to fundraise on if they are to raise enough money to purchase the hammocks.

c Find the maximum daily percentage decrease in the money they raise if they are to reach their goal of raising €300 in 10 days.

a $S_{10} = \dfrac{50\left(1 - 0.85^{10}\right)}{1 - 0.85} = €267.71$

The amount will not be enough in order to purchase the hammocks.

This is a geometric series with $u_1 = 50$ and $r = \dfrac{100 - 15}{100} = 0.85$

Use the second form of the formula for the sum of a geometric series as $r < 1$.

b $S_n = \dfrac{50\left(1 - 0.85^n\right)}{1 - 0.85} \geq 300 \Rightarrow n \geq 14.2$

$\Rightarrow n \geq 15$. They would need at least 15 days in order to collect the amount.

The students will need to fundraise for n days, such that the sum to n of the geometric progression is greater than or equal to 300.

c $S_{10} = \dfrac{50\left(1 - r^{10}\right)}{1 - r} = 300 \Rightarrow r = 0.879$

$\Rightarrow \dfrac{100 - p}{100} = 0.879 \Rightarrow p = 12.1\%$

There should only be a decrease of 12.1% each day in order to achieve the goal of raising €300 in 10 days.

In order to raise 300 in 10 days, the amounts must form a geometric progression with $u_1 = 50$ and $S_{10} = 300$.

Find r as a percentage, p.

TOK

Is mathematics a language?

Exercise 7C

1 Maria, a jewellery designer, is designing an earring in the shape shown below

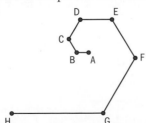

The straight-line segments from which the earring is made follow a geometric sequence with common ratio 1.4. The first and smallest segment is 1 cm long.

a Find the length of the longest segment of the earring.

b Find the total length of material required for this earring.

2 A biologist is running an experiment with a certain colony of bacteria in a petri dish. Every hour the number of new bacteria that are created is 10% more than the previous hour. There were approximately 72 million bacteria at the beginning of the experiment and during the first hour the number of bacteria that were created was approximately 12 million.

  a Find the number of bacteria that were created during the 6th hour of the experiment.

  b Find the total number of bacteria that were created during the first 6 hours.

  c Find the total number of bacteria in the petri dish 10 hours later.

  d Determine how long it will take for the number of bacteria to exceed 1 billion.

3 The numbers of email users increase by 6.2% each year. The number of email users in 2008 was approximately 1.7 billion.

  a Find the common ratio of the sequence.

  b Find the number of email users in 2019.

  c What is the percentage increase from 2008 to 2019?

  d Find the first year in which the number of email users will exceed 3 billion.

  e Comment on why this sequence is likely to have a limited lifetime.

4 The sum of the first 10 terms of a geometric sequence is 33 times the sum of its first five terms. The first term of the sequence is 3.

  a Find the common ratio of the series.

  b Find the greatest term in the sequence which is less than 1000.

  c Find the smallest value of n such that the sum of the first n terms of the series is greater than 1000.

  d Given that the sum of the first k terms of the series is 33825 times the sum of the first five terms, find the value of k.

5 Find the value of the following geometric series.

  a $2 + 10 + 50 + \ldots + 781\,250$

  b $6.4 + 9.6 + 14.4 + \ldots + 164.025$

  c $\dfrac{8}{3} + \dfrac{2}{3} + \dfrac{1}{6} + \ldots + \dfrac{1}{6144}$

6 Anna Louisa is practicing for the interschool swimming championships. She records the best time from every day's practice in order to monitor her performance. She noticed that her times go down by 0.2% after each day of practice. She started with a time of 30.4 seconds. The record of the competition is 29.3 seconds and the competition is in 20 days from the day she started practicing.

  a What is the common ratio of the geometric sequence?

  b What time is she expected to swim after five days of practice?

  c Will she manage to break the record time on the day of the championship?

Investigation 4

1 For a geometric sequence with $u_1 = 1$ and $r = 1.1$ find u_{10}, u_{50} and u_{100}.

2 Repeat for the sequence with $u_1 = 1$ and $r = 0.9$.

3 State the main differences between the results of **1** and **2** and justify your answer using the formula $u_n = u_1 r^{n-1}$.

If as n increases a sequence, u_n, approaches a value but never quite reaches it, we say it displays **asymptotic behavior** and can talk about its limit as n **tends to infinity**, which is written as as $\lim_{n \to \infty}(u_n)$.

4 When $-1 < r < 1$ write down $\lim_{n \to \infty}(u_n)$ and justify your answer.

5 Why does it make no sense to talk about $\lim_{n \to \infty}(u_n)$ when $r > 1$ or $r < -1$ (we can also write $|r| > 1$)?

Consider a piece of paper of area $1\,m^2$ which is divided as shown in the diagram. First one half is shaded, then one half of the remainder is shaded, then one half again.

Let u_n be the area shaded on the nth "shading". Hence $u_1 = \dfrac{1}{2}$,

$u_2 = \dfrac{1}{4}$ etc.

6 a Find an expression for u_n.

   b State the value of r for the sequence.

   c In the context of the diagram explain what is meant by S_n.

   d From the diagram write down $\lim_{n \to \infty}(S_n)$.

   e Use the formula $S_n = \dfrac{u_1\left(1 - r^n\right)}{1 - r}$ to justify your answer to **6d**.

   f Hence right down a formula for the limit as n tends to infinity for the sum of a geometric series giving the condition on r for it to be valid.

This limit is referred to as the sum to infinity of the series and is written as S_∞.

7 Use your formula to find the sum to infinity of the following geometric sequences.

   a $1, 0.1, 0.01, 0.001, \ldots$ **b** $8, -4, 2, -1, \ldots$

8 **Conceptual** When does an infinite sum of a geometric series converge to a finite sum?

The **sum to infinity** of a geometric sequence is:

$$S_\infty = \frac{u_1}{1 - r}, \text{ for } |r| < 1$$

TOK

How do mathematicians reconcile the fact that some conclusions conflict with intuition?

Example 6

Sheldon is carrying out an experiment that involve adding decreasing amounts of a chemical to a collection of test solutions.

He adds $60\,ml$ to the first and $50\,ml$ to the second. The amounts added form a geometric sequence.

a Find the amount added to the fifth solution.

b Find which solution will be the first to have less than $10\,ml$ added.

c Given Sheldon has $400\,ml$ of the chemical, prove that he will have enough however many test solutions he has included in his experiment.

Continued on next page

a $r = \dfrac{5}{6}$

Let the amount added on the nth experiment be u_n.

$$u_5 = 60 \times \left(\dfrac{5}{6}\right)^4 = 28.9\,\text{ml}$$

b $u_n < 10 \Rightarrow u_1 r^{n-1} < 10$

$$\Rightarrow 60 \times \left(\dfrac{5}{6}\right)^{n-1} < 10$$

$n = 11$

As a whole number answer is required this can most easily be solved using the table function in the GDC. Alternatively the graphing or numerical solving function can be used to first show $n > 10.8$

c   Maximum needed can be given by the sum to infinity.

$$S_\infty = \dfrac{60}{1 - \dfrac{5}{6}} = 360\,\text{ml}$$

Using $S_\infty = \dfrac{u_1}{1-r}$

So Sheldon will have enough of the chemical.

Exercise 7D

1   Determine whether the following infinite series possess a finite sum. If they do, determine the value of the infinite sum.

   a $0.001 + 0.002 + 0.004 + \ldots$

   b $1\,000\,000 + 500\,000 + 250\,000 + \ldots$

   c $1 - 3 + 9 - 27 + \ldots$

   d $\dfrac{1}{2} + \dfrac{1}{4} + \dfrac{1}{8} + \ldots$

2   The sum of an infinite geometric sequence is seven times the value of its first term.

   a   Find the common ratio of the sequence.

   b   Find the least number of terms of the sequence that must be added in order for the sum to exceed half the value of the infinite sum.

3   The value of an infinite series is 24. The first term of the sequence is 4.

   a   Find the common ratio of the sequence.

   b   Find the first three terms of the sequence.

   Now all the terms of the sequence are squared.

   c   Find the first three terms of the new series.

   d   Find the common ratio of the new sequence. What do you notice?

   e   Find the infinite sum of the new sequence.

   f   Find the ratio of the infinite sum of the new sequence to the square of the infinite sum of the original sequence. Comment on your result.

4   In Physics class, Zoe learned that because of energy losses, when a basketball is dropped to the ground, it would bounce to 75% of its original height.

If the ball is dropped from an initial height of 2 m:

   a   Determine the height it would rise after the first bounce.

   b   Determine the height it would rise after the second bounce.

   c   Determine the height it would rise after the third bounce.

   d   Determine the common ratio of the sequence of bounce heights.

e Comment on whether or not the ball would ever stop bouncing.

f If the bouncing continues indefinitely, calculate the total distance covered by the ball.

5 In a HL Mathematics class, the teacher gave the following project to his students. He gave them a piece of paper with an empty circle of radius 4 cm drawn in the middle. He then asked each student to shade half of the empty shape, determine in terms of pi the area of the whole shape that has been shaded and give it to the next student. These are the first few shaded circles:

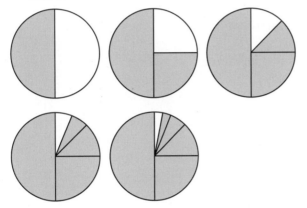

a Find the area shaded by the first student.

b Find the area shaded by the second student.

c Find the area shaded by the first two students.

d Find the area shaded by the fifth student.

e Find the area shaded by the first five students.

f Find the number of students required to shade 99% of the circle.

g If the process was continued indefinitely, find what area of the circle would eventually be shaded. Verify your answer using the formula for the sum of an infinite series.

6 A mathematics teacher has taken his daughter to the playground. While she was on the swing, he noticed that the amplitude of each successive swing was significantly less than the previous and he had to give her a push every now and then.

Going back home he decided to analyze the motion of the swing. The amplitude of the first oscillation was 1 m and every subsequent oscillation was 89% of the previous one.

The swing needs a push whenever the amplitude falls below 0.5 m.

a Find the amplitude of the third oscillation.

b Find after how many oscillations he will need to push the swing again.

c Find the total distance travelled up to the point that he needs to push the swing again.

d If he left the swing to oscillate indefinitely, calculate the total distance covered.

Developing inquiry skills

Look back to the opening problem at the start of the chapter.

You should now be able to answer questions 1–5.

1 What do you notice about the scaling of the axes?

2 Describe how the scale on the x-axis increases.

3 Would the x-axis ever reach zero?

4 Describe how the scale on the y-axis increases.

5 What would be the problem in using the same scale on both axes?

7.2 Financial applications of geometric sequences and series

As soon as she was born, Zaira's parents decided to put some money into an account for her to have on her 18th birthday. They were offered the following investment schemes from the different banks that they approached:

- Scheme A: To invest 10 000 MAD at a simple interest rate of 5% per annum for 18 years.
- Scheme B: To invest 10 000 MAD at a compound interest rate of 4% per annum compounded annually for 18 years.
- Scheme C: To invest 10 000 MAD at a compound interest rate of 4% per annum compounded monthly for 18 years.
- Scheme D: To invest 10 000 MAD and get back double this amount at the end of the 18 years.

How much interest would they receive under each one of the schemes?

Compound interest

If the interest paid is **simple interest**, then the interest remains the same for each year that you have your money in the bank.

If the interest paid is **compound interest**, then the interest is added to the original amount and the new value is used to calculate the interest for the next period.

Compound interest is not always calculated per year, it could also be calculated per month, per week, etc.

It is also possible to have yearly interest with several **compounding periods** within the year, for example monthly compounding.

In the previous section you saw that when any quantity increases by $p\%$ per time period then the value at the end of n time periods can be given as $u_n = u_0 \left(\dfrac{100+p}{100} \right)^n = u_0 \left(1 + \dfrac{p}{100} \right)^n$ where u_0 is the initial amount.

In this section we shall consider the case where p represents the interest rate received on an investment which can be added at varying intervals. When a yearly interest rate is given it can be referred to as $p\%$ per annum (year)

Investigation 5

Eric decides to put his money into a compound interest scheme in a bank. He is going to invest €10 000. The interest rate is 5% per annum compounded yearly.

1　How much interest will he receive on the amount of his investment during the first year?

2　What is the total amount that he will have at the end of the first year?

3　Write down an expression for the total amount he will have in the account at the end of n years.

4　Hence find the total amount he will have in his account at the end of the 10th year.

5　**Conceptual**　How can you model compound interest?

Another bank pays the same annual interest rate but compounded monthly (ie the interest is added each month rather than just at the end of the year).

Assume that the monthly interest rate is one twelve of the annual interest rate.

6　State the number of times interest is added in the first year (these are the compounding periods).

7　Hence find how much money he will have in the account after
  i one year
  ii ten years.

8　By considering by how much his investment has increased in the first year, give the actual percentage interest he has received from the bank.

The interest rate given assuming that the interest is added just once is called the **nominal** rate; the interest rate which takes into account the compounding is called the **effective** rate.

9　What do you notice about the two investment schemes and the interest that they pay?

As the number of compounding periods within a year increase, the interest rate per compounding period decreases and can be calculated as $\frac{1}{k} \times r\%$, where $r\%$ is the nominal annual interest rate and k is the number of compounding periods within a year.

If the amount is invested for n years, the times (periods) at which the investor will receive interest increase and become $k \times n$.

If PV is the present value, FV the future value, r the nominal interest rate, n the number of years and k the compounding frequency, or number of times interest is paid in a year (ie $k = 1$ for yearly, $k = 2$ for half-yearly, $k = 4$ for quarterly and $k = 12$ for monthly, etc), then the general formula for finding the future value is

$$FV = PV \times \left(1 + \frac{r}{100k}\right)^{k \times n}$$

EXAM HINT

In this course, you should be able to calculate compound interest using technology, including the financial packages of your GDC. When answering exam questions, you should show your working clearly, including the information from the financial package.

Example 7

1 Rafael invests BRL 5000 (Brazilian real) in a bank offering 2.5% interest compounded annually.

    a Calculate the amount of money he has after five years.

After the five years, Rafael withdraws all his money and puts it in another bank that offers 2.5% interest per annum compounded monthly.

    b Calculate the amount of money that he has in the bank after three more years.

2 Alexis invests RUB 80000 (Russian ruble) in a bank that offers interest at 3% per annum compounded quarterly.

    a Calculate how much money Alexis has in the bank after six years.

    b Calculate how long it takes for his original amount of money to double.

---

1 a $FV = 5000\left(1 + \dfrac{2.5}{1 \times 100}\right)^{1 \times 5}$

        $= \text{BRL } 5657.04$

   $PV = 5000,\ r = 2.5,\ k = 1,\ n = 5$

b $FV = 5657.04\left(1 + \dfrac{2.5}{12 \times 100}\right)^{12 \times 3}$

      $= \text{BRL } 6097.16$

   $PV = 5657.04,\ r = 2.5,\ k = 12,\ n = 3$

Or, using the Finance app on your GDC:

a $N = 5$

   $I\% = 2.5$

   $PV = -5000$

   $PMT = 0$

   $FV =$

   $PpY = 1$

   $CpY = 1$

Move the cursor back to FV and press enter to get the answer.

b $N = 3$

   $I\% = 2.5$

   $PV = -5657.04$

   $PMT = 0$

   $FV =$

   $PpY = 1$

   $CpY = 12$

Move the cursor to FV and press enter.

PV is usually negative because you have given it to the bank.

PMT is periodic money transfers (also called annuity payment) and you don't need it here.

PpY is periods in the year; when you are dealing with years, this is always 1.

CpY is compounding periods: 1, 2, 4 or 12 depending on how often interest is paid.

2 a $FV = 80\,000\left(1 + \dfrac{3}{4 \times 100}\right)^{4 \times 6}$

$= \text{RUB } 95\,713.08$

N = 6

I% = 3

PV = −80 000

PMT = 0

FV =

PpY = 1

CpY = 4

Move the cursor back to FV and press enter.

b $160\,000 = 80\,000\left(1 + \dfrac{3}{4 \times 100}\right)^{4 \times n}$

Using the Finance app:

$n = 23.19$

So it would take 23 years for his money to double.

Double the original amount is RUB 160 000

N =

I% = 3

PV = −80 000

PMT = 0

FV = 160 000

PpY = 1

CpY = 4

Move the cursor back to N and press enter.

Example 8

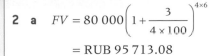

Zoe deposits €25 000 in a bank offering 2.4% annual interest rate compounded quarterly.

From this account she wishes to pay her rent, which is €600 per month. Find how long it will take until the account can no longer be used to pay the rent.

Using the finance app on your GDC: N = I% = 2.4 PV = −25000 PMT = 600 FV = 0 PpY = 12 CpY = 4 Move the cursor back to N and press enter to get the answer. N = 43.5 months, meaning that she will be able to pay the rent from this account for 43 complete months.	In this case, money is also withdrawn from the account, so PMT = 600. The Future Value is set to zero, since you are looking for the value of *n* at the time when the account will have no more money. PpY is set to 12 since Zoe has to pay the rent 12 months per year. CpY is set to 4 since the interest she receives is compounded 4 times per year.

Inflation measures the rate that prices for goods increase over time and, as a result, how much less your money can buy.

This means that if inflation is at $i\%$ an investment which receives $r\%$ interest compounded annually will actually have its **real value** increased by only $(r - i)\%$.

Therefore when adjusting for inflation to find the real value of an investment replace r by $(r - i)$ in the compound interest formula.

TOK

"Debt certainly isn't always a bad thing. A mortgage can help you afford a home. Student loans can be a necessity in getting a good job. Both are investments worth making, and both come with fairly low interest rates" – Jean Chatzky

Do all societies view investment and interest in the same way?

What is your stance?

Example 9

Kathryn would like to buy a new house in five year's time. The average price of houses in the area she is considering is €120 000. She has €110 000 in an investment account, which is earning 5.2% interest per year compounded yearly. House inflation is expected to be 3.1% per year. Will she be able to afford an average price house in five year's time?

Investment will be worth $$110\,000\left(1 + \frac{5.2 - 3.1}{100}\right)^5$$ $= €122\,045$ So she will be able to afford it	This can also be done using the financial application on your GDC entering the interest as 2.1%.

Exercise 7E

1 Oswald and Martha both have €5000 to invest. Oswald invests his money in a bank that offers to pay 3.7% nominal annual interest compounded annually. Martha invests her money in a bank that offers to pay 3.5% nominal annual interest compounded monthly.

Calculate who has the most money at the end of 15 years.

2 Adam invests 50 000 NIS (New Israeli Sheqel) in a bank that pays 3.2% nominal annual interest compounded annually.

a Calculate the amount he will have in the bank after 10 years.

b Find how many complete years it will take for his money to double?

c Calculate the interest rate he should ask for if he wants to double his investment in 20 years.

3 Celia plans to invest £4500 in a bank that offers $r\%$ nominal annual interest compounded monthly. After 5 years, she has £5803.94 in the bank.

a Find the interest rate.

b Find how many years it will take for Celia to increase her initial amount by 50%.

4 Tony wants to buy a scooter that costs $1500. He deposits $1000 in a bank that pays 7.5% interest compounded quarterly. Determine after how many years he will be able to buy the scooter.

5 Leon invests an amount in euro in a bank that offers 1.2% interest compounded half-yearly. 10 years later his account has €6762.56. Calculate the original amount of his investment.

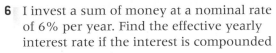
6 I invest a sum of money at a nominal rate of 6% per year. Find the effective yearly interest rate if the interest is compounded

 a quarterly

 b monthly.

7 Celia is planning to invest $20 000 in the United States. The inflation rate is projected to be 2.1%. She found an investment scheme in a bank that pays a nominal annual interest rate of 2.4% compounded monthly.

 a Determine the real interest rate she will receive next year.

 b Determine the worth of her investment after one year.

8 The inflation rate in Ecuador is negative (deflation) meaning that the price of basic commodities decreases every year. The projection for the next year is −0.5%.

 Juliana is planning to invest an amount of $2000 at an interest rate of 0.1%.

 a Determine the real interest rate that she will receive.

 b Determine the worth of her investment at the end of one year.

Annuities and amortization

When a constant investment, P, is made for n periods always compounded with the same interest rate, r%, it is called an **annuity**.

Investigation 6

Laura deposits $3000 at the beginning of each year for 10 years in a pension scheme.

The rate of interest is fixed at 6% per annum. Interest is compounded yearly.

1 Write down an expression for the final value (after 10 years) of the $3000 invested at the beginning of the first year.

2 Write down an expression for the final value of the $3000 invested at the beginning of the second year.

3 Similarly, write down an expression consisting of the sum of ten terms for the **total** value of the pension fund at the end of 10 years.

4 What type of series does your expression represent?

5 How much will the deposit be worth after 10 years?

6 Conceptual How does an annuity represent compounded growth?

> The formula for working out an annuity is:
>
> $$FV = A\frac{(1+r)^n - 1}{r}$$
>
> where FV is the future value, A is the amount invested each year, r is the interest rate and n is the number of years.

When a constant payment, P, to repay a loan is made for a certain number of n periods always compounded with the same interest rate, r%, it is called **amortization**.

Investigation 7

Pim borrows $1000 from a bank that charges 4% interest compounded annually. He wants to pay the loan back in six months in monthly instalments. The bank informs Pim that he must pay $168.62 back each month.

1 Work out how much he has to pay in total.

If the interest is 4% compounded annually, then that would be 2% for half a year.

2 Work out 2% of $1000.

3 Explain why the amount that Pim pays back in total is less than $1000 + 2% of $1000.

Pim sets up a spreadsheet to monitor his payments.

He pays $168.62 each month, but the bank also charges interest each month on the amount owed.

4 If the interest rate is 4% per annum, work out what it is per month.

5 Calculate the interest for the first month.

6 Describe how you worked out how much is paid off the loan each month.

7 The spreadsheet shows the first two lines of Pim's payments. Fill in the next few lines.

Amount owed	Payment	Interest	Payment – Interest	Remaining loan
1000	168.62	3.33	165.29	834.71
834.71	168.62	2.78	165.84	668.87

After six months, the remaining loan should be $0.

Example 10

Jack receives a loan of $5000 from a bank at an annual interest rate of 7.5% compounded monthly. It is to be repaid in monthly installments within a five-year period.

a Determine the monthly installments in order to repay the loan on time.

b Jack starts repaying the $5000 loan with the monthly installments calculated in part **a**. Calculate the amount he still owes after the 10th installment.

a $N = 60$ as the number of installments is 60 $I\% = 7.5$ ie the annual interest rate $PV = -5000$, the loan received $PMT = $ blank as you are looking for it $FV = 0$, to totally repay the loan $P_pY = 12$, for 12 payments per year $C_pY = 12$ The GDC gives the amount of the monthly installments (PMT) to be $100.19.	Use your GDC to find the PMT (ie the required monthly installments). The number of repayments will be $12 \times 5 = 60$

b PM2 = 10, which is the month of the last payment

I% = 7.5 ie the annual interest rate

PV = −5000, the loan received

PMT = 100.189743 (found in part **a**)

P_pY = 12, for 12 payments per year

C_pY = 12

The GDC gives the amount of amount of principal that remains to be repaid (BAL) to be $4290.89.

Use your GDC to find the BAL (ie the balance on the debt of a loan received).

Exercise 7F

1 Brandt receives a loan of $10 000 from a bank at an annual interest rate of 6% compounded monthly to be repaid in monthly installments within a 10-year period.

   a Determine the monthly installments in order to repay the loan on time.

   b Find how much she still owes after the fifth year.

2 Spyro takes out a loan of 40 000 AED from a bank at an annual interest rate of 6.3% compounded quarterly to be repaid in quarterly installments within a six-year period.

   a Determine the monthly installments in order to repay the loan on time.

   b Find how much he still owes after the end of the 3rd year.

3 Maude decides to invest in a 25-year private pension scheme, where she will have to deposit TRY1000 every month. The rate of interest is fixed at 8% per annum. Interest is compounded monthly.

   a Determine the future value of her investment at the end of the 25 years.

   After the 25-year period, when she will have retired, she will receive (according to the pension scheme) a monthly pension of TRY1200.

   b Calculate how long it will be until she breaks even with the amount that she invested?

4 Donny received a loan of €11,000 at an interest rate of 5.19% compounded monthly. He agreed to pay back the loan in 72 equal monthly instalments over the next six years.

   a Determine the amount of each one of the 72 equal monthly installments.

   Five years after he started repaying his loan, Donny decided to repay the rest in a final single installment.

   b Determine the amount still owing at the end of the five years.

5 Larry wants to make a decision on a six-year amortized loan for him to buy a new car. The value of the car is $33 560. The annual interest rate of the loan is 14.06% compounded monthly. He can afford to pay up to $700 monthly in order to repay the loan. Determine if it is enough for him to agree on this contract.

Developing inquiry skills

- Scheme A: Investing 10 000 MAD at a simple interest rate of 5% per annum for 18 years.
- Scheme B: Investing 10 000 MAD at a compound interest rate of 4% per annum compounded annually for 18 years.
- Scheme C: Investing 10 000 MAD at a compound interest rate of 4% per annum compounded monthly for 18 years.
- Scheme D: Investing 10 000 MAD and getting back double this amount at the end of the 18 years.

Which scheme is the most rewarding?

TOK

"A government's ability to raise and lower short-term interest rates is its primary control over the economy" – Alex Berenson

How can knowledge of mathematics result in individuals being exploited or protected from extortion?

7.3 Exponential functions and models

The marathon is a 42 kilometre race that has been held in the Olympics since 1896. Originally, it was run by a Greek messenger reporting the victory of the Battle of Marathon to Athens. The winning time has dropped considerably over the years: from around 3 hours down to almost 2 hours.

Can you predict the shortest time in which an athlete will ever be able to run a Marathon?

Investigation 8

Helen is examining the rate of growth of the bacteria lactobacillus acidophilus. At the beginning of her experiment she introduced 200 bacteria into a petri dish. Under a fixed environment she measured that after one hour the bacteria had doubled. This rate of growth remained the same as the bacteria doubled in number again within the next hour.

a Copy and complete the table below showing the number of bacteria at the specified number of hours after the beginning of the experiment

Hours after	0	1	2	3	4
Number of bacteria	200				

b What sequence does the trend of the number of bacteria follow?

c What is the formula of the nth term of the above sequence of numbers?

Assume that we now want to determine the number of bacteria 1.5 hours after the experiment begun.

d Why is a sequence insufficient to determine this value?

If the same relation is used with the independent variable being any positive real number it now becomes a function.

e Use this function in order to determine the number of bacteria present after 1.5 hours.

f Sketch the graph of the function representing the number of bacteria.

g What do you notice? What is the domain and range of this function?

The function found in Investigation 8 is an example of an exponential function, one in which the independent variable is the **exponent** of a number, called the **base**.

The basic exponential function is of the form $f(x) = a^x$, $a > 0$. Investigation 9 looks at some properties of all such exponential functions.

Investigation 9

1 Use technology to sketch the graphs of these functions.

   a $f(x) = 2^x$ **b** $f(x) = 3^x$ **c** $f(x) = 0.5^x$

   d $f(x) = 0.2^x$ **e** $f(x) = 2^{-x}$

2 Explain why the exponential equation $f(x) = \left(\dfrac{1}{2}\right)^x$ can be written as $f(x) = 2^{-x}$.

3 Give two different conditions on the base and the exponent for an exponential function to be a decreasing function.

4 How are these functions different from power functions?

5 How can you describe the shape of these graphs? Do they have any asymptotes? Are they increasing or decreasing?

6 How are they the same and how are they different?

7 What happens as x tends to $+\infty$ and $-\infty$?

8 How many zeros do these functions have and why?

9 Could you sketch the graph of the function $f(x) = (-2)^x$? If not, why?

10 **Conceptual** Describe the main features of the graphs of all exponential functions of the form $f(x) = a^x$, $a > 0$.

The independent or input variable is the exponent.

The general equation is of the form $f(x) = a \times b^x + c$, $b > 0$, $a \neq 0$.

The simplest form of an exponential function is $f(x) = b^x$, $b > 0$.

Since any positive power raised to any power is still a positive number, the range of these functions is $f(x) > 0$.

International-mindedness

The term "power" was used by the Greek mathematician Euclid for the square of a line.

International-mindedness

The word "exponent" was first used in the 16th century by German monk and mathematician Michael Stifel. Samuel Jeake introduced the term "indices" in 1696.

All exponential functions have a **horizontal asymptote**.

Exponential functions of the form $f(x) = b^x$ have the line $y = 0$ as a horizontal asymptote. Unlike inverse proportion functions, the asymptotic behavior occurs either as $x \to \infty$ or as $x \to -\infty$, but not both.

The general form $f(x) = ab^x + c$, has a horizontal asymptote at $y = c$ since the exponential term ab^x can never become equal to zero.

Investigation 10

1 Consider the transformation of the graph of $y = 2^x$ onto the graph of each of the following functions.

For each function:

i state the sequence of transformations which maps $y = 2^x$ onto that function

ii sketch the graph of the new function

iii write down the equation of the asymptote

iv write down the value of the y-intercept.

a $y = 3 \times 2^x$ b $y = 2^x - 3$ c $y = 2^{-x}$ d $y = -2^x$

e $y = 3 \times 2^x - 4$ f $y = 2^{-x} + 4$

2 Describe the key features of the function $f(x) = ka^x + c$ for $a > 1$.

3 State the difference in the curve when $0 < a < 1$ or when the function is rewritten as $f(x) = ka^{-x} + c$, $a > 1$.

4 Write the following two functions in the form $f(x) = ka^x + c$.

a $f(x) = 3^{x+2} + 5$ b $f(x) = 3^{2x} + 7$

5 Hence explain why all exponential functions of the form $f(x) = k_1 a_1^{bx+d} + c$ can be written in the form $f(x) = ka^x + c$ and state the values of k and a in terms of k_1 and a_1.

6 **Conceptual** How do the parameters of the exponential function affect the graph of the function?

The exponential function $f(x) = ka^x + c$ has the following properties:

The straight line $y = c$ is a horizontal asymptote .

It crosses the y-axis at the point $(0, k + c)$.

Is increasing for $a > 1$ and decreasing for $0 < a < 1$.

The exponential function $f(x) = ka^{-x} + c$ has the following properties:

The straight line $y = c$ is a horizontal asymptote as $x \to \infty$.

It crosses the y-axis at the point $(0, k + c)$

Is decreasing for $a > 1$ (exponential decay)

Functions of the form $f(x) = k_1 a_1^{bx+d} + c$ can also be written in the form $f(x) = ka^x + c$ where $k = k_1 \times a_1^d$ and $a = a_1^b$. Either form is acceptable, and the choice will often depend on the context.

Example 11

For each of the following functions:

i find the equation of the horizontal asymptote

ii find the coordinates of the point where the curve cuts the y-axis.

iii state if the function is increasing or decreasing.

a $f(x) = 3^x + 2$

b $f(x) = 5 \times 0.2^x - 3$

a **i** The horizontal asymptote has equation $y = 2$.	2 is the value for c.
ii The curve cuts the y-axis at the point $(0, 3)$.	$k = 1$ and $c = 2$, so, $1 + 2 = 3$
iii The function is increasing because 3 is greater than 1.	
b **i** The horizontal asymptote has equation $y = -3$.	-3 is the value for c.
ii The curve cuts the y-axis at the point $(0, 2)$.	$k = 5$ and $c = -3$, so $5 - 3 = 2$
iii The function is decreasing because 0.2 lies between 0 and 1.	

Exercise 7G

1 For the graphs of the following equations:

  i find the y-intercept

  ii find the equation of the horizontal asymptote

  iii state whether the function shows growth (increasing) or decay (decreasing).

  a $f(x) = 4^x + 1$ **b** $f(x) = 0.2^x - 3$

  c $f(x) = 5^{2x}$ **d** $f(x) = 3^{0.1x} + 2$

  e $f(x) = 3(2)^x - 5$ **f** $f(x) = 4(0.3)^{2x} + 3$

  g $f(x) = 5(2)^{0.5x} - 1$ **h** $f(x) = 2(2.5)^{-x} - 1$

2 Write the following functions in the form $f(x) = ka^x + c$.

  a $f(x) = 2(4)^{2x} + 5$

  b $f(x) = 7(0.5)^{-3x} + 2$

3 John is a photographer and he is practicing the 19th technique called the "Collodion process" producing ambrotypes. In this process he has to be very precise with the timing of the use of the various chemicals.

In order to perfect his technique, he created several mathematical models relating the time that he applies the various chemicals to the sharpness of his images.

The model function that he created for Ethyl ether is $S(t) = 12 + 10 \times 1.2^{-t}$.

a Find the initial value of the sharpness.

b Find how long it will take for the sharpness to drop to 15.

For another chemical Ethyl alcohol, the sharpness is 2 units higher than with Ethyl ether.

c Use graph transformations to determine the function for Ethyl alcohol.

For another chemical, nitrocellulose the sharpness is the same as with Ethyl ether but takes double the time.

d Use graph transformations to determine the function for nitrocellulose.

For a final chemical that he uses, iodide, the sharpness is double that of Ethyl ether.

e Use graph transformations to determine the function for iodide.

> **TOK**
>
> The phrase "exponential growth" is used popularly to describe a number of phenomena.
>
> Do you think that using mathematical language can distort understanding?

Investigation 11

A bank is offering to pay 100% interest per year on a special account.

1 If the initial investment is P find in terms of P the value of the investment after one year if the interest is compounded

    a yearly **b** monthly **c** weekly **d** daily.

2 Comment on the values obtained.

3 If k is the number of compounding periods explain why the value of the investment after one year is $P\left(1 + \dfrac{1}{k}\right)^{k}$

4 Use your GDC or other technology to investigate $\lim\limits_{k \to \infty}\left(1 + \dfrac{1}{k}\right)^{k}$

The limit is an irrational number which is denoted by the letter e. Like π it is a number that appears often in many unexpected places. In the sciences most exponential equations use e as their base when the growth is continuous.

5 Suppose now that the interest rate is $R\%$. Let $r = \dfrac{R}{100}$

    a Show that the value of the investment after one year is $P\left(1 + \dfrac{r}{k}\right)^{k}$

    b By writing $\left(1 + \dfrac{r}{k}\right)^{k}$ as $\left(1 + \dfrac{1}{\left(\dfrac{k}{r}\right)}\right)^{k}$ show that the $\lim\limits_{k \to \infty}\left(1 + \dfrac{r}{k}\right)^{k} = e^{r}$

If a quantity is growing at a rate of r per time period, where r is the proportion of the original added on rather than the final amount (eg the interest rate in our example), then after one time period it will have increased by a factor of e^{r}.

After t time periods it will have increased by a factor of $\left(e^{r}\right)^{t} = e^{rt}$

6 **Conceptual** What is the connection between e and rate of growth of a quantity?

Exercise 7H

1 Determine the missing entries in the following table with the value of each function at the specified x-values:

		y-intercept	Horizontal Asymptote	Growth or Decay	Range
a	$f(x) = e^x + 3$				
b	$f(x) = 2e^{-x} + 4$				
c	$f(x) = 2e^{0.3x} - 2$				
d	$f(x) = 5 - 2e^{-3x}$				

2 Sketch the graph of each of the functions from Question 1, clearly showing all the information that you found.

3 A cup is filled with hot water and left to stand. The temperature T of the water after t minutes have elapsed is modelled by $T(t) = 24.5 + 55.9\,e^{-0.0269t}$, for $t \geq 0$.

   a Determine the y-intercept of the graph of function.

   b State a contextual interpretation of the y-intercept.

   c State whether the function displays growth or decay.

   d State how the growth or decay relates to the cooling of the water.

   e Determine the horizontal asymptote of the function.

   f State how the horizontal asymptote relates to the physics of the cooling of the water.

   g Determine the range of the function in the given domain and explain its significance.

   h Sketch the graph of the function.

4 Find the value of a if the following piecewise functions are continuous.

   a $f(x) = \begin{cases} ax^3 & x < 3 \\ 2e^x & x \geq 3 \end{cases}$

   b $f(x) = \begin{cases} ax^2 + 8 & x < 4 \\ 2^{x+1} & x \geq 4 \end{cases}$

Exponential modelling

Example 12

The function $M(t) = 85.7 \times 0.966^t$ models the amount (M) in grams of a radioactive material t years from its production.

a Determine the original mass of the radioactive material

b Determine the mass of the radioactive material after one decade?

c Calculate the complete number of years it would take for the radioactive material to reduce below 55 grams.

d Determine the half-life of the material

a At $t = 0 \Rightarrow M(0) = 85.7$ grams	All these values should be found directly from the GDC.
b At $t = 10 \Rightarrow M(10) = 60.6$ grams	
c $M(t) < 55 \Rightarrow t > 12.8 \Rightarrow t = 13$ years	
d $M(t) = \dfrac{85.7}{2} \Rightarrow t = 20$ years	

HINT

The half-life of a material is how long it takes for the material to reduce to half its original amount.

Example 13

The function that determines the value of an investment in a fund is $V(t) = V_0 e^{kt}$, where t is measured in years.

a Given that the initial amount in the account was €5000, determine the value of V_0.

b The amount in the account increased by 25% after 6 years. Determine the value of k correct to 3 significant figures.

c Using the parameters found in parts **a** and **b**, determine the value of the investment after exactly eight and a half years.

d Calculate the number of complete years for the investment to double.

a	$5000 = V_0 e^{k0} \Rightarrow V_0 = €5000$	Using $t = 0$ and $V = €5000$
b	$6250 = 5000 e^{k6} \Rightarrow k = 0.0372$	Using $t = 6$ and $V = 5000 \times 1.25 = €6250$
c	$V(8.5) = 5000e^{0.0372 \times 8} = €6859.52$	As a whole number of years is being looked
d	$5000 e^{0.0372t} > 10000 \Rightarrow t > 18.6$	for the value 19 can also be found directly
	$\Rightarrow$ the investment will double after 19 complete years.	from the table function of a GDC without the need to find 18.6.

Example 14

A rock band the VKs published a new video on their YouTube channel. The weekly views up to and including the 20th week of publication were as follows:

Week	1st	2nd	3rd	4th	5th	6th	7th	8th	9th	10th
Views	102365	38716	21617	24305	9321	14148	2103	8285	5098	3777
Week	11th	12th	13th	14th	15th	16th	17th	18th	19th	20th
Views	831	1007	834	34	378	204	6	42	54	31

A scatter plot of the data is shown below:

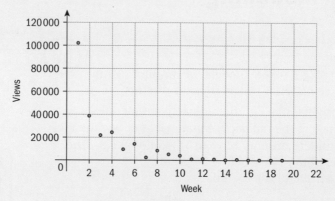

a Explain why an exponential model would be suitable to model this set of data.

b Use exponential regression to determine the best fit exponential model.

c Determine R^2 the coefficient of determination of the model function.

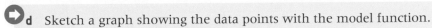

d Sketch a graph showing the data points with the model function.

e For their next video, the band wants to start advertising it as soon as it falls below 1000 views per week. Assuming it follows the same pattern as the first video, predict after how many **days** they should do so.

---

a The data shows the sales decaying at a diminishing rate continuous decay, which is a major characteristic of exponential decay functions.

Also the data have a physical horizontal asymptote as the number of views can never fall below zero.

b The exponential function that models the data is $f(x) = 129\,000 \times 0.642^x$.

Exponential regression will give the function in the form ab^x. The next section will explain how to convert to base e if required.

c $R^2 = 0.888$

d

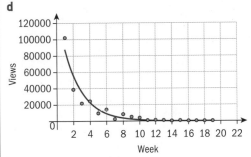

e $129\,000 \times 0.642^x = 1000$

$\Rightarrow x = 10.97$ weeks.

$\Rightarrow d = 7 \times 10.97 = 76.8$ days.

They have to start advertising their video again after 77 days.

Exercise 7I

1 The number of bacteria, n, in a dish, after t minutes is given by $n = 8e^{kt}$.

   a Given that the number of bacteria after 23 minutes is 252, determine the value of k giving your answer to two decimal places.

   b Find the value of n after one hour giving your answer to the nearest integer.

   c After T minutes, the value of n becomes greater than $100\,000$. Find the least value of T, where $T \in \mathbb{Z}$.

2 The mass m in kg of a radioactive substance at time t hours is given by $m(t) = 952e^{-\frac{t}{3}}$

   a Find the initial mass of the radioactive substance.

   b Find the amount of radioactive substance after 2.5 hours.

   c Find the half-life of the radioactive substance.

   d Find how long would it take for the radioactive substance to reduce to 10% of its original mass.

3 Consider the function $f(x) = 3^{\frac{x}{2}} - 3$.

   a Determine the equation of the horizontal asymptote.

   b Sketch the graph of $f(x)$. In your graph, show clearly the horizontal asymptote and the exact coordinates of any intersections with the coordinate axes.

   c State clearly the domain and range of the inverse function.

4 A tank initially contains 5000 ml of water. At $t = 0$, a tap is opened, and water starts flowing out of the tank. The volume of liquid, V ml, which remains in the tank after t minutes is given by the function $V(t) = ae^{bt}$.

   a Determine the exact value of a.

   b Given that the volume after 35 seconds is 151 ml, find the value of the constant b, giving your answer correct to 1 decimal place.

   c After T minutes, the volume of water becomes less than 100 ml. Find the least value of T, where $T \in \mathbb{Z}$.

5 Jaroslav is trying to determine a pattern for the real estate prices in his area for similar houses to his. After collecting monthly data for the past year, he displayed them in the following table (1 accounting for the 1st month he collected data and so on).

Month	1st	2nd	3rd	4th	5th	6th
Value (CZK) millions	7.20	7.27	7.31	7.22	7.35	7.38
Month	7th	8th	9th	10th	11th	12th
Value (CZK) millions	7.24	7.27	7.47	7.47	7.33	7.47

   a Plot the data on an appropriate set of axes.

   b Explain why an exponential model would be suitable to model this set of data.

   c Determine the best fit exponential model.

   d Determine R^2 the coefficient of determination of the model function.

   e Sketch a graph showing the data points with the model function.

   Jaroslav wants to sell his house when its price reaches 9 million CZK.

   f Assuming that the values of the houses in this area keep on following the same pattern, find how long he will need to wait until he sells his house.

6 The health officer in a new district swimming pool is responsible for maintaining the bacterial levels in the water within health and safety specifications. Specifically, the heterotrophic plate count (HPC) should not exceed 100 colonies per 1 milliliter of water. To test the swimming pool, he took a sample of water every day since he first put in the disinfectant. The data are shown in the following table:

Day	1	2	3	4	5	6	7	8	9	10
HPC	3.5	2.2	16.8	11.5	17.5	41.0	73.9	114.1	181.7	279.4

   a Plot the data on an appropriate set of axes on your GDC.

   b Explain why an exponential model would be suitable to model this set of data.

   c Use exponential regression to determine the best fit exponential model.

   d Determine R^2 the coefficient of determination of the model function.

   e Plot a graph showing the data points with the model function.

The health officer wants to prevent the bacterial levels even reaching close to the safety levels and has thus decided to introduce disinfectants whenever the level of HPC reaches half the safety levels. In order not to take measurements every day, he decided to follow the model calculated above.

   f Find how often, in days, he should disinfect the swimming pool for HPC

7 The number of bacteria, n, in a petri dish, after t minutes is given by $n = 8e^{kt}$.

   a Given that the number of bacteria after 23 minutes is 252, determine the value of k giving your answer to two decimal places.

   b Find the value of n after one hour giving your answer to the nearest integer.

   c After T minutes, the value of n becomes greater than 1000. Find the least value of T, where $T \in \mathbb{Z}$.

8 Initially a tank contains 5000 ml of liquid. At the time $t = 0$ seconds a tap is opened, and liquid then flows out of the tank. The volume of liquid, V ml, which remains in the tank after t minutes is given by $V = ae^{bt}$.

   a Determine the value of a.

   b Given that the volume after 35 minutes is 151 ml, find the value of the constant b, giving your answer correct to 1 decimal place.

   c After T minutes, the volume of liquid becomes less than 100 ml. Find the least value of T, where $T \in \mathbb{Z}$.

9 The number of bacteria in a culture N, varies according to the function $N = 1000 \times 2^{k \times t}$, for $t \geq 0$, where t is measured in days and k is a constant.

   a Find the initial number of bacteria.

   b If the number of bacteria is 4000 after 4 days find the exact value of k.

   c Find the exact number of bacteria after 8 days.

   d Determine how long it will take for the number of bacteria to grow to 32 000.

Developing inquiry skills

Now return to the question posed at the start of this section. The following table shows what fraction of one hour was shaved off the original men's world record for running a marathon at various years after the original record was set.

Time since first record (years)	0	5	25	45	50	56	70	80	100	110
Reduction in world record time (hours)	0.98	0.74	0.56	0.41	0.35	0.33	0.25	0.21	0.17	0.13

a What sequence do the "Reduction in world record times" approximately follow?

b What would be the formula of the nth term of these times?

You want to determine the record time 63.2 years since records were first recorded.

c Why is a sequence insufficient to determine this value?

If the same relation is used with the independent variable being any positive real number, it now becomes a function.

d Use this function in order to determine the record time 63.2 years since records were first recorded.

e Sketch the graph of the function representing the record time since records were first recorded.

f What do you notice? What is the domain and range of this function?

g Can you predict the shortest time in which an athlete will ever be able to run a marathon?

h What information will you need and what assumptions will you make?

i How will you choose an appropriate model? Will it be different for men and women?

7.4 Laws of exponents – laws of logarithms

Investigation 12

a Consider the exponential equation $2^x = 8$. How could you describe the solution in words? What is the exact solution?

b Consider the exponential equation $2^x = 5$. How could you describe the solution in words? Why can't you determine the exact numerical solution without the use of technology? Sketch the graph $f(x) = 2^x$ and the horizontal line $y = 5$ in order to solve the equation.

c Consider the exponential equation $2^x = -2$. Does this equation have a solution?

d Consider the equation $a^x = b$. Can you describe the solution in words?

e Do all exponential equations have a solution? How can you find the solution to an exponential equation?

Some mathematical equations do not have an exact numerical solution. For this reason, mathematicians have "invented" symbols in order to describe the exact solution.

In general, the solution of the exponential equation $a^x = b$ is the **logarithmic function** $x = \log_a b$, where $a, b > 0$ and $a \neq 1$.

Here a is called the **base** of the logarithm. Any positive number can be used as a base for logarithms, but the only ones you need to know about for this course are 10 and Euler's number e.

You can write $\log_{10} x$ as $\log x$.

You can write $\log_e x$ as the **natural logarithm** $\ln x$.

Some examples follow.

Two fundamental exponential equations with their solutions are:
- $10^x = c \Rightarrow x = \log c$
- $e^x = c \Rightarrow x = \ln c$

and two fundamental logarithmic equations are:
- $\log x = c \Rightarrow x = 10^c$
- $\ln x = c \Rightarrow x = e^c$

On your GDC, $\log_{10}$ is called "LOG" and $\log_e$ is called "LN".

Example 15

Find the exact value of x for each of the following equations.

1 $10^x = 5$ **2** $e^{2x} = 12$ **3** $\log x = 3$ **4** $3\ln x = 7$

1 $x = \log 5$	By the definition of log or by using the result above.
2 $2x = \ln 12 \Rightarrow x = \dfrac{1}{2}\ln 12$	
3 $x = 10^3 = 1000$	
4 $\ln x = \dfrac{7}{3} \Rightarrow x = e^{\frac{7}{3}}$	It is important to isolate the log term before applying the rule.

Investigation 13

1 Consider the equations $10^x = 1$ and $e^x = 1$ or even the general case $a^x = 1$.

Find the value of x.

What is the solution in terms of logs?

2 Consider the equations $10^x = 10$ and $e^x = e$ or even the general case $a^x = a$.

Find the value of x.

What is the solution in terms of logs?

3 Consider the equations $10^x = 10^n$ and $e^x = e^n$ or even the general case $a^x = a^n$, where x is the unknown variable and n is a constant parameter.

Find the value of x.

What is the solution in terms of logs?

4 Use your GDC to copy and complete the following table, giving your answers to three significant figures.

log 2		log 3		log 6	
log 3		log 4		log 12	
ln 5		ln 7		ln 35	

What do you notice? What can you conjecture about $\log_a x + \log_a y$?

5 Use your GDC to copy and complete the following table, giving your answers to three significant figures.

log 12		log 2		log 6	
log 15		log 3		log 5	
ln 11		ln 7		$\ln \dfrac{11}{7}$	

What do you notice? What can you conjecture about $\log_a x - \log_a y$?

International-mindedness

Logarithms do not have units but many measurements use a log scale such as earthquakes, the pH scale and human hearing.

 Continued on next page

6 Use your GDC to copy and complete the following table, giving your answers to three significant figures.

$\log(3^2)$		$\log 3$		$2\log 3$	
$\ln\sqrt{2}$		$\ln 2$		$\frac{1}{2}\log 2$	

What do you notice? What can you conjecture about $\log_a(x^n)$?

$\log 1 = 0$, $\ln 1 = 0$ and in general, $\log_a 1 = 0$

$\log 10 = 1$, $\ln e = 1$ and in general, $\log_a a = 1$

$\log 10^n = n$, $\ln e^n = n$ and in general, $\log_a a^n = n$

Laws of logarithms:

- $\log_a x + \log_a y = \log_a xy$

- $\log_a x - \log_a y = \log_a \dfrac{x}{y}$

- $\log_a (x)^n = n\log_a x$

Example 16

Write each of the following as a single logarithm:

a $3\log x$ **b** $\dfrac{\log x}{2}$ **c** $2\log x + \log y$ **d** $\log x - 2\log y$

e $-\ln x$ **f** $1 + \ln x$ **g** $\ln x + \ln y - \ln z$

a $3\log x = \log(x^3)$

b $\dfrac{\log x}{2} = \dfrac{1}{2}\log x = \log\left(x^{\frac{1}{2}}\right) = \log\sqrt{x}$

c $2\log x + \log y = \log(x^2) + \log y = \log(x^2 y)$

d $\log x - 2\log y = \log x - \log(y^2) = \log\left(\dfrac{x}{y^2}\right)$

e $-\ln x = -1\ln x = \ln(x^{-1}) = \ln\left(\dfrac{1}{x}\right)$

f $1 + \ln x = \ln e + \ln x = \ln(ex)$

g $\ln x + \ln y - \ln z = \ln(xy) - \ln z = \ln\left(\dfrac{xy}{z}\right)$

Exercise 7J

1 Find the value of each of the following logarithms.

a $\log 100$ **b** $\log 0.1$ **c** $\ln e$

d $\ln \dfrac{1}{e}$ **e** $\ln e^2$ **f** $\log \sqrt{10}$

g $\ln\left(\dfrac{1}{\sqrt{e}}\right)$

2 Find the solution to the following exponential equations giving the answer as a logarithm where appropriate.

a $10^x = 10$ **b** $10^x = 100$

c $10^x = 38$ **d** $e^x = e^2$

e $e^x = 3$ **f** $e^x = 0.3$

g $e^x = 1$

3 Write each of the following as a single logarithm:

a $2\log x$ **b** $\dfrac{\log x}{3}$

c $3\log x + 2\log y$ **d** $\log x - 3\log y$

e $-2\ln x$ **f** $2 + \log x$

g $\ln x - \ln y - \ln z$

4 Find the exact value of a if the following piecewise functions are continuous for $x > 0$

a $f(x) = \begin{cases} 4x^3 - 3 & x \leq 1 \\ 2e^{ax} & x > 1 \end{cases}$

b $f(x) = \begin{cases} 3x^2 - 4 & x \leq 2 \\ 2\ln ax & x > 2 \end{cases}$

TOK

The phrase "exponential growth" is used popularly to describe a number of phenomena.

Do you think that using mathematical language can distort understanding?

Investigation 14

1 a Verify that if $f(x) = \log x$ and $g(x) = 10^x$ then $f \circ g(x) = g \circ f(x) = x$.

b Hence state the connection between the two functions f and g.

2 Use the result of **1 a** to sketch the graphs $y = 10^x$ and $y = \log x$ on the same axes.

3 State the domain and range of $f(x) = \log x$.

4 a Find the inverse of $h(x) = e^x + 2$.

b Sketch the graph of $y = h(x)$ and its inverse on the same axes.

5 State the domain and range of h and h^{-1}.

6 **Factual** What are the domain and range of the function $f(x) = \log_a x$?

7 **Conceptual** What is the relationship between the logarithmic function and the exponential function?

The fuctions $y = 10^x$ and $y = \log x$ are inverse functions and so their composition gives x.
Similarly, the same thing holds for the functions $y = e^x$ and $y = \ln x$.
$$10^{\log x} = x \text{ and } e^{\ln x} = x$$

Exercise 7K

1 Solve the following exponential equations using logarithms. Give your answers as a logarithm.

a **i** $10^x = 3$, **ii** $\dfrac{10^x}{5} = 15$ **iii** $e^x = 5$

b **i** $3e^x - 1 = 14$, **ii** $\dfrac{10^x}{2} + 3 = 5$,

iii $3(e^x - 1) = 5$

2 Solve the following exponential equations using logarithms, given that all parameters are positive real numbers and $a \neq 1$.

a $a^x - c = 0$ **b** $be^x = 2$, **c** $2 \times 10^x = k$

3 Simplify the following:

a $10^{3\log x}$ **b** $e^{\ln x - \ln y}$

c $10^{2\log x - \log y}$ **d** $e^{-2\ln x}$

4 Given the functions $f(x) = \ln(x + 2)$ and $g(x) = 2e^x$

a Find $(g \circ f)(x)$, giving your answer in the form $ax + b$.

b For the function $f(x)$, determine the equation of any possible asymptotes and the exact coordinates of any possible intersections with the coordinate axes.

c Hence, sketch the curve of $f(x)$.

d Determine the inverse function of $f(x)$ and sketch it on the same set of coordinate axes, indicating any possible asymptotes and intercepts with the coordinate axes.

5 Consider the function $f(x) = 10^x - 3$.

a Find its inverse function $f^{-1}(x)$.

b Sketch the graph of $f^{-1}(x)$. On your graph, show clearly any possible asymptotes with their equations and the exact coordinates of any possible intersections with the coordinate axes.

c State clearly the domain and range of the inverse function $f^{-1}(x)$.

6 Consider the function $f(x) = 2e^x - 6$.

a Sketch the graph of $f(x)$. On your graph, show clearly any possible asymptotes with their equations and the exact coordinates of any possible intersections with the coordinate axes.

b Find its inverse function $f^{-1}(x)$.

c State clearly the domain and range of the inverse function $f^{-1}(x)$.

Investigation 15

Kim recorded the battery remainder indication on her laptop during the course of a day with respect to the time of the day and gathered the following data, where t is the time in hours since she started the experiment and B is the battery left on her laptop.

t	1.6	3	4.4	6	6.8	9	10	12	14.8	16.4
B	96	79	65	52	47	34	30	23	15	12

She plotted the data and produced the following scatter diagram:

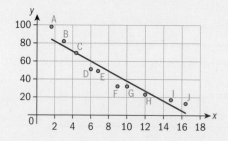

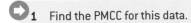

1 Find the PMCC for this data.

The scatter diagram she created did not have strong enough linear correlation for her to conclude that the relation between her variables is linear.

Her physics teacher suggested that in fact the relationship was more likely to be exponential of the form $B = ae^{ct}$ and suggested she draw a semi-log graph of $\ln B$ against t.

2 By taking the natural log of both sides of the equation, explain why a graph of $\ln B$ against t for this function would be a straight line and give expressions for of the gradient and the y-intercept of this line.

3 a Copy and completed the table below

t	1.6	3	4.4	6	6.8	9	10	12	14.8	16.4
$\ln B$										

b Create a scatter diagram based on the table in part **a** with t on the horizontal axis and $\ln B$ on the vertical axis. This is called a semi-log graph—one varible plotted against the logarithm of the other variable.

c Find the PMCC for this data and compare your result with the one for a linear model.

d Use your values for the gradient and for the y-intercept to estimate the parameters for the equation $B = ae^{ct}$

Her chemistry teacher suggested that in fact the relationship was more likely to be of the form $B = at^c$ and suggested she draw a log-log graph of $\ln B$ against $\ln t$.

4 By taking the natural log of both sides of the equation, explain why a graph of $\ln B$ against $\ln t$ for this function would be a straight line and give an expression for the gradient of the line and for the y-intercept.

5 a Copy and complete the table below

$\ln t$										
$\ln B$										

b Create a scatter diagram based on the table in part **a** with $\ln t$ on the horizontal axis and $\ln B$ on the vertical axis. This is called a **log-log graph** – the logarithm of one variable plotted against the logarithm of the other variable.

c Find the PMCC for this data and compare your result with the previous two models.

d Use your values for the gradient and for the y-intercept to estimate the parameters for the equation $B = at^c$.

6 By considering the value of B when $t = 0$ which of the two non-linear models might you prefer irrespective of the values of the PMCC?

7 [Conceptual] How does logarithmic scaling of graphs help you identify the relationship between variables?

A power function of the form $y = ax^b$ can be **linearized** as $\ln y = b\ln x + \ln a$.

A graph of $\ln y$ against $\ln x$ will have a gradient of b and a y-intercept of $\ln a$.

An exponential function of the form $y = ae^{bx}$ can be **linearized** as $\ln y = bx + \ln a$.

A graph of $\ln y$ against x will have a gradient of b and a y-intercept of $\ln a$.

EXAM HINT

In most cases the parameters for the function can also be found by using either power or exponential regression on your GDC. But if instructed to find them using linearization techniques you must show sufficient method to demonstrate you have found them this way.

Some GDCs will give the exponential regression function in the form $y = ab^x$. This can be converted into base e by writing $b = e^r \Rightarrow r = \ln b$ and hence $y = a(e^r)^x = ae^{rx}$ or $y = ae^{x\ln b}$.

Investigation 16

a Sketch the following data on a scatter diagram.

x	3	5	7	9	11	13	15	17
y	95	1071	9812	103 201	1 100 458	9 526 983	107 247 384	993 485 029

b Write down the domain and the range of the data. What do you notice? What is the problem with viewing this scatter diagram?

c Complete the following table to include the logarithm of the y-values.

y	95	1071	9812	103 201	1 100 458	9 526 983	107 247 384	993 485 029
$\log y$								

d Sketch the following data on a scatter diagram.

x	3	5	7	9	11	13	15	17
$\log y$								

e Write down the domain and the range of the new set of data. What do you notice? How was the problem resolved?

Exercise 7L

1 In a set of data, for reasons of manageable scaling the logarithm (in base 10) of the measurements have been found and recorded. The new set of data is as follows.

Value	A	B	C	D	E	F	G	H	I	J
log y	1.7	3.2	4.1	4.7	5.2	6	6.6	7.2	8	10.1

a Find the value of y for measurement B and measurement G. How many times is G greater than B?

b State the range of values in this set of data

c Comment on the advantages of using a log scaling of the original data

2 Data linking the life expectancy in countries of the European Union to their gross national income (GNI) index are shown below.

Country	AUT	BEL	BGR	HRV	CZE	CNK	EST	FIN	FRA
GNI	42 080	39 270	13 980	19 330	24 280	42 300	20 830	38 500	35 650
L.E.	80.7	80.2	74.2	77.1	77.8	79.9	76.3	80.3	81.6
Country	DEU	GRC	HUN	IRL	ITA	LVA	LTU	LUX	NLD
GNI	39 970	26 090	20 260	33 230	32 710	17 820	19 690	64 410	43 260
L.E.	80.5	80.5	75	80.6	82	74.6	74.3	81.5	80.9
Country	POL	PRT	ROU	SVK	SVN	ESP	SWE	GBR	
GNI	20 480	24 480	15 140	22 230	26 960	31 660	42 200	35 940	
L.E.	76.5	80.2	74.5	76.1	79.9	82	81.7	80.5	

a Calculate the log of both sets of data and include your results in an enlarged table.

Let the value of GNI be x and the value of L.E. be y.

It is thought that the relation ship between the two variables is of the form $y = ax^b$

b Find the line of best fit for log y against log x.

c Hence find estimates for a and b.

d Use the power regression function on the GDC to verify your values of a and b.

---

3 Frances suspects that the time taken (t minutes) to answer one question in a multiple-choice quiz increases with the total time (q minutes) that she has spent working on the quiz.

She times herself over different periods and collects the following data.

Total time working on the quiz, q (minutes)	5	20	30	40	50
Time taken to answer a question, t (minutes)	2.4	2.8	3.4	4.0	5.1

Frances thinks t and q are related by an equation of the form $q = ae^{bt}$.

a Find the values of $\ln q$ for the values of q given in the table.

b Plot a graph of $\ln q$ against t.

c Either by measuring values from your graph, or by using the linear regression function on your GDC, find the values of b and $\ln a$.

d Hence, suggest a suitable model for the time taken to answer questions.

e Use the model to estimate how long it would take Frances to answer a question after working on the quiz for one hour in total.

4 Yenni owns a small factory that manufactures shirts. She wants to model the relationship between the daily total cost of manufacturing shirts ($\$s$) and the number of shirts that are produced (n).

She believes the model is of the form $s = an^b + c$

She knows that, even if she were making no shirts, the daily cost of running the factory would be $\$1000$.

a Find the value of c.

Yenni collects data and estimates the following values

n	50	100	150	200
s	2000	2800	3400	3800

b Write down a linear equation of $\ln(s - c)$ against $\ln n$.

c Plot a graph of $\ln(s - c)$ against $\ln n$.

d Find values for b and $\ln a$ using your graph or linear regression.

e Hence find a model for the cost of producing the shirts.

f Yenni would like to produce 500 shirts a day. Use the model from part **e** to estimate the total daily cost.

g Describe the dangers of using this model to estimate the cost of producing 500 a day.

h i Describe how you could enter data into your GDC to find the model using the power regression function.

ii Hence, verify your answer to part **e**.

5 The velocity (v) of a falling body is recorded at different distances (d) from the point at which it was launched. Consideration of the physics involved leads to the following model being proposed:

$v = a\sqrt{d} + b$

Data for v and d is collected and shown below.

d	1	2	3	4
v	8.4	10.3	11.7	12.9

a Plot a graph of v against $\sqrt{d}$.

b Estimate values of a and b.

7.5 Logistic models

The progression of the world record for men's high jump at the beginning of each year since 1912 is shown on the scatter diagram.

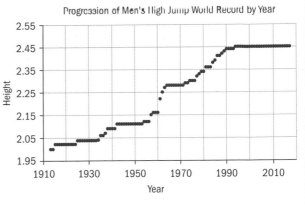

Progression of Men's High Jump World Record by Year

a How could you describe the basic features of the progression of the world record?

b How is it different from a linear graph?

c How is it different from an exponential graph?

d Where else do you encounter this shape?

The logistic function is used to model situations where there is a restriction on the growth. For example, population on an island, bacteria in a petri dish, or the increase in height of a person or seedling.

Logistic functions have a horizontal asymptote at $f(x) = L$.

> The equation of a logistic function has the standard form $f(x) = \dfrac{L}{1 + Ce^{-kx}}$,
>
> where L, C and k are the parameters of the function and e is Euler's number.

TOK

Mathematics is all around us in patterns, shapes, time and space.

What does this tell you about mathematical knowledge?

Investigation 17

a Sketch the graph of the following functions.

i $f(x) = \dfrac{10}{1 + e^{-x}}$ **ii** $f(x) = \dfrac{20}{1 + e^{-x}}$ **iii** $f(x) = \dfrac{30}{1 + e^{-x}}$

What is the relation of the value of the numerator to the graph of the function?

How does this link with graph transformations?

How does the rate of change vary at different points on the graph?

At what point does the rate of change seem greatest?

Give the equations of any asymptotes.

b Sketch the graph of the following functions:

i $f(x) = \dfrac{10}{1 + e^{-x}}$ **ii** $f(x) = \dfrac{10}{1 + e^{-2x}}$ **iii** $f(x) = \dfrac{10}{1 + e^{-3x}}$

What is the relation of the parameter multiplying x to the graph of the function?

How does this link with graph transformations?

How does the rate of change vary at different points on the graph?

HINT

In a logistic equation $f(x) = \dfrac{L}{(1 + Ce^{(-kx)})}$, $f(x) = L$ is an asymptote to the curve and L is referred to as the carrying capacity for the model being considered.

Number and algebra

Functions

Logistic functions have a varying rate of change. The most usual shape of a logistic function starts with the data being almost constant (close to zero rate of change), then the data show a rapid increase and finally become almost constant again (close to zero rate of change again). Thus the data show two different horizontal asymptotes, one for small data values and one for large data values.

HINT

In some real-life situations the change will begin at a certain time and so the lower horizontal asymptote will not be part of the function.

Exercise 7M

1 The function that models the percentage of people globally with access to broadband Internet with respect to time is given by the logistic function $P(t) = \dfrac{100}{1 + 10e^{-0.5t}}$, $t \geq 0$.

   a Sketch the graph of the function.

   b Write down the range of values of the function and interpret their significance.

   c Use the model to predict how long it will take for half the people to have access to broadband Internet.

   d Calculate the percentage of people who will have access to broadband Internet in 20 years.

2 Data for the population of the Virgin Islands from 1950 to 2015 have produced the following logistic function model.
   $P(t) = \dfrac{107000}{1 + 4e^{-0.135t}}$, where t is the number of years that have passed since 1950.

   a Estimate the population of the Virgin Islands in 1950.

   b Estimate the population of the Virgin Islands in 2015.

   c Assuming that this model will also be valid in the future, state the largest population that the Virgin Islands will ever be able to accommodate.

3 A flu epidemic is spreading throughout Europe. An estimated 120 million people are susceptible to this particular strain and it is predicted that eventually all of them will get infected. There are 10 000 people already infected when $x = 0$ and it is projected that the number of people who will have been infected will double in the next two weeks.

   The logistic function $f(x) = \dfrac{L}{1 + Ce^{-kx}}$ models the number of people infected where x is measured in weeks.

   a Determine the approximate values of the parameters L, C and k.

   b Use the model to determine how many people will be infected for after four weeks.

   c The infection is considered terminated when 90% of the people have been infected. Use the model to determine how long it will be until the infection can be considered terminated.

Chapter summary

- A sequence of numbers in which each term can be found by multiplying the preceding term by a **common ratio**, r, is called a geometric sequence. For a sequence to be geometric, $r \neq 1$.

- The nth term of a geometric sequence is given by the formula:
$$u_n = u_1 r^{n-1}, r \neq 1$$

- Percentage change is a form of a geometric sequence.

- When terms **increase** by $p\%$ from the preceding term, their common ratio corresponds to $r = \dfrac{100 + p}{100}$.

- When terms **decrease** by $p\%$ from the preceding term, their common ratio corresponds to $r = \dfrac{100 - p}{100}$.

- The sum of the first n terms of a geometric sequence is called a geometric series and is given by the formula:
$$S_n = \frac{u_1\left(r^n - 1\right)}{r - 1} = \frac{u_1\left(1 - r^n\right)}{1 - r}, r \neq 1$$

- The **sum to infinity** of a geometric sequence is:
$$S_\infty = \frac{u_1}{1 - r}, \text{ for } |r| < 1$$

- If PV is the present value, FV the future value, r the interest rate, n the number of years and k the compounding frequency, or number of times interest is paid in a year (ie $k = 1$ for yearly, $k = 2$ for half-yearly, $k = 4$ for quarterly and $k = 12$ for monthly, etc), then the general formula for finding the future value is
$$FV = PV\left(1 + \frac{r}{100k}\right)^{kn}$$

- When a constant investment of $\$P$ is made for a certain number of n periods always compounded with the same interest rate, it is called an annuity.

- All exponential functions have a **horizontal asymptote**.

- Exponential functions of the form $f(x) = b^x$ have the line $y = 0$ as a horizontal asymptote. Unlike inverse proportion functions, the asymptotic behavior occurs either as $x \to \infty$ or as $x \to -\infty$, but not on both.

- The exponential function $f(x) = ka^x + c$ has:
  - The straight line $y = c$ as a horizontal asymptote.
  - It crosses the y-axis at the point $(0, k + c)$.
  - Is increasing for $a > 1$ and decreasing for $0 < a < 1$.

- In general, the solution of the exponential equation $a^x = b$ is the **logarithmic function** $x = \log_a b$, where $a, b > 0$ and $a \neq 1$.

- Here a is called the **base** of the logarithm. Any positive number can be used as a base for logarithms, but the only ones you need to know about for this course are 10 and Euler's number e.

- You can write $\log_{10} x$ simply as $\log x$.

- You can write $\log_e x$ simply as the **natural logarithm** $\ln x$.

Continued on next page

- Two fundamental exponential equations with their solutions are:
  - ○ $10x = c \Rightarrow x = \log c$
  - ○ $e^x = c \Rightarrow x = \ln c$

  and two fundamental logarithmic equations are:
  - ○ $\log x = c \Rightarrow x = 10^c$
  - ○ $\ln x = c \Rightarrow x = e^c$

Laws of logarithms:

- $\log_a x + \log_a y = \log_a xy$

- $\log_a x - \log_a y = \log_a \dfrac{x}{y}$

- $\log_a (x^n) = n\log_a x$

The functions $y = 10^x$ and $y = \log x$ are inverse functions and so their composition gives x. Similarly, the same thing holds for the functions $y = e^x$ and $y = \ln x$.

$10^{\log x} = x$ and $e^{\ln x} = x$

The equation of a logistic function has the standard form $f(x) = \dfrac{L}{1 + Ce^{-kx}}$, where L, C and k are the

parameters of the function and e is Euler's number. The logistic function is used in situations where there is a restriction on the growth. L is referred to as the carrying capacity.

Developing inquiry skills

If you keep doubling a number, how long will it take before it becomes more than 1 million times its original value?

Can something that grows indefinitely never exceed a certain value?

What is the equation that models a skateboard quarter pipe ramp?

Does the same amount of money have the same value today, yesterday and tomorrow?

How can you decide on which is the best investment plan?

Will an ice cube left outside of the freezer or a boiling cup of water that has been removed from heat ever reach room temperature?

Chapter review

Click here for a mixed review exercise

1 The first four terms of a geometric sequence are 2, 5, 12.5, 31.25.

  a Find the common ratio.

  b Find the 8th term.

  c Find the sum of the first eight terms.

2 Saul bought a new bicycle for US$350. Every year the value of the bicycle decreased by 12%. Find the value of the bicycle at the end of five years.

3 Molly bought a flat. At the beginning of the third year, the value of Molly's flat had increased to 363 000 euros. At the beginning of the fifth year, the value had increased to 439 230 euros. Assume that the value of the flat increases by a constant rate each year.

a Calculate the rate of increase as a percentage of the value of the house.

b Calculate how many euros Molly originally paid for the flat.

c Find how much the flat is worth at the beginning of the ninth year.

4 A finite geometric sequence has terms 2, 6, 18, …, 118 098.

a Calculate the number of terms in this sequence.

b Find the sum of the sequence.

5 The school fees increase each year by the rate of inflation. When Barnaby joined the school, the fees were UK£9500. At the end of the first year the rate of inflation was 1.16%.

a Find the cost of the school fees for the second year.

The following year the rate of inflation was 1.14%.

b Find the cost of the school fees for the third year.

6 Wei invested SGD 3000 (Singapore dollars) in a bank that paid 2.35% interest per year compounded monthly.

a Find how much Wei had in the bank after six years.

b Find the number of years before he had SGD 5000 in the bank.

7 Omar invested JOD 4500 (Jordanian dinar) in a bank that paid interest per annum compounded quarterly. After six years he has JOD 5179.27 in the bank. Find the interest rate.

8 Silvia is left an annuity of US$4000 in her uncle's will. The annuity is for five years at 4% per annum and is to be paid out monthly. Find the monthly payments.

9 Nathalie borrows 6500 euros for a motorbike. The loan is for five years at 2.5% interest per annum. Find how much Nathalie's monthly payments are to clear the loan.

10 A population of rabbits can be modelled by the function $f(x) = 24\,000 \times 1.12^x$, where x is the time in years.

a Find the number of rabbits after five years.

b Calculate how long it will take for the population of rabbits to double.

11 The temperature, $T°C$, of a cup of soup can be modelled by the equation $T(x) = 21 + 74 \times (1.2)^{-x}$, where x is the time in minutes.

a Find the initial temperature.

b Find the temperature after 10 minutes.

c Find how many minutes it takes for the soup to reach 40°C.

d Write down the room temperature.

12 An exponential function is $f(x) = 4 \times 2.3^x + 16$.

a Write down the equation of the horizontal asymptote.

b Write down the coordinates of the point where the curve cuts the y-axis.

13 The spread of a disease can be modelled by the equation $y = 4 + e^x$, where x is the time in days from the time the disease was first detected.

a Find the number of people with the disease after seven days.

b Find the number of days it takes for 25 000 people to be infected.

14 The height, in metres, of a runner bean plant increases each week according to the model function $h(t) = 0.25 + \log(2t - 0.6)$, $t > 0$, where t is the time in weeks.

a Find the height of the plant after four weeks.

b Find the number of weeks it takes for the plant to reach a height of 2 m.

15 a Find the value of the following in the most simplified form: $\sum_{r=1}^{n}(5 \times 2^r)$.

b Find the value of the following in the most simplified form: $\sum_{r=1}^{2n}(5 \times 2^r)$

16 $900 is invested at the beginning of each year into an account earning 4% per annum compounded annually. Find the total value of the investments at the end of the tenth year.

Exam-style questions

17 P1: Maria's parents will not let her have a pet animal, so instead she has a pet rock. She keeps it in her pocket and strokes it, but sadly this wears it away. Its mass is given by the equation

$m = 0.1e^{-0.4}t$, where m is mass in kg and t is time in years.

a Write down the initial mass of Maria's pet rock. (1 mark)

b Find how long it takes for the mass of the rock to be half the original mass. (3 marks)

When the mass of the pet rock is less than 0.01 kg it becomes too small for Maria to find.

c Find how long it takes for this sad event to occur. (3 marks)

18 P2: Let $\log x = p$ and $\log y = q$. Express the following in terms of p and q.

a $\log xy$ (1 mark)

b $\log \dfrac{x}{y}$ (1 mark)

c $\log \sqrt{x}$ (1 mark)

d $\log x^2 y^5$ (2 marks)

e $\log(x^y)$ (3 marks)

f $\log 0.01 x^3$ (3 marks)

19 P1: The Martian high jump record height, h m, is given by $h = \dfrac{a}{b + e^{-0.1t}}$, where t is the time in years from when records

were first kept. The first recorded height was 2 m. As t increases, the record tends to a limit of 3 m.

a Find the values of a and b. (4 marks)

b Calculate the record height after 10 years. (2 marks)

c Find the value of t for which $h = 2.8$. (3 marks)

20 P1: Carbon dating can be used to estimate the age of a piece of wood. Scientists measure the ratio r of carbon 14 in the sample to carbon 14 in living wood. They can then estimate the time (t years) since the tree was cut down using the model $t = \dfrac{-6000}{\ln 2}\ln(r)$ where $r < 1$.

a Calculate t if

i $r = 0.5$ **ii** $r = 0.25$. (3 marks)

If $r < 0.01$ then there is insufficient carbon 14 for the test to be reliable.

b Find the age of the oldest piece of wood for which the test would just cease to be reliable, giving your answer to the nearest 10 000 years. (2 marks)

c Express r in terms of t. (2 marks)

d Hence find r if $t = 10000$. (2 marks)

21 P1: A geometric sequence has 3rd term 18 and 6th term of 486.

a Find the first term a and the common ratio r. (3 marks)

b Find:

i the 8th term

ii the sum of the first 8 terms. (3 marks)

c Find the smallest value of n such that the nth term is greater than 10^6. (2 marks)

22 P1: A geometric sequence has first term a and common ratio r, where a and r are both positive.

a Write down an expression in terms of a and r for

  i the nth term, u_n

  ii the sum S_N of the first N terms of u_n.   (2 marks)

A new sequence is defined by $v_n = \log u_n$.

b By writing v_n in terms of a and r, determine what type of sequence v_n defines, and find an expression for the nth term v_n. You must clearly show your working and justify your answer.   (4 marks)

c Find an expression for the sum T_N of the first N terms of v_n (2 marks)

d Determine whether or not $T_n = \log S_n$.   (2 marks)

23 P1: a If the sum to infinity of a geometric sequence is 3 times the first term, find the common ratio.   (2 marks)

b If the sum to infinity of a geometric sequence is $\frac{2}{3}$ times the first term, find the common ratio.   (2 marks)

c Determine whether the sum to infinity of a geometric sequence can be $\frac{1}{3}$ times the first term. Justify your answer.   (3 marks)

24 P2: In this question all monetary values are to be given to 2 decimal places.

Anna invests her money in a bank that gives her 3% compound interest per year.

a Calculate how much money Anna would have to deposit in the bank now, for it to be worth £100 in one year's time.   (2 marks)

b Calculate how much money Anna would have to deposit in the bank now, for it to be worth £100 in ten years' time.   (2 marks)

Anna decides to invest ten instalments of £M each, with each instalment being deposited in the bank on 1st January each year. On the 31st of December of final year (when her last instalment will have been invested for one year) she wishes her investment to be worth £1000.

c Find the value of M.   (6 marks)

25 P1: Bonjana has 5000 euros that she wishes to invest for five years. There are two schemes that she can choose between.

Scheme 1 offers 4% annual compound interest, compounded yearly.

Scheme 2 offers 3.8% annual compound interest, compounded monthly.

a If Bonjana wants to gain much interest as possible, determine which option she should choose.   (4 marks)

b For the scheme you identified in part **a**, calculate the interest that Bonjana will earn over five years. Give your answer correct to 2 decimal places.   (2 marks)

c Determine whether your answer to part **a** would change if Bonjana had a different amount to invest, for a different number of complete years.   (3 marks)

Click here for further exam practice

A passing fad?

Approaches to learning: Communication, Research

Exploration criteria: Presentation (A), Mathematical communication (B), Reflection (D), Use of mathematics (E)

IB topic: Exponentials and logarithms

Look at the data

Fortnite was released by Epic Games in July 2017 and quickly grew in popularity.

Here are some data for the total number of registered players worldwide from August 2017 to June 2018:

Date	August 2017	November 2017	December 2017	January 2018	June 2018
Months since launch, t	1	4	5	6	11
Number of registered players, P (million)	1	20	30	45	125

The data is taken from the press releases of the developers, Epic Games.

Are these data reliable?

Are there any potential problems with the data that has been collected?

What other data might be useful?

Plotting these data on your GDC or other graphing software gives this graph:

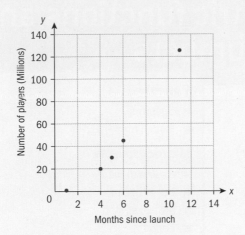

Describe the shape of the graph.

What could be some possible explanations for this growth?

Model the data

Why might it be useful to find a model that links the number of players of Fortnite to the number of months since the launch of the game?

Who might this be useful for?

Let t be the number of months since July 2017.

Let P be the number of players in millions.

Assume that the data is modelled by an exponential function of the form $P = a.b^t$ where a and b are constants to be found.

Use the techniques from the chapter or previous tasks to help you.

Consider different models **by hand** and **using technology**.

How do these models differ? Why?

Which one is preferable? Why?

What alterations could be made to the model?

Use the model to predict the number of users for the current month.

Do you think this is likely to be a reliable prediction?

How reliable do you think the models are at predicting how many Fortnite players there are now? Justify your answer.

Research the number of players there are in this current month who play Fortnite.

Compare this figure with your prediction based on your model above. How big is the error?

What does this tell you about the reliability of your previous model?

Plot a new graph with the updated data and try to fit another function to this data.

Will a modified exponential model be a good fit?

If not, what other function would be a better model that could be used to predict the number of users now?

Extension

Think of another example of data that you think may currently display a similar exponential trend (or exponential decay).

Can you collect reliable and relevant data for your example?

Find data and present it in a table and a graph.

Develop a model or models for the data (ensure that your notation is consistent and your variables are defined) – you could use technology or calculations by hand.

For how long do you think your model will be useful for making predictions?

Explain.

8 Modelling periodic phenomena: trigonometric functions and complex numbers

Many natural, and human-made, phenomena repeat themselves regularly over time. Tides rise and fall, the sun rises and sets, the moon changes its appearance, a clock's pendulum swings, crystals vibrate when an electrical current is applied. All of these things happen in a predictable fashion.

Concepts
- Systems
- Modelling

Microconcepts
- Radian measure
- Length of arc
- Area of sector
- Period
- Amplitude
- Phase shift
- Principal axis
- Sinusoidal models: $f(x) = a\sin(b(x-c)) + d$
- Cartesian form of complex numbers
- Polar form of complex numbers
- Exponential form of complex numbers
- Modulus
- Argument
- Powers
- Complex numbers
- The complex plane.

> Given the times of high and low tides on a given day, how would you decide when there would be enough water in a harbour to enter with a boat?

> If two sources of electricity are combined, how could you find the overall voltage?

> If there is a full moon tonight, how can we predict when the next new moon will occur?

> How can we predict the number of hours of daylight on a particular date?

The harbour in Aberdeen, Scotland has the depth of water varies with the tide. As a result, boats can only enter or leave at certain times.

On 1 January 2017, high tides were at 3:02 and 15:09 where the water had a depth of 4m. The low tide occurs at 8:54 where the depth of water is 1.1m. A boat requires 2m of water to be able to move. What was the latest a boat could leave the harbour on that day?

The water depth over the course of January is shown on the graph with red lines. The height of alternate low tides is marked with a green dot. An attempt has been made to approximate that to a function, in blue.

- In what ways is the model a good fit?
- In what ways does the model not fit the data well?
- What features can you identify about the model that might enable you to find its equation?
- What other information is shown on the graph?

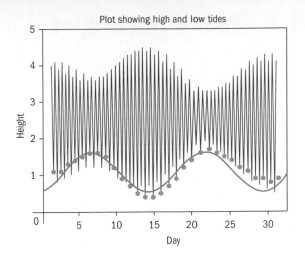

Plot showing high and low tides

Developing inquiry skills

What other climate phenomena could have a repeating pattern? What questions could you ask for your country? What data would you need?

Think about the questions in this opening problem and answer any you can. As you work through the chapter, you will gain mathematical knowledge and skills that will help you to answer them all.

Before you start

Click here for help with this skills check

You should know how to:

1 Transform graphs of functions.
   e.g. The transformations needed to transform $y = x^2$ onto $y = 2(3x - 1)^2 + 4$ are:

   - A translation of $\begin{pmatrix} 1 \\ 0 \end{pmatrix}$

   - Then a stretch parallel to the y-axis scale factor $\frac{1}{3}$

   - Then a stretch parallel to the x-axis scale factor 2

   - Then a translation of $\begin{pmatrix} 0 \\ 4 \end{pmatrix}$

Skills check

1 The graph shows $y = f(x)$.

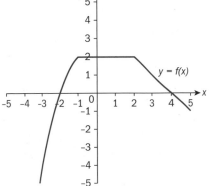

Draw the graphs of:

a $y = 2f(x) + 1$ **b** $y = f(2x + 1)$

8.1 Measuring angles

Units of measurement are often varied and equally often quite arbitrary in how they have been developed. Lengths may be measured in feet, metres, chains, etc, all of which have been established in a certain manner and have their different uses. Equally there are ways to convert between different measures.

The measurement of angles is the same, and there have been many measures that have been adopted over the years. We are probably most comfortable with using degrees for the measurement of angles and we know that a full circle is comprised of 360 degrees. However, in some more advanced mathematics we use a mathematical unit of measurement called the **radian**.

TOK

Which is a better measure of angle: radian or degree? What are the "best" criteria by which to decide?

A radian is defined as the angle subtended at the centre of a circle of radius 1 by an arc of length 1 as shown in the diagram.

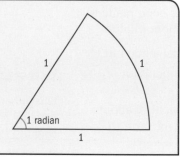

Investigation 1

1 If a sector has radius 1 and angle 2 radians, what will be the length of the arc?

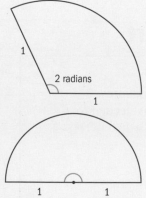

It is clear that if the angle is doubled, then the length of the arc will be doubled too.

We can consider a semicircle to establish the conversion between degrees and radians.

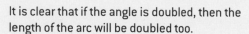

2 What is the angle shown in degrees?

3 **Factual** What is the length of the arc? Hence state the size of the angle in radians.

We can see that 180 degrees are equivalent to π radians or approximately 3.14 radians. Note the difference between a numerical value and an exact value.

4 **Factual** What would be the exact radian equivalence of 90°? 45°? 120°?

In degrees the arc length of a sector subtended by an angle θ is given by the formula $\dfrac{\theta}{360} \times 2\pi r$

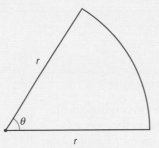

5 **a** Explain how this formula can be derived.

  b Give the formula for arc length when θ is measured in radians.

  c Explain why this matches the definition for one radian given at the start of the investigation.

6 **a** Write down the formula for the area of a circle with radius r.

  b Hence give the formula for the area of the sector of a circle with radius r subtended by an angle θ, when θ is measured in radians.

7 **Conceptual** Why might you choose to use radians rather than degrees when finding the lengths of arcs and areas of sectors?

International-mindedness

Why are there 360 degrees in a complete turn?

- π radians are equivalent to 180 degrees.

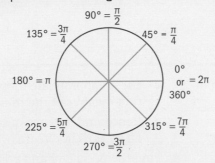

$$90° = \frac{\pi}{2}$$
$$135° = \frac{3\pi}{4} \qquad 45° = \frac{\pi}{4}$$
$$180° = \pi \qquad \begin{array}{c} 0° \\ \text{or} = 2\pi \\ 360° \end{array}$$
$$225° = \frac{5\pi}{4} \qquad 315° = \frac{7\pi}{4}$$
$$270° = \frac{3\pi}{2}$$

- The length of arc, L, of a sector radius r, is given by $L = r\theta$, if θ is in radians.

- The area, A, of a sector radius r, is given by $A = \dfrac{1}{2}r^2\theta$, if θ is in radians.

Example 1

The diagram below shows a sector of a circle of radius 5m, subtended by an angle of 1.1 radians inside a rectangle with a length 6m.

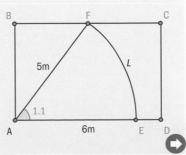

Continued on next page

a Find the length, L, of the arc FE.

The rectangle ABCD represents a garden of length 6m. A security light is placed at point A which has a range of 5m.

b Find the length BF.

c Hence find the area of the garden which is covered by the security light.

a $L = 5 \times 1.1 = 5.5$ m	Using the formula $L = r\theta$
b $BF = 5\cos(1.1) = 2.27$ m	The trig buttons on the calculators are used in the normal way, but if inputting an angle in radians the calculator needs to be set to radians mode.
c Area of sector = $\frac{1}{2} \times 5^2 \times 1.1 = 13.75 \text{m}^2$	Using the formula $A = \frac{1}{2}r^2\theta$ Area of yard covered by the security light is the area of the sector plus the area of the triangle ABF.
Area of triangle ABF = $\frac{1}{2} \times 2.27 \times 5 \times \sin(1.1) = 5.05 \text{m}^2$	Using Area of a triangle $= \frac{1}{2}ab\sin C$
Total area $= 13.75 + 5.05$ $= 18.8$ m²	

International-mindedness

Seki Takakazu calculated π to ten decimal places in 17th century Japan.

Exercise 8A

1 State the exact radian equivalent for each of the following angles.

   a 30°   **b** 165°

   c 270°   **d** 300°   **e** 210°

2 State the degree equivalent to each of the following radian measures.

   a $\dfrac{\pi}{3}$ **b** $\dfrac{4\pi}{3}$

   c $\dfrac{3\pi}{5}$ **d** 3π **e** 1

3

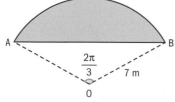

   a Find the length of the arc AB.

   b Find the area of sector OAB.

c Use an appropriate formula to find the area of the triangle OAB.

d Hence find the area of the segment, cut off by the chord AB.

4 Find the perimeter and area of each of the shaded regions below:

   a

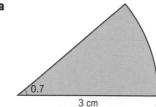

   b

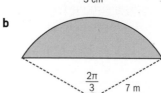

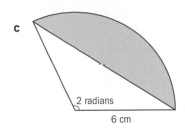

c

2 radians

6 cm

5 A goat is attached by a rope of length 3 m in the corner of a small, fenced rectangular field. The dimensions of the field are 6 m by 2.5 m.

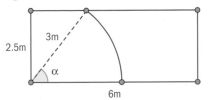

2.5m

3m

α

6m

a Find the value of α.

b Hence find the area of grass that can be reached by the goat.

6 The diagram below shows two circles with radii 3 cm and 5 cm and centres 6 cm apart. For the shaded region, find:

a the perimeter **b** the area.

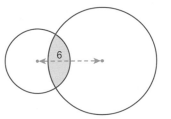

6

7 Find the area of the shaded region in the diagram below.

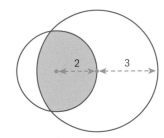

2 3

8.2 Sinusoidal models:
$$f(x) = a\sin(b(x-c)) + d$$

In Chapter 1 you saw how a right-angled triangle with hypotenuse of 1 unit length had other sides of lengths $\sin x$ and $\cos x$ if one of its angles was x.

This gave us a way to define the sine and cosine of acute angles. What about other angles? For example, a carriage on a Ferris wheel rotates 360 degrees around its centre point.

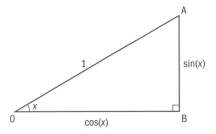

A

1

sin(x)

0 x cos(x) B

How would we extend the idea of sine and cosine for angles from 0 to 360 and beyond? What would these tell us about the position of the Ferris wheel car?

When dealing with angles greater than 90°, it is useful to have a more general definition for sine and cosine.

The definition used is based on the idea of the **unit circle**, which is a circle with radius of 1 unit, centred on the origin.

Angles on a unit circle are always measured clockwise, from the positive x-axis.

Investigation 2

On the diagram of the unit circle below, the points A, B and C represent angles of 90°, 180° and 270°.

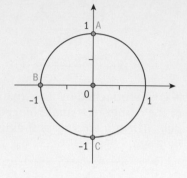

1 Write 90°, 180° and 270° in radians.

2 Where might you place

   a 225° **b** 360° **c** 3π?

3 Where might you place

   a $-\dfrac{\pi}{2}$ **b** $-45°$ **c** $-400°$?

4 a From the unit circle explain why $\cos \theta = x$ and $\sin \theta = y$.

   b Give the value of $\tan \theta$ in terms of x and y and hence in terms of $\sin \theta$ and $\cos \theta$.

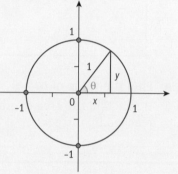

The results of question 4 can be extended to all angles, both positive and negative.

> On the unit circle the position of an angle $-\theta$ is found by moving clockwise around the unit circle through an angle θ.
>
> In general a negative angle represents a clockwise rotation. A rotation of $-45°$ and a rotation of $45°$ **clockwise** define the same movement.

> For all values of θ:
> - $\sin \theta$ is the y-coordinate of the point on the unit circle that represents an angle θ
> - $\cos \theta$ is the x-coordinate of the point on the unit circle that represents the angle θ.
> - $\tan \theta = \dfrac{\sin \theta}{\cos \theta}$

5 Use the definitions above to complete the following table.

θ	$-90°$	$0°$	$90°$	$180°$	$270°$	$360°$	$450°$
$\sin \theta$							
$\cos \theta$							

6 Copy the axes below and on them plot the points found above. Join these points to form a smooth curve for $y = \sin \theta$ and $y = \cos \theta$.

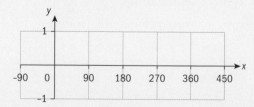

7 **Conceptual** How do we describe the sine function beyond the first quadrant?

8 **Conceptual** How do we describe the cosine function beyond the first quadrant?

9 Draw the graph of $y = \sin x$ on your GDC with your GDC set to:

   a **i** degrees   **ii** radians.

   b Comment on the differences and the similarities.

10 a With your GDC set to either degrees or radians, draw the graph of $y = \sin^2 x + \cos^2 x$. What do you notice?

   b Use the unit circle definition of sine and cosine to explain why this must always be true.

11 a Use the unit circle to explain why $\cos(-\theta) = \cos\theta$.

   b Find an expression for $\sin(-\theta)$.

   c Justify the answers for parts **a** and **b** from the graphs of the functions shown below.

You should know the following trigonometric identities:

$$\sin^2 x + \cos^2 x \equiv 1 \qquad \tan x \equiv \frac{\sin x}{\cos x}$$

$$\sin(-\theta) \equiv -\sin\theta \qquad \cos(-\theta) \equiv \cos\theta$$

The graphs of $y = \sin x$ and $y = \cos x$ repeat every $360°$ or 2π radians.

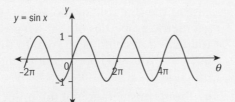

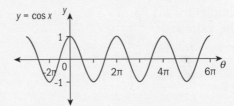

If solving for $\sin x = a$ or $\cos x = a$ you should always consider the multiple possible values for x.

Example 2

Use your GDC to find all values of x, $-\pi \le x \le 2\pi$ for which:

a $\sin x = \dfrac{1}{2}$ **b** $\cos x = -0.2$.

a 0.524, 2.62	Using the button for the inverse of sine on your GDC will only give one result. You should always plot a graph to ensure you find all the solutions in the range required by the question.
b $-1{,}77$, $1{,}77$, 4.51	This time there are three solutions.

Example 3

a Use the triangle shown to find an exact expression for:

    i $\sin 45°$ **ii** $\cos 45°$.

b Hence write down the exact values of the following:

    i $\sin(-45°)$ **ii** $\cos\left(-\dfrac{\pi}{4}\right)$

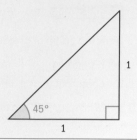

a $\sqrt{1^2 + 1^2} = \sqrt{2}$ **i** $\sin 45° = \dfrac{1}{\sqrt{2}}$ **ii** $\cos 45° = \dfrac{1}{\sqrt{2}}$	Using Pythagoras' theorem to find the hypotenuse, and then right-angled trigonometry to find sine and cosine.
b i $\sin(-45°) = -\dfrac{1}{\sqrt{2}}$	Using $\sin(-\theta) = -\sin\theta$.
ii $\cos\left(-\dfrac{\pi}{4}\right) = \dfrac{1}{\sqrt{2}}$	Using $\cos\left(-\dfrac{\pi}{4}\right) = \cos(-45°)$ and $\cos(-\theta) = \cos\theta$.

Exercise 8B

1 From your knowledge of the unit circle or the graphs $y = \sin x$ and $y = \cos x$ write down the values of:

  a $\sin 0$ **b** $\cos 0$ **c** $\sin \pi$

  d $\cos\left(\dfrac{\pi}{2}\right)$ **e** $\sin\left(-\dfrac{\pi}{2}\right)$ **f** $\cos(-\pi)$

  g $\sin\left(\dfrac{3\pi}{2}\right)$ **h** $\cos\left(-\dfrac{\pi}{2}\right)$

2 a For each of the following equations, find all solutions for $0 \le x \le 720°$.

    i $\sin x = \sin 10°$ **ii** $\sin x = 0.3$

    iii $\cos x = \cos 200°$

  b For each of the following equations, find all solutions for $0 \le x \le 3\pi$.

    i $\sin x = \sin\left(\dfrac{2\pi}{5}\right)$ **ii** $\cos x = -0.1$

    iii $\cos x = 0$

3 a Find the coordinates of all the intersection points for the graph of $y = \sin x$ and:

    i $y = 1 - x$ **ii** $y = 1 - 0.2x$.

  b In each case justify the fact that there are no further solutions.

4 In Chapter 1 you considered the ambiguous case of the sine rule by looking at the geometric properties of the two possible triangles that could be drawn. In this question you will approach it using the sine function.

  a From consideration of the unit circle explain why $\sin\theta = \sin(180 - \theta)$.

  b i Use your GDC to find a value of θ in degrees for which $\sin\theta = \dfrac{1}{2}$.

    ii Use the result of part **a** to write down another solution to $\sin\theta = \dfrac{1}{2}$.

  Consider the triangle ABD such that AB = 5 cm, BÂC = 20° and BC = 3 cm.

  c i Show that $\sin B\hat{C}A = \dfrac{5\sin 20°}{3}$.

    ii Use your GDC to find a value for BĈA.

    iii Use the result of part **a** to write down a second value for BĈA.

    iv Sketch the triangle ABC for both these angles.

5 A triangle PQR is such that $\hat{P} = 25°$, PQ = 7cm, and QR = 5cm. Find the two possible values for PR.

6 a Use the equilateral triangle shown to find an exact expression for

    i   sin60°   **ii**   cos60°

    iii   sin30°   **iv**   cos30°.

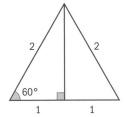

b Hence find the exact values of

    i $\cos(-60°)$ **ii** $\sin\dfrac{\pi}{6}$

    iii $\cos\left(-\dfrac{\pi}{6}\right)$ **iv** $\sin\left(-\dfrac{\pi}{3}\right)$.

7 It is given that $\cos x = \dfrac{1}{3}$, $0 \le x \le \dfrac{\pi}{2}$.

a Use the identities $\sin^2 x + \cos^2 x \equiv 1$ and $\tan x \equiv \dfrac{\sin x}{\cos x}$ to find the exact values of:

    i $\sin x$ **ii** $\tan x$.

b Write down the exact values of

    i $\cos(-x)$ **ii** $\sin(-x)$.

8 It is given that $2\sin x = \cos x$, $0 \le x \le \dfrac{\pi}{2}$

a Write down the value of $\tan x$.

b Find the exact value of

    i $\sin x$ **ii** $\cos x$.

c Why is it not possible that $-\dfrac{\pi}{2} \le x \le 0$?

The graph of $y = \sin x$ is shown:

The curve is **periodic**, as it repeats itself continually, and it oscillates either side of its **principal axis**.

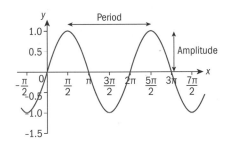

The **period** of a function is defined as the distance along the horizontal axis between a point and the corresponding point in the next cycle.

For $y = \sin x$ the period is 2π or $360°$.

The **amplitude** of a periodic function is defined as the distance from the principal axis to the maximum or minimum.

For $y = \sin x$ the amplitude is 1.

TOK

Sine curves model musical notes and the ratios of octaves. Does this mean that music is mathematical?

Investigation 3

In this investigation you will consider the graph of $y = a\sin(b(x - c)) + d$ for different values of the parameters a, b, c and d.

1 a Use your GDC to draw $y = \sin x$ and $y = \sin 2x$ on the same axes and comment on your results.

    b Use your knowledge of the transformations of functions covered in Chapter 6 to write down the transformation that takes the graph $y = f(x)$ to $y = f(bx)$.

Continued on next page

c   Hence give the period for the functions with graphs:

      i $y = \sin 2x$ **ii** $y = \cos 4x$.

2   **Factual**   How does changing the parameter b change the graph?

3   Deduce the period of $y = \sin bx$.

4   **a**   Write down the transformation that takes the graph $y = f(x)$ onto the graph $y = af(x)$.

    b   Draw graphs of $y = 2\sin x$, $y = 3\sin x$, $y = \dfrac{1}{2}\sin x$, $y = -\sin x$.

    Find the amplitude of each of the functions.

5   **Factual**   How does changing the parameter a change the graph?

6   Deduce the amplitude of $y = a\sin x$.

7   Two transformations will map the graph of $y = \sin x$ onto the graph of $y = 2\sin x + 3$.

    Describe the two transformations, taking care to state the order of the transformations. Illustrate the two steps using technology.

8   **Factual**   How does changing the value of d affect the graph?

9   Write down the transformation that will take $y = \sin x$ onto $y = \sin(x - c)$

10   The curve $y = \cos x$ undergoes two transformations:

    i   a stretch parallel to the x-axis, scale factor $\dfrac{1}{2}$

    ii   a horizontal translation of 1 unit.

    a   Sketch the curve after each of these transformations indicating the coordinates of the first maximum with $x \geq 0$.

    b   Explain why the equation of this curve is $y = \cos(2(x - 1))$.

11   The curve $y = \cos x$ undergoes two different transformations:

    i   a horizontal translation of 2 units

    ii   a stretch parallel to the x-axis, scale factor $\dfrac{1}{2}$.

    a   Sketch the curve after each of these transformations indicating the coordinates of the first maximum.

    b   Write down the equation of this curve.

    c   Verify that the equations in parts **10b** and **11b** are equal. Explain why the translations are different depending on the order of the transformations.

12   **Factual**   How does changing the value of the parameter c affect the graph?

    The phase shift is the horizontal translation of the curve, which takes place after the horizontal stretch. In the equation $y = a\sin(b(x - c)) + d$ the phase shift is c.

    Conceptual   What is the difference of having values inside the sine function and outside?

13   **Conceptual**   How does changing the parameters generally alter a trigonometric graph?

•   The graph of $f(x) = a\sin x + d$ can be obtained from the graph of $f(x) = \sin x$ by stretching vertically by a scale factor of a (giving an amplitude of a), then translating d units upwards (in the positive y direction). If $a < 0$ then the curve has also been reflected in the x-axis. In this case the amplitude is $|a|$

- The graph of $f(x) = \sin(b(x+c))$ can be obtained from the graph of $f(x) = \sin x$ by stretching horizontally by a scale factor of $\dfrac{1}{b}$ (giving a period of $\dfrac{2\pi}{b}$), then translating c units to the left (in the negative y direction).
- Similarly the graph of $f(x) = \sin(bx+c)$ can be obtained from the graph of $f(x) = \sin x$ by translating c units to the left then stretching horizontally by a scale factor of $\dfrac{1}{b}$.
- The graph of $f(x) = -\sin x$ can be obtained from the graph of $f(x) = \sin x$ by reflecting the graph in the x-axis.
- The graph of $f(x) = \sin(-x)$ can be obtained from the graph of $f(x) = \sin x$ by reflecting the graph in the y-axis.

Example 4

For the function $f(x) = a\sin(b(x+c)) + d$, the graph of $y = f(x)$ is drawn. The first maximum point shown has coordinates $(1, 2)$ and the first minimum point has coordinates $(5, -8)$.

a   State the equation of the principal axis.

b   Hence find the value of d.

c   Find the amplitude of the function.

d   Hence find the value of a.

e   Find the period of the function.

f   Hence find the value of b.

g   Find the smallest positive value for c.

h   State the values of $f(x)$ for $x = 0, 1, 5, 8, 9$ and use those data points to verify a sinusoidal regression calculation on your GDC gives the same result.

a $y = -3$	The graph reaches maximum points of 2, and minimum points of -8. Halfway between the two is -3.
b $d = -3$	The principal axis would normally be $y = 0$ so it has been translated down by -3.
c 5	$2 - (-3) = -3 - (-8) = 5$
d 5	The amplitude would normally be 1 so it has stretched by a scale factor of 5.
e 8	The two maximums occur when $x = 1$ and $x = 9$. The distance between is 8.

Continued on next page

f $b = \dfrac{\pi}{4}$

g $c = 1$

h $f(0) = f(8) = 5\sin\dfrac{\pi}{4} - 3$

$f(1) = f(9) = 2$

$f(5) = -8$

The equation is
$y = 5\sin(0.785x + 0.785) - 3$.

$\dfrac{2\pi}{b} = 8 \Rightarrow b = \dfrac{\pi}{4}$

Substituting the point $(1, 2)$ and solving the

equation $2 = 5\sin\left(\dfrac{\pi}{4}(1+c)\right) - 3$.

Exercise 8C

1 For the following curves state

  i the amplitude

  ii the equation of the principal axis

  iii the period

  iv the phase shift

  a $y = 2\sin(3(x-4)) - 5$

  b $y = -3\cos(\pi(x+1)) + 3$

  c $y = 4\sin(3x - 6)$

  b $y = \cos(2x + 5) - 1$.

2 Find the equations of the following curves in the form $y = a\sin(bx) + d$.

a

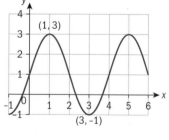

b

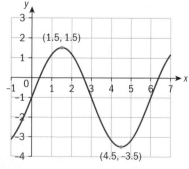

3 a Find the equations of the following curves in the form $y = a\sin(b(x - c)) + d$.

  i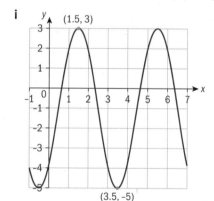

  ii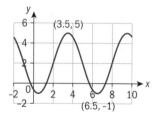

b What would be the equation of the curves if they were to be given as $y = a\cos(b(x - c)) + d$?

c The transformation that takes the graph of the curve $y = a\sin(b(x - c)) + d$ onto the graph of $y = a\cos(b(x - c)) + d$ is a horizontal translation of $k \times$ the period.

  State the value of k.

4 The times of sunrise in London for every other Monday of 2018 are given. You are required to provide a model for the times.

Date	Sunrise	Day-number	Hours after midnight
01/01/2018	08:06	1	8.1
15/01/2018	08:00	15	8
29/01/2018	07:44	29	7.733
12/02/2018	07:21	43	7.35
26/02/2018	06:53	57	6.883
12/03/2018	06:22	71	6.367
26/03/2018	06:50	85	6.833
09/04/2018	06:19	99	6.317
23/04/2018	05:49	113	5.817
07/05/2018	05:23	127	5.383
21/05/2018	05:01	141	5.017
04/06/2018	04:48	155	4.8
18/06/2018	04:44	169	4.733

Date	Sunrise	Day-number	Hours after midnight
02/07/2018	04:49	183	4.817
16/07/2018	05:03	197	5.05
30/07/2018	05:22	211	5.367
13/08/2018	05:43	225	5.717
27/08/2018	06:06	239	6.1
10/09/2018	06:28	253	6.467
24/09/2018	06:50	267	6.833
08/10/2018	07:13	281	7.217
22/10/2018	07:37	295	7.617
05/11/2018	07:01	309	7.017
19/11/2018	07:25	323	7.417
03/12/2018	07:47	337	7.783
17/12/2018	08:01	351	8.017
31/12/2018	08:06	365	8.1

a Explain why a daynumber will need to be used rather than the date.

b The hours after midnight are used instead of the time. Explain how they were calculated.

c Use the sine regression function on your GDC to establish a model for the time of sunrise against the daynumber.

d Use your model to predict the time of sunrise for the 2 February 2019.

e Comment on the reliability of your prediction.

5 If the period of a wave is P (seconds) then its frequency (Hz) is defined as $f = \dfrac{1}{P}$.

An electronic signal has amplitude 4 and frequency, $f = 500$Hz.

The strength of the signal (S) at time t seconds is given by the equation

$S = 4\sin(bt)$.

a Find the value of b.

A second signal of equal strength is sent out with a time delay of 1 millisecond. Its equation is $S = 4\sin(b(t - c))$.

b State the time delay in seconds and hence write down the equation for the strength of the second signal at time t.

The strength of the signal given by the two curves interacting is given by
$S_T = 4\sin(b(t - c)) + 4\sin(bt)$.

c Use your GDC to plot the graph of $y = S_T$ and comment on your result with reference to the graphs of the two signals.

6 The strength of two sound waves with the same frequency but different amplitudes and phase can be represented by the equations $S_1 = 3\sin(200t)$ and $S_2 = 2\sin(200(t - 0.001))$.

The combined effect of the two waves is given by $S_T = S_1 + S_2$.

a Plot the graph of $y = S_T$ for $0 \le t \le 0.1$.

b Find the coordinates of the first maximum and minimum points.

c Find the value of i the amplitude ii the period of the combined waves.

d Hence find the equation for S_T in the form $S_T = a\sin(b(t - c)) + d$.

7 The heights of the water in Aberdeen were measured every two hours on 1st January 2017. The high and low tides on that day were also recorded. All the data is shown on the table below.

Time (hours after midnight)	0	2	3.033	4	6	8	8.9	10	12
Height (m)	2.48	3.8	4	3.84	2.57	1.24	1.1	1.15	2.41
Time (hours after midnight)	14	15.15	16	18	20	21.32	22	24	—
Height (m)	3.76	4.1	3.88	2.65	1.28	.8	1.02	2.33	—

It is assumed that the height of water $h(t)$ can be modelled against time, t, by a function $h(t) = a\sin(bt + c) + d$.

a One possible way to estimate a and d might be to take the mean height for high tide and the mean height for low tide as the maximum and minimum values of the function. Find a and d using this method.

b In a similar way an approximation for the period of the function might be to find the mean of the time difference between the two high tides and between the two low tides. Using this method show that your estimate of b would be 0.512.

c Use the value of t and h at the first high tide to find an approximate value for c. Hence write down an equation to model the height of the tides.

d Use the sine regression function on your GDC to find a model for the height of the water. Compare this answer with the one obtained in part **c**.

e The rowing club shows the times when it is possible to row.

Unrowable Start	Unrowable End	Unrowable Start	Unrowable End
07:24	10:24	19:49	22:49

Use your model to estimate the depth of water necessary to be able to row.

Developing inquiry skills

Could you now make a better estimate for the earliest that the boat in the opening section would be able to leave Aberdeen harbour?

8.3 Completing our number system

Number sets

When you first encountered numbers, you were only aware of counting numbers. As your mathematical awareness grew, so new sets of numbers had to be introduced, fractions, negative numbers, irrational numbers all gradually needed to make sense of your expanding mathematical world. The historical development of mathematics has followed a similar course. When you were very young, and were only aware of counting numbers, you were told things like "you can't take 5 from 2" or "3 cannot be split into 5 parts", but with the introduction of negative integers, and fractions, you found these things are possible. The same is true of the next step in our mathematical development. Until now you have probably understood that there are no solutions to $x^2 = -4$ or $x^2 + x + 2 = 0$. We shall see that with the introduction of the next level of sophistication in our number system that there are.

The number sets we have been introduced to, in increasing complexity, are:

$\mathbb{N}$ – Natural numbers – counting numbers. 1, 2, 3, ...

$\mathbb{Z}$ – Integers – positive and negative whole numbers and zero. ... −3, −2, −1, 0, 1, 2, 3 ...

$\mathbb{Q}$ – Rational numbers – any number that can be expressed as a fraction with integer numerator and denominator.

$\mathbb{R}$ – Real numbers – up to now any number you have used. Includes irrational numbers such as π, e, $\sqrt{2}$.

Each new number set contains all the previous sets. Real numbers include all rational numbers which include all integers, etc.

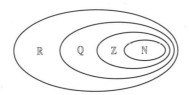

Complex numbers, $\mathbb{C}$, is the next set and contains all real numbers in addition to the inclusion of an "imaginary" concept, i, where $i^2 = -1$. Complex numbers provide solutions to previously unsolvable equations; for example, i is one of the solutions to the equation $x^2 = -1$.

Investigation 4

The quadratic equation $ax^2 + bx + c = 0$ can be solved using the quadratic

formula $x = \dfrac{-b \pm \sqrt{b^2 - 4ac}}{2a}$ (note – this is in your formula book).

1 Use the quadratic formula to find exact solutions of the equations:

   a $2x^2 + 2x - 1 = 0$ **b** $x^2 - 5x + 3 = 0$.

2 What happens when you try to solve the following equations?

   a $x^2 - 8x + 16 = 0$ **b** $x^2 + 2x + 5 = 0$

The part of the quadratic formula within the square root is called the **discriminant**, often written as a capital *delta*, Δ.

Continued on next page

3   If $i^2 = -1$, use your knowledge of the laws of indices to find: $(2i)^2$, $(-i)^2$, $(-2i)^2$, $(5i)^2$, $(-5i)^2$

4   Use your answers to conclude the values of x which satisfy:
$x^2 = -4$, $x^2 = -9$, $x^2 = -2$, $x^2 = -18$

A complex number is written as $a + bi$ where a and b are real numbers.

5   We now return to $x^2 + 2x + 5 = 0$.

Write down the two complex solutions to this equation.

Factual When does a quadratic equation have complex roots?

6   Show that each of the following also have two solutions, and write both the solutions in the form $a + bi$.

$x^2 - 6x + 13 = 0$, $x^2 + 2x + 26 = 0$, $x^2 - 4x + 6 = 0$, $x^2 - 10x + 26 = 0$.

7   Comment on the solutions of each equation.

8   **Factual** Given one complex solution of a quadratic equation, how could you find the other?

9   **Conceptual** Why do we need complex numbers?

For the equation $ax^2 + bx + c = 0$, $\Delta = b^2 - 4ac$

- When $\Delta > 0$ the equation has two real roots.
- When $\Delta = 0$ the equation has one real root.
- When $\Delta < 0$ the equation has no real roots.

TOK

Solving an equation has given you an answer in mathematics, but how can an equation have an infinite number of solutions?

A **complex number** has two parts, and can be written in the form $a + bi$ where $a, b \in \mathbb{R}$. a is known as the **real part** and b is known as the **imaginary part**.

The notation used is: $\text{Re}(a + bi) = a$ and $\text{Im}(a + bi) = b$.

The **conjugate** of a complex number $a + bi$ is defined as $a - bi$.

Complex solutions to quadratic equations with real coefficients always occur in conjugate pairs.

The arithmetic of complex numbers

As ever, when a new set of numbers is introduced, the associated arithmetic also needs to be developed. When you were introduced to the concepts of fractions or of negative numbers, you very soon had to develop the ability to add, subtract, multiply and divide those different types of numbers. Complex numbers are no different, but since you already have algebraic skills, those can be simply applied to the arithmetic of complex numbers.

Investigation 5

1 Collect like terms to simplify $2 + a - 3 + 3b + 4a$.

Apply the same logic to simplify $3 + 2i + 4 + 5i$.

It should follow that the sum or difference of any complex numbers can be found easily:

If $a = 2 + 3i$, $b = 3 - i$ and $c = -4 + 2i$, calculate $a + b$, $b - c$ and $2a$.

If $z_1 = x_1 + y_1 i$ and $z_2 = x_2 + y_2 i$ deduce expressions for $z_1 + z_2$, $z_1 - z_2$, $p z_1 + q z_2$.

2 **Conceptual** What rules of algebra do we use to be able to add or subtract complex numbers?

3 Show that $\left(2 - 3\sqrt{2}\right)\left(1 + 2\sqrt{2}\right) = -10 + \sqrt{2}$.

Apply the same logic to simplify $(2 - i)(3 + 2i)$.

If $a = 2 + 3i$, $b = 3 - i$ and $c = -4 + 2i$, calculate ab, bc and a^2.

4 **a** Find the product of $(1 + 2\sqrt{2})(1 - 2\sqrt{2})$.

   b Show that $\dfrac{2 - 3\sqrt{2}}{1 + 2\sqrt{2}} = -2 + \sqrt{2}$.

   Apply the same logic to simplify $\dfrac{2 - i}{3 + 2i}$.

   If $a = 2 + 3i$, $b = 3 - i$ and $c = -4 + 2i$, calculate $\dfrac{a}{b}$, $\dfrac{b}{c}$ and $\dfrac{ac}{b^2}$.

5 **Conceptual** How do we simplify and manipulate complex numbers?

6 Make sure you know how to find i on your GDC. Check the answers you have found in the investigation.

> **HINT**
>
> i^2 should be simplified to -1.

Example 5

Let $z_1 = 2 + 3i$ and $z_2 = 3 - i$.

a Calculate each of the following, writing your answers in the form $a + bi$.

   i $2z_1 + 3z_2$;   **ii** $z_1 z_2$ **iii** $\dfrac{z_1 + z_2}{z_1 - z_2}$

b If $\operatorname{Im}(z_1 + p z_2) = 0$ find p.

a **i** $13 + 3i$	These values can be calculated using the rules given above or directly on a GDC.	
ii $9 + 7i$		
iii $\dfrac{3 - 22i}{17}$		
b 3	$z_1 + p z_2 = (2 + 3p) + (3 - p)i$	
	If imaginary part is zero then $3 - p = 0 \Rightarrow p = 3$	

Example 6

One solution of the equation $x^2 + px + q = 0$ is $2 - 3i$. Find the value of p and the value of q.

$p = -4, q = 13$	If one solution is $2 - 3i$ then the other is $2 + 3i$.
	The equation is therefore: $(x - (2 - 3i))(x - (2 + 3i)) = 0$
	Multiplying out gives:
	$x^2 - (2 - 3i + 2 + 3i) + (2 - 3i)(2 + 3i) = 0$
	$x^2 - 4x + 13 = 0$

Exercise 8D

1 Find the exact solutions to the following equations:

  a $2x^2 - 4x + 1 = 0$ **b** $x^2 - 4x + 5 = 0$

  c $4x^2 - 8x + 5 = 0$ **d** $x^2 + 10 = 0$

2 If $a = 2 + i$, $b = 3 - 2i$ and $c = 1 - i$, find:

  a $2a - 3b$ **b** ab **c** $\dfrac{a}{b}$

  d b^2 **e** c^3 **f** $\dfrac{a^4}{b}$

You should find each calculation without a GDC and check your answers with the GDC.

3 Find the solutions to $x^2 - 4x + 5 = 0$. Hence write $x^2 - 4x + 5$ as the product of two linear factors.

4 One solution of $x^2 + px + q = 0$ is $3 - i$. Find the value of p and the value of q, assuming both are real.

8.4 A geometrical interpretation of complex numbers

The complex plane

Much of our understanding about numbers to date has been enhanced by placing the numbers on a number line. Complex numbers have two parts, a real and an imaginary part, and so can be thought of as two dimensional numbers. Much understanding about complex numbers can be developed by placing them on the complex plane, also called an **Argand diagram**.

Traditionally we have the horizontal axis as the Real axis and the vertical axis as the Imaginary axis. Consequently the number $a = 2 + 3i$ can be represented by the point shown.

International-mindedness

Jean-Robert Argand was an 18th-century amateur mathematician born in Geneva, Switzerland.

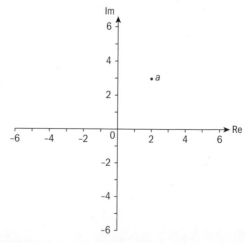

$|z|$, the **modulus** of a complex number, z, is defined as its distance from O. $\arg z$, the **argument** of a complex number, z, is defined as the angle between the positive real axis and the line from O to z. The argument is normally given in radians with $-\pi < \arg z \le \pi$.

TOK

Why is it called the Argand plane and not the Wessel plane?

Example 7

Let $z_1 = 2 + 2i$, $z_2 = 3 - 4i$ and $z_3 = -\sqrt{3} + i$.

a Calculate the modulus of: **i** z_1 **ii** z_2 **iii** z_3.

b Calculate the argument of: **i** z_1 **ii** z_2 **iii** z_3, giving your answers in radians.

c Find the area of the triangle with vertices at z_1, z_2 and z_3.

a **i**	$\sqrt{8}$	**i** $\sqrt{2^2 + 2^2} = \sqrt{8} \left(= 2\sqrt{2} \right)$
ii	5	**ii** $\sqrt{3^2 + 4^2} = 5$
iii	2	**iii** $\sqrt{\left(\sqrt{3}\right)^2 + 1^2} = 2$
b **i**	$\dfrac{\pi}{4}$	From the diagram it is clear that the argument will be 45° and hence $\dfrac{\pi}{4}$. The numerical answer 0.785 is equally acceptable.
ii	-0.927 (3 s.f.)	When looking for the argument it is often best to ignore any negative values and use right angled trigonometry to find the angle made with the real axis. The actual value for the argument can then be calculated from the position of the point in the Argand plane. In this example the GDC gave 0.927 and the argument is -0.927.
iii	2.62	Find $\arctan\left(\dfrac{1}{\sqrt{3}}\right) = 0.524$. The required angle is therefore $\pi - 0.524 = 2.62$. If working in degrees the GDC would have given the exact answer $30° = \dfrac{\pi}{6}$, so $\pi - \dfrac{\pi}{6} = \dfrac{5\pi}{6}$ would also be acceptable.

Continued on next page

c $A_1 = \dfrac{1}{2} \times \sqrt{8} \times 5 \sin\left(\dfrac{\pi}{4} + 0.927\right) = 2.73$

$A_2 = \dfrac{1}{2} \times 5 \times 2 \sin\left(2\pi - 0.927 - 2.62\right) = 1.96$

$A_3 = \dfrac{1}{2} \times \sqrt{8} \times 2 \sin\left(2.62 - \dfrac{\pi}{4}\right) = 7$

Total area $= 11.7$ (3s.f.)

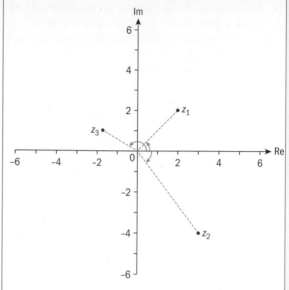

The total area can be found by adding the area of each of the 3 triangles, found using the formula $A = \dfrac{1}{2} ab \sin C$.

The required angles can be easily found from the arguments of the points.

If the complex number $a + bi$ has a modulus of r and an argument of θ we can use right-angled trigonometry to write down $a = r \cos \theta$ and $b = r \sin \theta$.

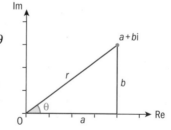

Hence $a + bi = r \cos \theta + r \sin \theta i = r(\cos \theta + \sin \theta i)$. This expression is often abbreviated to $a + bi = r \operatorname{cis} \theta$.

> **HINT**
>
> This form has many names, including **modulus-argument** form, **polar** form or **cis** form.

The form $a + bi$ is called **Cartesian** form (after René Descartes (1596–1650)) or **rectangular** form.

The definition of sine and cosine on the unit circle ensures that

$a + bi = r \operatorname{cis} \theta$ is also valid when $\theta < 0$ and $\theta > \dfrac{\pi}{2}$.

Example 8

a   Write the complex number $2 + 3i$ in modulus argument form.

b   Find in the form $a + bi$ the complex numbers with the following modulus (r) and argument (θ) values.

    i $r = 3,\ \theta = 0.4$ **ii** $r = 5,\ \theta = 3.4$

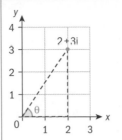

a   modulus $= \sqrt{13}$

argument $= \arctan\left(\dfrac{3}{2}\right) = 0.983$

$2 + 3i = \sqrt{13}\,\text{cis}\,(0.983)$

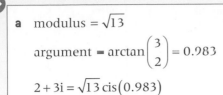

b **i** $a + bi = 3\big(\cos 0.4 + \sin 0.4\,i\big)$

$= 2.76 + 1.17i$

ii $a + bi = 5(\cos 3.4 + \sin 3.4\,i)$

$= -4.83 - 1.28i$

Applying the formula, ensuring the GDC is set to radian mode.

$3.4 > \pi$ so the complex number must lie in the fourth quadrant and so we expect a and b to be negative, which is what is given by the formula.

A complex number, z, can be expressed in different forms:

- In Cartesian form, $z = a + bi$
- In polar form, $z = r(\cos\theta + i\sin\theta)$, where $r = |z|$ and $\theta = \arg z$. This is often abbreviated to $z = r\,\text{cis}\,\theta$.

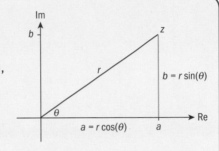

Exercise 8E

1 Plot the following complex numbers on an Argand diagram and hence give their values in modulus and argument form.

a 8i   **b** −7   **c** 12   **d** −5i

2 Find the modulus and argument of the following complex numbers, giving your answers to 3 significant figures.

a $2 - 3i$ **b** $2 + 5i$ **c** $3 - i$

d $-4 - 2i$ **e** $-5 + 2i$ **f** $1 - 3i$

3 Given that

$\tan\dfrac{\pi}{6} = \dfrac{1}{\sqrt{3}}$, $\tan\dfrac{\pi}{4} = 1$ and

$\tan\dfrac{\pi}{3} = \sqrt{3}$, find exact values for

the modulus and argument for each of the following complex

numbers. Hence write the numbers in the form $r\text{cis}\theta$.

a $4 + 4i$ **b** $2 + 2\sqrt{3}i$

c $3\sqrt{3} - 3i$ **d** $-\sqrt{3} - i$

e $-5 + 5i$ **f** $7 - 7\sqrt{3}i$

4 Use the expression $a + bi = r\cos\theta + r\sin\theta i$ to find in the form $a + bi$ the complex numbers with the following modulus (r) and argument (θ).

a $r = 3, \theta = 60°$

b $r = 4, \theta = 120°$

c $r = 2, \theta = -150°$

d $r = 5, \theta = 0.4$

e $r = 2.4, \theta = 1.9$

f $r = 3.8, \theta = -0.6$

TOK

Imagination is one of the ways of knowing in TOK. How does this relate to imaginary numbers?

Around 1740 the mathematician Leonard Euler proved the following link between exponential and trigonometric functions:

$e^{i\theta} = \cos\theta + i\sin\theta$ which is known as Euler's formula.

A result of this formula is that the complex number
$a + bi = r\cos\theta + r\sin\theta i = r(\cos\theta + \sin\theta i)$ can also be written as $a + bi = re^{i\theta}$

This form is referred to as **exponential** or **Euler** form, and like cis it is also an example of polar or modulus-argument form as the parameters are the modulus and the argument.

HINT

Most GDCs will convert from Cartesian to modulus-argument form (rectangular to polar form) and vice versa. When they do they are likely to use the exponential form for the modulus-argument form.

Investigation 6

The diagram shows the complex numbers $z_1 = 1 + 3i$, $z_2 = 4 + i$ and their sum.

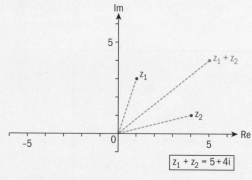

$z_1 + z_2 = 5 + 4i$

1 If the points represented by O, z_1, $z_1 + z_2$ and z_2 were joined, what would be the shape formed?

Experiment with other values of z_1 and z_2.

What conclusion can you reach about the geometrical interpretation of addition of two complex numbers?

How can the addition/subtraction be visualized geometrically?

2 By examining different values of z_1 and z_2 conclude a similar geometrical interpretation of subtraction of two complex numbers.

3 **Conceptual** How can the addition and subtraction of complex numbers compare to the addition and subtraction of vectors?

4 The effect of multiplying $1 + 3i$ by i is shown.

Experiment multiplying other numbers by i and draw a conclusion as to the geometrical effect of multiplying a number by i. Repeat for multiplying by $2i$.

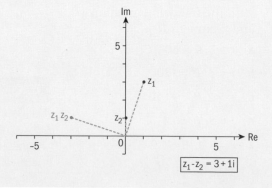

$z_1 - z_2 = 3 + 1i$

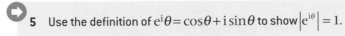

5 Use the definition of $e^{i}\theta = \cos\theta + i\sin\theta$ to show $\left|e^{i\theta}\right| = 1$.

6 a State the modulus and argument of i and hence write i in the form $re^{i\theta}$. A general complex number is written as $re^{i\theta}$.

  b Use your answer to part **6a** to find $i \times re^{i\theta}$ in exponential form. Does this confirm your conjecture in question **4**?

7 Two complex numbers z_1 and z_2 are written in exponential form as $z_1 = r_1 e^{\theta_1 i}$ and $z_2 = r_2 e^{\theta_2 i}$, Find expressions for

  a $z_1 z_2$ **b** $\dfrac{z_1}{z_2}$.

8 Describe the geometrical effect of multiplying the complex number z by the complex number $z_1 = re^{\theta i}$, in terms of a stretch and a rotation.

> **HINT**
>
> Transformations are covered in detail in Chapter 9. It is sufficient for now to refer to an increase in the modulus of a complex number by a factor of a as a stretch with scale factor a.

9 a Find $3i \times \left(\sqrt{2} + \sqrt{2}i\right)$.

  b Show $3i$, $\sqrt{2} + \sqrt{2}i$ and $3i \times \left(\sqrt{2} + \sqrt{2}i\right)$ on an Argand diagram.

  c Write $\sqrt{2} + \sqrt{2}i$ in exponential form. Use the diagram drawn in part **b** to verify your conjecture in question **8**.

  Factual What is the exponential form of a complex number?

  Conceptual What will be the geometrical effect of multiplying z_1 by z_2 when $|z_2| = r$ and $\arg z_2 = \theta$?

Powers of complex numbers

The exponential form provides an easy way to find powers of complex numbers.

If $z = re^{i\theta}$ then $z^n = \left(re^{i\theta}\right)^n = r^n e^{in\theta}$ If z is raised to the power n then its modulus is also raised to the power n and the argument is multiplied by n.

This can also be written expressed in cis form:

If $z = r\text{cis}\theta$ then $z^n = r^n \text{cis}(n\theta)$.

Example 9

a Given $\tan\left(\dfrac{\pi}{6}\right) = \dfrac{1}{\sqrt{3}}$ find the modulus and argument of $z = -\sqrt{3} - i$.

b Find an expression for z^n and hence find the smallest value of n for which $\text{Im}(z^n) = 0$ and for this value of n give z^n in Cartesian form.

---

a $|z| = \sqrt{1+3} = 2$

$\arg z = -\pi + \dfrac{\pi}{6} = -\dfrac{5\pi}{6}$

The modulus and argument can be found using the diagram below:

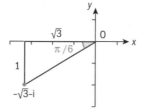

An alternative solution is:

$\arg z = \pi + \dfrac{\pi}{6} = \dfrac{7\pi}{6}$

z^n can easily be found using exponential form.

b $z^n = 2^n e^{\frac{-5\pi}{6} ni}$

$\dfrac{-5\pi}{6} n = k\pi$, where $k \in \mathbb{Z}$.

Hence smallest value of n is 6

$z^6 = 2^6 e^{-5\pi i} = -64$

If $\text{Im}(z^n) = 0$ then the argument has to be a multiple of π so the point lies on the real axis.

An argument of -5π will place the number on the negative real axis.

This could also be done on a GDC.

Movement in the Argand plane

Investigation 7

Complex numbers can be used to define curves on the Argand plane.

For example as t varies the points given by $z = 2e^{ti}$ will form a circle, centre $(0, 0)$ with a radius of 2.

What curve will the points given by $z = te^{ti}$ form as t varies?

To see the curve enter the expression into suitable software

Investigate the effect on the curve of changing r and a and write down your conclusions.

How can complex numbers be used to create spiral curves?

Exercise 8F

1 **a** Given that $a = 1 + \sqrt{3}\,i$, $b = -1 + i$ and $c = \sqrt{3} - i$, find a, b and c in modulus-argument form using the values

$$\tan\frac{\pi}{6} = \frac{1}{\sqrt{3}}, \quad \tan\frac{\pi}{4} = 1 \text{ and } \tan\frac{\pi}{3} = \sqrt{3}.$$

   b Hence find each of the following in Cartesian form:

   i ac **ii** $\dfrac{a}{c}$ **iii** b^4

   iv $\dfrac{a^3}{b^2}$ **v** $\dfrac{a^2 b}{c^2}$

2 If $z = 3 + i$, find the values of n for which $\text{Im}(z^n) = 0$.

3 **a** Write the number $\sqrt{2} + \sqrt{2}i$ in exponential form.

   b Draw the point $3 + 3i$ on an Argand diagram.

   c Without calculating the values plot the approximate positions of u, v and s where:

   $$u = (3 + 3i) + \left(\sqrt{2} + \sqrt{2}i\right)$$

   $$v = (3 + 3i) \times \left(\sqrt{2} + \sqrt{2}i\right) \qquad s = \frac{(3 + 3i)}{\left(\sqrt{2} + \sqrt{2}i\right)}$$

   d Describe the geometrical transformation(s) that will take $3 + 3i$ onto of u, v and s.

4 Let $z = re^{i\theta}$. Write z^* (the conjugate of z) in exponential form and hence prove $\text{Im}(zz^*) = 0$.

5 Use Euler's formula $e^{i\theta} = \cos\theta + i\sin\theta$ to obtain Euler's identity $e^{i\pi} + 1 = 0$.

TOK

This formula is widely regarded as the most beautiful in mathematics as it combines the five fundamental numerical constants into a simple formula.

6 **a** Describe the line formed on the Argand plane by all the points, z, for which $\arg z = \dfrac{\pi}{4}$

   The diagram below shows the complex numbers given by the expression $z = 0.5te^{\frac{\pi}{2}ti}$, along with those points, z, for which $\arg z = \theta$.

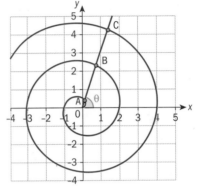

   b Find the values of t at which the curve first crosses:

   i the imaginary axis

   ii the real axis.

   c Give the values of z for each of these points in Cartesian form.

   The curve and line shown intersect at points, A, B and C.

   d Find in exponential form and in terms of θ, the complex numbers, z_1, z_2 and z_3 which are at the points A, B and C.

   e Write down $|z_2| - |z_1|$ and $|z_3| - |z_2|$. Would you expect this pattern to continue? Justify your answer.

8.5 Using complex numbers to understand periodic models

It is surprising that complex numbers, that have been developed in a very abstract context, turn out to be very important in practical applications where sinusoidal functions are found. They have a particular importance in electronics where currents or voltages are following sinusoidal waves.

Investigation 8

1 The diagram shows the output of the "sine function"

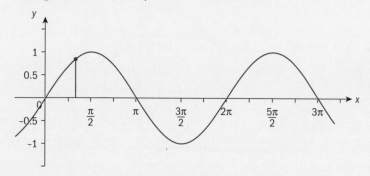

It shows how we can plot the imaginary part of a complex number z, with fixed modulus (r_1), as a function of its argument (angle), x.

Show that $f(\theta) = \mathrm{Im}(r_1 \operatorname{cis} \theta)$ is a sinusoidal function.

2 **Conceptual** What effect will changing the modulus of z (ie r_1) have on the function?

3 Describe the function $f(\theta) = \mathrm{Im}\left(r_1 \operatorname{cis}\left(\theta + \dfrac{\pi}{6}\right)\right)$.

4 Show that the function $f(x) = a\sin(x+c)$ can be written $f(x) = \mathrm{Im}(a\,e^{xi}e^{ci})$.

If two functions are defined $f(x) = \sin(x)$ and $g(x) = 2\sin\left(x + \dfrac{\pi}{2}\right)$, you can

use your knowledge of complex numbers to understand the nature of $h(x) = f(x) + g(x)$.

5 a Use the result from question 4 to write $f(x)$ and $g(x)$ in the form $\mathrm{Im}(a\,e^{xi}e^{ci})$.

   b Hence show that $h(x) = \mathrm{Im}\left(e^{ix}\left(1 + 2e^{\frac{\pi}{2}i}\right)\right)$

   c Use your GDC to write $1 + 2e^{\frac{\pi}{2}i}$ in exponential form.

   d Hence show that $h(x) = 2.24\sin(x + 1.11)$.

e Verify your answer by using your GDC to plot both

$$h(x) = \sin x + 2\sin\left(x + \frac{\pi}{2}\right) \text{ and } h(x) = 2.24\sin(x + 1.11).$$

f State the amplitude of the combined trigonometric functions.

6 If two functions are defined $f(x) = \sqrt{2}\sin\left(x + \frac{\pi}{4}\right)$ and

$g(x) = 2\sin\left(x + \frac{2\pi}{3}\right)$, show that $h(x) = \text{Im}\left(e^{ix}\left(\sqrt{2}e^{i\frac{\pi}{4}} + 2e^{2i\frac{\pi}{3}}\right)\right)$

and hence that $h(x) = \text{Im}\left(e^{ix}\left(ae^{bi}\right)\right)$, $a, b \in \mathbb{R}$.

a Find the values of a and b.

b Deduce $h(x)$ can be written as $h(x) = 2.73\sin(x + 1.57)$.

7 [Conceptual] What can you deduce about the sum of two sine functions with the same frequency and amplitudes r_1 and r_2 and phase shifts α_1 and α_2?

8 If $f(x) = r_1\sin(ax + \alpha_1)$ and $g(x) = r_2\sin(ax + \alpha_2)$, show that

$$f(x) + g(x) = \text{Im}\left(e^{iax}\left(r_1 e^{i\alpha_1} + r_2 e^{i\alpha_2}\right)\right).$$

Hence show that if $f(x) + g(x) = r\sin(ax + \alpha)$, then $r = \left|r_1 e^{i\alpha_1} + r_2 e^{i\alpha_2}\right|$
$\alpha = \arg\left(r_1 e^{i\alpha_1} + r_2 e^{i\alpha_2}\right)$.

HINT

When adding sine functions of the form $\sin(b(x + c))$ or $\sin(bx + bc)$ it is normal to refer to the phase shift as bc rather c. In exams the questions will always make it clear which definition is being used.

Example 10

The voltage of an AC electrical source can be modelled by the equation $V = a\sin(bt + c)$, where c is the phase shift. Two AC sources with equal frequencies are combined. One has a maximum voltage of 60V and the other of 80V. The amplitude of the sine function gives the maximum voltage of each electrical source. The first electrical source has a phase shift of 30° and the other of 120°. Find the maximum voltage and the phase difference of the combined source.

amplitude = $\left\|60e^{30i} + 80e^{120i}\right\| = 100$	These are found using the formula derived in the investigation. A fuller solution is below.
Phase shift = $\arg\left(60e^{30i} + 80e^{120i}\right) = 83.1°$	The two voltages can be written as $V_1 = 60\sin(bt + 30)$ $V_2 = 80\sin(bt + 120)$ $V_1 + V_2 = \text{Im}(e^{bit}(60e^{30i} + 80e^{120i}))$ $\qquad = \text{Im}(e^{bti}(100e^{83.1i}))$ $\qquad = 100\sin(bt + 83.1°)$

HINT

Some GDCs will only work in radians for some complex number operations. If you are not obtaining the answers shown here, then you should convert the phase shift to radians before calculating.

1 Show that if two AC electrical sources each output a maximum of 110V and have a phase difference of 60° then the combined output will have a maximum of $110\sqrt{3}$ volts.

2 A three phase electrical supply has three sources, each with a maximum 110V output and a phase difference of $\dfrac{2\pi}{3}$ between each.

   a Show that if the three phases are added together the output will be zero.

   b If one of the three sources is connected in reverse the value of the voltage is the negative of the previous value. Explain why that would be equivalent to adding an extra π to the phase shift.

   c Show that the new output in this case would be 220V.

3 Two electrical sources have maximum outputs 6V AC and 10V AC and a phase difference of 40°. Find the output of the combined sources.

4 Two functions are defined as
   $$f\left(x\right) = 3\sin\left(3x + \frac{\pi}{12}\right) \text{ and}$$
   $$g\left(x\right) = 4\sin\left(3x + \frac{3\pi}{4}\right)$$
   Find r and α if
   $$f(x) + g(x) = r\sin(3x + \alpha).$$

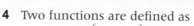

TOK

Is there always a trade-off between accuracy and simplicity?

5 In Exercise 8C, question 1 you found that the times of sunrise, in hours after midnight, was given by $f(t) = 2.14\sin(0.0165t + 1.81) + 5.97$ where t is the number of days after midnight on 31 December.

   In a similar way, the times of sunset can be modelled by the function
   $g(t) = 2.19\sin(0.0165t - 1.23) + 18.0$.

   a Show that the length of day can be modelled by the function
   $h(t) = 2.19\sin(0.0165t - 1.23) + 2.14\sin(0.0165t + 4.95) + 12.03$

   b Hence find the length of the longest and shortest days according to the model.

   c According to the model, determine the dates on which the longest and shortest days fall.

Chapter summary

- A radian is defined as the angle subtended at the centre by an arc of length 1 and radius 1.

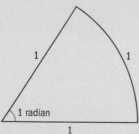

- π radians are equivalent to 180 degrees.
- The length of arc, L, of a sector radius r, is given by $L = r\theta$, if θ is in radians.
- The area, A, of a sector radius r, is given by $A = \dfrac{1}{2}r^2\theta$, if θ is in radians.
- The **period** of a function is defined as the length to complete one cycle before repeating. For $y = \sin x$ the period is 2π.

- The **amplitude** of a function is defined as the distance from the principal axis to the maximum or minimum. For $y = \sin x$ the amplitude is 1.
- The **phase shift** of a periodic function is defined as the distance the graph has moved to the left.
- The graph of $f(x) = a\sin x + d$ can be obtained from the graph of $f(x) = \sin x$ by stretching vertically by a scale factor of a (giving an amplitude of a), then translating d units upwards (in the positive y direction).
- The graph of $f(x) = \sin b(x + c)$ can be obtained from the graph of $f(x) = \sin x$ by stretching horizontally by a scale factor of $\dfrac{1}{b}$ (giving a period of $\dfrac{2\pi}{b}$), then translating c units to the left (in the negative y direction).
- Similarly the graph of $f(x) = \sin(bx + c)$ can be obtained from the graph of $f(x) = \sin x$ by translating c units to the left then stretching horizontally by a scale factor of $\dfrac{1}{b}$.
- The graph of $f(x) = -\sin x$ can be obtained from the graph of $f(x) = \sin x$ by reflecting the graph in the x-axis.
- The graph of $f(x) = \sin(-x)$ can be obtained from the graph of $f(x) = \sin x$ by reflecting the graph in the y-axis.

  A **complex number** has two parts, and can be written in the form $a + b\mathrm{i}$ where $a,\ b \in \mathbb{R}$. a is known as the **real part** and b is known as the **imaginary part.** The notation used is: $\mathrm{Re}(a + b\mathrm{i}) = a$ and $\mathrm{Im}(a + b\mathrm{i}) = b$

- The **conjugate** of a complex number $a + b\mathrm{i}$ is defined as $a - b\mathrm{i}$.
- Complex solutions to quadratic equations with real coefficients always occur in conjugate pairs.

  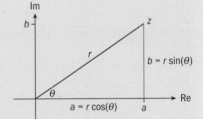

  $|z|$, the **modulus** of a complex number, z, is defined as its distance from O. $\arg z$, the **argument** of a complex number, z, is defined as the angle between the positive real axis and the line from O to z, measured anticlockwise.

  A complex number, z, can be expressed in different forms:

- In Cartesian form, $z = a + b\mathrm{i}$.
- In polar form, $z = r(\cos\theta + \mathrm{i}\sin\theta)$, where $r = |z|$ and $\theta = \arg z$. This is often abbreviated to $z = r\,\mathrm{cis}\,\theta$.
- In exponential form (also known as Euler form), $z = r\mathrm{e}^{\mathrm{i}\theta}$, where $r = |z|$ and $\theta = \arg z$.

Developing inquiry skills

Return to the opening problem. You were given a graph showing high and low tides in the harbour at Aberdeen.

How has what you have learned in this chapter changed the way you understand this problem?

Chapter review

Click here for a mixed review exercise
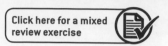

1 A circle has radius R and [AB] is a diameter. The point P is the midpoint of the arc AB and the angle APB is 90°. A circle with centre P passes through A and B to give the shaded region shown in the diagram.

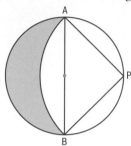

Find the area of the shaded region in terms of R.

2 In the triangle drawn AB = 1, AC = 2 and angle A is $\frac{2\pi}{3}$.

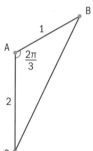

   a Find the area of the triangle.

   b Find BC.

3 Find the perimeter and area of the sector of radius 5 cm and internal angle 2 radians shown here.

4 Calculate the argument of the complex number $\left(\sqrt{3}+i\right)^{10}$ giving your answer in radians between $-\pi$ and π.

5 Given that $\tan\left(\frac{\pi}{4}\right)=1$ and $\tan\left(\frac{\pi}{6}\right)=\frac{1}{\sqrt{3}}$ find $z_1 = 1+i$ and $z_2 = \sqrt{3}-i$ in modulus-argument(polar) form. Hence express, in polar form:

   a $z_1 z_2$ b $\dfrac{z_1}{z_2}$ c $\dfrac{z_1^{3} z_2^{3}}{i}$

6 In the following Argand diagram the point A represents the complex number $-1 + 4i$ and the point B represents the complex number $-3 + 0i$. The shape of ABCD is a square. Determine the complex numbers represented by the points C and D.

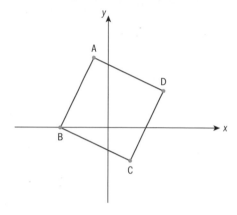

7 a If $w = 2 + 2i$, find the modulus and argument of w.

   b Given $z = \cos\left(\dfrac{5\pi}{6}\right)+i\sin\left(\dfrac{5\pi}{6}\right)$, find in its simplest form, $w^4 z^6$.

8 The complex numbers z_1 and z_2 have arguments between 0 and π radians. Given that $z_1 z_2 = -\sqrt{3}+i$ and $\dfrac{z_1}{z_2} = 2i$, find the modulus and argument of z_1 and of z_2.

9 Find the amplitude of $f(x) = 2\cos(2x + 60°) + 3\sin(2x + 30°)$.

10 An electric source of 20 amps has another source of 10 amps and a phase difference of 60° added to it. Find the total current of the combined power source. If the second source is connected in reverse, determine the combined current?

HINT

If one of the three sources is connected in reverse the value of the voltage is the negative of the previous value. Explain why that would be equivalent to adding an extra π to the phase shift.

Exam-style questions

11 **P2:** The following shows a portion of the graph of $y = p + q\cos(rx)$ (where x is given in degrees).

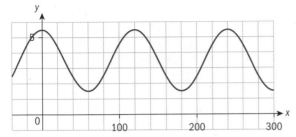

a Determine the values of the constants p, q and r. (6 marks)

b Hence, using technology, solve the inequality $p + q\cos(rx) < q + p\sin(rx)$ for $0° \le x \le 180°$ (4 marks)

12 **P1:** The following diagram shows the sector of a circle OBC, where O is the centre of the circle, and length OA = 10 cm. AD is the arc of a smaller circle, centre O.

$$A\hat{O}D = \left(\frac{6}{5}\right)^c.$$

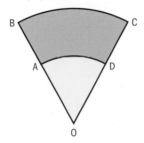

Given that the blue and yellow shaded areas are equal, determine the perimeter of ABCD. Give your answer in the form $a\sqrt{2} + b$, where a and b are integers. (8 marks)

13 **P1:** The following shows a portion of the graph of $y = p - q\sin(rx)$ $(p > 0, q > 0, r > 0)$, where x is measured in degrees.

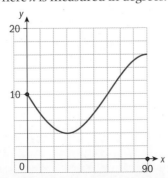

a On the same axes, sketch the graph of $y = p + \dfrac{q}{2}\sin(rx)$. (2 marks)

b Determine the values of the constants p, q and r. (7 marks)

14 **P1:** Two sources of electrical alternating current (AC) have voltages of 100 V and 180 V respectively. The first source has a phase shift of 45° and the second has a phase shift of 135°.

The two sources of current are combined.

a Find the voltage of the combined source. (2 marks)

b Find the phase shift of the combined source. (3 marks)

15 **P2:** Given $z_1 = 4\operatorname{cis}\left(-\dfrac{\pi}{3}\right)$ and $z_2 = 3\operatorname{cis}\left(\dfrac{5\pi}{6}\right)$, find expressions for the following. In each case, give your answers in the form $a + bi$, $a, b \in \mathbb{R}$.

a $z_1 z_2$ (3 marks)

b $\left(\dfrac{z_1}{z_2}\right)^3$ (5 marks)

c $\left(z_1^2\right)^*$ (3 marks)

16 **P1:** Two functions are given such that $f(x) = \sin\left(2x + \dfrac{\pi}{3}\right)$ and $g(x) = 2\sin\left(2x + \dfrac{\pi}{4}\right)$.

Given that $f(x) + g(x) = r\sin(2x + \alpha)$ $(r > 0, \alpha > 0)$, determine possible values for r and α, giving your answers to 3 significant figures. (8 marks)

Making a Mandelbrot!

Approaches to learning: Critical thinking, Communication,
Exploration criteria: Mathematical communication (B), Personal engagement (C), Use of mathematics (E)
IB topic: Complex numbers

Fractals

You may have heard about fractals.

This image is from the Mandelbrot set, one of the most famous examples of a fractal:

This is not only a beautiful image in its own right. The Mandelbrot set as a whole is an object of great interest to mathematicians. However, as yet there have been no practical applications found!

This image appears to be very complicated, but is in fact created using a remarkably simple rule.

Exploring an iterative equation

Consider this iterative equation:

$Z_{n+1} = (Z_n)^2 + c$

Consider a value of $c = 0.5$, so you have $Z_{n+1} = (Z_n)^2 + 0.5$.

Given that $Z_1 = 0$, find the value of Z_2.

Now find the value of Z_3.

Repeat for a few more iterations.

What do you think is happening to the values found in this calculation?

A different iterative equation

Now consider a value of $c = -0.5$, so you have $Z_{n+1} = (Z_n)^2 + 0.5$.

Again start with $Z_1 = 0$.

What happens this time?

The Mandelbrot set

The Mandelbrot set consists of all those values of c for which the sequence starting at $Z_1 = 0$ does **not** escape to infinity (those values of c where the calculations zoom off to infinity).

That is only part of the story however.

The value of c in the function does not need to be real.

It could be complex of the form $a + b$i.

If you pick a complex number for c, is it in the Mandelbrot set or not?

Consider starting with a value of $Z_1 = 0 + 0$i, rather than just "0".

Consider, for example, a value of c of $1 + $i, so you have $Z_{n+1} = (Z_n)^2 + (1 + i)$.

Find Z_2.

Repeat to find Z_3, Z_4, etc.

Does this diverge or converge? (Does it zoom off to infinity or not?)

Repeat for a few more values of c.

Try, for example:

a $c = 0.2 - 0.7$i

b $c = -0.25 + 0.5$i

What happens if $c = $i?

Try some values of your own.

You may find a GDC will help with these calculations as it can be used for complex numbers. When the number gets very big, the calculator will not be able to give a value. You may also notice that some numbers get "big" a lot quicker than others.

It is clearly a time-consuming process to try all values!

There are programs that can be used to calculate the output after several iterations when you input a number for c. This will indicate which values of c belong to the Mandelbrot set and which don't.

The Mandelbrot set diagram is created by colouring points on an Argand diagram of all those values of c which do not escape to infinity in one colour (say black) and all those that remain bounded in another colour (say red).

HINT

One way to check is to plot the different values of Z_1, Z_2, Z_3, Z_4, etc, on an Argand diagram and to see whether the points remain within a boundary square, or you could calculate the modulus of each value and see whether this is increasing.

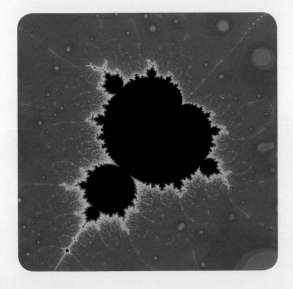

Extension

- Try to construct your own spreadsheet or write a code that could do this calculation a number of times for different chosen values of c.

- Explore what happens as you zoom in to the edges of the Mandelbrot set.

- What is the relationship between Julia sets and the Mandelbrot set?

- What is the connection to Chaos Theory?

- What are Multibrot sets?

- How could you find the area or perimeter of the Mandelbrot set?

9 Modelling with matrices: storing and analysing data

How can urban planners determine the population of different cities if people are constantly moving between them?

How can athletes ensure their diet provides all the nutrients they need?

How do computers simulate movement?

How do we send messages securely?

Is it possible to create a snowflake using mathematical formulae?

The Koch snowflake is an attempt to describe the patterns like those found in an ice crystal.

When an ice crystal is magnified we see that smaller versions of the ice crystal can be found at each level of magnification. This property is called self-similarity and structures that display it are called *fractals*. By identifying and describing the smallest piece in this pattern with a mathematical process we can create the entire structure simply by carrying out this process repeatedly.

Each stage of the Koch snowflake is described by the iterative process shown.

We begin by dividing the line segment in stage 0 into thirds and creating an equilateral triangle in the middle third of the segment.

Stage 0

Stage 1

Stage 2

- Write down step-by-step instructions describing geometrically how you could use the shape in stage 1 to create the shapes in stages 2, 3 and 4.

- Construct graphs of stages 1 and 2 of the Koch snowflake on square millimetre graph paper using the scale 1 unit = 30mm like the one shown. Determine the exact coordinates of each vertex and endpoint for each figure.

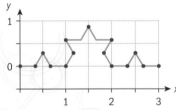

- Is there a pattern in the values of the coordinates of each of these points that you could use to determine the coordinates of the points on stage 3?

Save your work as you will need the results to check your answers to the investigation at the end of the unit.

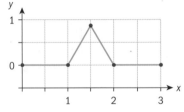

Developing inquiry skills

Where else do fractals appear in the real world?

Can we use fractal formulae to model real-life situations? How might these be useful?

Think about the questions in this opening problem and answer any you can. As you work through the chapter, you will gain mathematical knowledge and skills that will help you to answer them all.

Before you start

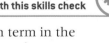

Click here for help with this skills check

You should know how to:

1 Identify and write the general term of a geometric sequence.
   eg The general term of 4, −8, 16, −32, ...
   is $u_n = 4 \times (-2)^{n-1}$

2 Find the sum of geometric series.
   eg The sum of 8 terms of the series
   $12 + 6 + 3 + 1.5 + ...$ is
   $$S_8 = \frac{12(1 - 0.5^8)}{1 - 0.5} = 23.9.$$

Skills check

1 Find a formula for the nth term in the
   sequence: $\left\{18, -12, 8, -\dfrac{16}{3}, ...\right\}$

2 Determine the sum of the first 15 terms of each sequence in question 2.

3 Write an expression for S_n for the series

   $6 + 6\left(\dfrac{1}{2}\right) + 6\left(\dfrac{1}{2}\right)^2 + 6\left(\dfrac{1}{2}\right)^3 + \cdots$ then use it to

   find S_{12}.

9.1 Introduction to matrices and matrix operations

Computers store large amounts of data using a programming structure called an array. Understanding how data is stored and manipulated leads you to a study of matrices and matrix operations.

A **matrix** A with dimensions $m \times n$ is a rectangular array of real (or complex) numbers containing m rows and n columns where $a_{i,j}$ refers to the element located in row i and column j. Such a matrix is said to have order $m \times n$.

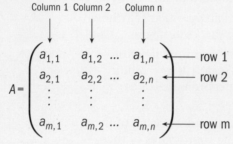

$$A = \begin{pmatrix} a_{1,1} & a_{1,2} & \cdots & a_{1,n} \\ a_{2,1} & a_{2,2} & \cdots & a_{2,n} \\ \vdots & \vdots & & \vdots \\ a_{m,1} & a_{m,2} & \cdots & a_{m,n} \end{pmatrix} \begin{matrix} \leftarrow \text{row 1} \\ \leftarrow \text{row 2} \\ \\ \leftarrow \text{row m} \end{matrix}$$

Column 1   Column 2   Column n

International-mindedness

English mathematician and lawyer, James Sylvester, introduced the term "matrix" in the 19th century and his friend, Arthur Cayley, advanced the algebraic aspect of matrices.

For example, matrix $\boldsymbol{P} = \begin{pmatrix} -1 & 3 & 4 & 2 \\ 1 & 5 & 0 & 7 \\ -3 & 4 & -2 & 6 \end{pmatrix}$ has dimensions 3×4 where

$a_{2,3}$ is the element located in the 2nd row and 3rd column and has a value of 0. Note that matrix $\boldsymbol{P}$ contains $3 \times 4 = 12$ elements.

If $m = n$ (ie the number of columns is equal to the number of rows) then we say that $\boldsymbol{P}$ is a **square matrix of order** n.

Consider the 3×5 matrix $\boldsymbol{C}$ showing the cost (in euros) of manufacturing 3 different products for 5 different manufacturers.

	Manufactuer 1	Manufactuer 2	Manufactuer 3	Manufactuer 4	Manufactuer 5
Product 1	3.50	4.25	3.82	4.10	3.95
$\boldsymbol{C} =$ Product 2	8.25	10.50	.75	9.45	7.80
Product 3	10.50	9.75	8.95	11.00	10.80

For example, the cost of producing product 3 with manufacturer 4 is given by element $a_{3,4}$ and is €11.00.

Matrices $\boldsymbol{A}$ and $\boldsymbol{B}$ are equal if and only if the matrices have the same dimensions and their corresponding elements are equal.

Matrix addition

Three models of a particular brand of television undergo two manufacturing processes each carried out in different factories. The elements of matrices **A** and **B** represent the shipping and manufacturing costs (in USD) for each of the three models at each of two factories.

$$A = \begin{matrix} \text{Manufacturing} & \text{Shipping} \\ \left(\begin{matrix} 125 & 35 \\ 275 & 40 \\ 180 & 55 \end{matrix}\right) & \begin{matrix} \text{Model 1} \\ \text{Model 2} \\ \text{Model 3} \end{matrix} \end{matrix} \quad \text{and} \quad B = \begin{matrix} \text{Manufacturing} & \text{Shipping} \\ \left(\begin{matrix} 300 & 50 \\ 210 & 35 \\ 325 & 65 \end{matrix}\right) & \begin{matrix} \text{Model 1} \\ \text{Model 2} \\ \text{Model 3} \end{matrix} \end{matrix}$$

Adding $a_{1,1} + b_{1,1} = 425$ indicates that the total manufacturing cost of Model 1 is \$425. Similarly, adding $a_{3,2} + b_{3,2} = 120$ and indicates that the total shipping cost of Model 3 is \$120.

Thus,

$$A + B = \begin{pmatrix} 125 & 30 \\ 275 & 40 \\ 180 & 55 \end{pmatrix} + \begin{pmatrix} 300 & 50 \\ 210 & 35 \\ 325 & 65 \end{pmatrix} = \begin{pmatrix} 425 & 85 \\ 485 & 75 \\ 505 & 120 \end{pmatrix}$$

> To add or subtract two or more matrices, they must be of the same order. You add or subtract corresponding elements.

The zero matrix **0** is the matrix whose entries are all zero.

For 2 × 2 matrices $\begin{pmatrix} 0 & 0 \\ 0 & 0 \end{pmatrix}$ is the zero matrix, for 2 × 3 matrices it is

$\begin{pmatrix} 0 & 0 & 0 \\ 0 & 0 & 0 \end{pmatrix}$.

For any matrix **A**, **A** + **0** = **A** and **A** − **0** = **A**.

Scalar multiplication for matrices

Consider the situation where manufacturer A increases both its shipping and manufacturing costs by 10%. That is, each new cost is 110% of its old cost. Therefore, multiplying each value by 1.10 gives a matrix representing the new costs.

$$1.10A = \begin{pmatrix} 125(1.10) & 35(1.10) \\ 275(1.10) & 40(1.10) \\ 180(1.10) & 55(1.10) \end{pmatrix} = \begin{pmatrix} 137.50 & 38.50 \\ 302.50 & 44 \\ 198 & 60.5 \end{pmatrix}$$

In this way, we define **scalar multiplication** of matrices.

> Given a matrix **A** and a real number k then kA is obtained by multiplying every element of **A** by k where k is referred to as a scalar.

TOK

"There is no branch of mathematics, however abstract, which may not someday be applied to phenomena of the real world." – Nikolai Lobatchevsky

Where does the power of mathematics come from? Is it from its ability to communicate as a language, from the axiomatic proofs or from its abstract nature?

HINT

A scalar is a quantity that is one-dimensional. Some examples of scalars are temperature and weight.

Example 1

Find a and b if $2P - 5Q = \mathbf{0}$, $P = \begin{pmatrix} 1 & 2b \\ 3c & 1 \end{pmatrix}$ and $Q = \begin{pmatrix} a & -1 \\ -1 & 0.4 \end{pmatrix}$

$2\begin{pmatrix} 1 & 2b \\ 3c & 1 \end{pmatrix} - 5\begin{pmatrix} a & -1 \\ -1 & 0.4 \end{pmatrix} = \begin{pmatrix} 0 & 0 \\ 0 & 0 \end{pmatrix}$	The zero matrix is a matrix all of whose elements are 0.
$\begin{pmatrix} 2 - 5a & 4b + 5 \\ 6c + 5 & 0 \end{pmatrix} = \begin{pmatrix} 0 & 0 \\ 0 & 0 \end{pmatrix}$	
$2 - 5a = 0 \Rightarrow a = \dfrac{2}{5}$	If two matrices are equal then their corresponding elements are equal.
$4b + 5 = 0 \Rightarrow b = \dfrac{-5}{4}$	
$6c + 5 = 0 \Rightarrow c = \dfrac{-5}{6}$	

Exercise 9A

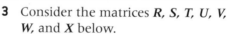

1 Given that

$A = \begin{pmatrix} 2 & -3 & 5 \\ 4 & -2 & 6 \end{pmatrix}$, $B = \begin{pmatrix} 3 \\ -4 \\ 5 \end{pmatrix}$,

and $C = \begin{pmatrix} 8 & 5 & 2 \\ -4 & 0 & 3 \\ 1 & -1 & 7 \end{pmatrix}$, write down the values

of $a_{1,2}$, $a_{2,3}$, $b_{3,1}$, $c_{2,2}$ and $c_{3,1}$.

2 The matrix Q describes the number of units of each of three products that are produced by each of four manufacturers where $q_{i,j}$ represents the amount of product i produced by manufacturer j.

$Q = \begin{pmatrix} 420 & 250 & 145 & 0 \\ 340 & 575 & 420 & 100 \\ 200 & 375 & 425 & 235 \end{pmatrix}$

  a Write down the dimensions of Q.

  b Write down the value of $q_{2,4}$ and describe its meaning.

  c Find a 4×1 matrix T representing the total number of products produced by each manufacturer.

3 Consider the matrices R, S, T, U, V, W, and X below.

$R = \begin{pmatrix} 0 & -1 \\ 3 & 7 \\ -5 & 4 \end{pmatrix}$ $S = \begin{pmatrix} 3 & -2 & 1 \\ 4 & 1 & -7 \\ -9 & 6 & 2 \end{pmatrix}$

$T = \begin{pmatrix} -3 & -9 \\ 6 & 12 \end{pmatrix}$ $U = \begin{pmatrix} 8 & -3 & -2 \\ 6 & 7 & 2 \\ 0 & 1 & -1 \end{pmatrix}$

$V = \begin{pmatrix} -2 & 0 \\ -4 & -8 \end{pmatrix}$ $W = \begin{pmatrix} 1 & -2 & 3 \\ 3 & 2 & -1 \end{pmatrix}$

$X = \begin{pmatrix} 7 & -2 \\ -6 & 4 \end{pmatrix}$

Find each of the following if possible. If not possible, explain why. Check your answers using technology.

  a $3W$ **b** $R - W$ **c** $4U + S$

  d $\dfrac{1}{3}T - \dfrac{1}{2}V$

4 The matrix $P = \begin{pmatrix} 32450 \\ 18725 \\ 24175 \\ 19250 \end{pmatrix}$ describes the prices

(in USD) of four types of cars. The sales tax rate is 7.5% of the purchase price.

a Write down $T = kP$ where T represents the amount of tax paid for each car.

b The matrix C represents the cost of each car including tax. Write a matrix equation that describes C in terms of P.

5 A column vector can be regarded as a 2×1 matrix. The point $P = (-3, 6)$ is written in matrix form as $X = \begin{pmatrix} -3 \\ 6 \end{pmatrix}$.

a Determine the points:

i $2X$

ii $\dfrac{1}{3}X$

iii $-X$.

b Show each of these the points on a graph.

c Make a conjecture about the set of points described by kX.

6 Find real values of μ and λ if

$$\mu A + \lambda B = \begin{pmatrix} -8 & 12 \\ -10 & 4 \end{pmatrix}, \text{ where } A = \begin{pmatrix} -9 & 12 \\ -6 & 3 \end{pmatrix}$$

and $B = \begin{pmatrix} 1 & -2 \\ 3 & -1 \end{pmatrix}$.

9.2 Matrix multiplication and properties

Consider a matrix F whose elements represent the number of each of three types of medium size drinks (frappé, cappuccino, and iced coffee) sold at a café on each day of the first week in June.

	Frappé	Cappuccino	Iced coffee
Sun	28	32	16
Mon	34	51	8
Tues	40	31	15
$W =$ Wed	37	24	20
Thurs	75	47	29
Fri	38	29	19
Sat	47	34	12

The price for a frappe is €4.00, cappuccino is €3.50 and iced coffee is €2.50.

The following calculation can be used to determine the revenue R for each day:

day	revenue	=	# frappes sold	×	price	+	# cappuccinos sold	×	price	+	# iced coffee	×	price
Sunday	$264	=	28	×	4.00	+	32	×	3.50	+	16	×	2.50

Similarly, the revenue for each day is obtained by summing the products of the number of each type of drink sold and the corresponding prices for each drink on each day of the week. That is,

$$R = \begin{pmatrix} 28(4.00)+32(3.50)+16(2.50) \\ 34(4.00)+51(3.50)+8(2.50) \\ 40(4.00)+31(3.50)+15(2.50) \\ 37(4.00)+24(3.50)+20(2.50) \\ 75(4.00)+47(3.50)+29(2.50) \\ 38(4.00)+29(3.50)+19(2.50) \\ 47(4.00)+34(3.50)+12(2.50) \end{pmatrix} = \begin{pmatrix} 264 \\ 334.50 \\ 306 \\ 282 \\ 537 \\ 301 \\ 337 \end{pmatrix}$$

A more compact way of expressing R would be to represent the price of each drink as a 3×1 matrix $P = \begin{pmatrix} 4.00 \\ 3.50 \\ 2.50 \end{pmatrix}$.

so that $R = WP = \begin{pmatrix} 28 & 32 & 16 \\ 34 & 51 & 8 \\ 40 & 31 & 15 \\ 37 & 24 & 20 \\ 75 & 47 & 29 \\ 38 & 29 & 19 \\ 47 & 34 & 12 \end{pmatrix} \begin{pmatrix} 4.00 \\ 3.50 \\ 2.50 \end{pmatrix} = \begin{pmatrix} 264 \\ 334.50 \\ 306 \\ 282 \\ 537 \\ 301 \\ 337 \end{pmatrix}$

Sunday's revenue $= 28(4.00)+32(3.50)+16(2.50)$

$$= (28 \quad 32 \quad 16)\begin{pmatrix} 4.00 \\ 3.50 \\ 2.50 \end{pmatrix} = 264$$

Friday's revenue $= 38(4.00)+29(3.50)+19(2.50)$

$$= (38 \quad 29 \quad 19)\begin{pmatrix} 4.00 \\ 3.50 \\ 2.50 \end{pmatrix} = 301$$

If $P = AB$ then each element of P (named as $P_{i,j}$) is found by summing the products of the elements in row i of A with the elements in column j of B.

For example, if $A = \begin{pmatrix} 1 & 5 & -3 \\ -1 & 4 & 2 \end{pmatrix}$ and $B = \begin{pmatrix} -1 & 2 \\ -3 & 4 \\ 2 & 1 \end{pmatrix}$ then

$$P = \begin{pmatrix} 1 & 5 & -3 \\ -1 & 4 & 2 \end{pmatrix}\begin{pmatrix} -1 & 2 \\ -3 & 4 \\ 2 & 1 \end{pmatrix}$$

$$= \begin{pmatrix} 1(-1)+5(-3)-3(2) & 1(2)+5(4)-3(1) \\ -1(-1)+4(-3)+2(2) & -1(2)+4(4)+2(1) \end{pmatrix} = \begin{pmatrix} -22 & 19 \\ -7 & 16 \end{pmatrix}.$$

Investigation 1

Consider the matrices $A = \begin{pmatrix} 2 & 4 \\ -1 & 1 \end{pmatrix}$, $B = \begin{pmatrix} 2 & -1 & 3 \\ 0 & -3 & 4 \end{pmatrix}$, $C = \begin{pmatrix} 1 \\ 2 \end{pmatrix}$,

$D = \begin{pmatrix} 1 & 2 & -2 \\ 0 & 3 & 1 \\ -1 & -3 & 1 \end{pmatrix}$, and $E = \begin{pmatrix} -2 \\ 1 \\ -1 \end{pmatrix}$.

1   **Factual**   Find the products of **AB, AC, BD, DE,** and **BE.**

2   Complete the table below to determine the dimensions (order) of the products **AB, AC, BD, DE,** and **BE.**

Product	Dimensions of first matrix	Dimensions of second matrix	Dimensions of product
AB	2 x 2	2 x 3	
AC			
BD			
DE			
BE			

3   **Factual**   Based upon the results in question **1** explain how you could determine the dimensions of the product of two matrices using the dimensions of the two matrices being multiplied?

4   Explain why the products **BA, CB,** and **DB** cannot be determined.

5   **Conceptual**   When does the product of two matrices exist?

If **A** has dimensions $m \times n$ and **B** has dimensions $p \times q$ then
- the product **AB** is defined only if the number of columns in **A** is equal to the number of rows in **B**
  (that is, $n = p$)
- and when the product does exist, the dimensions of the product is $m \times q$.

TOK

How are mathematical definitions different from definitions in other areas of knowledge? How are mathematical definitions different from properties, axioms, or theorems?

Example 2

A diet research project consists of adults and children of both sexes. The number of participants in the survey is given by the matrix:

$$A = \begin{matrix} & \text{Adults} & \text{Children} \\ \begin{matrix} \text{Male} \\ \text{Female} \end{matrix} & \begin{pmatrix} 75 & 180 \\ 110 & 250 \end{pmatrix} & \end{matrix}$$

Continued on next page

The number of daily grams of protein, fat, and carbohydrates consumed by each child and adult is given by the matrix:

$$B = \begin{pmatrix} \overset{\text{Protein}}{15} & \overset{\text{Fat}}{20} & \overset{\text{Carbohydrate}}{25} \\ 8 & 16 & 20 \end{pmatrix} \begin{matrix} \text{Adult} \\ \text{Child} \end{matrix}$$

a Determine AB.   **b** Explain the meaning of $AB_{3,2}$ **c** Explain why BA does not exist.

a $AB = \begin{pmatrix} 75 & 180 \\ 110 & 250 \end{pmatrix}\begin{pmatrix} 15 & 20 & 25 \\ 8 & 16 & 20 \end{pmatrix}$ $= \begin{pmatrix} 75(15)+180(8) & 75(20)+180(16) & 75(25)+180(20) \\ 110(15)+250(16) & 110(20)+250(16) & 110(25)+250(20) \end{pmatrix}$ $= \begin{pmatrix} 2565 & 4380 & 5475 \\ 5650 & 6200 & 7750 \end{pmatrix}$	Multiply the matrices.
b $AB_{2,3} = 110(25) + 250(20) = 7750$ and represents the total number of carbohydrates consumed by females in the project. **c** BA is not possible since the number of columns in B is not equal to the number of rows in A.	Total carbohydrates consumed by the 110 adult females is $110(25)$ and the total carbohydrates consumed by 250 child females is $250(20)$.

Investigation 2

Use the matrices $A = \begin{pmatrix} -2 & -3 \\ 4 & 1 \end{pmatrix}$, $B = \begin{pmatrix} -1 & 5 \\ 6 & -2 \end{pmatrix}$ and $C = \begin{pmatrix} -2 & 1 \\ 3 & -4 \end{pmatrix}$ to answer each question.

1 Multiplication of real numbers a and b is commutative since $ab = ba$, for example $5 \times 4 = 4 \times 5 = 20$. Determine AB and BA. Is matrix multiplication commutative?

Multiplication of real numbers is distributive since $a(b+c) = ab + ac$ and $(b+c)a = ab + ac$.

2 Determine each of the following then describe your observations.

  i $A(B+C)$ **ii** $(B+C)A$ **iii** $AB+AC$ **iv** $BA+CA$

3 Based upon your observations is matrix multiplication distributive? Is $A(B+C) = AB+BC$? Is it correct to write $(B+C)A = AB+CA$?

4 Multiplication of real numbers is associative which means that $a(bc) = (ab)c$. Is matrix multiplication associative? You can answer this by showing whether or not $A(BC) = (AB)C$.

5 Consider the marix $I = \begin{pmatrix} 1 & 0 \\ 0 & 1 \end{pmatrix}$

  a Find AI and IA **b** Write down what you notice.

6 **Conceptual** How do matrix and matrix multiplication work in terms of the commutative and associative properties?

Properties of multiplication for matrices
For matrices A, B, and C:
- Non-commutative $AB \neq BA$
- Associative property $A(BC) = (AB)C$
- Distributive property $A(B + C) = AB + AC$ and $(B + C)A = BA + CA$

These properties only hold when the products are defined.
- In $A(B + C)$, $B + C$ is pre-multiplied by A.
- In $(B + C)A$, $B + C$ is post-multiplied by A.

Multiplicative identity for matrices

The multiplicative identity for real numbers is 1 since $a \times 1 = 1 \times a = a$ for any real number a.

If A is any square matrix and I is the identity matrix, then $A \times I = I \times A = A$. In other words, if any square matrix is pre- or post-multiplied by the identity matrix, then the answer is the original matrix.

The multiplicative identity of a square $n \times n$ matrix A is given by

$$I_n = \begin{pmatrix} 1 & 0 & \cdots & 0 \\ 0 & 1 & \cdots & 0 \\ \vdots & \vdots & \ddots & \vdots \\ 0 & 0 & \cdots & 1 \end{pmatrix}.$$

Note that both $A \times I_n = A$ and $I_n \times A = A$ hold only in the case where A is a square matrix.

Unless needed for clarity, n is not normally written, and I is used alone to denote the identity matrix, whatever the size.

Exercise 9B

1 Using the matrices

$$A = \begin{pmatrix} 1 & -2 \\ 2 & 3 \end{pmatrix}, \quad B = \begin{pmatrix} 2 & -4 & 1 \\ -1 & 0 & 3 \end{pmatrix},$$

$$C = \begin{pmatrix} 1 & 0 \\ -1 & 2 \\ -2 & 3 \end{pmatrix}, \quad D = \begin{pmatrix} 1 & -2 & -1 \\ 3 & 0 & -4 \\ -3 & 2 & 1 \end{pmatrix},$$

$$E = \begin{pmatrix} 2 \\ 1 \\ -3 \end{pmatrix}, \quad \text{and} \quad F = \begin{pmatrix} -3 & -1 \\ 2 & 4 \\ 5 & -2 \end{pmatrix},$$

find each of the following matrices if possible. If it is not possible, state the reason.

a $(C + F)A$ **b** DE **c** ABC

d CF **e** $2A - 3I_2$

2 Given that P is a $4 \times m$ matrix, Q is a $2 \times n$ matrix, determine the values of m and n if PQ is a 4×3 matrix.

3 Find a matrix that has the effect of summing the entries in every row of a 3×3 matrix. That is, if $A = \begin{pmatrix} a & b & c \\ d & e & f \\ g & h & i \end{pmatrix}$ find

a matrix B such that $AB = \begin{pmatrix} (a + b + c) \\ (d + e + f) \\ (g + h + i) \end{pmatrix}$.

4 Consider the matrix $A = \begin{pmatrix} 3 & -2 & 1 \\ -1 & 5 & -6 \end{pmatrix}$.

   a Find a matrix B such that $AB = A$.

   b Find a matrix C such that $CA = A$.

   c Explain why A does not have a multiplicative identity.

5 A manufacturer makes three types of products P_1, P_2, and P_3 at each of its four plant locations L_1, L_2, L_3, and L_4. Matrix A gives the daily amount (in kilograms) of carbon monoxide, sulfur dioxide, and nitric oxide produced during the manufacturing process of each product.

$$A = \begin{array}{c} \\ P_1 \\ P_2 \\ P_3 \end{array} \begin{pmatrix} \overset{\text{carbon}}{\underset{\text{monoxide}}{}} & \overset{\text{sulfur}}{\underset{\text{dioxide}}{}} & \overset{\text{nitric}}{\underset{\text{oxide}}{}} \\ 20 & 35 & 15 \\ 18 & 28 & 12 \\ 45 & 72 & 32 \end{pmatrix}$$

New federal laws require that the manufacturer reduce its daily emissions of carbon monoxide, sulfur dioxide, and nitric oxide by 60%, 20%, and 40% of its current levels. The manufacturer takes corrective measures to reduce emissions to meet the minimum daily standards.

   a Let matrix N be a matrix whose entries are the total daily number of kilograms of pollutants released for each product after the corrective measures. Write down the matrix R such that $N = AR$ then find N.

The daily cost (in USD) of removing each kilogram of carbon monoxide, sulfur dioxide, and nitric oxide at each of the four plants is given by the matrix C:

$$C = \begin{array}{c} \\ \\ \\ \end{array} \overset{\begin{array}{cccc} L_1 & L_2 & L_3 & L_4 \end{array}}{\begin{pmatrix} 10 & 8 & 12 & 8 \\ 3 & 2 & 4 & 3 \\ 7 & 9 & 6 & 11 \end{pmatrix}} \begin{array}{l} \text{carbon monoxide} \\ \text{sulfur dioxide} \\ \text{nitric oxide} \end{array}$$

   b Find AC and describe the meaning of its entries.

Investigation 3

Consider the matrix $A = \begin{pmatrix} 2 & -3 \\ 4 & 7 \end{pmatrix}$, $B = \begin{pmatrix} 2 & 0 \\ 0 & -3 \end{pmatrix}$, $C = \begin{pmatrix} 0 & 2 \\ -3 & 0 \end{pmatrix}$, $D = \begin{pmatrix} 2 & 0 \\ 0 & -1 \end{pmatrix}$ and $I_2 = \begin{pmatrix} 1 & 0 \\ 0 & 1 \end{pmatrix}$.

1 Using the fact that $A^2 = A \times A$ show that $A^2 \neq \begin{pmatrix} 2^2 & (-3)^2 \\ 4^2 & 7^2 \end{pmatrix}$.

2 Find B^2, C^2, and $(I_2)^2$.

3 If $A = \begin{pmatrix} a & b \\ c & d \end{pmatrix}$ under what conditions is $A^2 = \begin{pmatrix} a^2 & b^2 \\ c^2 & d^2 \end{pmatrix}$? Does this same condition apply to all $n \times n$ matrices? Explain.

4 Determine D^2, D^3, and D^4. Write a formula for D^k where $k \in \mathbb{Z}^+$.

5 Without using technology write your own definition for the *zeroth power of a square matrix A^0*. Explain your reasoning. How does the GDC interpret A^0 and is this result consistent with your definition?

If $A = \begin{pmatrix} a & b \\ c & d \end{pmatrix}$ then $A^k = \underbrace{A \times A \times \cdots \times A}_{k \text{ factors of } A}$.

In the case where $b = c = 0$ then $A^k = \begin{pmatrix} a & 0 \\ 0 & d \end{pmatrix} = \begin{pmatrix} a^k & 0 \\ 0 & d^k \end{pmatrix}$.

Exercise 9C

Complete each exercise using the definitions and properties you learned in this section then check your answers using technology.

1 If $A = \begin{pmatrix} -1 & 2 & 4 \\ 3 & 1 & 0 \end{pmatrix}$ and $B = \begin{pmatrix} 3 & -2 \\ -1 & 1 \end{pmatrix}$. Find each if possible. If not possible, explain why.

a AB **b** BA

c A^2 **d** B^2

Use the following matrices to answer questions 2–6.

$$R = \begin{pmatrix} 0 & -1 \\ 3 & 7 \\ -5 & 4 \end{pmatrix}, \quad S = \begin{pmatrix} 3 & -2 & 1 \\ 4 & 1 & -3 \\ -7 & 5 & 2 \end{pmatrix},$$

$$T = \begin{pmatrix} 1 & 2 \\ -1 & 3 \end{pmatrix}, \quad U = \begin{pmatrix} 4 & -3 & -2 \\ 5 & -4 & 2 \\ 0 & 1 & -1 \end{pmatrix},$$

$$W = \begin{pmatrix} 1 & -2 & 3 \\ 3 & 2 & -1 \end{pmatrix}, \quad X = \begin{pmatrix} 7 & -2 \\ -6 & 4 \end{pmatrix}$$

2 Calculate each of the following if possible. If not possible, explain why.

a SR **b** TR **c** $WR + X$ **d** $W(S - U)$

e $(S - U)W$

3 Use the properties of matrices to show that $UR + R = (U + I)R$. Verify your answer.

4 In algebra, $(a + b)(a - b) = a^2 - b^2$ and $(u + b)^2 = a^2 + 2ab + b^2$ where $a, b \in \mathbb{R}$. Expand $(T + X)(T - X)$ and $(T + X)^2$ using properties of matrices. Explain why $(T + X)(T - X) \neq T^2 - X^2$ and $(T + X)^2 \neq T^2 + 2TX + X^2$

5 Show that $(SU)^2 \neq S^2 U^2$. Explain why using matrix multiplication.

6 Show that $2(RT) = (2R)T = R(2T)$. What does this suggest about scalar multiplication?

7 Consider the matrices $A = \begin{pmatrix} -3 & 5 \\ 1 & -2 \end{pmatrix}$ and $B = \begin{pmatrix} -2 & -5 \\ -1 & -3 \end{pmatrix}$.

a Show that $AB = BA = I_2$.

b Determine $(2AB)^{10}$.

8 Michael makes the following conjectures for all square matrices A and B.

a $(AB)^n = A^n B^n$ **b** $(kA)^n = k^n A^n$

If you agree with Michael's claims, prove them. If you disagree, write down counter-examples.

9.3 Solving systems of equations using matrices

One of the many useful applications of matrix multiplication is that it gives you an efficient way to express and solve systems of linear equations. Any system containing n variables and n equations can be expressed as a matrix equation.

For example,

$\begin{cases} 10x - 5y = 35 \\ -3x + 7y = 23 \end{cases}$ is equivalent to $\begin{pmatrix} 10 & -5 \\ -3 & 7 \end{pmatrix} \begin{pmatrix} x \\ y \end{pmatrix} = \begin{pmatrix} 35 \\ 23 \end{pmatrix}$.

$\begin{cases} 4s - 3t - 2z = 0 \\ 2s + 2t + 3z = -6 \\ 6s + t - z = 2 \end{cases}$ is equivalent to $\begin{pmatrix} 4 & -3 & -2 \\ 2 & 2 & 3 \\ 6 & 1 & -1 \end{pmatrix} \begin{pmatrix} s \\ t \\ z \end{pmatrix} = \begin{pmatrix} 0 \\ -6 \\ 2 \end{pmatrix}$.

In general, an $n \times n$ system of equations can be expressed in the form $AX = B$ where A is an $n \times n$ matrix containing the coefficients, B is a $n \times 1$ matrix containing the constants, and X is an $n \times 1$ matrix containing the variables.

Since you are interested in the values of the variables that solve all equations in the system, our goal is to determine X. At first glance you notice that $AX = B$ looks similar to the more familiar linear equation such as $2x = 10$, where you would simply divide both sides by 2. However, solving the matrix equation by dividing both sides by the matrix A would not lead you to $X = \dfrac{B}{A}$. Unfortunately, matrix division is not defined in the same way as other matrix operations. The key to unlocking the answer to this problem utilizes the multiplicative inverse property.

Recall that if a is a real number then $\dfrac{1}{a}$ is referred to as the multiplicative inverse of a since $a \times \dfrac{1}{a} = 1$ and $\dfrac{1}{a} \times a = 1$. For example, $-\dfrac{3}{2}$ and $-\dfrac{2}{3}$ are multiplicative inverses since $\left(-\dfrac{3}{2}\right)\left(-\dfrac{2}{3}\right) = 1$ and $\left(-\dfrac{2}{3}\right)\left(-\dfrac{3}{2}\right) = 1$. Note that there are two conditions for which a number has a multiplicative inverse. First, both the number and its inverse must have a product equal to 1 and second, this product must satisfy the commutative property of multiplication.

Similarly, $n \times n$ matrices A and B are called multiplicative inverses if $AB = I_n$ and $BA = I_n$ where I_n is the identity matrix. For example

$$A = \begin{pmatrix} 3 & 1 \\ 2 & 1 \end{pmatrix} \text{ and } B = \begin{pmatrix} 1 & -1 \\ -2 & 3 \end{pmatrix} \text{ are multiplicative inverses since}$$

$$AB = \begin{pmatrix} 3 & 1 \\ 2 & 1 \end{pmatrix}\begin{pmatrix} 1 & -1 \\ -2 & 3 \end{pmatrix} = \begin{pmatrix} 1 & 0 \\ 0 & 1 \end{pmatrix} \text{ and } BA = \begin{pmatrix} 1 & -1 \\ -2 & 3 \end{pmatrix}\begin{pmatrix} 3 & 1 \\ 2 & 1 \end{pmatrix} = \begin{pmatrix} 1 & 0 \\ 0 & 1 \end{pmatrix}.$$

Thus, the central question is, given a square matrix A how do you find its multiplicative inverse? The following investigation will guide you through this process for a 2×2 matrix.

> ### International-mindedness
>
> Matrix methods were used to solve simultaneous linear equations in the second century BC in China in the book "Nine Chapters on the Mathematical Art" written during the Han Dynasty

Investigation 4

Determine the multiplicative inverse of $A = \begin{pmatrix} 8 & -6 \\ -5 & 4 \end{pmatrix}$.

a **i** Let $B = \begin{pmatrix} w & x \\ y & z \end{pmatrix}$ be the multiplicative inverse of A. Use the fact that $AB = I$ to show that

$$\left.\begin{array}{l} 8w - 6y = 1 \\ -5w + 4y = 0 \end{array}\right\} \text{ and } \left.\begin{array}{l} 8x - 6z = 0 \\ -5x + 4z = 1 \end{array}\right\}.$$

ii Solve each system in **i** to find the values of $w, x, y,$ and z. Check your answer by verifying that $AB = I$ and $BA = I$.

b Consider that you are given a matrix $A = \begin{pmatrix} a & b \\ c & d \end{pmatrix}$ where a, b, c and d are real numbers and you wish to determine the multiplicative inverse of A.

Let $B = \begin{pmatrix} w & x \\ y & z \end{pmatrix}$ be the multiplicative inverse of A.

i Use the fact that $AB = I$ to show that $\begin{Bmatrix} aw + by = 1 \\ cw + dy = 0 \end{Bmatrix}$ and $\begin{Bmatrix} ax + bz = 0 \\ cx + dz = 1 \end{Bmatrix}$.

ii Solve each system in **i** to find the values of w, x, y, and z in terms of a, b, c, and d.

Verify that $AB = I$ and $BA = I$.

The multiplicative inverse of a 2 × 2 matrix

Investigation 4 reveals that if $A = \begin{pmatrix} a & b \\ c & d \end{pmatrix}$ then the inverse of A is given by:

$$A^{-1} = \frac{1}{ad - bc}\begin{pmatrix} d & -b \\ -c & a \end{pmatrix} \text{ where } ad - bc \neq 0$$

You can thus determine the inverse of $\begin{pmatrix} a & b \\ c & d \end{pmatrix}$ using the following steps.

1 Subtract the product of the values on the minor diagonal from the product of the numbers on the main diagonal.

2 Interchange the elements on the main diagonal and change the sign of the numbers on the minor diagonal.

3 Divide each element of $\begin{pmatrix} d & -b \\ -c & a \end{pmatrix}$ by $(ad - bc)$.

You will see in later sections of this chapter as well as in future chapters that the value $(ad - bc)$ has geometric significance. For this reason, this value is given a name and is defined as the **determinant of matrix A** and is written as det A or $|A|$. Restating the formula for A^{-1} you now have:

$$A^{-1} = \frac{1}{|A|}\begin{pmatrix} d & -b \\ -c & a \end{pmatrix} \text{ where } ad - bc \neq 0$$

In the case where $|A| = 0$, A^{-1} does not exist and A is said to be a **singular matrix or non-invertible**.

International mindedness

Carl Gauss first used the term "determinant" in 1801.

$\nearrow ad - bc \nwarrow$

$\begin{pmatrix} a & b \\ c & d \end{pmatrix}$

$\begin{pmatrix} a & -b \\ -c & d \end{pmatrix}$

$$A^{-1} = \begin{pmatrix} \dfrac{d}{ad - bc} & \dfrac{-b}{ad - bc} \\ \dfrac{-c}{ad - bc} & \dfrac{a}{ad - bc} \end{pmatrix}$$

EXAM HINT

Finding the multiplicative inverse for square matrices beyond a 2 × 2 requires using technology, and you will need to know how to do this for your exams.

Example 3

Find the inverse of $\begin{pmatrix} 1 & -2 \\ 3 & -4 \end{pmatrix}$.

$\dfrac{1}{1 \times (-4) - (-2) \times 3} \begin{pmatrix} -4 & 2 \\ -3 & 1 \end{pmatrix}$	
$= \dfrac{1}{2} \begin{pmatrix} -4 & 2 \\ -3 & 1 \end{pmatrix} = \begin{pmatrix} -2 & 1 \\ -1.5 & 0.5 \end{pmatrix}$	Either of these two forms can be used, choose whichever is most appropriate for the context.

EXAM HINT

In examinations you should be able to demonstrate the use the formula

$$A^{-1} = \frac{1}{|A|} \begin{pmatrix} d & -b \\ -c & a \end{pmatrix}$$

to compute the inverse of a 2×2 matrix but are expected to use the matrix utility using technology to find the inverse of a matrix that is larger than a 2×2.

Example 4

Use technology to determine the inverse of $P = \begin{pmatrix} 4 & -3 & -2 \\ 2 & 2 & 3 \\ 6 & 1 & -1 \end{pmatrix}$.

Verify that $PP^{-1} = P^{-1}P = I_3$.

$$P^{-1} = \begin{pmatrix} \dfrac{1}{12} & \dfrac{1}{12} & \dfrac{1}{12} \\ -\dfrac{1}{3} & -\dfrac{2}{15} & \dfrac{4}{15} \\ \dfrac{1}{6} & \dfrac{11}{30} & -\dfrac{7}{30} \end{pmatrix}$$

$$PP^{-1} = \begin{pmatrix} 4 & -3 & -2 \\ 2 & 2 & 3 \\ 6 & 1 & -1 \end{pmatrix} \begin{pmatrix} \dfrac{1}{12} & \dfrac{1}{12} & \dfrac{1}{12} \\ -\dfrac{1}{3} & -\dfrac{2}{15} & \dfrac{4}{15} \\ \dfrac{1}{6} & \dfrac{11}{30} & -\dfrac{7}{30} \end{pmatrix} = \begin{pmatrix} 1 & 0 & 0 \\ 0 & 1 & 0 \\ 0 & 0 & 1 \end{pmatrix} = I_3$$

$$PP^{-1} = \begin{pmatrix} \dfrac{1}{12} & \dfrac{1}{12} & \dfrac{1}{12} \\ -\dfrac{1}{3} & -\dfrac{2}{15} & \dfrac{4}{15} \\ \dfrac{1}{6} & \dfrac{11}{30} & -\dfrac{7}{30} \end{pmatrix} \begin{pmatrix} 4 & -3 & -2 \\ 2 & 2 & 3 \\ 6 & 1 & -1 \end{pmatrix} = \begin{pmatrix} 1 & 0 & 0 \\ 0 & 1 & 0 \\ 0 & 0 & 1 \end{pmatrix} = I_3$$

You are now ready to unlock the solution to the problem proposed at the beginning of section 9.3, which was to solve the matrix equation $AX = B$ for X.

$$AX = B$$
$$A^{-1}AX = A^{-1}B \quad \left(\text{pre-multiplying both sides by } A^{-1}\right)$$
$$I_n X = A^{-1}B \quad \left(\text{multiplicative inverse property}\right)$$
$$X = A^{-1}B \quad \left(\text{Multiplicative identity property}\right)$$

TOK

Do you think that one form of symbolic representation is preferable to another?

Example 5

Solve the systems of equations by first forming a matrix equation.

a $\begin{cases} 10x - 5y = 35 \\ -3x + 7y = 23 \end{cases}$

b $\begin{cases} 4s - 3t - 2z = 0 \\ 2s + 2t + 3z = -6 \\ 6s + t - z = 2 \end{cases}$

Geometry and trigonometry

a $\begin{cases} 10x - 5y = 35 \\ -3x + 7y = 23 \end{cases} \Leftrightarrow \begin{pmatrix} 10 & -5 \\ -3 & 7 \end{pmatrix}\begin{pmatrix} x \\ y \end{pmatrix} = \begin{pmatrix} 35 \\ 23 \end{pmatrix}$

Rewriting the system in the form $AX = B$

$\begin{pmatrix} 10 & -5 \\ -3 & 7 \end{pmatrix}^{-1}\begin{pmatrix} 10 & -5 \\ -3 & 7 \end{pmatrix}\begin{pmatrix} x \\ y \end{pmatrix} = \begin{pmatrix} 10 & -5 \\ -3 & 7 \end{pmatrix}^{-1}\begin{pmatrix} 35 \\ 23 \end{pmatrix}$

Pre-multiplying both sides by A^{-1}

$\begin{pmatrix} 1 & 0 \\ 0 & 1 \end{pmatrix}\begin{pmatrix} x \\ y \end{pmatrix} = \dfrac{1}{70-15}\begin{pmatrix} 7 & 5 \\ 3 & 10 \end{pmatrix}\begin{pmatrix} 35 \\ 23 \end{pmatrix}$

$AA^{-1} = I_2$

$\begin{pmatrix} x \\ y \end{pmatrix} = \dfrac{1}{55}\begin{pmatrix} 360 \\ 335 \end{pmatrix}$

$I_2 X = X$

$\begin{pmatrix} x \\ y \end{pmatrix} = \begin{pmatrix} \dfrac{72}{11} \\ \dfrac{67}{11} \end{pmatrix}$

The calculation $\begin{pmatrix} 10 & -5 \\ -3 & 7 \end{pmatrix}^{-1}\begin{pmatrix} 35 \\ 23 \end{pmatrix}$ could have been done directly on a GDC. Use GDC to obtain the result.

The solution to the system is $x = \dfrac{72}{11}$ and $y = \dfrac{67}{11}$

b $4s - 3t - 2z = 0$
$2s + 2t + 3z = -6 \quad \Rightarrow$
$6s + t - z = 2$

$\begin{pmatrix} 4 & -3 & -2 \\ 2 & 2 & 3 \\ 6 & 1 & -1 \end{pmatrix}\begin{pmatrix} s \\ t \\ z \end{pmatrix} = \begin{pmatrix} 0 \\ -6 \\ 2 \end{pmatrix}$

Continued on next page

$$\begin{pmatrix} s \\ t \\ z \end{pmatrix} = \begin{pmatrix} 4 & -3 & -2 \\ 2 & 2 & 3 \\ 6 & 1 & -1 \end{pmatrix}^{-1} \begin{pmatrix} 0 \\ -6 \\ 2 \end{pmatrix}$$

$$\begin{pmatrix} -\dfrac{1}{3} \\[2mm] \dfrac{4}{3} \\[2mm] -\dfrac{8}{3} \end{pmatrix}$$

The solution to the system is
$$s = -\frac{1}{3}, \; t = \frac{4}{3}, \text{ and } z = -\frac{8}{3}$$

Applications to cryptography

Protecting sensitive electronic information such as a password relies upon a process called data encryption. Data encryption protects data by translating it into an unrecognizable form using an algorithm called a *cipher*.

To encrypt your bank account password "CharLie578Sam*!" you assign a number to each lowercase and uppercase letter along with the special characters and the digits 0 through 9 as shown below.

a	b	c	d	e	f	g	h	i	j	k	l	m	n	o	p	q	r	s	t	u	v	w	x	y	z
1	2	3	4	5	6	7	8	9	10	11	12	13	14	15	16	17	18	19	20	21	22	23	24	25	26
A	B	C	D	E	F	G	H	I	J	K	L	M	N	O	P	Q	R	S	T	U	V	W	X	Y	Z
27	28	29	30	31	32	33	34	35	36	37	38	39	40	41	42	43	44	45	46	47	48	49	50	51	52
!	@	#	$	%	^	&	*	"	?	:	;	/	\	0	1	2	3	4	5	6	7	8	9	space	
53	54	55	56	57	58	59	60	61	62	63	64	65	66	67	68	69	70	71	72	73	74	75	76	77	

Using table above converts the password "CharLie578Sam*!":

Original "word"	C	h	a	r	L	i	e	5	7	8	S	a	m	*	!
Converted word	29	8	1	18	38	9	5	72	74	75	45	1	13	60	53

Next, you decide upon the length of the block you will use to divide the password. In this case you will use a block of three which will divide the word into five blocks giving the following 3×5 matrix **M**.

> **HINT**
>
> If the word length was not a factor of 5 then the remaining spaces could simply be filled with zeros.

$$\begin{pmatrix} 29 \\ 8 \\ 1 \end{pmatrix}, \begin{pmatrix} 18 \\ 38 \\ 9 \end{pmatrix}, \begin{pmatrix} 5 \\ 72 \\ 74 \end{pmatrix}, \begin{pmatrix} 75 \\ 45 \\ 1 \end{pmatrix}, \begin{pmatrix} 13 \\ 60 \\ 53 \end{pmatrix} \Leftrightarrow M = \begin{pmatrix} 29 & 18 & 5 & 75 & 13 \\ 8 & 38 & 72 & 45 & 60 \\ 1 & 9 & 74 & 1 & 53 \end{pmatrix}$$

To encode the message, you can choose any 3×3 matrix for our

cipher. For example, if you choose $C = \begin{pmatrix} 7 & 2 & 1 \\ 0 & 3 & -1 \\ -3 & 4 & -2 \end{pmatrix}$ then our

encrypted message E is

$$E = CM = \begin{pmatrix} 7 & 2 & 1 \\ 0 & 3 & -1 \\ -3 & 4 & -2 \end{pmatrix} \begin{pmatrix} 29 & 18 & 5 & 75 & 13 \\ 8 & 38 & 72 & 45 & 60 \\ 1 & 9 & 74 & 1 & 53 \end{pmatrix} = \begin{pmatrix} 220 & 211 & 253 & 616 & 264 \\ 23 & 105 & 142 & 134 & 127 \\ -57 & 80 & 125 & -47 & 95 \end{pmatrix}$$

That is, the bank password is stored in the document in matrix form as

$$\begin{pmatrix} 220 & 211 & 253 & 616 & 264 \\ 23 & 105 & 142 & 134 & 127 \\ -57 & 80 & 125 & -47 & 95 \end{pmatrix}.$$

To decrypt the password requires you to solve $E = CM$ for M:

$$E = CM \Leftrightarrow C^{-1}E = C^{-1}CM \quad \therefore M = C^{-1}E$$

$$M = C^{-1}E = \begin{pmatrix} 7 & 2 & 1 \\ 0 & 3 & -1 \\ -3 & 4 & -2 \end{pmatrix}^{-1} \begin{pmatrix} 220 & 211 & 253 & 616 & 264 \\ 23 & 105 & 142 & 134 & 127 \\ -57 & 80 & 125 & -47 & 95 \end{pmatrix}$$

$$= \begin{pmatrix} -2 & 8 & -5 \\ 3 & -11 & 7 \\ 9 & -34 & 21 \end{pmatrix} \begin{pmatrix} 220 & 211 & 253 & 616 & 264 \\ 23 & 105 & 142 & 134 & 127 \\ -57 & 80 & 125 & -47 & 95 \end{pmatrix}$$

$$= \begin{pmatrix} 29 & 18 & 5 & 75 & 13 \\ 8 & 38 & 72 & 45 & 60 \\ 1 & 9 & 74 & 1 & 53 \end{pmatrix}$$

So the decrypted password is

29 8 1 18 38 9 5 72 74 75 45 1 13 60 53

C h a r L i e 5 7 8 S a m * !

Exercise 9D

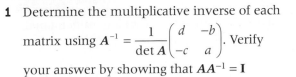

1 Determine the multiplicative inverse of each

matrix using $A^{-1} = \dfrac{1}{\det A}\begin{pmatrix} d & -b \\ -c & a \end{pmatrix}$. Verify

your answer by showing that $AA^{-1} = I$

a $\begin{pmatrix} 2 & -4 \\ 3 & -5 \end{pmatrix}$

b $\begin{pmatrix} -2 & -3 \\ -1 & 0 \end{pmatrix}$

c $\begin{pmatrix} \dfrac{3}{4} & \dfrac{1}{2} \\ \dfrac{1}{2} & \dfrac{3}{4} \end{pmatrix}$

d $\begin{pmatrix} 0.25 & 0.8 \\ 0.75 & 0.2 \end{pmatrix}$

2 Determine the multiplicative inverse of each matrix using technology expressing the elements as exact values. Verify your answer by showing that $AA^{-1} = I$.

a $\begin{pmatrix} 2 & -1 & 4 \\ 1 & 2 & 0 \\ -1 & 1 & -2 \end{pmatrix}$ b $\begin{pmatrix} 1.2 & -2.5 & 3 \\ 0.8 & -1 & 4 \\ 1.5 & -0.75 & 1 \end{pmatrix}$

c $\begin{pmatrix} \frac{2}{3} & -\frac{3}{4} & \frac{1}{2} \\ 1 & \frac{1}{3} & -1 \\ \frac{5}{2} & 0 & 1 \end{pmatrix}$

3 Write each system in the form of $AX = B$ then solve the system using $X = A^{-1}B$.

a $\begin{cases} x + y + 3z = 30 \\ 3x + 2y - z = 20 \\ 2x + y + z = 10 \end{cases}$ b $\begin{cases} 5x - 7y = 12 \\ -2x + 5y = 20 \end{cases}$

c $\begin{cases} 2a + b - c + 4d = -2 \\ 5b - 3c = 4 \\ 4a - 3b + d = 1.75 \\ a + 2c - 8d = -0.5 \end{cases}$

For questions 4–6 create a system of equations that represents each situation then solve the system using matrices. Be sure to define all variables.

4 In 2016, Sonya invested a total of $175,000 in three different index funds $F_1, F_2,$ and F_3. After one year, the combined value of all of her investments was $181,615. Data collected on each of these investments showed that each investment made average annual gains of 2.5%, 4.8%, and 3.5% respectively during the year. If Sonya invested twice as much money in F_2 than in F_1, calculate the amount she invested in each fund.

5 A manufacturer wishes to produce four different products A, B, C, and D. The table below shows the number of minutes required on each of four machines to produce each product.

Machine	Product A	Product B	Product C	Product D
I	2	1	1	3
II	1	3	2	4
III	2	1	2	2
IV	3	4	1	2

The maximum amount of time available for each machine I, II, III, and IV is 240 minutes, 380 minutes, 280 minutes, and 400 minutes respectively. Calculate how many of each product can be manufactured if each machine uses all of its available time.

6 **a** Jonathan makes the conjecture that $(AB)^{-1} = A^{-1}B^{-1}$. Show that Jonathan's conjecture does not hold using the matrices $A = \begin{pmatrix} -1 & 2 \\ 2 & -3 \end{pmatrix}$ and $B = \begin{pmatrix} 4 & 1 \\ 3 & 1 \end{pmatrix}$.

b Michelle claims that $(AB)^{-1} = B^{-1}A^{-1}$ does hold using the matrices A and B above.

i Verify that Michelle's claim is correct

ii Choosing your own 2×2 matrices for A and B show that $(AB)^{-1} = B^{-1}A^{-1}$.

iii Prove that $(AB)^{-1} = B^{-1}A^{-1}$ using the fact that $(AB)(AB)^{-1} = I_2$

7 Using the conversion table on page 386 decrypt the famous quote by James Joseph Sylvester [James Joseph Sylvester (1814–1897) – an English mathematician who made fundamental contributions to matrix theory, invariant theory, number theory, partition theory, and combinatorics.]

Encrypted message:
$$\begin{pmatrix} 224 & 288 & 84 & 192 & 279 & 75 & 38 & 158 & 103 & 96 & 83 & 220 \\ 144 & 202 & 50 & 109 & 182 & 49 & 28 & 80 & 71 & 60 & 50 & 150 \\ 83 & 163 & 49 & 89 & 174 & 44 & 15 & 79 & 51 & 51 & 47 & 131 \end{pmatrix}$$

Encryption matrix:
$$\begin{pmatrix} 1 & 2 & 3 \\ 1 & 1 & 2 \\ 0 & 1 & 2 \end{pmatrix}$$

8 Develop your own cipher using matrices to encrypt a sensitive piece of information. Design your own conversion table and encryption matrix by assigning different numbers to each of the characters and numbers. Check your work by having a friend decrypt your message by giving them your encrypted message, encryption key, and conversion table.

9.4 Transformations of the plane

For this section you need to be familiar with the ideas of rotation, reflection and enlargement, as illustrated in the example below.

Example 6

Draw the image of the triangle shown after the following transformations:

a rotation of 90° counter clockwise (or anticlockwise) about (0, 0)

b reflection in the line $x = 0$

c enlargement scale factor 2 centre (0, 0)

d a stretch parallel to the x-axis, scale factor 2.

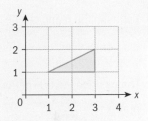

a

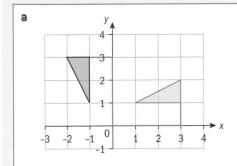

The rotation can be done using tracing paper or drawing an L shape from the origin to the point and rotating the L shape the required angle.

b

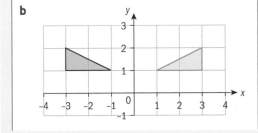

Reflection in the line $x = 0$ means all points are transformed to a position an equal distance the other side of the **mirror line**.

Continued on next page

c

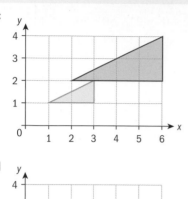

An enlargement scale factor 2 centre (0, 0) means the **image** of each point moves twice as far from the origin as before. Their new positions can easily be calculated by multiplying all their coordinates by 2.

d

A stretch scale factor 2 parallel to the x-axis (or horizontally) just multiplies all the x-coordinates by 2 and leaves the y-coordinates unchanged. Similarly for a stretch parallel to the y-axis.

Investigation 5

Points in the plane can be represented by their position vectors. In the diagram below, for example, the position vector of A is $\begin{pmatrix} 1 \\ 1 \end{pmatrix}$.

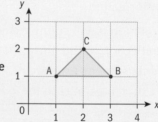

The position vectors of the vertices of the triangle ABC can be put in a single matrix $\begin{pmatrix} 1 & 2 & 3 \\ 1 & 2 & 1 \end{pmatrix}$.

1 Find the product of $\begin{pmatrix} 1 & 0 \\ 0 & -1 \end{pmatrix}\begin{pmatrix} 1 & 2 & 3 \\ 1 & 2 & 1 \end{pmatrix}$.

Let the columns of the new matrix be the position vectors of the **image** of triangle ABC under the transformation represented by the matrix $\begin{pmatrix} 1 & 0 \\ 0 & -1 \end{pmatrix}$.

2 On a copy of the diagram above draw the triangle ABC and its image after the transformation.

What is the transformation?

3 In the same way use the matrix $\begin{pmatrix} 1 & 0 \\ 0 & -1 \end{pmatrix}$ to find the image of (1, 0) and (0, 1) under this transformation.

What do you notice about the image matrix?

4 Test your conjecture by considering the image of (1, 0) and (0, 1) under this transformation represented by the matrix $\begin{pmatrix} a & b \\ c & d \end{pmatrix}$.

5 By considering the images of $(1, 0)$ and $(0, 1)$ suggest a matrix that represents an enlargement scale factor 2, centre $(0, 0)$.

Verify your answer by multiplying the points from the triangle above by this matrix and seeing if all the coordinates are multiplied by two.

How can you use the points $(1, 0)$ and $(0, 1)$ to find a transformation matrix?

All standard transformations of the xy-plane, including rotations, reflections, stretches and enlargements can be represented by 2×2 matrices provided the point $(0, 0)$ is invariant. These are often referred to as **linear transformations.**

A matrix representing a linear transformation can be written $\begin{pmatrix} a & c \\ b & d \end{pmatrix}$ where (a, b) is the image of $(1, 0)$

and (c, d) the image of $(0, 1)$.

6 Find the matrix that represents a rotation of 90° clockwise about $(0, 0)$.

7 Find the matrix that represents a stretch parallel to the x-axis with a scale factor of 2 and the y-axis invariant.

Using the same method some general formulae can be found.

8 a In the diagram below A and B are the images of $(1, 0)$ and $(0, 1)$ under a counter clockwise rotation of θ about $(0, 0)$. Use the diagram to show this rotation is represented by the matrix $\begin{pmatrix} \cos\theta & -\sin\theta \\ \sin\theta & \cos\theta \end{pmatrix}$.

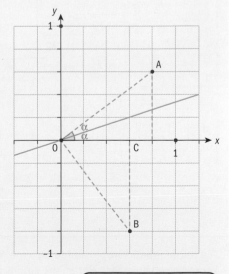

b What will be the matrix for a clockwise rotation of magnitude θ?

c Hence write down the matrix that represents a rotation of 60° clockwise about $(0, 0)$.

9 a The line $y = mx$ can be written as $y = (\tan\alpha)x$, where α is the angle made with the x-axis.

In the diagram below A and B represent the images of $(1, 0)$ and $(0, 1)$ respectively under a reflection in the line $y = (\tan\alpha)x$.

a Explain why the image of $(1, 0)$ has coordinates $(\cos2\alpha, \sin2\alpha)$.

b By finding $O\hat{B}C$ in terms of α find the image of $(0, 1)$ under the transformation.

c Hence verify that the matrix that represents a reflection in the line $y = (\tan\alpha)x$ is $\begin{pmatrix} \cos2\alpha & \sin2\alpha \\ \sin2\alpha & -\cos2\alpha \end{pmatrix}$.

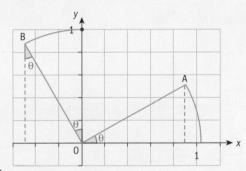

d By first finding α, determine the matrix that represents a reflection in the line $y = \sqrt{3}x$.

10 By considering the images of $(1, 0)$ and $(0, 1)$ find the general matrices for:

a a one-way stretch, parallel to the x-axis, scale factor k

b an enlargement scale factor k, centre $(0, 0)$.

> **HINT**
> These formulae are all in the formula book

Example 7

a Write down the matrix that represents a rotation of 45° anticlockwise about the origin given that $\cos 45° = \sin 45° = \dfrac{1}{\sqrt{2}}$.

b Write down the matrix that represents a horizontal stretch of scale factor $\sqrt{2}$.

c Hence find the image of (2, 3) after a rotation of 45° anticlockwise about (0, 0) followed by a horizontal stretch of scale factor $\sqrt{2}$.

d Write down the single matrix that represents a rotation of 45° anticlockwise about (0, 0) followed by a horizontal stretch of scale factor $\sqrt{2}$.

a $\begin{pmatrix} \dfrac{1}{\sqrt{2}} & -\dfrac{1}{\sqrt{2}} \\ \dfrac{1}{\sqrt{2}} & \dfrac{1}{\sqrt{2}} \end{pmatrix}$	This is using the formula for an anticlockwise rotation.
b $\begin{pmatrix} \sqrt{2} & 0 \\ 0 & 1 \end{pmatrix}$	This is using the formula for a one-way stretch. Both these formulae are in the formula book.
c $\begin{pmatrix} \sqrt{2} & 0 \\ 0 & 1 \end{pmatrix}\left(\begin{pmatrix} \dfrac{1}{\sqrt{2}} & -\dfrac{1}{\sqrt{2}} \\ \dfrac{1}{\sqrt{2}} & \dfrac{1}{\sqrt{2}} \end{pmatrix}\begin{pmatrix} 2 \\ 3 \end{pmatrix} \right)$ $= \begin{pmatrix} \sqrt{2} & 0 \\ 0 & 1 \end{pmatrix}\begin{pmatrix} -\dfrac{1}{\sqrt{2}} \\ \dfrac{5}{\sqrt{2}} \end{pmatrix} = \begin{pmatrix} -1 \\ \dfrac{5}{\sqrt{2}} \end{pmatrix}$	The point is first rotated and then its image is stretched.
d $\begin{pmatrix} \sqrt{2} & 0 \\ 0 & 1 \end{pmatrix}\begin{pmatrix} \dfrac{1}{\sqrt{2}} & -\dfrac{1}{\sqrt{2}} \\ \dfrac{1}{\sqrt{2}} & \dfrac{1}{\sqrt{2}} \end{pmatrix} = \begin{pmatrix} 1 & -1 \\ \dfrac{1}{\sqrt{2}} & \dfrac{1}{\sqrt{2}} \end{pmatrix}$	

> If a transformation represented by a matrix A is followed by a transformation represented by matrix B then the single matrix that represents both transformations is BA.

Example 8

Find the 2×2 matrix that will transform the point $(2, 1)$ to $(1, 4)$ and the point $(1, -3)$ to $(4, 9)$.

Let $T = \begin{pmatrix} a & b \\ c & d \end{pmatrix}$.	
Therefore, $$\begin{pmatrix} x' \\ y' \end{pmatrix} = \begin{pmatrix} a & b \\ c & d \end{pmatrix}\begin{pmatrix} 2 \\ 1 \end{pmatrix} = \begin{pmatrix} 1 \\ 4 \end{pmatrix} \Leftrightarrow 2a + b = 1 \text{ and } 2c + d = 4$$	Write down the matrix equation that describes the transformation.
$$\begin{pmatrix} x' \\ y' \end{pmatrix} = \begin{pmatrix} a & b \\ c & d \end{pmatrix}\begin{pmatrix} 1 \\ -3 \end{pmatrix} = \begin{pmatrix} 4 \\ 9 \end{pmatrix} \Leftrightarrow a - 3b = 4 \text{ and } c - 3d = 9$$	Develop two 2×2 systems of equations and solve each system using elimination or technology.
$\begin{cases} 2a + b = 1 \\ a - 3b = 4 \end{cases}_{\times (-2)} \Leftrightarrow 7b = -7 \quad \therefore b = -1 \text{ and } a = 1$	
and $\begin{cases} 2c + d = 4 \\ c - 3d = 9 \end{cases}_{\times (-2)} \Leftrightarrow 7d = -14 \quad d = -2 \text{ and } c = 3$	
Therefore, $T = \begin{pmatrix} 1 & -1 \\ 3 & -2 \end{pmatrix}$.	

Investigation 6

Consider the triangle ABC with vertices $\mathbf{A}(0, 0)$, $\mathbf{B}(2, 2)$, $\mathbf{C}(-1, 5)$.

1 Show that $\triangle ABC$ is a right-angled triangle and find its area.

2 Triangle ABC is enlarged by a factor of 3 to obtain triangle A′B′C′.

   a Use matrix multiplication to determine the coordinates of A′B′C′.

   b Determine the area of triangle A′B′C′. By what factor has the area of triangle ABC changed? By what factor will the area change if it is enlarged by a factor of k?

3 Triangle ABC is transformed by $T = \begin{pmatrix} 1 & 2 \\ 2 & -1 \end{pmatrix}$.

   a Find the coordinates of the image points of triangle ABC.

   b Show that the new triangle is a right-angled triangle and determine its area. By what factor has the area of triangle ABC changed under T?

   c Calculate $\det(T)$ and show that the area of triangle ABC enlarged by a factor of $|\det(T)|$.

Continued on next page

4 Consider triangle ABC under the transformation $T = \begin{pmatrix} 2 & 1 \\ -1 & 3 \end{pmatrix}$

   a Use graphing software to show that area of A′B′C′ = 42. Is ABC a right triangle? How do you know?

   b Show that this area is equal to $|\det(T)| \times$ Area of triangle ABC.

5 Consider the transformation of triangle ABC under $T = \begin{pmatrix} 2 & 1 \\ 6 & 3 \end{pmatrix}$. Does the relationship $|\det(T)| \times$ Area of triangle ABC hold for T? Explain why.

In the investigation above you discovered a very useful relationship between the area of a figure's pre-image and the area of its image under a linear transformation T.

$$\text{Area of the image} = |\det(T)| \times \text{Area of the pre-image}$$

Exercise 9E

1 Find the transformation matrix for:

   a A reflection in the x-axis

   b An anticlockwise rotation about the origin of 45°

   c A clockwise rotation of $\dfrac{\pi}{2}$

   d A reflection in the line $y = -x$

   e A vertical stretch of scale factor 3

   f An enlargement scale factor 2, centre $(0, 0)$

   g A reflection in the line $y = \sqrt{3}x$.

2 a Write down the transformation matrix for an enlargement scale factor 4, centre $(0, 0)$.

   b Write down the transformation matrix for a rotation of 180° about $(0, 0)$.

A rotation of 180° about the origin followed by an enlargement of scale factor k where $k > 0$ is often referred to as an enlargement with scale factor $-k$.

   c Find the product of the two matrices found in parts **a** and **b** and hence explain why this definition is justified.

3 Consider the triangle ABC whose vertices are described by the matrix

$$P = \begin{pmatrix} 2 & 6 & 10 \\ 4 & 7 & 6 \end{pmatrix}.$$

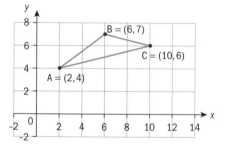

a Use matrix multiplication to determine the image of triangle ABC when it is reflected across the x-axis to obtain triangle A′B′C′. Sketch the triangle and its image on the same axis.

Triangle A′B′C′ is reflected across the y-axis to obtain A″B″C″.

b Write a single matrix equation to find the image of P under the composition of both reflections. Sketch triangle A″B″C″ on the same axis.

c Show that if triangle ABC is reflected across the x-axis then again across the x axis that the resulting image is triangle ABC.

d What transformation is equivalent to reflection in the x-axis followed by reflection in the y-axis.

4 a Write down the transformation matrix for a reflection in the line $y = (\tan\alpha)x$.

b Verify that a reflection followed by a second reflection in the same line is equivalent to the identity matrix.

5 a Write down the exact matrix R for a rotation of 45° clockwise about the origin, given that $\cos 45° = \sin 45° = \dfrac{1}{\sqrt{2}}$.

b Find the value of R^8 and interpret your result.

6 a Find the area of the triangle with vertices at $(0,5)$, $(4,5)$ and $(2,7)$.

b Use the result, area of image = $|\det (T)| \times$ area of object to find the area of the image of the triangle:

i after a vertical stretch with scale factor 2, followed by an enlargement, centre $(0, 0)$, scale factor 3

ii after undergoing the transformation represented by the matrix $\begin{pmatrix} 2 & 2 \\ -3 & 5 \end{pmatrix}$.

7 Prove that neither transformation will change the area of an object by considering the determinant for the general matrix for:

a a reflection **b** a rotation.

8 Let T be a linear transformation such that $T = \begin{pmatrix} 3 & 5 \\ 2 & 4 \end{pmatrix}$. Find:

a the coordinates of the image of the point $P(14, 12)$ under T

b the coordinates of the point having an image of $(-12, 12)$.

9 Let T be a linear transformation such that $T = \begin{pmatrix} -1 & 2 \\ 1 & -2 \end{pmatrix}$. Find:

a the coordinates of the image of the point $P(-3, 4)$ under T

b the coordinates of the point having an image of $(-12, 12)$.

10 Find the 2×2 matrix that will transform the point $(2, 1)$ to $(1, 4)$ and the point $(1, -3)$ to $(4, 9)$.

11 A triangle with vertices $(1, 1)$, $(3, 1)$ and $(3, 3)$ is rotated $\dfrac{\pi}{2}$ clockwise about $(0, 0)$ and then reflected in the line $y = -x$. Let R represent the rotation and T represent the reflection.

a Write down the matrices R and T.

b Find the single matrix that represents R followed by T.

c Hence find the image of the triangle after both these transformations.

d From a sketch or otherwise describe the single transformation represented by RT.

12 Let E be a matrix representing an enlargment scale factor 0.5, centre $(0, 0)$.

a Write down the matrix E.

b Find the single matrix that represents a series of n enlargements scale factor 0.5, centre $(0, 0)$.

13 The point $P(-2, 5)$ undergoes two rotations R_1 followed by R_2.

a Given that R_1 is a counterclockwise rotation of 20° and R_2 is a counterclockwise rotation of 40°. Determine the coordinates of the image of P.

b Show that

$$\begin{pmatrix} \cos 60° & -\sin 60° \\ \sin 60° & \cos 60° \end{pmatrix}\begin{pmatrix} x \\ y \end{pmatrix} = \begin{pmatrix} \cos 20° \cos 40° - \sin 20° \sin 40° & -\cos 40° \sin 20° - \sin 40° \cos 20° \\ \sin 40° \cos 20° + \cos 40° \sin 20° & -\sin 40° \sin 20° + \cos 40° \cos 20° \end{pmatrix}\begin{pmatrix} x \\ y \end{pmatrix}$$

c Given that R_1 is a counterclockwise rotation of α and R_2 is a counterclockwise rotation of θ, show that

$$\cos(\alpha + \theta) \equiv \cos\alpha\cos\theta - \sin\alpha\sin\theta \text{ and } \sin(\alpha + \theta) \equiv \sin\theta\cos\alpha + \cos\alpha\sin\theta.$$

Affine transformations

Points in the plane can also be transformed using vectors (**translations**). For example, the point (3, 2) under the translation $\begin{pmatrix} 1 \\ -3 \end{pmatrix}$ will have position vector $\begin{pmatrix} 3 \\ 2 \end{pmatrix} + \begin{pmatrix} 1 \\ -3 \end{pmatrix} = \begin{pmatrix} 4 \\ -1 \end{pmatrix}$

or coordinates (4, −1).

An Affine transformation consists of a linear transformation (represented by a matrix) and a translation and is of the form $Ax + b$ where x is the point being acted on. Affine transformations are often used to describe or create objects for which the whole object is the same (or approximately the same) as part of itself (self-similar), many fractals are self-similar. A famous example is the Barnsley Fern.

Example 9

The square PQRS with vertices P(−2, 4), Q(−6, −3), R(1, −7), S(5, 0) undergoes a transformation described by

$$\begin{pmatrix} x' \\ y' \end{pmatrix} = \begin{pmatrix} -\dfrac{1}{2} & 0 \\ 0 & \dfrac{1}{2} \end{pmatrix} \begin{pmatrix} x \\ y \end{pmatrix} + \begin{pmatrix} 3 \\ 2 \end{pmatrix}.$$

a By multiplying two transformation matrices verify that $\begin{pmatrix} -\dfrac{1}{2} & 0 \\ 0 & \dfrac{1}{2} \end{pmatrix}$ is equivalent to an

enlargement of scale factor 0.5 followed by a reflection in the y-axis.

b Determine the coordinates of the vertices of the image of PQRS.

c Draw the square PQRS and its image on the same axes.

a $\begin{pmatrix} 0.5 & 0 \\ 0 & 0.5 \end{pmatrix} \begin{pmatrix} -1 & 0 \\ 0 & 1 \end{pmatrix} = \begin{pmatrix} -0.5 & 0 \\ 0 & 0.5 \end{pmatrix}$	Take each point in turn and find its image. The full working for the point (−2, 4) is shown.
b $\begin{pmatrix} x' \\ y' \end{pmatrix} = \begin{pmatrix} -\dfrac{1}{2} & 0 \\ 0 & \dfrac{1}{2} \end{pmatrix} \times \begin{pmatrix} -2 \\ 4 \end{pmatrix} + \begin{pmatrix} 3 \\ 2 \end{pmatrix} = \begin{pmatrix} 1 \\ 2 \end{pmatrix} + \begin{pmatrix} 3 \\ 2 \end{pmatrix} = \begin{pmatrix} 4 \\ 3 \end{pmatrix}$	
$(-6, -3) \rightarrow (6, 0.5)$	
$(1, -7) \rightarrow (2.5, -1.5)$	
$(5, 0) \rightarrow (0.5, 2)$	

c

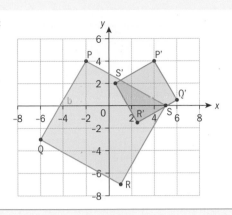

Investigation 7

Consider the series of squares S_0, S_1, S_2, ... where the sides of each successive square is one-half of the previous square, as shown. Each successive square is formed by a transformation of the form $AX + b$ where A is a 2×2 matrix and b is a 2×1 column vector.

Let (x_{n-1}, y_{n-1}) be a point in S_{n-1} and (x_n, y_n) be the image of this point in S_n such that

$$\begin{pmatrix} x_n \\ y_n \end{pmatrix} = A \begin{pmatrix} x_{n-1} \\ y_{n-1} \end{pmatrix} + b.$$

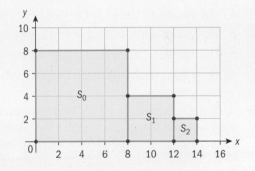

1 By considering the points $(0, 0)$, $(0, 8)$, and $(8, 0)$ in S_0 and their corresponding images in S_1 write down and solve a system of equations to determine A and b.

2 Using the coordinates of a point in the interior of S_1 along with the coordinates of its image in S_2 verify your answer in question 1.

3 Determine the coordinates of the image of $(6, 6)$ in S_3.

4 **a** Apply the transformation to find (x_1, y_1) in terms of (x_0, y_0).

b Apply the transformation again to find (x_2, y_2) in terms of (x_0, y_0).

c Hence show that $\begin{pmatrix} x_3 \\ y_3 \end{pmatrix} = \begin{pmatrix} \dfrac{1}{8} x_0 + 8 + 4 + 2 \\ \dfrac{1}{8} y_0 \end{pmatrix}$.

d Use the formula for a geometric series to find an expression for (x_n, y_n) in terms of (x_0, y_0).

5 Use your conjecture to determine the coordinates of the image of $(6, 2)$ in S_4.

1 The points A(−3, 4), B(2, −3), C(0, 4), and D(5, 8) are transformed to A′, B′, C′, D′ according to a linear transformation defined by $X = \begin{pmatrix} -4 & 0 \\ 1 & -4 \end{pmatrix} X + \begin{pmatrix} 6 \\ -2 \end{pmatrix}$. Find:

a the coordinates of the image points A′, B′, C′, D′

b the coordinates of the point whose image is P(−6, −3).

2 Under a transformation **T** the image (x′, y′) of a point (x, y) is obtained by the matrix equation $\begin{pmatrix} x' \\ y' \end{pmatrix} = \begin{pmatrix} -2 & 1 \\ -1 & 2 \end{pmatrix} \begin{pmatrix} x \\ y \end{pmatrix}$. Find

a the image of the point (−5, 8)

b the point with an image of (3, 6)

c the image of the point (a, a) where $a \in \mathbb{R}$

d the point with an image of (a, a) where $a \in \mathbb{R}$.

3 A shape is transformed by first undergoing a enlargement by a factor of 3 followed by a rotation of 90° anti-clockwise then lastly translated by the vector $\begin{pmatrix} 2 \\ 3 \end{pmatrix}$.

a Determine the 2 × 2 matrix **T** and the 2 × 1 column vector **b** that maps the pre-image point (x, y) to its image point (x′, y′) such that $\begin{pmatrix} x' \\ y' \end{pmatrix} = T \begin{pmatrix} x \\ y \end{pmatrix} + b$

The image point (x′, y′) is now reflected across the origin to obtain the image point (x'', y'')

b Determine the 2 × 2 matrix **A** and the 2 × 1 column vector **c** that maps the pre-image point (x, y) to its image point (x'', y'') such that $\begin{pmatrix} x'' \\ y'' \end{pmatrix} = A \begin{pmatrix} x \\ y \end{pmatrix} + c$.

4 a Find the 2 × 2 transformation matrices **P**, **Q**, **R**, and **S** given that

i matrix **P** represents a reflection in the x-axis

ii matrix **Q** represents a clockwise rotation of 135°

iii matrix **R** represents a reflection in the line $y = \sqrt{3}x$

iv matrix **S** represents a stretch of factor 2 parallel to the x-axis and a stretch of factor 4 parallel to the y-axis.

b Find a single transformation in the form of **AX** + **b** that transforms a point (x, y) by **Q** followed by **P** followed by **R** followed by **S**.

c Find a single transformation in the form of **AX** + **b** when a point (x, y) is translated by the vector $\begin{pmatrix} 4 \\ -2 \end{pmatrix}$ followed by **R**.

5 A sequence of equilateral triangles (T_n) are shown below. T_n is formed from T_{n-1} by rotating the triangle 60° clockwise about (0, 0) and enlarging by a factor 0.5 (centre (0, 0).

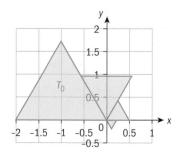

T_0 is the triangle shown with two vertices at (−2, 0) and (0, 0).

The perimeter of the shape formed from these triangles is the distance around the outside edge.

a Find the perimeter of the shape shown made up of triangles T_0 to T_3.

b Explain why the maximum perimeter is reached once T_5 is added to the diagram and find this value.

Let E be the enlargement matrix and R the rotation matrix.

c i Find $\det(E)$.

  ii Find the area of T_0.

  iii Hence find the total area covered by T_0 to T_6.

d Write down the matrix R.

e Find ER.

f Use your GDC to find the coordinates of all three vertices in T_8.

Developing inquiry skills

In the chapter opener, you found, using geometry, the exact values of the coordinates of each vertex and endpoint of stages 1 and 2 of the Koch Snowflake.

Stage 1

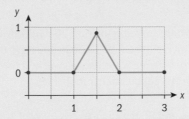

You may have noticed that the basic building block of the Koch Snowflake is given by stage 1– that is, using a series of transformations on stage 1 you can create each colored piece of the snowflake in stage 2.

Stage 2

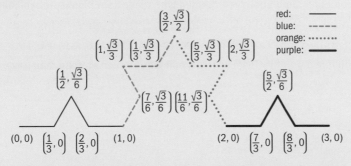

1 Describe the series of transformations that are necessary to map the red piece in stage 1 to the red piece in stage 2. Write your answer in the form of $AX + b$ where A is a 2×2 matrix, b is a 2×1 column vector, and X is a 2×1 column vector of the vertices and endpoints of stage 1. Name this transformation T_1. By applying T_1 to each vertex and endpoint in stage 1, determine the image points of the red piece in stage 2.

2 Repeat the steps in question **1** to determine the transformations of the form $AX + b$ that maps the vertices in stage 1 onto the blue, orange, and purple pieces of stage 2. Name these transformations T_2, T_3, and T_4 respectively. By applying these transformations determine the coordinates of each vertex and endpoint in each stage.

9.5 Representing systems

Some applications of probability consider sequences of events in which an outcome depends on the previous outcome. For example, the probability of our inheriting a particular genetic trait is dependent on the genes of our parents. Whether or not today sees heavy rainfall may be affected by the type of weather from the previous day.

Investigation 8

Sequences A and B are simulations of weather data over 21 days.
W represents the event "It was wet today" and D represents the event "It was dry today".

| A | D | D | D | D | W | D | W | W | D | D | W | D | W | D | W | W | W | D | D | D | D |
| B | W | D | D | W | W | D | W | W | W | W | W | W | W | D | D | D | W | D | W | W | W |

You can investigate this data to see if there is any evidence of the weather tomorrow being dependent on the weather today as follows.

In sequence A there are 8 wet days and 13 dry. You only consider the first 20 days however since you do not have information about the weather on the 22nd day. From the first 20 days you have this data: {WD, WW, WD, WD, WD, WW, WW, WD} to represent the days on which the weather was wet and then the weather on the next day. From this set you can find these experimental conditional probabilities:

$$P(\text{Wet tomorrow} \mid \text{Wet today}) = \frac{3}{8} \text{ and } P(\text{Dry tomorrow} \mid \text{Wet today}) = \frac{5}{8}$$

Show that for sequence B an estimate of the conditional probabilities are:

$$P(\text{Wet tomorrow} \mid \text{Dry today}) = \frac{4}{7} \text{ and } P(\text{Dry tomorrow} \mid \text{Dry today}) = \frac{3}{7}$$

One sequence was generated by a computer simulation programmed with these conditional probabilities:
$$P(\text{Wet tomorrow} \mid \text{Dry today}) = 0.4 \text{ and } P(\text{Dry tomorrow} \mid \text{Dry today}) = 0.6 \text{ and}$$
$$P(\text{Wet tomorrow} \mid \text{Wet today}) = 0.5 \text{ and } P(\text{Dry tomorrow} \mid \text{Wet today}) = 0.5$$

The other sequence was simulated by flipping a coin. Discuss in a small group which method may have generated each sequence

1   How did you decide?

2   Why is it difficult to be sure?

3   **Conceptual** How do you describe independent events?

The **states** of this system are "Dry" and "Wet" and the sequences A and B show the system changing state from one day to another. In this system, you cannot predict the outcome of a given trial with absolute certainty, but you can use probabilities to quantify the likely state of the system in any given trial.

> A **Markov Chain** is a system in which the probability of each event depends only on the state of the previous event.

TOK

How do "believing that" and "believing in" differ?

How does belief differ from knowledge?

You could represent the probabilities in the computer simulation given in investigation 8 in two tree diagrams as below. These are called **transition probabilities.**

Another convenient way to summarise and represent these probabilities is in this **transition state diagram:**

You can also represent the same information in a **transition matrix** in which the column headings refer to the **current state** of the system, shown here as the matrix T and the row headings the next (future) state.

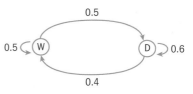

The entries in the transition matrix show the probability of the transition from the current state to the future state.

$$T = \begin{array}{c} \\ \text{Future state} \end{array} \begin{array}{c} \\ \begin{array}{cc} & \text{Current state} \\ & \begin{array}{cc} D & W \end{array} \end{array} \\ \begin{array}{c} D \\ W \end{array} \begin{pmatrix} 0.6 & 0.5 \\ 0.4 & 0.5 \end{pmatrix} \end{array}$$

In the following investigation you will find out how to interpret repeated multiplication of a transition matrix.

Investigation 9

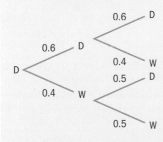

Coninuing with the situation described above You can use this tree diagram to find the probability that if is **dry** today, it is also dry two days from now by finding

$0.6 \times 0.6 + 0.4 \times 0.5 = 0.56$

and the probability that if it is **dry** today it will be wet two days from now by finding

$0.6 \times 0.4 + 0.4 \times 0.5 = 0.44$

1   Apply a tree diagram to find the probability that if is **wet** today, it is also wet two days from now.

2   Apply a tree diagram to find the probability that if is **wet** today, it is dry two days from now.

3   Given $T = \begin{pmatrix} 0.6 & 0.5 \\ 0.4 & 0.5 \end{pmatrix}$, Find T^2.

4   How do you interpret the values in the matrix T^2?

5   **Factual** What is more efficient to find the probabilities in T^2- matrix multiplication or drawing the two tree diagrams?

6   **Factual** How do you interpret the values in the matrix T^3?

7   **Factual** How can you interpret our results when multiplying by the transition matrix?

8   **Factual** What does n represent in T^n?

9   **Conceptual** How can the probabilities of Markov chains be represented?

A transition matrix is a square matrix which summarizes a transition state diagram. It describes the probabilities of moving from one state in a system to another state.

The sum of each column of the transition matrix is 1.

The transition matrix is extremely useful when there are more than two states in the system and when you wish to predict states of the system after several time periods.

International mindedness

Matrices play an important role in the projection of three-dimensional images into a two-dimensional screen, creating the realistic seeming motions in computer-based applications.

Example 10

Dockless bicycle company Mathbike hires bicycles in a city through a mobile phone app. Users can unlock a bicycle with their smartphone, ride it to their destination then lock the bicycle. Mathbike divides the city into three zones: Inner (I), Outer (O), and Central business district (C). By tracking their bicycles with GPS over several weeks, the company finds that at the end of each day:

- 50% of the bicycles rented in zone C remained in zone C, 30% were left in Zone I, and 20% were left in Zone O

- 60% of the bicycles rented in zone O remained in zone O, 30% were left in zone I, and 10% were left in zone C.

- 35% of bicycles rented in zone I remained in zone I, 35% were left in zone O, and 30% were left in zone C.

a Show this information in a transition state diagram.

b Show this information in a transition matrix.

c Determine the probability that after three days, a bicycle that started in C is now in O.

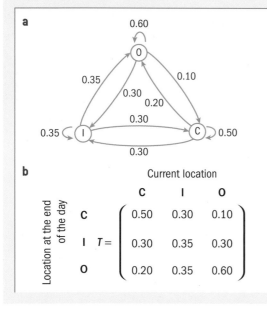

a

b Current location

$$\begin{array}{c}\text{Location at the end of the day}\end{array}\quad\begin{array}{c}\text{C}\\\text{I}\\\text{O}\end{array}\quad T=\begin{array}{ccc}\text{C} & \text{I} & \text{O}\\\begin{pmatrix}0.50 & 0.30 & 0.10\\0.30 & 0.35 & 0.30\\0.20 & 0.35 & 0.60\end{pmatrix}\end{array}$$

The diagram gives a quick way to check that the relationships given in the question are put in the right places.

Be careful to make the column headings represent the current state of the system and the row headings the future state.

c

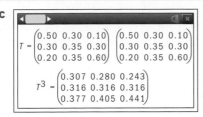

$$T = \begin{pmatrix} 0.50 & 0.30 & 0.10 \\ 0.30 & 0.35 & 0.30 \\ 0.20 & 0.35 & 0.60 \end{pmatrix} \begin{pmatrix} 0.50 & 0.30 & 0.10 \\ 0.30 & 0.35 & 0.30 \\ 0.20 & 0.35 & 0.60 \end{pmatrix}$$

$$T^3 = \begin{pmatrix} 0.307 & 0.280 & 0.243 \\ 0.316 & 0.316 & 0.316 \\ 0.377 & 0.405 & 0.441 \end{pmatrix}$$

The most efficient method is to store the matrix in a GDC as T and find T^3.

The probability that a bicycle starting in the central business district at the end of three days is in the outer zone is 0.441.

Read off the number in the C column and the O row, which is 0.441 and write a conclusion that interprets this number.

Reflect From what you have learned in this section, how can you best represent a system involving probabilities?

For **visualising** a system, would you choose a tree diagram, a transition state diagram or a transition matrix?

For **calculating probabilities**, would you choose a tree diagram, a transition state diagram or a transition matrix?

Exercise 9G

1 For these transition matrices, construct the corresponding transition diagrams:

a

Current state

$$\begin{array}{cc} & X \quad\; Y \\ \text{Future state} \;\begin{array}{c} X \\ Y \end{array} & \begin{pmatrix} \dfrac{5}{11} & \dfrac{1}{5} \\[2mm] \dfrac{6}{11} & \dfrac{4}{5} \end{pmatrix} \end{array}$$

b

Current location

$$\begin{array}{c} \\ T = \end{array} \begin{array}{c} A \\ B \\ C \end{array} \begin{array}{ccc} A & B & C \end{array} \begin{pmatrix} 0.2 & 0 & 0.47 \\ 0.5 & 0.9 & 0 \\ 0.3 & 0.1 & 0.53 \end{pmatrix}$$

2 This transition state diagram shows the findings from market research of the buying habits of consumers who shop weekly and buy either soft drink brand Ceko or Popsi. For example, the probability that a person buying Ceko will buy Popsi the next week is 0.25.

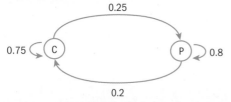

a Show this information in a transition matrix T by writing down the blank entries.

Current location

$$T = \begin{array}{c} \text{Future state} \end{array} \begin{array}{c} C \\ P \end{array} \begin{array}{cc} C & P \end{array} \begin{pmatrix} & 0.2 \\ 0.25 & \end{pmatrix}$$

b Calculate T^3 and hence find the probability that a person who buys Popsi now will change to Ceko three weeks from now.

3 Upon further research, it is found that a more realistic model is to create a third state N to represent a person buying neither Ceko nor Popsi. The transition state diagram is

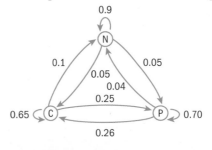

a Complete the transition matrix:

b Find the probability that a person buying neither Ceko nor Popsi now will buy Popsi five weeks from now.

4 A game begins in state 1 with two white coins in one box and two blue in another. A coin is chosen at random from each box and put into the other then the process is repeated many times.

State 1   State 2   State 3

a Construct the transition matrix to show the probabilities of transitioning from one state to another.

b The game is made more sophisticated by starting with three white coins in one box and three blue in another, represented as 3W3B. State the new number of states. the transition matrix to show the probabilities of transitioning from one state to another.

c Investigate the transition matrices for other situations such as 4W4B, 5W5B, 3W2B etc.

5 Two candidates A and B are running for an elected government office. Statistics gathered from a survey taken over several weeks prior to the election showed that after each week approximately 4.1% of the candidates who were planning to vote for candidate A changed their mind and decided to vote for candidate B and 3.2% of those who were planning to vote for candidate B changed their mind and decided to vote for candidate A.

Five weeks before the election a final survey showed that 45 520 people were planning to vote for candidate A and 38 745 people were planning to vote for candidate B.

a Write a matrix equation that describes the number of voters supporting each candidate n weeks after the final survey.

b Assuming that the trends revealed in the survey continue up until the day of the election determine which candidate will win. Calculate the margin of victory.

9.6 Representing steady state systems

You have seen in section 9.5 that if T is an $m \times m$ transition matrix and if

$$T^n = \begin{pmatrix} a_{11} & a_{12} & a_{13} & \dots & a_{1m} \\ a_{21} & a_{22} & a_{23} & \dots & a_{2m} \\ a_{31} & a_{32} & a_{33} & \dots & a_{3m} \\ \dots & \dots & \dots & \dots & \dots \\ a_{m1} & a_{m2} & a_{m3} & \dots & a_{mm} \end{pmatrix}$$

TOK

If we can find solutions of higher dimensions, can we reason that these spaces exist beyond our sense perception?

then a_{ij} is the probability that the system transitions from state j to state i *after n stages*. The sequence of transition matrices T^n, $n \in \mathbb{Z}^+$ behaves in different ways according to T, just as the geometric sequence $u_1 r^n$, $n \in \mathbb{Z}^+$ behaves in different ways according to the value of r.

Investigation 10

1   Use technology to find these powers of each transition matrix T.

	T	T^2	T^3	T^4	T^{20}	T^{50}	Term
a	$\begin{pmatrix} \dfrac{5}{11} & \dfrac{1}{5} \\[2mm] \dfrac{6}{11} & \dfrac{4}{5} \end{pmatrix}$						
b	$\begin{pmatrix} 0.2 & 0 & 0.47 \\ 0.5 & 0.9 & 0 \\ 0.3 & 0.1 & 0.53 \end{pmatrix}$						
c	$\begin{pmatrix} 0 & 0.5 & 0 \\ 1 & 0 & 1 \\ 0 & 0.5 & 0 \end{pmatrix}$						
d	$\begin{pmatrix} 0 & 0 & 0 & 0.8 \\ 0.3 & 1 & 0 & 0.1 \\ 0.3 & 0 & 1 & 0.1 \\ 0.4 & 0 & 0 & 0 \end{pmatrix}$						
e	$\begin{pmatrix} 0.25 & 0 & 0.65 \\ 0 & 0 & 0.35 \\ 0.75 & 1 & 0 \end{pmatrix}$						

2   What patterns are there in these sequences of matrices?

Each sequence above is classified by one of these terms: absorbing, regular, periodic.

An absorbing state is one that when entered, cannot transition to another.

3   What would a definition of the other terms be? Drawing a transition state diagram may help you distinguish between the different types.

4   Identify the appropriate term for each.

5   **Conceptual** What happens to a regular Markov chain with transition matrix T as n tends to infinity?

> A **regular** transition matrix T has the property that there exists $n \in \mathbb{Z}^+$ such that all entries in T^n are greater than zero. For high powers of n a regular transition matrix converges to a matrix in which all the columns have the same values. In the rest of this chapter you only consider regular transition matrices.

You can use this property to make predictions about the state of a system after many time periods. In practical applications you often need to consider a population in which a certain number are in either state at the beginning. For example, consider the transition matrix which represents the probabilities of transitioning between buying Ceko or Popsi each week:

$$T = \begin{array}{c} \\ \text{Future state} \end{array} \begin{array}{cc} & \text{Current location} \\ & \begin{array}{cc} \text{C} & \text{P} \end{array} \\ \begin{array}{c} \text{C} \\ \text{P} \end{array} & \begin{pmatrix} 0.75 & 0.2 \\ 0.25 & 0.8 \end{pmatrix} \end{array}$$

A survey of 126 consumers showed that 81 bought Ceko and 45 Popsi.

> The **initial state vector** S_0 shows the initial state of the system.

$$S_0 = \begin{array}{c} \\ \\ \text{C} \\ \text{P} \end{array} \begin{array}{c} \text{Number of} \\ \text{consumers} \\ \begin{pmatrix} 81 \\ 45 \end{pmatrix} \end{array}$$

You can predict the market share after one week by finding

$$S_1 = TS_0 = \begin{pmatrix} 0.75 & 0.2 \\ 0.25 & 0.8 \end{pmatrix} \begin{pmatrix} 81 \\ 45 \end{pmatrix} = \begin{pmatrix} 69.75 \\ 56.25 \end{pmatrix}$$

Hence you can predict that after one week, between 69 and 70 of these 126 consumers will purchase Ceko. Remember that some of these customers will have initially bought Ceko and some will have changed from Popsi. Also, some customers who originally bought Ceko will have changed to Popsi. The multiplication $S_1 = TS_0$ quantifies and represents all the transitions.

Similarly, you can multiply by T successively to predict the states in subsequent weeks, and look for patterns in our predictions.
$S_2 = TS_1 = T^2 S_0$. Repeating this process establishes the equation
$S_n = T^n S_0$

Investigation 11

1 Using the Ceko and Popsi matrix and vector above, use technology to complete the table.

$n =$ no. of weeks	Algebra representation of S_n	Matrix representations of S_n	Vector representation of S_n
0	S_0		$\begin{pmatrix} 81 \\ 45 \end{pmatrix}$
1	TS_0	$\begin{pmatrix} 0.75 & 0.2 \\ 0.25 & 0.8 \end{pmatrix}\begin{pmatrix} 81 \\ 45 \end{pmatrix}$	$\begin{pmatrix} 69.75 \\ 56.25 \end{pmatrix}$
2	$TS_1 = T^2 S_0$	$\begin{pmatrix} 0.75 & 0.2 \\ 0.25 & 0.8 \end{pmatrix}\begin{pmatrix} 69.75 \\ 56.25 \end{pmatrix} = \begin{pmatrix} 0.6125 & 0.31 \\ 0.3875 & 0.69 \end{pmatrix}\begin{pmatrix} 81 \\ 45 \end{pmatrix}$	$\begin{pmatrix} 63.5625 \\ 62.4375 \end{pmatrix}$
3	$TS_2 = T^3 S_0$	$\begin{pmatrix} 0.75 & 0.2 \\ 0.25 & 0.8 \end{pmatrix}\begin{pmatrix} 63.5625 \\ 62.4375 \end{pmatrix} = \begin{pmatrix} 0.536875 & 0.3705 \\ 0.463125 & 0.6295 \end{pmatrix}\begin{pmatrix} 81 \\ 45 \end{pmatrix}$	$\begin{pmatrix} 60.1594 \\ 65.8406 \end{pmatrix}$
4			
10			
20			
49			

2 **Factual** What are the converging **steady state** patterns in your results?

3 **Conceptual** Generalise these convergent patterns using the terms **long-term probability matrix** and **steady state vector**.

4 What interpretations can you make of these patterns regarding the long-term market share of each brand?

5 What assumptions are made?

6 **Conceptual** How can you use powers of the transition matrix to make predictions?

> If P is a square regular transition matrix, there is a unique vector q such that $Pq = q$. This q is called the **steady-state vector** for P.

Example 11

Dockless bicycle company Mathbike open their business by distributing a number of

bicycles in a city according to the initial state vector $S_0 = \begin{pmatrix} 110 \\ 80 \\ 50 \end{pmatrix}$.

Continued on next page

➡ **a** Calculate the likely number of bicycles in each zone of the city after five days using the transition matrix given in example 10.

b Find the likely steady state of Mathbikes.

c Comment on how the owners of Mathbikes should reflect on their choice of the initial state vector S_0. State the limitations of this model.

a $\begin{pmatrix} 0.50 & 0.30 & 0.10 \\ 0.30 & 0.35 & 0.30 \\ 0.20 & 0.35 & 0.60 \end{pmatrix}^5 \begin{pmatrix} 110 \\ 80 \\ 50 \end{pmatrix} = \begin{pmatrix} 65.746 \\ 75.789 \\ 98.465 \end{pmatrix}$

Find $S_5 = T^5 S_0$ with a GDC

There would be approximately 66 Mathbikes in zone C, 76 in Zone I and 98 in Zone O.

Make sure to interpret your findings.

b $\begin{pmatrix} 0.50 & 0.30 & 0.10 \\ 0.30 & 0.35 & 0.30 \\ 0.20 & 0.35 & 0.60 \end{pmatrix}^{50} \begin{pmatrix} 110 \\ 80 \\ 50 \end{pmatrix} = \begin{pmatrix} 65.263 \\ 75.789 \\ 98.947 \end{pmatrix}$

So, the system quickly reaches an equilibrium at 65 bikes in C, 76 in I and 99 in O.

Use your GDC to investigate higher powers of the transition matrix and look for convergence. As with geometric sequences, the rate of convergence depends on the values you are given.

A steady state matrix is reached earlier than this, after ten days.

c This shows that Mathbike's original distribution of bikes to zone I was a good guess, but they would have met the needs of the customers better by placing 50 bikes in C and 110 in O at the start.

This model does not account for broken or stolen bikes. Nor does it account for changing habits amongst the customers due to weather patterns or competition from other companies.

Think critically about the context.

Write a complete sentence that presents your findings.

Investigation 12

1 By investigating the sequence T^n show that if $T = \begin{pmatrix} 0.6 & 0.2 \\ 0.4 & 0.8 \end{pmatrix}$, then the

long-term probability matrix is $X = \begin{pmatrix} \dfrac{1}{3} & \dfrac{1}{3} \\ \dfrac{2}{3} & \dfrac{2}{3} \end{pmatrix}$.

2 Fill in the table with examples of your own initial state vectors and find values for the steady state population vector and the steady state probability vector.

➡

S_0	Total population (p) represented by S_0	$XS_0 = v$	$u = \dfrac{1}{p}v$ (the steady state probability vector)
$\begin{pmatrix} 63 \\ 18 \end{pmatrix}$	81	$\begin{pmatrix} 27 \\ 54 \end{pmatrix}$	
$\begin{pmatrix} 568 \\ 123 \end{pmatrix}$			
$\begin{pmatrix} 56358 \\ 2 \end{pmatrix}$			
...			

Then repeat with your own 2×2 regular transition matrix T.

3 **Factual** Does the steady state probability vector depend on the initial state vector?

4 What relationship exists between the steady state probability vector and the long-term probability matrix?

Let $T = \begin{pmatrix} 0.6 & 0.2 \\ 0.4 & 0.8 \end{pmatrix}$ with long-term probability matrix $X = \begin{pmatrix} \dfrac{1}{3} & \dfrac{1}{3} \\ \dfrac{2}{3} & \dfrac{2}{3} \end{pmatrix}$, and

let $u = \begin{pmatrix} u_1 \\ u_2 \end{pmatrix}$ be the steady state probability vector. Hence,

$$Tu = u \Rightarrow \begin{bmatrix} 0.6u_1 + 0.2u_2 = u_1 \\ 0.4u_1 + 0.8u_2 = u_2. \\ u_1 + u_2 = 1 \end{bmatrix}$$

5 Explain why each of the three equations hold and show that the solution of this system is $u = \begin{pmatrix} \dfrac{1}{3} \\ \dfrac{2}{3} \end{pmatrix}$.

6 With your own regular 2×2 matrix T, find the long-term probability matrix by repeated multiplication and then form three equations to solve $Tu = u$ using technology.

7 Repeat with your own regular 3×3 matrix.

8 **Factual** What do you notice?

9 **Conceptual** How can you find the steady state probabilities? Give two different methods.

1 Find the long-term probability matrices for the Markov processes with these transition matrices:

a $\begin{pmatrix} 0.13 & 0.71 \\ 0.87 & 0.29 \end{pmatrix}$

b $\begin{pmatrix} 0.24 & 0 & 0.31 \\ 0.42 & 0.85 & 0.05 \\ 0.34 & 0.15 & 0.64 \end{pmatrix}$

c $\begin{pmatrix} 0.1 & 0.6 & 0.2 & 0.7 \\ 0.05 & 0.2 & 0.2 & 0.05 \\ 0.4 & 0.05 & 0.2 & 0.2 \\ 0.45 & 0.15 & 0.4 & 0.05 \end{pmatrix}$

2 A regular transition matrix T in a given Markov process is defined as

$$T = \begin{pmatrix} 0.81 & 0.1 & 0.08 \\ 0.09 & 0.15 & 0.5 \\ 0.1 & 0.75 & 0.42 \end{pmatrix}.$$

Let $u = \begin{pmatrix} u_1 \\ u_2 \\ u_3 \end{pmatrix}$ be the steady state probability

vector such that $Tu = u$.

a Find u by solving a system of equations.

b Demonstrate your answer for part a is correct by finding the long-term probability matrix.

3 Three electricity providers A, B and C compete in a market. A survey of consumers has determined the probabilities that a person using an electricity provider in one year will either stay with that provider or will switch to another next year. The probabilities are given in this transition matrix:

Current provider

		A	B	C
Provider after one year	A	0.8	0.05	0.06
	B	0.12	0.92	0.1
	C	0.08	0.03	0.84

$T = \begin{pmatrix} 0.8 & 0.05 & 0.06 \\ 0.12 & 0.92 & 0.1 \\ 0.08 & 0.03 & 0.84 \end{pmatrix}$

At the present time, 45% of the customers are provided electricity by A, 25% by B and 30% by C.

a Find the percentage of the customers provided by each electricity provider after two years.

b Calculate the long-term percentage of customers who will be provided electricity by B. State your assumptions.

c By comparing the matrices T, T^2, T^5 and T^{20}, comment critically on the likelihood that the transition probabilities remain constant in the long term.

4 A hire car owned by Mathcar is in one of four possible states: A: functioning normally, B: functioning despite needing a minor repair, C: functioning despite needing a major repair, D: broken down. Mathcar only takes a car out of service if it breaks down.

The transition matrix

$$F = \begin{pmatrix} 0.9 & 0 & 0 & 0.96 \\ 0.03 & 0.85 & 0 & 0 \\ 0.02 & 0.05 & 0.6 & 0 \\ 0.05 & 0.1 & 0.4 & 0.04 \end{pmatrix} \text{ represents the}$$

probabilities of the car transitioning from one state to another after a period of a month.

a Interpret the zeros in the matrix in the context of the problem, and the entry in the fourth row fourth column.

b Verify C that F is a regular Markov matrix.

c Mathcar begins business with a fleet of 500 cars in state A, 25 in B, 0 in C and 0 in D. Find how many cars are in each state after 10 months.

d Comment on how Mathcar could change their practices so that changes are made to F which improve the availability of their cars.

9.7 Eigenvalues and eigenvectors

Investigation 13

Consider the transformation $T = \begin{pmatrix} 1 & 1 \\ -2 & 4 \end{pmatrix}$ applied to the points on the line

$L_1: y = 2x$.

i Write down the coordinates of any five points on L_1 then show that images of these five points lie on the same line.

Take a general point on the line with coordinates $(x, 2x)$ and find its image.

ii Based upon your observations in part **i** write down the value of λ for which

$\begin{pmatrix} 1 & 1 \\ -2 & 4 \end{pmatrix} \begin{pmatrix} x \\ 2x \end{pmatrix} = \lambda \begin{pmatrix} x \\ 2x \end{pmatrix}$. What does this tell you about how T transforms

the points on L_1 geometrically?

iii $T = \begin{pmatrix} 1 & 1 \\ -2 & 4 \end{pmatrix}$ also maps the points on line $L_2: y = x$ to image points that

are also on $y = x$. Determine the scale factor of the stretch that describes

this mapping by solving the equation $\begin{pmatrix} 1 & 1 \\ -2 & 4 \end{pmatrix} \begin{pmatrix} x \\ x \end{pmatrix} = \lambda \begin{pmatrix} x \\ x \end{pmatrix}$.

The investigation above reveals a special type of linear transformation that maps points on a line back onto the same line and is described as a stretch by a factor λ. In this section you will learn how this idea along with our knowledge of matrix algebra will allow you to determine large powers of matrices. These results lay the foundation for our study of modelling and analyzing dynamical systems and networks in chapters 12 and 14.

Eigenvalues and eigenvectors

Geometrically, you say that the lines $y = 2x$ and $y = x$ are invariant under the transformation T.

In general, you are interested in determining the equations of the invariant lines and their associated scale factors, λ, for a given transformation matrix A. That is, you wish to solve the equation

$A \begin{pmatrix} x \\ y \end{pmatrix} = \lambda \begin{pmatrix} x \\ y \end{pmatrix}$ or expressed more simply $Ax = \lambda x$. The values of λ

are referred to as the **eigenvalues** of matrix A. Each eigenvalue of A is associated with a particular line that is invariant under the transformation A whose equation is described by the **eigenvector** x.

Consider the problem of determining the eigenvalues and eigenvectors

of the transformation matrix $A = \begin{pmatrix} 1 & 4 \\ 2 & 3 \end{pmatrix}$.

You would like to find the eigenvalues λ and their associated eigenvectors such that $\begin{pmatrix} 1 & 4 \\ 2 & 3 \end{pmatrix} x = \lambda x$. Proceeding with the matrix algebra yields:

$$\begin{pmatrix} 1 & 4 \\ 2 & 3 \end{pmatrix} x = \lambda x$$

$$\begin{pmatrix} 1 & 4 \\ 2 & 3 \end{pmatrix} x - \lambda x = \mathbf{0} \qquad \text{(addition property of equality)}$$

$$\begin{pmatrix} 1 & 4 \\ 2 & 3 \end{pmatrix} x - \lambda \mathbf{I}_2 x = \mathbf{0} \qquad \text{(identity property)}$$

$$\left(\begin{pmatrix} 1 & 4 \\ 2 & 3 \end{pmatrix} - \lambda \begin{pmatrix} 1 & 0 \\ 0 & 1 \end{pmatrix} \right) x = \mathbf{0} \qquad \text{(distributive property)}$$

$$\begin{pmatrix} 1-\lambda & 4 \\ 2 & 3-\lambda \end{pmatrix} x = \mathbf{0} \qquad \text{(matrix addition)}$$

When the matrix $\begin{pmatrix} 1-\lambda & 4 \\ 2 & 3-\lambda \end{pmatrix}$ has an inverse then both sides of the equation can be multiplied by the inverse matrix to give the solution $x = \begin{pmatrix} 0 \\ 0 \end{pmatrix}$. If looking for additional solutions they must occur when the inverse does not exist which happens when the matrix $(A - \lambda I)$ is singular and therefore its determinant is equal to zero.

Thus:

$$\begin{vmatrix} 1-\lambda & 4 \\ 2 & 3-\lambda \end{vmatrix} = 0$$

$$(1-\lambda)(3-\lambda) - 8 = 0$$

$$\lambda^2 - 4\lambda - 5 = 0$$

$$\therefore \lambda_1 = -1 \text{ and } \lambda_2 = 5$$

Now, returning to the original equation $\begin{pmatrix} 1-\lambda & 4 \\ 2 & 3-\lambda \end{pmatrix} x = \mathbf{0}$ to find the corresponding eigenvector for each eigenvalue gives you:

$$\lambda_1 = -1 \iff \begin{pmatrix} 2 & 4 \\ 2 & 4 \end{pmatrix}\begin{pmatrix} x \\ y \end{pmatrix} = \begin{pmatrix} 0 \\ 0 \end{pmatrix} \iff \left. \begin{cases} 2x + 4y = 0 \\ 2x + 4y = 0 \end{cases} \right\} \text{ both equations give } y = -\frac{1}{2}x$$

$$\lambda_2 = 5 \iff \begin{pmatrix} -4 & 4 \\ 2 & -2 \end{pmatrix}\begin{pmatrix} x \\ y \end{pmatrix} = \begin{pmatrix} 0 \\ 0 \end{pmatrix} \iff \left. \begin{cases} -4x + 4y = 0 \\ 2x - 2y = 0 \end{cases} \right\} \text{ both equations give } y = x$$

The eigenvectors associated with the eigenvalue of $\lambda_1 = -1$ are described by the position vectors of the points on the line $y = -\frac{1}{2}x$

International-mindedness

Belgian/Dutch mathematician Simon Stevin use vectors in his theoretical work on falling bodies and his treatise "Principles of the art of weighing" in the 16th century.

and therefore have the form $x_1 = \begin{pmatrix} t \\ -\dfrac{t}{2} \end{pmatrix}$ where t is any real number.

That is, there are an infinite number of eigenvectors associated with the eigenvalue of $\lambda_1 = -1$. One particular eigenvector (when $t = 2$) is $x_1 = \begin{pmatrix} 2 \\ -1 \end{pmatrix}$. Similarly, there are an infinite number of eigenvectors associated with the eigenvalue of $\lambda_2 = 5$ described by the points on the line $y = x$ and these vectors have the form $x_2 = \begin{pmatrix} t \\ t \end{pmatrix}$ where t is any real number. One particular eigenvector (when $t = 1$) is $x_2 = \begin{pmatrix} 1 \\ 1 \end{pmatrix}$.

If $A = \begin{pmatrix} a & b \\ c & d \end{pmatrix}$ then the real number λ is called an eigenvalue of A if there exists a nonzero vector x such that $Ax = \lambda x$ where x is the associated eigenvector with the eigenvalue λ.

The eigenvalues of A are given by the solutions of $\begin{vmatrix} a - \lambda & b \\ c & d - \lambda \end{vmatrix} = 0$ referred to as the **characteristic equation**.

HINT

The process for finding the steady state vector of a Markov chain, ie solving $Tu = u$, is equivalent to finding the eigenvector for an eigenvalue of 1.

Matrix algebra provides you with a tool for modelling, analyzing, and predicting the long-term behaviour of systems that change over time (called dynamical systems).

Example 12

Find the eigenvalues and corresponding eigenvectors of $A = \begin{pmatrix} 0 & 1 \\ 3 & -2 \end{pmatrix}$.

Solve $\begin{vmatrix} -\lambda & 1 \\ 3 & -2-\lambda \end{vmatrix} = 0$	
$-\lambda(-2-\lambda) - 3 = 0$	This can be expanded or solved directly using technology.
$\lambda = -3$ or 1	
When $\lambda = -3$	

Continued on next page

$$\begin{pmatrix} 3 & 1 \\ 3 & 1 \end{pmatrix}\begin{pmatrix} x \\ y \end{pmatrix} = \begin{pmatrix} 0 \\ 0 \end{pmatrix}$$

$\Rightarrow 3x + y = 0$ or $y = -3x$

Similarly when $\lambda = 1$ $\begin{pmatrix} -1 & 1 \\ 3 & -3 \end{pmatrix}\begin{pmatrix} x \\ y \end{pmatrix} = \begin{pmatrix} 0 \\ 0 \end{pmatrix}$

$x + y = 0$ or $y = x$

Possible eigenvectors are therefore $\begin{pmatrix} 1 \\ -3 \end{pmatrix}$ and $\begin{pmatrix} 1 \\ 1 \end{pmatrix}$

Using $(A - \lambda I)\,x = 0$

An alternative equation to find the eigenvectors is $\begin{pmatrix} 0 & 1 \\ 3 & -2 \end{pmatrix}\begin{pmatrix} x \\ y \end{pmatrix} = -3\begin{pmatrix} x \\ y \end{pmatrix}$

In the first case any vector which has the y-coordinate $-3 \times$ the x-coordinate will do.

Exercise 9I

1 Determine the characteristic equation of each matrix in the form $\lambda^2 + p\lambda + q = 0$ then determine its eigenvalues.

a $A = \begin{pmatrix} -4 & -2 \\ 3 & 1 \end{pmatrix}$ **b** $B = \begin{pmatrix} 5 & 0 \\ -3 & -5 \end{pmatrix}$

c $C = \begin{pmatrix} -2 & 1 \\ -1 & 2 \end{pmatrix}$

2 Determine whether or not $\lambda = -1$ an eigenvalue of $\begin{pmatrix} 3 & 2 \\ 3 & 8 \end{pmatrix}$.

3 Find the eigenvalues and eigenvectors of each matrix.

a $C = \begin{pmatrix} 5 & -8 \\ 2 & -3 \end{pmatrix}$ **b** $Q = \begin{pmatrix} 2 & 4 \\ 5 & 3 \end{pmatrix}$

c $I_2 = \begin{pmatrix} 1 & 0 \\ 0 & 1 \end{pmatrix}$ **d** $P = \begin{pmatrix} 0 & -3 \\ -3 & 0 \end{pmatrix}$

e $T = \begin{pmatrix} 0.4 & 0.7 \\ 0.6 & 0.3 \end{pmatrix}$

4 Consider the transition matrix

$T = \begin{pmatrix} a & b \\ 1-a & 1-b \end{pmatrix}$ where $0 \leq a \leq 1$ and $0 \leq b \leq 1$.

a Show that $\lambda = 1$ is an eigenvalue of T and determine the other value of λ in terms of a and b.

b Determine eigenvectors for each eigenvalue of T in terms of a and b.

Diagonalization and powers of a matrix

Investigation 14

Consider the matrix $A = \begin{pmatrix} 5 & -3 \\ -6 & 2 \end{pmatrix}$.

1 Show that the eigenvalues of A are $\lambda_1 = -1$ and $\lambda_2 = 8$ and that the corresponding eigenvectors are

$x_1 = \begin{pmatrix} 1 \\ 2 \end{pmatrix}$ and $x_2 = \begin{pmatrix} 1 \\ -1 \end{pmatrix}$.

2 Let P be a matrix containing the eigenvectors x_1 and x_2 of A and $D = \begin{pmatrix} \lambda_1 & 0 \\ 0 & \lambda_2 \end{pmatrix}$. That is, $P = \begin{pmatrix} 1 & 1 \\ 2 & -1 \end{pmatrix}$

and $D = \begin{pmatrix} -1 & 0 \\ 0 & 8 \end{pmatrix}$.

a Find AP and show that $AP = PD$.

b Explain using the definition of eigenvalues and eigenvectors why this will always be the case.

3 a Use matrix algebra to show that if $AP = PD$ then $A = PDP^{-1}$

b Use the result in part **a** to show that $A^3 = PD^3P^{-1}$

c How did you use the fact that matrix multiplication is associative?

d How did you use properties of inverses?

4 a For the value of D given in question **2** find the value of D^3.

b Can you generalize your result for D^n.

5 a Determine A^3 by finding PD^3P^{-1}. Verify the result using the GDC to calculate A^3.

b Can you generalize your result for A^n?

Let $A = \begin{pmatrix} a & b \\ c & d \end{pmatrix}$ containing real number entries and having distinct real

eigenvalues λ_1 and λ_2 then you say that A is *diagonalizable* and can thus be written in the form of $A = PDP^{-1}$ where $P = (X_1 \ X_2)$ is the matrix of

eigenvectors and $D = \begin{pmatrix} \lambda_1 & 0 \\ 0 & \lambda_2 \end{pmatrix}$.

EXAM HINT

In an exam, matrices will always have distinct real eigenvalues.

Let A be a diagonalizable 2×2 matrix expressed in the form of

$A = PDP^{-1}$ then $A^n = PD^nP^{-1}$ where $P = (X_1 \ X_2)$ and $D = \begin{pmatrix} \lambda_1 & 0 \\ 0 & \lambda_2 \end{pmatrix}$.

International-mindedness

Vectors developed quickly in the first two decades of the 19th century with Danish-Norwegian Caspar Wessel, Swiss Jean Robert Argand and German Carl Friedrich Gauss.

Example 13

a Find the diagonalization of $A = \begin{pmatrix} 1 & 2 \\ 3 & 0 \end{pmatrix}$.

b Hence find an expression for A^4 in the form PD^4P^{-1}.

c Find an expression for A^4 as a product of 3 matrices with no exponents.

$\begin{vmatrix} A - \lambda I \end{vmatrix} = 0 \Leftrightarrow \begin{vmatrix} 1-\lambda & 2 \\ 3 & -\lambda \end{vmatrix} = 0 \Leftrightarrow \lambda^2 - \lambda - 6 = 0$ $\lambda_1 = 3$ and $\lambda_2 = -2$	Eigenvalues are the solutions of the characteristic equation $|A - \lambda I| = 0$

Continued on next page

$$\begin{pmatrix} 1 & 2 \\ 3 & 0 \end{pmatrix} x_1 = 3x_1 \Leftrightarrow \begin{pmatrix} 1 & 2 \\ 3 & 0 \end{pmatrix}\begin{pmatrix} x \\ y \end{pmatrix} = 3\begin{pmatrix} x \\ y \end{pmatrix} \Leftrightarrow y = x$$

$$x_1 = \begin{pmatrix} 1 \\ 1 \end{pmatrix}$$

There are an infinite number of eigenvectors of the form

$$x_1 = \begin{pmatrix} t \\ t \end{pmatrix} \text{ and } x_2 = \begin{pmatrix} 2t \\ -3t \end{pmatrix} \text{ where}$$

$t \in \mathbb{R}$ you arbitrarily choose $t = 1$ (for simplicity.)

$$\begin{pmatrix} 1 & 2 \\ 3 & 0 \end{pmatrix} x_2 = -2x_2 \Leftrightarrow \begin{pmatrix} 1 & 2 \\ 3 & 0 \end{pmatrix}\begin{pmatrix} x \\ y \end{pmatrix} = -2\begin{pmatrix} x \\ y \end{pmatrix} \Leftrightarrow y = -\frac{3}{2}x$$

$$x_2 = \begin{pmatrix} 2 \\ -3 \end{pmatrix}$$

Therefore,

$$P = \begin{pmatrix} 1 & 2 \\ 1 & -3 \end{pmatrix}, \, D = \begin{pmatrix} 3 & 0 \\ 0 & -2 \end{pmatrix}, \, P^{-1} = -\frac{1}{5}\begin{pmatrix} -3 & -2 \\ -1 & 1 \end{pmatrix}$$

Using $P^{-1} = \dfrac{1}{ad-bc}\begin{pmatrix} d & -c \\ -b & a \end{pmatrix}$.

Therefore:

$$A = -\frac{1}{5}\begin{pmatrix} 1 & 2 \\ 1 & -3 \end{pmatrix}\begin{pmatrix} 3 & 0 \\ 0 & -2 \end{pmatrix}\begin{pmatrix} -3 & -2 \\ -1 & 1 \end{pmatrix}$$

The $\dfrac{1}{5}$ can be taken out as a factor or placed inside one of the matrices, either is acceptable.

$$\text{or } A = \begin{pmatrix} 1 & 2 \\ 1 & -3 \end{pmatrix}\begin{pmatrix} 3 & 0 \\ 0 & -2 \end{pmatrix}\begin{pmatrix} 0.6 & 0.4 \\ 0.2 & -0.2 \end{pmatrix}$$

b $\quad A^4 = \begin{pmatrix} 1 & 2 \\ 1 & -3 \end{pmatrix}\begin{pmatrix} 3 & 0 \\ 0 & -2 \end{pmatrix}^4\begin{pmatrix} 0.6 & 0.4 \\ 0.2 & -0.2 \end{pmatrix}$

c $\quad A^4 = \begin{pmatrix} 1 & 2 \\ 1 & -3 \end{pmatrix}\begin{pmatrix} 81 & 0 \\ 0 & 16 \end{pmatrix}\begin{pmatrix} 0.6 & 0.4 \\ 0.2 & -0.2 \end{pmatrix}$

Return to transition matrices

In section 9.5 you saw how to find the steady state of a dynamical system by considering high powers of the transition matrices or by solving the equation $Tu = u$ where u is the steady state probability vector.

This section will show how the same results can be obtained using diagonalization. Though this is a initially a longer process, once the diagonalised form has been found it is much easier for you (or for computers) to calculate high powers using this than by performing successive multiplications.

An additional benefit is that it also gives you an easy way to find a formula for the state of the system after n transitions.

Investigation 15

Consider the situation where people move between two neighbourhoods in a particular city. Each year since 2015, 8% of people currently living in neighbourhood A move to neighbourhood B and 12% of people currently living in neighbourhood B move to neighbourhood A. You may assume any movement other than between the two neighborhoods exactly balances those arriving with those leaving.

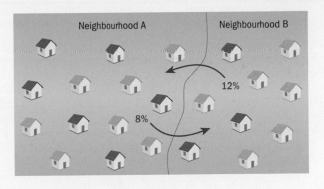

What will the population of each neighbourhood be in 2020 assuming the migration rates remain fixed?

1 Let T be the transition matrix where T_{ji} represents the probability of a person moving from neighbourhood i to neighbourhood j. Explain why the transition matrix is

$$T = \begin{matrix} & \begin{matrix} A & B \end{matrix} \\ \begin{matrix} A \\ B \end{matrix} & \begin{pmatrix} 0.92 & 0.12 \\ 0.08 & 0.88 \end{pmatrix} \end{matrix}$$

2 The populations of neighbourhoods A and B are 24,500 and 45,200 respectively at the beginning of 2015. After 1 year the population can be expressed as the matrix $P_1 = TP_0 = \begin{pmatrix} 0.92 & 0.12 \\ 0.08 & 0.88 \end{pmatrix}\begin{pmatrix} 24500 \\ 45200 \end{pmatrix}$

What is the population of neighbourhood A after 1 year? Neighbourhood B?

Let $S_0 = \begin{pmatrix} 24500 \\ 45200 \end{pmatrix}$. The population after n years is given by the expression $T^n S_0$.

3 Find the eigenvalues and eigenvectors for T.

4 Diagonalize T and use the relationship $T^n = PD^nP^{-1}$ to show that

$$T^n = \begin{pmatrix} 3 & 1 \\ 2 & -1 \end{pmatrix}\begin{pmatrix} 1^n & 0 \\ 0 & 0.8^n \end{pmatrix}\begin{pmatrix} 0.2 & 0.2 \\ 0.4 & -0.6 \end{pmatrix}.$$

5 As $n \to \infty$, what will $D^n = \begin{pmatrix} 1^n & 0 \\ 0 & 0.8^n \end{pmatrix}$ approach? What will T^n approach?

6 Hence find the long-term population of the neighbourhoods.

The administration of both neighborhoods would like a formula to tell them how many residents are expected to be in each community n years after 2015.

7 Multiply out your expression found in question 3 to find a suitable formula for each of the school boards.

8 Use your formula to write down the populations of neighborhood A in 2020.

Exercise 9J

1. Given that eigenvalues of $R = \begin{pmatrix} -2 & 1 \\ 2 & -3 \end{pmatrix}$ are $\lambda_1 = -4$ and $\lambda_2 = -1$ write R in the form $R = PDP^{-1}$.

2. Consider $A = \begin{pmatrix} 16 & -35 \\ 6 & -13 \end{pmatrix}$.

   a. Determine the eigenvalues and eigenvectors of A. State why A is diagonalizable.

   b. Express A in the form of $A = PDP^{-1}$.

   c. Find a general expression for A^n in terms of n.

   d. Use your expression in part **c** to find A^4. Verify your result using the matrix utility on the GDC.

3. Consider matrix $T = \begin{pmatrix} 0.4 & 0.75 \\ 0.6 & 0.25 \end{pmatrix}$.

   a. Express T in the form $T = PDP^{-1}$.

   b. Find T^4 using your answer in part **a**. Verify your result by finding $\begin{pmatrix} 0.4 & 0.75 \\ 0.6 & 0.25 \end{pmatrix}^4$ using the matrix utility on the GDC.

   c. Using the result from part **b** determine the long-term behavior of T.

4. Suppose only two rival companies, R and S, manufacture a certain product. Each year, company R keeps $\frac{1}{4}$ of its customers while $\frac{3}{4}$ of them switch to company S. Each year, company S keeps $\frac{2}{3}$ of its customers while $\frac{1}{3}$ of them switch to company R. At the beginning of the 2005, company R had 6500 customers while company S had 5200 customers.

   a. Write down a transition matrix T representing the proportion of the customers moving between the two companies.

   b. Find the distribution of the market after two years. Describe the change in this distribution from the 2005.

   c. Write T in the form $T = P\Lambda P^{-1}$

   d. Show that $T^n = \frac{1}{17}\begin{pmatrix} 8+9p^n & 8-9p^n \\ 9-9p^n & 9+8p^n \end{pmatrix}$ where $p = -\frac{5}{12}$.

   e. Hence, find an expression for the number of customers buying from R after n years.

   f. Verify your formula by finding how many customers are purchasing from R after two years.

   g. Find the long-term number of customers buying from R.

Chapter summary

- To add or subtract two or more matrices, they must be of the same order. You add or subtract corresponding elements.

- Given a matrix A and a real number k then kA is obtained by multiplying every element of A by k where k is referred to as a scalar.

- If $P = AB$ then each element of P (named as $P_{i,j}$) is found by summing the products of the elements in row i of A with the elements in column j of B.

- If A has dimensions $m \times n$ and B has dimensions $p \times q$ then
  - the product AB is defined only if the number of columns in A is equal to the number of rows in B (that is, $n = p$)
  - and when the product does exist, the dimensions of the product is $m \times q$.

- **Properties of multiplication for matrices**

  For matrices A, B, and C:
  - Non-commutive $AB \neq BA$
  - Associative property $A(BC) = (AB)C$
  - Distributive property $A(B + C) = AB + AC$ and $(B + C)A = BA + CA$

  These properties only hold when the products are defined.

- The multiplicative identity of a square $n \times n$ matrix A is given by $I_n = \begin{pmatrix} 1 & 0 & \cdots & 0 \\ 0 & 1 & \cdots & 0 \\ \vdots & \vdots & \ddots & \vdots \\ 0 & 0 & \cdots & 1 \end{pmatrix}$. Note that

  both $A \times I_n = A$ and $I_n \times A = A$ hold only in the case where A is a square matrix.

- If A is a square matrix then $A^k = \underbrace{A \times A \times \cdots \times A}_{k \text{ factors of } A}$.

- In the case where $b = c = 0$ then $A^k = \begin{pmatrix} a & 0 \\ 0 & d \end{pmatrix} = \begin{pmatrix} a^k & 0 \\ 0 & d^k \end{pmatrix}$.

- The matrices which represent rotations, reflections, enlargements and one way stretches are all given in the IB formula book.

- A **Markov Chain** is a system in which the probability of each event depends only on the state of the previous event.

- A transition matrix is a square matrix which summarizes a transition state diagram. It describes the probabilities of moving from one state to another in a stochastic system.
  - The sum of each column of the transition matrix is 1.
  - The transition matrix is extremely useful when there are more than two states in the system and when you wish to predict states of the system after several time periods.

- A **regular** transition matrix T has the property that there exists $n \in \mathbb{Z}^+$ such that all entries in T^n are greater than zero.

- The **initial state vector** S_0 shows the initial state of the system.

- If P is a square regular transition matrix, there is a unique probability vector q such that $\mathbf{P}q = q$. This q is called the **steady-state vector** for P.

- Let $A = \begin{pmatrix} a & b \\ c & d \end{pmatrix}$ containing real number entries and having distinct real eigenvalues λ_1 and λ_2 then

  you say that A is diagonalizable and can thus be written in the form of $A = PDP^{-1}$ where $P = (x_1 \, x_2)$ is

  the matrix of eigenvectors and $D = \begin{pmatrix} \lambda_1 & 0 \\ 0 & \lambda_2 \end{pmatrix}$.

- Let A be a diagonalizable 2×2 matrix expressed in the form of $A = PDP^{-1}$ then

  $A^n = PD^nP^{-1}$ where $P = (x_1 \, x_2)$ and $D = \begin{pmatrix} \lambda_1 & 0 \\ 0 & \lambda_2 \end{pmatrix}$.

Chapter review

Click here for a mixed review exercise
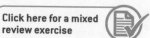

1 If $A = \begin{pmatrix} 5 \\ -2 \end{pmatrix}$, $B = \begin{pmatrix} 1 \\ -1 \\ 2 \end{pmatrix}$, $C = \begin{pmatrix} -1 & 3 \\ -2 & 4 \end{pmatrix}$, $D = \begin{pmatrix} -3 & 1 \\ 0 & -5 \end{pmatrix}$, $E = \begin{pmatrix} -1 & 2 & 1 \\ -2 & 1 & 0 \\ -3 & -1 & 4 \end{pmatrix}$, $F = \begin{pmatrix} 1 & 2 & -3 \\ -1 & 4 & -2 \end{pmatrix}$ find

each of the following without using the matrix utility on the GDC. If it does not exist state why it does not.

a $2C + 3D$ **b** $A - B$ **c** DF **d** FE

e E^2 **f** $(C + D)^2$ **g** $EB + B$ **h** C^{-1}

i CDA **j** $C - 2I_2$

---

2 Determine the values of a and b such that

$$\begin{pmatrix} 3a & 2 \\ -1 & 2b \end{pmatrix} + 4\begin{pmatrix} -1 & -2b \\ 1 & -\dfrac{a}{2} \end{pmatrix} = \begin{pmatrix} 8 & 6 \\ 3 & -9 \end{pmatrix}.$$

3 Solve each equation for X.

a $3X - \begin{pmatrix} 2 & -1 \\ 1 & -2 \end{pmatrix} = \begin{pmatrix} 3 & 5 \\ -7 & 0 \end{pmatrix}$

b $\begin{pmatrix} 1 & 3 \\ -1 & 2 \end{pmatrix} X = \begin{pmatrix} -5 & 2 \\ 1 & -10 \end{pmatrix}$

c $X\begin{pmatrix} 3 & -1 \\ -4 & 2 \end{pmatrix} + 3I_2 = \begin{pmatrix} 5 & 4 \\ 2 & 6 \end{pmatrix}$

4 Write each system as a matrix equation then solve the system using matrix algebra (if possible). Write your answers in exact form.

a $\begin{aligned} 7y &= 4x - 20 \\ 3x &= 2y + 10 \end{aligned}$ **b** $\begin{aligned} w &= 3 + 2y + 2z \\ 3y - 4z &= 6 - w \\ 4w + 5y - 3 &= 2z \end{aligned}$

c $\begin{aligned} 6x &= 5y + 18 \\ 27 - 9x &= -7.5y \end{aligned}$

5 Parallelogram PQRS with vertices P($-4, -2$), Q($-1, 7$), R($8, 4$), T($5, -5$) is translated by the

vector $\begin{pmatrix} -3 \\ 5 \end{pmatrix}$ then enlarged by a factor of $\dfrac{1}{2}$

then reflected across the x-axis.

a Determine a single transformation of the form of $AX + b$ that maps PQRS to its image P'Q'R'S'.

b Determine the coordinates of P', Q', R', and S'.

c Area of P'Q'R'S' = $k \times$ Area of PQRS. Determine the value of k.

6 The linear transformation

$$\begin{pmatrix} x' \\ y' \end{pmatrix} = \begin{pmatrix} -3 & 1 \\ -1 & 4 \end{pmatrix}\begin{pmatrix} x \\ y \end{pmatrix} + \begin{pmatrix} -1 \\ 2 \end{pmatrix}$$ maps the points

(x, y) to (x', y'). Find

a the coordinates of the image of $(-3, 5)$

b the coordinates of the point who image is $(-7, 0)$

c the coordinates of the image of $(a, 2a)$ where $a \in \mathbb{R}$.

7 A series of triangles T_0, T_1, T_2,... are formed by rotating each consecutive triangle anti-clockwise by $\theta°$ then enlarging the triangle by a factor of k.

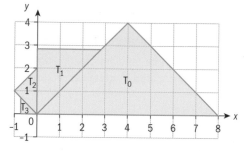

a Given that the series of transformations

can be described by $\begin{pmatrix} x_n \\ y_n \end{pmatrix} = A\begin{pmatrix} x_{n-1} \\ y_{n-1} \end{pmatrix}$

determine

i the 2×2 matrix A

ii the exact coordinates of the vertices of T_3.

b Given that $\begin{pmatrix} x_n \\ y_n \end{pmatrix} = \mathbf{C}_n \begin{pmatrix} x_0 \\ y_0 \end{pmatrix}$

   i write down $\mathbf{C}_1$

   ii find $\mathbf{C}_2, \mathbf{C}_3$, and $\mathbf{C}_4$

   iii find the sum of the areas of $T_0, T_1, T_2, \ldots$

Exam-style questions

8 **P1:** Given $A = \begin{pmatrix} 3 & -2 \\ 2 & -3 \end{pmatrix}$ and $B = \begin{pmatrix} 4 & 0 \\ 1 & -2 \end{pmatrix}$,

find the following matrices:

   a $2B$ (2 marks)

   b $A - B$ (2 marks)

   c AB (2 marks)

   d $(A + B)^2$ (2 marks)

9 **P1:** Given that the matrix $A = \begin{pmatrix} x & -1 \\ 4 & 3-x \end{pmatrix}$ is

singular, determine the possible value(s) of x.   (5 marks)

10 **P1:** $P = \begin{pmatrix} \dfrac{1}{2} & -\dfrac{\sqrt{3}}{2} \\ \dfrac{\sqrt{3}}{2} & \dfrac{1}{2} \end{pmatrix}$ and $Q = \begin{pmatrix} \dfrac{\sqrt{3}}{2} & \dfrac{1}{2} \\ -\dfrac{1}{2} & \dfrac{\sqrt{3}}{2} \end{pmatrix}$.

   a Find the matrix $(PQ)^3$.   (3 marks)

   b Hence, find the smallest value of n

     such that $(PQ)^n = \begin{pmatrix} -1 & 0 \\ 0 & -1 \end{pmatrix}$.

                        (2 marks)

11 **P2: a** Show that the matrix $A = \begin{pmatrix} 4 & 1 \\ 3 & 6 \end{pmatrix}$

     satisfies the equation
     $A^2 - 10A + 21I = 0$, where I is the
     2×2 identity matrix.   (4 marks)

   b Hence express A^3 in the form
     $pA + qI$.   (3 marks)

   c Hence express A^4 in the form
     $rA + sI$.   (3 marks)

12 **P1:** The matrix $A = \begin{pmatrix} 3 & 2 & -1 \\ 0 & 1 & 2 \\ 1 & 1 & 3 \end{pmatrix}$ and

$B = \begin{pmatrix} 1 & 0 & 1 \\ 0 & 1 & 0 \\ 1 & 0 & 1 \end{pmatrix}$

   a Find A^{-1}.   (2 marks)

   b Hence find the matrix C such that
     $AC = B$.   (3 marks)

13 **P1:** Consider the following system of equations:

$$5x + 3z = 23$$
$$x - 2y + 5z = 23$$
$$3y + 7z = 122$$

   a Write the system in the form $AX = B$,
     where A, X and B are matrices.
                      (2 marks)

   b Find the matrix A^{-1}.   (2 marks)

   c Hence solve the original system of
     equations.   (3 marks)

14 **P1:** At a particular opening night screening
of Galaxy Wars 2, one cinema had a
full attendance of 750 people. It
charged £8 for adults, £5 for children,
and £4 for OAPs.

The number of OAPs attending was
one-fifth of the total attendance.

The total amount received in entrance
tickets was £4860.

Use a matrix method to determine the
number of children that attended the
screening.   (9 marks)

15 **P2:** Consider the matrix $A = \begin{pmatrix} 4 & -2 \\ -2 & 4 \end{pmatrix}$

   a Find the eigenvalues and
     corresponding eigenvectors of A.
                      (7 marks)

   b Hence find a matrix P and a matrix
     D such that $D = P^{-1}AP$.   (2 marks)

   c Find a general expression for A^n in
     terms of n.   (5 marks)

MarComm phones and Markov chains

Approaches to learning: Communication, Critical thinking

Exploration criteria: Mathematical communication (B), Use of mathematics (E)

IB topic: Markov chains, Matrices

Example

A phone company, MarComm, has four package options, A, B, C and D.

A customer is initially allocated to package A for a year.

After this, every year, customers can either continue with their present option or change to one of the other options.

The probabilities of each possible change are given in this transition state diagram:

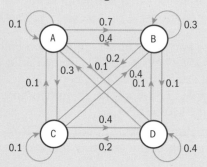

How would MarComm be able to determine the probabilities on the diagram?

Represent this information in a transition matrix, P, of the system.

If customers are all initially allocated to option A for the first year, then write down an initial state vector, $\vec{x}_0$,

in the form $\vec{x}_0 = \begin{bmatrix} w \\ x \\ y \\ z \end{bmatrix}$.

The probabilities for the next state can then be found by multiplying $\vec{x}_0$ by the transition matrix P.

Calculate the probabilities of being in each option after one year if the customer starts with option A.

Write down these probabilities in the form $\vec{x}_1 = \begin{bmatrix} a \\ b \\ c \\ d \end{bmatrix}$.

How might MarComm find this information useful?

Repeating this iteratively will give the probability of a customer being in any state in subsequent years.

Investigate the behaviour of the system over time.

Let π be the stationary distribution of the system, where $\pi = \begin{bmatrix} \pi_1 \\ \pi_2 \\ \pi_3 \\ \pi_4 \end{bmatrix}$.

You will now find the stationary distribution using three different methods.

Using technology

Calculate $\vec{x}_{19}$ and $\vec{x}_{20}$ (that is $P^{19}\vec{x}_0$ and $P^{20}\vec{x}_0$) using a calculator or computer. This will give an **indication** of the convergence to a stationary distribution (to a reasonable degree of accuracy).

Why would this **not** be considered a sophisticated approach to the problem?

Solving a system of equations

This method uses the fact that once the stationary distribution, π, is reached, multiplying by the transition matrix has no effect $\Rightarrow P\pi = \pi$.

So, by letting $\pi = \begin{bmatrix} \pi_1 \\ \pi_2 \\ \pi_3 \\ \pi_4 \end{bmatrix}$, you can solve the system of equations $[P]\begin{bmatrix} \pi_1 \\ \pi_2 \\ \pi_3 \\ \pi_4 \end{bmatrix} = \begin{bmatrix} \pi_1 \\ \pi_2 \\ \pi_3 \\ \pi_4 \end{bmatrix}$.

Use this method with the information in the example to calculate π and to verify that the result is equivalent to the answer obtained using the previous method using technology.

Does this feel more sophisticated than the previous process using technology? Justify your answer.

Using eigenvalues and eigenvectors

If the stationary distribution π is such that $P\pi = \pi$, then as you have seen in this chapter the matrix P must have an eigenvalue of 1 with corresponding eigenvector π scaled so that the sum of its elements is 1.

Calculate the eigenvalues of P from the example and the corresponding eigenvectors (using technology).

How could you demonstrate that you understand fully what you are finding here and that you understand the process that is taking place beyond just getting the correct answers?

How will you organize the mathematical calculations so that the process from posing the problem to answering the problem is logical?

These methods give MarComm π, the probabilities of a customer being in each of the four options in the long term.

How could the company use this information?

Clearly all three methods produce the same approximate vector π correct to four significant figures.

However, which method do you prefer?

Which method is the most sophisticated? Justify your answer.

Extension

Does a system always reach a steady state?

How quickly will the process converge to the steady state?

10 Analyzing rates of change: differential calculus

Calculus is a mathematical tool for studying change. This chapter will focus on differentiation, which looks at how quickly one variable is changing **with respect to** another.

Change is all around us. Examples in physics, include change of position, velocity, density, current and power; in chemistry, we have rates of reaction, and in biology, the growth of bacteria; in economics, rates include marginal cost and profit; in sociology, we might want to measure the speed at which a rumour spreads or periodic changes in fashion. All of these can be applications of differentiation. But how do we go about measuring these changes?

Concepts
- Change
- Relationships

Microconcepts
- Concept of a limit
- Derivatives of standard functions
- Increasing and decreasing functions
- Tangents and normals
- Optimization
- The chain rule
- The product rule
- The quotient rule
- The second derivative
- Kinematics

If you are given a model for the number of people who catch a disease, how would you work out how quickly it is spreading at a particular time?

How might you find the velocity of an asteroid if you were just given the equation for its position?

A company has a model that shows the profit it could make for different levels of output. How could it quickly find the output that would give maximum profit?

How do weather forecasters predict the weather when the changes seem so unpredictable?

A firm is about to launch a new product. They conduct a survey to find the optimum price at which it should be sold. They obtained the results shown in the table.

The firm decides that a **demand** equation is needed to model these results. Two models are suggested: a power model of the form $d = \dfrac{a}{x^b}$ and an exponential model of the form $d = ae^{-bx}$ or $d = a(c)^x$ where $c = e^{-b}$.

Price (x)	Percentage of the sample who would buy at this price (d)
5	68
10	55
15	43
20	33
25	22
30	14
35	8
40	4

- Plot the data on your GDC.
- Explain why these two models might be suitable.
- Find best fitting equations for each of the models.
- The business would like to maximize their profit. What other information would they need?
- If this information were available, how might you work out the maximum value of a profit function?
- The gradient of the demand curve is called the "marginal demand". What might the marginal demand tell you? How could you work out its value from the curve?
- The marketing team has a model that links extra demand with the amount of money spent on advertising. How can this be incorporated into your model?

Developing inquiry skills

What other information might you need to work out the profit?

What could the company do to persuade more people to buy the product?

How might this affect the model?

Think about the questions in this opening problem and answer any you can. As you work through the chapter, you will gain mathematical knowledge and skills that will help you to answer them all.

Before you start

You should know how to:	Skills check

Click here for help with this skills check

You should know how to:

1 Find the equation of a line.

eg Find the equation of the line with gradient 5 and passing through the point $(2, 1)$.

$1 = 5(2) + c$

$c = -9 \quad y = 5x - 9$

or use $y - 1 = 5(x - 2)$

2 Use the laws of indices.

eg Write the following with a single exponent.

a $\dfrac{x^5}{x^3} = x^{5-3} = x^2$ **b** $\dfrac{1}{x^2} = x^{-2}$ **c** $\sqrt{x} = x^{\frac{1}{2}}$

3 Find maximum and minimum values of a function using your GDC.

eg Find the coordinates of the maximum point of $y = x^3 - 8x^2 + 15$, where $0 \le x \le 3$.

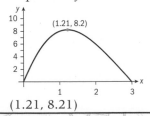

(1.21, 8.21)

Skills check

1 Find the equation of the line perpendicular to the line $y = 2x - 3$ and passing through the point $(3, 4)$.

2 Write the following with negative exponents.

a $\dfrac{x^2}{x^7}$ **b** $\dfrac{1}{x}$ **c** $\dfrac{3}{\sqrt{x}}$

3 Find the minimum value of $y = x^4 - 5x^3 - 4x^2 + 20$, $0 \le x \le 2$.

10.1 Limits and derivatives

The graph shows how the profits of a company increase with the number of widgets it sells.

From previous work on linear functions you will know that the rate at which the profit increases for each new widget made (profit per widget) is

$$\frac{2100 - 500}{160 - 0} = \$10 \text{ per widget.}$$

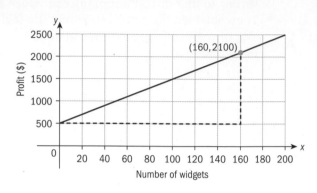

This is equivalent to the gradient of the curve. If the curve had a steeper gradient the profit per widget would be higher. If the gradient were less steep the profit per widget would be lower.

Hence, the rate of change of one variable with respect to another is equivalent to the gradient of the curve.

This is easy to calculate when the functions are linear. The following investigation will consider how the gradient at a point on a curve might be calculated.

Investigation 1

When a curve is increasing, we say that it has a positive gradient, and when it is decreasing we say that it has a negative gradient. Consider the curve $y = x^2$ shown in the diagram.

1 a Give the range of x values for which the gradient of the curve is

  i negative

  ii positive

  iii equal to zero.

  b At which point is the gradient of the curve greater, A or B?

The tangent to a curve at a point is the straight line that just touches but does not cross the curve at that point.

2 a On your GDC or other software, plot the curve $y = x^2$ and draw the tangent at the point $(1, 1)$, as shown in the second diagram.

  b Zoom in to the point $(1, 1)$.

  Factual What do you notice about the gradient of the tangent and the gradient of the curve at the point of contact?

  c Use your GDC or online software to draw tangents to $y = x^2$ at the points listed below and in each case write down the gradient of the tangent.

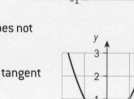

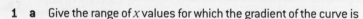

x	−1	0	1	2	3
Gradient of tangent at x			2		

  d Conjecture a function for the gradient of $y = x^2$ at the point on the curve with coordinates (x, x^2).

To justify the conjecture above we will consider the gradient of a chord from the point (x, x^2) to the point a distance h further along the x-axis. This is shown in the diagrams below for different values of h.

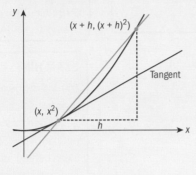

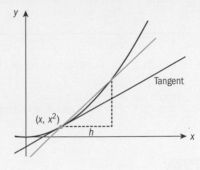

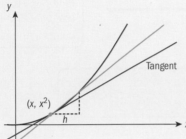

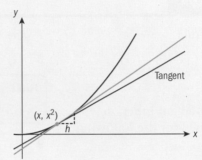

3 **a** What do you notice about the gradient of the chord as h decreases?

   b What will happen as h approaches zero? (Note: we could write this as $h \to 0$.)

The answer to **3b** can be used to work out an expression for the gradient of the curve at the point (x, x^2).

4 **a** Explain why an expression for the gradient of the chord between the two points (x, x^2) and

   $\left(x + h, (x+h)^2\right)$ is $\dfrac{\left(x+h\right)^2 - x^2}{h}$.

   b What would happen if you let $h \to 0$?

   c Expand and simplify your expression. What happens now if you let $h \to 0$?

   d Compare your answer with your answer to question **2d**.

5 **a** Now consider the curve $y = x^3$. Draw tangents to the curve at the points listed below and in each case write down the gradient of the tangent.

x	−2	−1	0	1	2	3
Gradient of tangent at x						

   b Conjecture a function for the gradient of $y = x^3$ at the point on the curve with coordinates (x, x^3).

   c Write down an expression for the gradient of the chord between (x, x^3) and $(x+h, (x+h)^3)$.

   d By first expanding and simplifying your answer to part **c** find an expression for the gradient of the curve at (x, x^3). Is it the same as the answer you conjectured in part **b**?

6 **Conceptual** How would you find the gradient of the curve at a point using the gradient of a chord from that point?

Calculus

The function that gives the gradient of the graph $y = f(x)$ at the point x is written as $f'(x)$ where $f'(x) = \lim_{h \to 0} \left(\dfrac{f(x + h) - f(x)}{h} \right)$.

HINT
The notation $\lim_{h \to 0} (A)$ is read as "the limit of A as h tends to zero".

The gradient function, $f'(x)$, is referred to as the **derivative** of x.

Reflect What does the derivative of a function tell you?

EXAM HINT
You will not be asked questions that require you to use this notation. However, the ideas behind functions approaching limits will reappear at various points in the course.

Exercise 10A

Use the formula

$$f'(x) = \lim_{h \to 0} \left(\frac{f(x + h) - f(x)}{h} \right)$$

to find the gradient function (the derivative) for the following functions.

1 $f(x) = 4x$ **2** $f(x) = -2$

3 $f(x) = 3x - 5$ **4** $f(x) = c$

5 $f(x) = mx$

6 $f(x) = x^2 - 3x + 7$

7 $f(x) = 2x^2$

8 $f(x) = x^4$

HINT
$(x + h)^4 = x^4 + 4x^3 h + 6x^2 h^2 + 4x h^3 + h^4$

9 $f(x) = \dfrac{1}{x}$

10 Conjecture an expression for $f'(x)$ given that $f(x) = ax^n$, a, $n \in \mathbb{R}$.

TOK
What value does the knowledge of limits have?

From the previous exercise, you may have conjectured the following rules:

- $f(x) = ax^n \Rightarrow f'(x) = anx^{(n-1)}$, $n \in \mathbb{R}$ (the power law)
- $f(x) = c \Rightarrow f'(x) = 0$
- $f(x) = mx \Rightarrow f'(x) = m$

Notice that the last two follow the same rule as the first if you write c as cx^0 and mx as mx^1.

In addition, if $h(x) = f(x) + g(x)$ then $h'(x) = f'(x) + g'(x)$.

Reflect What is the power law for differentiation?

Example 1

Use the power law to find the derivative of each of:

a $f(x) = 3x^2 + 2x + 7$ **b** $f(x) = \dfrac{3}{x^2}$ **c** $f(x) = 4\sqrt{x} + \dfrac{1}{\sqrt{x}}$

a $f'(x) = 6x + 2$

b $f(x) = 3x^{-2}$

$$f'(x) = -6x^{-3} = -\frac{6}{x^3}$$

c $f(x) = 4x^{\frac{1}{2}} + x^{-\frac{1}{2}}$

$$f'(x) = 2x^{-\frac{1}{2}} - \frac{1}{2}x^{-\frac{3}{2}}$$

$$= \frac{2}{\sqrt{x}} - \frac{1}{\sqrt{x^3}}$$

Use the rules above.

To use the power law you need to first write the expression using a negative index.

The answer can be left as a negative exponent, but sometimes writing it as a fraction makes subsequent work easier.

The first step again is to write the expression using fractional and negative powers.

There are different ways to write the final answer; all are acceptable in an exam unless you are told otherwise.

Example 2

For each of the functions below:

   i find $f'(x)$

   ii find the gradient of the curve at the point where $x = 2$

   iii sketch the graph of the function and its derivative on the same axes

   iv write down the set of values of x for which the function is increasing.

a $f(x) = 2x^2 + 3x - 5$

b $f(x) = \dfrac{2}{x} + x,\ x \neq 0$

a **i** $f'(x) = 4x + 3$

   ii $x = 2 \Rightarrow f'(2) = 11$

   iii

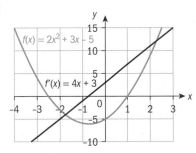

   iv $x > -0.75$

Use the laws given above.

The derivative at a point gives the gradient at that point.

This can be found by either finding the minimum point of $f(x) = 2x^2 + 3x - 5$ or by finding where $f'(x) > 0$.

Calculus

Continued on next page

b i $\dfrac{2}{x} = 2x^{-1} \Rightarrow f(x) = 2x^{-1} + x$

$f'(x) = -2x^{-2} + 1 = \dfrac{-2}{x^2} + 1$

ii $x = 2 \Rightarrow f'(2) = -0.5 + 1 = 0.5$

iii

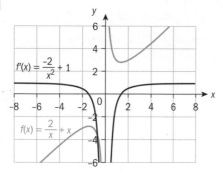

iv $x > 1.41,\ x < -1.41$

Again the range in which the curve is increasing can be found by finding the maximum and minimum points using a GDC or by finding where $f'(x) > 0$.

Reflect What is the relationship between the gradient of a curve and the sign of its derivative?

Example 3

In economics, the marginal cost is the cost of producing one more unit. It can be approximated by the gradient of a cost curve.

A company produces motorbike helmets and the daily cost function can be modelled as

$C(x) = 600 + 7x - 0.0001x^3$ for $0 \le x \le 150$

where x is the number of helmets produced and C the cost in US dollars.

a Write down the daily cost to the company if no helmets are produced.

b Find an expression for the marginal cost, $C'(x)$, of producing x helmets.

c Find the marginal cost if **i** 20 helmets are produced **ii** 80 helmets are produced.

d State the units of the marginal cost.

a $600	This is the value when $x = 0$.
b $C'(x) = 7 - 0.0003x^2$	
c i $C'(20) = 6.88$	C' represents the marginal cost.
ii $C'(80) = 5.08$	
d $ per helmet	This is the extra cost in $ for each new helmet made.

Alternative notation

There is an alternative notation for the derivative, which is very widely used.

For example, if $y = 2x^2 + 5$ then its derivative is $\dfrac{dy}{dx} = 4x$.

The notation comes from the fact that the gradient of a line is $\dfrac{\text{difference in } y}{\text{difference in } x}$.

One useful aspect to this notation is that it indicates clearly the variables involved, so if $s = 3t^3 + 4t$ then the derivative would be written as $\dfrac{ds}{dt} = 9t^2 + 4$.

> Usually the prime notation, $f'(x)$, is used when dealing with functions and the fractional notation, $\dfrac{dy}{dx}$, is used when dealing with equations relating two variables.

HINT

There are no set rules, however. $y' = 2x - 1$ and $\dfrac{df}{dx} = 3x$ are both correct, though less frequently seen.

Example 4

The tangent to the curve $y = 2x^2 + 3x - 4$ at the point A has a gradient of 11.

Find the coordinates of A.

$\dfrac{dy}{dx} = 4x + 3$	First find the derivative.
$4x + 3 = 11$ $\quad 4x = 8$ $\quad\;\; x = 2$	You know that the derivative is the same as the gradient of the tangent – so, equate the derivative to 11 and solve for x.
When $x = 2$, $y = 2(2)^2 + 3(2) - 4 = 10$,	Now substitute 2 for x into the original equation.
So, the coordinates of A are $(2, 10)$,	

The following exercise contains a mixture of both notations. Remember that they both indicate that the derivative of a function gives the gradient, or rate of change, of the variable.

Calculus

Exercise 10B

1 Find the derivative of each of the following functions with respect to x and find the gradient of the curve at the point where $x = 2$.

   a $y = 6$

   b $y = 4x$

   c $f(x) = 3x^2$

   d $f(x) = 5x^2 - 3x$

   e $f(x) = 3x^4 + 7x - 3$

   f $f(x) = 5x^4 - 3x^2 + 2x - 6$

2 Find the derivative of each of the following functions with respect to x and find the gradient of the curve at the point where $x = 1$.

   a $f(x) = \sqrt[3]{x}$ **b** $y = 2\sqrt{x} + 3$

   c $y = 2x^2 - \dfrac{3}{x}$ **d** $y = \dfrac{6}{x^3} + 4x - 3$

   e $y = \dfrac{7}{x^3} + 8x^4 - 6x^2 + 2$

3 Find the derivative of each of the following functions, and find the gradient of the associated curve when $t = 16$.

   a $s = 4t - \dfrac{8}{\sqrt{t}}$

   b $v = 4t^{\frac{3}{4}} - \dfrac{16}{t^{\frac{1}{4}}}$

4 For each of the functions below:

   i find the derivative

   ii find the set of values of x for which the associated function is increasing.

   a $y = (2x - 1)(3x + 4)$

   b $f(x) = 2x(x^3 + 4x - 5)$

   c $g(x) = x^3 + 3x^2 - 9x - 8$

5 The area, A, of a circle of radius r is given by the formula $A = \pi r^2$.

   a Find $\dfrac{dA}{dr}$.

   b Find the rate of change of the area with respect to the radius when $r = 2$.

6 The profit, $\$P$, made from selling c cupcakes is modelled by the function $P = -0.056c^2 + 5.6c - 20$.

   a Find $\dfrac{dP}{dc}$.

   b Find the rate of change of the profit with respect to the number of cupcakes when $c = 20$ and $c = 60$.

   c Comment on your answers for part **b**.

7 The distance of a bungee jumper below his starting point is modelled by the function $f(t) = 10t - 5t^2$, $0 \le t \le 2$, where t is the time in seconds from the moment he jumps.

   a Find $f'(t)$.

   b State the quantity represented by $f'(t)$.

   c Find $f'(0.5)$ and $f'(1.5)$ and comment on the values obtained.

   d Find $f(2)$ and comment on the validity of the model.

8 Points A and B lie on the curve $f(x) = x^3 + x^2 + 2x$ and the gradient of the curve at both A and B is equal to 3.

Find the coordinates of points A and B.

9 The outline of a building can be modelled by the equation $h = 2x - 0.1x^2$ where h is the height of the building and x the horizontal distance from one corner of the building, as shown in the diagram below.

An observer stands at A. The angle of elevation from his position to the highest point he can see on the building is $45°$.

Find the height of that point above the ground.

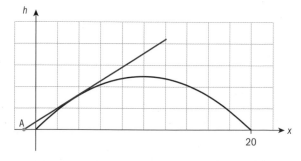

Equations of tangents and normals

The equation for the tangent to a curve at a given point can easily be found using the gradient to the curve and the coordinates of the point.

Example 5

Find the equation of the tangent to the curve $y = 2x^2 + 4\sqrt{x}$ at the point where $x = 4$.

$y = 2x^2 + 4x^{\frac{1}{2}}$ $\dfrac{dy}{dx} = 4x + 2x^{-\frac{1}{2}}$ $\qquad = 4x + \dfrac{2}{\sqrt{x}}$	Write in exponent form so the power rule can be used. If working without a GDC, it is easier to write the derivative as a fraction when working out its value.
When $x = 4$, $\dfrac{dy}{dx} = 17$. When $x = 4$, $y = 2 \times 4^2 + 4 \times 2 = 40$ so $(4, 40)$ lies on the curve and on the tangent.	The gradient of the tangent is equal to the gradient of the curve so we know the tangent is of the form $y = 17x + c$. To find c, we need a point on the curve.
Equation of the tangent is $y - 40 = 17(x - 4)$ or $y = 17x - 28$.	The point–gradient form of the equation is often the easiest to use. Your answer can be left like this, though it is usual to write it in gradient–intercept form.

The **normal** to a curve at a point is the line that is perpendicular to the tangent to the curve at that point.

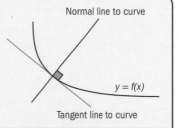

Normal line to curve

$y = f(x)$

Tangent line to curve

International-mindedness

The ancient Greeks used the idea of limits in their "Method of exhaustion".

Example 6

Find the equation of the normal to the curve for equation $f(x) = 2x^3 + 3x - 2$ at the point where $x = 1$.

$f(1) = 2(1)^3 + 3(1) - 2 = 3$ So the point is $(1, 3)$.	Find the y-coordinate of the point.
$f'(x) = 6x^2 + 3$	Next find $f'(x)$.
$f'(1) = 6(1)^2 + 3 = 9$	Find $f'(1)$ to work out the gradient of the tangent line.

HINT

If two lines are perpendicular then the product of their gradients is -1.

If the gradient of the tangent is $\dfrac{a}{b}$, then the gradient of the normal is $-\dfrac{b}{a}$.

Continued on next page

Calculus

The gradient of the tangent line is 9.	
Gradient of the normal line $= -\dfrac{1}{9}$	Gradient of normal $= \dfrac{-1}{\text{gradient of tangent}}$
$3 = -\dfrac{1}{9}(1) + c$	Substitute the coordinates $(1, 3)$ into the equation of the normal.
$c = 3\dfrac{1}{9}$	
The equation of the normal is $y = -\dfrac{1}{9}x + 3\dfrac{1}{9}.$	In the general form, this is $x + 9y - 28 = 0$.

Example 7

The gradient of the normal to the graph of the function defined by $f(x) = kx^3 - 2x + 1$ at the point $(1, b)$ is $-\dfrac{1}{4}$. Find the values of k and b.

$f'(x) = 3kx^2 - 2$	
If the gradient of the normal is $-\dfrac{1}{4}$, then the gradient of the tangent is 4.	
So,	
$f'(1) = 3k(1)^2 - 2 = 4$ $\qquad\qquad 3k = 6$ $\qquad\qquad\; k = 2$	The derivative is the gradient of the tangent at any point. Here the point is where $x = 1$. So, you put $x = 1$ into the derivative and equate it to 4 (which is the gradient of the tangent at that point).
$f(1) = 2(1)^3 - 2(1) + 1 = 1$	
So, $b = 1$.	To find b you need to substitute 1 for x into the original equation.

Exercise 10C

1 Find the equation of the tangent to the graph of the function defined by $f(x) = 2x^2 - 4$ at the point where $x = 3$.

2 Brian makes a seesaw for his children from part of a log and a plank of wood. The shape of the log can be modelled by the function $f(x) = -x^2 + 2x$ for $0 < x < 2$.

When the seesaw is level, the plank of wood is a tangent to the log at the point where $x = 1$.

By differentiating $f(x)$, find the equation of the line containing the plank.

3 Find the equation of the normal to the graph of the function defined by $f(x) = 3x^2 - 4x + 5$ at the point $(1, 4)$.

4 Find the equations of the tangent and the normal to the functions defined by

   a $y = x^4 - 6x + 3$ at the point where $x = 2$

   b $y = 6\sqrt{x}$ at the point where $x = 9$.

5 The edge of a lake can be modelled by the function $f(x) = x^2$.

   A fountain is to be placed in the lake at the point where the normals at $x = 2$ and $x = -2$ meet.

   Find the equations of these two normals and the coordinates of the point where the fountain will be placed.

6 The gradient of the tangent to the graph of the function defined by $f(x) = ax^2 + 3x - 1$ at the point $(2, b)$ is 7. Find the values of a and b.

7 The gradient of the tangent to the graph of the function defined by $f(x) = x^2 + kx + 3$ at the point $(1, b)$ is 3. Find the values of k and b.

8 The gradient of the normal to the graph of the function defined by $y = ax^2 + bx + 1$ at the point $(1, -2)$ is 1. Find the values of a and b.

GDC techniques and local maximum and minimum points

There are many websites that will give the derivative of a function as an equation and indeed some calculators do this as well. Be aware these calculators are not allowed in exams.

It will be expected in exams that you can work out numerical values for the derivatives at given points and also draw the graph of the derivative. This widens the range of functions that you might need to find the gradient for.

> **EXAM HINT**
>
> Unless told otherwise, always use your GDC if it makes answering the question simpler.

> **TOK**
>
> Mathematics and the real world: the seemingly abstract concept of calculus allows us to create mathematical models that permit human feats, such as getting a man on the Moon. What does this tell us about the links between mathematical models and physical reality?

Example 8

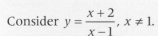

Consider $y = \dfrac{x+2}{x-1}$, $x \neq 1$.

Find the gradient of the curve at the points where $x = 2$ and $x = 3$.

-3 and -0.75	The gradient is found using the numerical derivative function on your GDC.

Investigation 2

Consider the curve $s = 3t^3 + 3t^2 - 4t + 2$.

1 Find $\dfrac{ds}{dt}$.

2 On the same axes, sketch $s = 3t^3 + 3t^2 - 4t + 2$ and its derivative.

3 Solve the equation $\dfrac{ds}{dt} = 0$ and find the coordinates of the points at which this occurs.

4 What feature of $s = 3t^3 + 3t^2 - 4t + 2$ is indicated by these points.

Continued on next page

Calculus

5 What feature of the graph of $\dfrac{ds}{dt}$ allows you to say which of the points where $\dfrac{ds}{dt} = 0$ is a maximum and which is a minimum?

6 If the domain of the function is restricted to $-2 \leq x \leq 2$, find the actual maximum and minimum values of the function.

7 **Conceptual** On a function with a restricted domain, where might the maximum and minimum points occur?

A local maximum or minimum point on a curve is a point at which the gradient moves from positive to negative or negative to positive, respectively.

For a differentiable function $f(x)$, $f'(x) = 0$ at a local maximum or minimum point.

For a continuous curve, the maximum and minimum values will occur either at local maximum or minimum points or at the end points of the domain.

> A differentiable function is a function whose derivative exists at every point in its domain.

Reflect How could you use the derivative to find a local maximum or minimum on a curve?

Example 9

Consider the derivative function $\dfrac{dy}{dx} = 1 - \dfrac{1}{x^2}$, $x \neq 0$.

a Plot the curve on a GDC.

b Find the values of x at which $\dfrac{dy}{dx} = 0$.

c State whether these points represent local maximum or minimum points on the curve for y, justifying your answer.

EXAM HINT

A sketch of the curve is usually sufficient to justify whether or not a point is a maximum or minimum. However, you may be asked to determine maximum and minimum points from a graph of the derivative.

a

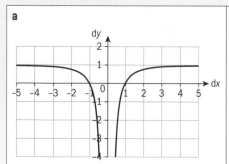

b $x = \pm 1$	These points can be found directly from the GDC.
c $x = 1$ will be a minimum point as the gradient changes from negative to positive. $x = -1$ will be a maximum point as the gradient changes from positive to negative.	The graph of the derivative is sufficient justification of the change of sign of the gradient. It is not necessary in this case to find actual values.

International-mindedness

German mathematician Gottfried Leibnitz represented the derivative by $\dfrac{dy}{dx}$ in the 17th century.

Exercise 10D

1 Use your GDC to find the gradient of the following curves at the point where $x = 3$.

   a $y = \dfrac{x^2}{x-1}$ **b** $y = x \ln x$

2 Sketch the following curves and hence find the coordinates of any point where $\dfrac{dy}{dx} = 0$.

In each case, state whether the point is a local maximum or a local minimum.

   a $y = 3x^3 - 6x^2 - 15x + 7$

   b $y = x + \dfrac{1}{x-1}$

   c $y = xe^x, x > 0$

3 For each of the curves below, find the values of x at which $\dfrac{dy}{dx} = 0$ and, by considering the sign of $\dfrac{dy}{dx}$, state whether the curve y has a local maximum or minimum point at these values.

   a $\dfrac{dy}{dx} = 2x - 4$ **b** $\dfrac{dy}{dx} = 3x^2 - 12$

   c $\dfrac{dy}{dx} = 8 - \dfrac{2}{x^2}$

4 A business buys engine parts from a factory. The business is currently deciding which of three purchasing strategies to use for the next stage of their development. Their researchers produce models for each of the strategies. In these models, P is the expected profit in €10000 and n is the number of parts they buy (in 1000s). The largest number of parts the factory can sell them is 5000 and there is no minimum.

   a For each model find the maximum profit and the number of parts they need to buy to make this profit.

   i $P = 0.5n + 1.5 + \dfrac{4}{n+1}$

   ii $P = \dfrac{n^3}{3} - \dfrac{5n^2}{2} + 6n - 4$

   iii $P = \dfrac{n^3}{24} - \dfrac{5n^2}{8} + 3n$

   b State which strategy they should adopt.

5 John is a keen cyclist and is planning a route in the Alps. The profile of the route he would like to take can be modelled by the equation $y = -0.081x^4 + 0.89x^3 - 2.87x^2 + 3x, 0 \le x \le 6$, where y ($\times 100$m) is the height of the point on the route which is a distance x ($\times 10$ km) from his starting point.

Sketch the graph and find the total height John will climb on this route.

6 If $y = 2^x$ then $\dfrac{dy}{dx} = k2^x$ where k is a constant. Find the value of k.

Optimization

If a function to be optimized has only one variable, then either a GDC or differentiation can be used directly to find the maximum or minimum point.

If a function to be optimized has more than one variable then a **constraint** must also be given. This constraint can then be written as an equation and substituted into the function to eliminate one of the variables.

International-mindedness

French mathematician Joseph Lagrange invented an alternative notation with a prime mark to denote a derivative as $f'(x)$.

Example 10

A can of dog food contains 500 cm³ of food. The manufacturer, wanting to make sure that the company receives maximum profits, would like to make sure that the surface area of the can is as small as possible. Let the radius of the can be r cm and the height, h cm.

a Find an expression for the surface area S in terms of r.

b Find $\dfrac{dS}{dr}$.

c Hence, find the dimensions of the can that will result in the minimum surface area.

a Surface area, $S = 2\pi rh + 2\pi r^2$	
	Because the equation has two variables, you cannot find the minimum, so will need to eliminate h or r. The question is asking us to eliminate h.
$V = \pi r^2 h \Rightarrow \pi r^2 h = 500$	This is the constraint, written as an equation.
So, $h = \dfrac{500}{\pi r^2}$	By rearranging the expression we can substitute for h in the equation for surface area.
$S = 2\pi r\left(\dfrac{500}{\pi r^2}\right) + 2\pi r^2 = \dfrac{1000}{r} + 2\pi r^2$	
b $S = 1000r^{-1} + 2\pi r^2$ $\dfrac{dS}{dr} = -1000r^{-2} + 4\pi r$	If the only instructions in the question were to find the minimum value, this function could now be plotted and the minimum found directly from the GDC. The question though is guiding us towards solving the equation $\dfrac{dS}{dr} = 0$.
c $\dfrac{dS}{dr} = 0$ at a maximum or minimum point. So, $-1000r^{-2} + 4\pi r = 0$ $r = 4.3$.	Because the question says "hence", you need to provide some evidence that you know the local minimum will occur when the gradient is equal to 0.
So, the best dimensions for the can are $r = 4.3$ cm and $h = 8.6$ cm.	h is found using the equation from part **a**.
	If asked to justify this is a minimum, the graph of S or $\dfrac{dS}{dr}$ can be plotted or values of r either side of 4.3 can be substituted in to $\dfrac{dS}{dr}$ to show that the gradient changes from negative to positive across the point.

Exercise 10E

1 A vegetable garden is in the shape of a rectangle. The garden is surrounded by 100 metres of fencing.

   a If the width of the garden is x metres, find an expression for the length.

   b Show that the area of the garden is $A = x(50 - x)\,\text{m}^2$.

   c Find $\dfrac{dA}{dx}$.

   d Hence find the maximum area of the garden and the corresponding dimensions that give this area.

2 An open cylinder has a volume of $400\,\text{cm}^3$. The radius of the base is r cm and the height is h cm.

   a Explain why $\pi r^2 h = 400$.

   b Rearrange the equation in part **a** to make h the subject.

   c Write down an expression for the surface area, A, of the open cylinder.

   d Show that this can be written as $A = \pi r^2 + \dfrac{800}{r}$.

   e Sketch the graph of $A = \pi r^2 + \dfrac{800}{r}$.

   f Find the minimum area and the value of r when this occurs.

3 The total surface area of a closed cylinder is $5000\,\text{cm}^2$.

Find the dimensions of the cylinder that will maximize its volume and state this maximum volume.

4 A cone has radius r cm and height $(18 - r)$ cm.

   a Find an expression for the volume V of the cone and hence show $\dfrac{dV}{dr} = \pi r(12 - r)$.

   b Hence find the radius that will maximize the volume of the cone. Use the expression given in part **a** to justify the value found is a maximum.

5 A rectangular piece of card measures 20 cm by 24 cm. Equal squares of side x cm are cut out of each corner.

The rest of the card is folded up to make a box.

   a Show that the volume, V, of the box can be expressed as $V = 4x^3 - 88x^2 + 480x$ and state the domain for this function.

   b Find $\dfrac{dV}{dx}$.

   c Find the value of x for which $\dfrac{dV}{dx} = 0$.

   d Verify that the global maximum does not occur at the end points of the domain.

   e Hence find the maximum volume of the box.

6 A school council does a survey to see how many students would buy charity cakes at different prices.

The survey revealed that if they sold each cake for $\$x$, the demand ($d$) in the school could be expressed as the function.

$d = \dfrac{100}{x^2}$. The cost to produce the cakes is $\$0.75$ per cake.

   a Explain why the profit the council makes can be expressed by the equation $P = \dfrac{100}{x} - \dfrac{75}{x^2}$.

   b Find $\dfrac{dP}{dx}$.

   c Show that the solution to $\dfrac{dP}{dx} = 0$ is $x = 1.5$.

   d By substituting $x = 1$ and $x = 2$ into the expression for $\dfrac{dP}{dx}$ justify that selling the cakes for $\$1.50$ will bring in maximum profit.

7 A rectangle is inscribed inside a circle of radius 6. Let the width of the rectangle be $2x$ and the height be $2y$.

   a Show that the area (A) of the rectangle is $A = 4x\sqrt{36 - x^2}$, $0 \le x \le 6$.

   b Find the dimensions of the rectangle of largest area that can be inscribed in a circle with radius 6 cm and state the area of the rectangle.

8 A right circular cylinder is inscribed in a sphere of radius 8 cm.

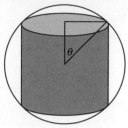

If θ is the vertical angle made by the line segment from the centre of the sphere to the point at which the cylinder touches the sphere,

a show that the curved surface area of the cylinder is, $A = 256\pi \cos\theta \sin\theta$ cm^2, $0 \le \theta \le 90°$

b find the radius and height of the cylinder having the largest curved surface area and state this area.

Developing inquiry skills

In the opening problem for the chapter, a possible power model for the demand curve was found using the best fit function on a GDC to be

$d = \dfrac{855}{x^{1.25}}$ where d is the percentage demand within the market for the new product at price $\$x$.

Given the cost ($\$C$) of producing n items is $C = 3n$ and the market size is estimated to be 10 000 people and assuming only sufficient items to match the demand are made, find an expression for the profit (P).

By differentiating this expression and solving $\dfrac{\mathrm{d}P}{\mathrm{d}x} = 0$, find the maximum profit and the price at which the product should be sold to achieve this.

10.2 Differentiation: further rules and techniques

The chain rule

Investigation 3

Consider the polynomial function $y = (2x^2 - 5)^2$, which is differentiable for all $x \in \mathbb{R}$.

1 Expand the brackets and simplify. Hence find $\dfrac{\mathrm{d}y}{\mathrm{d}x}$.

2 Note that y is a composite function.

Let $u(x)$ be the first function in the composite, hence $u(x) = 2x^2 - 5$.

a Write y as a function of u.

b Find $\dfrac{dy}{du}$ and $\dfrac{du}{dx}$.

c Hence find the product $\dfrac{dy}{du} \times \dfrac{du}{dx}$ in terms of x.

3 Compare your answers from questions **1** and **2c**. What do you notice?

4 Consider the composite function $y = (x+1)^3$.

   a Expand the function and hence find $\dfrac{dy}{dx}$.

   Let $u(x)$ be the first function in the composite.

   b Write down an expression for $u(x)$.

   c Write y as a function of u.

   d Find $\dfrac{dy}{du} \times \dfrac{du}{dx}$.

   e What do you notice?

5 If $y(x)$ is a composite function, and $u(x)$ is the first function of the composite, conjecture an expression for $\dfrac{dy}{dx}$.

6 Test your conjecture by differentiating $y = (x + 2x^{-1})^2$

   a by first expanding the function

   b by using your conjectured expression.

7 **Conceptual** How do you find the derivative of a composite function?

> The chain rule for composite functions can be written as $\dfrac{dy}{dx} = \dfrac{dy}{du} \times \dfrac{du}{dx}$.

HINT

This relation is not the result of cancelling du, but the idea of treating the notation for a derivative as a fraction is often useful and provides a convenient way to remember the rule.

Example 11

Find the derivative of

a $y = \sqrt{3x^2 - 2}$

b $f(x) = \dfrac{1}{2x+3}$

a $u = 3x^2 - 5 \Rightarrow y = u^{\frac{1}{2}}$	Identify the first function and call it u.
$\dfrac{dy}{du} = \dfrac{1}{2}u^{-\frac{1}{2}}$ and $\dfrac{du}{dx} = 6x$	Find $\dfrac{dy}{du}$ and $\dfrac{du}{dx}$.
	Use the chain rule.
$\dfrac{dy}{dx} = \dfrac{1}{2}u^{-\frac{1}{2}} \times 6x = \dfrac{3x}{\sqrt{3x^2 - 5}}$	Substitute u and simplify.

Continued on next page

b $f(x) = \dfrac{1}{2x+3}$

$u = 2x + 3, \quad f(u) = \dfrac{1}{u} = u^{-1}$

$\dfrac{du}{dx} = 2, \quad \dfrac{df}{du} = -u^{-2} = -\dfrac{1}{u^2}$

$f'(x) = \dfrac{df}{du} \times \dfrac{du}{dx}$

$f'(x) = -\dfrac{1}{u^2} \times 2 = -\dfrac{2}{(2x+3)^2}$

Again we need to identify the first function in the composite and call it u.

Write the fraction as a negative power to make differentiating easier.

Though we often write $f'(u)$, $\dfrac{df}{du}$ is also correct notation.

Use the chain rule.

Substitute u and simplify.

When you have practised a few of these you may find it is no longer necessary to explicitly write down an expression for u. Many people use the informal rule: the derivative of the inside function (u) multiplied by the derivative of the outside function.

For the first example above, this would be:

The derivative of $u = 3x - 5$, multiplied by the derivative of u to the power one-half.

Hence, $3 \times \dfrac{1}{2}(3x - 5)^{-\frac{1}{2}}$.

Exercise 10F

1 For each composite function below

    i identify the two functions that make up the composite function and write them as $u(x)$ and $y(u)$

    ii find $\dfrac{dy}{du}$.

  a $y = (x^2 + 4)^3$ **b** $y = (5x - 7)^2$

  c $y = 2(x^3 - 3x^2)^4$ **d** $y = \sqrt{4x - 5}$

  e $y = \dfrac{1}{(x^2 + 1)^2}$ **f** $y = \dfrac{2}{\sqrt{5x - 2}}$

2 Find the derivative of each of the following functions.

  a $f(x) = (x^2 + 1)^3$ **b** $g(x) = 6(5x + 2)^{\frac{1}{3}}$

  c $h(x) = \left(\sqrt{x} - 4\right)^3$ **d** $s(t) = 3(t^2 - 2)^2$

  e $v(t) = \dfrac{4}{5t - 1}$ **f** $a(t) = \left(2 - \dfrac{1}{t}\right)^3$

3 The table gives values for f, g, f' and g'.

x	$f(x)$	$g(x)$	$f'(x)$	$g'(x)$
1	5	3	−2	1
3	1	5	5	2
5	5	3	2	−2

  a If $F(x) = f \circ g(x)$, find $F'(1)$.

  b If $H(x) = g \circ g(x)$, find $H'(3)$.

The product rule

When differentiating a product of two functions, it is not possible to differentiate the two functions separately and then multiply.

For example, if $y = 5x \times x^3$ then

$$y = 5x^4 \Rightarrow \frac{dy}{dx} = 20x^3$$

This is not the same as $\dfrac{d(5x)}{dx} \times \dfrac{d(x^3)}{dx}$, which is $5 \times 3x^2 = 15x^2$.

To differentiate a product of two functions, we need to use the product rule.

The product rule

If y, u and v are all differentiable functions of x and if $y = uv$ then

$$\frac{dy}{dx} = u\frac{dv}{dx} + v\frac{du}{dx}$$

Proof of product rule

Let $h(x) = f(x)g(x) \Rightarrow h'(x) = \lim\limits_{h \to 0}\left(\dfrac{f(x+h)g(x+h) - f(x)g(x)}{h}\right)$.

This uses the limit definition of the derivative we met in the last section.

The next part looks complicated but it is just a trick. The term $f(x+h)g(x)$ is both added and subtracted in the denominator.

$$h'(x) = \lim\limits_{h \to 0}\left(\frac{f(x+h)g(x+h) - f(x+h)g(x) + f(x+h)g(x) - f(x)g(x)}{h}\right)$$

The rules of limits allow us to split this into two separate parts and then take out the factors in the next line.

$$h'(x) = \lim\limits_{h \to 0}\left(\frac{f(x+h)g(x+h) - f(x+h)g(x)}{h}\right) + \lim\limits_{h \to a}\left(\frac{f(x+h)g(x) - f(x)g(x)}{h}\right)$$

$$= \lim\limits_{h \to 0} f(x+h)\lim\limits_{h \to 0}\left(\frac{g(x+h) - g(x)}{h}\right) + \lim\limits_{h \to o} g(x)\lim\limits_{h \to 0}\left(\frac{f(x+h) - f(x)}{h}\right)$$

The larger expressions are simply the limit formulae for the derivatives of $g(x)$ and $f(x)$, respectively, hence

$$h'(x) = f(x)g'(x) + g(x)f'(x).$$

> **EXAM HINT**
>
> You will not be required to reproduce this proof in an exam. The formula for the product rule is given in the formula book.

Calculus

Example 12

Use the product rule to find $f'(x)$ if $f(x) = (x^2 + 2x)\left(\dfrac{1}{x} + 3\right)$.

Let $u(x) = x^2 + 2x$, then $u'(x) = 2x + 2$. Let $v(x) = \dfrac{1}{x} + 3$, then $v'(x) = -\dfrac{1}{x^2}$.	Define $u(x)$ and $v(x)$ and find their derivatives.
$f'(x) = \left(x^2 + 2x\right)\left(-\dfrac{1}{x^2}\right) + \left(\dfrac{1}{x} + 3\right)(2x + 2)$ $f'(x) = 6x + 7$	The product rule can be thought of as, "Differentiate one term and leave the other the same, plus differentiate the other term and leave the first the same".

Example 13

Find the derivative of $y = (x^2 - 4)^2(x^3 - 1)^4$.

$u(x) = (x^2 - 4)^2$ and $v(x) = (x^3 - 1)^4$ $\dfrac{du}{dx} = 2(x^2 - 4)(2x) = 4x(x^2 - 4)$ $\dfrac{dv}{dx} = 4(x^3 - 1)^3(3x^2) = 12x^2(x^3 - 1)^3$	In this case, we need to use the chain rule to differentiate u and v first.
$\dfrac{dy}{dx} = (x^2 - 4)^2\,12x^2(x^3 - 1)^3 + (x^3 - 1)^4\,4x(x^2 - 4)$	Use the product rule for $\dfrac{dy}{dx}$.
$\Rightarrow \dfrac{dy}{dx} = 12x^2(x^2 - 4)^2(x^3 - 1)^3 + 4x(x^3 - 1)^4(x^2 - 4)$ $\quad = 4x(x^2 - 4)(x^3 - 1)^3(3x(x^2 - 4) + x^3 - 1)$ $\quad = 4x(x^2 - 4)(x^3 - 1)^3(4x^3 - 12x - 1)$	Often the product rule will generate factors that can be used to simplify the expression.

The quotient rule

Similar to the product of two functions, a quotient cannot be differentiated by differentiating the two parts separately, but has to be differentiated using the quotient rule.

> **The quotient rule**
> If u and v are differentiable functions of x and if $y = \dfrac{u}{v}$ then
> $$\dfrac{dy}{dx} = \dfrac{v\dfrac{du}{dx} - u\dfrac{dv}{dx}}{v^2}$$ for $v(x) \neq 0$. The formula for the quotient rule is given in the formula book.

TOK

What is the difference between inductive and deductive reasoning?

The result is proved in Exercise 10G.

Example 14

If $y = \dfrac{x^2 + 3}{x + 1}$, $x \neq -1$, find

a $\dfrac{dy}{dx}$

b the equations of   **i** the tangent and   **ii** the normal at the point $(-2, -7)$.

a Let $u(x) = x^2 + 3$, then $u'(x) = 2x$. Let $v(x) = x + 1$, then $v'(x) = 1$.	Define $u(x)$ and $v(x)$ and find their derivatives.
$\dfrac{dy}{dx} = \dfrac{(x+1)\,(2x) - (x^2 + 3)1}{(x+1)^2}$	Use the quotient rule.
$\qquad = \dfrac{2x^2 + 2x - x^2 - 3}{(x+1)^2} = \dfrac{x^2 + 2x - 3}{(x+1)^2}$	
b i Gradient of tangent $= m = \dfrac{-3}{1} = -3$ $y = -3x + c$ $-7 = 6 + c$ $c = -13$ Hence, the equation of the tangent is $y = -3x - 13$	Substitute $x = -2$ into the derivative function. Point $(-2, -7)$ lies on the tangent. An alternative method is to use the formula $y - y_1 = m(x - x_1)$.
ii Gradient of normal $= \dfrac{1}{3}$ Hence, the equation of the normal is $y + 7 = \dfrac{1}{3}(x + 2)$ $\Rightarrow y = \dfrac{1}{3}x - \dfrac{19}{3}$ or $x - 3y - 19 = 0$	If the gradient of the tangent is m then the gradient of the normal is $-\dfrac{1}{m}$. Point $(-2, -7)$ lies on the normal as well. As the question does not ask for a particular form, any of these answers would be acceptable.

Calculus

HINT

It is important to use the correct technique in a particular question:

- Avoid rearranging a quotient into a product when using the product rule.

  For example, avoid writing $y = \dfrac{x^2 + 3}{x + 1}$ as $y = (x^2 + 3)(x + 1)^{-1}$.

  This will give the correct answer but the answer will not be set over a common denominator and so will be more difficult to manipulate in the later parts of a question.

Continued on next page

An expression in which the numerator is a constant term should be differentiated using the chain rule and not the quotient rule.

For example, $y = \dfrac{2}{x^2 + 3}$, should be written as $y = 2(x^2 + 3)^{-1}$

$$\Rightarrow \frac{dy}{dx} = -4x\left(x^2 + 3\right)^{-2}$$

Exercise 10G

1 Use the product rule to find the derivative of the following equations. Write down your answers in factorized form where possible.

a $y = x^2(2x + 1)$

b $y = (x + 2)(x^2 + 3)$

c $y = (x^2 + 2x + 1)(x^3 - 1)$

d $s = (2t^2 + 3)(4 - t)^5$

e $f(x) = \dfrac{1}{x}(2x^3 + x + 4)$

f $g(t) = (2t + 1)^4(t^3 + 1)^2$

2 Use the quotient rule to find the derivative of the following equations. Write down your answers as fractions, with any simple cancellations performed, where possible.

a $y = \dfrac{2x^3 + x + 4}{x}$ **b** $y = \dfrac{1 - x}{x^2 + 1}$

c $y = \dfrac{x}{\sqrt{x + 1}}$ **d** $s = \dfrac{4t}{2t + 1}$

e $f(x) = \dfrac{x^3 - 1}{x + 1}$ **f** $g(t) = \dfrac{t^{\frac{1}{3}}}{t^{\frac{1}{3}} - 4}$

3 Find the derivative of each of the following.

a $y = x^2(x^2 + 1)^3$ **b** $y = \dfrac{4}{2x + 3}$

c $y = \dfrac{x}{\sqrt{2x + 1}}$ **d** $s = 4t\sqrt{2t - 3}$

e $f(x) = \dfrac{x}{(3 - 2x)^2}$ **f** $g(t) = \dfrac{4t(t + 1)^2}{2t - 3}$

4 P is the point on the curve $y = x(2x - 1)^2$ with coordinates $(1, 1)$.

a Find $\dfrac{dy}{dx}$.

b Hence find the equation of

   i   the tangent at P

   ii   the normal at P.

The tangent and normal at P meet the x-axis at Q and R, respectively.

c Find the area of the triangle $\triangle$QPR.

5 Consider the curve $y = \dfrac{4x - 2}{x + 1}, x \neq -1$.

a Find the equation of the normal to the curve at the point $(2, 2)$.

b Find the coordinates of the second point at which the normal intersects the curve.

6 By writing $y = \dfrac{u}{v}$ as $y = u(v)^{-1}$, use the chain and product rules to prove $\dfrac{dy}{dx} = \dfrac{v\dfrac{du}{dx} - u\dfrac{dv}{dx}}{v^2}$.

Derivatives of trigonometric functions

Investigation 4

1 a With your GDC in radian mode, draw the graph of $y = \sin x$ for $0 \le x \le 2\pi$.

b From your graph, estimate the gradient of the curve at the points where $x = 0, \dfrac{\pi}{2}, \pi, \dfrac{3\pi}{2}$ and 2π. Take into consideration the possible different scales on the two axes.

2 Use the numerical derivative function on your GDC to complete the following table. $(\sin x)'$ denotes the derivative of $\sin x$.

x	0	$\dfrac{\pi}{4}$	$\dfrac{\pi}{2}$	$\dfrac{3\pi}{4}$	π	$\dfrac{5\pi}{4}$	$\dfrac{3\pi}{2}$	$\dfrac{7\pi}{4}$	2π
$\sin x$									
$(\sin x)'$									
$\cos x$									
$(\cos x)'$									

3 Conjecture an expression for the derivative of

a $\sin x$ **b** $\cos x$.

4 Put your GDC into degree mode. Use the numerical derivative function to calculate the gradient of

a $\sin x$ when $x = 0$ **b** $\cos x$ when $x = 90°$.

c Explain why these results are different from those obtained in question **2**.

5 Use the definition of $\tan x = \dfrac{\sin x}{\cos x}$ and the quotient rule to show that the derivative of $\tan x$ is $\dfrac{1}{\cos^2 x}$.

6 **Factual** What units do you use when differentiating trigonometric functions?

7 From your answers to questions **3**, **4** and **5**, what can you say about the derivatives of $\sin x$ and $\cos x$?

TOK

Euler was able to make important advances in mathematical analysis before calculus had been put on a solid theoretical foundation by Cauchy and others. However, some work was not possible until after Cauchy's work.

What does this suggest regarding intuition and imagination in mathematics?

Calculus

- $f(x) = \sin x \Rightarrow f'(x) = \cos x$
- $f(x) = \cos x \Rightarrow f'(x) = -\sin x$
- $f(x) = \tan x \Rightarrow f'(x) = \dfrac{1}{\cos^2 x}$

HINT

All these derivatives are in the formula book.

Example 15

Use the chain rule to find the derivative of

a $y = \sin 2x$ **b** $y = \cos 4t$.

a $\dfrac{dy}{dx} = \cos 2x \times 2$	Let $u = 2x$, $y = \sin u$
$\phantom{\dfrac{dy}{dx}} = 2\cos 2x$	$\dfrac{du}{dx} = 2$, $\dfrac{dy}{du} = \cos u$
b $\dfrac{dy}{dt} = -\sin 4t \times 4$	Let $u = 4t$, $y = \cos u$
$\phantom{\dfrac{dy}{dt}} = -4\sin 4t$	$\dfrac{du}{dt} = 4$, $\dfrac{dy}{du} = -\sin u$

> **HINT**
>
> Differentiating expressions of the form $y = \sin ax$ and $y = \cos ax$ is so
>
> common that it is useful to learn the derivatives: $y = \sin ax \Rightarrow \dfrac{dy}{dx} = a\cos ax$
>
> and $y = \cos ax \Rightarrow \dfrac{dy}{dx} = -a\sin ax$

Example 16

Find the derivative of $y = \dfrac{\cos x}{x^2}$.

Let $u(x) = \cos x$ and $v(x) = x^2$.	We will use the quotient rule so we need to identify u and v.
$\dfrac{du}{dx} = -\sin x$ and $\dfrac{dv}{dx} = 2x$	Find the derivatives of u and v.
$\dfrac{dy}{dx} = \dfrac{(x^2)(-\sin x) - (\cos x)(2x)}{(x^2)^2}$	Use the quotient rule.
$\dfrac{dy}{dx} = \dfrac{-x\sin x - 2\cos x}{x^3}$	Factorize and simplify.

Exercise 10H

1 Find the derivative of the following functions.

a $y = 4 \sin x$

b $y = 2 \cos x - x^2$

c $y = 5 \tan x$

d $y = 2 \cos 4t$

e $f(x) = \sin 5x + 4x^3$

f $g(t) = \sin 3t - 3\cos 2t - t^2 + 1$

2 Use the product and quotient rules to find the derivative of the following.

a $y = x \sin x$

b $y = \sin x \cos x$

c $y = 2x^2 \tan x$

d $y = \dfrac{\sin t}{t}$

e $f(x) = \dfrac{\cos x}{\sin x}$

f $g(t) = \dfrac{\sin 2t}{\cos t}$

3 Find the derivative of the following.

a $y = \sin(x^2)$

b $y = 2 \cos(3x)$

c $y = \tan(3x - 1)$

d $y = \sin^2 t$

e $f(x) = 3 \cos^3 x$

f $g(t) = 2 \sin 4t \cos 4t$

g $f(x) = \sin^2(3x)$

h $g(t) = \sin^2 t \cos t$

4 A performance hall is in the shape of a prism whose cross-sectional area can be modelled by the curve $y = 5.1 \cos\left(\dfrac{\pi}{10}x\right)$, $-5 \leq x \leq 5$.

A temporary screen is to be fitted at one end of the hall. The cross-section of the screen will be in the shape of a rectangle.

A possible screen is shown in the diagram below.

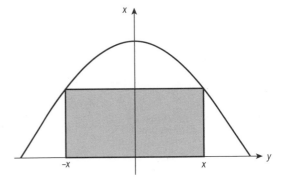

The cross-sectional area of the screen should be as large as possible.

a Write down a model for the cross-sectional area (A) of the screen in terms of x, the x-coordinate of the right-hand vertical side.

b Find $\dfrac{dA}{dx}$.

c Find the maximum value for the cross-sectional area of the screen.

Derivatives of e^x and $\ln x$

Investigation 5

The diagrams below show the graphs of $y = 2^x$ and $y = 3^x$ in green and the graphs of their derivatives in red.

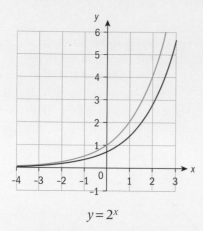

$y = 2^x$

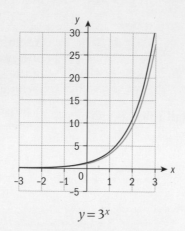

$y = 3^x$

1 Comment on the any similarities or differences between the two graphs.

2 A function f is such that $f(x) = f'(x)$. Where might you look for such a function?

3 a Use the numerical derivative function on your GDC to complete the following table.

x	-1	0	1	2	3
e^x					
$(e^x)'$					

b Conjecture an expression for the derivative of e^x.

4 Consider the graph of $y = \ln x$ shown in this diagram.

Sketch a possible graph showing the gradients of points on the curve $y = \ln x$ and comment on its key features.

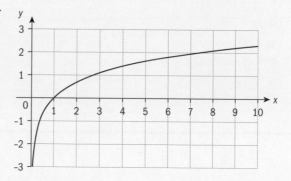

5 a Use the numerical derivative function on your GDC to find the value of the gradient of $y = \ln x$ at the following points.

x	1	2	3	4	5
$(\ln x)'$					

b i Conjecture an expression for the derivative of $\ln x$.

ii Does your sketch from question **4** support your answer?

iii Test your conjecture by finding the derivative when $x = 10$.

Differentiating exponentials and logarithmic functions in other bases gives a multiple of the results obtained here, so it is usual to use base e, as this is the simplest, and this is the only one required by the course.

6 **Factual** What base should be used when differentiating exponential or logarithmic functions?

7 **Conceptual** Why is the exponential function with base e so special?

- $f(x) = e^x \Rightarrow f'(x) = e^x$
- $f(x) = \ln x \Rightarrow f'(x) = \dfrac{1}{x}$

HINT

These derivatives are in the formula book.

HINT

The results in Investigation 5 can be proved using the definition of e^x as

$$e^x = \lim_{n \to \infty}\left(1 + \frac{x}{n}\right)^n$$

which you met in Chapter 7.

Example 17

Find the derivative of **a** $y = x \ln x$ **b** $y = e^{4x}$.

a $\dfrac{dy}{dx} = \ln x + x \times \dfrac{1}{x}$	Use the product rule.
$\quad = \ln x + 1$	
b Let $u = 4x$ and $y = e^u$	Identify the two functions that make up the composite.
$\dfrac{du}{dx} = 4$, $\dfrac{dy}{du} = e^u$	
$\dfrac{dy}{dx} = 4 \times e^u = e^{4x}$	Use the chain rule.

HINT

Differentiating expressions of the form $y = e^{ax}$ is so common that it is useful to learn the derivative:

$$y = e^{ax} \Rightarrow \frac{dy}{dx} = ae^{ax}.$$

Example 18

Find the derivative of $f(x) = \sin(\ln x)$.

Let $u(x) = \ln x$, then $f(u) = \sin(u)$	Identify the composite function.
$\dfrac{du}{dx} = \dfrac{1}{x}$ and $\dfrac{df}{du} = \cos(u)$	Find $\dfrac{du}{dx}$ and $\dfrac{df}{du}$.
$f'(x) = \cos(u) \times \dfrac{1}{x}$	Use the chain rule.
$\Rightarrow f'(x) = \dfrac{1}{x}\cos(\ln x) = \dfrac{\cos(\ln x)}{x}$	

Calculus

Exercise 10I

1 Find the derivative of each of the following.

   a $y = \ln(x^2 + 1)$ b $y = xe^x$

   c $y = e^{2x^2}$ d $y = t^2 \ln t$

   e $f(x) = (2x + 1)e^{2x}$ f $f(t) = \dfrac{\ln t}{t}$

   g $s = 3t \ln(t^2 - 2)$ h $g(x) = \dfrac{2e^{4x}}{x}$

   i $h(t) = te^{3t^2}$

2 Find $\dfrac{dy}{dx}$ using the log laws to simplify the expressions given.

   a $y = \ln x^5$ b $y = \ln(2x + 3)^4$

   c $y = \ln(x(x - 3)^2)$ d $y = \ln\left(\dfrac{2x + 1}{x}\right)$

   e $y = \ln(e^{x^2})$ f $y = \ln\left(\dfrac{x^2}{(2x + 1)^3}\right)$

3 a   By writing $\ln(ax)$ as $\ln x + \ln a$, deduce an expression for the derivative of $\ln ax$.

   b   Verify that the chain rule gives the same result.

4 i   Find the derivative of each of the following functions.

   ii   Find the smallest positive value of x for which $f(x) = f'(x)$.

   a $f(x) = 20 \sin(\ln x)$

   b $f(x) = \ln(\cos x + 2)$

   c $f(x) = e^{2\sin x}$

5 Consider the curve $y = \dfrac{e^{2x}}{x + 3}$.

   a   Find the **exact** value of the coordinates of the point at which the tangent to the curve is parallel to the x-axis.

   b   Write down the equation of the normal to the curve at this point.

Developing inquiry skills

In the opening problem for the chapter, a possible exponential model for the demand curve was found, using the best fit function on a GDC, to be $d = 130e^{-0.0792x}$ where d is the percentage demand within the market for the new product at price $\$x$.

Given the cost ($\$C$) of producing n items is $C = 3n$ and the market size is estimated to be 10 000 people, and assuming only sufficient items to match the demand are made,

1 find an expression for the profit (P)

2 by differentiating this expression and solving $\dfrac{dP}{dx} = 0$, find the maximum profit and the price at which the product should be sold to achieve this.

TOK

Who do you think should be considered the discoverer of calculus?

10.3 Applications and higher derivatives

The second derivative

Investigation 6

In section 10.1 it was shown that for a function f

- if f is increasing at x then $f'(x) > 0$
- if f is decreasing at x then $f'(x) < 0$.

1 Consider the two curves shown below. Write down for which of the two curves

    a   the gradient of the curve is increasing

    b   the gradient of the curve is decreasing.

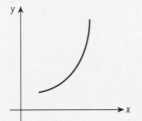 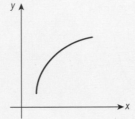

The first curve is an example of a curve that is **concave up** and the second an example of a curve that is **concave down**.

2 Consider the curve $y = (x - 1)^3$.

    a   Sketch the curve showing clearly the x-intercept.

    b   Find $\dfrac{dy}{dx}$.

    c   Explain from your answer to part **b** why the curve is always increasing.

The second derivative is obtained by differentiating the first derivative of a function. The notation is either $\dfrac{d^2y}{dx^2}$ (said as "d two y by dx squared") or $f''(x)$.

3 **a**   Find the second derivative of $y = (x - 1)^3$.

    b   State the values of x for which

       i $\dfrac{d^2y}{dx^2} > 0$ **ii** $\dfrac{d^2y}{dx^2} < 0$.

4 **Factual** What feature of a graph is indicated by the sign of the second derivative?

5 **a**   Write down the value of x for which $\dfrac{d^2y}{dx^2} = 0$.

    b   What is significant about this point in terms of the concavity of the curve?

The point on a curve at which the concavity changes sign is called a **point of inflexion**.

6 **Conceptual** Given the equation of a curve, how would you find a point of inflexion if one exists?

Calculus

The first and second derivatives indicate the following features of a curve:

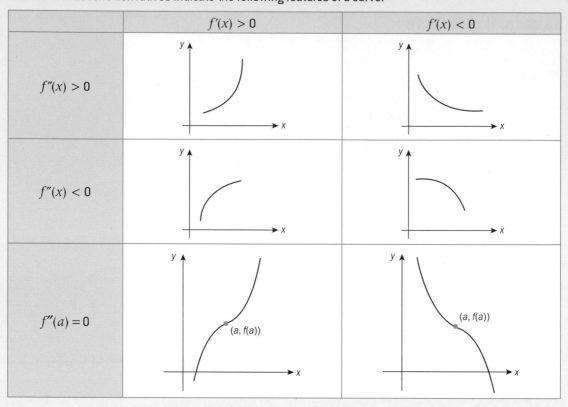

	$f'(x) > 0$	$f'(x) < 0$
$f''(x) > 0$		
$f''(x) < 0$		
$f''(a) = 0$		

Example 19

For the function $f(x) = x^4 - 3x^2 + 2$

a find the local maximum and minimum points, justifying the nature of each

b find the interval in which the curve is concave down.

a From the GDC, the local maximum point is $(0, 0)$ and the minimum points are $(1.225, -0.25)$ and $(-1.225, -0.25)$. 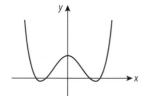	Often the easiest way to locate maxima and minima is by using the inbuilt functions on the GDC. The sketch is sufficient justification of the nature of the points.

b $\dfrac{dy}{dx} = 4x^3 - 6x$

$\dfrac{d^2y}{dx^2} = 12x^2 - 6$

$12x^2 - 6 < 0 \Rightarrow x^2 < 0.5$

$-0.707 < x < 0.707$

It is difficult to find the point at which the concavity changes directly from a GDC and so this question is best done algebraically.

When the graph is concave down, the second derivative is less than 0.

The graph indicates that the range required is between the two boundaries of the inequality.

The second derivative provides an alternative way to distinguish whether or not the point $(a, f(a))$ at which $f'(a) = 0$ is a maximum, a minimum or a point of inflexion.

- If $f''(a) > 0$ the curve is concave up and so $(a, f(a))$ is a minimum point.
- If $f''(a) < 0$ the curve is concave down so $(a, f(a))$ is a maximum point.
- If $f''(a) = 0$ the result is inconclusive because, though it is likely to be a point of inflexion, there are a few curves for which it could be either a maximum or a minimum.

For example, if $f(x) = x^4$ then $f''(x) = 0$ but the curve clearly has a minimum point at $x = 0$.

In these cases it is important to check the sign of $f''(x)$ either side of the point to see if the concavity changes.

Reflect If $(a, f(a))$ is a local maximum, what is the sign of $f''(a)$?
If $(a, f(a))$ is a local minimum, what is the sign of $f''(a)$?

International-mindedness

The Greeks' mistrust of zero meant that Archimedes' work did not lead to calculus.

EXAM HINT

In exams, a sketch of the curve is also sufficient to identify the nature of a point where the gradient is equal to zero.

Example 20

Consider the curve $y = 2x^3 - 9x^2 + 12x + 5$.

a Find $\dfrac{dy}{dx}$.

b Hence, find the coordinates of the points on the curve at which $\dfrac{dy}{dx} = 0$.

c Find $\dfrac{d^2y}{dx^2}$.

d Hence, determine whether the points are local maxima or local minima.

e Find the coordinates of the point of inflexion on the curve.

Continued on next page

Calculus

a $\dfrac{dy}{dx} = 6x^2 - 18x + 12$

b $6x^2 - 18x + 12 = 0$

$\Rightarrow x = 1, 2$

$(1, 10), (2, 9)$

It would be easy to find the maximum and minimum values by sketching the curve on your GDC to justify their nature, but because the question says "hence", you must use the previous result and show working to demonstrate that you have.

c $\dfrac{d^2y}{dx^2} = 12x - 18$

d When $x = 1$, $\dfrac{d^2y}{dx^2} = -6 < 0$; hence, it is a maximum point.

When $x = 2$, $\dfrac{d^2y}{dx^2} = 6 > 0$; hence, it is a minimum.

e $\dfrac{d^2y}{dx^2} = 0 \Rightarrow 12x - 18 = 0$

$\Rightarrow x = 1.5$

$(1.5, 9.5)$

Because the question says there is one point of inflexion and there is only one point at which the second derivative is equal to zero, there is no need to check for a change in concavity.

Exercise 10J

1 Find the second derivative for the following functions.

  a $y = x \sin x$

  b $f(x) = \dfrac{2}{(x-3)^2}$

  c $s = 2t \ln t$

2 Let $y = x^5 - 3x^2 + 5$.

  a Find any local maximum or minimum points on the curve, justifying whether they are maxima or minima.

  b Find a point of inflexion on the curve.

  c Hence, give the range of values of x for which the curve is concave up.

3 Let $y = \dfrac{e^x}{x}$, $x \neq 0$.

  a Find   **i** $\dfrac{dy}{dx}$ **ii** $\dfrac{d^2y}{dx^2}$.

  b **Hence**, show that there is a minimum point at $x = 1$.

  c Prove that there are no points of inflexion on the curve.

4 If $f(x) = \dfrac{x}{x-3}$, $x \neq 3$,

  a show that f is decreasing for all x values in its domain

  b show that f has no points of inflexion.

5 For each function below

   i find any local maximum or minimum points

   ii find an expression for $\dfrac{d^2y}{dx^2}$

   iii find any points of inflexion

   iv determine the intervals where the function is concave up and where it is concave down.

   a $y = (x - 2)^3(x + 1)$

   b $h(x) = e^{-x}\cos x,\ 0 \le x \le 2\pi$

   c $f(x) = x^3 e^{-2x}$

6 A population p at time t is given by the following logistic equation $p(t) = \dfrac{10}{1 + 4e^{-2t}}$.

a i Find an expression for $p'(t)$.

   ii Explain why $p'(t) > 0$ for all $t \ge 0$ and interpret your result in the context of population growth.

b i Find an expression for $p''(t)$.

   ii Hence, find the value of t at which $p''(t) = 0$.

   iii Explain the significance of this point in the context of the rate of population growth.

c i For the value of t found in part **b ii** find the value of $p(t)$.

   ii Explain the significance of this point in the context of the carrying capacity of the population.

Kinematics

In Chapter 3 motion with constant velocity was introduced along with the idea of the displacement of an object being its position relative to an origin.

In this section, motion with a variable velocity in one dimension will be considered.

Though the focus will be on just one dimension, it is important to remember that velocity is still a vector quantity and hence has both magnitude and direction.

In the diagram below, A is moving along the x-axis and has a positive displacement. Because it is moving in a negative direction its velocity is -2.

Speed is the magnitude of the velocity and so is always positive. The speed of A is 2.

Let $s(t)$ be the displacement of an object at time t.

The average velocity between times t_1 and t_2 is

$$\frac{\text{change in displacement}}{\text{time}} = \frac{s(t_2) - s(t_1)}{t_2 - t_1}$$

And the velocity at time t will be the rate of change of the displacement at that time, $s'(t)$ or $\dfrac{ds}{dt}$.

In the same way as velocity is the rate of change of displacement (that is, a measure of how quickly displacement is changing), **acceleration** is the rate of change of velocity and hence is equal to $\dfrac{dv}{dt}$.

> **TOK**
>
> Does the fact that Leibnitz and Newton came across calculus at similar times support the argument of Platonists over Constructivists?

Calculus

Using the chain rule leads to another expression for acceleration.

$a = \dfrac{dv}{dt} = \dfrac{ds}{dt} \times \dfrac{dv}{ds} = v\dfrac{dv}{ds}$, which is useful when velocity is given as a function of displacement rather than time.

> If an object has displacement $s(t)$, velocity $v(t)$ and acceleration $a(t)$ then
>
> $$a(t) = \frac{dv}{dt} = \frac{d^2s}{dt^2} \ \text{ or } \ a = v\frac{dv}{ds}$$

Example 21

The height (m) of a rocket projected vertically into the air until it returns to the ground is represented by the function $h(t) = -0.11t^2 + 1.32t + 1.5$, $t \geq 0$, where t is the number of seconds after the rocket was launched.

a State the height at which the rocket was launched.

b Find the maximum height reached by the rocket.

c Calculate the velocity of the rocket at $t = 7.5\,$s and state whether it is ascending or descending at this time.

d Find the other time at which the rocket is travelling at the same speed as when $t = 7.5\,$s.

a 1.5 m	The initial height occurs when $t = 0$.
b $v(t) = -0.22t + 1.32 = 0$ $t = \dfrac{1.32}{0.22} = 6$ $h(6) = 5.46\,$m	The maximum height will occur when $\dfrac{dh}{dt} = 0$, which is equivalent to $v(t) = 0$. Substitute the value for t into the equation for height.
c $v(7.5) = -0.22 \times 7.5 + 1.32$ $\qquad\quad = -0.33\,$m s^{-1} Descending	Because the velocity is negative, the height is decreasing and so the rocket is descending. Parts **a** to **c** could be done by sketching the curve on the GDC and using the maximum and numerical derivative functions. However, the simplest way to do part **d** is by using differentiation.
d $-0.22t + 1.32 = 0.33 \Rightarrow t$ $\qquad\qquad\qquad\quad = 4.5$ seconds	The rocket has the same speed, so its velocity is ±0.33. We already know where it is −0.33 so we need to solve $v = 0.33$.

The "dot" or Newton's notation is often used to signify a rate of change (derivative) with respect to time. If x is an object's displacement then $v = \dot{x}$ and $a = \ddot{x}$.

This notation is particularly useful when considering motion in more than one direction.

HINT

If a derivative has time as its variable then Newton's dot notation is often used.

Hence, $v = \dot{s}$ and $a = \dot{v} = \ddot{s}$.

Exercise 10K

1 A ball is thrown vertically upwards.

The path of the ball can be modelled by the equation $h(t) = 12t - 4t^2$ where $h(t)$ is the height of the ball in metres after t seconds.

a Find the average velocity between 1 and 1.5 seconds.

b Find the instantaneous velocity at 1 second.

2 A particle moves in a straight line and its displacement from a fixed point is given as

$s(t) = -t^3 + 2t^2 + 4t - 2$

where t is measured in seconds and s in metres.

a Find its average velocity in the first 3 seconds.

b Find its velocity and acceleration at $t = 3$.

c Determine if the speed of the particle is increasing or decreasing at $t = 3$.

d Find the value of t when the direction of the particle changes.

e i Find the value of t at which the acceleration of the particle changes direction.

ii Explain the geometrical significance of this point on the graph
$s(t) = -t^3 + 2t^2 + 4t - 2$.

3 The velocity of a particle as a function of its displacement x is given as $v = 5\sin 3x$.

Use the expression $a = v\dfrac{\mathrm{d}v}{\mathrm{d}s}$ to find the

particle's acceleration when $x = 2$.

4 A rocket is fired into the air from a platform which is 1 m above the ground.

The path of the rocket can be modelled by a quadratic function with equation

$y(t) = -0.2t^2 + 2t + 1$, where $t \geq 0$ represents the time, in seconds, since the rocket took off, and $y(t)$ represents the height, in metres, of the rocket above the ground.

a Find an expression for the velocity of the rocket at time t.

b Hence, find

i the initial velocity of the rocket

ii the maximum height of the rocket

iii the speed at which the rocket hits the ground.

5 A marble is dropped from a certain height into a large tube containing a viscous liquid. The distance (s) fallen by the marble t seconds after the marble enters the liquid is given by the equation

$s = 0.4(2 + t - 2e^{-0.5t})$.

a i Find the distance fallen by the marble after 2 seconds.

ii Find the value of t at which the marble will have fallen 2 m.

b Find an expression for the velocity of the marble at time t.

c Write down the velocity of the marble as it enters the liquid.

The terminal velocity of a falling object is the velocity approached by the object as it falls.

d Write down the terminal velocity of the marble in the liquid.

e Find the time at which the marble is first moving within 1% of its terminal velocity.

6 A cyclist is cycling up a hill. The distance (x metres) cycled from the foot of the hill can be modelled by the equation $x = 3t + \ln(2t + 1)$ where t is the number of seconds after the cyclist begins the climb. The road up the hill is 200 m long.

   a Find the value of t at which the cyclist reaches the top of the hill.

   b Find an expression for the velocity of the cyclist at time t.

   c Find

     i the initial velocity of the cyclist

     ii the velocity of the cyclist at the top of the hill.

   d Show that the cyclist is always decelerating when climbing the hill.

7 The displacement from the equilibrium position (x cm) of a weight attached to a spring is given by the equation $x = 4e^{-0.4t} \sin(4t)$.

   a Sketch the curve for $0 \leq t \leq 10$.

   b Find the greatest value of t at which the weight is 1.2 cm from the equilibrium position.

   c Find an expression for $\dot{x}$, the velocity of the weight at time t.

   d Find

     i the value of t at which the weight first returns to the equilibrium position

     ii the velocity of the weight at this time.

Rates of change and related rates of change

The previous section considered the rates of change of displacement (velocity) and velocity (acceleration) but there are many other quantities that change with time.

For example, in a town, the temperature (T°C) t hours after midnight might be modelled by the equation $T = 4\sin\left(\dfrac{\pi(t-9)}{12}\right) + 13$.

In this case $\dfrac{dT}{dt}$ will represent the rate of change of temperature with time and the units will be °C per hour.

Related rates

Investigation 7

A spherical balloon is being inflated at a constant rate of 10 cm³ s⁻¹.

This represents the rate of change of the volume of the balloon and so can be written as $\dfrac{dV}{dt} = 10$.

Suppose you now wish to find out how quickly the radius is increasing when $r = 1$ and $r = 3$.

1 At which of the two radii will the rate of increase of the radius be greater?

2 Write down the rate of increase of the radius as a derivative.

Clearly, the rates of increase of the radius and the volume are related. If the rate of increase of the volume changed, so would the rate of increase of the radius. This connection can be used to find one quantity if the other is known.

TOK

How can you justify a tax rise for plastic containers, eg plastic bags and plastic bottles, using optimization?

Recall that if y is a function of u and u is a function of x then by the chain rule $\dfrac{dy}{dx} = \dfrac{dy}{du} \times \dfrac{du}{dx}$.

3 Use the chain rule to find an expression for the rate of change of the volume in terms of the rate of change of the radius and one other quantity.

4 What do you still need to find?

5 Given the balloon remains spherical, find the relation between the two rates as a function of the radius.

6 Hence, find the rate of change of the radius at $r = 1$ and $r = 3$.

7 [Conceptual] How can you find an expression connecting two related rates?

If you are given a rate $\dfrac{dx}{dt}$ and wish to find the related rate $\dfrac{dy}{dt}$, the chain rule can be used to give $\dfrac{dy}{dt} = \dfrac{dx}{dt} \times \dfrac{dy}{dx}$.

This can be found if the equation relating y and x is known and is differentiable.

HINT

If it is easier to calculate $\dfrac{dx}{dy}$ than $\dfrac{dy}{dx}$, then the chain rule may be written as $\dfrac{dy}{dt} = \dfrac{dx}{dt} \div \dfrac{dx}{dy}$.

Example 22

A water tank is in the shape of an inverted circular cone with base radius 3 m and a height of 6 m. If water is being poured into the tank at a rate of $5\,\mathrm{m^3\,min^{-1}}$, find the rate at which the water is rising when the water has a depth of 2 metres.

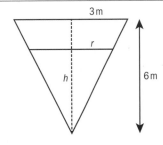	Draw a diagram.
Define: t: time in minutes from the point when the water began to be added h: depth of the water at time t r: radius of the surface of the water at time t V: volume at time t.	Define variables and write down the given information.

Continued on next page

Calculus

Rate given is $\dfrac{dV}{dt} = 5$

Rate required is $\dfrac{dh}{dt}$

Hence, $\dfrac{dh}{dt} = \dfrac{dV}{dt} \times \dfrac{dh}{dV}$

$V = \dfrac{1}{3}\pi r^2 h$

$\dfrac{h}{r} = \dfrac{6}{3} \Rightarrow r = \dfrac{h}{2}$

$\Rightarrow V = \dfrac{1}{12}\pi h^3$

$\Rightarrow \dfrac{dV}{dh} = \dfrac{1}{4}\pi h^2$

$\dfrac{dh}{dt} = \dfrac{dV}{dt} \div \dfrac{dV}{dh}$

$= \dfrac{20}{\pi h^2}$

When $h = 2\,\text{m}$,

$\dfrac{dh}{dt} = \dfrac{20}{4\pi} = 1.59\,\text{m min}^{-1}.$

The process is always to write down the rate that you are given and the rate that you want and to use the chain rule to find the connection between the two.

An equation connecting V and h is required. As the equation for the volume of a cone contains r, which is also a variable, it needs to be replaced with a function of h.

This result is obtained from the diagram above using similar triangles.

As it was easier to calculate $\dfrac{dV}{dh}$ than $\dfrac{dh}{dV}$, the alternative form of the chain rule is used.

Exercise 10L

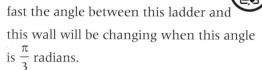

1 If V is the volume of a cylinder with radius r and height h, write down the rate of change of the volume when

   a the height is increasing at a rate of $\dfrac{dh}{dt}$ whilst r is kept constant

   b the radius is increasing at a rate of $\dfrac{dr}{dt}$ whilst h is kept constant.

2 The volume of a cube is increasing at a rate of $2\,\text{m}^3\text{s}^{-1}$. Find the rate of increase of its surface area when the cube has a volume of $27\,\text{m}^3$.

3 A ladder 4 m long rests against a vertical wall. If the bottom of the ladder slides away from the wall at $1.5\,\text{m s}^{-1}$, find how fast the angle between this ladder and this wall will be changing when this angle is $\dfrac{\pi}{3}$ radians.

4 A 4 m long water trough is in the shape of a prism whose cross-section is an isosceles triangle with height 1.2 m and base length of 1.0 m. If the trough is being filled at a rate of $1200\,\text{cm}^3\text{min}^{-1}$, find how fast the water level will be rising when the water is 45 cm deep.

5 A and B are two points on a circle with centre O and radius 5 cm.

   Let the angle AOB be θ and be increasing at a rate of 0.2 radians s^{-1}.

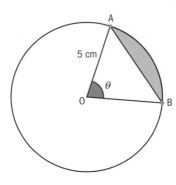

5 cm

θ

O

A

B

Find the rate at which the area of the minor segment formed by the chord AB is increasing when $\theta = 1$.

6 **a** Show that if $f(x) = \dfrac{1}{\tan x}$ then

$$f'(x) = -\dfrac{1}{\sin^2 x}.$$

b A plane is flying at a constant height of 2000 m. An observer watching from the ground directly beneath the flight path of the plane measures the angle of elevation to the plane as 0.5 radians and the rate of change of the angle of elevation as 0.01 radians s^{-1}.

Find how fast the plane is travelling.

Chapter summary

Differentiation rules

- $f(x) = c \Rightarrow f'(x) = 0$ where $c \in \mathbb{R}$
- $f(x) = ax^n \Rightarrow f'(x) = anx^{n-1}$ where $a, n \in \mathbb{R}$
- $f(x) = e^x \Rightarrow f'(x) = e^x$
- $f(x) = \ln x \Rightarrow f'(x) = \dfrac{1}{x}$

If x is in radians, the derivatives of the trigonometric functions are

- $f(x) = \sin x \Rightarrow f'(x) = \cos x$
- $f(x) = \cos x \Rightarrow f'(x) = -\sin x$
- $f(x) = \tan x \Rightarrow f'(x) = \dfrac{1}{\cos^2 x}$

The chain rule for composite functions $y \times u(x)$

- $\dfrac{dy}{dx} = \dfrac{dy}{du} \times \dfrac{du}{dx}$

The product rule

- $\dfrac{d(uv)}{dx} = v\dfrac{du}{dx} + u\dfrac{dv}{dx}$

The quotient rule

- $\dfrac{d\left(\dfrac{u}{v}\right)}{dx} = \dfrac{v\dfrac{du}{dx} - u\dfrac{dv}{dx}}{v^2}$

Continued on next page

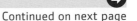

Calculus

Increasing and decreasing functions

- $f'(x) > 0 \Rightarrow f(x)$ is increasing
- $f'(x) < 0 \Rightarrow f(x)$ is decreasing

Second derivative

- $f''(x) > 0 \Rightarrow y = f(x)$ is concave up
- $f''(x) < 0 \Rightarrow y = f(x)$ is concave down
- If the concavity of the curve $y = f(x)$ changes either side of $x = c$ then $(c, f(c))$ is a point of inflexion.
- If the curve is differentiable then $f''(c) = 0$.

Optimization

Optimization is the process of finding the maximum or minimum points of a function.

This can be done using a GDC or solving $f'(x) = 0$.

If the function is continuous and the domain is restricted, the global maximum or minimum may occur at the boundary of the domain or where $f'(x) = 0$.

To decide whether a point, $(c, f(c))$, at which $f'(c) = 0$ is a maximum, a minimum or a horizontal point of inflexion, either

- plot the curve on a GDC
- find the value of $f''(c)$ to see if the curve is concave up, down or neither, or
- find the sign of $f'(x)$ either side of c.

Related rates

- Related rates look at the effect that a change in a particular rate has on another rate.
- To solve a related rates problem, write down the rate you are given and the rate you want and connect the two using the chain rule.

Developing inquiry skills

The marginal profit is the extra profit made or lost when increasing production by one unit.

1 Explain why the derivative of the profit function with respect to the number of goods produced is often used as an approximation for marginal profit.

Use the equation for profit found previously, namely, $P = 13000e^{-0.0792x}(x-3)$ where x is the price of the goods and the original equation for demand $d = 13000e^{-0.0792x}$. Assume that the amount produced is equal to the demand.

2 Use related rates to find an expression for the marginal cost, $\dfrac{\mathrm{d}P}{\mathrm{d}d}$ in terms of d.

3 Find an expression for $\dfrac{\mathrm{d}^2P}{\mathrm{d}d^2}$ and hence show the marginal profit is always decreasing.

Generally, if the marginal cost is positive, it is worth increasing production.

4 Use this rule to find the maximum value of d at which the factory should produce goods.

Click here for a mixed review exercise
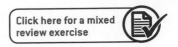

Chapter review

1 a Find the gradient of the curve

$$y = \frac{3}{2}x + 4x^2 \text{ at the point } (4,70).$$

b Find the point(s) on the curve

$$f(x) = 4x^{\frac{5}{4}} - 80x - 8 \text{ where the gradient}$$

is zero.

c Given that $r = 6 + 10t - 7t^2$, find the rate of change of r with respect to t at the instant when $t = 5$.

2 Find the derivative of the following functions.

a $f(x) = 2 \cos x + \sin 2x$ **b** $f(x) = \ln(\tan x)$

c $y = \dfrac{\cos x}{\sin x}$ **d** $y = xe^{2x}$

3 Find the first and second derivatives of each of the following.

a $f(x) = \dfrac{12}{x^2} + 3\sqrt{x}$ **b** $f(x) = (x-1)(3x-7)$

c $y = \dfrac{x-12}{x^2}$ **d** $y = \dfrac{x^2}{x-12}$

4 A function is defined by $f(x) = \dfrac{1}{e^{2x} + 1}$.

Show that the function is increasing for all values of x.

5 Find the point of intersection of the normals to the curve $y = 3x^2 - 7x + 8$ at the points $(2, 6)$ and $(0, 8)$.

a Find the coordinates of the point at which $\dfrac{dy}{dx} = 0$ for the curve

$$y = 7x - 14\sqrt{x}.$$

b Find an expression for $\dfrac{d^2y}{dx^2}$.

c **Hence**, state and justify whether the point found in part **a** is a maximum or minimum.

6 A rectangular enclosure is to be made in a field, using an existing wall as one side of the enclosure and 128 m of fencing to create the other three sides. Let x represent the length of the sides of the enclosure perpendicular to the wall.

a Find an expression for the area, A, of the enclosure in terms of x in its simplest form.

b Find the value of x for which A is a maximum.

c Find the maximum area of the enclosure.

7 The graph below represents the velocity v, in metres per second, of a particle moving along the x-axis over the time interval $t = 0$ to $t = 10$ seconds.

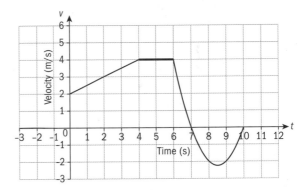

a At $t = 2$ s, determine whether the particle is moving to the right or left.

b Find the interval(s) in which the particle is moving **i** to the right **ii** to the left.

Explain your answer.

c At $t = 3$ s, determine whether the acceleration is positive or negative.

d Describe the motion of the particle in each of the intervals [0,4], [4,6], [6,7], [7, 8.5] and [8.5,10] in terms of direction of the motion, velocity and acceleration.

e Determine the time in the given interval when the particle is farthest to the right.

Calculus

8 Determine the value of x for which the gradient of the logistic function

$$f(x) = \frac{70}{1+e^{-2x+19}}$$ is at its maximum.

Hence, find the coordinates of the point of inflexion of $f(x - 5)$.

9 A particle is moving along the curve $y = \sqrt{x} + 3$. As the particle passes through the point $(1, 4)$, its x-coordinate is increasing at a rate of $2\,\mathrm{cm\,min^{-1}}$. Determine the rate of change of distance between the origin and the particle at this point.

Exam-style questions

10 P1: Find the equation of the normal to the curve $y = 2 - \dfrac{x^4}{2}$ at the point where $x = 1$

(7 marks)

11 P1: A curve is given by the equation

$$y = \frac{2x^3}{3} - \frac{7x^2}{2} + 2x + 5.$$

a Determine the coordinates on the curve where the gradient is -3. You must show all your working, and give your answers as exact fractions. (6 marks)

b Find the range of values of x for which the curve is decreasing.

(2 marks)

12 P2: A rectangular piece of paper, measuring 40 cm by 30 cm, has a small square of side length x cm cut from each corner. The flaps are then folded up to form an open box in the shape of a cuboid.

a Show that the volume V of the cuboid may be expressed as $V = 1200x - 140x^2 + 4x^3$. (3 marks)

b Find an expression for $\dfrac{dV}{dx}$.

(2 marks)

c Hence show that the cuboid will have a maximum volume when

$$x^2 - \frac{70}{3}x + 100 = 0.$$ (2 marks)

d Using technology, find the maximum possible volume of the cuboid.

(4 marks)

13 P2: Consider the function defined by

$$f(x) = \frac{x^2}{2x^3 - 1}, \quad x \neq \sqrt[3]{\frac{1}{2}}$$

a Find an expression for $f'(x)$.

(3 marks)

b Find the equation of the tangent to the curve at the point where $x = 1$.

(4 marks)

c Find the coordinates of the points on the curve where the gradient is zero.

(4 marks)

d Determine the range of values of x for which $f(x)$ is an increasing function. (2 marks)

14 P1: A right circular cone with fixed height 50 cm is increasing in volume at a rate of 2 cm³ min⁻¹. Find the rate at which the radius of the base r is increasing when $r = 0.4$ cm. Give your answer in exact form. (6 marks)

15 P1: A small object travels in a straight line so that its displacement, x metres, from a fixed point O after t seconds (where $0 \leq t < 5$) is given by the equation

$$x = \frac{t}{t-5} + 2\ln(1+t).$$

a Find the distance travelled by the object in the first two seconds.

(2 marks)

b Find an expression for $\dfrac{dx}{dt}$ and hence find the value of t when the particle is stationary. (6 marks)

16 P2: A small metal bearing is attached to the end of a vertical spring inside a tube of dense liquid.

At time t seconds ($t \geq 0$), the displacement (x metres) of the bearing from its equilibrium position is given by the equation $x = e^{-2t} \cos\sqrt{12}t$.

a Show that $\dfrac{d^2x}{dt^2} + 4\dfrac{dx}{dt} + 16x = 0$.

(6 marks)

b Sketch a graph of x against t for $0 \leq t \leq 2$.

(2 marks)

c Find the time when the bearing first comes to instantaneous rest and its distance from its equilibrium position at this time.

(4 marks)

d Find the maximum speed of the particle during its first second of motion and its distance from its equilibrium position at this time.

(5 marks)

River crossing

Approaches to learning: Thinking skills: Evaluate, Critiquing, Applying

Exploration criteria: Personal engagement (C), Reflection (D), Use of mathematics (E)

IB topic: Differentiation, Optimisation

Modelling and investigation activity

The problem

You are standing at the edge of a slow-moving river which is 1 kilometre wide. You want to return to your campground on the opposite side of the river. You can swim at 3 km/h and run at 8 km/h. You must first swim across the river to any point on the opposite bank. From there you must run to the campground, which is 2 km from the point directly across the river from where you start your swim.

What route will take the least amount of time?

Visualize the problem

Here is a diagram of this situation:

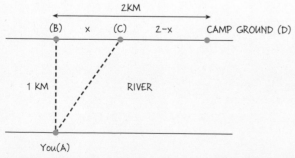

Discuss what each label in the diagram represents.

Solve the problem

What is the length of AC in terms of x?

Using the formula for time taken for travel at a constant rate of speed from this chapter, write down an expression in terms of x for:

1 the time taken to swim from A to C

2 the time taken to run from C to D.

Hence write down an expression for the total time taken, T, to travel from A to D in terms of x.

You want to minimize this expression (find the minimum time taken).

Find $\dfrac{dT}{dx}$.

Now solve $\dfrac{dT}{dx} = 0$ to determine the value of x that minimizes the time taken.

How do you know this is a valid value?

Use the second derivative test to show that the value you found is a minimum value.

For this value of x, find the minimum time possible and describe the route.

Assumptions made in the problem

The problem is perhaps more accurately stated as:

You are standing at the edge of a river. You want to return to your campground which you can see further down the river on the other side. You must first swim across the river to any point on the opposite bank. From there you must run to the campground.

What route will take the least amount of time?

Look back at the original problem.

What additional assumptions have been made in the original question?

What information in the question are you unlikely to know when you are standing at the edge of the river?

What additional information would you need to know to determine the shortest time possible?

The original problem is a simplified version of a real-life situation. Criticize the original problem, and the information given, as much as possible.

Extension

In an exploration it is important to reflect critically on any assumptions made and the subsequent significance and limitations of the results.

In this chapter you have been introduced to some classic optimisation problems in the examples and exercises. For example, there is the open-box problem in Q5 of Exercise 10E and Example 10 involving the surface area of a cylindrical can.

If you were writing an exploration and these problems were forming the basis or inspiration of that exploration, then:

- What assumptions have been made in the question?

- What information in the question are you unlikely to know in real-life?

- How could you find this missing information?

- What additional information would you need to know?

- Criticise the questions as much as possible!

11 Approximating irregular spaces: integration and differential equations

What do the graphs of functions that have the same derivative have in common? How do they differ?

This chapter explores integration, the reverse of differentiation. The area of an island, the surface area and volume of a building and the distance travelled by a moving object can all be represented by integrals. Integrals give you a way to estimate the values of areas and volumes that cannot be found using existing formulae.

Concepts
- Space
- Approximation

Microconcepts
- Lower limit
- Upper limit
- Antiderivative
- Definite integral
- Indefinite integral
- Numerical integration
- Reverse chain rule
- Area under the curve
- Volumes of revolution
- Exact solutions of differential equations
- Slope fields
- Euler's method

How can you find the distance travelled when the equation velocity is given?

How can you estimate the area covered by oil spills out at sea?

How can the volume of a building be found?

How can you find the amount of glass in this building?

San Cristóbal is the eastern most island of the Galapagos. Here is a map of the island.

It is claimed that the total area of the island is 558 km². How can you test this value?

Use a rectangle to estimate the area of the island.

How did you use the map scale?

Does your result underestimate or overestimate the claimed area? Why?

What would you do to improve your estimate?

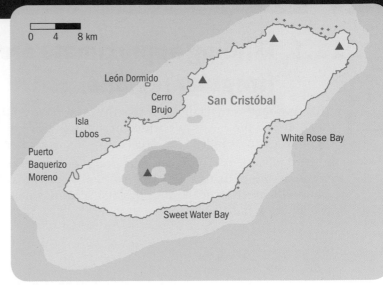

0   4   8 km

León Dormido

Cerro
Brujo

San Cristóbal

Isla
Lobos

White Rose Bay

Puerto
Baquerizo
Moreno

Sweet Water Bay

Developing inquiry skills

Write down any similar inquiry questions you might ask to model the area of something different, for example the area of a national park, city or lake in your country.

Think about the questions in this opening problem and answer any you can. As you work through the chapter, you will gain mathematical knowledge and skills that will help you to answer them all.

Before you start

Click here for help with this skills check

You should know how to:

1 Find the area of a trapezium.
   eg

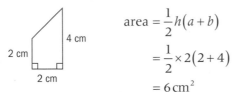

   $$\text{area} = \frac{1}{2}h(a+b)$$

   $$= \frac{1}{2} \times 2(2+4)$$

   $$= 6\,\text{cm}^2$$

2 Differentiate functions, including with the chain rule.
   eg If $f(x) = \sin 2x - \cos x^2$ then
   $f'(x) = 2\cos 2x + 2x \sin x^2$

Skills check

1 Find the area of the trapezium.

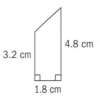

   4.8 cm

   3.2 cm

   1.8 cm

2 Differentiate each function.

   a $y = 3x^3 - 2\sqrt{x} + \dfrac{4}{x^2}$

   b $f(x) = \cos 5x + \sin^2 x$

   c $s = \ln 5t - 2e^{t^2}$

11.1 Finding approximate areas for irregular regions

In this chapter, you will discover that the area between the graph of a function and the x-axis can represent many things – distance, costs, total production or indeed an actual area – depending on the function.

Finding this value is clearly very important. For some functions the area can be found using calculus; for others, approximation methods or your GDC need to be used. In this first section, we use a GDC and approximation methods.

International-mindedness

Egyptian mathematician Ibn al-Haytham is credited with calculating the integral of a function in the 10th century.

Investigation 1

1 Consider the area bounded by the graph of the function $f(x) = x^2 + 1$, the vertical lines $x = 0, x = 2$ and the x-axis.

Estimate the area of the region. Is your estimation an overestimation or an underestimation of the actual area? Discuss your method with a classmate.

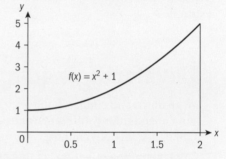

2 In this investigation, you will be using rectangles or vertical strips to estimate this area. At the end of the investigation you can check how close your estimation was to the actual area.

This graph shows four rectangles of the same width. The area under the graph of the function $f(x) = x^2 + 1$ between the vertical lines $x = 0, x = 2$ is also shown.

a What is the width of the rectangles? How did you calculate it?

b What is the relationship between the height of each rectangle and the graph of the function?

c Find the height of each of these rectangles.

d Find the area of each of these rectangles and then find **the sum** of the areas of these rectangles.

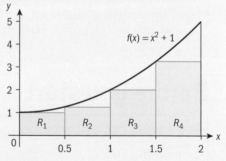

e Is this an underestimation or an overestimation of the actual area? Why?
The sum of these areas will be a **lower bound** of the area of under the curve. This will give an **underestimation** of the area.

3 This second graph shows another set of four rectangles with the same width. The area under the graph of the function $f(x) = x^2 + 1$ between the vertical lines $x = 0, x = 2$ is also shown.

a What is the width of each of these rectangles?

b Find the height of each of these rectangles.

c Find the area of each of these rectangles and then find **the sum** of the areas of these rectangles.

d Is this an underestimation or an overestimation of the actual area? Why?

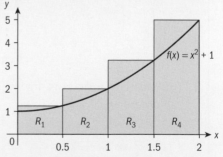

The sum of these areas will be an upper bound of the area under the curve. This will give an overestimate of the area.

e If L_S represents the lower bound, A represents the actual area and U_S represents the upper bound, write an inequality relating L_S, U_S and A.

4 In each of the following graphs there are six rectangles. The area under the graph of $f(x) = x^2 + 1$ between the vertical lines $x = 0$, $x = 2$ and the x-axis is also shaded.

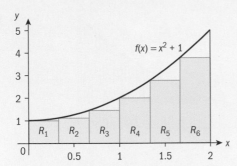 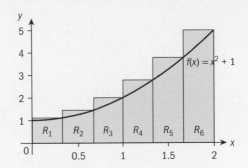

The area under the curve will now be approximated by finding new upper and lower bounds.

a Why do you think that more rectangles are being used?

b Complete the following tables to organize the information. You can create a table with your GDC to calculate the height of the rectangles. How would you calculate the widths? Remember that they are all equal.

Lower bound with six rectangles:

Rectangle	Width	Height	Area
R_1			
R_2			
R_3			
R_4			
R_5			
R_6			
			$L_S =$

Upper bound with six rectangles:

Rectangle	Width	Height	Area
R_1			
R_2			
R_3			
R_4			
R_5			
R_6			
			$U_S =$

c Have the lower and upper bounds approached each other if you compare their values to those found with four rectangles? How do you think these estimations can be improved?

d Write a new inequality relating L_S, U_S and A.

5 Look at the graphs below. The number of rectangles, n, has been increased in each case. L_S and U_S are also given.

$n = 20$, $L_S = 4.47$, $U_S = 4.87$:

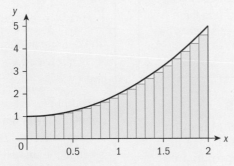 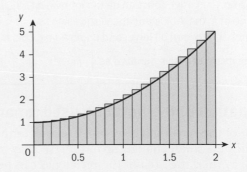

Continued on next page

Calculus

$n = 50$, $L_S = 4.5872$, $U_S = 4.7472$:

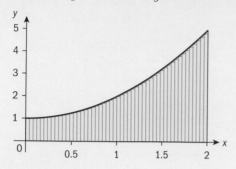
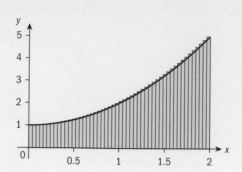

$n = 100$, $L_S = 4.6268$, $U_S = 4.7068$:

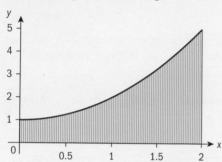
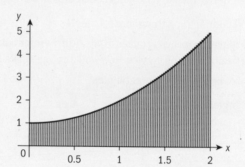

a   What can you say about the values of L_S as n increases?

b   What can you say about the values of U_S as n increases?
The table shows more values for n, L_S and U_S.

n	L_S	U_S
500	4.65867	4.67467
1000	4.66267	4.67087
10 000	4.66627	4.66707

c   What happens as n tends to infinity (gets larger and larger)? What can you say about the value of A?

When f is a non-negative function on the interval $a \leq x \leq b$, the area enclosed by the graph of f, the x-axis and the vertical lines $x = a$ and $x = b$ is the **unique** number between all lower and upper sums. This number is said to be the **definite integral** and is denoted as $\int_a^b f(x)\,dx$ or $\int_a^b y\,dx$.

HINT

$\int_a^b f(x)\,dx$ is read as

"the definite integral of $f(x)$ between $x = a$ and $x = b$".

The number a is called the **lower limit** of integration and b is called the **upper limit** of integration.

An explanation of the notation used for areas

If the width of the rectangle is δx (the Greek letter δ (delta) is often used to indicate a small change, so δx represents a small change in the value of x) then the area of the rectangles can be approximated as

$A \approx \sum_{i=1}^{n} y_i \times \delta x$. The actual area will be $A = \lim_{\delta x \to 0} \left(\sum_{i=1}^{n} y_i \delta x \right)$. To indicate that the limit is being taken, the Σ (Greek letter sigma) becomes an elongated S $\left(\int \right)$, the δx becomes dx and the bounds for x are added, hence the notation $\int_a^b y \, dx$.

Investigation 1 (continued)

6 What is the lower limit of integration in the investigation? What is the upper limit of integration? Is the function positive between the lower and the upper limit? How would you represent A using definite integral notation?

7 **Conceptual** How do areas under curves within a given interval relate to the definite integral and to lower and upper rectangle sums on the same interval?

Reflect What is a definite integral?

Example 1

a Write down a definite integral that gives the area of the shaded region.

b Calculate the definite integral by using the formula for a trapezoid.

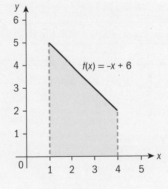

a $\int_1^4 (-x+6)\,dx$	The lower limit is $x = 1$.
	The upper limit is $x = 4$.
	The function is $f(x) = -x + 6$.
b $\int_1^4 (-x+6)\,dx = \dfrac{3}{2} \times (2+5) = 10.5$	The shape is trapezoidal.
	$a = f(1) = -1 + 6 = 5$
	$b = f(4) = -4 + 6 = 2$
	Height $= 4 - 1 = 3$ and substitute this into the trapezoid area formula.

Calculus

Exercise 11A

1 The equation for a circle centred at $(0,0)$ with radius 3 is $x^2 + y^2 = 9$. The sector of the circle in the first quadrant is shown below.

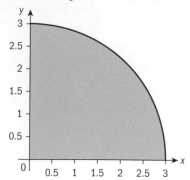

a **i** Find the equation of this sector in the form $y = f(x)$, carefully stating the domain.

ii Write an expression for the area of the sector in the form $\int_a^b f(x)\,dx$.

Parts **b** and **c** should be done using a spreadsheet or other technology.

b Calculate the values of y for the given values of x.

x	0	0.5	1.0	1.5	2.0	2.5	3.0
y							

c Use the table and the following diagrams to calculate the sum of the areas of the rectangles that form:

i a lower bound

ii an upper bound for the area of the sector.

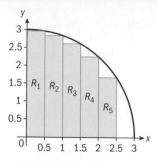

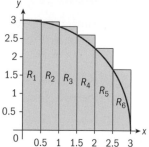

d Find the mean of your upper bound and lower bound.

e Find the percentage error in using the answer to part **d** as an estimate for the area of the quarter circle.

2 A region R is formed by the curve $y = \dfrac{1}{x}$, the x-axis and the lines $x = 1$ and $x = 6$.

a Sketch the graph of the curve and shade the region R.

b Write an expression for the area R in the form $\int_a^b f(x)\,dx$.

c Use five rectangles to find

i a lower bound

ii an upper bound for the area of R.

d Write down an expression for the area of R as an inequality in the form $p < R < q$.

Using the GDC to evaluate areas

It is a requirement in the exam that your GDC can calculate areas between the curve and the x-axis (equivalent to finding the **definite integral** when the function is positive).

Use your GDC to find the value of $\int_0^2 (x^2 + 1)\,dx$ and compare your answer with the bounds obtained in Investigation 1.

International-mindedness

The definite integral notation was introduced by the German mathematician Gottfried Wilhelm von Leibniz towards the end of the 17th century.

Example 2

Find the area shown by

a using the formula for the area of a trapezium

b using the integral function on your calculator.

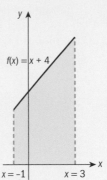

$f(x) = x + 4$

$x = -1$ $x = 3$

a The function in this case is $f(x) = x + 4$. The lower limit is $x = -1$ and the upper limit is $x = 3$. Hence the two parallel lines have lengths of 3 and 7. The area is therefore $\dfrac{1}{2} \times 4(3+7) = 20$.	The shape is trapezoidal. The parallel sides of the trapezium are a and b. $a = f(-1) = -1 + 4 = 3$ $b = f(3) = 3 + 4 = 7$ Height $= 3 - (-1) = 4$ Substitute into the trapezium area formula.
b $\displaystyle\int_{-1}^{3}(x+4)\,\mathrm{d}x = 20$	The area can be calculated directly from the GDC.

Example 3

Consider the area A of the region enclosed between the curve $y = -x(x-3)$ and the x-axis.

a Write down the definite integral that represents this area A.

b Find A.

a $\displaystyle\int_{0}^{3} -x(x-3)\,\mathrm{d}x$	You first have to identify the region. Using the GDC: 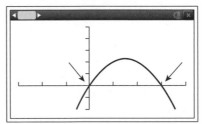 From the graph it can be seen that the lower and upper bounds are the **roots** of the parabola. $x = 0$ is one of the roots, the lower bound of the definite integral. $x = 3$ is the other root, the upper bound of the definite integral.
b $A = 4.5$	Once you have identified the region, write down the definite integral.

Example 4

The region bounded by the graph of $f(x) = x^2 + 3$, the x-axis and the vertical lines $x = -1$ and $x = a$ with $a > -1$ has area equal to 12.

Find the value of a.

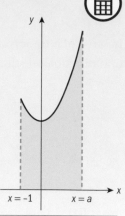

$\displaystyle\int_{-1}^{a}\left(x^2 + 3\right)dx = 12$	The unknown, a, is the upper bound of this area.
$a = 2$	First write down the definite integral.
	Use your GDC to find the value of a.

Exercise 11B

1 For each of the following:

  i write down the definite integral that represents the area of the enclosed region.

  ii find the area.

  a $y = x^2$, the x-axis and the lines $x = 2$ and $x = 4$

  b $y = 2^x$, the x-axis and the lines $x = -1$ and $x = 1$

  c $y = \dfrac{1}{1 + x^2}$ and the x-axis in the interval $-1 \le x \le 1$

  d $y = \dfrac{1}{x}$ and the x-axis in the interval $0.5 \le x \le 3$

  e $f(x) = -(x - 3)(x + 2)$, the vertical axis and the vertical line $x = 1$

  f $f(x) = -(x - 3)(x + 2)$, the vertical axis and the horizontal axis

  g $f(x) = -(x - 3)(x + 2)$ and the horizontal axis

  h $f(x) = -x^2 + 2x + 15$ and the vertical lines $x = -2$ and $x = 4.5$

  i $f(x) = -x^2 + 2x + 15$ and the line $y = 0$

  j $f(x) = 3 - e^x$, the vertical line $x = -1$ and the x-axis

  k $y = (x + 2)^3 + 5$ and the coordinate axes

2 Consider the curve $y = -x^2 + 4$.

  a Find the x-intercepts of this curve.

  b Find the point where this curve cuts the y-axis.

The following graph shows a piecewise function f made up of a horizontal line segment and part of the parabola $y = -x^2 + 4$. The area under the graph of f and above the x-axis has been shaded.

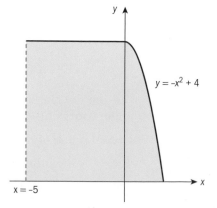

c Find the area under the graph of f in the interval $-5 \le x \le 0$.

d **i** Write down an expression for the area under the graph of f and above the x-axis for $x > 0$.

ii Find the area.

e Find the shaded area.

3 The region bounded by the graph of $f(x) = -(x+1)(x-5)$, the x-axis, the y-axis and the line $x = a$ where $0 \le a \le 5$ has area equal to 24. Find the value of a.

4 The region bounded by the graph of $f(x) = 2^{-x}$ and the x-axis between $x = -3$ and $x = a$ where $a > -3$ has area equal to 9. Find the value of a. Give your answer correct to 4 significant figures.

Negative integrals

Investigation 2

1 Use your GDC to evaluate the following definite integrals.

a $A = \int_0^1 (x^2 - 1)\mathrm{d}x$ **b** $B = \int_1^2 (x^2 - 1)\mathrm{d}x$ **c** $C = \int_0^2 (x^2 - 1)\mathrm{d}x$

2 Find an equation linking A, B and C.

3 **a** Sketch the curve $y = x^2 - 1$ for $0 \le x \le 2$.

b Why is the **area** bounded by the curve, the x-axis and the lines $x = 0$ and $x = 2$ not equal to $\int_0^2 (x^2 - 1)\mathrm{d}x$?

c **Factual** What do you notice about the definite integral when a function is below the x-axis?

4 **a** Sketch the graph of $y = |x^2 - 1|$.

b How might you use your GDC to find the **area** bounded by the curve, the x-axis and the lines $x = 1$ and $x = 2$?

5 **Conceptual** When evaluating areas bounded by curves, what must you consider when evaluating the definite integral?

If $f(x) < 0$ throughout an interval $a \le x \le b$ then $\int_a^b f(x)\,\mathrm{d}x < 0$.

If the area bounded by the curve $y = f(x)$ and the lines $x = a$ and $x = b$ is required and if $f(x) < 0$ for any values in this interval then the area should be calculated using $\int_a^b |f(x)|\,\mathrm{d}x$.

Example 5

a Sketch the curve $y = 2e^{0.5x} - 3$ for $0 \leq x \leq 3$.

b Find the area of the region bounded by the curve, the x-axis and the lines $x = 0$ and $x = 2$.

a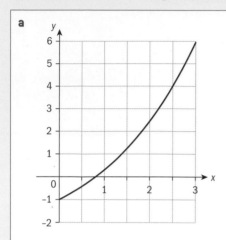

b $\displaystyle\int_0^2 \left| 2e^{0.5x} - 3 \right| dx \approx 1.74$

Because some of the curve lies below the x-axis, the modulus of the function is integrated.

1 a Sketch $y = \sin 2x$ for $0 \leq x \leq \pi$.

b Find the area of the region bounded by the curve, the x-axis and the following pairs of lines.

   i $x = 0$ and $x = 0.5$

   ii $x = 2$ and $x = 3$

   iii $x = 0$ and $x = 2.5$

2 a Sketch the curve $y = \dfrac{4}{x-2} - 2$.

b Explain why it is not possible to calculate $\displaystyle\int_0^3 \left(\dfrac{4}{x-2} - 2 \right) dx$.

c Find the area of the region bounded by the curve, the x-axis and the lines given.

   i $x = 3$ and $x = 4$ **ii** $x = 4$ and $x = 6$

d Hence or otherwise find the area of the region bounded by the curve, the x-axis and the lines $x = 3$ and $x = 6$.

The trapezoidal (trapezium) rule

Sometimes it is not possible to use a calculator to work out areas, in particular in those cases where the equation of the function is not known. Though it would be possible to approximate the area using rectangles and finding the sum, a more accurate method is usually to divide the area between the curve and the x-axis into a series of trapezoids, as shown in the investigation below.

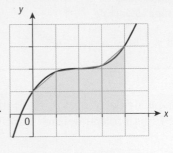

Investigation 3

The area beneath the curve $y = f(x)$ is to be found by approximating it using four trapezoids.

The formula for the area of a trapezoid is $A = \dfrac{1}{2}h(a+b)$ where a and b

are the lengths of the two parallel sides and h is the perpendicular distance between the two sides. h is often referred to as the height of the trapezoid, though in the trapezoids shown it would be more natural to refer to the width.

Let the width of each trapezoid be h and the lengths of the parallel sides be y_0, y_1, y_2, y_3 and y_4.

1 Write down an expression for the area of each trapezoid and show that the sum can be written as

$$\frac{1}{2}h\left(y_0 + y_4 + 2\left(y_1 + y_2 + y_3\right)\right).$$

2 Conjecture an expression for the approximate area between a curve and the x-axis found by using n trapezoids with the first parallel line having length y_0 and the last y_n.

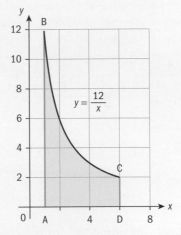

3 Consider the curve $y = \dfrac{12}{x}$, where $1 \le x \le 6$.

The area of the region enclosed between the graph of $f(x) = \dfrac{12}{x}$

and the x-axis in the interval $1 \le x \le 6$ will be called S.

a Write down an expression for S and find its value using your GDC. Give your answer correct to 2 decimal places.

This graph shows the shaded area subdivided into five trapezoids.

b Find the width (h) of each of the trapezoids.

c Use $f(x) = \dfrac{12}{x}$ to find the lengths of the vertical sides for

each of the trapezoids.

d Hence, use the rule conjectured in question **2** to find an approximation for S.

e Find the percentage error for this approximation.

The area of S will now be approximated using 10 trapezoids.

f Find the value of h.

g Find the lengths of the parallel sides of the trapezoids and hence, use the formula conjectured in question **2** to show that $S \approx 21.74$ correct to 2 decimal places.

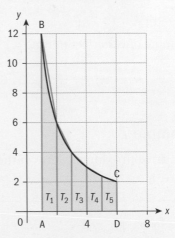

h Find the percentage error for this approximation.

i What will be the limit of the sum of the areas of the trapezoids as the number of trapezoids tends to infinity?

4 **Conceptual** How can we estimate the area underneath a curve?

5 **Conceptual** How do we make this approximation more accurate?

For a positive continuous function, the area (A) between the graph of the function, the x-axis and the lines $x = a$ and $x = b$ can be approximated by the trapezoidal rule.

$$A \approx \frac{1}{2}h\big(y_0 + y_n + 2(y_1 + \dots + y_{n-1})\big) \text{ where } h = \frac{b-a}{n}$$

It is particularly useful when the values on a curve are known, but not the function that defines the curve.

Example 6

The cross-section of a river in which the water is flowing at $0.8\,\text{m s}^{-1}$ is shown in the diagram. Use the trapezoidal rule, with seven trapezoids, to find an approximation for the volume of water passing this point in one minute. All lengths are in metres.

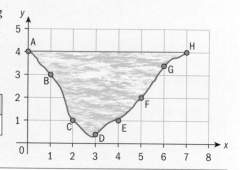

A	B	C	D	E	F	G	H
(0, 4)	(1, 3)	(2, 1)	(3, 0.4)	(4, 1)	(5, 2)	(6, 3.4)	(7, 4)

$A \approx \dfrac{1}{2} \times 1\big(4 + 4 + 2(3 + 1 + 0.4 + 1 + 2 + 3.4)\big)$	The lengths of the parallel lines are given by the y-coordinates in the table.
$= \dfrac{1}{2} \times 29.6 = 14.8\,\text{m}^2$	The trapezoidal rule is applied to these values.
Cross-sectional area of river is	
$28 - 14.8 = 13.2\,\text{m}^2$	
Volume of water per minute $= 13.2 \times 0.8 \times 60$ $\approx 634\,\text{m}^3$	Volume of water is the amount that passes per second multiplied by 60.

Example 7

Find an approximate value of the integral $\displaystyle\int_1^4 \sin^2 x\,dx$ using the trapezoidal rule with four intervals.

$A \approx \displaystyle\int_1^4 (\sin^2 x)\,dx$	The definite integral is the same as the area under the graph of the function when the function is always positive. You must always use radians for trigonometric functions unless told otherwise.
$h = \dfrac{4-1}{4} = 0.75$	

$$A = \frac{0.75}{2}\left[\begin{array}{c} \sin^2(1) + \sin^2(4) + 2\sin^2(1.75) \\ + 2\sin^2(2.5) + 2\sin^2(3.25) \end{array}\right]$$

$A \approx 1.4839$

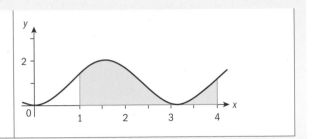

Exercise 11D

1 Use the trapezoidal rule to estimate the area under a curve over the interval $1 \le x \le 9$, with the x and y values given in the following table.

x	1	3	5	7	9
y	5	7	6	10	4

2 Use the trapezoidal rule to estimate the area under a curve over the interval $0 \le x \le 6$, with the x and y values given in the following table.

x	0	1.5	3	4.5	6
y	1	4	2	5.5	0

3 Use the trapezoidal rule to estimate the area under the graph of $y = f(x)$ using the data points given in the diagram.

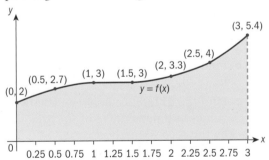

4 Use the trapezoidal rule to estimate the area under the graph of $y = f(x)$ using the data points given in the diagram.

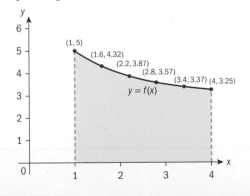

5 Use the trapezoidal rule to estimate the area between each curve and the x-axis over the given interval. Give your answers to 4 significant figures.

a $f(x) = \sqrt{x}$, interval $0 \le x \le 4$ with $n = 5$

b $f(x) = 2x$, interval $-1 \le x \le 4$ with $n = 4$

c $f(x) = \dfrac{10}{x} + 1$, interval $2 \le x \le 5$ with $n = 6$

d $y = -0.5x(x - 5)(x + 1)$, interval $0 \le x \le 5$ with $n = 5$

6 The diagram below shows the outline of a lake. The coordinates of seven points on the edge of the lake are given. All measurements are in kilometres.

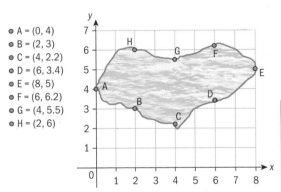

A = (0, 4)
B = (2, 3)
C = (4, 2.2)
D = (6, 3.4)
E = (8, 5)
F = (6, 6.2)
G = (4, 5.5)
H = (2, 6)

a Use the trapezoidal rule with four intervals to find the area below the curve marking the upper boundary of the lake (through the points A, H, G, F and E) and the x-axis.

b Repeat for the area below the curve marking the lower boundary of the lake.

c Hence find an approximation for the area of the lake.

Calculus

485

7 Consider the region enclosed by the curve $y = -2(x - 3)(x - 6)$ and the x-axis.

  a Sketch the curve and shade the region.

  b **i** Write down a definite integral that represents the area of this region.

  ii Find the area of this region.

  c Use the trapezoidal rule with $n = 6$ trapezoids to estimate the area of this region.

  d Find the percentage error made with the estimation made in part **c**.

8 Consider the region enclosed by the graph of the function $f(x) = 1 + e^x$, the x-axis and the vertical lines $x = 0$ and $x = 2$.

  a Sketch the function f and shade the region.

  b **i** Write down a definite integral that represents the area of this region.

  ii Find the area of this region. Give your answer correct to 4 significant figures.

  c Use the trapezoidal rule with $n = 5$ trapeziums to estimate the area of this region. Give your answer correct to 4 significant figures.

  d Find the percentage error made with the estimation found in part **c**.

9 The picture below shows the L'Oceanogràfic, a building in Valencia, Spain. Use the trapezoidal rule with four trapezoids to estimate the area of the window, given that the points A, B, C, D and E have coordinates $(0,0)$, $(1, 1.8)$, $(2, 3.7)$, $(3, 5)$, and $(4, 5.5)$.

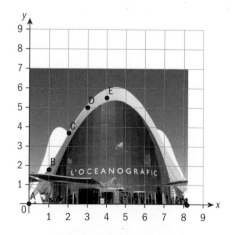

10 A surveyor needs to work out the area of the old window shown in the diagram below. Based on a coordinate system with the origin in the bottom left-hand corner of the window, the points A, B, C and D have coordinates $(0,6)$, $(1, 8.5)$, $(2, 9.4)$ and $(3, 10)$

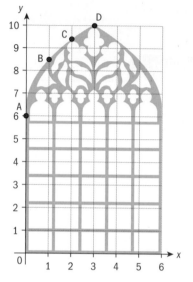

  a Use the trapezoidal rule to find an approximation for the area of the window.

A mathematician suggests to the surveyor that he might get a more accurate result if he fits a cubic curve through the four points.

  b Find the area of the window using this method.

  c Find the difference between the two values as a percentage of the area found by the second method.

Developing inquiry skills

In the opening problem for this chapter you looked at how to estimate the area of San Cristobal.

Use the trapezoidal rule to work out an estimate of the area using the points given. Compare your answer with the officially given figure of 558 km².

A	B	C	D	E	F	G	H	I	J
$(5, 15)$	$(14, 22)$	$(23, 27.5)$	$(32, 37)$	$(41, 40)$	$(50, 37)$	$(41, 26)$	$(32, 16)$	$(23, 12.5)$	$(14, 11)$

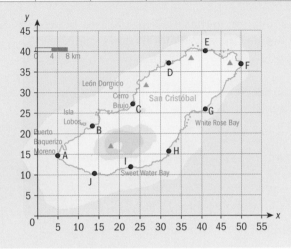

11.2 Indefinite integrals and techniques of integration

Investigation 4

With your GDC in radian mode, on the same set of axes, sketch the graphs of

   i $y = \sin x$ **ii** $y = \sin x + 1$ **iii** $y = \sin x - 1$ **iv** $y = \sin x + 2$.

1   How can you describe their relative positions?

2   Write down the gradient of each of these curves when $x = \dfrac{\pi}{2}$.

3   Use your GDC to find the gradient of each of these curves when $x = 0$.

4   Differentiate each of these functions to find an expression for the gradient at x.

5   Write down another curve for which the gradient at x is the same as the gradient of any of these curves.

6   **Factual**   What is the formula of **any** curve whose gradient is the same as the gradient of the above curves?

7   **Conceptual**   What does finding the indefinite integral lead to?

All these curves make up a **family of functions** with the same derivative.

The family of curves whose derivative is $\cos x$ can be written using the following notation:

$$\int \cos x \, dx = \sin x + c$$

$\int \cos x \, dx$ is the **indefinite integral** of $\cos x$.

We would say, "the integral of $\cos x$ is $\sin x + c$".

Reflect What is an indefinite integral?

The reason for the similar notation to that used for the area between a curve and the x-axis will become apparent later in this section.

Anti-derivatives

A function F is called an antiderivative or integral of f on an interval $[a, b]$ if $F'(x) = f(x)$ for all $x \in [a, b]$. That is,

$$\int f(x) \, dx = F(x) + c$$

The process of finding an antiderivative is called **integration**.

For example,

- $F(x) = 3x$ is an integral of $f(x) = 3$ because $F'(x) = 3$.

- $F(x) = x^2 + 1$ is an integral of $f(x) = 2x$ because $F'(x) = 2x$.

- $F(x) = \cos x$ is an integral of $f(x) = -\sin x$ because $F'(x) = -\sin x$.

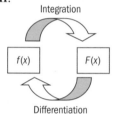

> **TOK**
>
> Is imagination more important than knowledge?

> **HINT**
>
> $[a, b]$ is equivalent to writing $a \leq x \leq b$.

Investigation 5

1 Write down the antiderivative of

   a $f(x) = x$ **b** $f(x) = x^2$ **c** $f(x) = x^3$

2 Conjecture an expression for the antiderivative of $f(x) = x^n$ where $n \in \mathbb{R}$.

3 Verify your conjecture by first integrating then differentiating the following expressions for

   a $f(x) = x^5$ **b** $f(x) = \sqrt{x}$ **c** $f(x) = \dfrac{1}{x^2} + x$

4 Conjecture an expression for the antiderivative of $f(x) = ax^n$ where $n, a \in \mathbb{R}$.

5 Write down the antiderivative of $f(x) = 12x^5 + 3x^2 + 4x + 7$, and verify your answer by differentiating.

6 **a** Use your conjectured formula to try to find the antiderivative of $f(x) = x^{-1}$.

   b Explain why you cannot obtain a solution.

   c From your knowledge of Chapter 10, write down the antiderivative of $f(x) = x^{-1}$, $x > 0$.

   d The graph of $y = \ln|x|$ is shown here. Given your conjecture in part **c** explain why the antiderivative of $f(x) = x^{-1}$, $x \neq 0$ will be $\ln|x|$.

7 Write down the antiderivative of

   a $f(x) = \sin x$ **b** $f(x) = \cos x$ **c** $f(x) = \dfrac{1}{\cos^2 x}$ **d** $f(x) = e^x$

8 a Use the chain rule to differentiate

    i $f(x) = \sin 4x$ **ii** $f(x) = \cos 5x$ **iii** $f(x) = e^{7x}$

b Hence, find the antiderivatives of

    i $f(x) = \cos 4x$ **ii** $f(x) = \sin 5x$ **iii** $f(x) = e^{7x}$

c Conjecture an expression for the antiderivatives of

    i $f(x) = \cos ax$ **ii** $f(x) = \sin ax$ **iii** $f(x) = e^{ax}$

9 **Factual** What are the antiderivative rules?

10 **Conceptual** How can you evaluate antiderivatives given what you already know about derivatives?

$\int f(x)\,dx$ is an indefinite integral and the process of finding the **indefinite integral** is called **integration**.

If $\dfrac{d}{dx}\big[F(x)\big] = f(x)$, then $\int f(x)\,dx = F(x) + c$ where c is an arbitrary constant.

$F(x)$ is an antiderivative of $f(x)$.

Rules for integration can be derived from those for differentiation:

- The sum/difference of functions: $\int\big(f(x) \pm g(x)\big)\,dx = \int f(x)\,dx \pm \int g(x)\,dx$

- Multiplying a function by a constant: $\int af(x)\,dx = a\int f(x)\,dx$

- Power rule: $\int ax^n\,dx = \dfrac{ax^{n+1}}{n+1} + c$

- $\int \sin x = -\cos x + c$

- $\int \cos x = \sin x + c$

- $\int \dfrac{1}{x}\,dx = \ln|x| + c$

- $\int e^x\,dx = e^x + c$

- $\int \dfrac{1}{\cos^2 x}\,dx = \tan x + c$

In addition:

- $\int \sin ax\,dx = -\dfrac{1}{a}\cos ax + c$

- $\int \cos ax\,dx = \dfrac{1}{a}\sin ax + c$

- $\int e^{ax}\,dx = \dfrac{1}{a}e^{ax} + c$

International-mindedness

The successful calculation of the volume of a pyramidal frustum was conducted by ancient Egyptians and seen in the Moscow mathematical papyrus.

Calculus

Example 8

Find each of the following.

a $\int(x^2+3)dx$ **b** $\int\dfrac{x^2+3}{x^2}dx$ **c** $\int\cos 3t\,dt$

a $\int(x^2+3)dx = \dfrac{1}{3}x^3+3x+c$	Apply the power rule of integration.
b $\int\dfrac{x^2+3}{x^2}dx = \int(1+3x^{-2})dx$	Separate the terms and write as a negative exponent.
$= x-\dfrac{3}{x}+c$	Apply the power rule.
c $\int\cos 3t\,dt = \dfrac{\sin 3t}{3}+c$	As with differentiation, any letter can be used for the variable.

Example 9

The curve $y=f(x)$ passes through the point $(1,3)$. The gradient function of the curve is given by $f'(x)=2-\dfrac{x}{3}$. Find the equation of the curve.

$f(x)=\int(2-\dfrac{x}{3})dx = 2x-\dfrac{1}{3}\times\dfrac{x^2}{2}+c$	Apply the power rule to find an antiderivative of $f'(x)$.
$= 2x-\dfrac{x^2}{6}+c$	
$f(1)=2\times 1-\dfrac{1^2}{6}+c$	If the curve passes through the point $(1,3)$ then $f(1)=3$.
$3=2-\dfrac{1}{6}+c$	
$c=\dfrac{7}{6}$	
Therefore, $f(x)=2x-\dfrac{x^2}{6}+\dfrac{7}{6}$	

Exercise 11E

1 Find the following indefinite integrals.

a $\int 10\,dx$

b $\int 0.6x^2 dx$

c $\int x^5 dx$

d $\int(7-2x)dx$

e $\int(1+2x)dx$

f $\int\left(5+x-\dfrac{1}{3}x^2\right)dx$

g $\int\left(-x+\dfrac{3x^2}{4}+0.5\right)dx$ **h** $\int\left(1-x+\dfrac{x^3}{2}\right)dx$

i $\int\left(x^2-\dfrac{1}{2}x+4\right)dx$

2 For $f(x) = x^2 - \dfrac{x}{3} + 4$, find

  a $f'(x)$ **b** $\int f(x)\,dx$

3 a Find $\int (t - 3t^2)\,dt$.

  b Find $\int (4t^3 - 3t + 1)\,dt$.

4 a Sketch on the same axes the curves $y = f(x)$ given that $f'(x) = 4x + 8$ and:

    i $f(0) = 1$ **ii** $f(0) = 4$

  b Write down the vertex for each of the curves.

5 Find

  a $\int 2\sin x\,dx$

  b $\int 4\cos x\,dx$

  c $\int \dfrac{\sin x}{3}\,dx$

  d $\int \dfrac{3}{\cos^2 x}\,dx$.

6 Find

  a $\int 2e^x\,dx$

  b $\int \left(3e^x + \dfrac{1}{x}\right)dx$

  c $\int \left(\dfrac{4}{x} - 3e^x\right)dx$.

7 Find

  a $\int 2e^{3x}\,dx$

  b $\int 2\sin 5t\,dt$

  c $\int (4 - 2e^{-3x})\,dx$

  d $\int (\cos 2t - \sin 3t)\,dt$.

8 Find the following indefinite integrals.

  a $\int \sqrt{5t}\,dt$

  b $\int \pi x^{-\frac{2}{3}}\,dx$

c $\int (a^3 - 3a^2 + 2)\,da$

d $\int \sqrt{\dfrac{1}{x}}\,dx$

e $\int \dfrac{x^2 + 2x + 3}{x}\,dx$

f $\int (e^{2x} + 3\sin 4x)\,dx$

g $\int \dfrac{\sqrt{x} - \cos 4x}{3}\,dx$

9 a If $y = \dfrac{1}{\sin(x)}$

    i find $\dfrac{dy}{dx}$

    ii hence, find $\int \dfrac{\cos x}{\sin^2 x}\,dx$.

  b If $y = \sqrt{4x - 1}$

    i find $\dfrac{dy}{dx}$

    ii hence, find $\int \dfrac{1}{\sqrt{4x-1}}\,dx$.

10 It is given that $\dfrac{dy}{dx} = x + \dfrac{x^2}{5} + 2$ and that $y = 3$ when $x = 4$. Find an expression for y in terms of x.

11 It is given that $f'(x) = 3 - x$ and $f(3) = 2$. Find $f(x)$.

12 Given $\dfrac{dy}{dx} = \cos 2x + 2\sin 2x$ and $y = 5$ when $x = \dfrac{\pi}{4}$, find an expression for y in terms of x.

13 Given $\dfrac{dy}{dx} = 8e^{4x} + 3x^2 + 1$ and $y = 4$ when $x = 0$, find an expression for y in terms of x.

Chain rule and reverse chain rule

The **chain rule** is a **rule** for differentiating compositions of functions.

If $y = f(g(x))$ then $\dfrac{dy}{dx} = f'(g(x)) \times g'(x)$.

We can reverse this rule to extend the range of functions we can integrate.

$$\int g'(x) \times f'(g(x)) dx = f(g(x)) + c$$

To use this method, we need to look for a composite function multiplied by the derivative of the interior (first) function.

Consider $\int 2x(x^2 + 5)^4 dx$. We see that this is of the required form.

When you have had plenty of practice at these, they can be quickly solved but initially it might be helpful to use a similar method to when you learning the chain rule, and call the interior function u.

The integral becomes $\int 2x(u)^4 dx$, but dx needs to become du to match the variable we wish to use for the integration.

We know that $u = x^2 + 5$ so $\dfrac{du}{dx} = 2x$.

A trick is to say that this can be split to give the equation $du = 2x\,dx$

or $dx = \dfrac{du}{2x}$.

Although the derivative notation is not really a fraction, it is often used like one.

The integral now becomes $\int 2xu^4 \dfrac{du}{2x} = \int u^4 du$.

This can now be integrated in the usual way:

$$\int u^4 du = \frac{1}{5}u^5 + c$$

Finally, substitute back the expression for u:

$$\int 2x(x^2 + 5)^4 dx = \frac{1}{5}(x^2 + 5)^5 + c$$

The reverse chain rule methods can be used whenever the integral consists of the product of a composite function and a multiple of the derivative of the interior function. In these cases, this function will cancel when the substitution is made.

- The interior function is replaced by the variable u.

- $\dfrac{du}{dx}$ is evaluated and dx is replaced by $\dfrac{du}{\left(\dfrac{du}{dx}\right)}$

- Any possible cancelling should then be carried out.

- The remaining function is integrated.

- The expression for x is substituted back in for u.

Example 10

Find the indefinite integral $\int x\sqrt{3-x^2}\,dx$.

$u = 3 - x^2$	Define u.
$\dfrac{du}{dx} = -2x$	Evaluate $\dfrac{du}{dx}$.
$\Rightarrow dx = \dfrac{du}{-2x}$	
$\displaystyle\int xu^{\frac{1}{2}}\dfrac{du}{-2x}$	Rearrange and substitute into the integral.
$= -\dfrac{1}{2}\displaystyle\int u^{\frac{1}{2}}du$	Cancel and move any constant factors outside the integral.
$= -\dfrac{1}{3}u^{\frac{3}{2}} + c$	Integrate the remaining function.
$= -\dfrac{1}{3}\left(3 - x^2\right)^{\frac{3}{2}} + c$	Substitute back into the original integration.

Example 11

Find the equation of the curve passing through $(2, 1)$ with $\dfrac{dy}{dx} = e^{2x-2}$.

$y = \displaystyle\int \left(e^{2x\ 2}\right)dx$	e^{2x-2} is a composite function. Although it does not look like a product, the derivative of the interior function is 2 rather than a function of x, hence the method can be used.
$u = 2x - 2$	Define u.
$\dfrac{du}{dx} = 2 \Rightarrow dx = \dfrac{1}{2}du$	
$\displaystyle\int e^u \dfrac{1}{2}du = \dfrac{1}{2}\displaystyle\int e^u du$	Substitute u and du.
$= \dfrac{1}{2}e^u + c$	
$\Rightarrow y = \dfrac{1}{2}e^{2x-2} + c$	

Continued on next page

Calculus

$1 = \dfrac{1}{2}e^2 + c$	
$\Rightarrow c = 1 - \dfrac{1}{2}e^2 \approx -2.69$	Substitute $(2, 1)$ and solve for c.
$\Rightarrow y = \dfrac{1}{2}e^{2x-2} - 2.69$	Write down the equation of the curve passing through $(2, 1)$.

Exercise 11F

1 Using the substitution $u = 4x - 1$, find the following indefinite integrals.

  a $\displaystyle\int (4x-1)^2\, dx$ **b** $\displaystyle\int \dfrac{1}{(4x-1)^2}\, dx$

  c $\displaystyle\int \dfrac{1}{\sqrt{4x-1}}\, dx$ **d** $\displaystyle\int \dfrac{3}{4x-1}\, dx$

2 Find

  a $\displaystyle\int 4(2x+3)\, dx$ **b** $\displaystyle\int 2xe^{1+x^2}\, dx$

  c $\displaystyle\int 4\sec^2(4+2x)\, dx$ **d** $\displaystyle\int \dfrac{1}{2x+3}\, dx$

  e $\displaystyle\int 4x\cos(x^2+2)\, dx$ **f** $\displaystyle\int \cos x\sin^2 x\, dx.$

3 Given that the gradient function of a curve is $\dfrac{dy}{dx} = x + \dfrac{1}{x+2}$ and the curve passes through the point $(0, 3)$, find the equation of the curve.

4 Use a suitable substitution or the reverse chain rule to find the following integrals.

  a $\displaystyle\int \cos(3x)e^{\sin 3x}\, dx$

  b $\displaystyle\int (x-3)(x^2-6x+4)^5\, dx$

5 **a** Find $\displaystyle\int \tan x\, dx$ using the identity $\tan x = \dfrac{\sin x}{\cos x}.$

  b Hence, solve $\dfrac{d^2y}{dx^2} = \dfrac{1}{\cos^2 x}$ given that $\dfrac{dy}{dx} = 3$ when $x = \dfrac{\pi}{4}$ and $y = 4$ when $x = 0.$

6 **a** Find an expression in the form $\dfrac{y^2}{a} + \dfrac{x^2}{b} = 1$ for the curve (an ellipse) with gradient function $\dfrac{dy}{dx} = -\dfrac{3}{2}\dfrac{x}{\sqrt{4-x^2}},$ given that when $x = 2$, $y = 0.$

  b Find the y-intercepts and hence, sketch the curve.

  c Find the area contained within the ellipse.

  d If the area is equal to $c\pi$ where $c \in \mathbb{Z}$, find the value of $c.$

7 In economics, marginal cost is the derivative of the cost function. A firm calculates that the marginal cost of producing its product is $\dfrac{dC}{dn} = \dfrac{4n}{n^2+1}$ where C is the total cost of production (in €1000) and n the number of items produced. Given that when no items are produced the cost to the firm is €1500, find:

  a an expression for C

  b the cost of producing seven items.

  c Sketch the curve and comment on its shape as n increases.

8 The rate of spread of a rumour is modelled by the equation $R'(t) = \dfrac{18e^{-0.5t}}{5\left(1+12e^{-0.5t}\right)^2}$

where $R(t)$ is the proportion of the population that knows the rumour at time t hours.

a Given $R(0) = \dfrac{1}{5}$, find an expression for $R(t)$.

b Estimate how long it would take for 70% of the population to hear the rumour.

c Find the percentage of the population who will eventually hear the rumour.

9 Water is flowing from a tank at a rate modelled by the function $R'(t) = 5\sin\left(\dfrac{t}{120}\right)$.

Water flows into the tank at a rate of

$$S'(t) = \dfrac{10t}{1 + 2t^2}.$$

Both R' and S' have units m³ per hour, and t is measured in hours for $0 \le t \le 5$.

a Find the intervals of time in $0 \le t \le 5$ during which the amount of water in the tank is increasing.

At $t = 0$, there is 25 m³ of water in the tank.

b Find an expression for T, the amount of water in the tank at time t.

c Find the value of the maximum amount of water in the tank and the time, t, at which this occurs.

Definite integrals

In this section you will explore the link between the definite integral used to find areas in Section 11.1 and the antiderivative (indefinite integral) from this section.

The following illustrates why the antiderivative gives the area under a curve.

Let $A(x)$ be the area under a curve $y = f(t)$ in the interval $[a, x]$.

For a small value of h, $A(x + h)$ will be approximately $A(x)$ plus the area of the rectangle below the curve between $t = x$ and $t = x + h$, as shown.

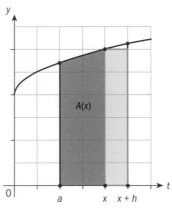

Therefore,

$$A(x + h) \approx A(x) + hf(x).$$

As seen in Section 11.1, this result will become increasingly accurate as $h \to 0$.

The expression can be rearranged to give

$$f(x) \approx \dfrac{A(x + h) - A(x)}{h}$$

and as $h \to 0$, we can write

$$f(x) = \lim_{h \to 0}\left(\dfrac{A(x + h) - A(x)}{h}\right).$$

From Chapter 10, you will recall that this is the equation for the derivative. Hence, we obtain

$$f(x) = \frac{dA}{dx} \Rightarrow A = \int f(x)\,dx = F(x) + c$$

The $+c$ term of the indefinite integral just reflects the arbitrary choice for the limits of the area. The reason it is not needed when calculating a definite integral is indicated below.

Consider the area under the curve $y = x^2 + 1$ between $x = 2$ and $x = 3$, which can be written as $\int_2^3 x^2 + 1\,dx$.

We know the area from an arbitrary point a to any value x is given by

$$F(x) = \int x^2 + 1\,dx = \frac{1}{3}x^3 + x + c$$

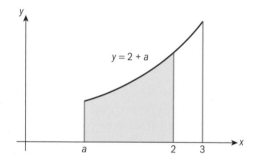

From the diagram, it can be seen that the shaded area is $F(2)$ and

hence, the required area is $F(3) - F(2) = \left(\frac{1}{3} \times 27 + 3 + c\right) - \left(\frac{1}{3} \times 8 + 2 + c\right)$

$$= 12 + c - \frac{14}{3} - c = \frac{22}{3}.$$

Hence, $\int_2^3 x^2 + 1\,dx = \frac{22}{3}$.

Thus, for a positive continuous function, the area between the curve $y = f(x)$, the x-axis and the lines $x = a$ and $x = b$ is given by

$\int_a^b f(x)\,dx = F(b) - F(a)$ where $F(x)$ is the antiderivative of $f(x)$.

This is **the fundamental theorem of calculus** and gives us a new way of calculating areas under a curve without using approximation methods or a GDC.

International-mindedness

The **fundamental theorem of calculus** shows the relationship between the derivative and the integral and was developed in the 17th century by Gottfried Wilhelm Leibniz and Isaac Newton.

Example 12

Find the area of the region bounded by the curve $y = 3x^2 + \dfrac{2}{\sqrt{x}}$, the x-axis and the lines $x = 1$ and $x = 4$.

$\displaystyle\int_1^4 \left(3x^2 + 2x^{-\frac{1}{2}}\right)dx$	This is the definite integral required. Normally this would be found using your GDC but here it will be calculated using the antiderivative.

$= \left[x^3 + 4x^{\frac{1}{2}} + c \right]_1^4$	Note the new notation. The square brackets with the limits are telling us to substitute the two values and subtract.
$= (64 + 8 + c) - (1 + 4 + c)$	From the fundamental theorem of calculus, $\int_a^b f(x)\,dx = F(b) - F(a)$ where $F(x)$ is the antiderivative of $f(x)$.
$= 72 + c - 5 - c = 67$	The $+c$ term will always cancel and so is omitted when working out a definite integral.

Example 13

Given $y = \cos 2x$:

a Find the area between the curve, the x-axis and the lines $x = 0$ and $x = \dfrac{\pi}{4}$.

b Show that the area between the curve, the x-axis and the lines $x = 0$ and $x = a$, where $\dfrac{\pi}{4} < a < \dfrac{3\pi}{4}$, is equal to $1 - \dfrac{1}{2}\sin 2a$.

a $\displaystyle\int_0^{\frac{\pi}{4}} \cos 2x \, dx = \left[\frac{1}{2}\sin 2x \right]_0^{\frac{\pi}{4}}$	Because the curve is positive for the interval $x = 0$ to $x = \dfrac{\pi}{4}$, the area is equal to $\displaystyle\int_0^{\frac{\pi}{4}} \cos 2x \, dx$.
$\quad = \dfrac{1}{2}\left(\sin\dfrac{\pi}{2} - \sin 0 \right)$	
$\quad = \dfrac{1}{2}$	Note that this time the $+c$ terms are not included.
	The can also be checked using your GDC.
b $\displaystyle\int_{\frac{\pi}{4}}^{a} \cos 2x \, dx = \left[\frac{1}{2}\sin 2x \right]_{\frac{\pi}{4}}^{a} = \frac{1}{2}\sin 2a - \frac{1}{2}\sin\frac{\pi}{2}$	$y = \cos 2x$ is negative for $\dfrac{\pi}{4} < x < \dfrac{3\pi}{4}$.
Hence, area =	Hence, the area between this part of the curve and the x-axis will need to be worked out separately and is equal to
$\dfrac{1}{2} + \left(-\dfrac{1}{2}\sin 2a + \dfrac{1}{2}\sin\dfrac{\pi}{2} \right) = 1 - \dfrac{1}{2}\sin 2a$	$-\displaystyle\int_{\frac{\pi}{4}}^{a} \cos 2x \, dx$

Exercise 11G

1 Find the **exact** area of the region bounded by the curve, the x-axis and the lines given.

a $y = e^{2x} + 1$, $x = 0$, $x = 1$

b $y = \dfrac{2}{x}$, $x = 2$, $x = 4$

c $y = x\sqrt{x^2 - 5}$, $x = 3$, $x = 4$

2 Show that $\displaystyle\int_{1}^{4} \dfrac{x}{x^2 + 2} = \dfrac{1}{2}\ln 6$.

3 Given that $\sin\left(\dfrac{\pi}{3}\right) = \dfrac{\sqrt{3}}{2}$ show that

$$\int_{\frac{\pi}{6}}^{\frac{\pi}{4}} \cos 2x \, dx = \dfrac{2 - \sqrt{3}}{4}.$$

4 The area under a power against time curve, between the times t_1 and t_2, will give the energy used during this time.

Find an expression for the energy used between $t = 0$ and $t = t_1$ given the power at time t is given by the equation

$$P = \dfrac{4t}{t^2 + 2}$$

5 The diagram below shows a company logo created by the curve $y = x^4 - 5x^2 + 4$ inside a circle of radius 4 cm.

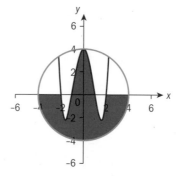

Find the area of the logo that is coloured red.

11.3 Applications of integration

In this section, we will look at some of the applications of definite integration, such as areas between curves, volumes of solids, displacement and total distance travelled.

The O2 Arena in London is one of the largest buildings by volume in the world. How might you calculate the volume contained, given it has a diameter of 365 m and a height of 50 m?

Areas between curves

From the diagram, it is clear that the area A between the two curves can be calculated by $A = \displaystyle\int_{a}^{b} f(x)\,dx - \int_{a}^{b} g(x)\,dx$ where a and b are the two intersection points of the curves.

However, it is often simpler to find the area by combining the two integrals, hence

$A = \displaystyle\int_{a}^{b} \big(f(x) - g(x)\big)\,dx$

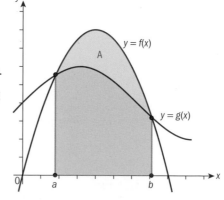

Example 14

Sketch the region bounded by $y = \sqrt{x+2}$, $y = \dfrac{1}{2x+4}$ and $x = 3$. Find the area of the region.

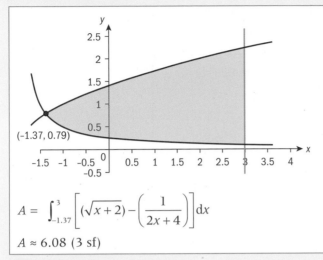

Sketch both graphs using your GDC or dynamic geometry software.

Find the intersection point of the two curves and identify the area to be calculated.

Remember that, even if you are using technology to find the value of the integral, you should always write down the definite integral representing the enclosed region.

$$A = \int_{-1.37}^{3} \left[\left(\sqrt{x+2}\right) - \left(\frac{1}{2x+4}\right) \right] dx$$

$A \approx 6.08$ (3 sf)

The expression $A = \int_a^b \left(f(x) - g(x) \right) dx$ is valid even when either of the curves is below the x-axis. However, if $f(x)$ is below $g(x)$, the integral (though not the area) will be negative.

In these cases, the expression $A = \int_a^b |f(x) - g(x)| dx$ should be used.

Example 15

Find the area of the region bounded by $y = \sin x$, $y = \cos x$, $x = 0$ and $x = 2\pi$.

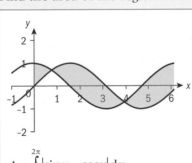

$$A = \int_0^{2\pi} |\sin x - \cos x| \, dx$$

$A \approx 5.66$ (3 sf)

Sketch the graph and shade the enclosed area.

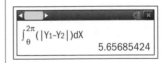

As $\cos x > \sin x$ in some intervals and $\sin x > \cos x$ in others, we need to use the absolute value.

The area A of the region bounded by the curves $y = f(x)$, $y = g(x)$ and the lines $x = a$ and $x = b$, where f and g are continuous, is given by

$$A = \int_a^b |f(x) - g(x)| dx$$

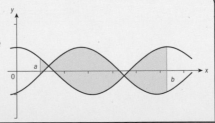

Calculus

Finding the area between a curve and the y-axis

If the equation is given in the form $x = f(y)$ then the method is very similar to finding the area between a curve and the x-axis.

If the equation is given as $y = f(x)$ then it will need to be rearranged to make y the subject.

> The area A of the region bounded by the curve $x = h(y)$, and the lines $y = a$ and $y = b$, where h is continuous for all y in $[a, b]$, is given by
> $$A = \int_a^b |h(y)|\,\mathrm{d}y$$

Note that, if we are trying the find the integral, we do not need the absolute value, but for areas we must use the absolute value to ensure we have positive values.

Example 16

Find the area of the region bounded by the curve $y = x^2$ and the y-axis, $x \in [-2, 0]$.

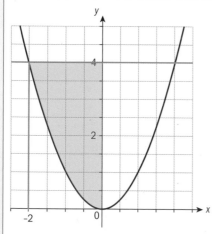

Sketch the graph and shade the required area.

$x = 0 \Rightarrow y = 0$ and $x = -2 \Rightarrow y = 4$

$y = x^2 \Rightarrow x = -\sqrt{y}$

$A = \int_0^4 \left| -\sqrt{y} \right| \mathrm{d}y$

$A \approx 5.33$ (3 sf)

Identify the lower and upper boundaries of y.

Write x as a function of y for the given region.

Write the area A as a definite integral.

You can use your GDC or integration rules to find the value of the integral.

$\int_0^4 (|-\sqrt{Y}|)\mathrm{d}Y$

5.333333544

Exercise 11H

1 Find the area of the shaded regions.

a

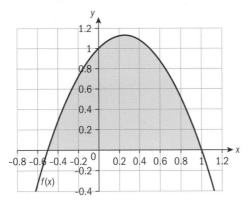

$f(x) = -2x^2 + x - 1$

b

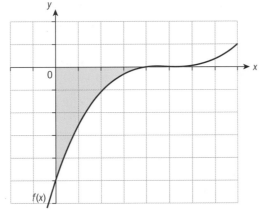

$f(x) = (x - 3)^3$

c

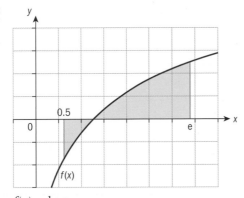

$f(x) = \ln x$

d

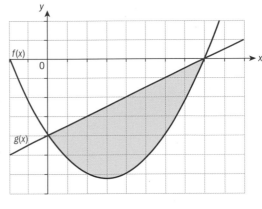

$f(x) = x^2 - 3x - 4$

$g(x) = x - 4$

e

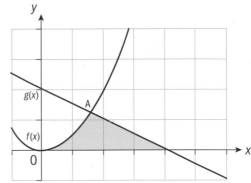

$f(x) = x^2$

$g(x) = 4 - x$

f

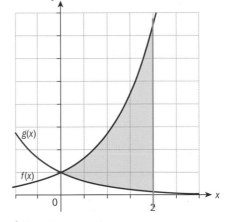

$f(x) = e^x$

$g(x) = e^{-x}$

2 Find the area of the shaded region bounded by $y = \dfrac{3}{x}$, the y-axis and the lines $y = 1$ and $y = 3$.

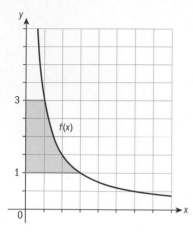

3 Find the area of the region bounded by $x = \sin y$, the y-axis and the lines $y = 0$ and $y = 2\pi$.

4 A building is in the shape of a prism with cross-section as shown in the diagram below. The building has a concrete roof that is 1 m thick when measured vertically. The outside of the cross-section of the roof forms a curve of the form $y = a\sin(bx)$ when placed on a coordinate system as shown. This curve touches the ground at the points A(0, 0) and C(5, 0) and the highest point of the roof is at $(2.5, 4)$.

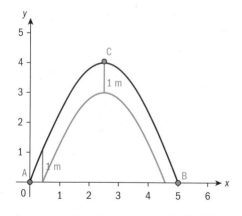

a Find the values of a and b.

b Write down the equation for the inner surface of the roof.

The building is 15 m long.

c Find the volume of concrete in the roof.

5 In economics, a supply function relates the quantity (q) that a manufacturer is willing to supply for a particular price per unit (p).

The diagram below shows the supply curve $p = \dfrac{1}{2}\ln(q+1)$.

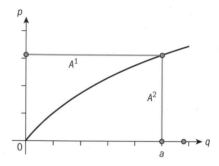

For a particular quantity, the area of the region above the curve (A_1) gives the producer surplus for selling that quantity and the area below the curve (A_2) gives the revenue needed by the producer. The area of the whole rectangle is the actual producer revenue. A quantity $q = a$ is produced.

a Find an expression in terms of a for:

   i the producer surplus

   ii the revenue needed.

b If the surplus is at least 50% more than the revenue needed by the producer, find the maximum integer value of a for this to occur.

Developing inquiry skills

Look again at the opening problem. To work out the area, we will now fit two curves through the points found previously: one curve through A, B, C, D, E and F and one through A, J, I, H, G and F.

Use cubic regression to find an equation for each curve and hence, an estimate for the area of San Cristobal.

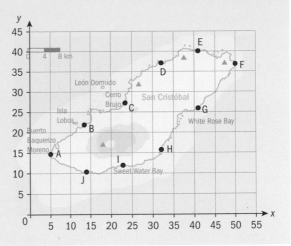

Solids of revolution

How do we calculate the volumes of irregular shapes?

We have formulae to calculate the volumes of regular shapes, for example a cylinder or a pyramid. We can extend our knowledge of volumes of regular shapes and integration to volumes of irregular shapes.

Consider $f(x) = \cos(0.5x - 1) + 2$ in the interval $[0, 12]$.

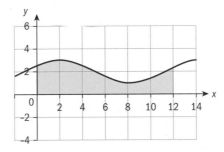

When you rotate this curve through 2π radians around the x-axis, you would get a 3D shape, like a vase.

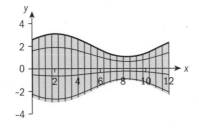

Calculus

On a closer look at the shape, you can see that it has circular cross-sections when sliced perpendicular to the x-axis, centred on the x-axis, each with a radius of $y = f(x)$.

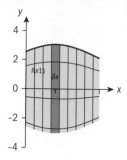

If we divide the shape into n cylindrical discs, each of width δx (remember from Section 11.1 that δx is used to indicate a small change in the value of x), we can approximate the total volume.

The cross-sectional area of the disk with x-coordinate x_i is $A_i = \pi[f(x_i)]^2$ using the formula for the area of a circle $A = \pi r^2$.

Using the formula for the volume of a cylinder, each disc has a volume of approximately

$V_i = \pi[f(x_i)]^2 \, \delta x$.

Thus, the volume formed by the revolution of the continuous function $y = f(x)$ through 2π radians around the x-axis is approximately

$$V \approx \sum_{i=1}^{n} \pi \left[f\left(x_i\right) \right]^2 \delta x.$$

As $\delta x \to 0$, the approximation will become more accurate.

Hence, $V = \displaystyle\lim_{\delta x \to 0} \left(\sum_{i=1}^{n} \pi \left[f\left(x_i\right) \right]^2 \delta x \right)$

Recall from Section 11.1 that we can write the limit with the integral sign and that δx becomes dx.

Hence, the formula for a volume formed by rotating $y = f(x)$ through 2π radians about the x-axis between $x = a$ and $x = b$ is

$$V = \int_a^b \pi \left(f(x) \right)^2 \mathrm{d}x.$$

We can now use the formula to find the volume of the solid formed by rotating $f(x) = \cos(0.5x - 1) + 2$ through 2π radians about the x-axis between $x = 0$ and $x = 12$:

$$V = \int_0^{12} \pi \left[\cos(0.5x - 1) + 2 \right]^2 \mathrm{d}x \approx 167.27 \, \text{unit}^3 \, (2 \text{ dp})$$

To find the volume formed when rotating about the y-axis, we simply interchange x and y.

EXAM HINT

This section has given an indication of the origin of the formula rather than a proof of the formula. Knowledge of the derivation is not required for the examinations.

TOK

You have been using radians to measure angles instead of degrees in recent chapters.

Why has this change been necessary? What are its advantages?

Volumes of revolution

- The volume formed when a continuous function $y = f(x)$ is rotated through 2π radians about the x-axis is

$$V = \int_a^b \pi \left[f(x) \right]^2 \, dx \text{ or } V = \pi \int_a^b \left[y \right]^2 \, dx$$

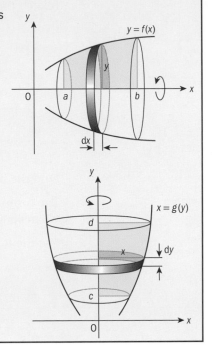

- The volume of the solid formed by revolution of $y = f(x)$ through 2π radians about the y-axis in the interval $y = c$ to $y = d$ is

$$V = \int_c^d \pi x^2 \, dy$$

Example 17

Let $f(x) = \dfrac{2x + 4}{x + 1}$, $0 \le x \le 4$. Find the volume of revolution formed when the curve $f(x)$ is rotated through 2π radians about

a the x-axis   **b** the y-axis.

a 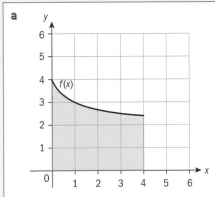	Sketch the graph of the curve.
$$V = \int_0^4 \pi \left[\frac{2x + 4}{x + 1} \right]^2 \, dx$$ $$V \approx 101 \ (3\,\text{sf})$$	Use the formula and evaluate the definite integral on the GDC.

Continued on next page

Calculus

b

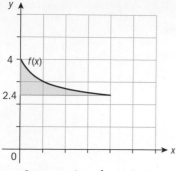

$x = 0 \Rightarrow y = 4$ and $x = 4 \Rightarrow y = 2.4$

$y = \dfrac{2x+4}{x+1} \Rightarrow x = \dfrac{-y+4}{y-2}$

$V = \displaystyle\int_{2.4}^{4} \pi \left[\dfrac{-y+4}{y-2} \right]^2 dy$

$V \approx 9.93 \ (3\,\text{sf})$

Sketch the graph of the curve.	

Find the boundaries for y.

The formula requires x as a function of y, so we need to rearrange the formula.

Use the formula and evaluate on a GDC.

Example 18

a Sketch $f(x) = \cos x$ and $g(x) = e^{-x}$ on the same axes for $0 \le x \le 1.5$.

b Find the intersection points of the two curves in the given interval.

c Find the volume of revolution formed when the region enclosed by the curves f and g is rotated through 2π radians about the x-axis.

a

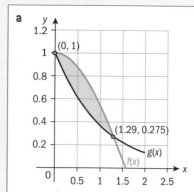

Sketch the graphs within the given domain.

Use your GDC to find the intersection points remembering to use at least 3 sf.

b Intersection points are $(0, 1)$ and $(1.29, 0.275)$.

c $V = \pi \displaystyle\int_0^{1.29} \left[\cos x\right]^2 dx - \pi \displaystyle\int_0^{1.29} \left[e^{-x}\right]^2 dx$

If we subtract the volume formed by $y = e^{-x}$ from the volume formed by $y = \cos x$, we get the volume formed by the region between the two curves.

$V \approx 0.993 \ (3\,\text{sf})$

Use your GDC.

Exercises 11I

1 Each of the following functions are sketched on the domain $0 \le x \le 1$ and rotated about the x-axis by 2π radians. Find the volumes of the generated solids of revolution.

  a $a(x) = x$
  b $b(x) = x^2$
  c $c(x) = x^3$
  d $e(x) = e^x$

2 The same parts of the functions in question **1** are rotated about the y-axis by 2π radians. Find the volumes of the generated solids of revolution.

3 A teardrop-shaped earring is being designed. Its shape is based on the graph of

  $y = \dfrac{x}{100}\sqrt{900 - x^2}$ for $0 \le x \le 30$ (where

  x and y are measured in mm), which is revolved by 2π radians around the x-axis as shown below.

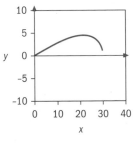 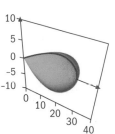

  a Find $\displaystyle\int \left(\dfrac{x}{100}\sqrt{900 - x^2}\right)^2 \, dx$.

  b Hence, find the volume of one earring.

  c If $1\,\text{cm}^3$ of gold weighs $19\,\text{g}$, and $1\,\text{g}$ of gold costs £30, find the cost of the gold used for the earring.

4 The line segment [AB] is placed as shown, where A = (0, 4) and B = (3, 0).

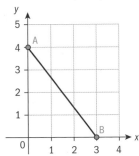

a Write down integrals that represent the volume obtained by rotating [AB] by 2π radians:

  i about the x-axis

  ii about the y-axis.

b Calculate the integrals and confirm your answers using the formula for the volume of a cone: $V = \dfrac{1}{3}\pi r^2 h$.

5 Hany and Ahmed are trying to model an American football. Hany's model is

  $s(x) = -4 + \sqrt{72.25 - x^2}$ and Ahmed's is

  $f(x) = 4.5 - 0.079x^2$.

  a Choose the best model and hence estimate the volume of the American football in cubic units using the information given in the diagram.

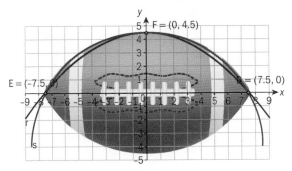

  b Given that the length of the football is 11 inches, convert your answer to part **a** into

  i cubic inches

  ii cubic centimetres.

6 The following regions are rotated about the x-axis by 2π radians. For each region:

  i Sketch the information given.

  ii Write down the integrals that quantify the volumes required.

  iii Hence, calculate the volumes.

  a The region bounded by $x = 0$, $y = x^2$ and $y = e^x$.

  b The region bounded by $y = 0$, $y = \ln(x)$ and $y = 4 - x^2$.

7 a Use technology to sketch the functions

$y_2 = 40 + \sqrt{4 - x^2}$ and $y_1 = 40 - \sqrt{4 - x^2}$.

b Sketch the shape generated by rotating the region bounded by y_2 and y_1 about the x-axis by 2π radians.

c Write down an integral that quantifies the volume of this shape and hence, find its volume.

8 In the diagram below, A is the centre of a circle with radius r and the line segment [AD] passes through the middle of [BC].

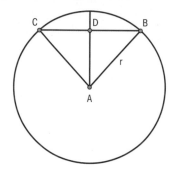

a Prove that $A\hat{D}B$ is 90°.

The cross-section of the O2 Arena in London can be thought of as a segment of a circle with a radius r m formed by a chord of length 365 m.

Given that the height of the O2 is 50 m and the equation of a circle of radius r with centre at (0, 0) is $x^2 + y^2 = r^2$, find:

a the value of r

b the volume of the O2.

Kinematics

The following results for an object with displacement s, velocity v and acceleration a at time t were derived in Chapter 10: $v = \dfrac{ds}{dt}$ and $a = \dfrac{dv}{dt} = \dfrac{d^2s}{dt^2}$.

We can now reverse the process to obtain $s = \displaystyle\int v \, dt$ and $v = \displaystyle\int a \, dt$.

TOK

Does the inclusion of kinematics as core mathematics reflect a particular cultural heritage?

Example 19

A stone is thrown vertically upwards with an initial velocity of 4.9 m s⁻¹ from a point 2 m above the ground.

Take the ground as the origin of the coordinate system with the upward direction as positive.

The acceleration due to gravity is $a = -9.8$ m s⁻².

a Find the maximum height reached by the stone.

b Find the speed with which it hits the ground.

a $a = -9.8$	Using $v = \int a\,dt$.
$v = \int -9.8\,dt = -9.8t + c$	Using the boundary condition to find c.
When $t = 0$, $v = 4.9 \Rightarrow c = 4.9$	
$\Rightarrow v = 4.9 - 9.8t$	
$s = \int (4.9 - 9.8t)dt$	Using $s = \int v\,dt$.
$\quad = 4.9t - 4.9t^2 + c$	
When $t = 0$, $s = 2 \Rightarrow t = 2$	
$\Rightarrow s = 4.9t - 4.9t^2 + 2$	
When $v = 0$, $t = \dfrac{4.9}{9.8} = 0.5$	The maximum height will occur when the velocity is equal to 0.
Hence,	
$s = 4.9 \times 0.5 - 4.9 \times 0.5^2 + 2 = 3.225$	This value for time is put into the displacement equation to find the maximum height.
b When $s = 0$,	When the stone hits the ground, its displacement will be 0 as we are measuring displacement from ground level.
$4.9t - 4.9t^2 + 2 = 0$	
$\Rightarrow t = 1.31$ seconds	
$v = 4.9 - 9.8 \times 1.31^2 = -7.95 \ \text{m s}^{-1}$	The velocity is negative as the stone is moving in the negative direction.
Speed $= 7.95 \ \text{m s}^{-1}$	The question asks for the speed, which is the magnitude of the velocity.

Example 20

A particle moves so that its velocity at time t is given by the equation

$v = 4t \sin(t^2)$.

a Given that it is initially at the origin, find an expression for its displacement at time t.
b Find the first time at which it returns to its starting point.

a $s = \int 4t \sin\left(t^2\right)dt$	"Initially" implies when $t = 0$.
$\quad = -2\cos(t^2) + c$	
When $t = 0$, $s = 0$	
$\Rightarrow 0 = -2\cos 0 + c$	It is important not to assume that c will always be equal to 0 just because initially $s = 0$.
$\Rightarrow c = 2$	
$s = 2 - 2\cos(t^2)$	

Continued on next page

Calculus

b $0 = 2 - 2\cos\left(t^2\right)$

$\Rightarrow \cos\left(t^2\right) = 1$

First positive solution is when

$t = 2.51$ seconds

The zeros can be found from rearranging and solving or by drawing a graph.

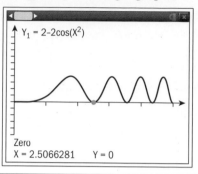

$Y_1 = 2 - 2\cos(X^2)$

Zero
X = 2.5066281   Y = 0

Exercise 11J

1 a Find expression for the velocity and displacement of a particle with acceleration $a(t) = \dfrac{3}{(t+1)^2}$, $t \geq 0$, if the particle is initially at rest at the origin.

b Determine the time it will take the particle to reach a distance of 50 m from the origin.

2 A particle moves so that its velocity $(m\,s^{-1})$ at time t seconds is given by the formula $v = e^{2\sin 3t} \cos 3t$.

a Find:

i an expression for the acceleration of the particle

ii the time t at which the particle's acceleration is first equal to $-0.5\,m\,s^{-2}$.

b Find an expression for the displacement of the particle (s) from its initial position at time t.

c Write down the exact value of the maximum displacement of the particle.

3 A particle moves so that its velocity at time t is given by the equation $v(t) = \dfrac{t}{e^{kt^2}}$ for $k > 0$.

At time 0, it is 1 cm from the origin.

a Determine the maximum acceleration of the particle.

b Find the set of values of k for which the particle will travel at least 5 cm from the origin.

4 a Show that the vertical height of a projectile after t seconds, if it is acted on only by gravity (acceleration $g = -9.8\,m\,s^{-2}$) is given by $s(t) = \dfrac{1}{2}gt^2 + v_0 t + y_0$, where v_0 is its initial vertical velocity and y_0 is its initial vertical position.

b Hence determine a formula for the maximum height reached by the particle.

c Determine, with reasons, whether a rocket fired with an initial vertical velocity of 310 m/s from 10 m above ground level is capable of reaching a target at a height of 4 km.

Area under a velocity–time graph

Investigation 6

The graph shows a **velocity–time graph** for the journey of an object. The horizontal axis shows the time taken from the start of the journey in seconds and the vertical axis shows the velocity of the object in m s^{-1}.

The equation for the velocity of the particle is $v = 10 - 2t$, $0 \leq t \leq 8$.

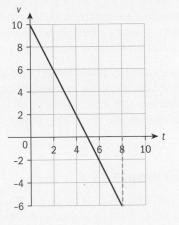

1   Explain why the particle has its maximum displacement when $t = 5$.

2   **a**   Find an equation for the displacement (s) of the particle, given that $s = 0$ when $t = 0$.

    b   Sketch the displacement graph for $0 \leq t \leq 8$.

3   **a**   Find the maximum displacement of the particle.

    b   Find the displacement at $t = 8$.

4   Hence, write down the total distance travelled by the particle for $0 \leq t \leq 8$.

5   Find the area between the curve, the t-axis, $t = 0$ and $t = 8$.

6   **Conceptual** How do you find the distance travelled by a particle?

7   Explain why this is not the same as $\int_0^8 (10 - 2t)\mathrm{d}t$.

$\int_a^b f(t)\,\mathrm{d}t$ and $\int_a^b |f(t)|\,\mathrm{d}t$

The value of $\int_a^b v(t)\mathrm{d}t = s(b) - s(a)$, which is the change in displacement of the particle between $t = a$ and $t = b$.

Consider an object moving along a line with a velocity at time t given by $v(t) = \cos t$.

Using $v = \dfrac{\mathrm{d}s}{\mathrm{d}t}$ and $a = \dfrac{\mathrm{d}v}{\mathrm{d}t}$, we obtain

$\int_a^b a(t)\mathrm{d}t = v(b) - v(a)$, the net change in the velocity of the particle

$\int_a^b v(t)\mathrm{d}t = s(b) - b(a)$, the net change in the displacement (or position)

of the particle.

> The **definite integral of a rate of change** in a given interval calculates the **net change**. This is a restatement of the fundamental theorem:
>
> If f is a **continuous** function on $a \leq x \leq b$ and F is any antiderivative of f then
>
> $$\int_a^b f(x)\,\mathrm{d}x = F(b) - F(a)$$

> If the rate of change of a function $F(x)$ is given by $f(x)$ then the total change in F between a and b is $\int_a^b |f(x)|\mathrm{d}x$.

Calculus

As v is the rate of change of s then the **total distance travelled** between $t = a$ and $t = b$ is $\int_a^b |v(t)| \, dt$.

There are various applications of total and net change derived from equations for rates beyond kinematics. Whenever we are given an equation for a rate, the definite integral of the function will give us the net change between the two values and the definite integral of the modulus of the function will give us the total change.

For example, if we would like to know how much money is left in our bank account, we would use net change, but if we would like to calculate the total value of all transactions into and out of the account, we would use the total change.

TOK

Why do we study mathematics?

What's the point?

Can we do without it?

Example 21

A hydro-electric power station generates electricity from water flowing through a pipe. During periods of low demand, water is pumped back up the pipe to the reservoir above.

Let the volume of water in the reservoir be V and assume that the only water that enters or leaves the lake during this period is through the pipe. The rate at which water flows through the pipe during a 24-hour period is given by the following equation:

$$\frac{dV}{dt} = -8.2\sin\left(\frac{\pi}{12}t + \frac{15\pi}{12}\right) - 5$$

where t is measured in hours after midnight and V is measured in millions of litres.

a Sketch the curve for $\dfrac{dV}{dt}$ against time for a 24-hour period.

b By calculating an appropriate definite integral, find the net change in the volume of water in the reservoir over a 24-hour period.

c By calculating an appropriate definite integral, find the total amount of water that has passed through the pipe in a 24-hour period.

d i Determine a formula for the volume of water in the reservoir at time t, given that the volume is V_0 at midnight.

   ii Find the value of V when $t = 24$ and use this value to verify your answer to part **b**.

a

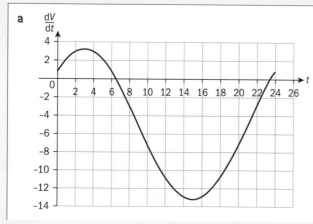

For most of the time the rate is negative, indicating that water is flowing out of the reservoir.

b $V = \int_0^{24} \left(-8.2\sin\left(\frac{\pi}{12}t + \frac{15\pi}{12}\right) - 5 \right) dt$

   $= -120\,\text{m}^3$

To find the net change, you take the definite integral between the two points.

c $V = \int_0^{24} \left| -8.2\sin\left(\frac{\pi}{12}t + \frac{15\pi}{12}\right) - 5 \right| dt$

   $= 149.4\,\text{m}^3$

To find the total change, you take the definite integral of the modulus function between the two points.

d i $V = \int \left(-8.2\sin\left(\frac{\pi}{12}t + \frac{15\pi}{12}\right) - 5 \right) dt$

The reverse chain rule is needed to integrate the expression.

$= \frac{98.4}{\pi}\cos\left(\frac{\pi}{12}t + \frac{15\pi}{12}\right) - 5t + c$

When $t = 0$, $V = V_0$

$\Rightarrow c = V_0 - \frac{98.4}{\pi}\cos\left(\frac{15\pi}{12}\right) = V_0 + 22.15$

$V = \frac{98.4}{\pi}\cos\left(\frac{\pi}{12}t + \frac{15\pi}{12}\right) - 5t + V_0 + 22.15$

ii When $t = 24$,

$V = \frac{98.4}{\pi}\cos\left(2\pi + \frac{15\pi}{12}\right) - 120 + V_0 + 22.15$

$= -120 + V_0$

So the difference is $-120 + V_0 - V_0 = -120$

The difference is independent of V_0 in the same way as you do not need to know the $+c$ term when working out definite integrals.

Both methods of working out a change are acceptable but generally, given the availability of technology, the method of part **b** is the more straightforward.

Exercise 11K

1 In an experiment, a liquid is cooled and then heated. The rate of change of the temperature of the liquid is given as $T'(t) = t^2 - 4t - 8$ where t is the time in minutes and $T(t)$ the temperature in °C. When $t = 8$, find:

  a how many degrees higher the liquid is than it was at $t = 0$

  b the total change in temperature over that period.

2 The graphs show the velocity–time graphs of four particles for a 5-second period of time. The x-axis is time (s) and the y-axis is velocity (m s^{-1}).

  a For each graph, find the total distance travelled and the displacement after 5 seconds.

i Particle A

$v(t) = 10$

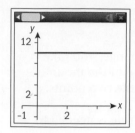

ii Particle B

$v(t) = 10 - 2t$

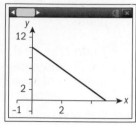

iii Particle C

$v(t) = 10 - 4t$

iv Particle D

$$v(t) = \begin{cases} 10 - 4t, & 0 \le t \le 2.5 \\ 4t - 10, & 2.5 < t \le 5 \end{cases}$$

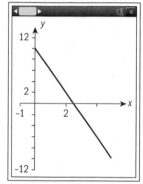

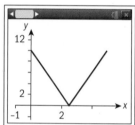

b Identify which of the particles changes direction.

3 Use technology to help sketch the velocity–time graphs for each of the following moving bodies and hence, find the total distance travelled and the displacement on the time intervals given. Time is in hours and velocity in $km\,h^{-1}$.

a $v(t) = \cos t$, $\left[0, \dfrac{\pi}{2}\right]$

b $v(t) = 3.1\sin 2t - 1$, $\left[\dfrac{\pi}{6}, \dfrac{3\pi}{2}\right]$

c $v(t) = 17 - 2t^2$, $[1, 4.1]$

d $v(t) = 1 - e^t$, $[0, 2.39]$

4 A particle moves with velocity function

$$v(t) = \begin{cases} 4, & 0 \le t \le 5 \\ 4 - \dfrac{4}{25}(t - 5)^2, & 5 < t \le 10 \\ -1.6t + 16, & t > 10 \end{cases}$$

where time is measured in seconds and distance in metres.

a Find the total distance travelled by the particle after

  i 5 seconds   **ii** 10 seconds.

b Calculate the time taken for the particle to return to its original position.

5 A suspension bridge is being designed. Immediately after the bridge sustains a heavy load, the vertical movement of a point on the bridge is modelled with a damped oscillation model, $v(t) = 5(0.65^t)$ $(\cos 5t - 0.08616 \sin 5t)$, where time is measured in seconds and v is measured in $cm\,s^{-1}$.

a Calculate the displacement of the point 5 seconds after sustaining a heavy load, and

b Find the total distance travelled by the point at this time.

6 Two objects A and B are launched from a balloon at a height of 1000 m, with velocity functions $v_a(x) = 16 - 4e^{\frac{-t}{16}}\ m\,s^{-1}$ and $v_b(x) = 18 - 7e^{\frac{-t}{16}}\ m\,s^{-1}$. The downward direction is taken as positive.

a **i** Graph both velocity functions for $0 \le t \le 20$.

  ii Calculate after how many seconds the objects are first travelling at the same velocity.

b Calculate how far above the ground A is at this time.

7 The derivative of the energy, $E\,(\text{mJ})$, of a particle is given as $\dfrac{dE}{dt} = \sin(0.5t) + a$. It is known that the change in the particle's energy between $t = 0$ and $t = \pi$ is 4 mJ. Find the value of a.

8 The rate of change in the area (A) covered by mould on a petri dish after t days is given as $\dfrac{dA}{dt} = 2e^{rt}$ where r is the rate of growth. Between the times $t = 2$ and $t = 4$, the area covered by the mould increases by 7.2 cm². Find the value of r.

9 The rate of change of the number of mosquitoes (N), measured in 10 000s, is modelled by the equation

$$\frac{dN}{dt} = 4\sqrt{t}\cos\left(\frac{\pi}{6}t - \frac{1}{2}\right) \text{ where } t \text{ is measured}$$

in months from the beginning of a year (1 January).

a Find in which month each year the population of mosquitoes is a minimum.

b By how much does the population of mosquitoes increase:

i the first year

ii the second year.

The average increase in population is the actual increase divided by the duration.

c Find the average increase in population for the first two years.

11.4 Differential equations

> A differential equation is an equation that contains a derivative.

For example, $\frac{dy}{dx} = 2x^2 + 5$.

You have already met several of these and solved them by integrating.

When no boundary condition is given then the solution to the equation will have an unknown constant (the $+c$ term). If a boundary condition is given, the particular solution can be found.

The equation above is written in the form $\frac{dy}{dx} = f(x)$, but often the context of the question will mean that the differential equation is of the form $\frac{dy}{dx} = f(x, y)$. These equations can often not be solved directly, so numerical solutions need to be found.

One situation in which they can be solved is when $\frac{dy}{dx} = f(x)g(y)$.

This form is called a **separable** differential equation.

It can be written as $\frac{1}{g(y)}\frac{dy}{dx} = f(x)$ and both sides are then integrated with respect to x:

$$\int \frac{1}{g(y)}\frac{dy}{dx}dx = \int f(x)dx$$

It can be shown that $\int \frac{1}{g(y)}\frac{dy}{dx}dx = \int \frac{1}{g(y)}dx$ as if we were cancelling the two dx's. This is very similar to the process used when integrating using the reverse chain rule.

Both sides of the expression $\int \frac{1}{g(y)}dy = \int f(x)dx$ can now be integrated.

International-mindedness

French mathematician Jean d'Alembert's analysis of vibrating strings using differential equations plays an important role in modern theoretical physics.

Calculus

In practice, many people often go from $\dfrac{dy}{dx} = f(x)g(y)$ to

$\dfrac{1}{g(y)}dy = f(x)dx$ and then add the integral operators. Although

this middle stage is meaningless, notationally it can be a convenient shortcut.

Example 22

Find the solution of the differential equation $y\dfrac{dy}{dx} = x^2 + 1$ given that $y(0) = 4$.

$\displaystyle\int y\,dy = \int (x^2 + 1)dx$	The variables have been separated to give $y\,dy = (x^2 + 1)dx$.
$\dfrac{1}{2}y^2 = \dfrac{1}{3}x^3 + x + c$	We do not need to have an integrating constant, c, for both sides of the equation.
	If the question asks for the solution to be given in a particular form, we may need to rearrange the answer obtained from the integration.
$y = 4$ when $x = 0$ $\Rightarrow 8 = c$	Substitute the given values to find c.
So $\dfrac{1}{2}y^2 = \dfrac{1}{3}x^3 + x + 8$	

Example 23

Find a solution in the form $y = f(x)$ to the differential equation $\dfrac{dy}{dx} = 6x^2 y$ given that $y = 2$ when $x = 0$.

$\displaystyle\int \dfrac{1}{y}dy = \int 6x^2 dx$	Separate the variables and integrate.
$\ln y = 2x^3 + c$	
$y = Ae^{2x^2}$	Converting the $+c$ term into a coefficient when eliminating a natural log operator is so common that it is often done in a single step. The full process is $y = e^{2x^2 + c} = e^c e^{2x^2} = Ae^{2x^2}$ where $A = e^c$.
$y = 2$ when $x = 0$ $\Rightarrow 2 = A$	Substitute to find A.
So $y = 2e^{2x^2}$	

Such an exponential model from a differential equation occurs whenever the growth or decay of a variable is proportional to the amount present.

Example 24

The rate of growth of mould on a large petri dish is directly proportional to the amount of mould present. The area covered by the mould (A) is initially $2\,\text{cm}^2$ and after 2 days it is $9\,\text{cm}^2$.

a Find an expression for the area covered by the mould at time t days.

b Find the value of t at which the mould will cover $20\,\text{cm}^2$.

a $\dfrac{dA}{dt} = kA$	If two variables a and b are proportional to each other, then $a = kb$.
$\displaystyle\int \dfrac{1}{A}\,dA = \int k\,dt$	
$\ln A = kt + c$	
$A = Be^{kt}$ where $B = e^c$	There are two unknowns in the equation, so two sets of boundary conditions need to be used.
$A = 2$ when $t = 0 \Rightarrow B = 2$	
$A = 2e^{kt}$	
$A = 9$ when $t = 2$	
$\Rightarrow 9 = 2e^{2k}$	This equation and the one in part **b** can be solved using the log laws or directly on a GDC.
$2k = \ln\left(\dfrac{9}{2}\right) \Rightarrow k = 0.752$	
So $A = 2e^{0.752t}$	
b $20 = 2e^{0.752t}$	
$t = \dfrac{1}{0.752}\ln 10 = 3.06\,\text{days}$	

Exercise 11L

1 Solve $4\dfrac{dy}{dx} = xy$, given that $y = 2$ when $x = 0$.

2 Solve $(x^2 - 1)\dfrac{dy}{dx} = 2xy$, given that $y(2) = 9$.

3 a The rate of decay of a radioactive substance is proportional to the amount M g remaining. Form a differential equation in M and show that this solves to give $M = Ae^{-kt}$ where A and k are positive constants.

b Given that the amount initially is 40 g and there is only 20 g remaining after 2 hours, find the value of k.

4 a Find the derivative of $y = \sqrt{4 - x^2}$.

b Verify that $y = \sqrt{4 - x^2}$ satisfies the differential equation $\dfrac{dy}{dx} = -\dfrac{x}{y}$.

c Solve $\dfrac{dy}{dx} = -\dfrac{x}{y}$ to find the general solution to the differential equation.

5 Solve the following differential equations.

a $\dfrac{dy}{dx} = e^{x+y}$ **b** $\dfrac{dy}{dx} = \dfrac{y + y\cos x}{y^2 + 1}$

6 For each of the following differential equations, find the solution that satisfies the given initial condition.

a $\dfrac{dy}{dx} = \sqrt{\dfrac{x}{2y}}$, $y(1) = 2$

b $\dfrac{dy}{dx} = \dfrac{2x + \sin x}{y}$, $y(0) = 1$

c $y'\tan x = \tan y$, $y(2) = 2$

7 Newton's law of cooling states that the rate of change of temperature, $\dfrac{dT}{dt}$, of an object is proportional to the difference between its own temperature, $T(t)$, and the ambient temperature, T_a (ie the temperature of its surroundings), that is $\dfrac{dT}{dt} = -k(T - T_a)$.

Suppose you have just poured a cup of coffee with a temperature of 75°C in a room where the temperature is 24°C.

a State the time at which the coffee cools most quickly, justifying your answer.

b Write a differential equation using the initial conditions given.

c Solve the differential equation.

d Explain from the equation why the temperature will never go below 24°C.

8 The number of bacteria in a liquid culture is observed to grow at a rate proportional to the number of cells present. At the beginning of the experiment there are 10^4 cells and after 3 hours there are 3×10^5 cells.

a Calculate the number of bacteria after 1 day of growth if this rate of growth continues.

b Determine the **doubling time** of the bacteria.

9 Indium-111 has a short half-life of 2.8 days, which makes it a useful tracer. It is used in a variety of diagnostic methods, including isotopic labelling of blood cell components, diagnosing rare cancers etc.

In the early 19th century, F. Soddy and E. Rutherford derived the radioactive decay formula as

$\dfrac{dN}{dt} = -kN$, where N is the amount of a radioactive material and k is a positive constant that depends on the radioactive substance, with T being the half-life of the substance.

a Show that the formula for k is $k = \dfrac{\ln 2}{T}$.

b If $N(0) = 5\,g$, find the mass remaining after 1 day.

10 A cylindrical tank of radius r is filled with water. A hole of area A m^2 is made in the bottom of tank.

The velocity of water through the hole is v m s^{-1}. The volume of water in the tank at time t seconds after the hole is made is V m^3.

Let h be the height of water remaining in the tank after t seconds.

a Given that $v = \sqrt{2gh}$, show that

$\dfrac{dV}{dt} = -A\sqrt{2gh}$.

b **i** Hence, show that $\dfrac{dV}{dt} = -k\sqrt{V}$ where k is a constant.

ii State the value of k in terms of A, r and g.

The volume of the cylinder when full is V_0.

c Find how long it will take the cylinder to empty in terms of k and V_0.

Investigation 7

In this investigation, you can assume that the number i can be treated the same as any other number when differentiating or integrating.

1 Solve $\dfrac{\mathrm{d}x}{\mathrm{d}\theta} = \mathrm{i}x$ given $x = 1$ when $\theta = 0$.

Let $x = \cos\theta + \mathrm{i}\sin\theta$

2 Verify that $x = 1$ when $\theta = 0$.

Show that $\dfrac{\mathrm{d}x}{\mathrm{d}\theta} = \mathrm{i}x$.

3 **Conceptual** What can you conclude about $e^{\mathrm{i}\theta}$?

This is called Euler's formula: $e^{\mathrm{i}\theta} = \cos\theta + \mathrm{i}\sin\theta$

11.5 Slope fields and differential equations

It is not always possible to solve differential equations and find an explicit formula for the unknown function. **Slope fields,** or **direction fields,** are used to represent graphical solutions of differential equations. They are drawn using tangent lines at specific points. They can often be produced even when it is not possible to solve the differential equation and find an explicit formula for the unknown function.

International-mindedness

Differential equations first became solvable with the invention of calculus by Newton and Leibniz. In Chapter 2 of his 1736 work *Method of Fluxions*, Newton described three types of differential equations.

Investigation 8

Consider the differential equation $\dfrac{\mathrm{d}y}{\mathrm{d}x} = \dfrac{y - 3x}{2}$.

The gradient of the tangent drawn to the curve y
- at $(1, 1)$ will be -1
- at $(1, 2)$ will be $-\dfrac{1}{2}$.

These points can be plotted on a grid and small line segments drawn

with gradients of -1 and $-\dfrac{1}{2}$, respectively, as seen in the diagram.

The process can be continued and is shown below for all the integer values of x and y in the intervals $-4 \leq x \leq 4$ and $-4 \leq y \leq 4$.

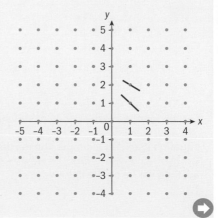

Calculus

Continued on next page

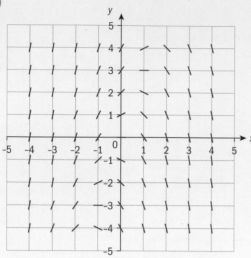

This type of diagram is called a **slope field**.

The slope field indicates the family of curves that satisfy the differential equation. At each point the direction of the curve is the same as the direction of the tangent. This means that given a starting point (a boundary condition), a solution curve can be drawn.

One way to think about this is that the slopes are like the current in a river and the curve follows the path a cork might take if released in the river at that point.

The diagrams below show the solution curves that pass through $(-1, 0)$ and $(-1, 1)$.

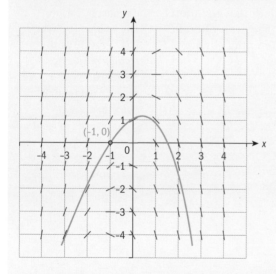

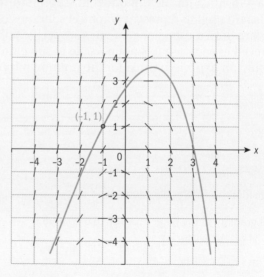

Certain features of the family of curves satisfying the differential equation can be worked out from the

equation itself. For example, the maximum points will occur when $\dfrac{\mathrm{d}y}{\mathrm{d}x} = \dfrac{y - 3x}{2} = 0$.

So, they will lie on the line $y = 3x$.

Exercise 11M

1 Consider the differential equation $y' = x^2 + y$.

a Find the missing values of the gradients of the tangents to the solution curves at the integer points for $-3 \le x \le 3$ and $-3 \le y \le 3$.

x \ y	−3	−2	−1	0	1	2	3
−3	6	1	−2	−3	−2	1	6
−2	7	2	−1	−2	−1	2	7
−1	8	3	0	−1	0	3	8
0	9	4	1	0	1	4	9
1	10	5	2	1			
2	11	6	3	2			
3	12	7	4	3			

b Sketch the slope field for the differential equation.

c Use the slope field to sketch the solution curve that passes through $(2, -2)$.

2 By evaluating the gradient at various points, or otherwise, match each differential equation below with a slope field.

a $\dfrac{dy}{dx} = x - 2$ **b** $\dfrac{dy}{dx} = x + y$

c $\dfrac{dy}{dx} = y + 2$ **d** $y' = x^2 + y^2$

i

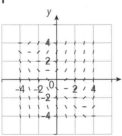

ii

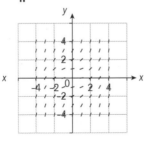

iii

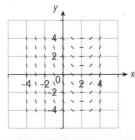

iv

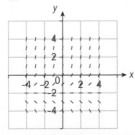

3 One of the following slope fields is for the differential equation $y' = \cos(x + y)$, and the other is for the differential equation $y' = \cos(x - y)$.

A   **B**

a For **i** $y' = \cos(x + y)$ **ii** $y' = \cos(x - y)$

write down the equation of a line along which the slope field would have a gradient of zero.

b State which is the slope field for

i $y' = \cos(x + y)$ **ii** $y' = \cos(x - y)$

4 The Gompertz equation is a model that is used to describe the growth of certain populations. In the 1960s, AK Laird used the Gompertz curve to fit the data on the growth of tumours. A tumour is a cellular population growing in a confined space where the availability of nutrients is limited.

If $T(t)$ is the size of a tumour then under this model $\dfrac{dT}{dt} = -T \ln\left(\dfrac{T}{2}\right)$.

a Sketch a slope field for $T(t)$ over the first 6 months, $0 \le t \le 6$. Take $0 \le T \le 3$.

b On your slope field, sketch a curve that shows the growth of the tumour given that its volume is 0.5 cm^3 when $t = 0$.

c Write down the maximum possible size of a tumour according to this model.

d Explain why this model might be suitable for modelling the growth of a tumour.

Calculus

Euler's method for numerically solving differential equations

The idea used in slope fields can also be applied to obtain numerical approximations of differential equations.

Consider the differential equation $\dfrac{dy}{dx} = f(x, y)$.

Let (x_{n-1}, y_{n-1}) be a point on the curve and let $x_n = x_{n-1} + h$ $(h > 0)$. The method will use the gradient of the curve at (x_{n-1}, y_{n-1}) to evaluate y_n, an estimate of the y coordinate of the point on the curve with x coordinate x_n.

The gradient of the tangent at the point (x_{n-1}, y_{n-1}) is $f(x_{n-1}, y_{n-1})$. The diagram shows that it is also $\dfrac{y_n - y_{n-1}}{h}$. Hence,

$f(x_n, y_n) = \dfrac{y_n - y_{n-1}}{h}$, which can be rearranged to give $y_n = y_{n-1} + hf(x_{n-1}, y_{n-1})$.

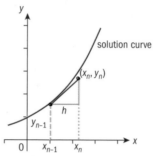

Generally, we are given a boundary condition, which can be written as (x_0, y_0). The formula is then used to find the coordinates (x_1, y_1). y_1 is unlikely to be on the curve, but if h is sufficiently small it should be quite close and so the coordinates can be used as the starting values to obtain (x_2, y_2).

This will create a series of approximations that might look similar to the red lines in the diagram.

This iterative numerical approximation of differential equations is named after Euler as **Euler's method**.

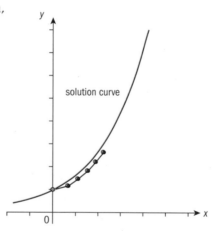

International-mindedness

The Euler method is named after Swiss mathematician Leonhard Euler (pronounced "oiler"), who proposed it in his book *Institutionum Calculi Integralis* in 1768.

Example 25

Use Euler's method with step size 0.1 to approximate the solution to the initial value problem $\dfrac{dy}{dx} = xy$ and $y(1) = 1$, and estimate the value of $y(2)$.

$y_n = y_{n-1} + hf(x_{n-1}, y_{n-1})$ $h = 0.1,\ f(x, y) = xy$	In examinations, it is important to write down the formula being used, as method marks can be awarded even if there are numerical errors in the calculations.

Hence,

$$y_n = y_{n-1} + 0.1x_{n-1}y_{n-1}$$
$$\Rightarrow y_n = y_{n-1}(1 + 0.1x_{n-1})$$

There is no need to simplify the formula, though sometimes this can make it easier to put into a GDC.

All the calculators recommended for this course have a simple way to calculate an iterative formula.

For this example, the full table of values is

Using technology,

$y(2) \approx 3.860891894$

n	x_n	y_n
0	1	1
1	1.1	1.1
2	1.2	1.221
3	1.3	1.36752
4	1.4	1.5452976
5	1.5	1.761639264
6	1.6	2.025885154
7	1.7	2.350026778
8	1.8	2.74953133
9	1.9	3.24444697
10	2	3.860891894

Exercises 11N

1 Consider the differential equation

$$\frac{dy}{dx} = \sqrt{\frac{x}{4y}}$$ where $y = 4$ when $x = 4$.

Use Euler's method with step size 0.1 to find an approximate value of y when $x = 4.5$.

2 Consider the differential equation $y' = 1 - y$ where $y = -1$ when $x = 0$.

Use Euler's method with step size 0.05 to find an approximate value of y when $x = 0.15$.

3 Consider the differential equation

$$\frac{dy}{dx} = \frac{2x^2 + 1}{xe^y}$$ where $y = 0$ when $x = 1$.

Use Euler's method with step size 0.025 to find an approximate value of y when $x = 1.1$.

4 a Consider the differential equation

$$\frac{dy}{dx} = -xy$$ where $y = 1$ when $x = 1$.

Use Euler's method with step size 0.1 to find an approximate value of y when $x = 1.5$.

b Solve the differential equation and hence, find the error in your approximation.

5 a Consider the differential equation

$$\frac{dy}{dx} = \frac{2xy}{1 + x^2}$$ where $y = 3$ when $x = 1$.

Use Euler's method with step size 0.1 to find an approximate value of y when $x = 1.3$.

b Solve the differential equation and hence, find the absolute error in your approximation.

Calculus

6 Let the population size of a colony of rare meerkats in units of 10 be N. At time t years, the rate of change of the population can be modelled by the differential equation

$$\frac{dN}{dt} = 0.5N - t.$$

a Given that $N = a + bt$, $a, b \in \mathbb{R}$ is a solution to the differential equation for a particular initial population, find the values of a and b.

The slope field for the differential equation is shown below.

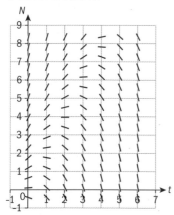

b On a copy of the slope field diagram, show
  i the line $N = a + bt$
  ii the trajectory of the population if at $t = 0$, $N = 2$.

c Find the least number of meerkats in the colony at $t = 0$ that will ensure the population does not become extinct.

An environmentalist measuring the population calculates it will reach a maximum after three years and then will begin to decline.

d What is the population of meerkats at this time?

At $t = 3$, they decide to introduce more meerkats from another colony.

e If the model remains valid, find the least number of meerkats that would need to be introduced for the colony to increase in size continually?

After the introduction of extra meerkats, the size of the population is 120.

f Use Euler's method with a step size of 0.1 to estimate the population one year later.

Chapter summary

- When f is a non-negative function for $a \le x \le b$, $\int_a^b f(x)\,dx$ gives the area under the curve from $x = a$ to $x = b$.

- If $f(x) < 0$ in an interval $[a, b]$ then $\int_a^b f(x)\,dx < 0$.

- If the area bounded by the curve $y = f(x)$ and the lines $x = a$ and $x = b$ is required and if $f(x) < 0$ for any values in this interval then the area should be calculated using $\int_a^b |f(x)|\,dx$.

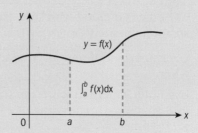

- For a positive continuous function, the area (A) between the graph of the function, the x-axis and the lines $x = a$ and $x = b$ can be approximated by the trapezoidal rule:

$$A \approx \frac{1}{2}h\left(y_0 + y_n + 2(y_1 + \dots + y_{n-1})\right) \text{ where } h = \frac{b-a}{n}.$$

- $\int f(x)\,dx$ is an indefinite integral and the process of finding the **indefinite integral** is called **integration**.

- If $\dfrac{d}{dx}\big[F(x)\big] = f(x)$, then $\int f(x)\,dx = F(x)+c$ where c is an arbitrary constant.

- $F(x)$ is the antiderivative of $f(x)$.

- Rules for integration can be derived from those for differentiation:

    ○ The sum/difference of functions: $\int\big(f(x)\pm g(x)\big)\,dx = \int f(x)\,dx \pm \int g(x)\,dx$

    ○ Multiplying a function by a constant: $\int af(x)\,dx = a\int f(x)\,dx$

    ○ Power rule: $\int ax^{n}\,dx = \dfrac{ax^{n+1}}{n+1}+c$

    ○ $\int \sin x = -\cos x + c$ ○ $\int \cos x = \sin x + c$

    ○ $\int \dfrac{1}{x}\,dx = \ln|x| + c$ ○ $\int e^{x}\,dx = e^{x} + c$

    ○ $\int \dfrac{1}{\cos^{2} x}\,dx = \tan x + c$

- In addition:

    ○ $\int \sin ax\,dx = -\dfrac{1}{a}\cos ax + c$ ○ $\int \cos ax\,dx = \dfrac{1}{a}\sin ax + c$

    ○ $\int e^{ax}\,dx = \dfrac{1}{a}e^{ax} + c$

- The reverse chain rule can be used whenever the integral consists of the product of a composite function and a multiple of the derivative of the interior function. In these cases, the derivative will cancel when the substitution is made.

- The area A of the region bounded by the curves $y=f(x)$, $y=g(x)$ and the lines $x=a$ and $x=b$, where f and g are continuous, is given by

$$A = \int_{a}^{b}\big|f(x)-g(x)\big|\,dx$$

- The area A of the region bounded by the curve $x=h(y)$, and the lines $y=a$ and $y=b$, where h is continuous for all y in $[a,\,b]$, is given by

$$A = \int_{a}^{b}\big|h(y)\big|\,dy$$

- The **definite integral of a rate of change** in a given interval calculates the **net change** and the definite integral of the modulus of a function gives the total change.

    If f is a **continuous** function on $[a,\,b]$ and F is any antiderivative of f then

$$\int_{a}^{b} f(x)\,dx = F(b) - F(a)$$

Developing inquiry skills

Write down any further inquiry questions you could ask and investigate how you could find the areas of irregular shapes and curved shapes.

Chapter review

Click here for a mixed review exercise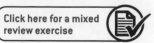

1 The graph shows how the velocity of a prototype drone designed to monitor large areas of rainforest changed in a trial lasting 90 hours.

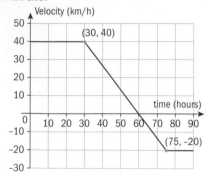

a Describe the motion of the drone during the entire trial.

b Write down the interval during which the acceleration of the drone is negative.

c Hence, determine when the drone is slowing down.

d Find the total distance travelled in the trial.

e Calculate the position of the drone at the end of the trial.

2 The graph gives information about the motion of a more advanced drone that is programmed to fly in a straight line and return to its starting point once it has collected enough photographic data to fill up its memory.

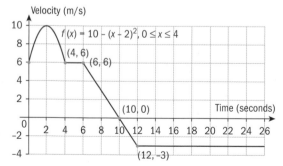

a Calculate the distance travelled in the first 6 seconds.

b Determine the time when the drone turns around to return to the starting point

c Hence, calculate how long the drone takes to complete its journey.

3 A prototype solar-powered vehicle is tested. Sensors in the car record the following data every 5 seconds.

Time (s)	Velocity (m/s)
0	6.7
5	15.3
10	26
15	27.3
20	29.4
25	32.1
30	35.5

Apply the trapezoidal rule to estimate the distance the car has travelled by the time its velocity reaches $35.5\,\mathrm{m\,s^{-1}}$.

4 Identify which of the following integrals can be found analytically and which need to be found using technology.

a $\displaystyle\int_0^4 \sin(4x+3)\,\mathrm{d}x$ **b** $\displaystyle\int_2^5 x\cos(x^2)\,\mathrm{d}x$

c $\displaystyle\int_2^5 x^2\cos(x)\,\mathrm{d}x$ **d** $\displaystyle\int_2^5 \cos(x^2)\,\mathrm{d}x$

e $\displaystyle\int_0^4 (\sin(4x)+3)\,\mathrm{d}x$ **f** $\displaystyle\int_5^{10} \frac{0.7x^4}{x^5-1}\,\mathrm{d}x$

g $\displaystyle\int_5^{10} \frac{x^5-1}{0.7x^4}\,\mathrm{d}x$ **h** $\displaystyle\int_5^{10} \frac{0.7x^4}{(x^5-1)^8}\,\mathrm{d}x$

i $\displaystyle\int_5^{10} \frac{0.7e^x}{x^5-1}\,\mathrm{d}x$

5 A population of midges in an area of western Scotland is to be controlled through sustainable changes to the environment. The rate of decrease of the population P is proportional to the number of midges at any time t. The population P decreases from 600 000 to 500 000 over four years.

a Write down the relationship between $\dfrac{\mathrm{d}P}{\mathrm{d}t}$ and P.

b Solve the differential equation for P.

c Hence, find the time taken for the population to decrease by 60%.

6 The diagram shows the function

$f(x) = \sqrt{r^2 - x^2}$, $0 \leq x \leq r$, and the area beneath it.

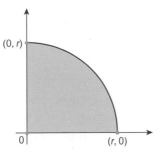

a State the geometrical shape of the solid of revolution generated by rotating $f(x)$ around the x-axis by 2π radians.

b Write down an integral that represents the volume of this solid.

c Hence, show that the volume V of a sphere of radius r is $V = \dfrac{4}{3}\pi r^3$.

7 a Consider the differential equation $y' = 2y(1 + x)$ where $y = 3$ when $x = 0$.

Use Euler's method with step size 0.1 to find approximate values of y when $x = 0.1$, 0.2 and 0.3.

b Solve the differential equation and hence, find the absolute errors for each of your approximations.

8 A water tank in the shape of a cylinder of radius 40 cm and height 100 cm collects rainwater for recycling.

Water flows out of a tap at the bottom of the tank at a rate directly proportional to the square root of the depth of the water.

After heavy rainfall, the tank is full but the owner needs to empty the tank so it can be cleaned.

The tap is opened and after 10 minutes the level of the water has dropped to 64 cm.

a Using V for the volume of water in the tank and h for the depth of the water, write down a differential equation relating these variables.

b Apply the chain rule and the formula for the volume of a cylinder to show that $\dfrac{dV}{dt} = \dfrac{4\pi}{25}\dfrac{dh}{dt}$. Hence, write your answer to part **a** in terms of h and t.

c Predict how long it will take for the tank to empty.

9 Xavier is designing an art installation in a public space. It is a large water tank in the shape of a prism. He builds a scale model in his studio. The constant cross-sectional area of the model is bounded by the functions

$f(x) = 2^x + 2^{-x}$ and $f(x) = \dfrac{9}{16}x^2 + 2$.

a Xavier sketches both functions on the domain $-2 \leq x \leq 2$. The x-axis is calibrated in metres. Calculate the area of the region bounded by the two graphs in square metres.

b Xavier uses his graph to build the model of the prism, which is 50 cm deep. Given that the model is 1:40 scale, calculate the volume of the art installation, correct to the nearest cubic metre.

Exam-style questions

10 P1: a Find the value of $\displaystyle\int_0^2 \dfrac{x}{x^2 + 4}$, giving your answer as a decimal correct to 3 significant figures. **(2 marks)**

b Find the integral $\displaystyle\int \dfrac{x}{x^2 + 4}\,dx$. **(3 marks)**

c Hence find the exact value of $\displaystyle\int_0^2 \dfrac{x}{x^2 + 4}\,dx$. **(2 marks)**

11 P1: Find the following indefinite integrals.

a $\int x^2 + 3x + 1 \, dx$ (2 marks)

b $\int \sin x + \cos(2x) \, dx$ (2 marks)

c $\int e^x + e^{-x} \, dx$ (2 marks)

d $\int (3x+1)^6 \, dx$ (2 marks)

e $\int \dfrac{x^2 + x}{x} \, dx$ (2 marks)

12 P1: Farmer Davies owns the land enclosed between two roads. The roads can be modelled by curves with equations $y = x^2 - 8x + 23$ and $y = x + 9$ for $0 \le x \le 10$, where x and y each represent a unit of 100 m.

Find the area of Farmer Davies' land. (6 marks)

13 P1: Alun, a geographer, measures the depth of a river at 1 m intervals from the bank using a boat and a marked piece of line with a heavy weight at the bottom.

Alun's results are presented in the table below, where x represents the perpendicular distance from the shore, and d represents the depth of the river (both measured in metres).

x	0	1	2	3	4	5	6	7	8	9	10	11	12
d	0	6.71	10.4	12.15	12.8	12.95	12.96	12.95	12.8	12.15	10.4	6.71	0

a Use the trapezium rule to estimate the cross-sectional area of the river, giving your answer correct to 2 decimal places. (3 marks)

It is later discovered that the equation connecting x and d is $d = \dfrac{1296 - (x-6)^4}{100}$.

b Calculate the true value of the cross-sectional area of the river. (3 marks)

c Find the percentage error in your estimation of the area you made in part **a**. (2 marks)

d Explain why, in this case, the trapezium rule underestimates the true value. (1 mark)

14 P1: The curve $y = e^{x^2}$ between $x = 0$ and $x = 1$ is rotated through 2π radians about the x-axis to form a solid of revolution. Find the volume of this solid. (4 marks)

15 P2: The acceleration of a small rocket-propelled craft is given by $a = 4e^{-0.2t} \, \text{ms}^{-2}$.

a Find an expression for the velocity of the craft, $v \, \text{ms}^{-1}$, as a function of time $t \, \text{s}$, given that the craft started from rest. (4 marks)

b Find an expression for the displacement of the craft, s m, as a function of time $t \, \text{s}$, given that the craft started from the origin. (4 marks)

c Write down the limiting velocity of the craft as t gets very large. (1 mark)

d Find the craft's displacement one minute after it begins to move. (2 marks)

16 P2: A differential equation is defined by $\dfrac{dy}{dx} = xy$, $x > 0$, $y > 0$ where $y(1) = 2$.

a Use Euler's method with a step size of 0.25 to find an approximation for $y(2)$. For each value of x, show the corresponding value of y in your working. (5 marks)

b Solve the differential equation, giving the answer in the form $y = f(x)$ for some function f. (7 marks)

c Hence, find the exact value of $y(2)$. (2 marks)

d Find the absolute percentage error in the value of $y(2)$ given by Euler's method. Give your answer to 2 significant figures. (2 marks)

17 P1: a Find the derivative of $x^2 \sin x$.

(3 marks)

b Hence find
$$\int 4\cos x + 6x \sin x + 3x^2 \cos x \,dx.$$

(2 marks)

18 P2: In a slope field, an *isocline* is defined as a curve on which the gradient is constant.

In other words, an *isocline* is a curve where $\dfrac{dy}{dx} = k$, with k a constant.

Consider the slope field of the following differential equation
$$\frac{dy}{dx} = \frac{x^2 + y^2}{2xy}, x \neq 0, y \neq 0.$$

a State which of the following equations are isoclines of the above differential equation.

If an equation is an isocline, state the constant value of the gradient.

If an equation is not an isocline, justify why it is not.

i $x^2 + y^2 - 8xy = 0$

ii $y = 1$

iii $y = x$

iv $y = x + 1$

v $y = -x$

(10 marks)

b Determine whether the solution to the differential equation

$$\frac{dy}{dx} = \frac{x^2 + y^2}{2xy}, x \neq 0, y \neq 0 \text{ has any}$$

turning points. Justify your answer.

(3 marks)

Click here for further exam practice

. . . .

In the footsteps of Archimedes

Approaches to learning: Research, Critical thinking

Exploration criteria: Mathematical communication (B), Personal engagement (C), Use of mathematics (E)

IB topic: Integration, Proof, Coordinate geometry

The area of a parabolic segment

A **parabolic segment** is a region bounded by a parabola and a line.

Consider this shaded region which is the area bounded by the line $y = x + 6$ and the curve $y = x^2$:

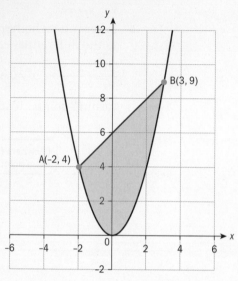

From this chapter you know that you can calculate the shaded area using integration.

On the diagram points A(-2, 4) and B(3, 9) are marked.

Point C is such that the x-value of C is halfway between the x-values of points A and B.

What are the coordinates of point C on the curve?

Triangle ABC is constructed as shown:

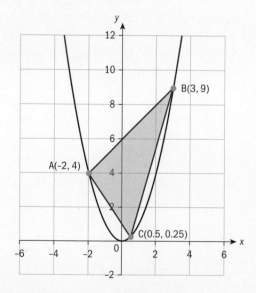

Archimedes showed that the area of the parabolic segment is $\frac{4}{3}$ of the area of triangle ABC.

Calculate the area of the triangle shown.

What methods are available to calculate the area of the triangle?

Use integration to calculate the area between the two curves.

Hence verify that Archimedes' result is correct for this parabolic segment.

You can show that this result is true for any parabola and for any starting points A and B on the parabola.

Consider another triangle by choosing point D on the parabola such that its x-value is halfway between the x-values of A and C, similar to before.

What are the coordinates of point D?

Calculate the area of triangle ACD.

Similarly, for line BC, find E such that its x-value is half-way between C and B.

What are the coordinates of point E?

Hence calculate the area of triangle BCE.

Calculate the ratio between the areas of the new triangles and original triangle ABC.

What do you notice?

You can see already that if you add the areas of triangles ABC, ACD and BCE, you have a reasonable approximation for the area of the parabolic segment.

You can improve this approximation by continuing the process and forming four more triangles from sides AD, CD, CE and BE.

If you add the areas of these seven triangles, you have an even better approximation.

How could the approximation be improved?

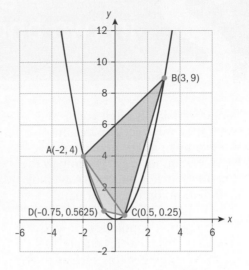

Generalise the problem

Let the area of the first triangle be X.

What is the total area of the next two, four and eight triangles in terms of X?

If you continued adding the areas of an infinite number of such triangles, you would have the *exact* area for the parabolic segment.

By summing the areas of all the triangles, you can show that they form a geometric series.

- What is the common ratio?
- What is the first term?
- What is the sum of the series?
- What has this shown?

Extension

This task demonstrates the part of the historical development of the topic of limits which has led to the development of the concept of calculus.

Look at another area of mathematics that you have studied on this course so far or one that interests you looking forward in the book.

- What is the history of this particular area of mathematics?
- How does it fit into the development of the whole of mathematics?
- How significant is it?
- Who are the main contributors to this branch of mathematics?

12 Modelling motion and change in two and three dimensions

Change in a single variable is often connected to changes in another variable. The height of a projectile, for example, might depend on horizontal displacement, its velocity through the air and the time for which it has been travelling. Growth in a population, on the other hand, might depend not just on resources but on the size of another competing population. How can you develop the ideas from earlier chapters to predict change in complex systems such as these?

Concepts

- Change
- Modelling

Microconcepts

- Vector quantities
- Component of a vector in a given direction evaluated using scalar or vector product
- Acceleration
- Two-dimensional motion with variable velocity
- Projectiles
- Phase portraits
- Euler method with three variables
- Coupled systems
- Eigenvalues and eigenvectors
- Asymptotic behaviour
- Second order differential equations

How much electricity can be generated by a solar panel?

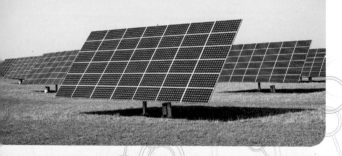

How much will a building move during an earthquake?

How might the shark population be affected by changes in the fish population?

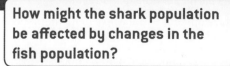

An aircraft needs to deliver a supply package to a polar research station. The package will be dropped from the aircraft from a height of 150 m. If the aircraft is flying at 180 km h^{-1} how far from the research station would the package need to be released if air resistance can be ignored?

- Make a guess at a possible answer to the question above.
- How would your answer change if the aircraft still had the same speed at the same height but was ascending at an angle of 30°?
- If air resistance cannot be ignored would the package need to be released further from or closer to the research station?

Developing inquiry skills

Think about the questions in this opening problem and answer any you can. As you work through the chapter, you will gain mathematical knowledge and skills that will help you to answer them all.

Before you start

Click here for help with this skills check

You should know how to:

1 Integrate exponential and trigonometric functions.

eg Find $\int 3e^{2x} + 2\sin 5x\, dx$

$\int 3e^{2x} + 2\sin 5x\, dx = \dfrac{3}{2}e^{2x} + \dfrac{2}{5}\cos 5x + c$

2 Find and use the scalar and vector products of two vectors.

eg

a Find the angle between $i + 2j - k$ and $2i - 3k$.

First take the scalar product
$1 \times 2 + 2 \times 0 + (-1) \times (-3) = 5$

If θ is the angle between the two vectors then

$\cos\theta = \dfrac{5}{\sqrt{6}\sqrt{13}} \Rightarrow \theta = 55.5°$

Skills check

1 Find:

a $\int 6e^{3x} - \dfrac{1}{e^{2x}}\, dx$

b $\int 3\cos 6x - 4\sin 2x\, dx$

2 a Find the angle between

$\begin{pmatrix} 2 \\ 3 \\ 1 \end{pmatrix}$ and $\begin{pmatrix} -4 \\ 2 \\ 3 \end{pmatrix}$

Continued on next page

b Find a vector perpendicular to

$\begin{pmatrix} 1 \\ 2 \\ -1 \end{pmatrix}$ and $\begin{pmatrix} 2 \\ 0 \\ -3 \end{pmatrix}$

A vector perpendicular to two vectors will be parallel to the vector product of the two vectors.

$\begin{pmatrix} 1 \\ 2 \\ -1 \end{pmatrix} \times \begin{pmatrix} 2 \\ 0 \\ -3 \end{pmatrix} = \begin{pmatrix} -6 \\ 1 \\ -4 \end{pmatrix}$

3 Find eigenvalues and eigenvectors.
eg Find the eigenvalues and eigenvectors for

$\begin{pmatrix} 2 & 3 \\ 1 & 4 \end{pmatrix}$

First solve the equation

$\begin{vmatrix} 2 - \lambda & 3 \\ 1 & 4 - \lambda \end{vmatrix} = 0$

$(2 - \lambda)(4 - \lambda) - 3 = 0$

$\lambda^2 - 6\lambda + 5 = 0 \Rightarrow \lambda = 1, 5$

For the eigenvalues above, solve

$\lambda = 1, \begin{pmatrix} 1 & 3 \\ 1 & 3 \end{pmatrix} \begin{pmatrix} x \\ y \end{pmatrix} = \begin{pmatrix} 0 \\ 0 \end{pmatrix}$

$x + 3y = 0 \Rightarrow x = -3y$

Eigenvectors are parallel to $\begin{pmatrix} -3 \\ 1 \end{pmatrix}$

Similarly the second eigenvector is $\begin{pmatrix} 1 \\ 1 \end{pmatrix}$

b Find a vector perpendicular to

$\begin{pmatrix} 2 \\ 3 \\ 2 \end{pmatrix}$ and $\begin{pmatrix} -2 \\ 2 \\ 3 \end{pmatrix}$

3 Find the eigenvalues and eigenvectors for

$\begin{pmatrix} 2 & 2 \\ 5 & -1 \end{pmatrix}$

12.1 Vector quantities

In Chapter 3 you met the idea of using vectors to describe position and straight-line movement in two-dimensional and three-dimensional space.

In the 19th century, physicists extended this idea of vectors to many other quantities. They realized that physical quantities could be usefully divided into those that needed a direction, as well as size, to define them completely, and those that did not.

For example an object's mass does not need a direction but its velocity does. A velocity of 10 ms^{-1} to the right is very different from 10 ms^{-1} to the left.

Quantities which need a direction to define them fully were classed as **vectors** and those that do not were called **scalars**.

Vector quantities include:

- velocity
- magnetic and electric fields
- acceleration
- momentum.
- force

EXAM HINT

In exams you will not need to understand the concepts of the quantities being used except for those listed in the syllabus (displacement, velocity and acceleration). Other quantities might appear in questions but the context will make it clear how the question is to be answered.

> The results obtained for displacement vectors in Chapter 3 apply equally well to any vector quantity.
> In particular the single vector which will have the same effect as several vectors acting together is called the **resultant** and is equal to the sum of all the vectors.

Geometry and trigonometry

Calculus

Example 1

A force is given by the vector $\begin{pmatrix} 2 \\ 5 \end{pmatrix}$ Newtons (N) and a second force by $\begin{pmatrix} 3 \\ -2 \end{pmatrix}$ N relative to horizontal and vertical axes.

A particle (A) is subjected to both these forces as shown.

1 What is the total horizontal force it experiences?
2 What is the total vertical force it experiences?
3 Hence write down as a column vector the resultant force experienced by the particle and show this force on a diagram.
4 Find the magnitude of the resultant force experienced by the particle.

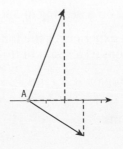

Continued on next page

1 $2 + 3 = 5 \text{N}$

2 $5 - 2 = 3 \text{N}$

3 $\begin{pmatrix} 5 \\ 3 \end{pmatrix} \text{N}$

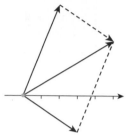

4 $\sqrt{5^2 + 3^2} = 5.83 \text{ N}$

The total horizontal force is found by adding the two horizontal components.

The total vertical force is found by adding the two vertical forces.

The resultant force is the sum of the two vectors. It is equivalent to the two individual vectors so its direction is the direction the particle would move if acted on by no other forces.

As can be seen from the diagram it can also be found geometrically by drawing the individual vectors following on from each other.

The magnitude of the resultant is not the sum of the magnitudes of the individual vectors unless they are all acting in the same direction. If not, parts of the individual vectors act against each other and so cancel each other out.

Exercise 12A

1 Find the magnitude and direction of the following forces. Give the direction as an angle measured counter-clockwise from the positive x-axis.

   a $(6\boldsymbol{i} + 3\boldsymbol{j})\text{N}$ **b** $\begin{pmatrix} -3 \\ 4 \end{pmatrix}\text{N}$

2 Write the following velocities as column vectors:

   a 7ms^{-1} on a bearing of $045°$

   b 12ms^{-1} on a bearing of $330°$.

3 A particle experiences the following accelerations as a result of three different forces acting on it $\begin{pmatrix} 2 \\ 4 \end{pmatrix}\text{ms}^{-2}$, $\begin{pmatrix} -1 \\ 2 \end{pmatrix}\text{ms}^{-2}$ and $\begin{pmatrix} -2 \\ 0 \end{pmatrix}\text{ms}^{-2}$

Find the magnitude and direction of the resultant acceleration experienced by the particle.

4 The torque (τ) produced when turning an object with a force $\boldsymbol{F}$ acting at the end of a lever a displacement $\boldsymbol{r}$ from the object is given by the equation $\tau = \boldsymbol{F} \times \boldsymbol{r}$.

   a State the direction of the torque in comparison to the other two vectors.

   b Find the magnitude of the torque produced when a force of $\begin{pmatrix} 3 \\ 4 \\ 0 \end{pmatrix}\text{N}$ is acting at a displacement $\begin{pmatrix} 2 \\ 1 \\ 0 \end{pmatrix}\text{m}$ from the object.

5 A sledge is being pulled by two dogs as shown. One of the dogs is pulling with a force of 150 N at an angle of 10° to the direction of travel and the second with a force of **D** N at an angle of 15° to the direction of travel.

The sledge is also subject to a resistance force of 70 N as shown.

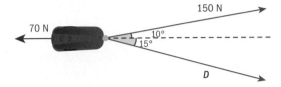

Take the components of the vectors to lie along the direction of travel and perpendicular to the direction of travel.

a Find expressions for the three forces as column vectors.

b Find the resultant force in terms of **D**.

c Find the value of **D** if the sledge is heading in the intended direction.

Newton's second law states that the resultant force (**F** N) acting on a body will be equal to the product of its mass (kg) and the acceleration (ms⁻²) of the body ($F = ma$).

d Given that the mass of the sledge and occupant is 60 kg find the magnitude and direction of the sledge's acceleration.

Components of vector quantities in given directions

It is often important to know how much of a vector quantity is acting in a given direction.

For example, if a book is lying on a table and is subject to a force of $3i + 4j$ N then 3 N will be acting to move the book along the table and 4 N will be acting to lift the book off the table. Whether or not this will result in the book moving depends on the frictional force in the first case and the weight of the book in the second.

The situation is less straightforward when we are trying to find the component of the vector which is acting in a direction which does not lie along one of our base vectors.

Investigation 1

Let θ be the angle between two non-parallel vectors a and b. Think of the direction of b as being along one of the axes.

1 Show that the component of a in the direction of b can be written as $|a|\cos\theta$ where $|a|$ is the magnitude of a.

2 Find a similar expression for the component of a perpendicular to b within the plane formed by the two vectors.

3 Rewrite the expression for the component of a in the direction of b in terms of the scalar product of a and b.

4 Rewrite the expression for the component of a perpendicular to the direction of b in terms of the vector product of a and b.

International-mindedness

Greek philosopher and mathematician, Aristotle, calculated the combined effect of two or more forces called the Parallelogram law.

Continued on next page

5 Hence find the components of $\begin{pmatrix} 1 \\ 2 \\ 1 \end{pmatrix}$

    a in the direction of $\begin{pmatrix} -3 \\ 4 \\ 0 \end{pmatrix}$ **b** perpendicular to $\begin{pmatrix} -3 \\ 4 \\ 0 \end{pmatrix}$.

6 Conceptual How do you find the component of a vector a acting

    i parallel to a vector b **ii** perpendicular to a vector b?

Given two vectors a and b the component of a in the direction of b is given by $\dfrac{a \cdot b}{|b|}$.

The component of a perpendicular to b, within the plane defined by the two vectors, is $\dfrac{|a \times b|}{|b|}$.

International-mindedness

René Descartes used (x, y, z) to represent points in space in the 17th century.

In the 19th century, Arthur Cayley reasoned that we might go further than three values.

Example 2

A sailboat is travelling on a bearing of 045°. The wind is blowing with a velocity of 40 km h^{-1} **from** a direction of 200°.

  a Write down the velocity of the wind as a column vector.

  b Find the component of the velocity of the wind in the same direction as the path of the boat.

a $\begin{pmatrix} 40\cos 70° \\ 40\sin 70° \end{pmatrix} = \begin{pmatrix} 13.7 \\ 37.6 \end{pmatrix}$	A diagram is helpful to make sure that the direction of the vector is correct. 
b Direction of sailboat $= \begin{pmatrix} 1 \\ 1 \end{pmatrix}$ Required component $= \dfrac{13.7 \times 1 + 37.6 \times 1}{\sqrt{1^2 + 1^2}} = 36.3 \,\mathrm{km\,h^{-1}}$	Any vector in the required direction will give the same answer, as the scalar product is divided by the magnitude.

Exercise 12B

1 a Find the magnitudes of the components of the vector $\begin{pmatrix} 1 \\ 4 \end{pmatrix}$ parallel and perpendicular to the vector $\begin{pmatrix} -1 \\ 2 \end{pmatrix}$.

b Find the magnitudes of the components of the vector $\begin{pmatrix} 2 \\ 0 \\ 5 \end{pmatrix}$ parallel and perpendicular, in the plane defined by the two vectors, to the vector $\begin{pmatrix} 2 \\ 2 \\ -1 \end{pmatrix}$.

2 Two forces are pulling a truck of mass 150 kg along a rail. The direction of the rail is $\begin{pmatrix} 12 \\ 5 \\ 0 \end{pmatrix}$ and the two forces are $\begin{pmatrix} 16 \\ 8 \\ 2 \end{pmatrix}$ N and $\begin{pmatrix} 18 \\ 10 \\ 5 \end{pmatrix}$ N.

a Find the component of the resultant force in the direction of the rail.

The acceleration of a body is equal to the resultant force divided by the mass of the body.

b Find the acceleration of the truck along the rail, assuming no other forces act in that direction.

3 In still water a boat can travel at $8\,\mathrm{km\,h^{-1}}$ on full power. On a certain day the boat is travelling in the direction $\begin{pmatrix} 1 \\ 1 \end{pmatrix}$ on full power.

A current is flowing with speed $10\,\mathrm{km\,h^{-1}}$ in the direction of $\begin{pmatrix} 3 \\ 4 \end{pmatrix}$.

a Write the velocity of the current as a column vector.

b Find the component of the current acting in the direction the boat is travelling.

4 A computer graphics technician needs to calculate the direction of the ray reflected off a flat surface (known as ray tracing). He knows the direction of the incident ray and the direction of the normal to the surface.

Let the incident ray have direction b_i, the reflected ray have direction b_r and the surface be perpendicular to the **unit** vector n.

Let a be a vector perpendicular to n as shown in the diagram.

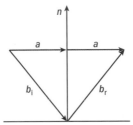

a Write down an expression for b_i in in the form $b_i = a + kn$, where k is a function of b_i and n.

b Find an expression for b_r in terms of b_i and kn.

c A ray with direction $\begin{pmatrix} 0 \\ -1 \\ 4 \end{pmatrix}$ strikes a surface with normal vector $\begin{pmatrix} 2 \\ 1 \\ -2 \end{pmatrix}$. Find the direction of the reflected ray.

12.2 Motion with variable velocity

A satellite is in a spiral descent back to the earth. What would the equation of its path look like? What features would it need to have?

In Chapter 3 you considered motion with constant velocity in two dimensions. In Chapters 10 and 11 you covered motion with variable velocity in one dimension. In this section the two concepts will be combined.

If the displacement of an object is given by $\boldsymbol{r}(t) = \begin{pmatrix} f_1(t) \\ f_2(t) \end{pmatrix}$ then

$$\boldsymbol{v} = \frac{\mathrm{d}\boldsymbol{r}}{\mathrm{d}t} = \begin{pmatrix} \dfrac{\mathrm{d}f_1}{\mathrm{d}t} \\ \dfrac{\mathrm{d}f_2}{\mathrm{d}t} \end{pmatrix} \text{ and } \boldsymbol{a} = \frac{\mathrm{d}^2\boldsymbol{r}}{\mathrm{d}t^2} = \begin{pmatrix} \dfrac{\mathrm{d}^2f_1}{\mathrm{d}t^2} \\ \dfrac{\mathrm{d}^2f_2}{\mathrm{d}t^2} \end{pmatrix}.$$

Integrating the acceleration vector (by integrating each component) gives the velocity vector, which can then be integrated to obtain the displacement vector. In the case of integration there will be two unknown constants which need to be found from the initial conditions.

Example 3

A particle has velocity $\boldsymbol{v}(t)$ where $\boldsymbol{v} = (4t - 6)\boldsymbol{i} - (3t)\boldsymbol{j}$.

a Find the speed of the particle when $t = 3$.

b Find the time at which the direction of movement of the particle is parallel to $\boldsymbol{j}$.

c Show that the acceleration of the particle is constant.

d Given that the displacement of the particle when $t = 0$ is $4\boldsymbol{i}$ find an expression for its displacement at time t.

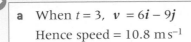
a When $t = 3$, $v = 6i - 9j$

Hence speed = 10.8 m s^{-1}

b $4t - 6 = 0 \Rightarrow t = 1.5$

	If parallel to j the component in the i direction must be equal to 0.
c $a = \dfrac{dv}{dt} = 4i - 3j$ hence constant	There is no variable in the acceleration equation, so acceleration is constant.
	Acceleration is a vector quantity and so should be left as a vector. If an answer of $\sqrt{13} \text{ m s}^{-2}$ were required, the question would need to ask for the magnitude of the acceleration.
d $r = \left(2t^2 + 6t + c_1\right)i - \left(\dfrac{3}{2}t^2 + c_2\right)j$ At $t = 0$, $r = 4i \Rightarrow c_1 = 4$, $c_2 = 0$ $r = \left(2t^2 - 6t + 4\right)i - \left(\dfrac{3}{2}t^2\right)j$	Because there are two components to the vector two different constants of integration are required.

TOK

Why might it be argued that vector equations are superior to Cartesian equations?

Exercise 12C

1 The position vector of a particle P at time t is given as $r = \begin{pmatrix} 4t + 2 \\ 3t^2 - t \end{pmatrix}$, where r is measured in metres and t in seconds.

   a Find the initial displacement of P.

   b Find the initial velocity and speed of P.

   c Show that the acceleration of P is constant and find its magnitude.

2 A particle moves with velocity v (m s^{-1}) given by $v = (4t - 1)i + (5 - 2t)j$.

   Given the initial displacement of the particle is $2i - j$ from the origin O,

   a find the displacement of the particle at time t

   b find the distance of the particle from O when $t = 2$.

3 A particle P moves with acceleration a where $a = \begin{pmatrix} 2 \\ 1 \end{pmatrix}$ m s^{-2}. The initial velocity of P is $\begin{pmatrix} 2 \\ 3 \end{pmatrix}$ m s^{-1}.

   a Find the velocity of P at time t.

   The initial displacement of P is $\begin{pmatrix} 4 \\ -1 \end{pmatrix}$.

   b Find the displacement of P at time t.

4 The velocity of a charged particle in a magnetic field at time t is given by $v = (2t - 1)i + 3t^2 j$.

   a Find the time at which the particle is moving parallel to the vector j.

   b Find the velocity of the particle when $t = 2$ and hence the angle its direction makes with the vector i.

   The initial displacement of the particle is $2i - 3j$.

   c Find an expression for the particle's displacement at time t.

   d Find the time at which the distance of the particle from the origin is 16.

Geometry and trigonometry

Calculus

5 During the first few seconds after take-off an aircraft's acceleration $\boldsymbol{a}$ ms^{-2} at time t seconds ($t \geq 0$) is given by $\boldsymbol{a} = \begin{pmatrix} 6t \\ 2 \end{pmatrix}$, where the two components represent horizontal and vertical motion. When $t = 1$ the velocity of the particle is $\begin{pmatrix} 7 \\ 14 \end{pmatrix}$ ms^{-1}.

  a Find an expression for the velocity at time t.

  b Find the time at which the direction of motion of the aircraft is at 45° to the horizontal.

6 A particle P has velocity vector $\boldsymbol{v}$ given by $\boldsymbol{v} = \begin{pmatrix} 4t - 2.5 \\ 3t^2 \end{pmatrix}$. The initial displacement of P from an origin O is $\begin{pmatrix} 2 \\ 0 \end{pmatrix}$.

  a Find an expression for the displacement of P at time t.

A second particle Q has a constant acceleration of $\begin{pmatrix} 0 \\ 4 \end{pmatrix}$. Its initial velocity is 10 ms^{-1} parallel to the vector $\begin{pmatrix} 3 \\ 4 \end{pmatrix}$.

  b Find an expression for its velocity at time t.

  c Given Q is initially at O show the two particles collide and state the time at which this occurs.

7 A boat has a displacement (km) given by $\boldsymbol{r} = (4t)\boldsymbol{i} + (t^2 - 3t)\boldsymbol{j}$ where t is time in hours from the beginning of its motion.

Find the minimum speed of the boat and the value of t at which it occurs.

Projectiles

Investigation 2

An object travelling under the force of gravity alone is called a projectile. For example, a baseball in flight would be a projectile.

The only acceleration experienced by a projectile is a downward acceleration of g ms^{-2} due to gravity. This acceleration is approximately equal to 9.81 m s^{-2} at the surface of the Earth.

1 Write down, in terms of g, the acceleration vector for a projectile, taking the positive y-direction as "up".

At $t = 0$ a projectile is launched with a speed of u m s^{-1} at an angle of α to the horizontal.

2 Find the initial velocity of the projectile as a column vector in terms of u and α.

3 Use integration to find the velocity vector for the projectile at time t.

International-mindedness

Belgian/Dutch mathematician Simon Stevin used vectors in his theoretical work on falling bodies and his treatise "Principles of the art of weighing" in the 16th century.

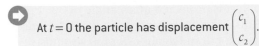

At $t = 0$ the particle has displacement $\begin{pmatrix} c_1 \\ c_2 \end{pmatrix}$.

4 Find an expression for the particle's displacement at time t.

A particle is projected from the point $(0, 0)$ on level ground.

5 Use your answer to question **3** to find the time at which the particle reaches its maximum height.

6 Use your answer to question **4** to find an expression for this height.

7 If the initial speed of the particle is fixed, which value of α will result in the particle maximizing the height reached?

8 a Use your answer to question **4** to find the time at which the particle hits the ground.

b Compare your answer to part **a** with your answer to question **5**. What does this tell you about the motion of the particle?

The range of the particle is the total horizontal distance travelled until it returns to the same height as that at which it began.

9 Find an expression for the range of the particle.

10 If the initial speed of the particle is fixed which value of α will result in the particle maximizing its range?

A ball is projected from ground level with an initial speed of $15\ \mathrm{m\,s^{-1}}$ at an angle of $30°$. The acceleration due to gravity is $9.81\ \mathrm{m\,s^{-2}}$.

11 Find the horizontal distance travelled by the ball before it hits the ground.

12 Find the maximum height reached by the ball.

13 In a more realistic model what additional force will need to be taken into account when predicting the flight of a ball?

14 **Factual** What does a column vector describe in projectile motion?

15 **Conceptual** How are vectors useful in describing projectile motion and how do we find the velocity equation?

Exercise 12D

In the following questions take $g = 9.81\mathrm{m\,s^{-2}}$.

$\begin{pmatrix} 1 \\ 0 \end{pmatrix}$ and $\begin{pmatrix} 0 \\ 1 \end{pmatrix}$ are unit vectors in the horizontal and vertical directions respectively. All external forces, such as air resistance, may be ignored.

1 An object is projected with an initial velocity of $\begin{pmatrix} 5 \\ 2 \end{pmatrix}\ \mathrm{m\,s^{-1}}$ from a point $1.5\,\mathrm{m}$ above ground level.

a Write down the acceleration vector for the particle while in flight.

b Find an expression for
   i the velocity
   ii the displacement
   of the object t seconds after it has been projected.

c Find the time at which the particle strikes the ground and the horizontal distance it has travelled during its flight.

2 A stone is thrown from the top of a vertical cliff 50 m high with an initial velocity of $4\mathbf{i} + 2\mathbf{j}$ m s^{-1}.

a Write down the velocity vector for the stone at time t seconds after the stone has been thrown.

b Find the displacement vector for the stone, taking the point of projection as the origin of the coordinate system.

c Find the time at which the stone hits the ground at the base of the cliff.

d Find its distance from the base of the cliff when it hits the ground.

3 An particle is projected from ground level at an angle of 30° to the horizontal and with a speed of 14.7 m s^{-1}.

a Write the initial velocity of the particle as a column vector.

b Find an expression for the velocity of the particle at time t.

c Find the time at which the particle attains its greatest height.

d Find an expression for the displacement of the particle.

e Find the greatest height reached by the particle.

f Find the horizontal distance travelled by the particle while in flight.

g Find the minimum speed attained by the particle during its flight.

Fully justify your answer.

4 An object is projected at an angle of 30° to the horizontal from a point at ground level. It hits the ground again after 6.0 seconds.

Find the initial speed of the object.

5 A ball is thrown from a height of 1.5 m with a speed of 10 m s^{-1} at an angle of 45° to the horizontal. It just clears a wall 10 m from the point of projection.

a Find an expression for the displacement of the ball at time t.

b Find the height of the wall.

c Find the horizontal distance travelled by the ball before it hits the ground.

6 A particle is projected at a speed of 50 m s^{-1} at an angle of 30° above the horizontal from a point 2 m above level ground.

a Write down the initial velocity vector.

b Find the displacement of the particle from the point of projection t seconds after the particle is projected.

c Find the time for which the particle's height above the ground is greater than 22 m.

d Find the time at which the particle hits the ground and the horizontal distance travelled during the flight.

Exponential and trigonometric motion

Investigation 3

Consider a particle moving so that its position at time t is given by the equation

$$\mathbf{r} = \begin{pmatrix} r\cos\omega t \\ r\sin\omega t \end{pmatrix}, \text{ where } r \text{ and } \omega \text{ are constant values.}$$

1 By considering the distance of the particle from the origin at time t, show that the path followed by the particle is a circle centred on the origin and state its radius. ➡

2 a Write down the initial position of the particle.

b Give the value of t when the particle first returns to its initial position.

3 a Find the velocity of the particle at time t.

b Show that the speed of the particle is constant and state its value.

c Show that the velocity is always perpendicular to the particle's displacement vector.

d Explain what this means geometrically about the direction of the motion of the particle.

4 a Find the acceleration of the particle at time t.

b Show that the acceleration is always perpendicular to the velocity vector.

Let a be the acceleration vector of the particle.

c Show that $|a| = \dfrac{|v|^2}{r}$.

d Show that $a = kr$ and state the value of k.

5 [**Conceptual**] How would you derive the velocity and acceleration equations for a particle moving in a circle from the general equation for its displacement?

TOK

How do we relate a theory to the author? Who developed vector analysis, Josiah Willard Gibbs or Oliver Heaviside?

Example 4

A particle has displacement r at time t where $r = \begin{pmatrix} 10e^{-0.5t}\cos t \\ 10e^{-0.5t}\sin t \end{pmatrix}$.

a Find the position of the particle when $t = 0, \dfrac{\pi}{2}, \pi, \dfrac{3\pi}{2}$ and 2π and show these points on a coordinate grid.

b Describe the long-term behaviour of the particle.

c Find the velocity of the particle at time t.

d Find the magnitude and the direction of the velocity when $t = 0$.

a $\begin{pmatrix} 10 \\ 0 \end{pmatrix}, \begin{pmatrix} 0 \\ 4.56 \end{pmatrix}, \begin{pmatrix} -2.08 \\ 0 \end{pmatrix}, \begin{pmatrix} 0 \\ -0.948 \end{pmatrix}, \begin{pmatrix} 0.432 \\ 0 \end{pmatrix}$

The position vectors are found by substituting the values of t into the equation for the displacement.

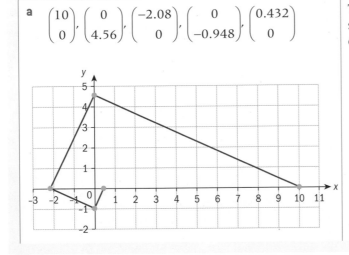

Continued on next page

Geometry and trigonometry

Calculus

b   The particle will spiral towards the point $(0,0)$.

c $v = \begin{pmatrix} -5e^{-0.5t}\cos t - 10e^{-0.5t}\sin t \\ -5e^{-0.5t}\sin t + 10e^{-0.5t}\cos t \end{pmatrix}$

The velocity is found by differentiating the displacement vector using the chain and product rules.

$= \begin{pmatrix} -5e^{-0.5t}(\cos t + 2\sin t) \\ -5e^{-0.5t}(\sin t - 2\cos t) \end{pmatrix}$

d $v = \begin{pmatrix} -5(1+0) \\ -5(0-2) \end{pmatrix} = \begin{pmatrix} -5 \\ 10 \end{pmatrix}$

Magnitude = 11.2, direction = 117° to the positive x-axis.

Exercise 12E

1   A particle moves such that its velocity at time t is given by

$v = \begin{pmatrix} 2e^{2t} \\ e^{2t} + 2 \end{pmatrix}$. At $t = 0$ the particle is at $(0,0)$.

a   Find an expression for the particle's acceleration at time t.

b   Find an expression for the particle's displacement at time t.

2   A particle has acceleration at time t given by

$a = \begin{pmatrix} 10e^{2t} - 1 \\ 4e^{2t} + 2 \end{pmatrix}$.

The particle is initially at rest at the origin. Find an expression for its displacement at time t.

3   A particle moves so that its acceleration is given by the expression $a = \begin{pmatrix} 8\cos 2t \\ 8\sin 2t \end{pmatrix}$.

Given the particle has initial velocity of

$v = \begin{pmatrix} 0 \\ -4 \end{pmatrix}$ and an initial displacement of $\begin{pmatrix} -2 \\ 0 \end{pmatrix}$:

a   Find an expression for the particle's displacement at time t.

b   Find the particle's distance from the origin at time t.

c   Hence describe the path of the particle.

d   Given that $a = kr$ state the value of k.

4   A particle moves such that its displacement at time t is given by $r = \begin{pmatrix} e^{2t} \\ 3e^{2t} \end{pmatrix}$.

a   Find an expression for the velocity of the particle at time t.

b   Find an expression for the acceleration of the particle at time t.

c   Given that $a = kr$ state the value of k.

5   A particle moves such that its displacement t seconds after its motion begins is given by

$r = \begin{pmatrix} e^{-t}\cos 4t + 2 \\ e^{-t}\sin 4t + 5 \end{pmatrix}$.

a   Find the particle's distance from $(2, 5)$ at time t.

b   Hence describe the path of the particle.

c   Show that the speed of the particle at time t is $\sqrt{17}e^{-t}$.

d   Find the value of t at which the speed of the particle is reduced by half.

6 A particle moves anti-clockwise at constant speed in a circle of radius 4 units centred on $(0, 0)$. Given that the time to complete one revolution is 6 seconds and the particle is initially at $(0, -4)$:

a Find an expression for the position of the particle at time t.

A second particle is moving anti-clockwise in a circle of radius 4 units centred on $(5, 4)$ with the same constant speed as the first particle. Initially it is at the point $(5, 0)$.

b Write down an expression for the displacement of this particle.

c Find the velocity vector at time t.

Developing inquiry skills

Return to the opening problem for the chapter. The package will be dropped from the aircraft from a height of 150 m. The aircraft has a speed of 180 km h^{-1}. If air resistance can be ignored, find how far from the research station the package should be released:

a if the aircraft is flying horizontally

b if the aircraft is ascending at an angle of 30°.

12.3 Exact solutions of coupled differential equations

Two fungi, X and Y, are growing on a tree. X is the faster growing fungus but when it encounters Y, Y will dominate and benefit from the nutrients in X.

What will happen as the two fungi spread out?

This section will look at simple models where the growth of one variable is affected by the presence of another.

A coupled system is one in which either the equation for the derivative of x contains a function of y or the equation for the derivative of y contains a function of x or both of these.

Investigation 4

Initially the investigation considers an uncoupled system.

1 Solve the differential equation $\dfrac{\mathrm{d}x}{\mathrm{d}t} = 2x$ given that $x = 5$ when $t = 0$.

2 Solve the system of differential equations $\begin{pmatrix} \dot{x} \\ \dot{y} \end{pmatrix} = \begin{pmatrix} 2x \\ 3y \end{pmatrix}$, given that

$\begin{pmatrix} x \\ y \end{pmatrix} = \begin{pmatrix} 3 \\ 5 \end{pmatrix}$ when $t = 0$.

The vector x is often used to stand for the general vector of the variables, so in the example above $x = \begin{pmatrix} x \\ y \end{pmatrix}$ and $\dot{x}$ will be the derivative of this vector with respect to time.

For any system of equations that can be written in the form $\dot{x} = Mx$, and for which the eigenvalues of M are distinct, the solution is
$$x = A\mathrm{e}^{\lambda_1 t} p_1 + B\mathrm{e}^{\lambda_2 t} p_2$$
where $A, B \in \mathbb{R}$, λ_1, λ_2 are the eigenvalues of M, and p_1 and p_2 are the corresponding eigenvectors.

3 a Verify the system of equations in question **2** can be written as $\dot{x} = Mx$.

   b Find the eigenvalues and eigenvectors of M and hence show that your solution can be written in the form $x = A\mathrm{e}^{\lambda_1 t} p_1 + B\mathrm{e}^{\lambda_2 t} p_2$, stating the values of A and B.

4 Verify that $x = A\mathrm{e}^{\lambda_1 t} p_1 + B\mathrm{e}^{\lambda_2 t} p_2$ is a solution to $\dot{x} = Mx$ more generally by differentiating the right-hand side and showing that it is equal to Mx.

   You will need to use the fact that from the definition of eigenvalues and eigenvectors, $Mp_1 = \lambda_1 p_1$ and $Mp_2 = \lambda_2 p_2$.

Two fungi, X and Y, are growing on a tree. X is the faster growing fungus but when it encounters Y, Y will dominate and benefit from the nutrients in X.

The area of tree covered by X is given as x and that of Y by y. The growth of the two fungi in cm^2 can be approximately modelled by the following system of differential equations where t is measured in weeks:

$\dot{x} = 0.4x - 0.2y$

$\dot{y} = 0.1x + 0.1y$

5 Explain why the signs of the different variables and the values of the coefficients indicate that these equations might be consistent with the information given.

6 Show that the right-hand side of this coupled system can be written in the form Mx where M is a 2×2 matrix and $x = \begin{pmatrix} x \\ y \end{pmatrix}$.

7 Hence, find expressions for the areas covered by X and by Y at time t, given that X covers $10\,\text{cm}^2$ and Y covers $6\,\text{cm}^2$ when $t = 0$.

8 a If this model continues to be a good approximation to growth what will be the long-term ratio of the area covered by X to the area covered by Y?

b Comment on why this model is unlikely to be valid as t increases.

9 [Conceptual] How are eigenvalues and eigenvectors useful when solving a system of equations?

The coupled linear system $\dot{x} = Mx$ has solution $x = Ae^{\lambda_1 t}p_1 + Be^{\lambda_2 t}p_2$, where $A, B \in \mathbb{R}$ and are dependent on the initial conditions.

Example 5

a Find the solution to the following system of differential equations, given that $x = 4$ and $y = -2$ when $t = 0$.
$$\dot{x} = 3x - 4y$$
$$\dot{y} = x - 2y$$

b Determine the long-term ratio of x to y.

a $\begin{vmatrix} 3-\lambda & -4 \\ 1 & -2-\lambda \end{vmatrix} = 0$ $\Rightarrow \lambda^2 - \lambda - 2 = 0 \Rightarrow \lambda = 2, -1$	The equations can be written as $\begin{pmatrix} \dot{x} \\ \dot{y} \end{pmatrix} = \begin{pmatrix} 3 & -4 \\ 1 & -2 \end{pmatrix}\begin{pmatrix} x \\ y \end{pmatrix}$. Hence the first stage is
Corresponding eigenvectors are $\begin{pmatrix} 4 \\ 1 \end{pmatrix}$ and $\begin{pmatrix} 1 \\ 1 \end{pmatrix}$.	to find the eigenvalues and eigenvectors for $\begin{pmatrix} 3 & -4 \\ 1 & -2 \end{pmatrix}$.
Hence $\begin{pmatrix} x \\ y \end{pmatrix} = Ae^{2t}\begin{pmatrix} 4 \\ 1 \end{pmatrix} + Be^{-t}\begin{pmatrix} 1 \\ 1 \end{pmatrix}$.	
Putting in initial conditions $\begin{pmatrix} 4 \\ -2 \end{pmatrix} = \begin{pmatrix} 4A \\ A \end{pmatrix} + \begin{pmatrix} B \\ B \end{pmatrix}$	The form of the general solution is given in the formula book.
$A = 2, \ B = -4$ $\begin{pmatrix} x \\ y \end{pmatrix} = 2e^{2t}\begin{pmatrix} 4 \\ 1 \end{pmatrix} - 4e^{-t}\begin{pmatrix} 1 \\ 1 \end{pmatrix}$	
b The long-term ratio is 4:1.	As t increases the second term tends to 0.

Phase portrait

It can be useful to show on a diagram how the values of the two variables change over time. Such a diagram is called a phase portrait.

Investigation 5

A system of linear equations has the following solution:

$$\begin{pmatrix} x \\ y \end{pmatrix} = A\mathrm{e}^{-t}\begin{pmatrix} 1 \\ 2 \end{pmatrix} + B\mathrm{e}^{5t}\begin{pmatrix} -1 \\ 1 \end{pmatrix}$$

1 **a** Show that the equations of the lines through the origin which are in the direction of each of the eigenvectors are $y = 2x$ and $y = -x$.

   b Choose an initial value for the system that lies on $y = 2x$, for example $(2, 4)$, and find this particular solution to the system of equations.

   c Choose an initial value for the system that lies on the line $y = -x$ and find this particular solution to the system of equations.

   d What do you notice?

2 A phase portrait indicates future **trajectories** for different initial values.

   a Draw a set of coordinate axes and on them draw $y = 2x$ and $y = -x$.

   b Indicate with arrows the direction of motion of any point initially on one of these lines.

3 For any initial values not on these lines, the values of both A and B will be non-zero.

   a Conjecture from your general solution the long-term trajectory for systems which are not initially on $y = 2x$ or $y = -x$.

   b Conjecture the "history" of the trajectory by considering what happens as t becomes increasingly negative.

   c Find the particular solution for an initial value of $(6, 6)$.

   d Enter the top and bottom lines of your solution into a GDC and use the table function to look at the values of x and y as t increases. Set the step interval on your table to 0.1. Consider the values of x and y as t increases in both the positive and negative directions. Does this support your conjectures in parts **a** and **b**?

   e Show $(6, 6)$ and the trajectory through that point on your phase portrait.

   f Use technology to plot trajectories within each of the quadrants in the diagram drawn in question **3**.

4 Now consider another system of coupled differential equations that has the following general solution:

$$\begin{pmatrix} x \\ y \end{pmatrix} = A\mathrm{e}^{t}\begin{pmatrix} 1 \\ 2 \end{pmatrix} + B\mathrm{e}^{3t}\begin{pmatrix} 2 \\ -1 \end{pmatrix}$$

   a Write down the equations of the two lines through the origin that are parallel to the eigenvectors.

   b By considering the values of A and B for a particular point on either of these two lines, describe the trajectory of any point initially on these lines.

   c For those trajectories beginning away from the two lines given in part **a** conjecture the direction the trajectory approaches as $t \to \infty$. Verify your answer using your GDC or Geogebra.

   d Which direction do the majority of trajectories tend towards as $t \to -\infty$?

e As they approach this point write down the approximate gradient for the trajectories that are not initially on either line through the origin parallel to the eigenvectors.

  f Sketch the phase portrait for the solution given.

  g How would your diagram change when drawing the phase portrait for the system with solution

  $$\begin{pmatrix} x \\ y \end{pmatrix} = A e^{-t} \begin{pmatrix} 1 \\ 2 \end{pmatrix} + B e^{-3t} \begin{pmatrix} 2 \\ -1 \end{pmatrix}?$$

5 **Conceptual** Why are phase portraits a useful way of depicting the solutions to differential equations?

An equilibrium point (or equilibrium solution) is a point at which $\dot{x} = 0$ and $\dot{y} = 0$. An equilibrium point is classed as **stable** or **unstable**. If **all** points close to an equilibrium point will move towards the equilibrium point, it is stable, otherwise it is unstable.

In both the examples in Investigation 5, (0, 0) is an **equilibrium point**. At this point $\dfrac{dx}{dt} = 0$ and $\dfrac{dy}{dt} = 0$ so if a particle were initially at (0, 0) it would stay there.

In both cases (0, 0) is an **unstable** equilibrium point because particles that begin close to the origin will generally move away from it rather than towards the origin.

In the first example (0, 0) is a **saddle point**.

In the second example (0, 0) is a **source**.

When the matrix representing a coupled system of linear first order differential equations has two distinct real eigenvalues, the lines through the origin in the direction of the eigenvectors of the matrix give the gradients for the long-term behaviour of the system as $t \to \infty$ and as $t \to -\infty$.

When both eigenvalues are positive all trajectories move away from the origin as t increases and towards the direction of the eigenvector associated with the larger eigenvalue. The origin is an unstable equilibrium point.

When both eigenvalues are negative all trajectories move towards the origin as t increases, and towards the direction of the eigenvector associated with the more negative eigenvalue. The origin is a stable equilibrium point.

When one eigenvalue is positive and the other negative then the origin is a saddle point. As t increases all trajectories not on the lines through the origin parallel to the eigenvectors move towards the direction of the eigenvector associated with the positive eigenvalue.

Geometry and trigonometry

Calculus

Exercise 12F

1   **a**   Find the solutions to the following systems of differential equations.

     i $\dot{x} = 2x + 2y$

         $\dot{y} = 5x - y$ $x = -6,\ y = 22$ when $t = 0$

     ii $\dot{x} = x + 2y$

         $\dot{y} = 3y$ $x = 3,\ y = 1$ when $t = 0$

     iii $\dot{x} = -2x + 2y$

         $\dot{y} = -x - 5y$ $x = 2,\ y = 1$ when $t = 0$

     iv $\dot{x} = x + 2y$

         $\dot{y} = 3x - 4y$ $x = 1,\ y = 11$ when $t = 0$

  b   Draw a phase portrait for the general solutions to the coupled differential equations obtained in part **a**. In each case give the Cartesian equations of the lines through the origin parallel to the eigenvectors.

2   Match each of these phase portraits with the associated solution to a system of coupled differential equations.

a

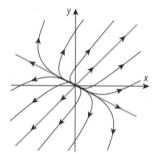

b

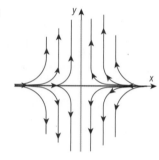

c

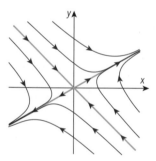

d

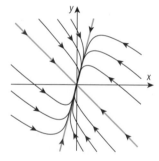

A $\begin{pmatrix} x \\ y \end{pmatrix} = A e^{t} \begin{pmatrix} 1 \\ 0 \end{pmatrix} + B e^{-t} \begin{pmatrix} 0 \\ 1 \end{pmatrix}$

B $\begin{pmatrix} x \\ y \end{pmatrix} = A e^{-t} \begin{pmatrix} 1 \\ 3 \end{pmatrix} + B e^{-3t} \begin{pmatrix} 1 \\ -1 \end{pmatrix}$

C $\begin{pmatrix} x \\ y \end{pmatrix} = A e^{t} \begin{pmatrix} 3 \\ 2 \end{pmatrix} + B e^{-2t} \begin{pmatrix} 1 \\ -1 \end{pmatrix}$

D $\begin{pmatrix} x \\ y \end{pmatrix} = A e^{4t} \begin{pmatrix} 3 \\ -2 \end{pmatrix} + B e^{5t} \begin{pmatrix} 1 \\ 1 \end{pmatrix}$

3   **a**   Find the general solution of the following system of differential equations:

     $\dot{x} = 2x + 3y$

     $\dot{y} = x + 4y$

  b   Sketch the phase portrait for this system of equations, making clear any asymptotic behaviour.

  c   Find the equation of the particular solution given that $x = -9,\ y = -1$ when $t = 0$.

4 a Find the general solution of the following system of differential equations. Give all final solutions correct to 3 significant figures.

$$\dot{x} = 3x + y$$
$$\dot{y} = 2x - y$$

b Sketch the phase portrait for this system of equations, making clear any asymptotic behaviour.

c Find the equation of the particular solution given that $x = 1$, $y = 1$ when $t = 0$.

5 a By considering the system of equations below explain what would happen when the initial conditions are $x = 0$, $y = 0$.

$$\dot{x} = ax + by$$
$$\dot{y} = cx + dy$$

b By considering the phase portraits and solutions from part **a**, or otherwise, write down conditions on the eigenvalues for $(0, 0)$ to be a stable equilibrium.

c Fred says that "Nearly all points close to the equilibrium point must tend towards it for the point to be stable?" Comment on Fred's statement.

6 In Investigation 4 the area of tree covered by two fungi X and Y was given by the variables x and y respectively, where

$$\begin{pmatrix} x \\ y \end{pmatrix} = Ae^{0.2t}\begin{pmatrix} 1 \\ 1 \end{pmatrix} + Be^{0.3t}\begin{pmatrix} 2 \\ 1 \end{pmatrix}$$ and the values

of A and B were dependent on the initial conditions.

a Draw a phase portrait for this general solution with $x, y \geq 0$.

The system of equations that led to this solution was

$$\dot{x} = 0.4x - 0.2y$$
$$\dot{y} = 0.1x + 0.1y$$

If the area covered by either of the fungi reaches 0 the fungus is extinct on that tree and will no longer grow.

b Write down the differential equations that will replace the system above if

i $x = 0$ **ii** $y = 0$

and give the general solution to these equations for times beyond this point.

Let the initial areas covered by the two fungi be x_0 and y_0 where $x_0, y_0 > 0$.

c Use your **phase portrait** to deduce the long-term proportions of $x:y$ if the initial conditions were such that:

i $0 < y_0 < \frac{1}{2}x$ **ii** $\frac{1}{2}x_0 < y_0 < x_0$

iii $y_0 > x_0$ **iv** $x_0 = y_0$

Systems with imaginary or complex eigenvalues

Sometimes the system will have complex eigenvalues. You do not need to find the corresponding eigenvectors or the solution to the system in this case, but you do need to be able to draw the phase portrait and predict the long-term behaviour of the trajectories. Because complex eigenvalues will come from solutions to the characteristic equation they will always be a conjugate pair, for example 2 + 3i and 2 − 3i.

Investigation 6

1 **a** Find the eigenvalues for the following system of equations:

$$\dot{x} = 2y$$

$$\dot{y} = -2x$$

In a similar way to the case of real eigenvalues, the general solution to a system of equations with imaginary eigenvalues $\pm b\mathrm{i}$ can be written in the form: $\begin{pmatrix} x \\ y \end{pmatrix} = A\mathrm{e}^{bit}\boldsymbol{v}_1 + B\mathrm{e}^{-bit}\boldsymbol{v}_2$, with $b \in \mathbb{R}$.

b State the value of b for the system given in part **a** and write e^{bit} in the form $\cos(bt) + \mathrm{i}\sin(bt)$.

> **HINT**
>
> A, B and the elements of the two eigenvectors can be complex numbers but values can be found in which both and x and y are real for all values of t. This is beyond this course but you need to note that the fact e^{bit} can be written as $\cos(bt) + \mathrm{i}\sin(bt)$ means the solution will be periodic with a period of $\dfrac{2\pi}{b}$.

c For the system given in part **a** find the value of t which gives the first positive time when the coordinates (x, y) are again equal to their initial value.

For imaginary eigenvalues the phase portrait will consist of concentric circles or ellipses centred on the origin.

2 **a** Find the eigenvalues for the systems below.

A	$\dot{x} = -3x - 4y$	**B**	$\dot{x} = 2x - y$
	$\dot{y} = 2x + y$		$\dot{y} = x + 2y$

b Write down what you notice about
  i the real part of the eigenvalue
  and **ii** the imaginary part in both **A** and **B**.

c Explain why this is always the case.

3 Write down a condition on a for the trajectory to spiral towards the origin.

To decide whether the spiral is clockwise or counter-clockwise you can evaluate $\dfrac{\mathrm{d}y}{\mathrm{d}t}$ at a point on the x-axis or $\dfrac{\mathrm{d}x}{\mathrm{d}t}$ at a point on the y-axis.

b For each of the systems in question **2** find the values of $\dfrac{\mathrm{d}y}{\mathrm{d}t}$ at the point $(1, 0)$ and deduce what this means about the direction of motion as t increases.

c Use the chain rule to also evaluate the gradient at $(0, 1)$.

d Hence sketch the phase portrait for the two systems given in question **2**.

4 **Conceptual** How is the motion of a particle different when the matrix for a coupled system has either imaginary or complex eigenvalues?

The result from question **2** means that a solution can be written in the form

$$\begin{pmatrix} x \\ y \end{pmatrix} = e^{at}\left(Ae^{bit}\mathbf{v}_1 + Be^{-bit}\mathbf{v}_2 \right) \text{ where } a, b \in \mathbb{R} \text{ and the periodic factor is the}$$

same as the one in question **1**.

The solution will be either a clockwise or counter-clockwise spiral with the trajectories either moving towards or away from the origin as shown below.

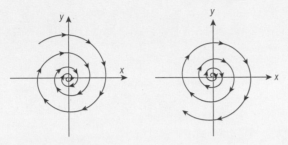

If the eigenvalues are $a \pm b\mathrm{i}$ then the trajectories will:

- form circles or ellipses with the origin as a centre if $a = 0$
- spiral away from the origin if $a > 0$
- spiral into the origin if $a < 0$.

The direction of movement can be found by evaluating $\dfrac{dy}{dt}$ for a point on the

x-axis or $\dfrac{dx}{dt}$ for a point on the y-axis.

Exercise 12G

1 For each of the systems below:

   i Find the eigenvalues.

   ii Find $\dfrac{dy}{dt}$ and the gradient of the curve at the point $(1, 0)$.

   iii Sketch the phase portrait for the system.

a $\dot{x} = 2x - 5y$
$\dot{y} = x - 2y$

b $\dot{x} = -x - 3y$
$\dot{y} = 4x + 3y$

c $\dot{x} = -0.2x + y$
$\dot{y} = -x - 0.2y$

d $\dot{x} = x + 5y$
$\dot{y} = -5x + y$

e $\dot{x} = 3x - 9y$
$\dot{y} = 4x - 3y$

2 A satellite is launched from the Earth. Its displacement at time t, measured with the Earth at the origin, is given as (x, y) with the coordinates lying in the plane of the satellite's motion. The velocity of the satellite at time t is given by the following system of equations:

$$\frac{dx}{dt} = 2x + y$$

$$\frac{dy}{dt} = -x + 2y$$

a Verify that the satellite's path will take it away from the Earth.

b Given that the satellite passes through the point $(1, 1)$ sketch a possible future trajectory for the satellite.

12.4 Approximate solutions to coupled linear equations

Many ecosystems contain species that are closely connected, often competing for limited resources. Is it possible to find population sizes where both species can exist together or will one always come to dominate over time? These kinds of equations are addressed through consideration of coupled non-linear differential equations.

Most systems of differential equations are not linear and cannot be solved exactly. Fortunately, there are many numerical methods that can be used to give approximate results, including the Euler method which you studied in Chapter 11.

For the equation $\dfrac{dy}{dx} = f(x, y)$ the Euler method equations are:

$x_{n+1} = x_n + h$, $y_{n+1} = y_n + hf(x_n, y_n)$, where h is the step size.

> **HINT**
>
> Though easy to apply, the Euler method is not much used in practice due to its inaccuracies. Other methods include the improved Euler method and the Runge–Kutta method. But these are not in the Higher Level course.

> For the coupled case in which
> $\dfrac{dx}{dt} = f_1(x, y, t)$, $\dfrac{dy}{dt} = f_2(x, y, t)$ the Euler method equations are:
> $t_{n+1} = t_n + h$
> $x_{n+1} = x_n + hf_1(x_n, y_n, t_n)$
> $y_{n+1} = y_n + hf_2(x_n, y_n, t_n)$

> **HINT**
>
> This is provided in the formula book.

Example 6

a Use the Euler method with a step size of 0.1 to find the approximate values of x and y when $t = 1$ and $t = 2$ for the following system of differential equations:

$\dot{x} = 3x - 4y$

$\dot{y} = x - 2y$

and $x = 4$ given $y = -2$ when $t = 0$.

b In Example 5 the exact solution to this system of differential equations was found to be

$\begin{pmatrix} x \\ y \end{pmatrix} = 2e^{2t}\begin{pmatrix} 4 \\ 1 \end{pmatrix} - 4e^{-t}\begin{pmatrix} 1 \\ 1 \end{pmatrix}$. Find the percentage error in your answers to part **a**.

a The two equations are:

$$x_{n+1} = x_n + 0.1(3x_n - 4y_n)$$
$$= 1.3x_n - 0.4y_n$$

$$y_{n+1} = y_n + 0.1(x_n - 2y_n)$$
$$= 0.1x_n + 0.8y_n$$

At $t = 1$, $x = 48.1$, $y = 11.0$

At $t = 2$, $x = 306$, $y = 76.2$

> There is no need to simplify the equation. Only do so if you feel it will make the next stages more straightforward.
>
> There is no need to list intermediate solutions in an exam but the recurrence relation used should be given.

b The exact values from the equation are:

At $t = 1$, $x = 57.6$, $y = 13.3$

At $t = 2$, $x = 436$, $y = 109$

Percentage errors are:

At $t = 1$, 16% and 17%

At $t = 2$, 30% and 30%

> Percentage errors are calculated using the formula $\dfrac{\text{actual error}}{\text{exact amount}} \times 100$.
>
> In this case, it is clear that the Euler method underestimates the actual values, and the errors increase as the iteration continues, though the asymptotic behaviour of the approximation is similar to the exact equation (y-value approximately four times x-value as expected from the exact equation).

Geometry and trigonometry

Exercise 12H

1 Solve each of the equations from question **1a** in Exercise 12F using the Euler method with a step size of 0.1 from $t = 0$ to $t = 1$. Use your results to sketch the trajectory from the initial point and compare your answer with the phase portrait drawn for question **1b**.

Comment on the accuracy of your answers, and in particular whether the ratio of x- to y-coordinates is tending towards the expected value.

2 Use the Euler method with a step size of 0.1 to find approximations for the values of x and y when $t = 1$ for the following systems.

a $\dfrac{dx}{dt} = 2xy - x$

$\dfrac{dy}{dt} = 2y - xy$

$x = 1$, $y = 1$ when $t = 0$

b $\dfrac{dx}{dt} = 2x^2 - xy$

$\dfrac{dy}{dt} = 2xy - y^2$

$x = 1$, $y = 1$ when $t = 0$

3 Use the Euler method with a step size of 0.1 to find approximations for the values of x and y when $t = 0.5$ for the following systems.

a $\dfrac{dx}{dt} = -2tx + 3y^2$

$\dfrac{dy}{dt} = -3x^2 + 3ty$

$x = -1$, $y = 2$ when $t = 0$

b $\dfrac{dx}{dt} = 2tx + y$

$\dfrac{dy}{dt} = -3x^2 + ty$

$x = 0$, $y = 1$ when $t = 0$

Calculus

Predator–prey and other real-life models

Investigation 7

When a population X of size x increases at a steady rate α, proportional to the size of the population, we can write the differential equation describing its rate of growth as $\dfrac{dx}{dt} = ax$. This equation leads to exponential growth.

Suppose now a different species Y, with population size y, is in competition with X.

The rate of increase of x is now affected by the size of y, such that as y increases the rate of increase of x will diminish.

The simplest equation that will do this is $\dfrac{dx}{dt} = \left(a - by\right)x$.

As the population of Y (y) increases, the rate of growth of X decreases as it depends on $a - by$.

If Y is competing with X for the same resources then the equation for the growth in population of Y is likely to have a similar structure:

$$\frac{dy}{dt} = \left(c - dx\right)y$$

However, if species Y is a predator and species X is the prey then an equation of the form

$\dfrac{dy}{dt} = \left(cx - d\right)y$ might be more appropriate.

1   Explain why this equation might be more appropriate than the previous one for a predator–prey situation.

The populations, **in thousands**, of fish (x) and of sharks, **in hundreds** (y) at time t (years) are given by the equations:

$$\frac{dx}{dt} = 3x - 3xy \text{ and } \frac{dy}{dt} = xy - 2y$$

2   Find the two equilibrium positions for the populations of fish and sharks.

Initially there are 3000 fish and 20 sharks.

3   Use the Euler method with a step size of 0.02 years to show that when $t = 0.02$ there are approximately 3144 fish and 20.4 sharks.

Use either a spreadsheet or a graphing calculator to answer the questions below.

4   **a**   Plot the values of x and y on a set of axes for $0 \le t \le 3$. Plot values every 0.2 years.

    b   Join the points to create a trajectory.

       What does this suggest about the non-zero equilibrium point?

5   Explain from a consideration of the differential equations why the population of sharks continues to grow once the population of fish has started to fall.

6   If using a spreadsheet draw a graph of x and y on the same axes, with t on the horizontal axis. Comment on the significant features of the graph.

7   Conceptual   How can we develop a predator–prey model and what can the model display?

> **HINT**
>
> These types of equations are often referred to as the **Lotka–Volterra equations.**

Exercise 12I

1 In the predator–prey model given by the following equations let P be the population of the predators and Q the population of the prey. All population values are measured in 1000s of individuals and time is measured in years.

$$\frac{dP}{dt} = (Q - 2)P$$

$$\frac{dQ}{dt} = (1 - P)Q$$

a Find the two equilibrium points for the populations.

b Use the equations to explain what would happen to the population of the prey if the predators were absent ($P = 0$).

c Use the equations to explain what would happen to the population of the predators if the prey were absent ($Q = 0$).

d If the initial population of prey is 2000 and of the predators is 2000 use the Euler method with a step size of 0.1 year to find the population of each after 1 year.

2 Populations of rabbits and foxes live together in a large area of countryside.

The numbers in each population are linked by the following equations:

$$\frac{dx}{dt} = x - 2xy \quad \text{and} \quad \frac{dy}{dt} = 1.8xy - 1.5y$$

where x is the size of the population of rabbits (in 1000s) and y is the population of foxes (in 100s).

a Find the non-zero equilibrium position for the populations of foxes and rabbits.

Initially there are 750 rabbits and 100 foxes ($x = 0.75$, $y = 1$).

b By putting the initial values into the differential equations state whether the populations of foxes and rabbits are initially increasing or decreasing.

c From the differential equations find:

i the size of the fox population when the rabbit population is a maximum

ii the size of the rabbit population when the fox population is a maximum.

d Using technology verify your answers to parts **b** and **c** and describe the change in the populations over one cycle.

> **HINT**
>
> Because of the approximations involved in the Euler method the trajectory becomes inaccurate and spirals out after the first cycle, rather than repeating the same cycle.

3 Two species of grazing animals, X and Y, are grazing on the same grass in competition with each other. The growth of their populations can be given by the following differential equations:

$$\frac{dx}{dt} = (2 - y)x$$

$$\frac{dy}{dt} = (3 - x)y$$

where x is the population of X and y is the population of Y, measured in hundreds.

a Use the Euler method with a step size of 0.1 to find the long-term outcome for the two populations if the initial population of X is 400 and of Y is 300. You may assume that when a population size is less than 1 (x or $y < 0.01$) the population is extinct.

Use the points evaluated to plot a trajectory for the populations.

b i Write down the differential equation for the population growth of Y if X becomes extinct.

ii Hence write down a general equation for the population of Y if t is the time from the extinction of X and A is the population of Y at this time.

c Use the fact that $\dfrac{dy}{dx} = \dfrac{dy}{dt} \div \dfrac{dx}{dt}$ to explain why the axes are asymptotes.

d From the differential equation explain why:

i If the initial populations have $x > 3$, $y > 2$ the population of Y will decrease.

ii If the initial populations have $x < 3$, $y > 2$ the population of X will decrease.

e State the two equilibrium points in the system.

f Draw a phase portrait for the populations.

Second order differential equations

A second order differential equation will contain a second derivative. We shall consider ones that can be written in the form:

$$\frac{d^2x}{dt^2} = f\left(x, \frac{dx}{dt}, t\right) \text{ or } \ddot{x} = f(x, \dot{x}, t).$$

These types of equations are a common occurrence in physics.

The questions can be approached by using the substitution $y = \dfrac{dx}{dt}$, and

hence $\dfrac{d^2x}{dt^2} = \dfrac{dy}{dt}$, and solving the resulting system of equations:

$$\frac{dx}{dt} = y$$

$$\frac{dy}{dt} = f(x, y, t)$$

> **EXAM HINT**
>
> An exam question is likely to set the differential equation in a context, but no knowledge of contexts outside the higher level Mathematics syllabus will be required to answer the question.

Example 7

A company's pricing policy is given by the following differential equation:

$$\frac{d^2P}{dt^2} + 5\frac{dP}{dt} + 18P = 117$$

Given that at $t = 0$ the price is \$10 and the rate of change of price is \$1, use the Euler method to find the long-term stable price for the product.

Let $\dfrac{dP}{dt} = y$. $\dfrac{dy}{dt} = -5y - 18P + 117$ $y_{n+1} = y_n + 0.1(-5y_n - 18P_n + 117)$ $P_{n+1} = P_n + 0.1y_n$ $P_0 = 20, \ y_0 = 1$ Stable price is \$6.50.	Because of the 117 this equation cannot be solved by considering the eigenvalues, so the Euler method must be used. Repeated iterations of the Euler method lead to a stable price.

Exercise 12J

1 By writing each as a coupled first order differential equation solve the following equations to find x in terms of t.

a $\dfrac{d^2x}{dt^2} - 3\dfrac{dx}{dt} + 2x = 0$

  $x = 2$, $\dfrac{dx}{dt} = 4$ when $t = 0$

b $\ddot{x} - 3\dot{x} - 4x = 0$, $x = 0$, $\dot{x} = 5$ when $t = 0$

c Draw a phase diagram for your solution and comment on the long-term relationship between x and $\dfrac{dx}{dt}$.

2 A particle moves such that its distance from the origin is given by the differential equation $\dfrac{d^2y}{dt^2} + 3\dfrac{dx}{dt} + 2x = 6t + 4$.

a Use the substitution $y = \dfrac{dx}{dt}$ to form a system of equations.

  When $t = 0$, $x = 6$ and $\dfrac{dx}{dt} = 5$.

b Use the Euler method with a step size of 0.1 to find the value of x when $t = 0.2$.

c Find the minimum value of x as given by the Euler approximation and the value of t at which it occurs.

d Find the limit of the velocity of the particle as time increases and hence write down an approximate solution for the particle's distance from the origin for large values of t.

3 A weight on a spring undergoes forced oscillations about an equilibrium point. The distance x cm from the point is given by the differential equation:

$$3\dfrac{d^2x}{dt^2} + 9\dfrac{dx}{dt} + 6x = 15\cos 5t$$

a Write this equation as a system of linear equations.

The weight is displaced by 2.5 cm and released $\left(\dfrac{dx}{dt} = 0\right)$.

b Use the Euler method with a step size of 0.1 to find the values of x from $t = 0$ to $t = 6$. Show the values on a graph with time on the horizontal axis. Comment on the key features of the graph.

> **HINT**
>
> Part **b** is best done on a spreadsheet.

Chapter summary

Components of vectors

- Acceleration and force are examples of vector quantities.
- The resultant vector has the same effect as all the individual vectors acting together.
- The component of vector a acting in the direction of vector b is $\dfrac{|a \cdot b|}{|b|} = |a|\cos\theta$.
- The component of a vector a acting perpendicular to vector b, in the plane formed by the two vectors, is $\dfrac{|a \times b|}{|b|} = |a|\sin\theta$.

Two-dimensional motion with variable velocity

- The acceleration vector can be integrated to find the velocity vector, which can be integrated to find the displacement vector.

Continued on next page

- Projectile motion occurs when the only acceleration is that due to gravity. The velocity and displacement vectors can be found by integrating $a = \begin{pmatrix} 0 \\ -g \end{pmatrix}$.

- The maximum height can be found when the vertical component of the velocity is equal to zero and the range found by setting the vertical component of the displacement to zero.

- Motion in a circle of radius r and centre $(0,0)$ can be given as $r = \begin{pmatrix} r\cos\omega t \\ r\sin\omega t \end{pmatrix}$. Acceleration and velocity for motion in a circle can be found by differentiating the expression for the displacement.

Coupled differential equations

- Solutions can be found to a linear coupled system if the eigenvalues are distinct and real.

- If the system is written in the form $\dot{x} = Mx$ the solution is:
$$x = A e^{\lambda_1 t} p_1 + B e^{\lambda_2 t} p_2$$
where $A, B \in \mathbb{R}$, λ_1, λ_2 are the eigenvalues of M, and p_1 and p_2 are the corresponding eigenvectors.

- Equilibrium points occur when all derivatives are equal to zero. If all points close to the equilibrium point move towards it, it is a stable equilibrium, if not it is unstable.

- Complex and imaginary eigenvalues lead to spiral or periodic motion. If the real part of the eigenvalue is positive the spiral will move away from the origin. If it is negative it will move towards the origin.

- Systems of non-linear coupled differential equations can be solved using the Euler method.

- For $\dfrac{dx}{dt} = f_1(x, y, t)$, $\dfrac{dy}{dt} = f_2(x, y, t)$ the Euler method equations are:
$$t_{n+1} = t_n + h$$
$$x_{n+1} = x_n + hf_1(x_n, y_n, t_n)$$
$$y_{n+1} = y_n + hf_2(x_n, y_n, t_n)$$

- Second order differential equations can be written as a first order coupled system by letting $\dot{x} = y$.

Developing inquiry skills

A plane needs to deliver a supply package to a polar research station. The package will be dropped from the plane from a height of 150 m. The plane has a speed of 180 kmh^{-1} and is flying horizontally. Air resistance acts on the package in such a way that the horizontal acceleration ($\ddot{x}$) and the vertical acceleration ($\ddot{y}$) are given by the following equations:

$$\ddot{x} = -0.05\dot{x} \qquad \ddot{y} = -9.8 + 0.02\dot{y}^2$$

a **i** Use the substitution $u = \dot{x}$ to write $\ddot{x} = -0.05\dot{x}$ in terms of u.

   ii Hence write down an equation for u in terms of t, the time in seconds from when the package was dropped.

iii Find an equation for x, the horizontal distance travelled by the package.

   iv If the package could be released from any height what would be the maximum horizontal distance from the research station that the package could be released.

b Use Euler's method with a step length of 0.1 seconds to find:

   i the time at which the package will hit the ground to the nearest tenth of a second

   ii the vertical speed at which the package will hit the ground.

c Hence find:

   i the distance from the research station at which the package should be released

   ii the speed (the magnitude of the resultant of horizontal and vertical velocity) at which the package hits the ground.

Chapter review

Click here for a mixed review exercise

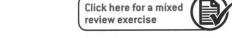

1 a Find the general solution for the following system of linear differential equations:

$$\dot{x} = y$$

$$\dot{y} = 6x - y$$

b Sketch the phase portrait for the system giving the equations of any asymptotes.

2 The displacement, x cm, of an object from an equilibrium position is given by the equation

$$\frac{d^2y}{dt^2} + 0.4x + e^{0.2t} = 0 \text{ and } x = 3, \ \dot{x} = 0 \text{ when}$$

$t = 0$ and t is measured in seconds.

Use the Euler method with a step size of 0.1 to find:

a the time when the displacement is first 1.0, to 2 significant figures

b the speed of the object at this point.

3 A particle has velocity given by the vector

$$v = \begin{pmatrix} 2t^{\frac{1}{2}} + 1 \\ 2t \end{pmatrix}.$$

a Given the particle is at the origin when $t = 0$ find the position of the particle at time t.

b Find the distance of the particle from the origin when $t = 1$.

4 Populations of lions (L) and zebra (Z) inhabit a national park. The two populations can be modelled by the following differential equations, where the lion population is measured in 10s and the zebra population in 1000s:

$$\frac{dL}{dt} = 2L + LZ - 2L^2$$

$$\frac{dZ}{dt} = 2Z - LZ$$

a Find the three equilibrium points for this system.

b Use the Euler method with a step size of 0.1 years to find the population after two years for initial populations of:

   i 30 lions and 4000 zebra

   ii 50 lions and 1000 zebra.

c Using your findings, explain whether it is possible to have a stable population of lions and zebra in the national park.

Geometry and trigonometry

Calculus

5 The energy expended by a force in moving an object is called the "work done". If a force F moves an object from point A to point B, the work done (W) is given by the equation $W = F \cdot \overrightarrow{AB}$.

  a Find the work done by a force of $\begin{pmatrix} 5 \\ 6 \end{pmatrix}$ newtons (N) in moving an object from (1, 3) to (6, 7) metres (the units of work done are the same as the units of energy, joules (J)).

  b If the direction of the force is the same as the direction of the motion, explain why the equation for work done can be written as $W = |F| \times |\overrightarrow{AB}|$.

  c An aircraft takes off in a straight line from the point (0, 0, 0) to the point A(40, 55, 3). Given the force produced by the engines is 100 000 N, use the result from part **b** to find the energy expended by the engine during this part of the flight.

6 The force produced by two engines in an aircraft during the first minute of its flight can be represented by the two vectors $\begin{pmatrix} 62 \\ 11 \\ 21 \end{pmatrix}$ and $\begin{pmatrix} 62 \\ -11 \\ 21 \end{pmatrix}$, measured in kN (1 kN = 1000 N).

The force due to the air passing over the wings is $\begin{pmatrix} 0 \\ 0 \\ 330 \end{pmatrix}$ kN. The weight of the aircraft produces a force of $\begin{pmatrix} 0 \\ 0 \\ -294 \end{pmatrix}$ kN and there is an air resistance of $\begin{pmatrix} 17 \\ 0 \\ 0 \end{pmatrix}$ kN.

  a Find the resultant force acting on the aircraft.

The acceleration (m s^{-2}) of an object subject to a resultant force of F N is given by the formula $a = \dfrac{F}{m}$, where m is the mass of the object in kilograms.

  b Given that the mass of the aircraft is 30 000 kg, find the acceleration of the aircraft in m s^{-2}.

The aircraft is initially at (0, 0, 0) and takes off with an initial velocity of $\begin{pmatrix} 55 \\ 0 \\ 0 \end{pmatrix}$ m s^{-1}.

  c Find:

    i the displacement of the aircraft at time t

    ii the displacement of the aircraft at $t = 60$.

7 A child is spinning a ball attached to a string around her head. The motion of the ball is in the form of a horizontal circle. The string is 40 cm long and is being spun at an angle of 30° to the vertical. The ball does a complete revolution every second.

Taking the centre of the circle as the origin of a coordinate system with the position of the ball at time $t = 0$ on the positive x-axis, find:

  a the radius of the circle

  b the equation for the displacement of the ball in the form $\begin{pmatrix} x \\ y \end{pmatrix} = \begin{pmatrix} r \cos bt \\ r \sin bt \end{pmatrix}$

  c the velocity vector.

  d The child releases the string. Find the initial speed of the ball as it is released, given that it is the same as its speed just before release.

8 In a two-dimensional computer game the protagonists simultaneously fire beanbags into the air from points A and B, 17 units apart.

The point A is at the origin of a coordinate system with B also on the horizontal axis. The velocity equations for the two beanbags are given by v_A and v_B where:

$$v_A = \begin{pmatrix} 5 \\ 3 - 2t \end{pmatrix} \text{ and } v_B = \begin{pmatrix} -4 \\ 5 - 2t \end{pmatrix}.$$

a Write down vector equations for the displacements, r_A and r_B, of the two beanbags.

b Find an expression for the vector joining the centres of the two beanbags.

c Hence find the shortest distance between the two beanbags.

The player firing beanbags from point A adjusts v_A to $\begin{pmatrix} a \\ b \end{pmatrix}$.

d Find the values of a and b if the two beanbags collide when $t = 1$.

e Find the angle to the horizontal at which the beanbag is fired from A.

9 A ball is thrown with an initial speed of $25\,\mathrm{m\,s^{-1}}$. After 3.5 seconds it is descending at an angle of $45°$ to the horizontal.

Find the possible angles of projection of the ball.

Exam-style questions

10 P2: The displacement $\mathbf{s}(t)$ of an object at time t is given by $\mathbf{s}(t) = \begin{pmatrix} x(t) \\ y(t) \end{pmatrix}$, where x and y are functions of t. The object's acceleration is given by $\mathbf{a} = \begin{pmatrix} t \\ 4 \end{pmatrix}$.

Initially, the object is at rest at the origin.

a In terms of t, find expressions for the object's

   i velocity $\mathbf{v}(t)$

   ii displacement $\mathbf{s}(t)$. (8 marks)

b When $t = 6$, find the object's

   i velocity

   ii displacement. (2 marks)

11 P1: A force $\mathbf{F} = -12\mathbf{i} - 24\mathbf{j}$ Newtons is applied to the head of a nail with a hammer. The head of the nail is at point $N(3\mathbf{i} + 4\mathbf{j})$ and the nail is embedded in a piece of wood at the origin.

The piece of wood lies along the x-axis.

a Find the scalar component of the force $\mathbf{F}$ in the direction of the vector $\overline{\mathrm{NO}}$. (3 marks)

b Find the scalar component of the force $\mathbf{F}$ which is perpendicular to the vector $\overline{\mathrm{NO}}$. (3 marks)

The force $\mathbf{F}$ can be resolved into two vector components; one acting in the direction of $\overline{\mathrm{NO}}$ and the other acting perpendicular to $\overline{\mathrm{NO}}$.

c Determine the component of the force $\mathbf{F}$ in the direction of the vector $\overline{\mathrm{NO}}$ (from part **a** in vector form. Give your answer in terms of the unit vectors $\mathbf{i}$ and $\mathbf{j}$. (3 marks)

12 P2: a Consider the differential equation $\dfrac{d^2x}{dt^2} - 3\dfrac{dx}{dt} - 10x = 0$.

An associated quadratic $\lambda^2 - 3\lambda - 10 = 0$ has roots of $\lambda = 5$ and -2.

   i Verify that $x = Ae^{5t} + Be^{-2t}$ is a solution to this differential equation.

   ii Find the solution given that $x(0) = 0$ and $\left.\dfrac{dx}{dt}\right|_{x=0} = 14$ (6 marks)

b Consider the differential equation $\dfrac{d^2x}{dt^2} + 3\dfrac{dx}{dt} = 0$.

An associated quadratic $\lambda^2 + 3\lambda = 0$ has roots of $\lambda = 0$ and -3.

   i Verify that $x = A + Be^{-3t}$ is a solution to this differential equation.

   ii Find the solution when $x(0) = 0$ and $\left.\dfrac{dx}{dt}\right|_{x=0} = 9$

   iii Find the limit that x tends towards as t tends to infinity. (7 marks)

13 P2: During prehistory, Homosapiens and Neanderthal man were competing for resources. Let x be the population of Homosapiens and y be the population of Neanderthal man, both measured in tens of thousands. Time t is measured in thousands of years.

This scenario can be modelled by the two coupled differential equations:

$$\begin{aligned} x'(t) &= 2x - 3y \\ y'(t) &= -y \end{aligned}$$, where initially $x = 6$ and $y = 4$.

a Use the matrix-eigenvalue method to find the solution to these two differential equations. (10 marks)

b Find the two populations after 1000 years, giving your answers to 2 significant figures. (2 marks)

c As $t \to \infty$

i give a simpler approximation for the population of Homosapiens

ii state what happens to Neanderthal man. (2 marks)

14 P2: Geraint is training on a stationary bike. There is a logo on the tyre of his back wheel which is initially at the point $(0, 75)$. At time t measured in seconds, it will be at position (x, y) where the distances are measured in centimetres. The logo's velocity vector is given by

$$\mathbf{v} = \begin{pmatrix} x'(t) \\ y'(t) \end{pmatrix} = \begin{pmatrix} -105\pi \cos 3\pi t \\ -105\pi \sin 3\pi t \end{pmatrix}.$$

a Find its acceleration vector
$$\mathbf{a} = \begin{pmatrix} \ddot{x}(t) \\ \ddot{y}(t) \end{pmatrix}.$$ (3 marks)

b Find its displacement vector $\mathbf{s} = \begin{pmatrix} x \\ y \end{pmatrix}$. (5 marks)

c When the vertical acceleration is zero, find the possible positions for the logo. (3 marks)

d State how many complete revolutions the wheel makes in one minute. (2 marks)

15 P2: For the following pairs of coupled differential equations, determine (with a worked reason) whether the solutions move away from the origin or move towards the origin.

a $$\begin{aligned} x'(t) &= 2x + y \\ y'(t) &= x + 2y \end{aligned}$$

b $$\begin{aligned} x'(t) &= -2x + y \\ y'(t) &= x - 2y \end{aligned}$$

c $$\begin{aligned} x'(t) &= 2x + y \\ y'(t) &= -x + 2y \end{aligned}$$

d $$\begin{aligned} x'(t) &= -2x - y \\ y'(t) &= x - 2y \end{aligned}.$$ (12 marks)

16 P2: On a large island there is a population of lemmings and a population of snowy owls. The owls like to eat the lemmings. Let x represent the number of lemmings (measured in thousands), and let y represent the number of owls (measured in hundreds). Let t represent time, in years.

Initially there are 1000 lemmings and 50 owls. The situation can be modelled by the coupled differential equations
$$\begin{aligned} x'(t) &= x - xy \\ y'(t) &= xy - 2y \end{aligned}$$

a State the two equilibrium points for this model. (3 marks)

b Use Euler's method with a step size of 0.25 years to estimate the population of lemmings and the population of owls after 2 years (to the nearest integer). Show the intermediate values that are obtained in the working, in the format of a table. (7 marks)

c Suggest whether stating the number of lemmings to the nearest integer is a valid level of accuracy when using Euler's method in part **b**. (2 marks)

17 **P1:** Show that $\left(\dfrac{\mathbf{a} \cdot \mathbf{b}}{|\mathbf{b}|}\right)^2 + \left(\dfrac{|\mathbf{a} \times \mathbf{b}|}{|\mathbf{b}|}\right)^2 = |\mathbf{a}|^2$.

(5 marks)

18 **P1:** Consider the differential equation
$\dfrac{d^2 x}{dt^2} + b\dfrac{dx}{dt} + cx = 0$, where $b^2 > 4c$.

The quadratic equation $\lambda^2 + b\lambda + c = 0$ will have two distinct real roots, let these roots be λ_1 and λ_2.

Let $\dfrac{dx}{dt} = y$ and so $\dfrac{dy}{dt} = -cx - by$.

Solve these two coupled differential equations by the matrix-eigenvalue method to show that the solution to the original differential equation is
$x = Ae^{\lambda_1 t} + Be^{\lambda_2 t}$. (11 marks)

Disease modelling

Approaches to learning: Communication, Critical thinking

Exploration criteria: Mathematical communication (B), Reflection (D), Use of mathematics (E)

IB topic: Differential equation (variables separable)

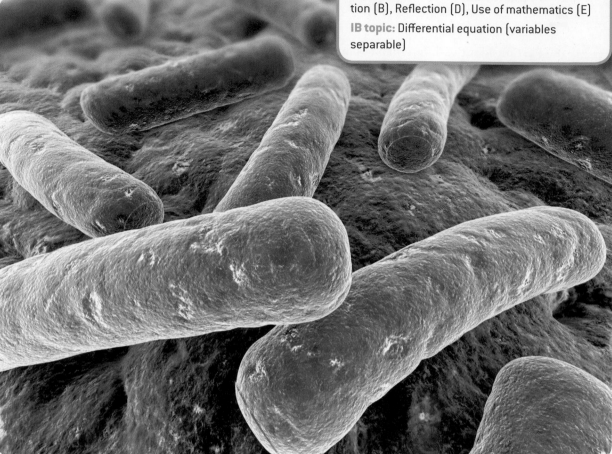

Hypothetical situation

Imagine a population threatened by an infectious disease.

Within the population there are two groups, those that are infected (I) and those that are healthy (H).

Assume that each year, the probability that a healthy person catches the disease is c, and the probability that an infected person recovers is r.

Let x be the proportion of the population that are infected and t be the number of years from the beginning of recording.

Show that a differential equation that will model the rate of change of the proportion of the population affected with respect to time is given by: $\dfrac{\mathrm{d}x}{\mathrm{d}t} = c(1 - x) - rx$

Reflect on the assumptions made in this hypothetical situation and how they may differ in a real-life situation involving an infectious disease in a population.

By separating the variables find the general solution of this differential equation.

Using this general solution what would you expect to happen to the proportion of people affected by the disease over time? (ie what happens as t tends towards infinity?)

Simulation

You are now going to simulate a specific case of this situation.

Assume that $c = 0.3$ and $r = 0.2$.

Use these values of c and r to simulate the proportion of infected people over time

To do this, assume a population size of 10 of which, in year 0, seven are healthy ($H = 7$) and three are infected with a particular disease ($I = 3$).

You are going to simulate what happens to each of the 10 people over 10 years.

Consider the first person (who starts off healthy in year 0). Generate a series of 10 random numbers from a list of numbers from 1 to 10.

If the number is a 1, 2 or 3 and the person is healthy ($c = 0.3$) then they will catch the disease. Otherwise they will remain healthy.

If the number is a 1 or a 2 and the person is infected they will recover. Otherwise they will remain infected

Example:

Year	0	1	2	3	4	5	6	7	8	9	10
Random number		5	3	7	3	8	2	5	5	9	6
Healthy or infected?	H	H	I	I	H	H	I	I	I	I	I

Conduct this simulation 10 times for each of the 10 people in your population.

For each year calculate the value of x, the proportion of people infected. Plot a graph of x against time.

What does the graph suggest will happen as x tends to infinity?

Now consider the differential equation again.

Rewrite the equation for $\dfrac{dx}{dt}$ but use the specific values of $c = 0.3$ and $r = 0.2$ from before.

Solve this differential equation by separating the variables and using the starting conditions of $t = 0$ and $x = 0.3$ to find the value of b in the equation.

Sketch the graph of x against t.

What happens as t tends to infinity?

How well does this fit with your data in your simulation?

Extension

What happens to the solution if you vary c and r?

What happens to the solution if you vary the starting conditions of the proportion of infected people in the population?

13 Representing multiple outcomes: random variables and probability distributions

Probability enables us to quantify the likelihood of events occurring and evaluate risk. The probabilities in the diverse situations described below can be modelled to help you make predictions and well informed decisions.

Concepts

- Representation
- Validity

Microconcepts
- Discrete random variables
- Binomial distribution
- Normal distribution
- Probability distribution function
- Continuous probability distribution function
- Discrete probability distribution function
- Probability distribution
- Cumulative distribution function
- Discrete and continuous data
- Expected value
- Variance
- Poisson distribution
- Parameters
- Probability density functions

> How many errors are likely in a new translation of a book?

> How can an engineer quantify the risk that an unacceptable number of microscopic flaws are present in an aircraft wing?

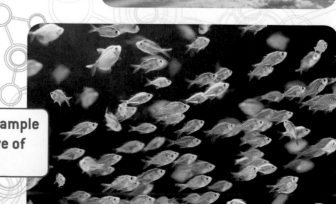

> How can an airline manage their booking system so that overbooking the flight maintains profitability while treating their customers fairly?

> How likely is it that a sample of fish is representative of the entire population?

I woke with a premonition: tomorrow my café would be inspected by the hygiene authority. I knew 3 months ago to expect a visit within a year, but not *when*. I'd expected longer than 3 months to prepare. I set out to arrive at the café early, but had to wait for 19 minutes at the bus stop. I usually have to wait 5 minutes for a bus on average. Then 3 came along at once!

On arrival I checked the machines. Two of the four percolators on the espresso machine were not functioning! Was this bad luck, I wondered? I knew that each percolator had a one in a thousand chance of not functioning on any given day … I started to think about this problem but decided to focus on fixing the percolators.

I had to open the espresso machine combination lock to access the percolators. I was given the 3-digit code years ago but had lost it! I could remember that the first two digits were the same. I decided to guess. After 34 trials I found the right code and the door swung open. I fixed the percolators: but did I have enough coffee? I knew the average weight of a bag was 3 kg and that it could range from 2.8 to 3.2 kg ... how sure could I be that I would not run out? Matt the barista rushed in. "Four inspectors came!" he exclaimed. "Why the past tense?" I enquired. "They were too heavy for the maximum elevator load of 300 kg and they didn't have time to use the stairs" came the answer … time to relax with an espresso I figured.

- How many situations are there in this tale that involve probability?
- What kind of variables are involved?
- How could you represent and quantify the variables?
- Write down some examples where chance has played a role in *your* life.

Developing inquiry skills

How could you estimate the probability of each event? Do the results surprise you? How good are people at evaluating risk?

Think about the questions in this opening problem and answer any you can. As you work through the chapter, you will gain mathematical knowledge and skills that will help you to answer them all.

Before you start

Click here for help with this skills check

You should know how to:

1 Find the mean of a data set.

eg Find the mean of:

x_i	4	7	8	10
f_i	2	1	5	7

$$\text{Mean} = \frac{\sum f_i x_i}{\sum f_i} = \frac{125}{15} \approx 8.33$$

2 Use technology to solve equations.

eg Use technology to solve $x^2 e^{-x} + x = 4$

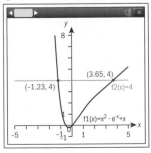

$x = -1.23$ or 3.65

Skills check

1 Find the mean value of x.

x_i	1	2	3	6	11
f_i	9	7	3	2	1

2 Solve the equation $x^3 e^{-x} + \ln(x) = 1$

13.1 Modelling random behaviour

You have learned in Chapter 5 how to quantify the probability of an event and the probability of combined events. In this chapter you will apply these concepts to model random behaviour in various processes that occur in real life.

For example, in Chancer's cafe in the opening scenario the number of failing percolators on a given day is a quantity that changes randomly. The number of buses that arrive at a bus stop in a 5-minute interval of time is another quantity that changes randomly. These quantities are determined by different processes.

We use the following terminology and notation:

Let X represent the number of failing percolators on a given day.

Terminology	Explanation
X is a **discrete random variable.**	Discrete: X can be found by counting.
	Random: X is the result of a random process.
	Variable: X can take any value in the $\{0, 1, 2, 3, 4\}$.

A first step in acquiring knowledge about X is to fill in a table:

Number of failing percolators (x)	0	1	2	3	4
P($X=x$)	P($X=0$)	P($X=1$)	P($X=2$)	P($X=3$)	P($X=4$)

The five probabilities must add to 1, and they must each satisfy $0 \le P(X=x) \le 1$.

You will determine the probabilities in the second row in section 13.2. This row establishes the **probability distribution** of X since the table then shows how the entire probability of 1 is distributed to each value of the random variable in its domain.

In this example you have explored data sets for patterns in order to determine the probability distribution. You can also explore processes.

Investigation 1

Daniel is playing a dice game in which he throws five fair cubical dice until he throws five equal numbers. He tires of this game after throwing the dice 617 times without success, and plans to carry out a simulation with a spreadsheet instead.

He writes down the definition of a discrete random variable T: "T is the number of trials taken until I throw five equal numbers with five fair cubical dice."

1 What is the sample space for T?

2 What is P($T=1$)?

3 How many trials would Daniel expect to carry out before he can expect to have thrown five equal numbers once?

➡

TOK

"Those who have knowledge, don't predict. Those who predict, don't have knowledge." – Lao Tzu.

Why do you think that people want to believe that an outside influence such as an octopus or a groundhog can predict the future?

You can test your answer with a spreadsheet as shown below:

	A	B	C	D	E	F	G	H	I	J	K	L
1	2	6	2	1	1		0		128			
2	3	2	6	6	3		0					
3	4	3	4	1	2		0		=MATCH(1,G1:G1500,0)			
4	6	5	5	5	1		0					
5	2		=RANDBETWEEN(1,6)		3	=IF(AND(A1=B1,B1=C1,C1=D1,D1=E1),1,0)						
6	6	6			1							

a Use a random number generator such as "= RANDBETWEEN(1, 6)" in each one of the first five columns of the first row to simulate the five dice.

b Typing "=IF(AND(A1=B1,B1=C1,C1=D1,D1=E1),1,0)" in the sixth column makes the spreadsheet give the answer 1 if five equal numbers are thrown, 0 otherwise.

c Copy and paste the first row down to the 1500th row to simulate 1500 throws of the five dice.

d Typing "=MATCH(1,G1:G1500,0)" will find the number of the first trial of the 1500, if any, in which five identical numbers were thrown. This is the value of the random variable T. Pressing F9 will generate another 1500 trials.

Find $P(T=2)$, $P(T=3)$, $P(T=4)$, ... Generalize to find a function $f(t) = P(T=t)$. This is called a **probability distribution function**.

4 What is the general statement for $f(t) = P(T=t)$?

5 What should the values of $f(t)$ add up to on its domain and why?

6 Find $\sum f(t)$ over all possible values of T.

7 **Conceptual** How can a discrete probability distribution function be found?

Definition

A **discrete probability distribution function** $f(t)$ assigns to each value of the random variable a corresponding probability. $f(t) = P(T=t)$.

$f(t)$ is commonly referred to by the abbreviation "pdf".

The **discrete cumulative distribution function** $F(t)$ assigns to each value of the random variable its corresponding cumulative probability.

$$F(t) = P(T \leq t) = \sum_{n=a}^{t} f(n) \text{ where } a \text{ is the minimum value of the domain of } f(t).$$

$F(t)$ is commonly referred to by the abbreviation "cdf".

Example 1

A fair cubical dice and a fair tetrahedral dice are thrown. The discrete random variable S is defined as the sum of the numbers on the two dice.

a Represent the probability distribution of S as:

   i a table of values   **ii** a bar chart.

b Hence find the probabilities:

   i $P(S > 7)$ **ii** $P(S$ is at most 5$)$ **iii** $P(S \leq 6 | S > 2)$.

Continued on next page

a

	1	2	3	4	5	6
1	2	3	4	5	6	7
2	3	4	5	6	7	8
3	4	5	6	7	8	9
4	5	6	7	8	9	10

Draw a sample space diagram.

i

s	2	3	4	5	6	7	8	9	10
$P(S=s)$	$\dfrac{1}{24}$	$\dfrac{1}{12}$	$\dfrac{1}{8}$	$\dfrac{1}{6}$	$\dfrac{1}{6}$	$\dfrac{1}{6}$	$\dfrac{1}{8}$	$\dfrac{1}{12}$	$\dfrac{1}{24}$

Read off the probability of each event $P(S = s)$ in turn from the sample space diagram.

ii

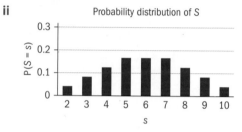

Probability distribution of S

Don't forget to label both axes.

b **i** $P(S > 7) = \dfrac{1}{8} + \dfrac{1}{12} + \dfrac{1}{24} = \dfrac{1}{4}$

ii $P(S \le 5) = \dfrac{1}{24} + \dfrac{1}{12} + \dfrac{1}{8} + \dfrac{1}{6} = \dfrac{5}{12}$

Take care to interpret "at most 5" correctly.

iii $P(S \le 6 | S > 2) = \dfrac{P(S \le 6 \cap S > 2)}{P(S > 2)}$

$= \dfrac{P(3 \le S \le 6)}{P(S > 2)} = \dfrac{\dfrac{13}{24}}{\dfrac{23}{24}} = \dfrac{13}{23}$

Use the formula for conditional probability and find the intersection of the two sets.

Example 2

The probability distribution of a discrete random variable U is defined by
$P(U = u) = k(u - 3)(8 - u)$, $u \in \{4, 5, 6, 7\}$.

a Find the value of k and hence represent the probability distribution of U.

b In 100 trials, calculate the expected value of each possible outcome of U.

c Hence predict the mean value of U after a large number of trials. Interpret your answer.

a

u	4	5	6	7
$P(U=u)$	$4k$	$6k$	$6k$	$4k$

Represent the probability distribution in a table.

$4k + 6k + 6k + 4k = 20k = 1 \Rightarrow k = \dfrac{1}{20}$, hence

Use the fact that the probabilities must add to 1 on the domain of the pdf.

u	4	5	6	7
$P(U=u)$	$\dfrac{1}{5}$	$\dfrac{3}{10}$	$\dfrac{3}{10}$	$\dfrac{1}{5}$

b The expected number of occurrences of $u = 4$ is $100 \times \dfrac{1}{5} = 20$. Similarly, the expected number of occurrences of 5, 6 and 7 are 30, 30 and 20 respectively.

Use the formula: Expected number of occurrences of $A = n\mathrm{P}(A)$.

c A grouped frequency table for these expected number of occurrences is

u	4	5	6	7
Frequency	20	30	30	20

Each number of occurrences is a frequency.

Hence the mean value of U with these frequencies is

$$\frac{20 \times 4 + 30 \times 5 + 30 \times 6 + 20 \times 7}{100} = \frac{550}{100} = 5.5$$

Use the formula for the population mean:

$$\mu = \frac{\sum\limits_{i=1}^{k} f_i x_i}{n} \text{ where } n = \sum\limits_{i=1}^{k} f_i$$

5.5 is not a number in the domain of the probability distribution function. Nevertheless, it models the central value of U expected in a data set of 100 trials.

Recall the definition of the mean as a measure of central tendency.

You can express the calculation in part **c** of the previous example more briefly as

$$\frac{20 \times 4 + 30 \times 5 + 30 \times 6 + 20 \times 7}{100} = 4 \times \frac{20}{100} + 5 \times \frac{30}{100} + 6 \times \frac{30}{100} + 7 \times \frac{20}{100} = 4 \times \frac{1}{5} + 5 \times \frac{3}{10} + 6 \times \frac{3}{10} + 7 \times \frac{1}{5}$$

Notice that this is the sum of the product of each value of the random variable with its corresponding probability, or $\sum\limits_{u} u\mathrm{P}(U = u)$. This leads to a further generalization for all discrete random variables.

> The **expected value** of a discrete random variable X is the mean score that would be expected if X was repeated many times. It is calculated using the formula: $\mathrm{E}(X) = \mu = \sum\limits_{x} x\mathrm{P}(X = x)$

Statistics and probability

Investigation 2

Consider the distribution in worked example 1: "A fair cubical dice and a fair tetrahedral dice are thrown. The discrete random variable S is defined as the sum of the numbers on the two dice." Consider an experiment in which 100 values of S are calculated in 100 trials.

Predict the average of these 100 values of S values by:

a deducing from the shape of the bar chart representation

b application of the formula for the expected value of a discrete random variable

c constructing a data set of 100 values of S with a spreadsheet and finding its mean by entering these formulae and dragging $A1, B1$ and $C1$ down to the 100th row.

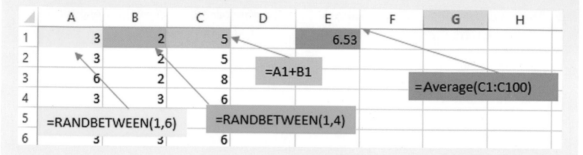

1 What are the strengths and weaknesses of each approach? Discuss.

2 [Conceptual] What does the expected value of a discrete random variable predict about the outcomes of a number of trials?

Application: Many countries organize national lotteries in which adults buy a ticket giving a chance to win one of a range of cash prizes. Profits are often invested in "good causes". For example, the UK National Lottery has distributed over £37 billion to good causes including sport, art and health projects since 1994.

It is possible to use the expected value formula to manage the prize structure of a lottery in order to maintain profitability.

Prize	Probability	Cash value per winner (£)
1st (Jackpot)	$\dfrac{1}{45\,057\,474}$	5 421 027
2nd	$\dfrac{1}{7\,509\,579}$	44 503
3rd	$\dfrac{1}{144\,415}$	1 018
4th	$\dfrac{1}{2180}$	84
5th	$\dfrac{1}{97}$	25
6th	$\dfrac{1}{10.3}$	Free ticket

⟹ Looking at the cash prizes only for simplicity, we can find the expected winnings as follows:

Expected cash winnings =

$$5\,421\,027 \times \frac{1}{45\,057\,474} + 44\,503 \times \frac{1}{7\,509\,579} + 1018 \times \frac{1}{144\,415} + 84 \times \frac{1}{2180} + 25 \times \frac{1}{97} \approx 0.430$$

This would appear to show that you would expect to make a profit (or a positive gain) playing this lottery! However, the cost of a ticket is £2.00 so you expect a *loss* (a negative gain) of £1.57. The attraction of the game is based on the desire to win a large prize and/or contribute to good causes. But it should not be a surprise that you would *expect* to make a loss on any one game.

If X is a discrete random variable that represents the gain of a player, and if $E(X) = 0$, then the game is **fair.**

Example 3

Some students have a meeting to design a dice game to raise funds for charity as part of a CAS project. Some of the decisions made in the meeting are lost.

This incomplete probability distribution table remains:

x (prize in $)	1	2	4	6	7
$P(X=x)$	$\frac{11}{40}$	$\frac{1}{4}$			$\frac{1}{8}$

The students also recall that $E(X) = \frac{67}{20}$.

a Determine the rest of the table. Given the probabilities follow a linear model, write down an expression for $P(X = x)$.

b What is the smallest cost the students could set for playing the game in order to predict a profit? What would you recommend as the cost of the game and why?

---

a Let the missing probabilities be represented by a and b.

Then $a + b = 1 - \dfrac{11}{40} - \dfrac{1}{4} - \dfrac{1}{8} = \dfrac{7}{20}$, also

$$1 \times \frac{11}{40} + 2 \times \frac{1}{4} + 4a + 6b + 7 \times \frac{1}{8} = \frac{67}{20}$$

Hence $a + b = \dfrac{7}{20}$ and $4a + 6b = \dfrac{17}{10}$

So $a = \dfrac{1}{5}$ and $b = \dfrac{3}{20}$

Representing the unknown quantities with a variable and writing down true statements involving them is a problem-solving strategy.

The probabilities must add to 1 and the formula for the expected value can be applied.

Solve the system of simultaneous equations.

Look for a pattern in the probability distribution table or alternatively apply the general equation for a linear function $y = mx + c$. This is called generalizing to a linear model.

Continued on next page

The completed table is :

x (prize in $)	1	2	4	6	7
$P(X=x)$	$\dfrac{11}{40}$	$\dfrac{10}{40}$	$\dfrac{8}{40}$	$\dfrac{6}{40}$	$\dfrac{5}{40}$

Hence $f(x) = P(X = x) = \dfrac{1}{40}(12 - x)$

b $E(X) = \dfrac{67}{20} = \$3.35$ so charging a player $3.35 would be a fair game. Therefore charging $3.36 would predict a small profit, but this could easily give a loss. Perhaps charging $4.00 would be more practical and it would predict a larger profit.

Apply the formula for the expected value and reflect critically.

Designing a CAS project

Students are working to raise money for charity in a CAS project during a school fair. Adults are invited to pay to play a simple game that gives the chance to win cash prizes. The rules are as follows:

A fair cubical dice is thrown. To play the game once costs $5. For each outcome the prizes are:

Outcome	1	2	3	4	5	6
Prize ($)	3	3	3	4	5	6

The expected gain from this game is

$$3 \times \frac{1}{6} + 3 \times \frac{1}{6} + 3 \times \frac{1}{6} + 4 \times \frac{1}{6} + 5 \times \frac{1}{6} + 6 \times \frac{1}{6} - 5 = 4 - 5 = -1$$

a Is this a fair game? Would you expect it to make a profit for the charity?

b You can test the profitability of the game using a spreadsheet to generate 100 trials.

Enter the prizes in cells A1, B1, C1, D1, E1, F1 and "=RANDBETWEEN(1,6)" in cell H1. Then type in cell J1: ="IF(H1=1,A1,IF(H1=2,B1,IF(H1=3,C1, IF(H1=4,D1,IF(H1=5,E1,IF(H1=6,F1))))))"

Copy and drag all cells down to the 100th row. Use the spreadsheet to find the total winnings and the total gain in the 100 trials.

Work in a small group on these design tasks for the CAS project:

c Suggest a change to the game to make it fair by changing the cost.

d Suggest changes to the game to make it fair by changing the distribution of the prizes.

e Suggest changes to the game that make it profitable but more attractive to players.

Exercise 13A

1 Consider these three tables. State which table(s) could not represent a discrete probability distribution and why.

a

b	1	2	3	4
$P(B=b)$	0.1	0.2	0.4	0.4

b

b	4	3	1	0
$P(B=b)$	−0.2	0.2	0.6	0.4

c

b	1	2	3.104	4
$P(B=b)$	0.1	0.2	0.3	0.4

2 The probability distribution of a discrete random variable A is defined by this table:

a	5	8	9	10	11	12
$P(A=a)$	0.5	0.05	0.04	0.1	0.2	$P(A=12)$

Find:

a $P(A = 12)$ **b** $P(8 < A \leq 10)$

c $P(A$ is no more than 9$)$

d $P(A$ is at least 10$)$

e $P(A > 8 | A \leq 11)$ **f** $E(A)$

3 X-squared potato crisps runs a promotion for a week. In 0.01% of the hundreds of thousands of bags produced there are gold tickets for a round-the-world trip. Let B represent the number of bags of crisps opened until a gold ticket is found.

a Find $P(B = 1)$, $P(B = 2)$, $P(B = 3)$.

b Hence show that the probability distribution function of B is
$f(b) = P(B = b) = 0.0001(0.9999)^{b-1}$

c State the domain of $f(b)$.

d Determined to win a ticket, Yimo buys ten bags of crisps. Find the probability that she finds a golden ticket after opening no more than ten bags.

4 The cumulative probability distribution function of a discrete random variable C is defined by this table:

c	1	2	3	4	5
$P(C \leq c)$	0.07	0.09	0.26	0.72	1

a Calculate the probability distribution of C.

b Find $E(C)$.

5 Two fair tetrahedral dice with faces numbered 1, 2, 3, 4 are thrown. The discrete random variable D is defined as the product of the two numbers thrown.

a Represent the probability distribution of D in a table.

b Find $P(D$ is a square number $| D < 8)$.

6 Marin throws three coins. He wins $15 if three heads occur, $5 if exactly two heads occur, y if only one head occurs and $2 if no heads occur. M is the discrete random variable representing Marin's winnings.

a Find $E(M)$ in terms of y.

b Find the value of y that makes the game fair if Marin pays $7 to play one game.

7 Two batteries are required to fit into a handheld whisk in a restaurant kitchen. The batteries are selected at random from a box holding three Fastcell and four Econbatt batteries. F is the number of Fastcell batteries selected to fit into the whisk.

a Find the probability distribution table.

b Find $E(F)$.

8 a Ten identically shaped discs are in a bag: two of them are black and the rest white. Discs are drawn at random from the bag and not replaced. Let G be the number of discs drawn until the first black one is drawn.

  i Find the probability distribution function $f(g) = P(G = g)$.

  ii Find $E(G)$.

 b If instead each disc is replaced before the next is drawn, repeat part **a**.

 c Show that for each case, the sum of all probabilities on the domain is 1.

9 The marketing team of Xsquared crisps wishes to explore how their marketing campaign can be generalized. If p represents the probability that a golden ticket is found in a randomly chosen bag of crisps then the probability distribution function of B, the number of bags of crisps opened until a gold ticket is found, is given by

$f(b) = P(B = b) = p(1 - p)^{b-1}$ where $b \in \mathbb{Z}^+$ and the cumulative distribution function is $F(b) = P(B \le b) = 1 - (1 - p)^b$.

a Show that for this discrete probability distribution, if $y \ge 0$ then $P(B \ge x + y \mid B \ge x) = P(B \ge y + 1)$.

b Interpret $P(B \ge 15 \mid B \ge 10) = P(B \ge 6)$.

Developing inquiry skills

Return to the opening problem.

Which of the situations in the café involve discrete probability distributions?

13.2 Modelling the number of successes in a fixed number of trials

You learned in section 13.1 that a probability distribution function can be found as a generalization of a random process. One example of the process you will learn about in this section is found in the work of cognitive psychologists Daniel Kahneman and Amos Tversky (1972). One question they posed in a survey was:

"All families of six children in a city were surveyed. In 72 families, the exact order of births of boys and girls was GBGBBG. What is your estimate of the number of families surveyed in which the exact order of births was BGBBBB?"

The median estimate was 30, suggesting the participants in the survey judged that GBGBBG was more than twice as likely an outcome as BGBBBB. Psychologists have studied this "representativeness fallacy" in further research of subjective judgments and biases. In this section, you will learn the mathematics needed to model situations like this.

You can model the family of six children as a sequence of six independent trials in which the probability of a male birth is constant over the six trials. A convenient way to experience this process is by flipping a coin six times.

TOK

Is it possible to reduce all human behaviour to a set of statistical data?

Investigation 3

Preliminary experience:

Carry out ten trials of flipping a coin six times, recording each trial as a sequence of H (heads) and T (tails). Compare your results with others in your class.

- How many of your trials resulted in outcomes like HTHTTH which *appear* more random than THTTTT?

- Discuss this claim: "The probability of a total of three heads in six trials is more than the probability of a total of one head in six trials". Justify your answer.

Investigation 4

In this investigation, represent all probabilities as fractions. Do not simplify the fractions.

A fair coin is tossed twice. Let X be the discrete random variable equal to the number of heads tossed in two trials of a fair coin. Use a tree diagram to represent all the possibilities in the sample space and hence find the probabilities to complete the probability distribution table.

x	0	1	2
$P(X=x)$			

Repeat these steps for three trials and then four trials.

1 What is the connection between your results and the pattern found here in Pascal's triangle?

2 What do these numbers represent?

```
                1
             1     1
          1     2     1
       1     3     3     1
    1     4     6     4     1
   ...   ...   ...   ...   ...   ...
```

3 Predict the probability distribution table for five trials.

4 Would the probability distribution tables for 0 trials and 1 trial be consistent with the pattern in Pascal's triangle?

The numbers in the Pascal's triangle are **binomial coefficients**. You can calculate them with technology. Make a prediction of the sum of a row and the next two rows and check your answer with technology.

Definition: The binomial coefficients in row $(n+1)$ of the triangle are represented by the following notation:

$$^nC_0, \, ^nC_1, \, ^nC_2, \, ..., \, ^nC_r, \, ^nC_{n-1}, \, ^nC_n.$$

EXAM HINT

In examinations, binomial probabilities will be found using technology.

Continued on next page

Statistics and probability

⮕ Use your probability distributions from parts **3** and **4** and binomial coefficients to make a general statement for the probability distribution function:

5 **Factual** Complete: "Let X be the discrete random variable equal to the number of heads tossed in n trials of a fair coin.

Then $P(X=x) = $ _____ for $x \in \{0, 1, ..., \_\_\}$"

6 **Factual** The experiment is changed so that the coin is not fair and it is thrown five times.
$P(H) = p, P(T) = 1 - p$

Complete the general statement $P(X=x) = $ _____ for $x \in \{0, 1, ..., \_\_\}$

This investigation leads to the formal definition of the **binomial distribution**:

In a sequence of n independent trials of an experiment in which there are exactly two outcomes "success" and "failure" with constant probabilities $P(\text{success}) = p$, $P(\text{failure}) = 1 - p$, if X denotes the discrete random variable equal to the number of successes in n trials, then the probability distribution function of X is

$$P(X = x) = {}^nC_x \, p^x (1 - p)^{n-x}, \; x \in \{0, 1, 2, ..., n\}$$

These facts are summarized in words as "X is distributed binomially with parameters n and p" and in symbols as $X \sim B(n, p)$.

The cumulative probability distribution function is

> **HINT**
>
> These probabilities can be worked out using your GDC.

$$P(X \leq x) = \sum_{i=0}^{x} {}^nC_i \, p^i (1 - p)^{n-i}, \, x \in \{0, 1, 2, ..., n\}$$

You can use the binomial distribution to reflect on the questions at the start of this section.

7 Use the binomial distribution to find the probability of having exactly three boys in a family of six.

8 What is the probability of the outcome GBGBBG?

9 **Factual** Which part of the formula for the binomial distribution counts possibilities?

10 **Conceptual** What situations are described by binomial distributions?

Example 4

For each situation, state if the random variable is distributed binomially. If so, find the probability asked for.

a A coin is biased so that the probability of a head is 0.74. The coin is tossed seven times. A is the number of tails. Find $P(A = 5)$.

b A bag contains 12 white chocolates and 7 dark chocolates. A chocolate is selected at random and its type noted and then eaten. This is repeated five times. B is the number of dark chocolates eaten. Find $P(B = 7)$.

c A bag contains 10 red, 1 blue and 7 yellow dice. A dice is selected at random and its colour noted and replaced. This is repeated 12 times. C is the number of yellow dice recorded. Find $P(C \leq 6)$.

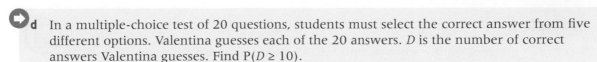
d In a multiple-choice test of 20 questions, students must select the correct answer from five different options. Valentina guesses each of the 20 answers. D is the number of correct answers Valentina guesses. Find $P(D \geq 10)$.

e Ciaran plays a lottery in which the probability of buying a winning ticket is 0.001. E is the number of tickets Ciaran buys until he wins a prize. Find $P(E < 7)$.

a Each toss of the coin is independent of the others. There are exactly two outcomes and a fixed number of trials. Therefore $A \sim B(7, 0.26)$.	Write the distribution. This clarifies your thoughts as well as awarding you method marks in the examination since you have demonstrated your knowledge and understanding.
	Use technology to find the binomial probability using the probability distribution function (pdf).
$P(A = 5) = 0.0137$	Write the answer to three significant figures.
b Since the probability of selecting a dark chocolate is dependent on what was selected in previous trials, the trials are not independent so the binomial distribution is not an appropriate model for A.	
c Since the dice are replaced at each trial, the probability of success is constant and equal to $\frac{7}{18}$. Therefore $C \sim B\left(12, \frac{7}{18}\right)$.	Use technology to find the binomial probability using the cumulative probability distribution function (cdf).
$P(C \leq 6) = 0.861$	Write the answer to three significant figures.
d Assuming Valentina pays no attention at all to the questions asked, $D \sim B\left(20, \frac{1}{5}\right)$.	Use technology to find the binomial probability using the cumulative probability distribution function (cdf). For some GDCs you need to use the fact that $P(D \geq 10) = 1 - P(D \leq 9)$.
$P(D \geq 10) = 0.00260$	Write the answer to three significant figures.
e There is not a fixed number of trials, so the binomial distribution is not an appropriate model for E.	

From your findings in the investigation and from this example, how can you understand from the context of a problem that the binomial distribution is an appropriate model to apply?

Example 5

Solve the problems, stating any assumptions and interpretations you make.

a In a family of six children, find

  i the probability that there are exactly three girls

  ii the probability that exactly three consecutive girls are born.

b A study shows that 0.9% of a population of over 4 000 000 carries a virus. Find the smallest size of sample from the population required in order that the probability of the sample having no carriers is less than 0.4.

a **i** $G \sim B(6, 0.5)$. $P(G = 3) = 0.3125$	Assuming that "boy" and "girl" are the only two outcomes, the probability of each is 0.5, the gender of each child is independent of the others and that G represents the number of girls, then $G \sim B(6, 0.5)$.

ii   Three consecutive girls are born:
 	
      GGGBBB
 	
      BGGGBB
 	
      BBGGGB
 	
      BBBGGG
	This is considerably smaller than 0.3125 since there are many more combinations of three girls that are not consecutive than are consecutive.

Each of these four outcomes has probability $\left(\dfrac{1}{2}\right)^6$, so P(three consecutive girls are born) $= 4 \times \left(\dfrac{1}{2}\right)^6 = \dfrac{1}{16} = 0.0625$	Examine your result critically and check that it is feasible.
b In a population this size, the binomial distribution is an appropriate model since sampling without replacement does not alter the probability of choosing a carrier significantly. If C is the number of carriers chosen in a sample of size n then $C \sim B(n, 0.009)$.	State the assumptions.
Find the smallest value of n so that $P(C = 0) < 0.4$ $P(C = 0) = (1 - 0.009)^n < 0.4$, so $0.991^n < 0.4$ $\Rightarrow \ln(0.991^n) < \ln(0.4)$ $\Rightarrow n\ln(0.991) < \ln(0.4)$ $\Rightarrow n > \dfrac{\ln(0.4)}{\ln(0.991)} = 101.351$	Write down the distribution. Translate the problem into an inequality. $\ln(x)$ is an increasing one-to-one function so the inequality sign does not change. $\ln(0.991) < 0$ so the inequality sign does change.
Hence $n = 102$ is the minimum value required.	Interpret the decimal. Alternatively, the problem can be solved using technology.

In section 13.1 you learned that the expected value of a discrete random variable X is $E(X) = \mu = \sum_x xP(X = x)$. You can use this to deduce that the expected value of the binomial distribution $X \sim B(n, p)$ is $E(X) = np$.

In statistics, you learned about the measures of central tendency (mean, median and mode), and measures of dispersion (range, interquartile range and standard deviation).

Probability distributions also have equivalents for the standard deviation and the variance.

The variance of a probability distribution X is written as $\text{Var}(X)$ and is the variance you would expect to find in the results if X was repeated many times. The standard deviation of X is written as $\text{Std}(X)$ and is the square root of the variance.

Investigation 5

A   An experimental perspective

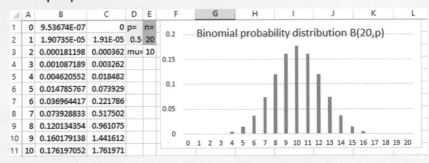

a   Use a spreadsheet to represent $X \sim B(20, p)$ as a probability distribution table and a bar chart by following these steps.

  i   In column A type the numbers 0, 1, 2, …, 20 down to cell A21.

  ii   Fill in cells D1, D2, E1 and E2 as shown above.

  iii   Type "=BINOM.DIST(A1,E2,D2,FALSE)" in cell B1. These are the probabilities of the events $P(X=0), P(X=1), …, P(X=20)$, where $X \sim B(20, p)$.

  iv   Type "=A1*B1" in cell C1.

  v   Copy and drag cells B1 and C1 down to row 21.

  vi   Type "=sum(C1:C21)" in cell E3.

  vii   Add a chart to display the values of X on the x-axis and the corresponding probabilities on the y-axis.

b   Which cell displays $E(X)$?

B   With your spreadsheet, alter the values of p and of n to explore the effect these parameters have on the spread of the distribution.

  • Compare and contrast the spread of $X \sim B(20, 0.15)$ with that of $X \sim B(20, 0.5)$.

  • Compare and contrast the spread of $X \sim B(20, 0.15)$ with that of $X \sim B(20, 0.85)$.

  • Compare and contrast the spread of $X \sim B(5, 0.85)$ with that of $X \sim B(20, 0.85)$.

Continued on next page

Statistics and probability

1 How can you make the spread greatest for a fixed number of trials by changing the probability of success?

2 How can you make the spread greater for a fixed probability of success by changing the number of trials?

3 Which parameters of $X \sim B(n, p)$ affect $Var(X)$?

If $X \sim B(n, p)$ then $E(X) = np$ and $Var(X) = np(1 - p)$

Exercise 13B

1 Given $X \sim B(6, 0.29)$ find the probabilities:

   a $P(X = 4)$ **b** $P(X \leq 4)$

   c $P(1 \leq X < 4)$ **d** $P(X \geq 2)$

   e $P(X \leq 4 | X \geq 2)$

   f Use your answers to determine if $X \leq 4$ and $X \geq 2$ are independent events.

2 A fair octahedral dice numbered 1, 2, …, 8 is thrown seven times. Find the probability that at least three prime numbers are thrown.

3 **a** Given $Y \sim B(n, 0.4)$ and $E(Y) = 5.2$, find n and $Var(Y)$.

   b Given $Z \sim B(9, p)$ and $Var(Z) = 1.44$, show that there are two possible values of p.

4 David plays a game at a fair. He throws a ball towards a pattern of ten holes in this formation:

The aim of the game is to have the ball fall into the red hole to win a point. One game consists of throwing ten balls. Assume David has no skill whatsoever at aiming, the ball is equally likely to fall in each of the holes and that a ball thrown must fall through one of the holes.

   a Find the probability that David scores at least 5 points in a game.

   b David plays six games. Find the probability that he scores no points in at least two games.

5 In a mathematics competition, students try to find the correct answer from five options in a multiple-choice exam of 25 questions. Alex decides his best strategy is to guess all the answers.

   a State an appropriate model for the random variable A, the number of questions Alex gets correct.

   b Find the probability that Alex gets at most five questions correct.

   c Find the probability that Alex gets at least seven questions correct.

   d Find the probability that Alex gets no more than three questions correct.

   e Write down $E(A)$ and interpret this value.

   f Find the probability that Alex scores more than expected.

   g In the test, a correct answer is awarded with 4 points. An incorrect answer incurs a penalty of 1 point. If Alex guesses all questions, find the expected value of his total points for the examination.

   h Four students in total decide to guess all their answers. What is the probability that at least two of the four students will get seven or more questions correct?

6 Calcair buys a new passenger plane with 538 seats. For the first flight of the new plane all 538 tickets are sold. Assume that the probability that an individual passenger turns up to the airport in time to take their seat on the plane is 0.91.

a Model the distribution of the random variable T as the number of passengers that arrive on time to take their seat, stating any assumptions you make.

b Find $P(T = 538)$ and interpret your answer.

c Find $P(T \geq 510)$ and interpret your answer.

d Calcair knows that it is highly likely that there will be some empty seats on any flight unless it sells more tickets than seats. Find the smallest possible number of tickets sold so that $P(T \geq 510)$ is at least 0.1.

e How many tickets should Calcair sell so that the expected number of passengers turning up on time is as close to 538 as possible?

f For this number of tickets sold, find $P(T = 538)$ and $P(T > 538)$. Interpret your answers.

7 You are given $X \sim B(n, p)$. Apply calculus to the formula for $\text{Var}(X)$ to find the value of p that gives the most dispersion (spread) of the probability distribution.

8 Johanna is designing a dice game. She buys three five-sided dice but is not convinced that they are fair dice. In her game, the three dice are thrown and the number of "1"s thrown is counted. In 200 trials, the following data is collected:

Number of 1s thrown	Frequency
0	79
1	83
2	9
3	29

a Assuming the dice are fair, model the data and calculate the expected frequencies of each outcome.

b Is there evidence that the dice are not fair?

13.3 Modelling the number of successes in a fixed interval

In this section, you will learn another discrete probability distribution that models a different process to the binomial distribution: the Poisson distribution.

Investigation 6

Nicolas is often late for school and he is reflecting on how bad his punctuality is, and the reasons for it. Nicolas collects data and identifies two discrete random variables of interest to him: L and U. L is the number of times in a school week of five days that Nicolas is late. Nicolas estimates that the probability that he is late on any given day is fixed at 0.05 and that lateness on any given day is independent of his punctuality or lack of it on any other day.

Nicolas relies on a bus service to pick him up near his home and drop him off near school.

Continued on next page

Statistics and probability

➡ *U* is the number of buses arriving in a five-minute interval at Nicolas's bus stop. The bus company tells him that there is on average one bus per five minutes arriving at Nicolas's stop, but he knows from experience that sometimes a full ten minutes go by with no buses arriving, whereas on other occasions three buses will arrive in the same minute. Nicolas notices that traffic congestion, roadworks, and competing bus companies serve to randomize when buses arrive at his stop as well as other factors like poor weather and breakdowns.

1 **Factual** What are all the similarities and differences between the random variables *L* and *U*?

U satisfies the assumptions for the Poisson distribution, which are:

U counts the number of occurrences of an event (a bus arrives) in a given interval. The interval may have dimensions of time or of space.

An average rate of occurrences in a given time interval is given and the rate is uniform over the whole time-interval being considered.

Occurrences in a time interval are independent and occurrences cannot occur at the same time or position.

2 **Factual** For the following random variables, which ones can be modelled by the Poisson distribution and which by the binomial distribution?

A is the number of gram- matical errors in five pages of a book translated from English to Albanian. The average number of errors per ten pages is four.	*B* is the number of faulty switches in a random sample of 10 switches chosen from a production line. The probability of a switch being faulty is 0.07.	*C* is the number of customers arriving between 0810 and 0820 at Chancer's café (from the opening problem) for morning coffee. On average, two cus- tomers arrive each minute between 0800 and 0900.
D is the number of goals recorded in a ten-minute interval during 60 football matches, assuming that on average 2.7 goals are scored per game.	*E* is the number of five-minute intervals in one hour in which there are at least 10 customers arriving at Chancer's café given that the probability of at least 10 custom- ers arriving in five minutes is fixed at 0.21.	*F* is the number of accidents on a motorway in seven weekends given that the average number of accidents per weekend is 2.1.

3 **Conceptual** What situations does the Poisson process model?

4 **Conceptual** How do the parameters and sample space of the Poisson distribution and the binomial distribution compare and contrast?

If *X* satisfies these requirements:

- *X* counts the number of occurrences of an event in a given interval. The interval may have dimensions of time or space.

- An average rate of occurrences in a given time interval is given (α in this case), and is uniform across all the time intervals being considered.

- Occurrences in a time interval are independent and occurrences cannot occur at the same time or position.

The probability distribution function of *X* is $P(X = x) = \dfrac{e^{-\alpha}\alpha^x}{x!}$,

$x \in \{0, 1, 2, \ldots\}$. This formula is not required for the exam.

These facts are summarized in words as "X follows a Poisson distribution with parameter α" and in symbols as $X \sim \text{Po}(\alpha)$.

EXAM HINT

In examinations, Poisson probabilities will be found using technology. Make sure you know how to do this.

Example 6

a Assume that the number of goals scored in a football match can be modelled by the Poisson distribution with parameter 2.9. Let G be the number of goals in a particular match. Find:

   i $P(G = 4)$ **ii** $P(G \leq 3)$ **iii** $P(G \geq 4)$.

b Let L be the number of goals scored in five matches. Write down the distribution of L and use it to find $P(L \leq 10 \mid L \geq 2)$.

a $G \sim \text{Po}(2.9)$	State the distribution.
	Use technology to find the probabilities.
i 0.162 **ii** 0.670 **iii** 0.330	Write the answers correct to three significant figures.
b $5 \times 2.9 = 14.5$	L must have parameter 14.5 by direct proportion since it is the average number of goals in five matches. State the distribution.
$L \sim \text{Po}(14.5)$ $$P(L \leq 10 \mid L \geq 2) = \frac{P(L \leq 10 \cap L \geq 2)}{P(L \geq 2)} = \frac{P(2 \leq L \leq 10)}{P(L \geq 2)}$$	Use the formula for conditional probability.
$P(L \leq 10 \mid L \geq 2) = 0.145$	Use technology to find the probabilities.
	Write the answer correct to three significant figures.

Statistics and probability

Example 7

Trains at a busy railway station are occasionally cancelled due to staff shortages, breakdowns, a lack of available trains and many other causes. Assume that there are on average 2.31 cancelled trains per day and that the number of cancelled trains C can be modelled by $C \sim \text{Po}(2.31)$.

a Find the probability that there will be four or more cancellations on a given day.

b Find the probability that there will be at least 81 cancellations in the month of March.

c Find, in two different ways, the probability that there are no cancellations in a working week of five days.

d In a working week of five days, find the probability that there will be four or more cancellations on exactly three of these days.

Continued on next page

a	$P(C \geq 4) = 1 - P(C \leq 3)$ $P(C \geq 4) = 0.203$	Interpret the problem, write down the event and apply complementary events to solve a smaller, related problem. Use technology to find the probability and write your answer to three significant figures.
b	Let M be the number of cancellations in March. Then $M \sim \text{Po}(71.61)$. $P(M \geq 81) = 0.147$	Write down the distribution with mean 2.31×31 since March has 31 days. Use technology to find the probability and write your answer to three significant figures.
c	One way is to find $(P(C = 0))^5$ where $C \sim \text{Po}(2.31)$, and the other is to find $P(W = 0)$ where $W \sim \text{Po}(11.55)$. Both methods give the probability 0.00000964 to three significant figures.	Apply the laws of independent events. Model the number of cancelled trains in one working week.
d	Let D be the number of days in a working week of five days on which there are at least four cancellations. Then $D \sim \text{B}(5, 0.203)$. $P(D = 3)$ is required. $P(D = 3) = 0.0531$	Define a random variable completely and clearly. Apply the binomial distribution to model the five days as independent trials with a probability of success 0.203 and write down the distribution and the event.

You have learned how to find the expected value and the variance of the binomial distribution. You can use technology to explore the mean and variance of the Poisson distribution.

Investigation 7

You can use technology to visualize the Poisson distribution with a spreadsheet. Enter the formula =POISSON.DIST(A2,C2,FALSE) in cell B2. Copy and drag down to row 31 to have 30 values of the probability distribution.

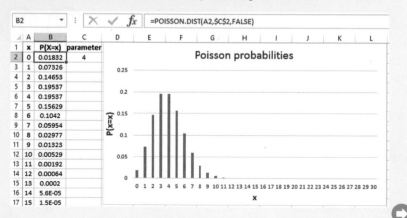

1 Use your spreadsheet and the formula for expected value,

$$E(X) = \sum_x xP(X = x),$$ to find the expected value of the Poisson

distribution for your chosen parameter.

Are 30 enough values to get an accurate result? Justify your answer.

Alter the value of the parameter in order to see the shape of the probability distribution function.

2 When is the shape of the distribution skewed? When is it more symmetrical?

3 **Factual** How do the mean and variance of the distribution change when the parameter is changed?

4 **Conceptual** How can you infer directly from the definition of the Poisson model that the parameter is the mean?

5 How can you infer from the shape of the distribution that the variance is related to the mean?

6 **Conceptual** What does the parameter of the Poisson distribution model?

If $X \sim \text{Po}(\alpha)$, then $E(X) = \text{Var}(X) = \alpha$

The proof of this result is beyond the scope of this book.

Example 8

The random variable T is modelled by a Poisson distribution. Given that $P(T > 2) = 0.53$, find the variance of T.

Let the Poisson parameter be λ $P(X > 3) = 1 - P(X \le 3) = 0.53$ $P(X \le 3) = 0.47$ $\lambda = 3.82$ Variance $= 3.82$	This equation can be solved using the cumulative Poisson probability function on the GDC with the Poisson parameter as the unknown variable. The variance is equal to the parameter for the Poisson distribution.

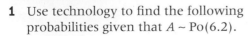
Exercise 13C

1 Use technology to find the following probabilities given that $A \sim \text{Po}(6.2)$.

  a $P(A = 2)$ **b** $P(A < 6)$

  c $P(A \ge 7 \mid A > 5)$

  d $P(A$ is no more than 4)

  e $P(A$ is more than 8 given that A is at least 3)

2 Given $Z \sim \text{Po}(\beta)$ and $P(Z = 0) = 0.301$, find the variance of Z.

3 Show that if $Y \sim Po(\alpha)$ and $P(Y = 1) = 0.15$ then there are two possible solutions for α. Explain how the two solutions both apply correctly to the event $P(Y = 1) = 0.15$.

4 A quantity of 278 pumpkin seeds are put in a dough mixture used to make 10 loaves of bread and mixed thoroughly. Let S be the number of pumpkin seeds in a loaf. State the probability distribution of S and any assumptions made. Find the most likely number of pumpkin seeds found in a loaf.

5 In Example 7, the train regulators decide to investigate how to punish poor punctuality with a penalty payment if there are four or more cancellations in a day and reward good punctuality for no cancellations with a bonus reward according to this table:

Number of cancellations in a day	4 or more	1, 2 or 3	0
Consequence	Penalty of £10 000	No penalty or reward	Bonus of ??

Given that the distribution of C, the number of cancellations per day, is Po(2.31) calculate the bonus payment that would make this fair.

6 The number of telephone calls per ten minutes to an IT support helpline is recorded in this table:

Number of calls	0	1	2	3	4	5 or more
Number of hours	15	30	28	14	7	8

Investigate whether this data appears to be modelled by a Poisson distribution.

7 Assume that the number of bacteria B in a petri dish are modelled by a Poisson distribution with a mean of two bacteria per square cm. A microbiologist selects two distinct areas of a petri dish at random and counts the number of bacteria. The first area measures 4.2 cm^2 and the second 1.7 cm^2.

Find the probability there are no bacteria in the petri dish by:

a considering each of the areas separately

b considering the two areas as a single area.

Verify that you get the same answer in each case.

8 The number of cars breaking down on a motorway is modelled by a Poisson distribution. The average number of breakdowns per kilometre of motorway is 0.597 per hour. Find the probability that:

a there are no breakdowns on a 5 km length of motorway in one hour

b there are three or more breakdowns on a 10 km length of motorway in a day

c there are fewer than 11 breakdowns per day on a 1 km section of motorway on at least five days of a week.

9 A car hire company has a fleet of ten cars that it hires out by the day. The number of requests for a day hire R is modelled by a Poisson distribution with mean 5.1 per day.

a Find the number of days in a year on which the owners of the company expect to have no custom.

b Find the number of days in 100 days on which the owners of the company expect to have to turn away customers because all the cars are rented out.

Developing inquiry skills

Look back at the opening scenario. Do any of the situations in the tale of Chancer's café involve the Poisson distribution?

13.4 Modelling measurements that are distributed randomly

So far you have studied two discrete probability distributions: the binomial and Poisson distributions, and how these distributions can model real-world data. While discrete random variables are quantities that can be **counted** using integers, there are many data sets in fields of nature, society and science that consist of **measurements** using real numbers. For example, the height Y metres of an adult human chosen at random is an example of a **continuous** random variable. The reaction times of a learner driver and the speeds of cars on a highway are other examples.

Terminology	Explanation
Y is a **continuous random variable.**	Continuous: Y can be found by measuring and is therefore a real number.
	Random: Y is the result of a random process.
	Variable: Y can take any value in a domain which is a subset of $\mathbb{R}$.
	If Y is the height of an adult human, Y could take any values such that $0.67 \leq Y \leq 2.72$ according to the *Guinness Book of World Records*.

Y can be measured to various degrees of accuracy and can take any value in its domain, hence the sample space of Y cannot be represented as a list of numbers that can be counted. You will learn how to model one example of a continuous random variable in this section: the normal distribution.

Consider the lifetimes L of 300 batteries measured to the nearest second in a quality control investigation. The data can be presented in many ways.

Statistics and probability

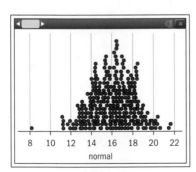

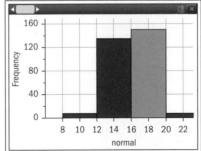

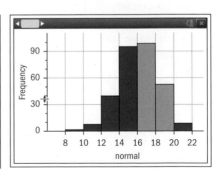

A dot plot of the 300 data points. Note the symmetry and the fact that batteries lasting very long or very short periods of time are very rare.

A frequency histogram with the interval $16 \leq L < 20$ showing a frequency of 150. The data is broadly symmetric in this representation.

The interval $16 \leq L < 18$ has a frequency of 98 and $18 \leq L < 20$ has a frequency of 52, confirming the total frequency of 150 for $16 \leq L < 20$.

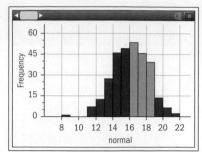 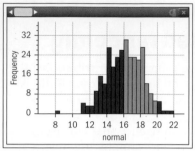 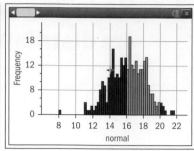

These three histograms have increasingly small widths to their bars. All three histograms have a symmetric shape and total frequency of 150 for $16 \leq L < 20$. The symmetric pattern fluctuates as the class intervals change in width.

The distribution of the battery lifetimes, shown above, display the characteristics of the normal distribution. When a data follows a normal distribution most of its values lie close to an average value and as you move away from the average there will be fewer and fewer values.

Probability density functions

All continuous random variables have an associated **probability density function**. This has the property such that if X is a continuous random variable with probability density function f then $P(a < X < b) = \int_a^b f(x)\,dx$.

Because $f(x) \geq 0$ for all values of x (as you cannot have negative probabilities) the $P(a < X < b)$ can also be thought of as the area under the curve $y = f(x)$ between a and b.

The probability density function for a normal distribution has the equation

$$f(x) = \frac{1}{\sigma\sqrt{2\pi}}\,e^{\frac{-(x-\mu)^2}{2\sigma^2}}.$$

Some properties of the curve depend on the parameters μ and σ but all curves with this probability density function have the same basic shape, often referred to a **bell curve**.

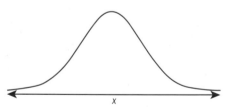

If you look back at the graphs for the distribution of battery life times you can see this shape is probably best illustrated by the histogram with a bar width of 0.5. If battery life did follow a normal distribution you would expect as the sample size increased the bar chart of frequencies would fit this theoretical model increasingly well.

Investigation 8

Using the dataset you are going to analyse W, the length from carpal joint to wing tip, of 4000 blackbirds.

1 Is W a discrete random variable?

E	F	G	H	I	J	K	L
Wing	Weight	Day	Month	Year	Time		
133	95	21	12	2006	14		114
134	106	25	11	2012	9		144
135	125	29	1	1994	9		112
135	113	5	2	1994	10		114
135	111	12	2	1994	8		116
134	105	15	2	1994	8		118
136	111	11	2	2004	8		120
127	103	23	2	2004	13		122
127	102	26	2	2004	9		124
126	104	25	2	2004	11		126
125	97	26	2	2004	9		128
135	102	27	2	2004	10		130
135	126	27	2	2004	15		132
135	121	2	3	2004	12		134
125	88	27	5	2004	14		136
123	90	8	6	2004	17		138
135	101	30	6	2004	13		140
129	100	7	9	2004	8		142
129	98	4	3	2005	16		144
129	97	6	3	2005	14		146

In cell L2 (green) type "=min(E2:E4001)".

In cell L3 (blue) type "=max(E2:4001)".

These give the maximum and minimum values of W in this sample of 4000.

Type 112, 114, 116 as shown and drag down to 146 in cell L21.

These will give your class intervals for a histogram. These are referred to as bins by the software.

Use the output to create a histogram of the 4000 values of W.

2 Does the histogram for W show a symmetric bell-shaped curve?

3 Can it be modelled by a normal distribution?

Repeat the experiment for E, the life expectancy at birth data for 224 countries, found on the CIA website: https://www.cia.gov/library/publications/the-world-factbook/rankorder/2102rank.html

4 **Factual** Is E a continuous random variable?

5 **Factual** Does the histogram for E show a symmetric bell-shaped curve?

6 **Factual** Can it be modelled by a normal distribution?

Repeat the experiment using other data sets that interest you.

7 Which of these measurements do you feel could be modelled by a normal distribution?

   a Baby birth weight

   b Age of mother of new baby

   c Number of hairs on head of a new baby

   d Number of toes on a new baby

   e Annual salary of adults aged between 20 and 25 years

   f Life expectancy in Sweden

   g The number of births on each day of January 1978 in the USA

   h Age of humans in Haiti

   i Journey time of a delivery van

   j Height of sunflowers

   k Annual salary of professional footballers

   l IQ scores of 2501 undergraduate students

8 **Conceptual** In which contexts do you expect the normal distribution to be an appropriate model?

Investigation 9

Use your GDC to explore the parameters of the normal distribution by varying the values of the mean and the standard deviation in the function $f(x) = \dfrac{1}{\sigma\sqrt{2\pi}} e^{\frac{-(x-\mu)^2}{2\sigma^2}}$ and seeing how this affects the shape of the curve.

1 **Conceptual** What does the shape of $f(x)$ tell you about where the probability is distributed most/least densely in the normal distribution?

2 What are the coordinates of the maximum point of the function in terms of μ and σ?

3 What is the equation of the asymptote of the function?

4 **Factual** Which parameter affects the position of the axis of symmetry of the function?

5 **Factual** Which parameter affects the gradient of the function?

6 **Factual** In a data set, how do you quantify the central tendency of the data? How do you quantify the spread of the data?

7 **Factual** What letters do we use to represent mean and variance?

8 **Factual** What is the normal distribution function?

9 **Conceptual** What do the parameters of $f(x) = \dfrac{1}{\sigma\sqrt{2\pi}} e^{\frac{-(x-\mu)^2}{2\sigma^2}}$ model?

A normal distribution is defined by the parameters μ and σ, where μ is the mean of the distribution and σ is its standard deviation.

If X is distributed with a mean of μ and a standard deviation of σ we would write $X \sim N\left(\mu, \sigma^2\right)$.

Notice that this notation gives the variance rather than the standard deviation.

Finding probabilities

$P\left(a < X < b\right)$ is the area under the probability density function of X between the values of a and b.

This area cannot be found by integrating the probability density function, but all GDCs will have a function that allows the area, and hence the probability, to be calculated if the mean and standard deviation are known.

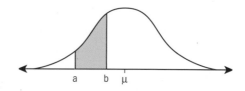

Example 9

If $X \sim N\left(10, 4\right)$ find

a $P\left(9 < X < 12\right)$ **b** $P\left(X < 13\right)$ **c** $P\left(X > 7\right)$.

a $P\left(9 < X < 12\right) = 0.533$	Most GDCs will require you to input the standard deviation rather than the area, so enter $\sigma = 2$.
b $P\left(X < 13\right) = 0.933$	
c $P\left(X > 7\right) = 0.933$	When sketching a normal curve the mean will always be on the line of symmetry, hence a sketch will demonstrate why the answers to parts **b** and **c** are equal.

Example 10

The lengths of trout in a fish farm are normally distributed with a mean of 39 cm and a standard deviation of 6.1 cm.

a Find the probability that a trout caught in the fish farm is less than 35 cm long.

b Cliff catches five trout in an afternoon. Find the probability that at least two of the trout are more than 35 cm long. State any assumptions you make.

c Find the probability that a trout caught is longer than 42 cm given that it is longer than 40 cm.

d Determine if the events $L > 42$ and $L > 40$ are independent.

a Let L represent the length of a randomly selected trout. Then $L \sim N(39, 6.1^2)$. $P(L < 35) = 0.256$	Write down the random variable, the distribution and the event to clarify your thoughts and to demonstrate knowledge and understanding. $P(L < 35)$ can be found on a GDC.
b Let C represent the event that five of the fish are more than 35 cm long. Then $C \sim B(5, 0.744)$, assuming that the length of each fish caught is independent of the others. $P(C \geq 2) = 0.983$	Five fish caught can be represented as five trials. Write down the distribution and the event to clarify your thoughts and to demonstrate knowledge and understanding of why this particular distribution was chosen. Demonstrate understanding that $1 - 0.256 = 0.744$ is the probability of success. $P(C \geq 2)$ can then be found on a GDC.
c $P(L > 42 \mid L > 40) = \dfrac{P(L > 42)}{P(L > 40)}$ $P(L > 42 \mid L > 40) = 0.716$	Apply the formula for conditional probability. $P(A \mid B) = \dfrac{P(A \cap B)}{P(B)}$
d Since $P(L > 42 \mid L > 40) = 0.716$ and $P(L > 42) = 0.311$, the events are not independent.	Apply the definition of independent events: If $P(A \mid B) = P(A)$ then A and B are independent.

Statistics and probability

Investigation 10

Given $X \sim N(7, 1.5^2)$, you can visualize a value $F(8)$ of the cumulative distribution function $F(8) = P(X \leq 8)$ on a sketch.

The shaded area shows the probability $P(X \leq 8) = 0.748$ quantified by $F(8)$.

1 In this diagram, why does the fact that $8 > 7$ guarantee that $P(X \leq 8) > 0.5$?

Use sketch diagrams to answer the following.

2 Find $P(X \geq 8)$ in terms of $F(8)$.

3 Find $P(X \leq 6)$ in terms of $F(8)$.

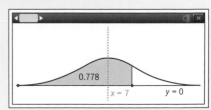

Continued on next page

4 Find $P(X \geq 6)$ in terms of $F(8)$.

5 Find $P(6 \leq X \leq 8)$ in terms of $F(8)$.

Check your answers using your GDC.

6 **Factual** What is the total area under the function?

7 How do $P(X \geq 6)$ and $P(X > 6)$ compare? Why?

8 Let $X \sim N(10, \ 1.7^2)$. Find the following probabilities.

$P(10 - 1.7 \leq X \leq 10 + 1.7), P(10 - 2 \times 1.7 \leq X \leq 10 + 2 \times 1.7), P(10 - 3 \times 1.7 \leq X \leq 10 + 3 \times 1.7)$

9 **Factual** Repeat question **8** with your own values of μ and σ. What do you notice?
Write your findings in a table:

If $X \sim N(\mu, \sigma^2)$, then:	
$P(\mu - \sigma \leq X \leq \mu + \sigma) =$	
$P(\mu - 2\sigma \leq X \leq \mu + 2\sigma) =$	
$P(\mu - 3\sigma \leq X \leq \mu + 3\sigma) =$	

10 **Conceptual** Given an interval of values of the random variable $X \sim N(\mu, \sigma^2)$, what does the cumulative probability function F quantify?

Up to this point we have been given values of the variable X and been asked to find probabilities. It is also possible to find a value of X given a probability.

If $F(x) = P(X < x) = p$ for some probability p, then we can write

$F^{-1}(p) = x$

This function is often referred to as the inverse cumulative normal function and is on all GDCs.

Example 11

For $X \sim N(21, 9)$,

1 find x given that:

   a $P(X < x) = 0.8$ **b** $P(X > x) = 0.4$

2 **a** find a and b given that $P(a < X < b) = 0.68$ and a and b are an equal distance either side of the mean.

   b Verify that this supports the statement that approximately 68% of all data for a normally distributed population is likely to lie within one standard deviation of the mean.

1 **a** $x = 23.5$	This is obtained from a GDC using the inverse cumulative normal function.
b $P(X > x) = 0.4 \Rightarrow P(X < x) = 0.6$	Some GDCs can work out the value of x without converting to $F(x)$, but for many finding $P(X < x)$ is the first stage.
$x = 21.8$	

2 a $P(X < b) = 0.5 + 0.34 = 0.84$

From a sketch it can be seen the $P(X < b)$ is half the whole area under the curve, plus half of 0.68.

$b = 24.0$

$a = 18.0$

b The two values are 21 ± 3

Example 12

The weights of cauliflowers purchased by a supermarket from their suppliers are distributed normally with mean 821 g and standard deviation 40 g.

Cauliflowers weighing less than 750 g are classified as small.

a Predict the number of cauliflowers classified as small in a sample of 400 cauliflowers.

b The heaviest 8% of cauliflowers are classified as oversized and re-packaged. Find the range of weights of cauliflowers classified as oversized.

a Let W represent the weight of a randomly selected cauliflower. Then $W \sim N(821, 40^2)$.

The expected number of cauliflowers classified as small is:

$400 \times P(W \le 750) = 15.1796$

15 cauliflowers are predicted to be classified as small.

Write down the random variable and the distribution to clarify your thoughts and to demonstrate knowledge and understanding.

Apply the formula for the expected number of occurrences and use technology to find the probability.

b

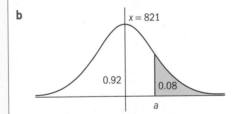

The value of a is 877.203.

Cauliflowers weighing at least 877 g will be classified as oversized.

A sketch helps you orientate the answer in the correct place. You can see already that the lower limit for classification as oversized must be greater than 821.

You have the probability, so you will need to use the inverse cumulative normal distribution on your GDC. Take care to use the correct cumulative probability of 0.92.

Interpret the result to state the range.

International-mindedness

The normal curve is also known as the Gaussian curve, and is named after the German mathematician, Carl Friedrich Gauss (1777–1855), who used it to analyse astronomical data. This is seen on the old 10 Deutsche Mark notes.

Statistics and probability

Exercise 13D

1 $T \sim N(17.1, 3.1^2)$. Estimate these probabilities without technology:

a $P(T < 17.1)$ **b** $P(T < 14)$

c $P(T > 20.2)$ **d** $P(14 \le T < 23.3)$

e $P(T < 7.8)$ **f** $P(T < 23.3 \mid T > 20.2)$

2 $Q \sim N(4.03, 0.7^2)$. Find these probabilities with technology:

a $P(Q < 4)$ **b** $P(Q < 3.4)$

c $P(Q > 5)$ **d** $P(3.5 \le Q < 4.5)$

e $P(T < 4.9 \mid T > 2.9)$

3 $R \sim N(22\,129, 300^2)$. Find the interquartile range of R, ie the values between which lie the middle 50% of the distribution.

4 $S \sim N(0, 1.35^2)$. Find the value of k if $P(|S| > k) = 0.57$

5 A random variable X is distributed normally with mean 372 and standard deviation 13.

a Find $P(X \le 381)$. Show your answer on a sketch.

b Given that $P(X > t) = 0.17$, find t. Show your answer on a sketch.

6 An electronics company produces batteries with a lifespan that is normally distributed with mean 182 days and a standard deviation of 10 days.

a Find the probability that a randomly selected battery lasts longer than 190 days.

b In a sample of seven batteries chosen for a quality control inspection, find the probability that no more than three of them last longer than 190 days.

c If a battery is guaranteed to last up to 165 days, find the probability that the battery will cease to function before the guarantee runs out.

d Hence predict the number of batteries in a batch of 10 000 that would not last the duration of the guarantee.

7 The distance travelled to and from work each day by employees in a central business district is modelled by a normal distribution with mean 16 km and standard deviation 5 km.

a Find the probability that a randomly chosen employee travels between 13 km and 15.3 km each day.

b 13% of employees travel more than x km each day to and from work. Find the value of x.

c Records show that when snow falls, 91% of employees who live further than 14 km from the central business district will fail to get to work. Assuming that all employes who live closer than 14 km do get to work, predict how many of the 23 109 employees will fail to get to work on a snow y day.

8 A courier service in a city centre analyzes their performance and finds that the delivery times of their drivers are normally distributed with a mean of 23 minutes and a standard deviation of 5 minutes. The management of the courier service want to promote "Delivery to you within m minutes or your money back!" in an advertising campaign. What value of m should they choose in order to be at least 99% sure not to pay the customer their money back?

9 A nurse has a daily schedule of home visits to make. He has two possible routes suggested to him by an app on his phone for the journey to his first patient, Nur. Assume that the journey times are normally distributed in each case.

Route A has a mean of 42 minutes and a standard deviation of 8 minutes.

Route B has a mean of 50 minutes and a standard deviation of 3 minutes.

a Distinguish between the advantages and disadvantages of each route.

b The nurse starts his journey at 8.15am and must be at Nur's house by 9.00am. Which route should he take?

c If on five consecutive days, the nurse leaves home at 8.15am and takes route A, find the probability that he arrives at Nur's house:

i by 9.00am on all five days

ii by 9.00am on at least three of the five days

iii by 9.00am on exactly three consecutive days.

13.5 Mean and variance of transformed or combined random variables

You have learned how to transform coordinates and graphs of functions.

You can transform random variables too: a random variable X may be transformed to a related random variable $Y = aX + b$ where $a, b \in \mathbb{R}$. This is a **linear transformation** of the random variable X.

Consider a random variable X, with the distribution shown below. If a fixed value of b is added to each of the possible values of X we would obtain the distribution $X + b$ shown on the right of the diagram.

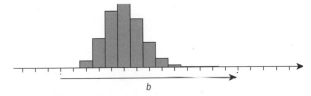

It can be seen that the expected value of the new distribution will be greater by the value b compared with X, hence $E(X + b) = E(X) + b$.

As the distribution is no more spread out than it was previously and as $\text{Var}(X)$ is a measure of spread it follows that $\text{Var}(X + b) = \text{Var}(X)$.

Now consider multiplying all the possible values of X by a. As all the values of X are multiplied by a then the expected value will also be multiplied by a. On this occasion the spread of the values will also increase by a factor of a. For example, if the lowest value was 4 and the highest 10 then the range would be 6. After the transformation the lowest value would be $4a$ and the highest $10a$ so the range would be $6a$. Hence the standard deviation would also be multiplied by a and so the variance by a^2.

This can be summarized as $E(aX + b) = aE(X) + b$ and $\text{Var}(aX) = a^2\text{Var}(X)$.

> Combining the ideas above we obtain
>
> $E(aX + b) = aE(X) + b$ and $Var(aX + b) = a^2 Var(X)$

Example 13

a T is a discrete random variable with $E(T) = 4.01$ and $Var(T) = 1.1$. Find:

   i $E(2.5T + 1)$ **ii** $Var(5T - 2)$ **iii** $E(-0.5T - 3)$ **iv** $Var(0.2T + 4)$

b $C \sim B(7, 0.2)$. Find: **i** $E(3C + 2)$ **ii** $Var(0.9T + 1.2)$

c $D \sim Po(4.2)$. Find: **i** $E(-1.7D + 5.1)$ **ii** $Var(0.9D + 1.2)$

a **i** $E(2.5T + 1) = 2.5 \times 4.01 + 1 = 11.025$	
ii $Var(5T - 2) = 5^2 \times 1.1 = 27.5$	Apply the formulae for the expected value and variance of a linear transformation of a random variable.
iii $E(-0.5T - 3) = -0.5 \times 4.01 - 3$ $= -5.005$	
iv $Var(0.2T + 4) = 0.044$	
b $E(C) = 7 \times 0.2 = 1.4$ $Var(C) = 7 \times 0.2 \times 0.8 = 1.12$, hence	Apply the formulae for the expected value and variance of the binomial distribution.
i $E(3C + 2) = 3 \times 1.4 + 2 = 6.2$	
ii $Var(0.9T + 1.2) = 0.9^2 \times 1.12 = 0.9072$	
c $E(D) = 4.2 = Var(D)$	Apply the formulae for the expected value and variance of the Poisson distribution.
i $E(-1.7D + 5.1) = -1.7 \times 4.2 + 5.1$ $= -2.04$	
ii $Var(0.9D + 1.2) = 0.9^2 \times 4.2 = 3.402$	

You can combine two or more random variables to make a new random variable, just as you can combine two functions to make a new function. For example two independent random variables X and Y may be combined to make a new random variable $Z = aX + bY$ where $a, b \in \mathbb{R}$.

Z is a **linear combination** of the random variables X and Y.

The results of the previous section can be applied to a linear combination of random variables. If X and Y are two random variables:

$E(aX \pm bY) = aE(X) \pm bE(Y)$

$Var(aX \pm bY) = a^2 Var(X) + b^2 Var(Y)$

In the case of the variance we need X and Y to be independent for this result to hold. Whether you add or subtract the two variables the variances are always added as demonstrated below:

$Var(X - Y) = Var(X + (-Y)) = Var(X) + Var(-Y)$

$= Var(X) + (-1)^2 Var(Y) = Var(X) + Var(Y)$

International-mindedness

French mathematicians Abraham De Moivre and Pierre Laplace were involved in the early work on the applications of the normal curve.

De Moivre developed the normal curve as an approximation of the binomial theorem in 1733 and Laplace used the normal curve to describe the distribution of errors in 1783, and in 1810 to prove the Central Limit Theorem.

The results above can be generalized to these results for linear combinations of n independent random variables X_i, $a_i \in \mathbb{R}$, $i = 1, 2, \ldots, n$.

$E(a_1X_1 + a_2X_2 + \ldots + a_nX_n) = a_1E(X_1) + a_2E(X_2) + \ldots + a_nE(X_n)$ and $Var(a_1X_1 + a_2X_2 + \ldots + a_nX_n) = a_1^2Var(X_1) + a_2^2Var(X_2) + \ldots + a_n^2Var(X_n)$.

The second result (with variances) is only valid when the random variables are independent.

Example 14

$A \sim Po(2.3)$, $M \sim B(8, 0.2)$ and $U \sim N(11.7, 1.7^2)$ are three independent random variables. Calculate:

a $E(3M - 2U)$ **b** $Var(A - 3M + 0.7U)$.

a $E(M) = 8 \times 0.2 = 1.6$, $E(U) = 11.7$	Apply your knowledge of the means of the binomial and normal distributions.
$E(3M - 2U) = 3E(M) - 2E(U)$ $= 3 \times 1.6 - 2 \times 11.7 = -18.6$	Apply the formula for the expected value of a linear combination of two independent random variables.
b $Var(A) = 2.3$, $Var(U) = 1.7^2$ $Var(M) = 8 \times 0.2 \times 0.8 = 1.28$	Apply your knowledge of the variance of the Poisson, binomial and normal distributions.
$Var(A - 3M + 0.7U)$ $= Var(A) + 9Var(M) + 0.49Var(U)$ $= 2.3 + 9 \times 1.28 + 0.49 \times 1.7^2$ $= 15.2361 \approx 15.2$	Take care to show the steps in your working because arithmetical errors are easy to make.
	Give the answer to three significant figures.

Exercise 13E

1 The random variable F is such that $E(3F + 1) = 6$ and $Var(3.1 - 2F) = 7$

Calculate **a** $E(F)$ **b** $Var(F)$

2 C and D are two independent Poisson random variables such that $E(C) = 3$ and $Var(D) = 6.1$. Calculate:

a $E(9C - 4D)$ **b** $Var(D + 0.2C)$

For questions **3**, **4**, **5**, and **6** use the following information:

Random variable	Expected value	Variance
U	4.01	1.2
V	2.7	0.4
W	12.9	3
X	7.81	2.11

3 Calculate:

a $E(2U + 9)$

b $E(4X - 0.1)$

c $Var(0.9W + 10)$

d $Var(7 - 3V)$

e $E(U + 4X - 2W)$

f $Var(2V + 0.8U - 0.9X + W)$

4 Given that $a > 0$, $E(aU + b) = 5.1$ and $Var(aV + b) = 2$, calculate a and b.

5 Given that $E(aW + bX) = 6$ and $E(aU + bV) = 2$, calculate a and b.

6 Given that $a > 0$, $E(aW + bX) = 15.1$ and $Var(aU + bV) = 2$, calculate a and b.

7 Denise has a fair three-sided spinner numbered 1, 2 and 2. David has a fair four-sided spinner numbered 3, 4, 5 and 5. Let T represent the number scored on Denise's spinner and H the number scored on David's.

a Construct probability distribution tables for T and for H.

b Hence find:

i $E(T)$

ii $E(H)$

Denise and David play a game in which they spin their spinners and add the numbers obtained. Let S represent the sum of the two numbers obtained.

c Find $E(S)$.

d Construct the probability distribution table for $S = T + H$ and use it to confirm your answer to part **c**.

8 Zeinab carries out an experiment to investigate two games she is designing. She uses two fair four-sided dice numbered 3, 4, 5 and 5.

In the first game, she takes her two dice, throws them and records the total as K.

In the second game, she throws one of her dice, doubles the number obtained and records the answer as L.

Karim argues that Zeinab is wasting her time thinking of these as two different games because the distributions of K and of L are identical, but Zeinab says otherwise. Determine who is correct and for what reason.

Developing inquiry skills

Return to the opening problem.

Do any of the situations in the café involve a linear combination of random variables?

13.6 Distributions of combined random variables

In section 13.5 you found the mean and variance of linear transformations of a random variable and of linear combinations of two or more random variables. In this section you will find out more about what distributions may be followed by random variables that are the results of linear transformations or combinations of other random variables.

For example, you can investigate the distribution of a sum of two independently distributed Poisson random variables using an intuitive argument and an exploration of data as follows.

TOK

How well do models, such as the Poisson distribution, fit real-life situations?

Investigation 11

Dulcinea counts the number of wild flowers in two fields as part of her biology fieldwork. She finds that the number of wild flowers in field A follows a Poisson distribution with mean 3 flowers per square metre whereas the number of wild flowers in a separate field B follows a Poisson distribution with mean 1.5 flowers

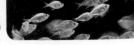

per square metre. Dulcinea conjectures that if $A \sim \text{Po}(3)$ and $B \sim \text{Po}(1.5)$ then if $T = A + B$, T must follow a Poisson distribution. She searches for evidence with which to justify her conjecture.

1 **Factual** What are $\text{E}(A+B)$ and $\text{Var}(A+B)$?

Is this information consistent with Dulcinea's conjecture? Discuss.

2 Since A and B both satisfy the conditions for the Poisson distribution and the two fields are separate and hence independent of each other, does it follow that $T = A + B$ must also satisfy the Poisson conditions? Discuss.

Dulcinea says she can't believe her conjecture until she sees some statistical evidence with her own eyes.

Follow these steps to create the same data sets as Dulcinea.

- Choose Data from the main menu and Data Analysis from the far right of the screen.

- Choose Random Number Generator and fill in the dialogue box as below to simulate 1000 Poisson experiments with mean (λ) 3 in the cells A1: A1000.

Repeat these steps to place 1000 random Poisson experiments with mean 1.5 in cells B1:B1000.

In cell C1 type "=A1+B1" and drag down to cell C1000.

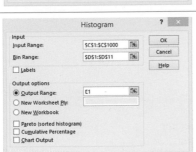

Type 0, 1, 2, 3, …, 10 in cells D1:D11.

These are the classes for the grouped frequency data that will be put in a table with the top left-hand corner in cell E1.

- Choose Data from the main menu and Data Analysis from the far right of the screen.

- Choose Histogram.

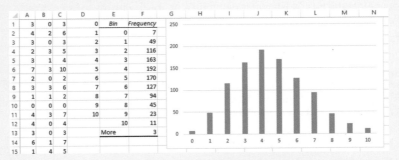

Dulcinea wants to check if the histogram that follows from the grouped frequency table really is from a Poisson distribution. Use the same steps to create 1000 Poisson experiments with mean 4.5 in column G and add this data to your histogram and compare.

3 **Conceptual** Given two independently distributed Poisson random variables $X \sim \text{Po}(\lambda)$ and $Y \sim \text{Po}(\alpha)$, what can you predict about the distribution of $Z = X + Y$?

Care must be taken when combining the average rates of two Poisson distributions, as shown in the next example.

Statistics and probability

Example 15

Richard is waiting for a bus. There are two bus companies, K Bus and L Express, who serve his bus stop. The numbers of arrivals follow Poisson distributions. On average, there is one bus every 5 minutes arriving from K Bus and one bus every 12 minutes from L Express. Richard can use either company to get to his destination.

Assuming that the buses arrive independently of each other, find the probability that at least two buses arrive in a 10-minute interval.

On average two K Buses arrive every 10 minutes. On average $\dfrac{5}{6}$ L Express buses arrive every 10 minutes. Then $K \sim \text{Po}(2)$ and $L \sim \text{Po}\left(\dfrac{5}{6}\right)$.	Use proportionality to find the parameters required for the distribution of the number of buses every 10 minutes. Write down the distributions to clarify your thoughts and show knowledge and understanding.
Let $T = K + L$. Then $T \sim \text{Po}\left(2\dfrac{5}{6}\right)$. We require $P(T \geq 2)$.	Write down the event.
$P(T \geq 2) = 0.775$	Find the answer with technology.

You can investigate the distribution of a sum of two independently distributed normal random variables in a similar way.

Investigation 12

Milagros explores the time taken for her daily commute. She found that the time taken for her bus to arrive T is distributed normally with mean 5 minutes and standard deviation 1.7 minutes. The time Y for all the passengers to embark and pay for their tickets before the bus can depart is distributed normally with mean 0.5 minutes and standard deviation 0.2 minutes. Milagros conjectures that the total time taken for her bus to arrive and then begin its journey $S = T + Y$ must be distributed normally as well but she wants to see evidence.

1 Find $E(S)$ and $\text{Var}(S)$.

   Milagros uses technology to create a sample of 1000 random numbers T such that $T \sim N(5, 1.7^2)$ and saves this in a list called t. She then creates a sample of 1000 random numbers Y such that $Y \sim N(0.5, 0.2^2)$ and saves this in a list called y.

   She adds the lists to find a new list $s = t + y$, and then finds the mean and the standard deviation of s.

2 Do her findings confirm your answer for **1**?

   Milagros constructs a histogram of the data in s.

   Use technology to investigate if a normal model fits the histogram.

3 Does the mean and standard deviation of the normal model for s fit your prediction?

4 **Factual** Is the normal distribution an appropriate model for $S = T + Y$?
Milagros wants to explore further.

She wants to know if she can predict the distribution of a linear combination $S = aT + bY$ of two independent normally distributed random variables.

Investigate by using a variety of examples such as $S = 3T - 2Y$ and repeating the above process.

5 **Conceptual** Given two independently distributed normal random variables $X \sim N(\mu_1, \sigma_1^2)$ and $Y \sim N(\mu_2, \sigma_2^2)$, what can you predict about the distribution of $T = aX + bY$?

6 **Conceptual** How can you determine the probability distribution of a linear combination of n independent normal random variables?

Note that the proof of your results is outside the scope of this course. The results of this investigation are very useful in applications and problem solving.

Example 16

Packing boxes used by a removal company come in three sizes: small, regular and large. After the boxes are filled weights S, R and L are all modelled by normal distributions with these parameters.

	Mean (kg)	Standard deviation (kg)
S	5	2
R	12.1	5
L	30.2	7

a One full box of each size is chosen at random. Find the probability that the large box weighs less than the regular box and three times the small box combined.

b One full large box and four small boxes are chosen at random. Find the probability that the total weight is more than 60 kg.

a $P(L < R + 3S)$ is required.	Write down the event.
$P(L < R + 3S) = P(L - R - 3S < 0)$	Rearrange the event into a linear combination of random variables.
$E(L - R - 3S) = E(L) - E(R) - 3E(S)$ $\qquad = 30.2 - 12.1 - 3 \times 5 = 3.1$	Apply the formula for the expected value of the linear combination.
$Var(L - R - 3S) =$ $Var(L) + Var(R) + 9Var(S) =$ $7^2 + 5^2 + 9 \times 2^2 = 110$	Apply the formula for the variance of the linear combination.
$L - R - 3S \sim N(3.1, 110)$ $P(L - R - 3S < 0) = 0.384$	State the distribution of the linear combination and find the probability of the event using technology, writing the answer to three significant figures.

Continued on next page

b Let the weights of the four small boxes be represented by S_1, S_2, S_3, S_4.

$P(L + S_1 + S_2 + S_3 + S_4 > 60)$ is required.

Write the event, showing that there are five separate independent random variables.

$E(L + S_1 + S_2 + S_3 + S_4) =$

$= E(L) + E(S_1) + E(S_2) + E(S_3) + E(S_4)$

$= 50.2$

Apply the formula for the expected value of the linear combination.

$\text{Var}(L + S_1 + S_2 + S_3 + S_4)$

$= \text{Var}(L) + \text{Var}(S_1) + \text{Var}(S_2) + \text{Var}(S_3) + \text{Var}(S_4)$

$= 7^2 + 2^2 + 2^2 + 2^2 + 2^2 = 65$

Apply the formula for the variance of the linear combination.

$L + S_1 + S_2 + S_3 + S_4 \sim N(50.2, 65)$

$P(L + S_1 + S_2 + S_3 + S_4 > 60) = 0.112$

State the distribution of the linear combination and find the probability of the event using technology, writing the answer to three significant figures.

Investigation 13

An important application of the distribution of a linear combination of independent normally distributed random variables is determining the distribution of the **sample mean** $\bar{X} = \dfrac{1}{n} \sum_{i=1}^{n} X_i$ in which each X_i, $i = 1, 2, \ldots, n$ in a sample of size n are selected from a large population without replacement that follows a normal distribution whose parameters are known: $X \sim N(\mu, \sigma^2)$.

You can assume X_i, $i = 1, 2, \ldots, n$ are independent even though the sampling is without replacement in a large population.

Apply the results from earlier in the section to answer the following.

1 What is the distribution of $X_1 + X_2$?

2 What is the distribution of $X_1 + X_2 + X_3$?

3 What is the distribution of $X_1 + X_2 + \ldots + X_n$?

4 Hence find the **distribution of the sample mean** $\bar{X} = \dfrac{1}{n} \sum_{i=1}^{n} X_i$.

Application: Adult passengers who book tickets for a flight can be thought of as a sample from a population. Assume that the adults booking tickets for a flight are from a population that follows the normal distribution with mean 80 kg and standard deviation 10 kg. You can visualise the distribution of the mean of the passengers' weights for different sizes of samples for each of these cases: commuter (19 passengers), regional (70 passengers), single-aisle (200 passengers) and double-aisle (400 passengers). Aircraft have a random selection of passengers on each flight and each aircraft has a total weight limit beyond which a flight is not safe and hence not permitted.

> **International-mindedness**
>
> Belgian scientist Lambert Quetelet applied the normal distribution to human characteristics (l'homme moyen) in the 19th century. He noted that characteristics such as height, weight and strength were normally distributed.

In this simulation you will create a population of 1000 passengers, select many samples of each size, find the mean of each sample and explore the distribution of your sample means.

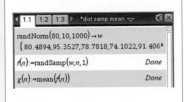	A list of 1000 random numbers drawn from the normal population following $N(80,10^2)$ is stored in the list w. The function $f(n)$ is defined with the symbol ":=" as a list of n numbers selected without replacement from w. The function $g(n)$ is defined as the mean of the numbers in the list $f(n)$
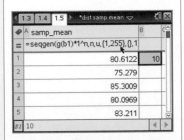	In a new spreadsheet, type 10 in cell B1. This will be the size of your first samples. Define the list of data in column 1 as samp_mean. You can type $\text{seqgen}(g(b1)*1\wedge(n),n,u,\{1,255\},\{\},1)$ or navigate to 'generate sequence' through the menu, as below
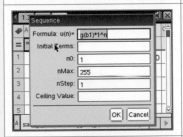	The $1\wedge n$ instructs the GDC to re-calculate the sequence and hence take a new sample. In total, 255 samples of size 10 are selected from the population of 1000 and their means calculated and placed in column A.
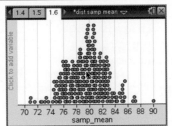	Add a new Data and statistics page. Select samp_mean on the x-axis. This dot plot shows the distribution of the 255 means of your 255 samples of size 10.
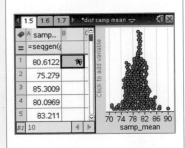	Group the page layout, so you can see the spreadsheet and the dotplot on the same screen. Now change the value in cell b1 to 19 to simulate the distribution of sample means for a commuter aircraft. Repeat for all the other sizes of aircraft. Use the GDC to find the mean and standard deviation of your 255 sample means for each size of aircraft.

Continued on next page

Statistics and probability

5   As the sample size is increased, what happens to the mean of the distribution of sample means?

6   As the sample size is increased, what happens to the standard deviation of the distribution of sample means?

7   How does your answer for question 4 help explain your answer for questions 5 and 6?

8   **Factual**   As the size of the aircraft increases, what is the effect on the confidence the pilot has about the average weight of the passengers in the aircraft?

9   **Factual**   As the size of a sample increases, what happens to the probability that the sample mean will differ from the population mean by a given amount?

10   **Conceptual**   What does the **distribution of sample means** of n independent normally distributed random variables help you to predict?

> Save your work for use in the next investigation.

Example 17

A food standards authority survey finds that the number of calories in takeaway meals from a national restaurant chain *Speedfood* is distributed normally with a mean of 1900 calories and a standard deviation of 80 calories.

Assume that the recommended daily intake of calories is 2000 calories.

Find the probability of the following.

a   A randomly chosen takeaway from *Speedfood* contains more than the recommended daily intake.

b   The average calorie intake of a family of five resulting from eating a meal from *Speedfood* is more than the recommended daily intake of calories.

c   Reflect on your results.

a Let C represent the calorific content in one randomly selected takeaway. Then $C \sim N(1900, 80^2)$. $P(C > 2000)$ is required. $P(C > 2000) = 0.106$	State the random variable, its distribution and the event. Give the answer to three significant figures.
b Let $\overline{C}$ represent the mean calorific content of the five randomly selected takeaway meals. Then $\overline{C} \sim N\left(1900, \dfrac{80^2}{5}\right)$ $P(\overline{C} > 2000)$ is required. $P(\overline{C} > 2000) = 0.00260$	Apply the formula for the distribution of sample means.
c The mean calorific content of five meals is far less likely to be above the daily limit than the calorific content of a single meal. This is due to a smaller standard deviation of the sample mean.	

You have investigated the distribution of the mean of a sample of n from a large population without replacement that follows a **normal distribution** whose parameters are known. But many populations follow other distributions. You can find, in a similar way, the distribution of the sample mean when the population follows **any** distribution.

TOK

Discuss the statement "Without the central limit theorem, there could be no statistics of any value within the human sciences."

Investigation 14

Using technology, change the population away from a normal population to **any** type of data set of 1000.

As an example, first try using the function $30\sin(n) + \ln(n)$ to create the list then create your own. For each example, note the mean and the standard deviation of your population.

Plot the values created in the suggested example and see in this case that the distribution followed is not normal. For the purposes of this investigation, we will call this a "concave up" distribution.

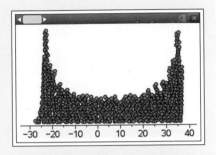

Using a random integer list is another good example to try – it may be referred to as a "uniform" distribution.

Then carry on the same analysis for the distribution of sample means as in Investigation 13.

Include distributions that are skewed or ones that show no obvious shape at all.

Note that you will re-calibrate the axes on your GDC each time.
Use sample sizes of at least 30.

In each case, read off the parameters of the normal model the GDC fits to the histogram.

Use your own examples and data to fill in a table:

Distribution	Population mean	Population standard deviation	Parameters of distribution of sample mean with sample size n, μ_n and σ_n		
			n	μ_n	σ_n
Concave up			30		
			50		
			100		
			n	μ_n	σ_n
Uniform			30		
			50		
			100		
			n	μ_n	σ_n
...	...		30		
			50		
			100		
...					

1 **Factual** In every distribution you create, is the distribution of sample means modelled by a normal distribution when the sample size n is at least 30?

Continued on next page

2 [Factual] Do your findings support this statement of the **central limit theorem:** "The mean $\bar{X}$ of a sample of size n taken from **any** population with mean μ and standard deviation σ can be modelled by a normal distribution with mean μ and standard deviation $\dfrac{\sigma}{\sqrt{n}}$ provided that n is at least 30"?

3 How do the assumptions and conclusions of the central limit theorem compare and contrast with those of the distribution of the sample means of n independently distributed random variables?

4 [Conceptual] What does the **central limit theorem** help you to predict?

Example 18

The number of emergency calls per hour to a hospital between 9.30am and 10.30am each day follows a Poisson distribution with parameter 6.3. Use the central limit theorem to find the probability that in 40 days the mean of the number of calls between 9.30am and 10.30am is less than 5.4.

The population sampled from has mean 6.3 and variance 6.3.	Apply your knowledge of the Poisson distribution.
Let $\bar{X}$ represent the mean of the number of calls in the 40 periods of time, 9.30am to 10.30am.	Define the random variable.
Then $\bar{X} \sim \mathrm{N}\left(6.3, \dfrac{6.3}{40}\right)$. $\mathrm{P}(\bar{X} < 5.4)$ is required.	Apply the central limit theorem and state the event.
$\mathrm{P}(\bar{X} < 5.4) = 0.0117$	Find the probability required with technology and give the answer to three significant figures.

Example 19

Scientists are comparing the growth of two types of wheat. Type A has an mean height of 23.0 cm with a standard deviation of 3.1 cm. Type B has a mean height of 22.5 cm with a standard deviation of 4.1 cm.

a Find the probability that a sample of 50 blades of wheat taken from type A has a mean greater than 24 cm.

b Find the probability that a sample of 50 blades taken from sample A has a greater mean than a sample of 50 blades taken from sample B.

a Let X be the distribution of the height of wheat from type A $$\bar{X} \sim \mathrm{N}\left(23.0, \frac{3.1^2}{50}\right)$$ $$\mathrm{P}\left(\bar{X} > 24\right) = 0.0113$$	Even though we do not know the distribution of X we can use the central limit theorem to find the distribution of $\bar{X}$
b Let Y be the distribution of height of wheat from type B $$\bar{Y} \sim \mathrm{N}\left(22.5, \frac{4.1^2}{50}\right)$$	

$$P(\bar{X} > \bar{Y}) = P(\bar{X} - \bar{Y} > 0)$$

The distribution of $\bar{X} - \bar{Y}$ is

$$N\left(23.0 - 22.5, \frac{3.1^2}{50} + \frac{4.1^2}{50}\right)$$

$$= N(0.5, 0.5284)$$

$$P(\bar{X} - \bar{Y} > 0) = 0.754$$

Rearranging to form a single distribution.

Developing inquiry skills

Look back at the opening scenario. Add a paragraph to the tale of the café that involves the central limit theorem.

Exercise 13F

1 A cookery book is translated from Russian into English. Each page has two separate sections, Ingredients and Method, which are translated by different translators working independently. Assuming the number of translation errors in the Ingredients section and the Method section follow Poisson distributions with parameter 0.7 and 0.6 respectively, find the probability that on a given page there is at least one error.

2 The maximum load a lift can carry is 375 kg. The weights of adult males and females are distributed normally with means 85 kg and 60 kg and standard deviations 10 kg and 7 kg respectively. Find the probability that a load of three women and two men would be too heavy for the lift to function, assuming that the weights of the five adults are independent of each other.

3 An emergency food parcel consists of three bottles of water, two bananas and two bars of chocolate. The weights of all the items comprising the parcel are distributed normally as follows:

Item	Mean (g)	Standard deviation (g)
Water	300	2
Banana	180	7
Chocolate	100	2
Box	16	0.5

What is the probability that the entire food parcel weighs more than 1.5 kg?

4 Saida collects data to investigate her email inbox. Find the probability that in a 24-hour period she receives more than 40 emails assuming that the emails arrive independently of each other at these constant rates. Saida receives junk email at an average rate of 1.5 per hour and personal emails at a rate of 2 per day.

5 Lengths of bamboo pole are cut in a hardware store into three sizes called short, regular and long. The lengths of each size follow normal distributions with parameters given in the following table:

Size	Mean (cm)	Standard deviation (cm)
Short	40	2.1
Regular	80	3.7
Long	120	4

Find the probability that:

a One short and one regular laid end to end are longer than one long.

b Three short lengths laid end to end are shorter than one long.

6 A supermarket purchases cut flowers from two suppliers, A and B. The heights of the flowers have parameters as shown in this table:

Supplier	Mean height (cm)	Standard deviation (cm)
A	110	25.0
B	123	8.1

a A random sample of 40 cut flowers is taken from each supplier. Find the probability that the mean of the sample from A is greater than that from B.

b Find the probability that the sample mean from A is between 108 and 112 cm.

c In 150 samples each of 50 flowers from B, in how many would you expect the sample mean to be greater than 125 cm?

7 A cylindrical part of an engine is manufactured with a radius that is distributed normally with a mean of 5.1 mm and a standard deviation of 0.1 mm. The cylinder must fit in a circular hole which has a diameter that is distributed normally with mean 10 mm and standard deviation 0.1 mm. What is the probability that the cylinder will fit in the hole?

8 Assume that the heights of adult males in Argentina and Egypt are distributed normally with means of 172 cm and 170 cm respectively and that the standard deviation of both populations is 7 cm. A sample of 25 adult males from each country is chosen at random. For each country find the probability that the sample mean is greater than 175 cm.

9 Assuming the heights of adult females in Croatia C are found to be distributed normally with mean 170 cm and standard deviation 6 cm, find the minimum sample size n such that $P(168 < \bar{C} < 172)$ is at least 0.9.

Chapter summary

- A **discrete random variable** T takes natural number values and varies randomly. A discrete random variable can be represented as a frequency histogram, a table of values or a **discrete probability distribution function.**

- The discrete probability distribution function (often abbreviated to pdf) $f(t) = P(T = t)$ represents the probability of the random variable taking a particular value in the domain.

- The values of the probability distribution function must be **at least zero** and their sum must be **exactly equal to 1**.

- The probability distribution function can be found by generalizing a process or by modelling a data set.

- The **cumulative distribution function** $F(t) = P(T \leq t) = \sum_{n=a}^{t} f(n)$, where a is the minimum value of the domain of $f(t)$, quantifies the probability of the random variable taking a value less than or equal to a particular value of the domain.

- The **expected value** of a discrete random variable X is $E(X) = \mu = \sum_{x} xP(X = x)$

- The **binomial distribution** models the process of a sequence of n independent trials of an experiment in which there are exactly two outcomes, "success" and "failure" with constant probabilities $P(\text{success}) = p$, $P(\text{failure}) = 1 - p$. You can use your GDC to calculate the probability distribution function of X.

- These facts are summarized in words as "X is distributed binomially with parameters n and p" and in symbols as $X \sim B(n, p)$.

- n and p are the **parameters** of the binomial distribution of X.

- The expected value of $X \sim B(n, p)$ is $E(X) = np$, and the variance is $Var(X) = np(1 - p)$.

- The **Poisson distribution** models the number of occurrences of an event in a given interval. The interval may have dimensions of time or of space. The average rate of occurrences α in a time interval is given and is uniform throughout all the times being considered. Occurrences in a time interval are independent and occurrences cannot occur at the same time or position. You can use your GDC to calculate the probability distribution function of X.

- These facts are summarized in words as "X follows a Poisson distribution with parameter α" and in symbols as $X \sim \mathrm{Po}(\alpha)$.

- The expected value of $X \sim \mathrm{Po}(\alpha)$ is $\mathrm{E}(X) = \alpha$, and the variance is $\mathrm{Var}(X) = \alpha$.

- Whereas discrete probability distributions involve **counting** outcomes, **continuous** probability distributions involve **measuring** a random variable.

- A continuous random variable can be represented as a **continuous probability density function** or its graph.

- The probability that a continuous random variable takes a particular value in the domain is zero. The area under the curve is 1.

- The parameters of the distribution are μ and σ^2. You write "X follows a normal distribution with a mean μ and variance σ^2" or $X \sim \mathrm{N}(\mu, \sigma^2)$.

- The graph of the normal probability density function is a symmetric bell shape with these properties:
  - The axis of symmetry is $x = \mu$
  - $\mathrm{P}(\mu - \sigma \le X \le \mu + \sigma) \approx 0.68$
  - $\mathrm{P}(\mu - 2\sigma \le X \le \mu + 2\sigma) \approx 0.95$
  - $\mathrm{P}(\mu - 3\sigma \le X \le \mu + 3\sigma) \approx 0.997$

- A random variable X can be transformed to the random variable $Y = aX + b$. The expected value and the variance of $Y = aX + b$ can be found by use of the formulae $\mathrm{E}(Y) = a\mathrm{E}(X) + b$ and $\mathrm{Var}(Y) = a^2\mathrm{Var}(X)$.

- Two independent random variables X and Y may be combined to make a new random variable $Z = aX + bY$ where $a, b \in \mathbb{R}$. The expected value and the variance of $Z = aX + bY$ can be found by use of the formulae $\mathrm{E}(aX \pm bY) = a\mathrm{E}(X) \pm b\mathrm{E}(Y)$ and $\mathrm{Var}(aX \pm bY) = a^2\mathrm{Var}(X) + b^2\mathrm{Var}(Y)$.

- This can be generalized for linear combinations of n independent random variables X_i, $a_i \in \mathbb{R}$, $i = 1, 2, \ldots, n$:

- $\mathrm{E}(a_1 X_1 \pm a_2 X_2 \pm \ldots \pm a_n X_n) = a_1 \mathrm{E}(X_1) \pm a_2 \mathrm{E}(X_2) \pm \ldots \pm a_n \mathrm{E}(X_n)$ and

  $\mathrm{Var}(a_1 X_1 \pm a_2 X_2 \pm \ldots \pm a_n X_n) = a_1{}^2 \mathrm{Var}(X_1) + a_2{}^2 \mathrm{Var}(X_2) + \ldots + a_n{}^2 \mathrm{Var}(X_n)$

- Given two independently distributed Poisson random variables $X \sim \mathrm{Po}(\lambda)$ and $Y \sim \mathrm{Po}(\alpha)$, $T = X + Y$ follows a Poisson distribution with parameter $\lambda + \alpha$.

- Given two independently distributed normal random variables
  $X \sim \mathrm{N}(\mu_1, \sigma_1{}^2)$ and $Y \sim \mathrm{N}(\mu_2, \sigma_2{}^2)$, $T = aX + bY$ follows a normal distribution $T \sim \mathrm{N}(a\mu_1 + b\mu_2, a^2\sigma^2{}_1 + b^2\sigma^2{}_2)$.

- An important application of this is the **distribution of sample means.**

- If $\bar{X} = \dfrac{1}{n}\displaystyle\sum_{i=1}^{n} X_i$ for which each X_i, $i = 1, 2, \ldots, n$ are selected from a large normally distributed population without replacement so that $X_i \sim \mathrm{N}(\mu, \sigma^2)$, then $\bar{X} \sim \mathrm{N}(\mu, \dfrac{\sigma^2}{n})$.

- Further, if $\bar{X} = \dfrac{1}{n}\displaystyle\sum_{i=1}^{n} X_i$ and each X_i, $i = 1, 2, \ldots, n$ come from **any** distribution, then the **central limit theorem** states that the distribution of $\bar{X}$ can be modelled by a normal distribution $\bar{X} \sim \mathrm{N}(\mu, \dfrac{\sigma^2}{n})$ provided that n is at least 30.

Developing inquiry skills

In Chancer's café in the opening scenario, how many examples of probability distributions can you find?

How many of them are discrete? How many are continuous?

How many of these distributions have you learned about in this chapter?

How many of the situations involve combinations of random variables?

Do you need any more information to help you be sure of your choice of model?

How can you name and define precisely the distributions in the Chancer's café scenario that you have not yet learned?

Chapter review

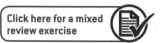

Click here for a mixed review exercise

1 The discrete random variable D is distributed as shown in this table:

d	0	1	2	3	4
$P(D = d)$	0.3	$p + q$	0.15	$p - q$	$p + 2q$

  a Given that $E(D) = 1.4$, find p and q.

  b Find $P(D = 3 | D > 1)$.

2 The sides of a fair cubical dice are numbered 2, 3, 3, 4, 4 and 5. The dice is thrown twice and the outcomes are added to give a total T.

  a Represent the probability distribution of T in a table.

  b A game is designed so that if T is prime, a prize of $\$T$ is won. If T is a square number, the player must pay $\$x$. If T is any other number, no prize or payment is made. Find the value of $\$x$ so that the game is fair.

3 **a** Show that there are 16 factors of 120.

  b A 120-sided dice is thrown six times. Find the probability that:

    i exactly three factors of 120 are thrown

    ii at least three factors of 120 are thrown

    iii at most three factors of 120 are thrown

    iv a factor of 120 is thrown on exactly three consecutive throws.

4 The number of accidents on a stretch of motorway follows a Poisson distribution with mean 1.21 accidents per day.

  a Find the probability that on a randomly chosen day there are three or more accidents.

  b Find the probability that on two consecutive days there is a total of exactly three accidents.

  c Find the probability that in one week there are more than four days on which there are no accidents.

5 Assume that the weights of 18-year-old males in a population follow a normal distribution with mean 65 kg and standard deviation 11 kg.

  a Find the probability that a randomly chosen male weighs more than 70 kg.

  b Find the interquartile range of the weights in the population.

  c Find the weight exceeded by 7.3% of the population.

  d Eight boys are chosen at random from the population. Find the probability that at most three of them weigh at least 70 kg.

  e In a sample of 1000 taken from the population, estimate how many would weigh below 60 kg.

6 A soft drinks manufacturer produces an energy drink in two sizes, R (regular) and F (family). A survey shows that the number of calories in each size follows a normal distribution with parameters as shown in this table:

Size	Mean (calories)	Standard deviation (calories)
R	160	5
F	430	9

a One bottle of each size is selected at random. Find the probability that the family bottle contains less than three times the calories of the regular bottle.

b One family bottle and three regular bottles are selected at random. Find the probability that the family bottle contains more that the total number of calories in the three regular bottles.

7 A computer game design is based on the straight line l with equation $y = 2x + 3$. The red point shown on the x-axis moves at varying speeds along the x-axis. The gamer must choose a time to "kick" a "ball" vertically at l. As the ball reaches l, it changes direction to move horizontally towards the y-axis.

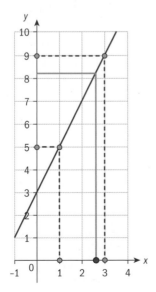

The score is determined by where the ball touches the y-axis as follows:

Interval	Points scored
$8 < y \le 9$	10
$6 < y \le 8$	5
$5 < y \le 6$	1

Let F represent the x value chosen by the gamer as the position she kicks the ball. If $F \sim N(2.3, 0.3)$, find the expected number of points she scores in 127 games.

8 a A and B are two independently distributed Poisson random variables such that $E(A) = 3.1$ and $Var(B) = 4.7$. For each of the following random variables, state if the random variable follows the Poisson distribution, giving a justification for those which do not.

$C = A - B$, $D = 3A + 9$, $E = A + B$, $F = 2.9B$

b An online retailer sells a special type of battery at a rate of seven per week. The number of batteries sold follows a Poisson distribution. Find the smallest number of batteries that the retailer should have in stock at the start of the week in order to be at least 99% certain that they can meet the demand for these batteries.

c The random variable U is modelled by a Poisson distribution. Given that $P(U > 2) = 0.401$ find the variance of U.

9 a X is a discrete random variable with expectation 3.07 and standard deviation 0.8. Y and Z are independent of each other and independent of X. Given that $Y \sim B(5, 0.27)$, $Z \sim Po(3.81)$ and $T = X + Y + 2Z$, find $E(T)$ and $Var(T)$.

b A sample of size 35 is from a population modelled by the distribution of T. Find $P(11 \le \bar{T} < 13)$.

c Find the minimum sample size n such that $P(11 \le \bar{T} < 13)$ is at least 0.95.

Exam-style questions

10 **P1:** In a game, the discrete random variable X represents the number of counters a player wins. The probability distribution for X is given in the table below.

$X = x$	−3	−2	−1	0	1	2	3
$P(X = x)$	$\frac{1}{20}$	$\frac{2}{20}$	a	b	$\frac{3}{20}$	$\frac{2}{20}$	$\frac{1}{20}$

The mean of X is zero.

Find the values of **i** a **ii** b. (4 marks)

11 **P2:** Sue has an electrical fault in her house. The random variable X represents the number of times that the power goes off in a day. It can be assumed that X satisfies the Poisson distribution with mean of 5.

    a Find the probability that Sue experiences exactly five power cuts in a day. (2 marks)

    b Find the probability that Sue experiences less than five power cuts in a day. (2 marks)

    c Find the probability that Sue experiences more than 33 power cuts in a week. (3 marks)

Mavis also has an electrical fault in her house. Let Y represents the number of times in a day that the power goes off in her house. Y satisfies a Poisson distribution with mean of 4.

It can be assumed that X and Y are independent, since Sue and Mavis live a large distance apart.

    d Find the probability that the combined number of power cuts that both Sue and Mavis experience in a day is 8 or less. (3 marks)

A new random variable is defined by $Z = 3X + 2Y$.

    e For the random variable Z, find **i** the mean **ii** the variance. (3 marks)

    f State (with a reason) whether Z could satisfy a Poisson distribution. (2 marks)

12 **P1:** On a particular piece of road, the probability that a car is speeding is $\frac{1}{4}$. The speeds of the cars are independent of each other.

A police officer sets up a speed-trap on this road.

    a If the police officer records the speeds of 10 cars, find the probability that exactly three cars are speeding. (3 marks)

    b If he records the speeds of 100 cars, find the probability that no more than 27 cars are speeding. (2 marks)

If he catches at least 50 cars for speeding, the policeman gets promoted.

    c Assuming he catches every car that is speeding, find the smallest number of cars whose speed he has to record, for him to be at least 75% certain of being promoted. (3 marks)

13 **P1:** The mass, M, of Olympic marathon runners is normally distributed with mean of 60 kg and standard deviation of 3 kg. Let T be the total mass of the three runners who gain the gold, silver and bronze medals. It can be assumed that their masses are independent.

    a Find the probability that $T > 175$. (4 marks)

The mass, H, of Olympic shot putters is normally distributed with mean of 160 kg and standard deviation of 5 kg.

    b Find the probability that the mass of the gold medallist in the shot put is smaller than 2.5 times the mass of the gold medallist in the marathon. (5 marks)

14 **P1:** The mass of hens' eggs is normally distributed with mean of 50 grams and standard deviation of 4 grams. An egg is classified as large if it weighs more than 55 grams.

    a Find the percentage of eggs that will be classified as large. (2 marks)

Eggs are put in boxes of six eggs.

b Find the probability that a random box of eggs has at least one large egg. (3 marks)

15 **P1:** The random variable, X, satisfies the Poisson distribution with mean of μ and $P(X = 9) = \frac{1}{2}P(X = 7)$.

a Find the value of μ. (3 marks)

16 **P2:** When Phil answers a multiple-choice question with four possible answers, he guesses the correct answer at random. Hence, the probability that he obtains the correct answer is $\frac{1}{4}$.

For a single multiple-choice question, let the discrete random variable X equal 1 if he has the question correct, and 0 if he has it wrong. Hence X satisfies the $B\left(1, \frac{1}{4}\right)$ distribution.

a For the random variable X, write down **i** the mean **ii** the variance. (2 marks)

A random sample of 100 values of X are taken (ie Phil takes an exam consisting of 100 multiple-choice questions). Let the sample mean $\dfrac{\sum_{1}^{100} X_i}{n}$ be denoted by $\bar{X}$. The Central Limit Theorem states that the distribution of $\bar{X}$ can be approximated by a normal distribution.

b Write down the **i** mean **ii** variance of $\bar{X}$, when approximated by a normal distribution. (3 marks)

c Use this normal approximation to find and estimate for $P(\bar{X} > 0.305)$. (2 marks)

d Hence, write down $P\left(\sum_{1}^{100} X_i > 30.5\right)$ when using this normal approximation. (2 marks)

e **i** State the true distribution that $T = \sum_{1}^{100} X_i$ satisfies and **ii** find the exact value of $P(T > 30.5)$, which can be construed as the probability of Phil passing the exam, if the pass mark was 31. (4 marks)

17 **P2:** A discrete random variable, X, has a probability distribution function given by

x	1	2	3
$P(X=x)$	$\frac{1}{2}$	$\frac{1}{3}$	$\frac{1}{6}$

a Find $P(X \le 2)$. (1 mark)

b Giving your answers as fractions, calculate:

  i $E(X)$ (3 marks)

The variance of X is $\frac{5}{9}$. Let the random variable $Y = 4X$.

c Find **i** $E(Y)$ **ii** $Var(Y)$. (3 marks)

Let the random variable $T = X_1 + X_2 + X_3$, be the total of three independent values of X.

d Find **i** $E(T)$ **ii** $Var(T)$. (3 marks)

e Let the random variable $R = \frac{1}{X}$.

  i Calculate $E(R)$ giving the answer as a fraction.

  ii Hence, determine whether or not the statement $E\left(\dfrac{1}{X}\right) = \dfrac{1}{E(X)}$ is true. You must justify your answer. (3 marks)

Fair game!

Approaches to learning: Collaboration, Communication, Self-management

Exploration criteria: Presentation (A), Mathematical communication (B), Personal engagement (C), Reflection (D), Use of mathematics (E)

IB topic: Probability, Expected value, Probability distributions

In this chapter you have been looking at probability distributions and understanding **expected value** and the meaning of a **fair game**.

The task

In your pairs or groups of three, your task is to design your own fully functioning game for other students to play.

In the task you will need to think about:

- What equipment can you use to create probabilities?

- How can you make your game exciting/appealing?

- How can you make sure you make a profit from your game?

Your game must be unique, and **not** copied from an existing game!

Part 1: Design and understand the probabilities involved in your game

In your groups decide on the game you will produce.

Brainstorm some ideas first.

You may need to trial the game in your group to check it works before you finalize everything.

Provide a brief overview of your game and make sure that you are able to explain the probabilities involved for your teacher to check through.

Think about:

- What equipment do players need to play the game?

- How much will the game cost to play?

- What will the prizes be?

Create a set of clear, step-by-step instructions to explain your game to players.

A player should be able to read the instructions and then be able to start playing your game immediately.

Part 2: Set up the game in a "class fair"

You will need to provide any required equipment for your game.

Your game needs to be attractive and eye-catching.

Play the games in class.

Part 3: Reflect on the success or otherwise of your game

Either in a written report, interview or in a video reflect on the success or otherwise of your game.

Think about:

- Explain how your game worked. What went well?

- What did you do as the game manager and what did your participants do as game players?

- Provide accurate analysis of the mathematics behind your game.

- Was your game popular? Why? Why not?

- What was your expected profit per game? Is this what you actually received? Why? Why not? Did the experimental probability match the theoretical probability?

- If the game was not fair, how could you change the game to make it fair?

- If anything didn't go as planned, what went wrong?

- What did you learn from other games that would improve your game? What would you improve or change if you were to do this task again?

Extension

As you reflect on this task and on this chapter as a whole, consider one, some or all of these questions regarding mathematics, probability and gambling.

You can approach each of these questions from a combination of mathematics and TOK concepts.

- What does "the house always wins" mean? Is it **fair** that casinos should make a profit? Is there such a thing as "ethical gambling"?

- Could and/or should mathematics and mathematicians help increase incomes in gambling? What is the ethical responsibility of a mathematician?

- What is luck? How would a mathematician explain luck?

Concepts

- Relationships
- Validity

Microconcepts

- Contingency tables
- Observed frequencies, expected frequencies
- Null hypothesis, alternative hypothesis
- Significance level
- Degrees of freedom
- Probability values (p-values)
- χ^2 test for independence, goodness of fit
- t-test
- Spearman's rank correlation

In order to discover the characteristics of a population you might look carefully at a sample from it. But how do you use the data you obtain? How can you tell whether or not the data supports a hypothesis you might have about the population? And how can you be sure that your data is reliable and the test you chose valid? This chapter will discuss many different tests you could use and enable you to decide which one should be chosen to test your ideas about the population.

How can manufacturers determine whether a new product will be successful or not?

How can a visitor to a casino determine if dice are biased or not?

Are your preferences for food positively or negatively correlated with their nutritional value? Or neither?

How can a teacher (or the IB) tell whether two different versions of a test are equally difficult?

Scientists are concerned with the effect of air pollution on the growth of trees. They measured the heights in metres of 24 young trees of the same species in each of two different forest areas. The data are shown in the table.

It is claimed that the trees in area A are, on average, taller than those in area B.

How could you test this claim?

How should the scientists have ensured that their samples were not biased?

Which statistics can you calculate from the data?

How could you display the data to help test the claim?

Do you think there is enough evidence in these samples to make any claims about the tree heights in general?

Which tests can the scientists use to find out if air pollution has had an effect on the growth of trees in either forest?

How valid will the results of these tests be?

Which test will be the most reliable?

Will scientists be able to use the results of these tests to give feedback on the effect of air pollution on the growth of the trees?

Area A		Area B	
5.30	5.17	5.64	4.73
5.26	4.97	3.90	4.21
3.74	4.87	4.38	5.07
5.55	5.17	4.91	4.82
4.77	5.85	4.87	4.84
6.00	5.48	3.89	5.14
4.44	5.24	4.61	4.95
4.53	4.96	4.88	3.12
4.04	5.61	4.47	4.02
4.73	6.14	5.12	4.12
4.83	5.10	4.46	5.23
5.12	5.75	4.64	5.06

Developing inquiry skills

Write down any similar inquiry questions you might ask to decide whether a statement about other sets of data was true or not. It might be, for example, the heights of children, or the sizes of pebbles on a beach, or the fuel consumption of cars. What would you need to think about in each case?

Think about the questions in this opening problem and answer any you can. As you work through the chapter, you will gain mathematical knowledge and skills that will help you to answer them all.

Before you start

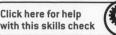

Click here for help with this skills check

You should know how to:

1 Find the probability of independent events.
eg A fair dice and an unbiased coin are thrown.

Show that the probability of getting a 6 on the dice and a head on the coin are independent events.

$$P(6) = \frac{1}{6}, \ P(\text{head}) = \frac{1}{2}$$

$$P(6 \cap \text{head}) = \frac{1}{36} = \frac{1}{6} \times \frac{1}{2}$$

2 Find probabilities from a normal distribution.

Heights are normally distributed with a mean of 156 cm and standard deviation of 7 cm.

Find the probability that a person chosen at random has a height between 152 cm and 161 cm.

The answer is 0.479.

3 Find Pearson's correlation coefficient.
eg The data below shows the position and the number of goals scored for a football league.

Position	Goals
1	63
2	59
3	55
4	48
5	46
6	37
7	35
8	28
9	21
10	13

Find the value of Pearson's correlation coefficient and comment on your answer.
$r = -0.994$. It is strong and negative.

Skills test

1 Numbers 1, 2, 3, 4, 5, 6 are written on cards.
S is the event of picking a square number.
E is the event of picking an even number.
Show that E and S are independent

2 The diameter of washers is normally distributed with mean = 35 mm and standard deviation = 3 mm. Find the probability that a washer chosen at random has a diameter less than 36 mm.

3 Find Pearson's correlation coefficient for the following data.

Weight (kg)	Height (cm)
36	128
38	131
39	134
41	138
39	140
42	142
41	145
42	146
54	149

14.1 Spearman's rank correlation coefficient

Investigation 1

Mould is grown in ten different petri dishes with different amounts of nutrients (X), and the area of the dish covered in mould after 48 hours (Y) is recorded. The results are given in the table and also shown on the graph.

X	Y
5.68	6.00
1.04	0.50
2.22	0.76
4.20	2.84
3.66	1.44
6.72	8.20
4.72	4.20
8.00	8.60

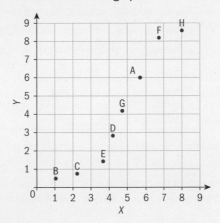

International-mindedness

In 1956, Australian statistician, Oliver Lancaster made the first convincing case for a link between exposure to sunlight and skin cancer using statistical tools including correlation and regression.

1 Calculate the Pearson's product moment correlation coefficient (PMCC) for this data and comment on your results.

Now give each data point a rank, which is the position of the point if the data were listed in order of size for each of the variables. For example, H would be ranked 1 for both X and Y. (It doesn't matter if we rank from largest to smallest, like this, or from smallest to largest; the result will be the same.)

2 a Complete the following table showing the ranks for each of the data points.

	A	B	C	D	E	F	G	H
X rank								1
Y rank								1

b Calculate the value of PMCC for these ranks.

c Comment on your result, relating it to the particular shape of the graph.

In another experiment the temperature (T) is varied and the area of the petri dish covered after 48 hours (Y) is recorded.

T	Y
4.95	4.50
10.49	4.86
16.40	4.36
19.80	3.86
23.90	3.38
27.70	3.14
32.30	3.06
36.40	0.22

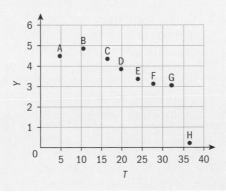

Continued on next page

Statistics and probability

3 a Calculate the value of PMCC for this data and comment on your results.

b Complete the following table showing the ranks for each of the data points.

	A	B	C	D	E	F	G	H
T rank								1
Y rank								8

c Calculate the value of PMCC for the ranks and comment on your results.

d Discuss the features of the data that led to this value.

The PMCC of the rank values is called Spearman's rank correlation coefficient.

4 **Factual** What type of data is used for Spearman's?

5 **Factual** What type of data is used for Pearson's?

6 **Conceptual** What do correlation coefficients tell you about the relationship between two variables? When do you use which?

TOK

What is the difference between correlation and causation?

To what extent do these different processes affect the validity of the knowledge obtained?

The product moment correlation coefficient of the ranks of a set of data is called Spearman's rank correlation coefficient. The notation used in IB is r_s.

Spearman's correlation coefficient shows the extent to which one variable increases or decreases as the other variable increases. Such behaviour is described as "monotonic".

A value of 1 means the set of data is strictly increasing and a value of -1 means it is strictly decreasing.

A value of 0 means the data shows no **monotonic** behaviour.

Example 1

Find Spearman's rank correlation coefficient for the following sets of data.

a

x	23	34	17	23	29	45
y	12	10	14	11	11	8

b

x	1	2	3	4	5
y	6	7	8	8	16

a The ranks are

x	4.5	2	6	4.5	3	1
y	2	5	1	3.5	3.5	6

$r_s = -0.956$

1 When more than one piece of data have the same value the rank given to each is the average of the ranks. For example, the two values of x equalling 23 would have ranks 4 and 5; hence each is given a rank of $\dfrac{4+5}{2} = 4.5$.

The ranked data is put into a GDC and the PMCC obtained.

b The ranks are

x	5	4	3	2	1
y	5	4	2.5	2.5	1

$r_s = 0.975$

Often, when one of the variables increases at a fixed rate, for example measurements taken at one-minute intervals, the order of the ranks will be the reverse of the order of the data.

Exercise 14A

1 Write down the value of Spearman's correlation coefficient for each of the sets of data shown. Justify your answers.

a

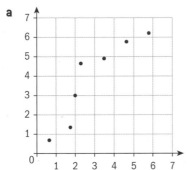

b

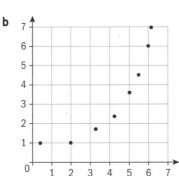

c

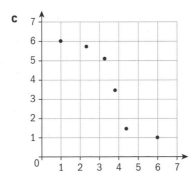

d

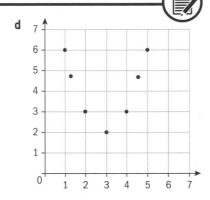

2 Find Spearman's rank correlation coefficient for the following data sets.

a

x	0	5	10	15	20	25	30
y	23	18	10	9	7	7	7

b

x	10	12	9	6	3	14	8
y	12	11	8	5	7	14	9

3 A sports scientist is testing the relationship between the speed of muscle movement and the force produced. In 10 tests the following data is collected.

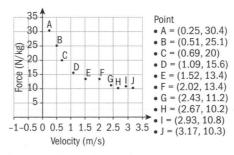

Point
- A = (0.25, 30.4)
- B = (0.51, 25.1)
- C = (0.69, 20)
- D = (1.09, 15.6)
- E = (1.52, 13.4)
- F = (2.02, 13.4)
- G = (2.43, 11.2)
- H = (2.67, 10.2)
- I = (2.93, 10.8)
- J = (3.17, 10.3)

Statistics and probability

a Explain why it might not be appropriate to use the PMCC in this case.

b Calculate Spearman's rank correlation coefficient (r_s) for this data.

c Interpret the value of r_s and comment on its validity.

---

4 A class took a mathematics test (marked out of 80) and an English test (marked out of 100) and the results are given in the table below.

Maths score	15	25	37	45	60	72	74	78	78	79	79
English score	44	47	42	49	52	44	54	59	69	78	89

a Calculate the PMCC for this data and comment on the result.

b Plot these points on a scatter diagram and comment on your result from part **a**.

c Calculate Spearman's rank correlation for this data and comment on your result.

d State, with a reason, which is the more useful measure of correlation.

---

5 In a blind tasting, customers are asked to rank ten different brands of coffee in terms of taste.

These rankings and the cost of the coffees in cents are given in the table below.

	A	B	C	D	E	F
Taste rank	1	2	3	4	5	6
Cost	450	360	390	320	350	300

a Explain why you cannot use PMCC in this case.

b Find Spearman's rank correlation coefficient for this data and comment on your answer.

6 Consider the following data set.

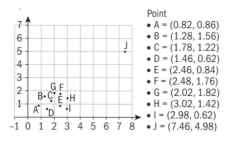

Point	
• A = (0.82, 0.86)
• B = (1.28, 1.56)
• C = (1.78, 1.22)
• D = (1.46, 0.62)
• E = (2.46, 0.84)
• F = (2.48, 1.76)
• G = (2.02, 1.82)
• H = (3.02, 1.42)
• I = (2.98, 0.62)
• J = (7.46, 4.98)

a For this data, calculate the PMCC

  i with the outlier J

  ii without the outlier J.

b Calculate Spearman's rank correlation coefficient

  i with the outlier J

  ii without the outlier J.

c Comment on the results.

The advantages of Spearman's over the PMCC are:

1 It can be used on data that is not linear.

2 It can be used on data which has been ranked even if the original data is unknown or cannot be quantified.

3 It is not greatly affected by outliers.

14.2 Hypothesis testing for the binomial probability, the Poisson mean and the product moment correlation coefficient

Until now you have been looking at samples of data and working out summary statistics related to the sample.

For example, if a scientist takes 20 plants from a field and measures their heights, he can use this data to find the mean or standard deviation of this particular sample of plants.

What does this tell us about the mean or standard deviation of all the plants in the field?

What might the accuracy of the prediction depend on?

Most of the work in statistics involves collecting a sample from a large population and from it estimating:

1 **parameters**; for example, the mean or correlation coefficient of a whole population

2 the **distribution** of the population; for example, whether or not the population is normally distributed.

Hypothesis testing

In statistics a **hypothesis** is a statement about unknown parameters or distributions.

The aim of a **statistical test** is to try and find data that supports your hypothesis.

Our initial hypothesis is called the **null hypothesis** and is written as H_0.

Every hypothesis test also has an **alternative hypothesis** that will be accepted if we reject H_0 and we write this as H_1.

Statistics and probability

For example, if we were interested in whether a population mean was 20 cm or more than 20 cm we could write

$H_0: \mu = 20$, $H_1: \mu > 20$

This is called a **one-tailed test** since you are only checking if the mean was more than 20 cm and not whether it could also be less than 20 cm.

If your alternative hypothesis is $H_0: \mu \neq 20$, then you have a **two-tailed test** as you are testing to see whether it is either greater than or less than 20.

Investigation 2

You need to test whether a coin is fair or biased in favour of either heads or tails. You decide to do an experiment in which you toss the coin ten times to see what happens.

1 In hypothesis testing it is important that you can test your null hypothesis mathematically. Suppose the probability of getting a head is p.

    a Explain why you would choose your null hypothesis to be $H_0: p = 0.5$ rather than $H_0: p \neq 0.5$

    b For your chosen null hypothesis, write down the alternative hypothesis.

2 a Without doing any calculations, write down a range of values for the number of heads to appear in the 10 tosses that will make you reject the null hypothesis that the coin is fair.

    b Also without doing any calculations, write down a range of values for the number of heads to appear in the 10 tosses for which you would not reject the null hypothesis but still might be suspicious that the coin is not fair. In this case, what might you do to try and be more certain about whether or not to reject the null hypothesis?

3 a Use the binomial distribution to work out the probability of the events listed in **2a** happening if the coin is fair.

    b Do you feel that this probability is small enough that you could reject the null hypothesis if one of the events listed occurred?

The events, such as those in **2a**, for which the null hypothesis is rejected are called the **critical region**. Statisticians will not normally reject a null hypothesis unless the probability of an outcome occurring in the critical region is less than 0.05. This means that data would appear by chance in the critical region when H_0 is true less than 5% of the time. This is referred to as a 5% **significance level**.

4   Conceptual   What is meant by a significance level of a test?

5 a Explain why your answer to **3a** is equal to the significance level of the test.

    b Find the significance level for a different choice of critical region.

    c Would you prefer this new one over the one chosen previously? Justify your answer.

    d Were your critical regions symmetrical in each case? Do they have to be?

TOK

If the result of a test is significant, what do we actually know?

6 a Can you ever be sure that a coin is biased? If so how, if not why not?

b Suppose the result of your experiment fell just outside the critical region, does this mean that the null hypothesis is true?

7 **Conceptual** What information do we obtain from a hypothesis test?

> If a statistic (a value) obtained from a sample falls in the critical region the null hypothesis is rejected.

Test for a binomial probability

> Each statistic obtained from a sample has an associated p-value. The p-value is the probability of obtaining this value (or a more extreme one) if the null hypothesis is true.
>
> If the p-value is less than the significance level the test is significant and the null hypothesis is rejected.

Example 2

A food scientist is trying to determine whether a new version of cheddar cheese is regarded as more tasty than the original type.

In order to do this he decides to carry out a test with 20 people in which they are given the two types of cheese without knowing which is the original and which is new, and he asks them to pick the one they prefer. His null hypothesis is that there is no preference, so each cheese is equally likely to be selected, and his alternative hypothesis is that the new cheese is preferred. He decides to perform the test with a 5% significance level.

Let X be the number of people in the test who prefer the new cheese.

1 If p is the proportion of people in the population who would prefer the new cheese, state the null and alternative hypotheses.

2 Find the critical region for this test.

3 State the lowest possible significance level of the test.

In the test, 18 out of the 20 people preferred the new cheese.

4 State the conclusion of the test.

5 a Find $P(X \geq 18)$ under the assumption that the null hypothesis is true.

b How does this confirm your answer to question **3**?

1 $H_0: p = 0.5$ $H_1: p > 0.5$	The alternative hypothesis is often the thing you would like to be true; in this case, that the new cheese is preferred.

Continued on next page

Statistics and probability

2 Let X be the number of people in the sample who prefer the new cheese.

The critical region has to be to the right-hand side of the distribution as our alternative hypothesis is that the proportion is larger than 0.5.

Suppose the critical region is $X \geq r$

The boundary for the critical region of this test will be the smallest value of r for which the probability of obtaining at least this number is less than or equal to 0.05.

$P(X \geq r) \leq 0.05$

$r = 15$

$P(X \geq 14) = 0.0577$

$P(X \geq 15) = 0.0207$

The critical region is $X \geq 15$

If your GDC only has a cumulative distribution function (cdf) find the acceptance region instead.

$P(X \leq s) > 0.95$

$P(X \leq 13) = 0.942$

$P(X \leq 14) = 0.979$

As the binomial distribution is discrete the critical region will therefore be $14 + 1 = 15$.

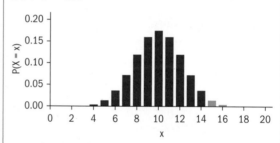

3 $P(X \geq 15) = 0.0207$

The probability is calculated using the function for the binomial distribution on the GDC.

The lowest possible significance level = 2.07%

The test could be given as a 2.07% test as the probability of being in the critical region if H_0 is true is equal to 0.0207. Normally though, a figure such as 5% or 1% is chosen.

4 As 18 lies in the critical region we reject the null hypothesis that the cheeses are preferred equally.

It can clearly be seen from the diagram above that 18 lies in the critical region and hence $P(X \geq 18)$ will be less than 0.05.

5 a P(X ≥ 18) = 0.000201

b This probability is less than 0.05 and so 18 lies in the critical region.

This is the ***p*-value** for the test – and should not to be confused with the binomial probability p.

Finding the *p*-value is often the easiest way to test the significance of the test as the critical region does not need to be calculated.

> The null hypothesis is rejected if either the test statistics falls in the critical region (it is beyond the critical value) or if the *p*-value is less than the significance level.

EXAM HINT

In examinations the test for a binomial probability will always be one-tailed.

Reflect How do you find a *p*-value for the binomial probability?

How do you find the critical region for the binomial probability?

Exercise 14B

1 Find the *p*-value for each of the following tests using the binomial distribution, where *x* is the number of successes. State whether or not H_0 should be rejected.

a H_0: $p = 0.3$, H_1: $p > 0.3$; $n = 12$, $x = 7$ and using a 5% significance level.

b H_0: $p = 0.4$, H_1: $p < 0.4$; $n = 20$, $x = 6$ and using a 10% significance level.

c H_0: $p = 0.7$, H_1: $p > 0.7$; $n = 10$, $x = 9$ and using a 10% significance level.

2 A medicine company claims that its treatment leads to a significant reduction in symptoms within one week for 60% of patients taking the treatment.

In order to test this claim a trial containing a sample of 30 people will take place.

a If *p* represents the proportion of people who benefit from the treatment, state null and alternative hypotheses for the test.

b Hence find the critical region for a test at the 5% significance level.

c When the test is performed, 14 people report a reduction in symptoms. State the conclusion of the test.

3 A show jumper claims the probability of their horse knocking down a fence (*p*) is only 0.1. A statistician wishes to test this claim by recording how many fences the horse knocks down in a single round of nine fences.

a Assuming a binomial distribution find the critical region for the test

H_0: $p = 0.1$, H_1: $p > 0.1$

b Give a reason why the binomial distribution might not be appropriate in this case.

4 A psychologist performs a test to see what proportion of 20 objects a subject can remember after viewing them for 30 seconds. The long-term proportion for the number of objects remembered is 0.3.

A student goes on a memory enhancement course and afterwards takes the same test and remembers 8 out of 20. Perform a hypothesis test to see whether the course improved the student's memory.

5 A bus company claims their buses are late less than 10% of the time. Jill notices that in a five-day period the bus is late two times.

Determine whether this is sufficient reason to reject the bus company's claim at the 5% significance level.

Statistics and probability

Reflect When is it appropriate to test for a binomial probability?

Test for the mean of a Poisson distribution

If a distribution is known to be Poisson, or if it has the characteristics of a Poisson distribution, a hypothesis test can be done to test for a particular value for the mean.

> ### International-mindedness
>
> The Poisson distribution is named after 19th century French mathematician Siméon Denis Poisson whose mentors were Lagrange and Laplace.

Example 3

The number of cars passing a school between 1 pm and 1.30 pm on a weekday can be modelled by a Poisson distribution with a mean of 32. A set of traffic lights is installed at one end of the road and it is hoped this will reduce the number of cars that use the road.

A teacher records the number of cars (X) that pass between 1 pm and 1.30 pm on five days during a school week.

a Find the critical region for a test at the 5% level.

b If the total number of cars is 140, state if there is there evidence at the 5% level that the number of cars has been reduced.

c Find the p-value for a test statistic of 140 cars and use it to verify your conclusion in part **b**.

a The total number of cars has a Po(160) distribution. $$H_0: \mu = 160, \quad H_1: \mu < 160$$ Let X be the number of cars that pass in the week. Critical region is $X \le 138$	The mean is calculated from $5 \times 32 = 160$. Critical value is the smallest value (r) of X for which $P(X \le r) < 0.05$.
b $140 \ge 138$, so not significant. Therefore, there is insufficient evidence at the 5% level to reject H_0. **c** $P(X \le 140) = 0.0592$ $0.0592 > 0.05$, so not significant. Therefore, there is insufficient evidence at the 5% level to reject H_0.	<table><tr><th>X</th><th>Y₁</th></tr><tr><td>134</td><td>0.0197</td></tr><tr><td>135</td><td>0.0241</td></tr><tr><td>136</td><td>0.0292</td></tr><tr><td>137</td><td>0.0352</td></tr><tr><td>138</td><td>0.0421</td></tr><tr><td>139</td><td>0.0501</td></tr><tr><td>140</td><td>0.0592</td></tr><tr><td>141</td><td>0.0696</td></tr><tr><td>142</td><td>0.0813</td></tr><tr><td>143</td><td>0.0943</td></tr><tr><td>144</td><td>0.1089</td></tr></table> X = 138
	Calculating the p-value is often the easiest way to do a test as the critical region does not need to be calculated.

Reflect How do you find a p-value for the mean of a Poisson distribution? How do you find the critical region for the mean of a Poisson distribution?

Exercise 14C

1 Let X have distribution $Po(\lambda)$, and let x be the number of occurrences of the events in the given time interval. By finding the appropriate p-value carry out the following tests.

   a $H_0: \lambda = 7.2$, $H_1: \lambda < 7.2$; $x = 5$, and using a 5% significance level

   b $H_0: \lambda = 5.9$, $H_1: \lambda > 5.9$; $x = 10$ and using a 5% significance level

   c $H_0: \lambda = 12.7$, $H_1: \lambda > 12.7$; $x = 23$ and using a 1% significance level

2 During the previous year the school bus has been late on average 1.8 times per week. A new route has been introduced for the new year and in the first two weeks the bus was late just twice. Determine whether this is sufficient evidence at the 5% significance level that the average has been reduced.

3 In the previous season a sports team conceded on average 2.2 goals per game. Over the summer they hired a specialist defence coach. The manager wants to use the first five games of the season to determine whether there is evidence of an improvement in their defence.

   a Assuming a Poisson distribution, state appropriate null and alternative hypotheses for the test.

   b Find the critical region for the test with a 5% significance level and state the actual significance level for the test.

   c State one reason why the Poisson distribution might not be suitable in this case.

4 A hospital ward is being inspected to see whether or not it has more incidents of infections than the national average. The national average is 0.25 cases per week and the ward is monitored for 16 weeks.

   a State a suitable test for whether or not the ward has a greater number of infections than the national average and state the critical region.

   b State one condition that needs to be assumed for a Poisson model to be valid.

> **Reflect** When is it appropriate to test for a Poisson mean?

Test for the product moment correlation coefficient

If you have a set of bivariate data, such as hours spent on homework by a student and his or her mid-term grades, then it would be possible to show these on a scatter diagram and find their correlation coefficient (r). This is unlikely to be the same value as the correlation coefficient for the whole population, which is normally written as ρ (pronounced "rho"), but for a large sample size it is likely to be quite similar.

If you need to calculate a line of best fit for your data you need to be sure that there is a linear correlation. Fortunately your GDC has an inbuilt function that allows you to do this by testing the null hypothesis

$H_0: \rho = 0$

against the alternatives $H_1: \rho < 0$, $H_1: \rho > 0$ or $H_1: \rho \neq 0$ depending on whether you are testing to see if there is a negative correlation, a positive correlation or either a negative or positive correlation.

In order to see whether the sample correlation is large enough so that the null hypothesis is rejected, a p-value is found. This is the probability of the sample correlation being at least as large as the one obtained if the two populations are in fact not correlated ($\rho = 0$). If the p-value is less than the significance level (normally 5% or 0.05) then there is strong evidence that the two variables have a linear correlation and as a consequence calculating the least squares regression line is appropriate.

Example 4

The number of times students are late for school and the distance they live from school is thought to be related. A sample of eight students is selected randomly and the data for the previous six weeks is checked. The following results were obtained.

Distance from school (km)	Number of times late	Distance from school (km)	Number of times late
5.2	5	2.3	1
1.4	2	2.8	3
6.7	0	7.0	2
8.8	6	0.5	0

Test at the 5% level whether there is a linear relationship between the two variables.

$H_0: \rho = 0$ $H_1: \rho \neq 0$	In a hypothesis test you must always clearly state both hypotheses. In this question you are not told to favour a positive or a negative correlation, so the alternative hypothesis is $H_1: \rho \neq 0$.
p-value $= 0.190$	There is no need to show any calculations, just give the p-value. All GDCs should be able to do this test directly.
$0.190 > 0.05$ hence no reason to reject the null hypothesis that there is not a linear relationship between the distance a student lives from school and the number of times they are late.	Notice that in the conclusion we are not saying that the null hypothesis is true, only that there is insufficient evidence to reject it. Notice the sample correlation coefficient is 0.516. Often this would be considered good evidence for a linear relationship but because the sample size is small it is not a significant result.

To do a hypothesis test for the population correlation coefficient (ρ) perform the following steps.

1 Write down the null hypothesis which is always H_0: $\rho = 0$.

2 Decide on the alternative hypothesis which will depend on whether you are looking for a positive correlation, a negative correlation or any linear relationship.

3 Find and write down the p-value.

4 Compare the p-value with the significance level of the test and write a conclusion.

If the p-value is less than the significance level, the result is **significant** and you "reject the null hypothesis that there is no correlation between the two variables".

If the p-value is greater than the significance level, the result is **not significant** and you would say "there is insufficient evidence to reject the null hypothesis that there is no correlation between the two variables".

You should not calculate a least squares regression line unless there is significant evidence of a linear relationship, though the level of significance you choose may vary depending on the context of the test.

Reflect How do you find a p-value when testing for PMCC = 0?

Exercise 14D

1 For each of the sets of data below:

i find the sample correlation coefficient

ii perform a test at the 10% significance level for the hypotheses

H_0: $\rho = 0$ and H_1: $\rho \neq 0$

iii if appropriate, write down the least squares line of regression for y on x.

a

x	y
12	4
15	6
16	5

b

x	y	x	y
7	9	5	7
6	7	9	8
8	8	11	9

c

x	y	x	y	x	y
42	68	34	60	82	75
35	75	70	78	61	79
56	77	54	72	25	47
24	43	38	78	35	51

2 A business is trying to assess demand for its product when it is sold at different prices. It organizes a trial in which the prices in several shops are varied on different days and the number of sales is recorded.

The results are shown below.

Price ($)	Sales	Price ($)	Sales
3.5	10	3	12
4	6	2	19
6	2	5	3
8	1	7	2

a Find the sample correlation coefficient.

b i Perform a test to see if there is a negative correlation between price and sales.

ii If the result of the test is significant, find the least squares regression line that would enable the business to estimate sales for a given price.

iii Use the line to find an estimate for the number of sales when the price is $5.50.

c Plot the original data on a graph and comment on the validity of the results obtained in parts **a** and **b**.

Statistics and probability

3 The total value of sales of ice cream from a shop and the maximum temperature were recorded over 10 days and the results are shown below.

Sales (€)	Temperature (°C)	Sales (€)	Temperature (°C)
156	23.2	191	27.3
175	25.6	182	26.6
178	28.4	187	24.6
201	31.3	162	22.3
207	30.2	158	18.5

a Test the hypothesis that there is a positive correlation between the total sales of ice cream at the shop and the maximum temperature.

b Find the equation of a regression line to estimate the sales of ice cream for a given maximum temperature.

c Hence find an estimate for the total sales when the temperature outside is 29 °C.

d Explain why the shop owner should not expect the regression line to give an accurate measure of sales for a maximum temperature of 35 °C. Justify your answer with reference to the context.

Reflect When is it appropriate to apply linear regression to bivariate data?

14.3 Testing for the mean of a normal distribution

There are many factors that affect the level of cholesterol in a person's bloodstream which makes it very difficult to know the probability distribution of cholesterol in a population as a whole.

This section explores how, for example, a research centre might test a new drug to see if it significantly reduces cholesterol, even without knowing the associated probability distribution.

The z-test

The normal distribution is the most common and important of all the distributions and has applications in many different disciplines. One of the main reasons for this is the **central limit theorem** which you met in chapter 13. An implication of the central limit theorem is that you do not need to know the distribution of the population you are sampling from in order to test for the population mean, so long as your sample size (n) is large enough. A figure of $n > 30$ is usually taken as sufficient, though this does depend on the distribution being sampled.

In the previous chapter the following result was demonstrated and is one of the most important results in Statistics.

> If X has a mean of μ and a standard deviation of σ and if X is normally distributed, or the sample size (n) is large enough for the central limit theorem to apply, then $\overline{X} \sim N\left(\mu, \dfrac{\sigma^2}{n}\right)$

International-mindedness

The standard version of the central limit theorem (CLT), was developed by the French mathematician Pierre-Simon Laplace in 1810 when he released and proved a generalization of his central limit theorem.

Investigation 3

A town council is trying to plan their budget for future years. To do this they need to know whether or not the average age of people in their town is older than the national average which is 40.0 years, with a standard deviation of 20.2 years.

They decide to test this belief by performing a hypothesis test and record the ages of a random sample of 100 people taken from the town records. They will then work out the sample average $\overline{x}$.

1 Explain why the ages of people in a large population are unlikely to follow a normal distribution.

2 Explain why the distribution of $\overline{X}$ can be assumed to be normal.

3 State null and alternative hypotheses for the council's test.

Because $\overline{X} \sim N\left(\mu, \dfrac{\sigma^2}{n}\right)$ we would expect $\overline{X}$ on average to be quite close to μ.

4 Explain why you would expect $\overline{X}$ to be particularly close to μ for larger sample sizes.

As a consequence of its distribution we would choose a test in which $H_0 : \mu = 40.0$, which would be accepted if $\overline{X}$ is close to 40.0 and rejected if it is far above it.

As before the test will have a critical region. If the value of $\overline{X}$ falls within this region then H_0 is rejected.

The town council decide to perform their test at the 5% significance level.

Let a be the critical value on the boundary of the critical region, so that $P(\overline{X} > a) = 0.05$.

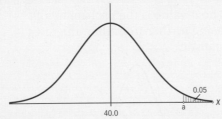

5 a Write down the distribution of $\overline{X}$ under the null hypothesis.

b Hence show that the critical region for the test is $P(\overline{X} > 43.32)$.

The value of the sample mean calculated by the town council was $\overline{x} = 42.3$.

6 State the conclusion of the town council's test.

7 Check your conclusion by calculating $P(\overline{X} > 42.3)$ when H_0 is true. Explain why this is the p-value for the test.

8 **Factual** How do you find the critical value of a one-tailed test?

9 **Conceptual** **a** What conditions are necessary to be able to use the normal distribution to test for a population mean?

b If the conditions in part **a** apply, which distribution is used to find the critical region for a test for a population mean?

TOK

When is the normal distribution a valid model?

Statistics and probability

The z-test uses the sample mean to test for the population mean. It can be used whenever the population standard deviation is known and when either the population is normally distributed, or the sample size is large enough for the CLT to apply.

Example 5

A machine fills bags of flour with a labelled weight of 1 kg. To make sure the bags are being filled correctly a sample of 40 is taken and their weights measured. The sample mean is found to be 995 g. From past experience it is known that the standard deviation of the bags filled by the machine is 20 g.

a Use the p-value to test whether there is sufficient evidence at the 5% level that the machine is filling the bags to less than the correct weight.

b Find the critical region for the test.

a $H_0: \mu = 1000$, $H_1: \mu < 1000$ p-value will be $P(\bar{X} < 995) = 0.0569$	μ is standard IB notation for the population mean, so does not need to be defined on each occasion it is used.
	The question does not tell us that the distribution of weights is normally distributed but, because the sample size is greater than 30, we can assume it is by the central limit theorem. This means we can use the z-test.
$0.0569 > 0.05$, not significant so insufficient evidence to reject H_0 that the bags are being filled to the correct average weight.	The p-value is the probability of being further from than the test statistic. 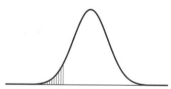
b $\bar{X} \sim N\left(1000, \dfrac{20^2}{40}\right)$ Let a be the boundary of the critical region (the critical value). $P(\bar{X} < a) = 0.05$	

EXAM HINT

Your GDC will have a function (z-test) that will enable you to obtain the p-value directly.

$$a = \text{invnorm}\left(0.05, 1000, \frac{20}{\sqrt{40}}\right) = 994.8$$

Critical region is $\overline{X} < 994.8$

The notation used here is for illustration only as it is a particular calculator notation and will vary on different calculators.

Note the distribution used for $\overline{X}$ is the one given above.

You can confirm your answer to part **a** as 995 does not lie in the critical region.

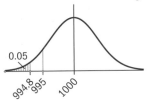

Two-tailed tests

When performing a two-tailed test (for example, one in which the alternative hypothesis is $H_1: \mu \neq 20$ rather than $H_1: \mu > 20$ or $H_1: \mu < 20$), the probability that the test statistic falls in the critical region is split between the two sides.

For example, for a 5% test we have the following critical regions:

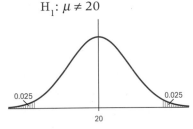
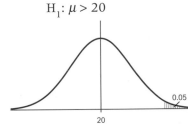
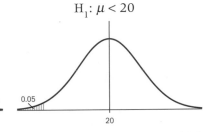

Example 6

The times taken by an athlete to run a circuit near his home can be modelled by a normal distribution with a mean of 15.4 minutes and a standard deviation of 0.62 minutes. The athlete's work takes him away from home for six months and on his return he is interested to see whether his average times have changed. He records his times over the first five days after his return and obtains the following times in minutes:

15.4, 15.5, 14.9, 15.2, 15.1

a Use the p-value to perform a test at the 5% significance level to see if his average time to complete the circuit has changed.

b Find the critical region for the test.

a H_0: $\mu = 15.4$, H_1: $\mu \neq 15.4$ p-value = 0.516 0.516 > 0.05, not significant so no reason to reject H_0 that his average time is still 15.4 minutes.	Note that this is a two-tailed test. As the test is performed on the GDC there is no need to show any method. The hypotheses, p-value and conclusion are all that are required.

Continued on next page

Statistics and probability

b Let the two critical values be a and b.

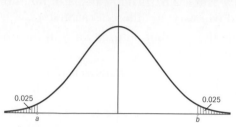

$P(\overline{X} < a) = 0.025$

$a = \text{invnorm}\left(0.025, 15.4, \dfrac{0.62}{\sqrt{5}}\right) = 14.86$

$P(\overline{X} > b) = 0.025$

$P(\overline{X} < b) = 0.975$

$b = \text{invnorm}\left(0.975, 15.4, \dfrac{0.62}{\sqrt{5}}\right) = 15.94$

Critical region is $\overline{X} < 14.86$, $\overline{X} > 15.94$

The 5% is split between the two critical regions.

Some GDCs will be able to find the value of b without converting it to $\overline{X} < b$.

b could also be found using the value of a as the two values will be symmetrical about the mean value, 15.4.

Reflect What are two-tailed tests?

Exercise 14E

1 The data below is taken from a normal population. Test to see whether it could have come from one with the given mean.

  a $H_0: \mu = 124$, $H_1: \mu \neq 124$; $\sigma = 10$. Use a 5% significance level.

    122, 134, 138, 128, 129

  b $H_0: \mu = 12.2$, $H_1: \mu \neq 12.2$; $\sigma = 1.3$. Use a 5% significance level.

    11.0, 9.4, 11.9, 12.1, 10.3

  c $H_0: \mu = 0.043$, $H_1: \mu \neq 0.043$; $\sigma = 0.012$. Use a 10% significance level.

    0.044, 0.051, 0.040, 0.054, 0.048

2 A pot of paint should cover 24 m² of wall. In a test, 32 pots of paint were tested and it was found that they covered on average 23.3 m². It is known that the standard deviation of the area covered is 1.8 m². The testers wish to determine whether this is sufficient evidence at the 5% significance level that the average coverage of the paint is less than 24 m².

  a Explain why it is possible to use a z-test in this case.

  b State the null and alternative hypotheses.

  c Determine the p-value for the test and the conclusion from the test.

  d Find the critical region for this test and use it to verify your result in part **c**.

3 It is known that the time between the arrivals of two buses is normally distributed with a standard deviation of 2.1 minutes. The bus company claims that the mean time between buses is 8.3 minutes.

John believes the average time is in fact longer than this so he decides to record some of the times between buses and this data is shown in the table below.

Time (minutes) between buses	8.0	8.7	9.2	8.4	8.5

a State the null and alternative hypotheses for John's test.

b Find the mean of John's sample ($\bar{x}$).

Let X be the times between buses.

c Write down the distribution of $\overline{X}$ under the null hypothesis.

d Hence find $P(\overline{X} > \bar{x})$ assuming the null hypothesis is true.

e Write down the conclusion of John's test.

f Verify your answer to part **d** by performing the test using the inbuilt function on your GDC.

g Find the critical region for the test.

The *t*-test

You will have noticed in the previous questions that though you were testing for an unknown population mean, you were assuming that you knew the population variance.

In most cases this is unrealistic, so the tester needs to estimate the population variance from the sample.

The value used is not the variance of the sample (s_n^2) but the

unbiased estimator of the population variance $\left(s_{n-1}^2\right)$. An unbiased estimator is one that will on average tend towards the value of the parameter being estimated; in this case σ^2.

The two values are linked by the equation $s_{n-1}^2 = \dfrac{n}{n-1} s_n^2$ which is given in the formula books.

> Calculators are likely to use different symbols for s_{n-1} and s_n. Make sure you know which is which.
>
> In examinations if using the inbuilt testing functions you need to be aware whether you have to enter s_{n-1} or s_n. Depending on what is given in the question you may need to use the formula above to convert between the two.

Unfortunately, using the data to estimate the population variance adds an extra degree of uncertainty. The level of uncertainty will depend on the sample size. If the sample is large then not much uncertainty will be introduced as the estimate of the variance will be close to the actual value. If the sample is small there will be more uncertainty.

The extra degree of uncertainty means the distribution of $\overline{X}$ can no longer be regarded as normally distributed but instead follows a *t*-distribution.

The particular *t*-distribution you need to use depends on the sample size. For a sample of size n we use the $T(n - 1)$ distribution where $n - 1$ is referred to as the degrees of freedom (the number of independent observations) and is often written as v. The term comes from the fact that you know the value of s_{n-1} so if you only knew $n - 1$ of the numbers you could work out the final one.

The *t*-distribution approaches the normal distribution for large values of n.

The graph on the right shows the *t*-distribution with one degree of freedom (green), two degrees of freedom (red) and the N(0,1) distribution.

The *t*-test is performed using the GDC in a very similar way to the *z*-test.

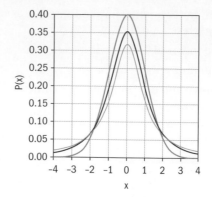

Example 7

a In order to test the hypotheses $H_0: \mu = 8.2$, $H_1: \mu < 8.2$ a sample of 14 is taken and the mean of the sample is found to be 8.15 and the standard deviation 0.07.

Test at the 5% significance level whether the sample is from the population given or one with a smaller mean.

b The sample below is thought to have come from a normal population with a mean of 34.5. Test this belief at a 5% significance level.

34.3	30.2	29.7	34.4	33.6	35.7	34.0	33.9	35.1	34.5

a $s_{n-1} = \sqrt{\dfrac{n}{n-1}}s_n = \sqrt{\dfrac{14}{13}} \times 0.07 = 0.0726$	If your GDC requires you to enter s_{n-1} you need to convert using this formula.
p-value = 0.0115 < 0.05, significant so reject H_0: $\mu = 8.2$	Use the *t*-test (one sample) on your GDC. If it asks for the sample size, input 14. If it asks for the degrees of freedom (ν) input $14 - 1 = 13$.
b $H_0: \mu = 34.5$, $H_1: \mu \neq 34.5$ p-value = 0.161 > 0.05, not significant so insufficient evidence to reject H_0	Because the answers are obtained directly from the GDC there is no need to show your method, just the hypotheses, the p-value and the conclusion.

Reflect When should the *t*-test be used instead of the *z*-test?

How do you calculate the degrees of freedom for a *t*-test?

How do you find the unbiased estimator for the variance if given the sample variance?

Exercise 14F

1 Let $\bar{x}$ be the mean of a sample of size n taken from a population with a normal distribution. Carry out the following tests.

a $H_0: \mu = 6.7$, $H_1: \mu < 6.7$; $\bar{x} = 6.4$, $s_{n-1} = 0.6$, $n = 8$ using a 5% significance level

b $H_0: \mu = 124$, $H_1: \mu \neq 124$; $\bar{x} = 121$, $s_n = 10$, $n = 9$ using a 5% significance level

c $H_0: \mu = 0.85$, $H_1: \mu > 0.85$; $\bar{x} = 0.864$, $s_n = 0.012$, $n = 6$ using a 5% significance level

2 The data below is taken from a normal population. Test to see whether it could have come from a population with the given mean.

a $H_0: \mu = 123$, $H_1: \mu \neq 123$. Use a 5% significance level

122, 134, 138, 128, 129

b $H_0: \mu = 12.2$, $H_1: \mu \neq 12.2$. Use a 5% significance level

11.0, 9.4, 11.9, 12.1, 10.3

c $H_0: \mu = 0.042$, $H_1: \mu \neq 0.042$. Use a 10% significance level

0.044, 0.051, 0.040, 0.054, 0.048

3 The average historic temperature in July is 28.2 °C. In a test the temperature is measured each day in two consecutive years (62 days). The average temperature recorded is 28.5 °C with a standard deviation of 3.2 °C. The researchers wish to determine whether this is sufficient evidence at the 5% significance level to state that the temperature is above the historical average.

a Explain why it is possible to use a t-test in this case.

b State the null and alternative hypotheses.

c Find the p-value for the test and state the conclusion from the test.

4 The time taken to travel between two towns by bus can be modelled as a normal distribution. The bus company claims that the mean journey time between the towns is 83 minutes.

Jackie believes the average time is in fact longer than this, so she decides to record some of her journeys on the bus and the data is shown below.

Journey time (minutes) between towns	82	87	92	84	85

a State the null and alternative hypotheses for Jackie's test.

b For this sample find

i the mean **ii** the standard deviation

iii the unbiased estimator of the population standard deviation.

c Find the p-value and write down the conclusion of the test.

Confidence intervals

Often, rather than testing data obtained from a sample against a single value for the population mean, it is more convenient to have a range of values within which the mean of the population is likely to lie.

These intervals always have a confidence level attached to them. For example, a 95% confidence interval means that on 95% of all occasions such a sample was selected the population mean would fall within the calculated boundaries.

When the population from which the sample is taken can be regarded as being normally distributed, confidence intervals for the population

TOK

In the absence of knowing the value of a parameter, will an unbiased estimator always be better than a biased one?

means can easily be worked out using the GDC. As with hypothesis testing, the normal distribution is used when the population variance is known and the $T(n-1)$ distribution is used when it has to be estimated from the data.

The GDC will always give a confidence interval that is centred on the sample mean.

Example 8

The sample below is taken from a population which can be modelled by a normal distribution. Find a 95% confidence interval for the population mean.

| 34.3 | 29.5 | 38.1 | 27.5 | 29.2 | 37.0 |

The 95% confidence interval is (27.91, 37.29).	This can be obtained directly from the calculator using the t-distribution. The interval can be stated in words or given using interval notation as has been done here.

Reflect What is a confidence interval?

Exercise 14G

1 Find the 95% confidence interval for the population mean given the samples below. The population can be assumed to be normally distributed.

a $\bar{x} = 12.4$, $s_{n-1} = 3.2$, $n = 12$

b $\bar{x} = 62.3$, $s_{n-1}^2 = 4.2$, $n = 120$

c $\bar{x} = 6.3$, $s_n^2 = 5.2$, $n = 10$

d $\bar{x} = 2.3$, $s_n = 0.2$, $n = 7$

e $\bar{x} = 4.6$, $\sigma = 0.2$, $n = 9$ (where σ is the population standard deviation)

2 Find the 99% confidence interval for the population mean based on the following samples.

a 12.4, 13.6, 10.9, 12.5, 11.9

b −2.3, −4.5, 0.2, 5.1, −0.9

3 A sample has a mean $\bar{x} = 21.2$ and $s_{n-1} = 1.4$.

a Find a 99% confidence interval for the population mean when

i $n = 10$ ii $n = 20$

iii $n = 50$ iv $n = 100$

b Comment on your answers to part **a**.

4 a Find the 95% confidence interval for the population mean based on the sample below.

12.2, 14.4, 11.6, 15.1, 13.7

b State one assumption that you made in your calculation.

c Comment on a claim that the population mean is 15.3.

Two-sample tests

One of the main uses for the t-test is in comparing two different samples and asking if they could have come from an identical population.

The assumption is always that the distributions are the same and the standard deviations are equal, so the test is just whether or not the populations they come from have the same mean. Before carrying out the test, you have to consider whether $\bar{X}$ can be regarded as normally distributed.

Example 9

Mr Arthur gives his two chemistry groups the same test. He wants to find out if there is any difference between the achievement levels of the two groups.

The results are:

Group 1	54	62	67	43	85	69	73	81	47	92	55	59	68	72
Group 2	73	67	58	46	91	48	82	81	67	74	57	66		

a Write down the null and alternative hypotheses.

b Perform a t-test at the 5% significance level.

c Write down the conclusion to the test.

Let the two population means be μ_1 and μ_2	Notice that the two groups do not need to be exactly the same size.
a $H_0: \mu_1 = \mu_2$ There is no difference between the grades in Group 1 and the grades in Group 2.	This will be a **two-tailed test** as you want to know if Group 1 is better or worse than Group 2.
$H_1: \mu_1 \neq \mu_2$ There is a difference between the grades in Group 1 and the grades in Group 2.	All GDCs will have a two-sample t-test option. If you are given the choice between pooled and not pooled, select pooled. This assumes the variances of the populations the samples are taken from are equal and is the assumption that will be used in examinations.
b p-value $= 0.816$	
c $0.816 > 0.05$, not significant so no reason to reject the null hypothesis that there is no significant difference between the two groups.	

Statistics and probability

1 Petra noticed that one of her apple trees grew in the shade and the other did not. She wanted to find out if apples from the tree in the shade weighed less than those in the sun. She picked nine apples from each tree and weighed them in grams.

Tree in shade	75	82	93	77	85	78	91	83	92
Tree not in shade	74	81	95	79	95	82	93	88	90

Perform a t-test at the 10% significance level to test whether the apples from the tree in the shade weigh less than those in the sun.

2 A pharmaceutical company claims to have invented a new pill to aid weight loss. They claim that people taking these pills will lose more weight than people not taking them. A total of twenty people are weighed and tested. Ten people are given the new pills and the other ten are given a placebo. After two months the people are weighed again and any weight loss, in kg, is noted in the table below.

New remedy	1.2	2.4	1.6	3.5	3.2	4.6	2.5	0.8	1.2	3.9
Placebo	0.6	0	1.0	1.3	2.1	0.7	1.9	2.4	0.3	1.0

Perform a t-test at the 1% significance level to see if those taking the pills are losing more weight on average.

Paired samples

A special type of two-sample test occurs when the two samples are paired in an obvious way. This might be the score of the same people in two different tests, or the time taken by a group of athletes to run two separate courses.

The null hypothesis is the same as in the previous test, namely the two populations have the same mean, but it is rephrased to say the difference in the two means is equal to zero and the test is done on the differences rather than on the two samples separately.

Example 10

Five candidates attended a revision course hoping to improve their chemistry grades. They were tested before the course started and again at the end of the course. The results were as follows.

Candidate	1	2	3	4	5
Score before course	64	43	29	56	61
Score after course	72	60	33	55	62

Determine at the 5% level whether the course improved the candidates' performance in their chemistry tests.

The differences between the scores after the course and before the course are:

| 8 | 17 | 4 | −1 | 1 |

Let μ_D be the population mean for the difference between the two scores.

H_0: $\mu_D = 0$, H_1: $\mu_D > 0$

p-value $= 0.0713 > 0.05$, not significant so no reason to reject H_0 that the grades have not improved.

It is possible to do the subtraction for each candidate in turn, but most GDCs allow you to subtract two lists. If the data set is larger, then this would be the best method to use.

The test is performed in the usual way using the differences and a one-sample t-test.

Reflect How is a paired-sample t-test different from a two-sample t-test?
What do you need to do before testing a paired sample?

Exercise 14I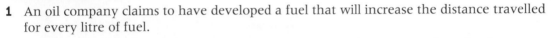

1 An oil company claims to have developed a fuel that will increase the distance travelled for every litre of fuel.

Ten scooters are filled with one litre of normal fuel and driven to see how far they can go. They are then filled with one litre of the new fuel and driven over the same track until the second litre is used up. The distances travelled, in km, are shown in the table below.

Original fuel	36	38	44	42	45	39	48	51	48	43
New fuel	43	39	51	49	53	48	52	46	53	49

Test at the 1% significance level whether the new fuel has increased the distance travelled.

2 A financial company claims to be able to increase any investment by 5% in six months.

To test this claim a reporter invested $100 six times over a period of a few weeks and checked the values of each when the six months were ended. The results are shown in the table below.

Value at start	100	100	100	100	100	100
Value at end	105	110	106	108	103	99

a State the null and alternative hypotheses.

b Carry out the test to see whether or not the company's claim can be rejected at the 5% level.

3 It is felt that a new drug has a positive effect in reducing cholesterol. A sample of ten patients was taken and the level of cholesterol measured at the start of the treatment and again six weeks later.

The results are shown in the table below.

Total cholesterol before (mmol/l)	8.5	9.2	8.7	9.6	7.9	8.8	8.9	9.5	10.0	8.4
Total cholesterol after (mmol/l)	7.9	7.5	8.5	8.1	6.2	6.8	7.5	8.8	9.4	7.6

Statistics and probability

a Use an appropriate test, with a 5% significance level, to see if the drug has had a positive effect on reducing the level of cholesterol.

It is now given that during the treatment the patients were also encouraged to eat more healthily. A large control group did not take the drug but were also encouraged to eat more healthily. It was found that their cholesterol on average dropped by 0.7 mmol/l.

b Given this new information, state an appropriate test to see if the drug has a beneficial effect and carry out this test.

c i State whether you would advise the drug manufacturers to do further tests.

ii If you were to do another test, comment on how the test could be improved.

14.4 χ^2 test for independence

> A **chi-squared (χ^2) test for independence** can be performed to find out if two data sets are independent of each other or not. It can be performed at various significance levels. In the examination it will only be tested at the 1%, 5% or 10% significance level.

Saanvi is a member of a sports club. She has noticed that more males play squash than females, and is interested to find out if there is any relationship between gender and favourite racket game. She sent around a survey to the other members in the club to find out which game they prefer: tennis, badminton or squash. The results of the survey are:

Male	Male	Male	Female	Female	Female
Tennis	Badminton	Badminton	Badminton	Badminton	Tennis
Tennis	Squash	Squash	Badminton	Squash	Badminton
Squash	Squash	Squash	Tennis	Badminton	Squash
Squash	Squash	Badminton	Tennis	Tennis	Badminton
Squash	Tennis	Squash	Squash	Badminton	Badminton
Squash	Tennis	Tennis	Tennis	Badminton	Tennis
Squash	Tennis	Tennis	Badminton	Squash	Squash
Badminton	Tennis	Tennis	Badminton	Tennis	Badminton
Tennis	Squash	Badminton	Tennis	Tennis	Badminton
Badminton	Squash	Squash			
Squash	Badminton	Squash			

Saanvi decides to perform a χ^2 test for independence at the 5% significance level to find out if the preferred game is independent of gender or not. She will need hypotheses for this test.

Her **null hypothesis** is

H_0: Preferred racket game is independent of gender.

And her **alternative hypothesis** is

H_1: Preferred racket game is not independent of gender.

Investigation 4

Complete the following table for Saanvi's data. This is the table of **observed frequencies**, f_o, and is called a contingency table.

Sport	Tennis	Badminton	Squash	Total	
Male	10				
Female					
Total				60	

1 Calculate the probability that a person chosen at random is male.

2 Calculate the probability that a person chosen at random likes tennis best.

3 If these two probabilities are independent, find the probability that a person chosen at random is male and likes tennis best.

4 There are 60 people in total. If the events were independent, find the expected number of males who like tennis best.

Under the null hypothesis that the two attributes are independent of each other, the column and row totals can be used to calculate expected frequencies (f_e) for each of the cells.

5 Complete the table of expected frequencies.

Sport	Tennis	Badminton	Squash	Total
Male				
Female				
Total				

In the table of expected frequencies, the **totals** of the rows and columns are fixed to match the numbers of males and females and players of each sport in the sample. In this example:

Sport	Tennis	Badminton	Squash	Total
Male				33
Female				27
Total	19	20	21	60

Continued on next page

6 Find the smallest number of entries that you need to calculate by multiplying probabilities before you can fill in the rest of the table from the numbers already there.

7 If your table had three rows and three columns, find the smallest number of entries that you would need to calculate by multiplying probabilities.

8 If your table had three rows and four columns, find the smallest number of entries that you would need to calculate by multiplying probabilities.

9 Find the smallest number of entries if the table had n rows and m columns.

This number is called the **degrees of freedom**, often written as ν. This is because you only have a "free" choice for the numbers that go into that many cells. After that, the remaining numbers are fixed by the need to keep the totals the same.

10 **Factual** What does the number of degrees of freedom represent?

11 **Conceptual** What do the "expected values" tell us?

> **EXAM HINT**
> In examinations, ν will always be greater than 1.

The formula for the degrees of freedom (ν) is:

$$\nu = (\text{rows} - 1)(\text{columns} - 1)$$

> **HINT**
> Expected values must be greater than 5. If there are expected values less than 5 then you will need to combine rows or columns. See Example 11.

Investigation 5

To decide whether two variables are likely to be independent it is necessary to compare the observed values with those expected. If the observed values are a long way from the expected values then you can deduce that the two variables are unlikely to be independent and reject the null hypothesis. But how do you measure how far away they are, and, if you have a measure, how do you decide when the difference is large enough to reject the null hypothesis?

1 Looking back at the results, which categories are furthest from the expected values? Which are closest?

2 Find the sum of the differences between the observed and expected values in the tables above and comment on how suitable this would be as a measure of how far apart they are.

3 Comment on an advantage of squaring the differences before adding them.

4 Comment on a disadvantage of using this sum as a measure of the distance between the observed and expected values.

In order to make sure that differences are in proportion, it would be better to divide each difference squared by the expected value (as long as the expected value is not too small).

This calculation will give you the χ^2 **test statistic**.

The χ^2 test statistic is

$$\chi^2_{calc} = \sum \frac{(f_o - f_e)^2}{f_e}$$

where f_o are the observed values and f_e are the expected values.
If this number is larger than a **critical value** then reject the null hypothesis. If it is smaller than the critical value then accept the null hypothesis.

Your GDC is likely to give you the p-value. This is often the easiest method to perform the test.

As before, the null hypothesis is rejected if the p-value is less than the significance level for the test.

Investigation 5 (continued)

The null and alternative hypotheses for a χ^2 test for independence are:

H_0: the two variables are independent of each other

H_1: the two variables are not independent of each other.

5   Use the entries in the tables above for the observed and expected frequencies to find the χ^2 test statistic. The calculation begins:

$$\chi^2_{calc} = \frac{(10 - 10.45)^2}{10.45} + \ldots$$

For a 5% significance level the critical value is chosen so that the probability of the test statistic being greater than this value if the two variables are independent is 0.05.

6   Will the critical value be larger or smaller for a 1% significance level than for a 5% significance level?

The size of the critical value also depends on the number of degrees of freedom, as more numbers are being added to create the test statistic. In examinations you will always be given the critical value if you need to use it.

The critical value for 2 degrees of freedom at the 5% significance level is $\chi^2_{5\%} = 5.991$.

7   Use this value and your test statistic to decide whether or not to accept the null hypothesis.

8   Use the inbuilt function on your GDC for the observed values given above and verify your previous answer for the test statistic.

Also make sure you know how to find the expected values on your GDC as you will need to check them each time to make sure they are all greater than 5.

Your GDC also gives you a p-value. As before this is the probability of obtaining the particular test statistic calculated or a higher value. If the p-value is smaller than the level of significance then you do not accept the null hypothesis.

EXAM HINT
In examinations you will use your GDC to find the value of your test statistic.

Continued on next page

Statistics and probability

9 Use the p-value that you found on your GDC and the significance level of 5% to reach a conclusion Saanvi's test.

10 **Factual** What are the null and alternative hypotheses for a χ^2 test for independence?

11 **Conceptual** How can you use the result of a χ^2 test to determine if there is a relationship between two variables?

Example 11

A randomly selected group of 80 people were asked what their favourite genre of music was: pop, classical, folk or jazz. The results are in the table below.

	Pop	Classical	Folk	Jazz	Total
Male	18	9	3	8	38
Female	22	6	7	7	42
Total	40	15	10	15	80

A χ^2 test was carried out at the 10% significance level.

a Write down the null and alternative hypotheses.

b Show that the expected value for a female liking pop is 21.

c Find the full table of expected values.

d Combine two columns so that all expected values are greater than 5 and write down the new observed and expected tables.

e Write down the degrees of freedom for the new table.

f Use your GDC to find the χ^2 test statistic and the p-value for this test.

g Determine whether the null hypothesis is accepted or not.

a H_0: Favourite genre of music is independent of gender. H_1: Favourite genre of music is not independent of gender.	Even if not told to do so, you must always state the null and alternative hypotheses when doing a test.
b $\dfrac{42}{80} \times \dfrac{40}{80} \times 80 = 21$	Because the command term is "show that" you cannot just get this value from your GDC.
c <table><tr><td></td><td>Pop</td><td>Classical</td><td>Folk</td><td>Jazz</td></tr><tr><td>Male</td><td>19</td><td>7.125</td><td>4.75</td><td>7.125</td></tr><tr><td>Female</td><td>21</td><td>7.875</td><td>5.25</td><td>7.875</td></tr></table>	You should always check the expected values to make sure all of them are greater than 5.

d

Expected	Pop	Classical	Folk and Jazz
Male	19	7.125	11.875
Female	21	7.875	13.125

Observed	Pop	Classical	Folk and Jazz
Male	18	9	11
Female	22	6	14

The Folk column could have been joined with either of the other two adjacent columns.

e $(3 - 1) \times (2 - 1) = 2$

Remember that you subtract one from the number of rows and columns, then multiply.

f $\chi^2 = 1.1629...$ and $p = 0.559...$

$0.559 > 0.10$ and so the result is not significant and there is no reason to reject the null hypothesis that favourite genre of music is independent of gender.

Reflect When do you need to combine columns/rows?

Exercise 14J

1 Sixty people were asked what their favourite flavour of chocolate was (milk, dark, white).

The results are shown in the table below.

	Milk	Dark	White	Total
Male	10	17	5	32
Female	8	6	14	28
Total	18	23	19	60

Perform a χ^2 test at the 1% significance level to see if favourite flavour of chocolate and gender are independent.

The critical value for this test is $\chi^2_{1\%} = 9.210$.

2 Nandan wanted to know whether or not the number of hours on social media had an influence on average grades (GPA). He collected the following information:

	Low GPA	Average GPA	High GPA	Total
0–9 hours	4	23	58	85
10–19 hours	23	45	32	100
>20 hours	43	33	9	85
Total	70	101	99	270

He decided to perform a χ^2 test at the 10% significance level, to find out if there is a connection between GPA and number of hours on social media.

a State the null hypothesis and the alternative hypothesis.

b Show that the expected frequency for 0–9 hours and a high GPA is 31.2.

c Show that the number of degrees of freedom is 4.

d Write down the χ^2 test statistic and the p-value for this data.

The critical value is $\chi^2_{10\%} = 7.779$.

e Comment on your result.

3 Hubert wanted to find out if the number of people walking their dog was related to the time of day. He kept a record during 120 days and the results are in the table below.

	Morning	Afternoon	Evening	Total
0–5 people	8	6	18	32
6–10 people	13	8	23	44
> 10 people	21	7	16	44
Total	42	21	57	120

Test, at the 5% significance level, if there is a connection between time of day and number of people walking their dog.

The critical value is $\chi^2_{5\%} = 9.488$.

4 Samantha wanted to find out if there was a connection between the type of degree that a person had and their annual salary in dollars. She interviewed 120 professionals and her observed results are shown in the table below.

	BA	MA	PhD	Total
< \$60 000	9	6	3	18
\$60 000–\$120 000	11	17	10	38
> \$120 000	7	13	24	44
Total	27	36	37	100

Test, at the 1% significance level, if there is a connection between type of degree and salary.

a State the null hypothesis and the alternative hypothesis.

b State which cell has an expected value less than 5.

c Combine two **rows** so that all expected values are greater than 5.

d Find the p-value for this data.

e Comment on your result.

Developing inquiry skills

Let the height of the trees in the opening problem be h. Divide the heights into small, medium and large where small is $h \le 4.5$ m, medium is $4.5 < h \le 5$ and large $h > 5.0$.

Use these categories to form a contingency table for the heights in areas A and B and test at the 5% significance level whether the height of a tree is independent of the area in which it is growing.

Does the conclusion of the test support the hypothesis that the trees from area A, on average, have a greater height than those from area B. Justify your answer.

TOK

What does it mean if a data set passes one test but fails another?

14.5 χ^2 goodness-of-fit test

The uniform and normal distributions

Investigation 6

Jiang wonders whether the die he was given is fair. He rolls it 300 times. His results are shown in the table.

Number	Frequency
1	35
2	52
3	47
4	71
5	62
6	33

1 Write down the probability of throwing a 1 with a fair die.

2 If you throw a fair die 300 times, how many times would you expect to throw a 1?

3 Write down the expected frequencies for throwing a fair die 300 times.

Since all the expected frequencies are the same, this is known as a **uniform distribution**.

4 **Factual** Is the formula for the χ^2 test suitable to test whether Jiang's results fit this uniform distribution?

The null hypothesis is H_0 : Jiang's die is fair.

5 Write down the alternative hypothesis.

6 Given that the critical value at the 5% significance level for this test is 11.07, use the formula for the χ^2 test, $\chi^2 = \sum \dfrac{(f_o - f_e)^2}{f_e}$, to find out if Jiang's results could be taken from a uniform distribution.

Normally you would solve this using your GDC, which may ask you to enter the degrees of freedom.

7 **Factual** What is the number of degrees of freedom in a χ^2 goodness-of-fit test? (Consider in how many cells you have free choices when completing the expected values table.)

8 Write down the number of degrees of freedom for this test.

9 Using your GDC verify the value for the test statistic found above and write down the associated p-value.

10 What is your conclusion from this test?

11 **Conceptual** What is the purpose of the χ^2 goodness-of-fit test?

These types of test are called "goodness-of-fit" tests as they are measuring how closely the observed data fits with the expected data for a particular distribution. The test for independence using contingency tables is an example of a goodness-of-fit test, but you can test for the goodness-of-fit with any distribution.

In a χ^2 goodness-of-fit test, the degrees of freedom $v = (n-1)$.

Example 12

Marius works in a fish shop. One week he measures 250 fish before selling them. His results are in the table below.

Length of fish, x cm	Frequency
$x < 12$	5
$12 \leq x < 15$	22
$15 \leq x < 18$	71
$18 \leq x < 21$	88
$21 \leq x < 24$	52
$24 \leq x < 27$	10
$27 \leq x$	2

Marius is told that the lengths of the fish should be modelled by a normal distribution with a mean of 19 cm and standard deviation of 3 cm, so he decides to perform a χ^2 goodness-of-fit test at the 5% significance level to find out if the fish that he measured could have come from a population with this distribution.

a Write down his null and alternative hypotheses.

b Find the probability that a fish is less than 12 cm long.

c Hence find the expected number of fish whose length is less than 12 cm.

The table below shows the expected values of 250 normally distributed fish with mean of 19 cm and standard deviation of 3 cm for the given intervals.

Length of fish, x cm	Probability	Expected frequency
$x < 12$		
$12 \leq x < 15$	0.0814	20.3
$15 \leq x < 18$		
$18 \leq x < 21$		
$21 \leq x < 24$	0.2047	51.2
$24 \leq x < 27$	0.04396	10.99
$27 \leq x$	0.00383	0.958

d Find the missing values.

e Perform the χ^2 goodness-of-fit test, writing down the degrees of freedom used.

(The critical value for this test is 9.488.)

---

a Let the length of the fish be X.

H_0: X is normally distributed with a mean of 19 cm and a standard deviation of 3 cm.

H_1: X is not normally distributed with a mean of 19 cm and a standard deviation of 3 cm.

b $P(X < 12) = 0.00981...$

c 2.45

Use the normal cdf function on your GDC to find the probability and then multiply your answer by 250 to get the expected number.

$250 \times 0.00981... = 2.45$

d

$18 \leq x < 21$	0.3781	94.5
$21 \leq x < 24$	0.2047	51.2

These values are calculated by first finding the probability and then multiplying by 250.

e Two of the expected frequencies are less than 5 so the rows need to combined.

Length of fish, x cm	Observed frequency	Expected frequency
$x < 15$	27	22.75
$15 \leq x < 18$	71	69.6
$18 \leq x < 21$	88	94.5
$21 \leq x < 24$	52	51.2
$24 \leq x$	12	11.9

Unlike the test for independence you will need to enter the expected values as well as the observed values.

Either critical values or p-values can be used, though in examinations the critical value will not always be given so the p-value must be used.

There are 4 degrees of freedom.

$\chi^2 = 1.28$ and the p-value = 0.864

Either: $1.28 < 9.488$,

or $0.864 > 0.05$

Hence not significant so no reason to reject the null hypothesis.

Reflect How do you perform a goodness-of-fit test for a uniform or normal distribution?

Exercise 14K

1 Terri buys 10 packets of sweets and counts how many of each colour, yellow, orange, red, purple and green, there are. In total she has 600 sweets.

According to the packaging, the colours should be evenly distributed with 20% of each colour in a bag.

The results for Terri's 10 bags are:

Colour	Frequency
Yellow	104
Orange	132
Red	98
Purple	129
Green	137

a Find the expected frequencies.

b Write down the degrees of freedom.

c Perform a goodness-of-fit test at the 5% significance level to find out if Terri's data fits a uniform distribution. Remember to write down the null and alternative hypotheses and to state your conclusion.

The critical value for this test is 9.488.

2 The last digit on 500 winning lottery tickets is recorded in the table below.

Last number	0	1	2	3	4	5	6	7	8	9
Frequency	44	53	49	61	47	52	39	58	42	45

a Each digit should be equally likely to occur. Write down the table of expected values.

b Perform a goodness-of-fit test at the 10% significance level to find out if the data fits a uniform distribution.

3 The grades for an economics exam for 300 university students are as follows.

Grade, $x\%$	Frequency
$x < 50$	8
$50 \leq x < 60$	72
$60 \leq x < 70$	143
$70 \leq x < 80$	71
$80 \leq x$	6

The guidelines for the exam state that grades should be normally distributed with mean of 65% and standard deviation of 7.5%.

a Complete the expected frequency table for this distribution.

Expected frequency	6.8			68.92	6.8

b Perform a goodness-of-fit test at the 10% significance level to find out if the data could have been taken from this normal distribution.

4 The heights of elephants are normally distributed with mean of 250 cm and standard deviation of 11 cm.

250 elephants are measured and the results shown in the table below.

Height, h cm	$h < 235$	$235 \leq h < 245$	$245 \leq h < 255$	$255 \leq h < 265$	$265 \leq h$
Frequency	10	69	88	63	20

a Complete the expected frequency table.

Expected frequency	21.6				

b Perform a goodness-of-fit test at the 5% significance level to find out if the observed data indicates that the population of elephants from which it was taken follows the given normal distribution.

5 The scores for IQ tests are normally distributed with mean of 100 and standard deviation of 10.

Cinzia gives an IQ test to all 200 IBDP students in the school. Her results are in the table below.

Score, x	Frequency
$60 \leq x < 90$	18
$90 \leq x < 100$	39
$100 \leq x < 110$	78
$110 \leq x < 120$	46
$120 \leq x < 130$	10
$130 \leq x < 140$	9

Cinzia wants to test if these results are taken from a population with the same distribution and performs a χ^2 goodness-of-fit test at the 1% significance level.

a Write down the null and alternative hypotheses.

b Explain why you should use the intervals $x < 90$ and $x \geq 130$ when working out the expected values for the lower and upper intervals.

c Hence calculate the expected values for each interval for an N(100,10) distribution.

d Combine rows to ensure all expected values are greater than 5 and give the new expected and observed values.

e Write down the number of degrees of freedom.

The critical value is 6.251.

f Find the χ^2 test statistic and the p-value and state the conclusion for the test.

g **i** Find the mean and standard deviation of the observed data.

ii From a consideration of the answers above and the distribution of the observed data, explain why the χ^2 test has not shown that the data is not normally distributed.

iii If you wished to test to see if the data was normally distributed, state how you might adapt the test.

The Poisson and binomial distributions

Example 13

Flaws in a length of material are thought to be modelled by a Poisson distribution with a mean of two flaws per metre.

Fifty 1 m lengths of material are inspected and the number of flaws in each are recorded in the table below.

Number of flaws	0	1	2	3	≥ 4
Frequency	5	10	18	11	6

a If $X \sim \text{Po}(2)$ find $P(X = 0), P(X = 1), P(X = 2), P(X = 3)$ and $P(X \geq 4)$.

b Hence find the expected values if the number of flaws follows a Poisson distribution with a mean of two flaws per metre.

c Write down the null and alternative hypotheses and the degrees of freedom for the test.

d Find the p-value.

e State the conclusion for this test.

a

Number of flaws	0	1	2	3	≥ 4
Probability	0.135	0.271	0.271	0.180	0.143

Most calculators have a function that will allow all these values to be read directly from a table.

To find $P(X \geq 4)$ you can use either the cumulative distribution function on the calculator or subtract the other values from 1.

Continued on next page

Statistics and probability

b

Number of flaws	0	1	2	3	≥ 4
Expected value	6.77	13.5	13.5	9.02	7.15

These results are obtained from multiplying the probabilities by the number of 1 m lengths.

c H_0: The number of flaws in the material follows a Poisson distribution with a mean of two flaws per metre.

H_1: The number of flaws in the material does not follow a Poisson distribution with a mean of two flaws per metre.

Degrees of freedom = $5 - 1 = 4$

As all the expected values are greater than 5 the degrees of freedom is just the number of cells minus one.

d p-value = 0.479

e $0.479 > 0.05$

This result is not significant so no reason to reject H_0 that the number of flaws follows a Poisson distribution.

Example 14

In a trial three coins are tossed.

a Find the probability of obtaining: 0 heads, exactly 1 head, exactly 2 heads, exactly 3 heads.

Hagar tosses three coins 200 times and makes a note of the number of heads each time.

Her results are as follows.

Number of heads	Frequency
0	28
1	67
2	83
3	22

She is interested to find out if her coins are fair and so performs a χ^2 goodness-of-fit test at the 5% significance level on her data.

b Use the probabilities for B(3, 0.5) and the fact that Hagar tossed the coins 200 times, to find the expected values for the number of heads.

c Write down the null and alternative hypotheses and the degrees of freedom for the test.

The critical value is 7.815.

d Find the χ^2 value and the *p*-value.

e State the conclusion for this test.

a	

Number of heads	Probability
0	0.125
1	0.375
2	0.375
3	0.125

Most calculators have a function that will allow all these values to be read directly from a table.

b	

Number of heads	Expected value
0	25
1	75
2	75
3	25

Multiply the list of probabilities obtained in part **a** by 200.

In binomial questions, take care not to confuse the number of times the experiment is repeated (200) with the number of times the action is repeated in each binomial trial (3).

An equivalent null hypothesis would be H_0: All the coins are fair.

c H_0: The number of heads has a B(3, 0.5) distribution.

H_1: The number of heads does not have a B(3, 0.5) distribution.

The number of degrees of freedom is 3.

Remember the number of degrees of freedom equals the number of cells minus one.

d $\chi^2 = 2.43$, *p*-value = 0.489. Either: 2.43 < 7.815, or 0.489 > 0.05

e The result is not significant, so there is no reason to reject the null hypothesis.

The conclusion could also be that not all the coins are fair.

Reflect How do you perform a goodness-of-fit test for a binomial or Poisson distribution?

TOK

In practical terms, is saying that a result is significant the same as saying that it is true?

How does language influence our perception?

Exercise 14L

1 Esmerelda rolls two dice 250 times. She records the number of sixes that she rolls.

Number of sixes	0	1	2
Frequency	135	105	10

a i Find the probabilities of scoring 0, 1 or 2 sixes when rolling two fair dice.

ii Hence, calculate the missing entries in the table of expected frequencies when rolling two fair dice.

Number of sixes	0	1	2
Expected frequencies			6.94

b Perform a goodness-of-fit test at the 5% significance level to find out if the data fits a $B\left(2, \dfrac{1}{6}\right)$ distribution. Remember to write down the null and alternative hypotheses.

The critical value for this test is 5.991.

2 It is thought that the number of goals scored in a sports match can be modelled by a Poisson distribution. To test this theory the number of goals in 50 games was collected and the data is shown in the table below.

Goals	0	1	2	3	4	5	≥6
Frequency	7	10	11	10	6	4	2

It is known that the average number of goals per game over a season is 2.4.

a Taking the mean as 2.4 and assuming a Poisson distribution, calculate the missing entries in the table below.

Goals	0	1	2	3	4	5	≥6
Probability							
Expected frequency							

b Use a hypothesis test at the 10% significance level to test whether the number of goals scored in a game follows a Poisson distribution with a mean of 2.4.

3 Advait sows three seeds in 50 different pots. The packet claims that the probability that a seed will germinate is 0.75 and the germination of a seed is independent of the other seeds in the packet.

The number of seeds that germinated in each pot is shown below.

Number of seeds germinating	0	1	2	3
Frequency	5	10	15	20

a Using the binomial distribution B(3, 0.75), find the expected probabilities of 0, 1, 2 or 3 seeds germinating.

Advait wishes to test the manufacturer's claim by using the χ^2 goodness-of-fit test and a 5% significance level.

b Write down the null and alternative hypotheses.

c Find the table of expected frequencies.

d Write down the degrees of freedom.

e Find the p-value for this test and hence whether the number of seeds germinating is consistent with a B(3, 0.75) distribution.

4 The number of people joining a queue at an airport during the hour before a flight departs is thought to follow a Poisson distribution with a mean of 4.2 in every five-minute interval.

To test this hypothesis, data is collected over a period of five days and the number of people arriving each five minutes is shown in the table below.

Number of people	0	1	2	3	4	5	6	7	≥8
Frequency	5	7	6	7	8	6	4	8	9

a Perform a χ^2 goodness-of-fit test at the 5% significance level to test the following hypotheses.

H_0: The number of people arriving in the queue each five minutes follows a Po(4.2) distribution.

H_1: The number of people arriving in the queue each five minutes does not follow a Po(4.2) distribution.

Show your table of expected values and clearly indicate any columns that have been combined.

b A test can be significant due to the data not following the particular distribution given, or through the wrong choice of parameters.

   i Find the mean and the variance of the original sample taken.

   ii Hence give two reasons why the significant result was probably due to the distribution not being Poisson rather than the parameter not being incorrect.

5 In an experiment a student has to guess the symbol on a card held up by a researcher. There are four possible symbols to choose from and each student will be tested five times.

a If a student is guessing randomly, write down the distribution of X, the number of cards they guess correctly.

b Hence find the probabilities that X is equal to 0, 1, 2, 3, 4 and 5.

A group of 500 students sit the test and the results are:

Number correct, x	0	1	2	3	4	5
Frequency	104	193	139	49	13	2

c Perform a goodness-of-fit test at the 5% significance level to find out if the data supports the hypothesis that the students are guessing randomly.

Developing inquiry skills

	Section A	Section B
Small $h \leq 4.5$	3	9
Medium $4.5 < h \leq 5.0$	7	9
Large $h > 5.0$	14	6

From previous research it is known that the heights of this species of tree follow a normal distribution with a mean of 4.9 m and a standard deviation of 0.5 m.

Use the data above to test the heights of the trees from each of the areas separately and see if the observed values are consistent with both samples being taken from this distribution.

Is there sufficient evidence to say these two samples were not taken from the given normal population?

What do your results suggest about the likelihood of the trees from area A having a greater height than those from area B?

Estimating parameters

Often in a χ^2 test you are not comparing the data with a fixed distribution but just want to test whether it is normal, binomial or Poisson. In these cases it makes no sense to choose an arbitrary mean, standard deviation or probability (in the case of binomial), but instead use values estimated from the observed data.

Estimating parameters from the data does affect the degrees of freedom used. For example, if you use the same mean as the observed data for your expected values then when all but two cells are filled in, the other two are fixed as there will be only two numbers which will ensure both the totals and the means match up between observed and expected.

> To obtain the number of degrees of freedom, take the number of cells minus one, and then subtract one for each of the parameters estimated.

For example if you have 10 cells and you have estimated the mean from the data, the number of degrees of freedom will be $10 - 1 - 1 = 8$.

Example 15

The lengths of fish caught in a lake are thought to be normally distributed. To test this belief 200 fish were caught and measured and the results are shown in the table below.

Length (x cm)	$0 < x < 10$	$10 < x < 15$	$15 < x < 20$	$20 < x < 25$	$25 < x < 30$	$30 < x < 40$
Number of fish	45	55	38	27	25	10

Using estimates of the mean and standard deviation of the population taken from the sample data, test the hypothesis at the 5% level that the lengths of the fish are normally distributed.

From the sample $\bar{x} = 16.1$ cm, $s_{n-1} = 8.46$ cm H_0: The fish in the lake have an N(16.1, 8.46²) distribution. H_1: The fish in the lake do not have an N(16.1, 8.46²) distribution. Expected values are: 41.3, 42.5, 45.9, 35.2, 19.3, 9.6 p-value = 0.0332 0.0332 < 0.05, the result is not significant so there is in sufficient evidence to reject the null hypothesis that the lengths of fish in the lake follow a normal distribution.	These values are obtained from the GDC using the mid-interval values. Make sure you use the unbiased estimator, and not the standard deviation of the sample. Expected values are calculated by multiplying the probabilities by 200. Make sure that you use $x < 10$ and $x > 30$ for the upper and lower intervals when calculating expected values.

Reflect How are the degrees of freedom calculated if extra parameters are estimated?

The binomial distribution

For the binomial distribution $B(n, p)$ you will need to estimate the value of p from the observed data. To do this, use the fact that the expected value for a binomial is np and hence p can be estimated using $\bar{x} = np$. Remember n is the number of trials within each of the experiments, not the number of times the experiment is repeated.

Example 16

An archer fires five arrows at a target, aiming for the "bullseye" in the centre. She feels that she has an equal chance of hitting the bullseye with each shot, that each shot is independent of the ones that have gone before and so the binomial distribution is a good model to use.

To test this belief she looks back over her records and notes the number of times she has hit the bullseye in the last 150 sets of five arrows fired. These results are recorded in the table below.

Number of bullseyes	0	1	2	3	4	5
Frequency	5	22	28	45	40	10

Perform a χ^2 goodness-of-fit test to test the following hypotheses.

H_0: The number of bullseyes follows a binomial distribution.

H_1: The number of bullseyes does not follow a binomial distribution.

Let the number of bullseyes be $X \sim B(5, p)$	
For the observed data $\bar{x} = 2.82$	
$\Rightarrow p = \dfrac{2.82}{5} = 0.564$	The formula used is $p = \dfrac{\bar{x}}{n}$.
Expected values are	These are obtained from the GDC.
2.36, 15.3, 39.5, 51.2, 33.1, 8.6	
Combine the first two columns to get	As the first column has expected value less than 5, it needs to be combined with the second column.
17.7, 39.5, 51.2, 33.1, 8.6	
Degrees of freedom $= 5 - 1 - 1 = 3$	p was estimated from the observed data so the degrees of freedom is the number of cells minus 2.
p-value $= 0.0137 < 0.05$	
The result is significant at the 5% significance level so we reject the null hypothesis that the data follows a binomial distribution.	

1 It is claimed that the lifespan of light bulbs is normally distributed with a mean lifespan of 1200 hours.

400 light bulbs are tested and the results shown in the table.

Lifespan, h hours	Frequency
$900 \leq h < 1000$	24
$1000 \leq h < 1100$	52
$1100 \leq h < 1200$	92
$1200 \leq h < 1300$	164
$1300 \leq h < 1400$	42
$1400 \leq h < 1500$	26

a Use the data given to estimate the standard deviation of the light bulbs.

b Copy and complete the expected frequency table assuming a normal distribution with a mean of 1200 and the standard deviation calculated in part **a**.

Expected frequency	19.7					19.7

c Write down the degrees of freedom.

d Perform a goodness-of-fit test at the 5% significance level to find out if the data fits a normal distribution.

2 The number of boys in 100 families with three children is shown below.

Number of boys	0	1	2	3
Frequency	16	29	32	17

A statistician wishes to check whether the probability of a boy being born into one of these families is always the same and the gender of each child is independent of all the others, so he decides to test for a binomial distribution.

a Find the mean of the data and hence the probability (p) that a child in the sample is a boy.

b Perform a goodness-of-fit test at the 1% significance level to find out if the data fits a binomial distribution with the probability of a boy equal to p.

3 The number of fish per day caught in a lake by each angler is thought to follow a Poisson distribution. To test this belief the number of fish caught in an hour by 80 anglers is recorded and the results are shown in the table below.

Number of fish	0	1	2	3	4	5	≥ 6
Frequency	7	10	15	21	14	9	4

a Given that the maximum number of fish caught be any angler was six find the mean of the sample.

b Using this mean as an approximation for the population mean perform a χ^2 goodness-of-fit test to see if the observed values are consistent with the data coming from a Poisson distribution.

4 The weights of grade 9 children are thought to be normally distributed.

The district nurse weighs 200 grade 9 students and her results are in the table below.

Weight, w kg	Frequency
$40 \leq w < 45$	12
$45 \leq w < 50$	59
$50 \leq w < 55$	52
$55 \leq w < 60$	68
$60 \leq w < 65$	9

a Find the mean and standard deviation of the sample.

b Using the calculated values for the mean and standard deviation, perform a χ^2 goodness-of-fit test at the 5% significance level to test whether the data is taken from a normal distribution.

c From a consideration of the observed data, conjecture why the results might not follow a normal distribution.

5 A scratch card has ten covered discs which are scratched off to reveal a prize. The company says the prizes are distributed randomly and independently among the cards. Abi is suspicious of this because she has heard of people who have won lots of prizes, whereas she has won very few. Scratch cards are normally sold in batches of five.

Abi contacts all her friends and family and asks them to record how many prizes are won in each batch of five. The results of the survey are shown below. No one won more than five prizes.

Number of prizes	0	1	2	3	4	5
Frequency	10	13	18	12	6	1

Abi decides to conduct a χ^2 goodness-of-fit test to see if the prizes are randomly distributed. Initially assume that the probability of winning a prize from a single disc is p.

a Write down the distribution for the number of prizes won in a batch of five cards if the prizes are distributed randomly.

b Use the data collected by Abi to find an estimate for p, the probability of winning a prize.

c Use a χ^2 goodness-of-fit test with this value of p to see whether the prizes are likely to be distributed randomly and independently.

6 The number of phone calls a company receives each five minutes between 1 pm and 2 pm is thought to follow a Poisson distribution with a mean of 2.0.

Over a one-week period the number of calls received every 5 minutes are recorded. The results are shown in the table.

Number of calls / 5 minutes	0	1	2	3	4	≥ 5
Frequency	4	8	21	12	10	5

a Perform a χ^2 goodness-of-fit test to see if the data supports the hypothesis that the number of calls is distributed as Po(2.0).

A statistician commented that a significant result did not show that the distribution of phone calls did not follow a Poisson distribution, only that it did not follow one with a mean of 2.

b Use a more appropriate value for the mean to test whether or not the phone calls coming into the business could follow a Poisson distribution.

You may assume that there were three intervals in which there were five calls to the business, one interval in which there was six calls, and one interval in which there were seven calls.

14.6 Choice, validity and interpretation of tests

The process of conducting a statistical test is far more than just analysing the data using one of the techniques covered in the previous sections. In this section we will look at the considerations you need to make in choosing which test to use, the checks to make sure your test is both valid and reliable and the limits on the interpretations you can make from your data.

Collection of data

In the natural sciences most data collected will have a numerical value. It is important to be aware of any possible errors in the collection methods. The errors might be **systematic** in which the errors will have a non-zero mean and often follow some kind of pattern, or **random** due to natural variation or other unknown factors, which might be expected to have a zero mean.

An example of systematic error might be a weighing machine that always adds on a fixed amount or a fixed percentage.

Though a systematic error might give a good correlation, any line of regression will be affected by it so it will give misleading results.

Selecting the sample

It is important that the sample chosen matches the needs of the test. In Chapter 2 you met simple random, convenience, systematic, quota and stratified sampling methods.

It is important that the right method is used for the question you are trying to answer.

For example, if you want to do a survey about the level of satisfaction with the provision of sport in a school you need to decide in advance whether you want all years represented (and if so in what proportions – quota or stratified).

Collecting data using questionnaires

A multiple-choice or short-answer survey will provide data that is easy to analyse but it needs to be used carefully for a variety of reasons.

- Answers may be restrictive, so not enough information is obtained.
- People might not answer honestly (particularly if the survey is not anonymous).
- The question might be interpreted in different ways.
- The questionnaire needs to be complete, as extra questions cannot be asked later.

TOK

Do you think that people from very different backgrounds are able to follow mathematical arguments, as they possess deductive ability?

Data mining

Data mining occurs when lots of pairs of variables are considered to see if any significant results can be found. If enough variables are compared it is very likely that such results can be found, as significant results will happen by chance 5% of the time for a 5% significance level. There might be a great temptation to publish these results, even though they have little meaning.

Example 17

A questionnaire is compiled asking a group of people a series of questions about five unrelated qualities. The answers to each set of questions are then compared with the answers to each of the other sets using a χ^2 test for independence, to see if there is significant evidence that they are not independent.

a State the number of tests the compiler of the questionnaire will have to perform if they are to compare every possible pair.

b Given that the tests are all at the 5% significance level, find the probability that at least one of them will prove to be significant, even if the qualities referred to in the questions are independent of each other.

a 10	This can be calculated by listing or reasoning that each of the five attributes needs to be paired with four others which makes 20 combinations. Because these count each pairing twice the answer needs to be divided by 2.
b P(at least one significant pairing) $= 1 - P(\text{none})$ $= 1 - 0.95^{10} = 0.401$	The probability of the 10 tests resulting in at least one significant result is about 40% so without further evidence nothing meaningful can be said about having found one.

Data mining is a useful technique to highlight possible connections between variables but if there is no external evidence in support of a connection then the test must be repeated to see if similar results are obtained. If this is not done then the test is not valid.

> **Reflect** What is a systematic error?
>
> What are the advantages and disadvantages of using a questionnaire to collect data?
>
> Why is important to collect appropriate data for a test?

Exercise 14N

1 The two sets of data below have been taken from a distribution in which $y = 2x + 1$. One has been subject to a systematic error and the errors for the other follow a normal distribution with a mean of 0.

x	1	2	3	4	5
y	2.9	4.2	7.1	9.2	10.6

x	1	2	3	4	5
y	3.2	5.4	7.6	9.8	12.0

Both sets of data are shown in the graph below.

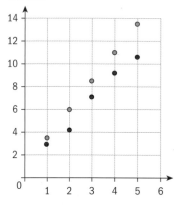

a State which data set shows a systematic error and which shows a random error.

b Comment on the results you would obtain if you found a correlation coefficient for each.

c Comment on the usefulness of any line of regression.

2 One hundred people were assessed in ten different attributes. The results for the comparison of two of these attributes are shown in the table below.

	0–10	11–20	21–30	Total
Positive	30	12	28	70
Negative	14	11	5	30
Total	44	23	33	100

a Perform the χ^2 test at the 5% significance level to see if there is evidence for the two attributes not being independent.

The assessor then carries out the test for all different pairings of the 10 attributes.

b Show that there are 45 different pairings for him to test.

c Assuming all the attributes are in fact independent, determine the probability that if all the pairs were tested at least one pair would yield a significant result at the 5% level.

d State what else you would need to know before producing a final conclusion about the result in part **a**.

3 Suppose two schools both teach the IB diploma programme. School A has approximately 60% girls and school B has approximately 40%. Each school has a very different style of teaching to the other.

Both schools agree to a sample of their students taking a standardized test at the start of the course, which will then be compared with their final results to see how much they have improved.

Given it is assumed that girls show more improvement between the test and the final result than boys, state how you would select your sample if you were interested in:

a **i** finding out which school is better in terms of how much their students improve

 ii finding out which of the two teaching methods are better

 iii testing whether in fact girls do perform better than boys.

b State a test you could use for each of the cases above, and comment on any assumptions being made.

4 To collect information on how many adults (defined as anyone who is no longer at school) in a particular area live with their parents, two methods of data collection were suggested.

A Use the results from the most recent census (data collected six years ago). In the census all households were visited and it was recorded if any children of the householders were also living there.

B Have pollsters visit 1000 homes chosen randomly from a database to find out the necessary information.

a State one reason why using the census might be a good way to collect this information, and one reason why it might not.

It is decided to use the pollsters to visit 1000 homes.

Assume that whether or not adult children live at home in a particular house is independent of all other houses. Assume also all households answer honestly.

b If the actual proportion of households with adult children living at home is 0.15 find the probability that the survey will obtain a figure for the proportion between

i 0.14 and 0.16 **ii** 0.1 and 0.2.

Comment on your results.

c Write down a possible question or questions that might be used by the pollsters to gain the required information.

5 A statistician wishes to test for differences between males and females so has them complete a survey answering questions in eight different categories. The answers to each of the questions consist of five boxes in which box 5 indicates "strongly agree" and box 1 indicates "strongly disagree".

The statistician carries out a t-test to compare the average of the answers for each of the eight categories with each of the other categories to see if there is a significant difference in the answers for males and for females. He finds that indeed one of the categories does show a significant difference and he publishes his findings.

As an external assessor you are asked to report on the validity of the test.

a State what you would want to know about the sample chosen.

b Calculate a probability to decide if his result is meaningful or not.

Choosing a valid test

A valid test is one that measures the quality it claims to be measuring.

For example, a chemistry test on the periodic table will provide data about how well the students have learned the periodic table.

A test such as this, which covers all the content being tested, is said to have **content** validity.

The assumption of content validity needs to be carefully considered. For example, if you are asking in a survey about how happy a person is, can you be sure that their response is a measure of their happiness or just a measure of how happy people say they are?

A test on quadratic equations certainly has content validity for testing how good a student is at doing quadratic equations.

In addition if previous experience with a test has shown that a high score in the test is a good indicator of success in more advanced algebra then it is said to also have c**riterion** validity as a test for the later success. If it relates particularly to future events then it is also referred to as **predictive** validity. An example of a test with predictive validity might be a total points score in the IB diploma and future success at university level.

Reliability of tests

A test or other means of collecting data is regarded as **reliable** if it produces similar results on each occasion it is carried out in similar circumstances. Its key attribute is repeatability.

A reliable test is not necessary a valid one. For example, a test on quadratic equations could be very reliable because students will obtain similar scores each time they take it, but it would be not valid as a test for assessing their ability in a visual arts course.

All valid tests though have to be reliable themselves and use data from a reliable source, so it is important to test for reliability if not sure.

Test–retest

To test that your means of collecting data is reliable the same test or questionnaire can be given to the same group after a period of time. If it is reliable there should be a strong correlation between the results on the two occasions the test is taken.

Of course there might be intervening factors between the two tests and hence even for the most reliable test there is unlikely to be a perfect correlation between the two, but a high value should be a good indication of reliability.

Parallel forms

A large number of questions is split into two parts, each part containing a range of questions designed to measure the required attributes and of as similar standard as possible.

One test is then given to a group of students and, very shortly afterwards, the second one is also given. If the test is reliable then there should be a strong correlation between the scores achieved on each of the tests.

The advantages and disadvantages of each method include the following.

- For parallel testing you have to create a large number of questions of equal difficulty to measure the same quality.
- Proving two parallel tests are equivalent is difficult.
- Test–retest can be affected by intervening factors.

> **TOK**
>
> Given that a set of data may be approximately fitted by a range of curves, where would we seek for knowledge of which equation is the "true" model?

Exercise 140

1 a State the necessary requirements on a population for the following tests to be valid.

   i a test for the binomial probability, p

   ii a test for the mean of a Poisson distribution

   iii a t-test.

b If you are not sure they do satisfy the necessary requirements, state the test you could perform to see if the data might come from the required distribution.

2 In a model for the spread of an infection in a small hospital, the average number of people a person will infect per day while he or she is infected is r. The hospital authorities collects data for the total number of people infected each day and compares the additional number infected with the number of people already infected and does this over a period of two weeks.

a The doctor wishes to test for the value of r to see if it is higher than what is normally expected, which might be a sign of bad practice in the hospital. To do this she assumes the number of infections can be modelled by a Poisson distribution with mean r. Comment on this assumption. Justify your answer.

b If it is a reasonable assumption, state a suitable statistical test, and comment on the reliabilty of any results.

3 A survey is done in a school to see if the weekly allowance received by a student is independent of the distance they live from school.

a State two tests which are used to test for independence.

b State the more appropriate in this case.

c Explain how you might set up the test having collected the data.

4 A school is experimenting with a survey to see how students rate the food served in the canteen. Before using the data they decide to test the survey for reliability and opt to do this by the test–retest method, giving the students the same questionnaire to answer four weeks after they first filled it in.

a Explain why a test–retest measure of reliability might be better than a parallel forms measure.

The average score given by eight students in each of the tests is recorded below.

Student	A	B	C	D	E	F	G	H
Test 1	4.2	6.4	5.4	4.0	4.8	5.0	4.8	5.6
Test 2	5.0	6.4	5.8	4.6	5.6	5.6	5.4	5.4

For a sample of size of eight a correlation coefficient above 0.8 will indicate good reliability.

b Find the correlation coefficient and state whether or not the survey is reliable.

c Find the median and the quartiles for the two sets of data and hence draw two box plots.

The canteen says that it has improved over the four weeks between the two tests.

d Comment on whether your answer to part **c** supports this. Justify your answer.

e Carry out a suitable test to decide whether or not this is true at the 5% significance level. Use your answer to part **c** to justify any assumptions you are making.

5 A statistician in a company thinks he has spotted a correlation between an employee's height and their salary. The managing director thinks this is nonsense and asks him to do a test which will hopefully demonstrate the two events are independent.

The statistician feels he can assume both variables are normally distributed and so decides to see whether there is evidence that the correlation between the two factors is positive. He then collects data from ten employees chosen randomly from the workforce and records their heights and salaries.

Height (cm)	145	178	167	155	182	186	191	150	162	177
Salary ($000s)	21	42	27	25	55	37	52	34	36	40

a Carry out an appropriate test and state the conclusion.

The statistician's form began with the following.

Employee no.	Male/female	Height	Salary
12 465	F	145	21
23 412	M	178	42
13 457	F	167	27

b Comment on the validity or otherwise of the test carried out.

c It is felt that a more significant factor affecting salary might be whether an employee is male or female. Assuming more data can be collected, state a test you might do to test this hypothesis.

Type I and type II errors and the importance of the significance level

Different significance levels can be used depending on how certain you want to be about the test results.

Suppose a vital component in a power station is tested to see if it is at a dangerous threshold or not. In this test a significant result would mean it is assumed to be safe when it is in fact dangerous.

Suppose testing takes place once a day.

A 5% significance level would mean that 5% of the time, roughly once every three weeks, a dangerous component would be kept in position. Though the consequences of keeping it in position need to be taken into consideration, this seems unreasonably high for a potentially dangerous situation, and so a lower significance level should be chosen.

A **type I** error is rejecting H_0 when H_0 is true; we can write its probability as $P(C|H_0 \text{ true})$ where C stands for the test statistic being in the critical region.

For the normal or t-distributions this is the same as the significance level, and for discrete distributions it is equal to the probability of rejecting H_0, which might not be exactly the same as the quoted significance level.

A **type II** error is accepting H_0 when it is not true; we can write its probability as $P(C'|H_1 \text{ true})$. The actual value of the probability depends on the particular value of the parameter.

Unfortunately, for a given sample size, reducing the chance of a type I error increases the chance of a type II error and vice versa.

It is therefore very important to consider the balance between the two. In some circumstances, such as the ones mentioned above, it is more important to avoid a type I error than to avoid a type II error. In the case of the power station a type II error would mean replacing a component before it needed to be replaced.

> **International-mindedness**
>
> In physics, during the search for the Higgs boson, the calculated p-value was 5.5×10^{-7}. It was felt necessary to have such a small value as the consequences were so large for our understanding of particle physics.

> **TOK**
>
> When is it more important not to make a type I error and when is it more important not to make a type II error?

Investigation 7

A laboratory test is being performed on a new drug. Previous drugs achieved a rating of 0.856 with a standard deviation of 0.01. The higher the rating, the more effective the drug. It is intended that the new drug will be tested on 40 samples to see if it has a higher rating. The test is initially conducted at a 5% significant level.

Assuming the standard deviation is the same as for the previous drugs:

1   state the null and alternative hypotheses for the test

2   find the critical region for the test and comment on the meaning of your answer in the given context

3 state the probability of a type I error for this test.

4 The probability of a type II error is $P(\bar{X} < a)$ if H_1 is true. State the value of a.

5 Why is it not possible to work out the probability of a type II error without further information?

Given that the population mean for the rating of the new drug is 0.858:

6 find the probability of a type II error and comment on your result.

7 If the significance level of the test was reduced to 1%

    a find the new critical region

    b hence find the probability of a type II error

    c comment on the effect of reducing the probability of a type I error.

8 On the same axes sketch the distribution of $\bar{X} \sim N\left(\mu, \dfrac{0.01}{\sqrt{40}}\right)$ for

$\mu = 0.856$ and $\mu = 0.858$

    a when $\mu = 0.856$ and shade the area that represents the probability of a type I error

    b when $\mu = 0.858$ and shade the area that represents the probability of a type II error.

9 **a** Investigate the effect of changing the size of the sample on the probability of a type II error for a fixed significance level.

    b Explain this effect by consideration of the standard deviation of $\bar{X}$.

10 **Factual** Explain what is meant by a type I and type II error and why is it important to considering both.

11 Due to extra funding the new drug is now tested on 500 samples and the sample mean is found to be 0.8568.

    a Find the p-value and state the conclusion of the test at the 5% level.

    b Medical testers might refer to a result as being 'statistically significant but not clinically significant'. Explain what this might mean for the result obtained in part **a**.

12 **Conceptual** Why is it important to consider type I and type II errors?

The probability of a type I error is the probability of rejecting H_0 when H_0 is true. For the normal distribution this will be equal to the significance level; for a discrete distribution this will be the probability of the statistic falling in the critical region.

In order to find the probability of a type II error, first find the critical region under the null hypothesis.

The probability of a type II error is the probability of the statistic not being in the critical region. This is calculated using a value for the parameter chosen from the alternative hypothesis.

Example 18

A machine produces components needed for a software company. The probability of a fault occurring in the production of a single component has to be less than 0.02. A sample of size 50 is taken from the output and tested to see if any were faulty. A test was performed with the hypotheses H_0: $p = 0.02$ and H_1: $p > 0.02$ at a 5% significance level.

a State a suitable model for the number of faults in the sample; include any additional assumptions you are making.

b Find

  i the critical region for the test

  ii the probability of a type I error.

c Earlier testing indicates that the probability of a fault is 0.04. If this is the case find the probability of a type II error.

a Let X be the number of faults in the sample. $X \sim B(50, 0.02)$ For the binomial model to be suitable we need to assume that the faults occur independently of each other.	
b i $P(X \geq a) < 0.05$ $P(X \leq a - 1) > 0.95$ $a - 1 = 3 \Rightarrow a = 4$ The critical region is $X \geq 4$	The critical value is the smallest value of a for which this inequality is satisfied. If your GDC will do right tail probabilities the answer can be obtained directly from the first line. If your GDC can only do cumulative probabilities (left tail) then find the acceptance region instead, which is $P(X \leq a - 1)$.
ii $P(X \geq 4) = 0.0178$ which is equal to the probability of a type I error.	This can be calculated as $1 - P(X \leq 3)$.
c $P(X \leq 3 \mid p = 0.04) = 0.861$ which is equal to the probability of a type II error.	A type II error is the probability of being in the acceptance region (not in the critical region) when H_0 is not true.

Example 19

In order to satisfy quality control the mean number of flaws in aluminium sheets must be less than or equal to 0.6 flaws per metre length. A length of 7 m is inspected.

Assuming the number of flaws follows a Poisson distribution:

a state the distribution of the number of flaws (X) in the length sampled, assuming an average of 0.6 flaws per metre

b state the hypotheses for the test

c find the critical region for the test at the 5% significance level

d find the probability of

   i a type I error

   ii a type II error, given the mean is in fact 0.72 flaws per metre.

a $X \sim \text{Po}(4.2)$	The mean is equal to $0.6 \times 7 = 4.2$.
b $H_0 : \mu = 4.2$, $H_1 : \mu > 4.2$	
c $P(X \geq a) \leq 0.05$	Some GDCs will be able to produce the critical region without the need to use the cumulative distribution function to find the acceptance region.
$P(X \leq a - 1) \geq 0.95 \Rightarrow a - 1 = 8$	
$a = 9$	
Critical region $X \geq 9$	
d **i** $P(X \geq 9 \mid \mu = 4.2) = 0.028$	The probability of a type I error is the probability of being in the critical region when H_0 is true.
ii $0.72 \times 7 = 5.04$	The probability of a type II error is the probability of falling outside the critical region under the assumptions of H_1.
$P(X \leq 8 \mid \mu = 5.04) = 0.929$	

Exercise 14P

1 For the samples below taken from a normal distribution, find the probability of a type II error, for a test at the 5% significance level.

  a $H_0 : \mu = 7$, $H_1 : \mu > 7$, $n = 30$, $\sigma = 0.4$, true value of $\mu = 7.1$

  b $H_0 : \mu = 12.1$, $H_1 : \mu < 12.1$, $n = 20$, $\sigma = 0.2$, true value of $\mu = 12.0$

2 For the samples below taken from a binomial distribution find the probability of

   i   a type I error   **ii**   a type II error

for a test at the 5% significance level.

  a $H_0 : p = 0.6$, $H_1 : p > 0.6$, $n = 30$, true value of $p = 0.68$

  b $H_0 : p = 0.45$, $H_1 : p < 0.45$, $n = 40$, true value of $p = 0.43$

3 A survey is taken to count the number of cars that pass a point each hour. For the hypothesis tests below n is the number of hours used in the survey. Assuming the number of cars can be modelled by a Poisson distribution, find the probability of

   i   a type I error   **ii**   a type II error

for a test at the 5% significance level.

  a $H_0 : \mu = 4.6$, $H_1 : \mu < 4.6$, $n = 30$, true value of $\mu = 4.5$

  b $H_0 : \mu = 2.1$, $H_1 : \mu > 2.1$, $n = 20$, true value of $\mu = 2.8$

Statistics and probability

4 A sample of size 15 is taken from a normal population with $\sigma = 5.3$.

The following hypotheses are tested at the 5% level.

$H_0: \mu = 51$, $H_1: \mu \neq 51$

  a Find the critical regions for the test.

  b Hence find the probability of a type II error if $\mu = 51.5$.

5 Two types of radioactive substances emit particles at different rates. A emits on average 50 particles per second and B emits on average 54 particles per second. The emission rates of both particles can be considered as being normally distributed with a known variance of 36.

Sophie believes she is testing substance A and records the emission rate in ten different experiments.

  a Given $H_0: \mu = 50$ and $H_1: \mu > 50$ find the critical region for her test at the 5% level of significance.

  b Find the probability of a type II error if the substance is in fact substance B.

  c State one way Sophie could reduce the probability of a type II error.

6 It is thought that in a crowded city with a large population the proportion of people who have a car is 0.3. To test this belief it is decided to take a sample of 50 people and record how many have a car. A 5% significance level is chosen.

  a State the distribution of the sample under H_0.

  b Find the critical region for rejecting the null hypothesis in favour of the alternative hypothesis that a larger proportion than 0.3 have a car.

  c For the above test calculate the probability of a type II error when the population proportion is in fact:

   i 0.4   **ii** 0.5

7 The number of people entering the casualty department at a hospital during a weekday evening, 6–10 pm, can be regarded as a Poisson distribution with a mean of 8.2 people per hour.

It is hoped that the introduction of a hospital phone line, which patients can call with concerns, will reduce this number and so a phone line is trialled for a period of several weeks.

During the trial the number of patients arriving over 10 randomly chosen hours during a weekday evening is recorded.

  a Explain why it was important to select the 10 hours for the survey randomly, rather than just record the numbers over three consecutive evenings.

  b Write down possible null and alternative hypotheses, based on the total number of people who come into the hospital during the 10 hours chosen, to test whether the number of patients arriving has been reduced.

If the mean number of patients arriving per hour in the sample is less than or equal to 7.5 per hour the management will assume the rate of arrivals has fallen and will continue the development of the phone line.

  c Describe what would be a type I error for this test and calculate its probability.

  d If the rate has gone down to 7.8 patients per hour, find the probability of a type II error and describe what this would mean in the given context.

8 A machine designed to put jam into doughnuts is set to deliver an average of 1.20 cm³ of jam per doughnut. The machine is checked regularly to ensure that the mean does not deviate from this amount. At each of the checks a sample of 20 is taken and the amount of jam dispensed is measured. Assume that the amount of jam follows a normal distribution with a standard deviation of 0.1 cm³, and the test is performed at the 5% significance level.

  a State the null and alternative hypotheses.

  b Write down the probability of a type I error.

Given that the actual amount of jam delivered is 1.17 cm³:

  c find the probability of a type II error.

Investigation 8

The actual meaning of a p-value is often misunderstood. It gives the probability of the data observed (or more extreme data) occurring if the null hypothesis is true, but what the testers often really want to know is the probability that the null hypothesis is true given the data, and that is not immediately accessible.

1 A test is performed with hypotheses $H_0: \mu = 5$ and $H_1: \mu \neq 5$. The p-value was equal to 0.02. The person performing the test claimed the result meant that the probability the mean is 5 is 0.98.

Using H_0 to signify the event the null hypothesis is true, and D to signify the event the data (or more extreme data) is obtained, write down:

   a an expression for the probability the researcher thinks he is giving.

   b the probability he is actually giving.

2 a In addition to the above notation let H_1 signify the alternative hypothesis is true. Draw a tree diagram to show the four possible situations for the test when the results D are obtained. The first two branches should be the events H_0 is true and H_1 is true.

   b On your tree diagram indicate the p-value.

   c i Hence explain why

$$P(H_0 \mid D) = \frac{P(H_0) \times P(D \mid H_0)}{P(H_0) \times P(D \mid H_0) + P(H_0) \times P(D' \mid H_0)}$$

   ii Find a similar formula linking $P(H_1|D)$ with $P(D|H_1)$.

3 It is felt that some athletic training camps have begun to use an illegal treatment to improve performance. In standardised tests of athletes before and after undergoing this treatment performance normally increases by 15%. Other indicators (investigative journalism, whistle-blowers etc) lead the athletics organisation to believe that 10% of all camps are using this method.

From previous data is known that the improvement in performance of athletes at a particular camp has been normally distributed with a mean of 10% and a standard deviation of 7.5%.

In a random check to see if the camp is now using the illegal treatment five athletes from the camp have their performance measured before and after the training, and a test is done with the following hypotheses,

H_0: The mean improvement (μ) is 10%, $H_1: \mu > 10\%$.

The test was carried out and it was found that $\bar{x} = 15.52$.

   a Assuming the standard deviation has not changed, verify the p-value for this result is 0.0499.

   ii Explain why this does not mean the probability the camp was using the illegal treatment is approximately 0.95.

   ii Without doing further calculations would you intuitively rate a value of 15.52% improvement as strong evidence for the athletes in the camp undergoing the illegal treatment?

   b Find the probability of obtaining this result (or a more extreme one) if the athletes had been undergoing the illegal treatment $(P(D|H_1))$.

   You may assume the standard deviation is unchanged.

   c i Use your values from **3a** and **3b**, plus the information given in the initial stem to add all the probabilities to the branches of a copy of the tree diagram from question **2a**.

   ii Hence find the probability of obtaining this test result (or a more extreme one), using all the information available $(P(D))$.

   iii Hence use the formula from c ii to find the probability the camp had been using the illegal treatment.

   iv What conclusion might you draw from the test?

4 Explain why the p-value is not the same as the probability the null hypothesis is true.

5 **Conceptual** What does a p-value actually tell you? What is a common misconception?

Statistics and probability

Exercise 14Q

1 Bruno claims he has extra sensory perception (ESP). A test is done in which three cards have one of five possible shapes drawn on them and Bruno has to guess the shape on the cards. If he possesses some form of ESP it is expected he will have a better than average chance of guessing the cards.

When the test is performed Bruno guesses the shapes on all three cards correctly.

a Explain why the p-value for this test is equal to 0.008.

b Bruno claims that this means the probability he has ESP is 0.992.

Explain why he is wrong.

c Explain what else you would need to consider if you were to try to find the probability of the existence of ESP.

Let H_0 be the event the results were obtained by chance and H_1 be the event Bruno has ESP. Let D be the event of obtaining the result or a more extreme one.

From other data the researcher believes that the probability ESP exists is 0.01.

d Draw a tree diagram to show the four possibilities from the test, with the first two branches indicating having ESP (H_1) and not having ESP (H_0). You may assume that if a person has ESP they will guess all three cards correctly.

e Hence find the probability that

i Bruno would guess all three cards correctly.

ii Bruno has ESP (note: this is $P(H_1|D)$).

f i Comment on which probability used was the least certain.

ii A different researcher believes the probability of ESP existing is 0.001.

If this was the case how would your answer to part **e ii** change?

2 It is known that a particular infection in a hospital will occur by chance in 1.0% of the patients admitted. It is known that poor practices in a hospital will lead to an increased likelihood of this infection occurring.

It is decided to look at 100 patients from a particular hospital and if three or more are found to have contracted the infection then the hospital will be required to review its practices.

The hypotheses used are H_0: $p = 0.01$, H_1: $p > 0.01$

a i Find the significance level of this test.

ii Does this mean the probability the hospital has bad practices is over 0.92?

It is know from previous research that 10% of hospitals have bad practices that lead to an increase infection rate. In these hospitals the probability of three or more infections is equal to 1.

A particular hospital is tested and it has three cases of the infection. No other information is available about this hospital.

b i Find the probability that the hospital has bad practices ($p > 0.01$).

ii What conclusion would you draw from this information?

3 Investigators have seized a package of drugs. They are keen to know whether this came from inside their country or from outside the country. A chemical in the drugs can be used to test the country of origin. On this test those from inside the country return a value which has a mean of 5.2 and those from outside the country a mean of 4.6. In each case the standard deviation can be assumed to be 1.2.

The drugs are sent away to be tested and 16 tests are run on the sample sent.

A one-tailed test of the sample mean $\bar{x}$ is set up with H_0: $\mu = 5.2$ and H_1: $\mu < 5.2$ and at a 5% significance level.

a Find the critical region for this test.

b Find the probability of a type II error if the drugs are in fact from outside the country.

It is known that generally 90% of the drugs in the area of the seizure are from inside the country and 10% from outside the country.

c Find the probability that $\overline{X}$ will fall in the critical region.

d If having done the tests the sample mean is found to lie in the critical region find the probability the drugs came from inside the country.

Chapter summary

- The product moment correlation coefficient of the ranks of a set of data is called Spearman's rank correlation coefficient. The notation used in IB is r_s.

- Spearman's correlation coefficient shows the extent to which one variable increases or decreases as the other variable increases.

- A value of 1 means the set of data is strictly increasing and a value of −1 means it is strictly decreasing.

- A value of 0 means the data shows no **monotonic** behaviour.

- The null hypothesis is rejected if either the test statistic falls in the critical region (it is beyond the critical value) or the p-value is less than the significance level.

- If a statistic is such that the null hypothesis is rejected we say the result is significant.

- The hypothesis test for the population correlation coefficient (ρ) will have $H_0: \rho = 0$. The p-value can be obtained from the GDC.

- When testing for a population mean, use the z-test if the population standard deviation is known and the t-test if not.

- When testing for the differences between two means use the pooled t-test.

- When the two groups are paired find the difference between each pair and test $H_0: \mu_D = 0$.

- Calculators are likely to use different symbols for s_{n-1} and s_n. Make sure you know which is which.

- In examinations if using the inbuilt testing functions you need to be aware whether you have to enter s_{n-1} or s_n. Depending on what is given in the question you may need to use the formula above to convert between the two.

- When testing for a binomial probability p which is not given in the question, p can be estimated from $\dfrac{\overline{x}}{n}$.

- A χ^2 **test for independence** can be performed to find out if two data sets are independent of each other or not. The GDC will produce a table of expected frequencies and a p-value. If any expected frequencies are less than 5 then adjacent rows or columns need to be merged.

- In a χ^2 goodness-of-fit test, the degrees of freedom $v = (n-1)$.

- To obtain the number of degrees of freedom, take the number of cells minus one, and then subtract one for each of the parameters estimated.

- A probability of a type I error is the probability of rejecting H_0 when H_0 is true. For the normal distribution this will be equal to the significance level, for a discrete distribution this will be the probability of the statistic falling in the critical region.

- In order to find the probability of a type II error, first find the critical region under the null hypothesis.

- The probability of a type II error is the probability of the statistic not being in the critical region. This is calculated using a value for the parameter chosen from the alternative hypothesis.

Developing inquiry skills

The initial claim was: the mean height of the trees from area A is smaller than the mean height of the trees from area B.

Which would be the best test to use to address this claim?

What conditions are necessary and have you tested to see if these conditions have been met?

Carry out the test and state the conclusion.

Chapter review

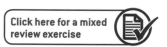

Click here for a mixed review exercise

1 Prabu took a note of the heights of 12 of her classmates and timed how many seconds it took them to run the 100-metre dash. Her data is in the table below.

Height (cm)	Time (seconds)
151	17.5
153	18
153	16.5
154	16
155	15.4
159	13.2
162	14
164	13.7
164	13.2
168	12.5
175	12
181	12

a Calculate Spearman's rank correlation coefficient (r_s) for this data.

b Interpret the value of r_s and comment on its validity.

2 The colour of eggs laid by three different types of hens was recorded.

	Leghorn	Brahma	Sussex
White eggs	5	23	14
Brown eggs	25	7	16

Phoebe was interested to find out if the colour of the eggs was independent of the type of hen. She decided to perform a χ^2 test at the 5% significance level on her data.

a Write down the null and alternative hypotheses.

b Show that the expected value of a Leghorn laying a white egg is 14.

c Write down the degrees of freedom.

d Find the χ^2 test statistic and the p-value.

e The critical value is 5.991; find the conclusion for this test, justifying your answer both in terms of the critical value and the p-value.

3 Marilu tosses two unbiased coins 60 times. The number of tails that she gets is given in the table below.

Number of tails	0	1	2
Frequency	12	34	14

a Show that the expected frequency for tossing 0 tails is 15.

b Find the table of expected frequencies.

c Write down the degrees of freedom.

d Perform a goodness-of-fit test at the 5% significance level to find out if the data fits a binomial distribution.

The critical value for this test is 5.991.

e State the conclusion for the test, justifying your answer.

4 Mrs Nelson gave her two grade 12 classes the same history test. She wanted to find out if they were, on average, of an equal standard.

The results of the test are:

Class 1	79	63	42	88	95	57	73	61	82	76	51	48
Class 2	65	78	85	49	59	91	68	74	82	56		

a Write down the null and alternative hypotheses.

b State whether this is a one-tailed test or a two-tailed test.

c Perform a t-test at the 5% significance level, stating your conclusion.

5 a Find a 95% confidence limit for the population mean if the following random sample is taken from the population which is assumed to have a normal distribution.

1.3, 1.5, 1.7, 1.4, 1.5, 1.6, 1.9

b Find the 90% confidence interval for the population mean if a sample of size 10 has a mean of 22.1 cm and a standard deviation of 0.8 cm.

6 For many years the number of tornadoes in a particular area during August has followed a Poisson distribution with a zmean of 7.5.

It is thought that climate change might be making the occurrence of more likely. The records for the two most recent years are looked at and the number of tornadoes is found to be 19.

Test at the 5% level the hypothesis that the number of tornadoes is now greater than 7.5.

7 The success rate of a medication is claimed to be 82%.

To test this claim the medication is given to a sample of 42 patients and the number of patients who benefit from the medication, X, is noted.

a Write down a suitable distribution for X and justify your answer.

b State suitable null and alternative hypotheses for the test.

c State the critical region for the test.

d State the probability of a type I error.

8 Consider the following one-tailed test.
$H_0: \mu = 30$ against $H_1: \mu > 30$.

The population is normally distributed with a known variance of 9 and a test is performed with a sample of size 4 with the following significance levels:

i 5%

ii 1%

a Write down the probability of a type I error in each case.

b Find the critical region in each case and hence the probability of a type II error given that $\mu = 32$.

c Comment on the effect on the probability of a type II error if:

i the sample size is increased

ii the significance level is reduced

iii the true value of μ increases, for example if $\mu = 34$.

9 A research team asks some employees about various aspects of the company they work for.

Following the survey the company takes action on some of the issues raised and later the company repeats the survey.

a Explain what is meant by the test–retest test for reliability.

A sample of the results is shown in the table below where the average level of satisfaction for each employee is given as a score out of 10.

	A	B	C	D	E	F	G	H
First test	5.4	6.6	4.3	8.1	5.5	3.2	4.6	7.1
Second test	5.6	7.0	4.7	8.1	5.0	3.8	4.3	7.7

b Find the product moment correlation coefficient for the sample and comment on the reliability of the test.

c Perform an appropriate test to see if the sample supports the belief that the levels of satisfaction have improved. State any assumptions you are making.

Exam-style questions

10 P1: A conman uses a coin to play a game. This might be an ordinary fair coin, with one side a Head and the other a Tail; or it might be a double-headed coin. The police are suspicious and formulate the following hypotheses.

H_0 : It is a fair coin

H_1 : It is a double headed coin.

A test is to be performed by tossing the coin four times. The following decision rules are made:

If there is at least one Tail, we will conclude that it is a fair coin.

If all four tosses produce a Head, we will conclude that it is a double-headed coin.

a Find the probability of making a Type I error. (3 marks)

b Find the probability of making a Type II error. (3 marks)

11 P2: In the country of Sodor there are three Television channels: Alphaview; Betaview; and Peppaview.

A sample of children were asked what their favourite TV channel was. The results are recorded in the table below.

	Alpha	Beta	Peppa
Up to 5 years old	10	10	40
Between 6 and 10 years old	15	25	30
Between 11 and 15 years old	15	35	20

a Perform a suitable test to decide, at the 1% significance level, whether the children's age and preference of TV channel are independent or not.

In your answer, you should include the test used, the test hypotheses, the degrees of freedom, the p-value and the conclusion (with a reason) of the test. (7 marks)

b Give the expected values in a table similar to the one above, and comment on their size in the context of the validity of the test. (4 marks)

12 P2: The heights of eight Welsh policemen were measured in centimetres as 170, 174, 176, 175, 171, 165, 179, 180

The heights of 10 Scottish policemen were measured in centimetres as 173, 176, 179, 180, 181, 178, 175, 177, 182, 177

a Find the sample mean height of **i** the Welsh policemen **ii** the Scottish policemen. (2 marks)

You can assume that both sets of values have a common unknown variance.

b Carry out a test at the 5% level to determine if the population mean of Welsh policemen is smaller than that of Scottish policemen. In your answer, you should include the test used (with a reason), the test hypotheses, the p-value and the conclusion of the test (with a reason). (7 marks)

c State if your conclusion would have been any different if working at the 1% significance level. (2 marks)

13 P1: The number of "likes" that Narcissus receives on his web site each hour is known to satisfy the Poisson distribution. Narcissus claims that on average he receives 20 "likes" every hour. We suspect that he is exaggerating. We monitor his web site over a period of 6 hours and find that he received 100 "likes" during this time.

Test Nar.issus's claim against our suspicion at the 5% significance level. In your answer, you should include whether this is a one-tailed or two-tailed test, the test hypotheses, calculation of the p-value, and the conclusion (with a reason) of the test. (7 marks)

14 P2: a State the central limit theorem. (4 marks)

Let the random variable X be the number of hours that a random student spends using their mobile phone each day. It is known that X has a population variance of $\sigma^2 = 1$ hour.

b A sample of 100 students were asked how many hours they spent using their phone in a day and the sample mean was $\bar{x} = 5$ hours. (3 marks)

Calculate the 95% confidence interval for the population mean, μ.

---

15 P1: It is claimed that the tread on the front tyres of rally cars wears more quickly than the tread on the rear tyres. To test this claim, the wear, in millimetres, on the front tyres and on the back tyres of 10 rally cars is measured at the end of a rally event.

The paired data is given in the table below.

Car	1	2	3	4	5	6	7	8	9	10
Front wear	4.1	4.0	4.2	3.9	4.8	4.5	4.6	5.0	4.7	4.7
Rear wear	3.9	4.0	3.8	4.0	4.2	4.5	4.4	4.9	4.8	4.4

Test the above claim at the 5% significance level. In your answer, you should include the test used (with a reason), the test hypotheses, the p-value and the conclusion of the test (with a reason). (8 marks)

---

16 P1: Let the random variable X be the height of a female, in centimetres, and let the random variable Y be the number of pets that she owns. A random sample of size 6 was taken and the paired data is shown in the table below.

Height	170	165	160	155	157	162
Number of pets	0	4	3	0	1	2

Use this data to test at the 5% significance level if there is a linear relationship between these two variables. (8 marks)

17 P1: The manufacturers of toys that come in surprise eggs claim that the colour of the toys;

Blue, Pink, Purple, and Green; appear in the ratios 3:4:2:1 respectively.

A sample of 100 toys was taken and the number of each colour is shown in the table below.

Colour	Blue	Pink	Purple	Green
Number	32	37	23	8

Test the manufacturer's claim at the 10% significance level. (9 marks)

Rank my maths!

Approaches to learning: Collaboration, Communication

Exploration criteria: Personal engagement (C), Reflection (D), Use of mathematics (E)

IB topic: Spearman's rank, hypothesis test

The task

In this task you will be designing an experiment that will compare the rankings given by different students in your class. You will then use your results to determine how similar they are and what agreement there is and then to test the significance of that relationship.

The experiment

Select one student in your group to be the experimenter. The other students in your group will be the subject of the experiment.

The experimenter is going to determine whether there is any similarity between the tastes of the other students in their group by asking them to rank a set of selections from the least to the most favourite.

Would you expect the rankings of the students in your group to be the same, similar or completely different?

What would help you to predict who might have similar tastes (where the strongest correlation would be)?

Under what circumstances might the rankings be similar and under what circumstances might they be different?

In your group, discuss:

What could you use the Spearman's rank method to compare?

What other ideas can you think of that this could be used to test?

The experimenter should prepare their own set of selections for the other members of the group to compare in the area they have chosen to investigate.

They should make a prediction about how strong they think the rank correlation will be between the other students with regards to the experiment they are doing.

The experimenter will give their set of selections to the group.

The other students will rank the set of selections from favourite (1) to least favourite (n), where n is the number of selections.

What does the experimenter need to be aware of when providing instructions?

The experimenter should record the rankings in a table.

The students who are doing the ranking should not collaborate or communicate with each other.

Why is this important?

The results

Now find the Spearman rank correlation between the students.

Do the students display strong correlations?

Are the results what were expected.

Discuss as a group why the original hypothesis may have been accurate or inaccurate.

Write a conclusion for the experiment based on the results you have found so far.

The statistical test

What spearman's rank value would mathematically be considered to be high?

It is possible to test the significance of a relationship between the two rankings. The test is similar to the one conducted for the product moment correlation coefficient.

Conduct a hypothesis test for the Spearman's rank value(s) you have found.

What conclusions can you draw from this? How confident are you in your results?

Extension

What other experiments or data collection exercises can you think of that will be suitable for a statistics-based exploration that will result in a hypothesis test like the one in this task?

Use the examples and questions in this chapter to give you some inspiration and then design your experiment and how you will conduct it.

15 Optimizing complex networks: graph theory

This chapter explores how diagrams (called graphs) can be used to model the connections between metro stations, components in electrical circuits and people within a social network. It also looks at how algorithms can be implemented to find optimal routes, for example for delivering parcels in a given area in the shortest possible time.

Concepts

- Representation
- Systems

Microconcepts

- Simple, weighted and directed graphs
- Minimum spanning tree
- Adjacency and transition matrices
- Eulerian circuits and trails
- Hamiltonian paths and cycles
- Graphs: directed, connected, complete; degree of a vertex, weight of an edge
- Adjacency matrix, lengths of walks, connectivity of a graph, transition matrix, steady state probabilities
- Spanning trees, minimum spanning trees, Prim's and Kruskal's algorithms, Prim's algorithm from a table
- Eulerian circuits and trails, leading to the Chinese postman problem
- Tables of least distances
- Classical and practical travelling salesman problems

What is the quickest route between two metro stations?

How can the driver of a snowplough ensure that they clear every road in a town after a blizzard as efficiently as possible?

How could an electrical engineer model the connections on a circuit board?

How can a postman deliver letters to every house on their route while minimizing the distance they travel?

A national park has bicycle trails connecting seven viewpoints. The distances between pairs of viewpoints are given in the table below. The entrance to the park is at A.

Viewpoints	A	B	C	D	E	F	G
A	0	5	4.5				
B	5	0	4	3.5			
C	4.5	4	0	2		6	
D		3.5	2	0	6	5.5	
E				6	0	4.5	3
F			6	5.5	4.5	0	3.5
G					3	3.5	0

- What do you think that a blank cell represents?
- Name three pieces of information represented in the table.
- Draw a diagram to represent the information in the table. Compare with others.
- How could you use your diagram to find the shortest route around all the viewpoints?

Developing inquiry skills

Write down any similar inquiry questions you could ask and investigate for your local park. What information would you need to find?

Could you write similar inquiry questions about your local supermarket or shopping mall? Or any other place?

Think about the questions in this opening problem and answer any you can. As you work through the chapter, you will gain mathematical knowledge and skills that will help you to answer them all.

Before you start

Click here for help with this skills check

You should know how to:

1 Raise a matrix to an integer power.

eg If $A = \begin{pmatrix} 2 & -1 \\ 1 & 0 \end{pmatrix}$ find A^4.

Using a GDC: $A^4 = \begin{pmatrix} 5 & -4 \\ 4 & -3 \end{pmatrix}$

2 Find the steady state vector for a transition matrix.

eg Find the steady state vector for the transition matrix $P = \begin{pmatrix} 0.1 & 0.6 \\ 0.9 & 0.4 \end{pmatrix}$.

Form equations $\begin{aligned} 0.1x + 0.6y = x \\ 0.9x + 0.4y = y \end{aligned}$

Solve either of these along with $x + y = 1$:

$x = 0.4$, $y = 0.6$

Skills check

1 If $A = \begin{pmatrix} 1 & -1 & 0 \\ 2 & 1 & 1 \\ -1 & 0 & 2 \end{pmatrix}$ find

a A^2 **b** A^4.

2 Let $P = \begin{pmatrix} 0.8 & 0.3 \\ 0.2 & 0.7 \end{pmatrix}$ be a transition matrix in

which the probability of moving from state i to state j is P_{ji}.

a By forming a system of linear equations find the steady state vector.

b Verify your answer is correct by calculating large powers of P.

c What is the long-term probability of being in state j?

691

15.1 Constructing graphs

For the opening problem you may have drawn a diagram like this. This is a **graph**.

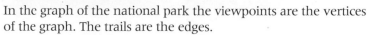

> A graph is defined as set of **vertices** and a set of **edges**.
> A vertex represents an object. An edge joins two vertices.

In the graph of the national park the viewpoints are the vertices of the graph. The trails are the edges.

In mathematical graph theory, graphs do not have to be drawn to scale and the positions of the vertices do not need to relate to their positions in the real world. A graph will always show which vertices are directly connected.

The graph above also shows the distances between vertices. A graph that shows values like these (called **weights**) is called a **weighted graph**. The "weight" can be any quantity, such as cost, time or distance.

The map of the London Underground is a famous example of an unweighted graph. It gives no information regarding the distances between the stations, only the connections between them.

> A **walk** is any sequence of vertices passed through when moving along the edges of the graph.

In the graph of the national park ABC and ABDBC are both walks from A to C.

The information in an unweighted graph can also be contained in an **adjacency table**. In an adjacency table the entries indicate the number of direct connections between two vertices.

TOK

Have you heard of the Seven Bridges of Königsberg problem? Königsberg is now Kaliningrad in Russia. Do all mathematical problems have a solution?

Example 1

The table shows the connections between stations on a small mountain railway. An empty cell indicates no direct connection between the stations.

a Show this information on a graph.

b Write down two possible walks from A to D.

	A	B	C	D
A		1	1	
B	1		1	
C	1	1		1
D			1	

a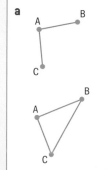

To draw the graph begin with vertex A.

From the first row in the table, A is connected to B and C, so add them to the graph.

From the second row, B is connected to A and C. The first of these is already included, so you only need to add the edge connecting B to C.

The third row shows that you need to add the edge CD.

The final row includes no extra edges. Use it to check your graph is drawn correctly.

b eg ABCD, ACD or ABACD

There are infinitely many answers to part **b** as you can pass through each vertex and along each edge as many times as you like.

Example 2

The table shows costs in dollars of travelling by bus between towns.

Show this information on a graph.

	A	B	C	D	E
A		4	7	6	
B	4		5		
C	7	5		3	6
D	6		3		2
E			6	2	

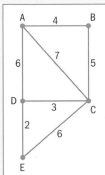

Because the costs are given in the table you must also show them on the graph.

Note that there are many different ways to draw the graph, eg:

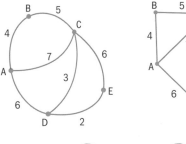

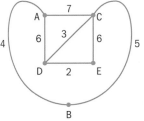

Any depiction is fine so long as you show the correct connections.

Reflect How do you construct a graph from information given in a table? What information can be readily obtained from a graph that cannot easily be seen in a table?

1 State which of the graphs represent the information given in the table.

	A	B	C	D	E	F
A		1		1		
B	1		1			1
C		1		1		
D	1		1		1	
E				1		1
F		1			1	

a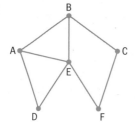

b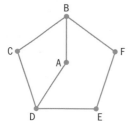

c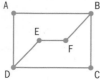

d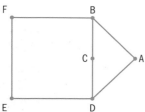

e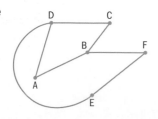

2 Draw a table to represent the number of direct connections between the vertices in the graphs below.

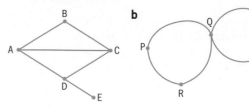

3 Draw the weighted graphs represented by the tables.

a

	A	B	C	D	E
A		15	12	10	
B	15			13	9
C	12				12
D	10	13			16
E		9	12	16	

b

	A	B	C	D	E
A		6	10		
B	6		7		
C	10	7			
D					5
E				5	

4 Draw weighted graphs represented by the tables below. Each table is read from row to column so the weight of the edge from A to B is 10. You will need to decide how to show the fact that A to B is not necessarily the same as B to A.

a

	A	B	C	D
A		10		7
B			8	
C		8		12
D				

b

	A	B	C	D
A		10		
B	10		6	
C		7		8
D	11			

5 Draw unweighted graphs to represent the tables below. A 1 in the intersection of row i and column j indicates that there is a connection from i to j.

a

	A	B	C	D
A		1		1
B	1			
C		1		1
D			1	

b

	A	B	C	D
A		1	1	1
B			1	
C		1		1
D			1	

6 A salesman needs to travel from Sheffield to Manchester to Nottingham and then back to Sheffield. A route finder algorithm has been programmed with the data in the table below, showing distances in miles between the major cities in England. Unfortunately the information on the distance from Manchester to Nottingham has not been included.

a Write down the distances from Sheffield to Manchester and from Nottingham to Sheffield.

In trying to give an estimate for the shortest distance the algorithm will find the shortest distance from Manchester to Nottingham via one other town. To do this efficiently it needs to reduce the table as much as possible.

b Explain why all those towns further than 77 miles from Manchester can be excluded from the search.

c Draw a graph showing all remaining routes from Manchester to Nottingham which go via one other town.

d Hence state an estimate for the shortest distance the salesman must travel to visit the two towns and return to Sheffield.

	Birmingham	Bristol	Derby	Exeter	Leeds	Liverpool	London	Manchester	Newcastle	Norwich	Nottingham	Oxford	Portsmouth	Sheffield	Southampton
York	129	217	88	292	25	97	194	65	82	181	80	174	252	53	239
Southampton	128	74	164	107	229	217	77	208	319	190	160	65	17	195	
Sheffield	76	164	37	240	34	72	160	38	128	146	39	130	208		
Portsmouth	141	94	175	124	242	231	71	222	332	184	173	78			
Oxford	63	70	90	141	163	153	56	144	254	141	95				
Nottingham	49	137	16	213	70	99	123		159	123					
Norwich	161	209	139	282	174	217	112	185	260						
Newcastle	204	288	161	364	94	155	274	131							
Manchester	81	162	59	238	41	34	184								
London	111	114	123	170	191	198									
Liverpool	90	161	81	237	73										
Leeds	110	196	70	271											
Exeter	164	75	203												
Derby	40	127													
Bristol	88														

> In a **connected** graph it is possible to construct a walk between any two vertices.
>
> A **subgraph** of a graph G consists entirely of vertices and edges that are also in G.

The graph from Exercise 15A question **3b** is an example of an **unconnected** graph.

It is unconnected because no walk exists from vertex A to vertex D, for example.

It is, however, made up of two connected **subgraphs.**

> In a **directed** graph all the edges are assigned a specific direction.
>
> A directed graph is **connected** if a walk can be constructed in at least one direction between any two vertices. A directed graph is **strongly connected** if it is possible to construct a walk in either direction between any two vertices.

The graphs from Exercise 15A question **4** are directed graphs.

The graph drawn in question **4a** is a connected, directed graph; sometimes this is referred to as **weakly** connected.

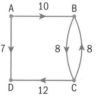

It is possible to go from A to D, for example, but not from D to A.

The graph drawn in question **4b** is strongly connected. It is possible to go in both directions between any two vertices.

The context often makes it clear whether a directed or undirected graph is required. For example, a bus may go from town A to town B but not make the reverse journey.

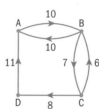

> **Reflect** When is it appropriate to use directed or undirected graphs?

Except in those cases where extra clarity is needed, the word **graph** will be taken to mean an undirected graph. If the graph is directed it will be explicitly mentioned.

> The **degree** (or order) of a vertex in a graph is the number of edges with that vertex as an end point.

A vertex whose degree is an even number is called an **even vertex** or is said to have **even degree**.

The degree of each vertex in the graph shown is:
A 2, B 3, C 2, D 4, E 3, F 2.

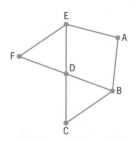

The **in-degree** of a vertex in a directed graph is the number of edges with that vertex as an end point. The **out-degree** is the number of edges with that vertex as a starting point.

In the graph shown A has an in-degree of 1 and an out-degree of 2.

Investigation 1

1   Five people shake hands before a meeting as indicated in the table.

	A	B	C	D	E
A		1		1	1
B	1		1		
C		1		1	
D	1		1		1
E	1			1	

   a   Show this information in a graph with each edge representing a handshake between two people.

   b   From the graph write down the total number of handshakes that take place before the meeting.

2   If possible, draw a graph consisting only of vertices with the degrees listed. If it is not possible, explain why not.

   a   1, 2, 2, 2, 3   b   1, 2, 2, 2   c   2, 2, 3, 3   d   2, 2, 2, 4

3   From your graphs in questions **1** and **2**, can you find a link between the degrees of the vertices in a graph and the number of edges? If necessary draw more graphs and record the degrees of the vertices and the number of edges.

4   Using your result from question **3**, explain why it is not possible to construct a graph with a degree sequence of 3, 2, 4, 1, 5, 2, 3, 3.

5   The link conjectured in question **3** is called the handshaking theorem. Explain why with reference to your answer to question **1**.

6   Can you find a similar theorem linking the degrees of the vertices in a directed graph and the number of edges?

Exercise 15B

1   A group of people share several attributes which can be shown in a graph, with the five people as the vertices. The edges represent the connections between them. For the following connections discuss whether it would be best to draw a directed or an undirected graph.

An edge represents:

   a   lives in the same block as

   b   is the sister of

   c   is a friend of

   d   is a follower on Twitter of.

2 a Draw a table to show the information contained in each of the following directed graphs.

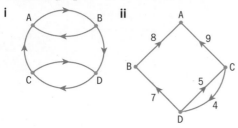

i

ii

b State whether each of the graphs is connected, strongly connected or not connected.

3 a i Draw an unweighted directed graph containing the information given in the following table.

	A	B	C	D
A		1		1
B			1	
C	1	1		1
D	1		1	

ii For each vertex state the in-degree and the out-degree.

b i Draw a weighted directed graph containing the information represented by the following table.

	A	B	C	D
A		6		4
B	6			
C		5		7
D			7	

ii For each vertex state the in-degree and the out-degree.

4 Without drawing the graph, write down the in-degree and the out-degree of each vertex given by the table below.

	A	B	C	D	E
A		1		1	1
B			1		
C		1			1
D			1		1
E	1			1	

5 The table shows part of the time-table for the ferries on Lake Starnberg in Germany.

Stop (village)	1	2	3
Starnberg	9.35	12.00	14.30
Possenhofen	10.07		14.44
Tutzing	10.31		15.06
Ammerland		12.44	15.22
Bernried	10.49		
Ambach		13.01	15.39
Seeshaupt	11.08	13.23	15.58
Ambach	11.32		
Bernried		13.48	16.23
Ammerland	11.51		
Tutzing	12.08	14.08	16.43
Possenhofen		14.34	17.09
Starnberg	12.28	14.50	17.25

a Show the connections between the towns on a directed graph.

b State one piece of information that is easier to see on the graph than on the timetable.

c Give two pairs of towns that are directly connected in one direction only.

d From your graph give four possible routes from Starnberg to Ambach which do not call at any town more than once.

e Use the timetable to find how many of the routes in part **d** could be completed in one day.

Developing inquiry skills

In the opening problem, you drew a graph to represent the information in the table. Check that your graph is a weighted graph that contains all of the information in the table.

Is the graph connected?

State the degree of each vertex.

15.2 Graph theory for unweighted graphs

Often, we are interested only in the connections between vertices and not in the weights of the edges.

Examples of such situations might be a map of a metro system, connections on an electronic circuit board or in a large file-storage system, or a network of friends on social media.

This information will normally be shown in an unweighted graph.

> Two vertices are said to be **adjacent** if they are directly connected by an edge. An element A_{ij} of an adjacency matrix A is the number of direct connections between vertex i and vertex j.

TOK

To what extent can shared knowledge be distorted and misleading?

Unlike in a table, when giving information about connections in a matrix, if there is no connection a 0 has to be put in as a place holder rather than leaving the entry empty.

Example 3

Find the adjacency matrices for the two graphs shown.

a

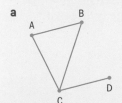

b

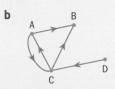

Continued on next page

a

$$\begin{array}{c} \\ A \\ B \\ C \\ D \end{array} \begin{array}{cccc} A & B & C & D \\ \begin{pmatrix} 0 & 1 & 1 & 0 \\ 1 & 0 & 1 & 0 \\ 1 & 1 & 0 & 1 \\ 0 & 0 & 1 & 0 \end{pmatrix} \end{array}$$

As the graph is undirected the matrix is symmetric in the diagonal from top left to bottom right (the leading diagonal).

b

$$\begin{array}{c} \\ A \\ B \\ C \\ D \end{array} \begin{array}{cccc} A & B & C & D \\ \begin{pmatrix} 0 & 1 & 1 & 0 \\ 0 & 0 & 0 & 0 \\ 1 & 1 & 0 & 0 \\ 0 & 0 & 1 & 0 \end{pmatrix} \end{array}$$

An adjacency matrix indicates possible movement from row to column; this is the opposite to the convention for transition matrices.

An edge from a vertex back to itself is called a **loop**.

If there are **multiple edges** between two vertices the graph is a **multigraph**.

A **simple graph** is one with no loops or multiple edges.

Reflect What can you deduce about the adjacency matrix of a simple graph from the above definition?

Example 4

Find the adjacency matrices for the two graphs shown.

a
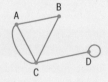

b
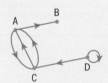

a

$$\begin{array}{c} \\ A \\ B \\ C \\ D \end{array} \begin{array}{cccc} A & B & C & D \\ \begin{pmatrix} 0 & 1 & 2 & 0 \\ 1 & 0 & 1 & 0 \\ 2 & 1 & 0 & 1 \\ 0 & 0 & 1 & 2 \end{pmatrix} \end{array}$$

In an undirected graph a loop is shown as a 2 in an adjacency matrix (as going both ways along it is possible).

b

$$\begin{array}{c} \\ A \\ B \\ C \\ D \end{array} \begin{array}{cccc} A & B & C & D \\ \begin{pmatrix} 0 & 1 & 1 & 0 \\ 0 & 0 & 0 & 0 \\ 2 & 0 & 0 & 0 \\ 0 & 0 & 1 & 1 \end{pmatrix} \end{array}$$

In this graph the loop is shown as a 1 in the adjacency matrix as the edge is directed.

Exercise 15C

1 Find the adjacency matrices for the following graphs.

a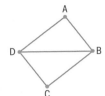

b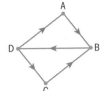

c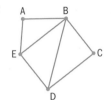

d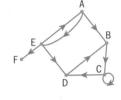

2 State the features of an adjacency matrix which tell you that a graph is simple.

3 Explain how you can use the adjacency matrix to find:

a the degree of each vertex in an undirected graph

b **i** the in-degree

  ii the out-degree

  of each vertex in a directed graph.

4 The following adjacency matrix shows the relationships between a group of people where a 1 in the entry in row i and column j indicates that person i knows the name of person j.

$$
\begin{array}{c}
\begin{array}{ccccc} A & B & C & D & E \end{array} \\
\begin{array}{c} A \\ B \\ C \\ D \\ E \end{array}
\begin{pmatrix}
1 & 1 & 0 & 0 & 1 \\
1 & 1 & 1 & 0 & 0 \\
0 & 1 & 1 & 1 & 1 \\
0 & 0 & 1 & 1 & 1 \\
0 & 0 & 0 & 1 & 1
\end{pmatrix}
\end{array}
$$

a **i** Explain why the matrix has a 1 in each entry on the leading diagonal.

  ii Explain why the graph does not have to be symmetric.

b Without drawing the graph find:

  i how many names A knows

  ii the number of people who know the name of C

  iii who knows the most names

  iv whose name is known by the largest number of people in the group.

c State whether there is anyone who does not know A's name and also does not know anyone who knows A's name.

Investigation 2

1 For this graph find the number of walks of the given length between the two given vertices. Write down each of the walks.

a length 2 between A and C

b length 2 between C and C

c length 3 between A and C

d length 3 between D and D

2 **a** Find the adjacency matrix M for the graph shown.

b Find M^2 and M^3.

c Conjecture a link between the powers of an adjacency matrix and the lengths of walks between vertices.

Continued on next page

➡ **3** Draw a **directed** graph of your own and verify that the conjecture in question **2c** still holds.

4 [Factual] How do you find the number of walks of length n between two vertices in a graph?

5 Explain how the matrices M, M^2 and M^3 can be combined to give a matrix which shows the number of walks of length 3 or less between the vertices of the graph.

6 [Factual] What can be calculated from the powers of an adjacency matrix?

7 [Factual] How can you use the powers of an adjacency matrix to find the **minimum** length of path between two vertices?

8 [Conceptual] How does the adjacency matrix allow you to analyse the paths between two points on a graph?

Let M be the adjacency matrix of a graph. The number of walks of length n from vertex i to vertex j is the entry in the ith row and the jth column of M^n.

The numbers of walks of length r or less between any two vertices are given by the matrix S_r where $S_r = M + M^2 + \ldots + M^r$

Exercise 15D

1 The adjacency matrices for the graphs in Exercise 15C question **1** are shown below.

a
$$\begin{array}{c@{}c} & \begin{array}{cccc} A & B & C & D \end{array} \\ \begin{array}{c} A \\ B \\ C \\ D \end{array} & \begin{pmatrix} 0 & 1 & 0 & 1 \\ 1 & 0 & 1 & 1 \\ 0 & 1 & 0 & 1 \\ 1 & 1 & 1 & 0 \end{pmatrix} \end{array}$$

b
$$\begin{array}{c@{}c} & \begin{array}{cccc} A & B & C & D \end{array} \\ \begin{array}{c} A \\ B \\ C \\ D \end{array} & \begin{pmatrix} 0 & 1 & 0 & 0 \\ 0 & 0 & 0 & 1 \\ 0 & 1 & 0 & 0 \\ 1 & 0 & 1 & 0 \end{pmatrix} \end{array}$$

c
$$\begin{array}{c@{}c} & \begin{array}{ccccc} A & B & C & D & E \end{array} \\ \begin{array}{c} A \\ B \\ C \\ D \\ E \end{array} & \begin{pmatrix} 0 & 1 & 0 & 0 & 1 \\ 1 & 0 & 1 & 1 & 1 \\ 0 & 1 & 0 & 1 & 0 \\ 0 & 1 & 1 & 0 & 1 \\ 1 & 1 & 0 & 1 & 0 \end{pmatrix} \end{array}$$

d
$$\begin{array}{c@{}c} & \begin{array}{cccccc} A & B & C & D & E & F \end{array} \\ \begin{array}{c} A \\ B \\ C \\ D \\ E \\ F \end{array} & \begin{pmatrix} 0 & 1 & 0 & 0 & 1 & 0 \\ 0 & 0 & 1 & 0 & 0 & 0 \\ 0 & 0 & 1 & 1 & 0 & 0 \\ 0 & 1 & 0 & 0 & 0 & 0 \\ 1 & 0 & 0 & 1 & 0 & 1 \\ 0 & 0 & 0 & 0 & 0 & 0 \end{pmatrix} \end{array}$$

Use these matrices to find the number of walks of length 3 between:

   i A and A   **ii** C and D.

In each case use the graphs in Exercise 15C question **1** to verify your result by listing all the possible walks.

2 By considering an appropriate power of a matrix, verify your answer to Exercise 15C question **4** part **c i**.

3 Use the adjacency matrices M to answer the following questions.

a

$$\begin{array}{cccc} & A & B & C & D \\ A & 0 & 1 & 1 & 0 \\ B & 1 & 0 & 1 & 0 \\ C & 1 & 1 & 0 & 1 \\ D & 0 & 0 & 1 & 0 \end{array}$$

b

$$\begin{array}{ccccc} & A & B & C & D & E \\ A & 0 & 1 & 0 & 0 & 0 \\ B & 1 & 0 & 1 & 0 & 0 \\ C & 0 & 1 & 0 & 1 & 1 \\ D & 0 & 0 & 1 & 0 & 1 \\ E & 0 & 0 & 1 & 1 & 0 \end{array}$$

i Find M^2 and M^3.

ii Write down the number of walks of length 2 between C and A.

iii Find the number of walks of length 3 or less between C and A.

The diameter of a graph is the length of the maximum shortest walk between any two vertices (so all the vertices can be reached from any other vertex in a walk of length less than or equal to the diameter of the graph).

iv Use the powers of the adjacency matrix to find the diameters of each graph. Justify your answer.

4 The following adjacency matrix shows the connections between some ports in the Shetland Islands off the coast of Scotland. The ferries go in both directions between each pair of ports.

	Castlebay	Eigg	Lochboisdale	Mallaig	Rum	Tiree	Tobermory
Castlebay	0	0	1	0	0	1	1
Eigg	0	0	0	0	1	0	0
Lochboisdale	1	0	0	0	0	0	1
Mallaig	0	0	0	0	1	0	0
Rum	0	1	0	1	0	0	0
Tiree	1	0	0	0	0	0	1
Tobermory	1	0	1	0	0	1	0

a Find the number of routes you can travel to get from Lochboisdale to Castlebay in three ferry trips.

b By considering the powers of the adjacency matrix find which ports it is possible to get to from Tiree using the ferry system.

An extra ferry route is now added between Mallaig and Lochboisdale.

c Write down the new adjacency matrix and hence state the two ports that are furthest apart.

5 a Use the directed graph you drew for Exercise 15B question **5** to write down an adjacency matrix for the ferry connections on Lake Starnberg.

b By taking a suitable power of the adjacency matrix find all the pairs of towns that are not connected directly or with at most one stop, stating clearly the direction of the connection.

Reflect How might you work out the maximum number of steps necessary to move between any two vertices on a graph?

How can we use powers of the adjacency matrix to determine whether or not a graph is connected?

TOK

Matrices are used in computer graphics for three-dimensional modelling.

How can this be used in real-life situations in other areas of knowledge?

Transition matrix

A random walk on a graph is a walk in which the vertex moved to is chosen randomly from those available.

In a graph with a finite number of vertices a random walk is a finite Markov chain.

A transition matrix can be constructed for both directed and undirected graphs.

HINT

See Chapter 9 for an introduction to Markov chains.

The probability of moving from one vertex to any of the adjacent vertices is defined to be the reciprocal of the degree of the vertex in an undirected graph and the reciprocal of the out-degree in a directed graph.

As discussed in earlier chapters, the probability of moving from vertex i to vertex j will be the entry in the ith **column** and jth **row** of the matrix.

The direction of movement in a transition matrix is **opposite** to that in an adjacency matrix.

EXAM HINT

Within the IB syllabus questions will only be set in which the graph is connected. In the case of a directed graph, it will be strongly connected.

The steady state probabilities indicate the proportion of time that would be spent at each vertex if a random walk was undertaken for a long period. The transition time between the vertices is ignored.

The Google PageRank algorithm was developed by Larry Page and Segei Brin in 1996 while working at Stanford University. They wanted to be able to rank web pages in an Internet search so that the ones most likely to be useful come towards the top of the list.

The algorithm they developed considered links from web pages as the edges in a directed graph. The steady state probabilities calculated from the transition matrix indicate which site would be visited most often if someone were randomly clicking on links in web pages. This site would come top of the list in a search.

EXAM HINT

If a walk around a graph is equally likely to take any of the edges leading from a vertex, it is called a **random walk**.

The justification for this ranking is that the sites most likely to be visited will either have lots of links to them, or be linked to by sites with lots of links going to them. In either case this is likely to reflect their relative importance.

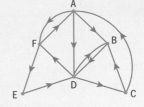

Example 5

In this graph vertices A to F represent web pages and the edges indicate links between the pages.

For example, page A has links from both C and F and contains links to B, D and F.

a Construct the transition matrix for a random walk around this graph.

b Find the steady state probabilities for the network.

c Hence rank the vertices in order of importance.

a The transition matrix is $$\begin{pmatrix} 0 & 0 & \frac{1}{2} & 0 & 0 & \frac{1}{2} \\ \frac{1}{3} & 0 & \frac{1}{2} & \frac{1}{3} & 0 & 0 \\ 0 & 0 & 0 & \frac{1}{3} & 0 & 0 \\ \frac{1}{3} & 1 & 0 & 0 & 1 & 0 \\ 0 & 0 & 0 & 0 & 0 & \frac{1}{2} \\ \frac{1}{3} & 0 & 0 & \frac{1}{3} & 0 & 0 \end{pmatrix}$$	For example, A has three edges connecting it to vertices B, D and F, and so each of these has a probability of $\frac{1}{3}$, which is shown in the first column of the matrix. Because the question does not specify which method to use, you can just look at high powers of the transition matrix using your GDC. You need to consider powers large enough to ensure there is no change in the third significant figure. An alternative would be to solve a system of six linear equations or diagonalize the matrix.
b The steady state probabilities are given by the vector $$\begin{array}{c} A \\ B \\ C \\ D \\ E \\ F \end{array} \begin{pmatrix} 0.130 \\ 0.207 \\ 0.109 \\ 0.326 \\ 0.076 \\ 0.152 \end{pmatrix}$$	
c The ranking would be D, B, F, A, C, E.	The vertex with the highest probability is placed at the top of the list.

Reflect How do you construct a transition matrix for a given graph?

Why might a random walk indicate the most important sites on a graph?

How can the steady state probabilities be used to rank lists?

Geometry and trigonometry

Exercise 15E

1 For each of the two graphs below find the transition matrix, **P**, and hence the steady state probabilities by:

  i considering high powers of **P**

  ii solving a system of linear equations.

a

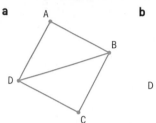

b

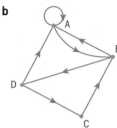

2 In an experiment on artificial intelligence a robot is put in a maze which has six rooms labelled A to F. Each of the rooms has gaps in the wall connecting it to adjacent rooms.

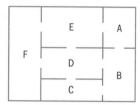

  a Draw the maze as a graph, with the vertices representing the different rooms and the edges representing the gaps between rooms.

The robot moves randomly and once in a room is equally likely to leave through any of the gaps.

  b Write down a transition matrix for the maze.

  c If the robot begins in room A, what is the probability it is again in room A after passing through four of the gaps?

  d i Find the two rooms which are most likely to be visited by the robot.

  ii Determine the percentage of time that the robot will be in each of these rooms.

3 The following diagram shows four websites. The arrows indicate a link from one of the pages to another; for example, there is a link from website D to website C.

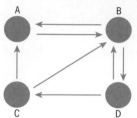

  a Write down the transition matrix to represent a random walk around this graph.

  b Show that it is not possible to link from B to C using exactly three links, and write down two other connections that are also not possible using exactly three links.

  c By solving four linear equations find:

  i the steady state probabilities

  ii the proportion of time that a person following random links will be on site B.

  d Based on this information write down the order in which the sites might be listed by a search engine, giving the one with the largest steady state probability first.

4 Within a large social network links can be created from one person's page to another. A small group of people share links according to the table below. For example, from Antoine's page it is possible to link directly to the pages of Belle, Charles and Emil.

Antoine	Belle	Charles	Dawn	Emil	Frances
Belle	Antoine	Antoine	Emil	Antoine	Dawn
Charles	Charles	Belle	Frances	Dawn	
Emil		Dawn			

George is also part of the network and friends with all those listed. He decides to visit the pages of each of them in the

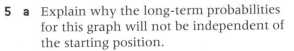

following way: having chosen a starting page he will then move to another page by choosing randomly from the list of possible links on his current page.

a Show the information from the table in a directed graph.

b From the graph explain why it is not possible for George to visit each of the friends' pages in the first six pages he looks at if he begins on Antoine's page.

c Determine whether it is possible to visit each of the friends' pages in the first six visits if he begins on another page. If so, give a possible order; if not, say why not.

d Construct a transition matrix for your graph.

George begins by visiting Antoine's page.

e Find the probability he is back on Antoine's page after visiting five further pages.

f Determine the probability he visited the pages in the order Antoine, Belle, Charles, Dawn, Emil, Antoine.

g George continues moving through the web pages in the same way for a long time. Find which page he is likely to visit:

   i the most   **ii** the least.

5 a Explain why the long-term probabilities for this graph will not be independent of the starting position.

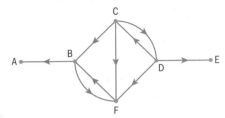

b Write down the probability that a random walk would end at vertex A if it began at vertex B.

c If X is the number of steps it would take for the walk to reach A from B find $E(X)$.

d Find the transition matrix for the graph.

e By evaluating high powers of the transition matrix find the long-term probability of being at vertex E if you began at vertex C.

Developing inquiry skills

In the opening problem, what is the minimum number of trips needed to travel between any two of the viewpoints?

A walker got lost in the park and was randomly travelling along trails. After a long period of time a rescuer went out to try and find him. Given that the rescuer decides to wait at one of the viewpoints, which one should they choose if they want to maximize the chance that the walker will pass through that viewpoint first.

15.3 Graph theory for weighted graphs: the minimum spanning tree

A **cycle** is a walk that begins and ends at the same vertex and has no other repeated vertices.
In the graph shown ABDGHA is a cycle.

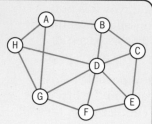

A **tree** is a connected graph which has no cycles, such as the one shown on the right.

A **spanning tree** for a graph is a subgraph which is a tree and contains all the vertices in the graph.

TOK

Is imagination more important than knowledge?

The two trees below are both spanning trees for the given graph.

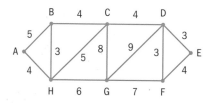

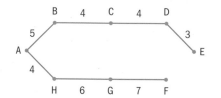

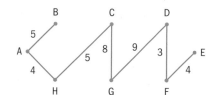

Let the graph represent new houses built on an extensive estate and the weighted edges the costs (in €1000s) of connecting them to mains electricity.

If connected using the first tree the total cost would be €33 000, and with the second it would be €38 000.

The problem that needs to be solved is finding the spanning tree of least weight, which is normally referred to as the **minimum spanning tree**.

The minimum cost solution cannot contain any cycles. If there were a cycle the edge with greatest weight could be removed and the houses would still be connected.

Reflect What would be the least-weight way to connect all the vertices in a graph?

You need to learn two algorithms to find the minimum spanning tree, Kruskal's and Prim's algorithms.

> ## Kruskal's algorithm
> 1 Find the edge of least weight anywhere in the graph. If there are two or more edges with the same weight any may be chosen.
> 2 Add the edge of least weight that has not already been selected and does not form a cycle with the previously selected edges.
> 3 Repeat the second stage until all the vertices are connected.

Example 6

Use Kruskal's algorithm to find the minimum cost of connecting all the houses on the estate. The costs of connecting each pair of houses are shown on the weighted graph. The weights are the costs in €1000 of connecting the houses.

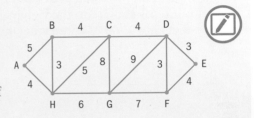

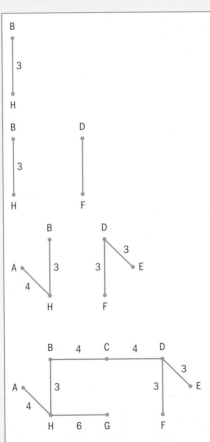

The minimum cost for connecting all the houses to electricity will be
4 + 3 + 4 + 4 + 3 + 3 + 6 = 27, ie €27 000

1 Find the edge of least weight anywhere in the graph. If there are multiple edges with the same weight any may be chosen.

In this example any of the edges of weight 3 can be selected.

2 Add the edge of least weight that has not already been selected and does not form a cycle with the previously selected edge.

Add another of the edges of weight 3.

3 Repeat the second stage until all the vertices are connected.

The next edge added will be the third of the edges with weight 3. The fourth one cannot be EF as this would create a cycle and so AH, BC or CD is added.

All the edges of weight 4 are added next. Neither of the edges of weight 5 can be added as they both form cycles, so GH of weight 6 is added. All the vertices are now connected.

> **Prim's algorithm**
>
> **1** Select any vertex and add the edge of least weight adjacent to it.
>
> **2** Add the edge of least weight that is incident to the tree formed in first step and does not connect to a vertex already in the tree.
>
> **3** Repeat this process until all the vertices have been added.

Example 7

Use Prim's algorithm to find the minimum cost of connecting all the houses on the estate. The costs of connecting each pair of houses is shown on the weighted graph. The weights are the costs in €1000 of connecting the houses.

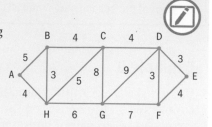

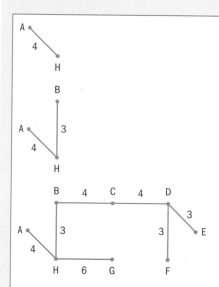

The minimum cost for connecting all the houses to electricity will be

$4 + 3 + 4 + 4 + 3 + 3 + 6 = 27$, ie €27 000

1 Select any vertex and add the edge of least weight adjacent to it.

For example, if vertex A is selected it is connected to H.

2 Add the edge of least weight that is incident to the tree formed in the first step and does not connect to a vertex already in the tree.

If two vertices adjacent to the tree being formed have the same weight then either can be used.

In this example the next edge would be HB.

3 Repeat this process until all the vertices have been added.

The tree formed will be a minimum spanning tree for the graph.

The order in which the edges were added to the tree was AH, HB, BC, CD, DE, DF, HG.

> All minimum spanning trees will have the same weight but may not consist of exactly the same edges.

> **EXAM HINT**
>
> Unless told which algorithm to use, you can use either Prim's or Kruskal's algorithm in an exam.

For very large graphs Prim's algorithm is usually quicker than Kruskal's as there is no need to check whether adding an edge will form a cycle.

It is possible to use Prim's algorithm directly from a table without needing to draw the graph.

Example 8

Find the minimum spanning tree for the graph represented by the table below.

	A	B	C	D	E
A	0	40	45	25	10
B	40	0	25	15	30
C	45	25	0	20	35
D	25	15	20	0	15
E	10	30	35	15	0

Begin with vertex A.

		A	B	C	D	E
①	A	0	40	45	25	(10)
	B	40	0	25	15	30
	C	45	25	0	20	35
	D	25	15	20	0	15
②	E	10	30	35	15	0

		A	B	C	D	E
①	A	0	40	45	25	(10)
	B	40	0	25	15	30
	C	45	25	0	20	35
③	D	25	15	20	0	15
②	E	10	30	35	(15)	0

Cross out the columns of vertices as they are added to the tree and indicate at the end of the rows the order in which they have been added. You can then look along these rows to find the entry with least weight. These entries should be circled.

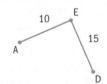

It is often easiest to draw the tree at each stage of the algorithm.

The sum of the circled entries will give the weight of the minimum spanning tree.

		A	B	C	D	E
①	A	0	40	45	25	(10)
④	B	40	0	25	15	30
	C	45	25	0	20	35
②	D	25	(15)	20	0	15
③	E	10	30	35	(15)	0

		A	B	C	D	E
①	A	0	40	45	25	(10)
④	B	40	0	25	15	30
⑤	C	45	25	0	20	35
②	D	25	(15)	(20)	0	15
③	E	10	30	35	(15)	0

Continued on next page

Geometry and trigonometry

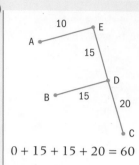

$0 + 15 + 15 + 20 = 60$

Reflect Why is Prim's a better algorithm than Kruskal's for a large graph or when the information is given in a table?

How should the algorithm be changed if extra restrictions are added, for example if there must be a direct connection between A and B?

Exercise 15F

1 Use Prim's algorithm to find the minimum spanning tree for the following graphs, beginning with vertex A.

State clearly the order in which the edges are selected.

EXAM HINT

It is likely an exam question will require this as evidence you have performed the algorithm correctly.

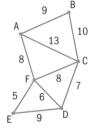

a

b

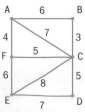

c

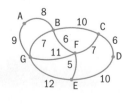

d

2 Use Kruskal's algorithm to find a minimum spanning tree for the graphs in question **1**. List the order in which the edges are selected.

3 Determine the number of edges there will be in a spanning tree containing v vertices Justify your answer through a consideration of the application of Prim's algorithm.

4 The following graph shows the offices of a finance company. The management wants to connect all the offices with extremely fast internet cables. The costs of doing so (in $1000s) are indicated on the graph below.

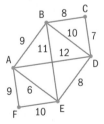

a Use Kruskal's algorithm to find the minimum cost for connecting all the offices. List the order in which the edges are connected.

b i State how you would adapt the algorithm if it is essential for offices B and D to be connected.

ii Find the minimum cost in this situation.

5 Use Prim's algorithm to find the weight of the minimum spanning tree for the following tables.

a

	A	B	C	D	E
A	0	40	25	15	20
B	40	0	25	45	30
C	25	25	0	15	35
D	15	45	15	0	20
E	20	30	35	20	0

b

	A	B	C	D	E
A	0	4	7	9	12
B	4	0	8	5	3
C	7	8	0	10	5
D	9	5	10	0	6
E	12	3	5	6	0

c Comment on why it would be more difficult to use Kruskal's algorithm than Prim's algorithm when the information is given in a table.

6 The following table shows the distances between homes needing to be connected to a mains water source at A.

	A	B	C	D	E	F	G
A	0	20	17	23	11	10	15
B	20	0	9	16	21	15	10
C	17	9	0	22	16	10	12
D	23	16	22	0	19	13	18
E	11	21	16	19	0	16	12
F	10	15	10	13	16	0	25
G	15	10	12	18	12	25	0

a Find the minimum length of pipe needed to connect all the houses and draw the corresponding spanning tree.

b It is decided that A and B must be directly connected. Find the extra length of pipe that will be required.

7 a i Use Prim's algorithm to find the minimum spanning tree for the graph represented by the table shown.

ii State the weight of the spanning tree.

	A	B	C	D	E	F	G	H
A		10	7	12	9			
B	10		8	5				
C	7	8						
D	12	5			9		7	6
E	9			9		5	6	
F					5		3	
G				7	6	3		4
H				6			4	

b A ninth vertex, I, needs to be added to the tree. In the graph I is connected to vertex A and to vertex B. By consideration of your tree from part **a** find the weight of the new minimum spanning tree if:

i the weight of the edge connecting I to A is 9 and to B is 10

ii the weight of the edge connecting I to A is 5 and to B is 6.

Developing inquiry skills

Look back to the opening question about the national park.

Extreme weather causes extensive damage to all of the trails. The park rangers decide to close some trails and repair the others to keep them open. All viewpoints still need to be accessible, and repair costs need to be kept to a minimum. Which trails should they keep open? What assumptions can you make about how the cost of the repairs relates to the length of a trail?

15.4 Graph theory for weighted graphs: the Chinese postman problem

Investigation 3

1   Find four different ways to draw this graph without taking your pen off the paper. Begin from at least two different vertices.

2   **a**   What do you notice about the degree of each vertex?

    b   What do you notice about the starting vertex and finishing vertex?

    c   **i**   **Conceptual** From the above results conjecture a sufficient condition for being able to traverse all the edges in a graph exactly once, ending at the vertex at which you began.

       ii   Verify your conjecture on a few graphs of your choosing.

       iii   Explain in your own words why your conjecture might also be a necessary condition.

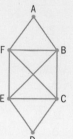

3   Is it possible to draw this graph without taking your pen off the paper? If so, find at least two ways this can be done, starting from at least two different vertices.

4   **a**   What do you notice about the starting and finishing vertices and the degrees of the vertices in the graph?

    b   **i**   **Conceptual** Conjecture necessary conditions for being able to draw a graph without taking your pen off the paper, ending at a different vertex from the one at which you began.

       ii   Draw some graphs to verify your conjecture.

       iii   Justify your conjecture.

International-mindedness

The Chinese postman problem was first posed by the Chinese mathematician Kwan Mei-Ko in 1962.

> A **trail** is a walk that repeats no edges. A **circuit** is a trail that starts and finishes at the same vertex.
>
> An **Eulerian trail** is a trail that traverses all the edges in a graph, and an **Eulerian circuit** is a circuit that traverses all the edges in a graph.

The results from Investigation 3 can therefore be summarized as follows:

● For a graph to have an Eulerian circuit all the vertices must have even degree.

● For a graph to have an Eulerian trail there must be exactly two odd vertices, and the trail must begin at one of these vertices and end at the other.

It can also be proved that every graph whose vertices are all even will have an Eulerian circuit and every graph with exactly two odd vertices will have an Eulerian trail.

Investigation 4

After a fall of snow the maintenance department in a school needs to clear all the paths before the students get to school. A graph of the school is shown. The weights on the graph show the time it would take to clear the paths. The time it takes to walk back along any cleared paths is one quarter of the time taken to clear them.

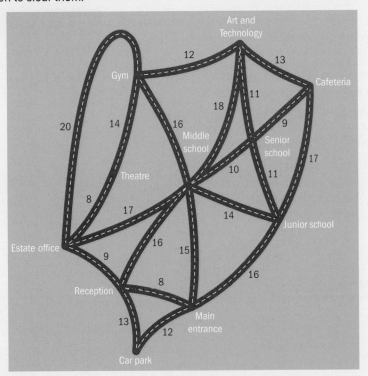

The maintenance department needs to begin and end their clearing at the estate office.

1   What would be the minimum time to clear all the paths if none of the paths needed to be repeated?

2   By considering the degrees of the vertices explain why it is not possible to clear all the paths without having to walk back along some of them.

3   The path between two buildings will need to be repeated; say which buildings these are.

4   In which order would you recommend the maintenance department clear the paths if they are to take the least possible time?

5   Given that there is an easy alternative to taking the path from the estate office to the gym (go via the theatre instead), it is decided that the direct path does not need to be cleared. How much time would be saved by not clearing this path?

Geometry and trigonometry

The Chinese postman problem is to find the route of least weight around a weighted graph and to return to the starting vertex. The question above was an example of a Chinese postman problem, modified slightly by having a reduced time to walk along the cleared paths.

Another context for the problem is that of a postman seeking to find the shortest way to walk along all the streets on their round, repeating as little distance as possible.

Clearly if the graph consists of just even vertices, you can find an Eulerian circuit and the least weight will simply be the sum of the weights of all the edges.

Recall from the handshaking theorem that it is not possible to have an odd number of odd vertices, so the minimum number of odd vertices in a graph is two. If there are exactly two odd vertices, you can find an Eulerian trail from one vertex to the other that goes along all the edges. You then must return to the starting vertex using the route of least weight.

One way to think about this is to add a second edge between the vertices on the repeated route. This creates a graph with just even vertices, and hence there is an Eulerian circuit.

> **TOK**
>
> What is most important in becoming an intelligent human being: nature or nurture?

Example 9

Solve the Chinese postman problem (find a route of least weight) for this graph, beginning and ending at A, and find the total weight for this route.

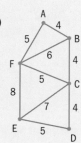

There are two odd vertices, B and E. 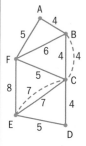	Begin by considering the degrees of all the vertices. In this example there are two odd vertices.
	By inspection find the route of least weight between these two vertices.
	Here it is BCE. Add extra edges to your graph to show this route.
	Use this second graph to find an Eulerian circuit beginning and ending at A.
A possible solution to the Chinese postman problem is ABCDEFBCECFA.	There are many possible routes and it is normally relatively easy to find one by inspection.
The total weight is 48 + 11 = 59	The weight of this route will be the weight of all the edges in the original graph plus the weights of the repeated edges.

Reflect How do the conditions for the existence of an Eulerian circuit or trail help in solving the Chinese postman problem?

Exercise 15G

1 Solve the Chinese postman problem for the graphs below, starting at vertex A. State the edges that are repeated and the weight of the route taken.

a

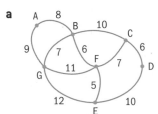

b

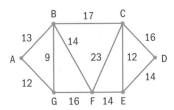

c

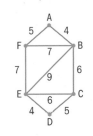

2 a Explain why the following graph has an Eulerian trail but not an Eulerian circuit.

b The weights on the graph represent the times taken in minutes for a postman to walk along the streets on his round, which begins and ends at vertex A. If he walks down any street for a second time it takes one third of the time, as he does not need to deliver letters.

i Find the minimum length of time it could take for the postman to complete his round, and which streets would need to be walked along twice.

ii If the postman has to walk down both sides of every street explain why no extra streets will need to be covered.

Give a possible route he could take.

3 The following graph represents bus routes between towns, and the weights are the costs of the journeys in dollars. A tourist staying at town A wishes to travel along all the routes and return to A as cheaply as possible.

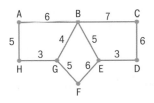

a Find the minimum possible total cost.

b A new direct bus route is added between towns G and E. Explain why the addition of this route will result in a lower cost for travelling all the routes and write down the new amount.

Investigation 5

1 The graph on the right has four odd vertices. List these vertices.

To solve the Chinese postman problem for this graph you will need to connect the odd vertices in pairs and find the route of least weight between them. You should then select the lowest of these as your solution.

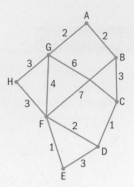

2 List the three pairings of the four vertices and state the weight of the least-weight route connecting the vertices in each of the pairs.

3 Show, on a copy of the graph, the routes connecting the pairs which have the least total weight. Hence solve the Chinese postman problem, beginning and ending at vertex A.

4 Find the total weight of the route of least weight that will traverse all the edges in the graph at least once.

The requirement to start and finish at the same vertex is now removed.

5 Use the weights listed in question **2** to find where you should now choose to start and finish.

6 **Factual** How many extra possible routes do we need to consider when the graph has four vertices of odd degree?

7 **Conceptual** How does an understanding of an Eulerian trail help determine how the algorithm should be adapted if the trail does not have to begin and end at the same vertex?

What does the solution to the Chinese postman problem represent?

Exercise 15H

1 For each of the following graphs list the three pairings that connect two vertices of odd degree, and find the minimum weight of the walk between the vertices in each pair.

Hence find which edges need to be repeated in the solution to the Chinese postman problem.

a

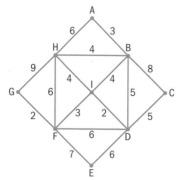

b

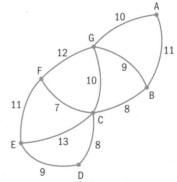

2 The graph below shows the lengths of connecting roads in a factory complex. Each evening a security guard walks along all of the roads and returns to his office at vertex A.

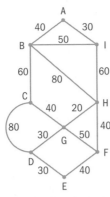

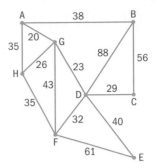

a Find a route which minimizes the length of his walk and state its length.

b A friend offers to drop him off at one of the vertices and to pick him up at another. State which two vertices should be chosen to minimize the distance the security guard has to walk.

3 The graph below shows the roads that need to be taken by a postman when delivering letters. The weights on the edges are the lengths of the roads in metres, and the postman needs to start and finish his deliveries at vertex A.

a Find a possible route he could take in order to minimize the distance he has to walk and state the length of this route. Fully justify your answer.

b A friend offers to pick him up from vertex H at the end of his round and take him back to A. Explain why this would not decrease the length he would have to walk.

c State where would you advise the postman to be collected in order to minimize the length he needs to walk, and find the total length of the repeated roads in this case.

Developing inquiry skills

Look back to the opening question about the national park.

What is the minimum distance you would need to cycle to travel along all the trails? Find one way of cycling along all the trails. Do you need to cycle along any trails more than once?

EXAM HINT

In an exam question there can only be 0, 2 or 4 vertices of odd degree.

15.5 Graph theory for weighted graphs: the travelling salesman problem

> A **table of least distances (weights)** shows the length of the shortest route between each pair of vertices in a graph.

Example 10

This graph shows the direct bus connections between four towns. The weights are the times of the journeys in minutes and the buses travel both ways along the routes.

Construct a table of least distances to show the shortest journey times between each pair of towns. Assume that there is no need to change buses on any of the journeys.

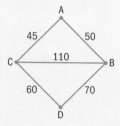

	A	B	C	D
A	0	50	45	105
B	50			
C	45			
D	105			

	A	B	C	D
A	0	50	45	105
B	50	0	95	70
C	45	95	0	60
D	105	70	60	0

From the graph we can see that the shortest routes from A to B and to C are just the direct connections, but from A to D the shortest route will be via C.

Because the graph is undirected both the first row and the first column can be completed.

Normally a direct route will be quicker than a route that passes through other vertices, but it is important to check. In this example it is shorter to go from B to C via A, which takes 95 minutes.

In the context it might be that the direct route is over poor roads or has more stops on the way.

A **path** is a walk which does not pass through any vertex more than once. A **cycle** is a walk that begins and ends at the same vertex, but otherwise does not pass through any vertex more than once.

A **Hamiltonian** path or cycle is a path or cycle which passes through all the vertices in a graph.

A **complete graph** is one in which every vertex is directly connected to every other vertex.

TOK

Hamiltonian paths and cycles are named after the 19th-century Irish mathematician William Rowan Hamilton.

The diagram on the right shows a complete graph with five vertices.

Investigation 6

There is just one Hamiltonian cycle in a complete graph with three vertices, ABC.

This is because a cycle which passes through the vertices in exactly the reverse order of another cycle is regarded as the same cycle. For example, CBA would be considered the same as ABC.

Any cycle with the vertices in the same order but beginning at a different vertex is also regarded as the same cycle. For example, BCA is the same as ABC.

Therefore, when counting cycles you can always start from the same vertex.

1 How many different Hamiltonian cycles are there in a complete graph with:

  a 4   **b** 5   **c** 6   vertices?

2 **Factual** Write down a formula for the number of Hamiltonian cycles in a complete graph with n vertices.

3 There are about 10^{80} atoms in the universe. How many vertices would there need to be in a complete graph for the number of Hamiltonian cycles to exceed the number of atoms in the universe?

Before doing the calculation guess what you think the answer might be, and then compare this guess with the calculated value.

Investigation 7

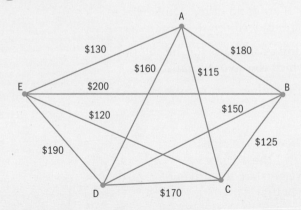

In the diagram the vertices represent towns and the edges represent the costs of flying between those towns. A salesman wishes to visit all the towns and return to his starting point at A.

1 What is the minimum number of flights he would need to take?

2 Explain why the total cost of visiting all the towns would be greater than $640.

Continued on next page

3 Find the weight of any Hamiltonian cycle beginning and ending at A.

4 Use your answers to questions **2** and **3** to give a lower and an upper bound for the cost of visiting all the cities.

5 In order to try and find a cheaper route the salesman decides that he will take the cheapest ongoing flight from each airport that takes him to a town he has not already been to and then back to A. Find the cost of the route if he follows this method beginning the algorithm at A.

6 Investigate the cost of visiting all the towns if he begins the algorithm at a different town.

7 Which of the routes you found would you recommend he take, beginning at town A?

8 Can you find a cheaper route? How likely do you think it is to be the cheapest? Justify your answer.

The **classical travelling salesman problem (TSP)** is to find the Hamiltonian cycle of least weight in a complete weighted graph.

The **practical TSP** is to find the walk of least weight that passes through each vertex of a graph, starting and finishing at the same vertex. In this case the graph need not be complete.

One context for the practical TSP would be a salesman needing to visit a number of towns and return to his starting point in the shortest possible time.

From the investigation you will have realized that finding the weight of each cycle individually to see which is shortest would take a considerable length of time.

Unfortunately, it has been shown that there is no other simple way to guarantee that a route you have found is indeed the shortest.

Instead you need to find **upper and lower bounds** for the solution which will give a range of values in which the solution must lie.

One procedure for doing so is illustrated below.

Finding an upper bound

The graph shows the connections between seven cities. A driver needs to make deliveries to all of these cities, beginning and ending at city A. The weights are the driving times between the cities, measured in hours.

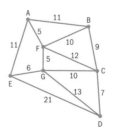

Any route that passes through all the vertices and returns to the starting point would be an upper bound for the solution to the TSP as the shortest route cannot have a greater weight than this route.

For example, by inspection ABFCDGEA is a cycle so its length would be an upper bound, namely $11 + 10 + 12 + 7 + 13 + 6 + 11 = 70$ hours. It is unlikely though that this is the best possible upper bound.

The **best upper bound** is the upper bound with the smallest value.

A method that is likely to give a better upper bound is the **nearest neighbour algorithm**.

The algorithm has two stages:

1 If the graph is not complete, create a table of least distances (weights) showing the shortest route between each pair of vertices.

2 Using your table (or the equivalent graph) choose a starting vertex and move around the graph, always going to the nearest vertex that has not already been included in the cycle. Once all the vertices have been visited, the shortest route back to the starting point is taken.

Completing a table of least distances converts a practical TSP into a classical TSP because it ensures that the graph is complete and so a Hamiltonian cycle exists.

The algorithm should only be used on a complete graph that satisfies the triangle inequality (which means the direct route between two adjacent vertices is always the shortest route). This will always be the case when working with a graph or table that shows the least distances.

EXAM HINT

In exams if there is more than one route between vertices the route of least weight between them is found by inspection.

If there is a direct route between two vertices this is often the shortest route, but it does not have to be.

Example 11

This graph shows the connections between seven cities. A driver needs to make deliveries to all of these cities, beginning and ending at city A. The weights are the driving times between the cities, measured in hours.

a The table of least distances is given below. Find the values of a, b and c.

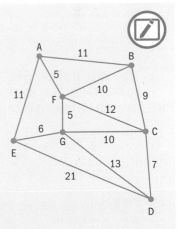

	A	B	C	D	E	F	G
A	0	11	a	23	11	5	10
B	11	0	9	16	b	10	15
C	a	9	0	7	16	12	10
D	23	16	7	0	c	18	13
E	11	b	16	c	0	11	6
F	5	10	12	18	11	0	5
G	10	15	10	13	6	5	0

Continued on next page

b Use the nearest neighbour algorithm, beginning at town A, to find an upper bound for the length of the driver's journey.

c If the driver were to follow this route, which towns would he pass through more than once?

---

a $a = 17, b = 21, c = 19$

The values are taken by inspection from the graph. It is important to check alternative routes as the most obvious is not always the shortest. For example, the route from B to E is longer going along the two outside edges than it is along the three edges through the centre of the graph.

Note also that the shortest route from D to E is not the direct route.

b

	A	B	C	D	E	F	G
A	0̶	11	a	23	11	⑤	10
B	1̶1̶	0	9	16	b	1̶0̶	15
C	0̶	9	0	7	16	1̶2̶	10
D	2̶3̶	16	7	0	c	1̶8̶	13
E	1̶1̶	b	16	c	0	1̶1̶	6
F	5̶	10	12	18	11	0̶	⑤
G	1̶0̶	15	10	13	6	5̶	0

When using the algorithm on a table of least weights it is a good idea to cross off the columns of the vertices already visited and to use the rows to find the nearest neighbours.

The final solution is:

AFGECDBA with weight
$5 + 5 + 6 + 16 + 7 + 16 + 11 = 66$

Hence an upper bound for the length of time the driver would take is 66 hours.

So beginning at A the shortest distance is to F. These two columns are crossed out as shown and the F row is used to find the next edge of least weight, which is [FG].

After reaching the final vertex you must return from this vertex to A.

c The actual route would be AFGE**G**CD**C**BA and so towns G and C would be passed through twice.

Though no vertices are repeated in the table, some of the shortest routes between towns pass through other towns. These need to be included if the driver's route has to be given.

Reflect What algorithms can you use to find an upper bound for the TSP for a particular graph?

TOK

How long would it take a computer to test all of the Hamiltonian cycles in a complete weighted graph with just 30 vertices?

Keep your answers to this exercise available as they will be needed for Exercise 15J.

1 For each of the following graphs:

  a Construct a table of least weights.

  b Hence use the nearest neighbour algorithm to find a Hamiltonian cycle around the complete graph and also the route that would need to be taken around the original graph.

  State the total weight of the route.

  If more than one route is possible give the upper bound for both routes and select the "better" upper bound.

a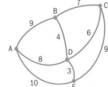

b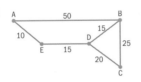

c

d

2 The following diagrams illustrate why the nearest neighbour algorithm should always be done on a complete graph which satisfies the triangle inequality. In each case apply the algorithm directly to the graph and comment on your findings.

a **b**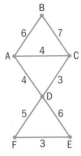

Finding a lower bound

For a graph with v vertices a solution to the TSP will need to traverse at least v edges, so one lower bound would clearly be v multiplied by the weight of the edge with least weight or the sum of the v lowest weights. In most cases this is not likely to be a good lower bound.

An alternative is to use the **deleted vertex algorithm**.

The procedure is as follows.

1 Choose a vertex and remove it and all the edges incident to it from the graph.

2 Find the minimum spanning tree for the remaining subgraph.

3 A lower bound is the weight of the minimum spanning tree plus the combined weight of the two edges of least weight removed in step 1.

4 The process can then be repeated by removing a different initial vertex. The best lower bound (the one with the largest weight) is then taken.

The example below includes an explanation of why this algorithm gives a lower bound.

HINT

This algorithm should also be used only on a complete graph that satisfies the triangle inequality. This will always be the case when working with a graph or table showing least distances.

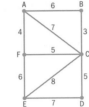

Example 12

Find a lower bound by deleting vertex A from the graph.

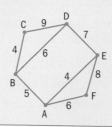

With vertex A deleted, the minimum spanning tree is	Explanation of why this will give a lower bound: The actual solution to the TSP is
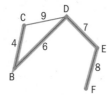 This has weight 25.	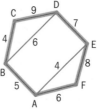
	When A is deleted the remaining part of the solution to the TSP will clearly be a tree, and so the weight of this part will be greater than or equal to the weight of the minimum spanning tree. In this example it is 28.
The two deleted edges of least weight have weights 5 and 4. 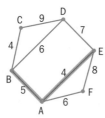	A is reconnected using the two edges of least weight. The combined weight of the two edges incident to A in the solution of the TSP will be greater than or equal to the combined weight of these two edges. In this example they add to 11.
Lower bound is 25 + 5 + 4 = 34	The total weight of edges produced using the algorithm will therefore be less than or equal to the weight of the solution of the TSP, which in the example is 28 + 11 = 37.

Reflect How do the algorithms used in the travelling salesman problem help address the fact that it is often not possible to test all the possible routes?

How can you make sure that the nearest neighbour algorithm and the deleted vertex algorithm will give the upper and lower bounds for a practical TSP?

HINT

If the weights are given in a table then Prim's algorithm can be used to find the minimum spanning tree, having removed the rows and columns of the deleted vertex.

Exercise 15J

1   For each of the tables of least weights produced for the graphs given in Exercise 15I, question **1**:

   i   find a lower bound using the deleted vertex algorithm and deleting vertex A

   ii   find a higher lower bound by deleting a different vertex

   iii   use the upper bound calculated in Exercise 15I plus your answer to part **ii** to give bounds for the solution of the TSP.

2   Answer the following questions which relate to the graph below.

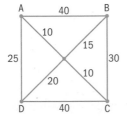

   a   By deleting vertex E on the graph, use the deleted vertex algorithm to find a lower bound for the TSP.

   b   Complete a table of least distances for this graph.

   c   Use the nearest neighbour algorithm to find an upper bound for the TSP.

   d   State what you notice and explain the reason for this.

3   In Example 10 an upper bound was found for the time it would take for a driver to travel between seven cities. The table of least distances is shown. Use the table and Prim's algorithm to find a lower bound for the above problem, by first deleting vertex A.

	A	B	C	D	E	F	G
A	0	11	17	23	11	5	10
B	11	0	9	16	21	10	15
C	17	9	0	7	16	12	10
D	23	16	7	0	19	18	13
E	11	21	16	19	0	11	6
F	5	10	12	18	11	0	5
G	10	15	10	13	6	5	0

4   The complete graph below shows the times in minutes to walk between five shops in a city.

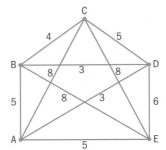

   a   Use the nearest neighbour algorithm to find an upper bound for the length of time to walk to all of the shops, starting and ending at A.

   b   Use the deleted vertex algorithm to verify that 21 minutes is a lower bound for the time to walk to all the shops.

   c   By consideration of the edges adjacent to C and to E explain why it is not possible to find a cycle with length 22 or less.

   d   The shopper decides they still need to start and finish at shop A but their last visit before returning to A has to be to shop B. State how the nearest neighbour algorithm might be adapted to allow for this.

Chapter summary

- A graph is a set of vertices connected by edges.
- When raised to the power n an adjacency matrix gives the number of walks of length n between two vertices.
- The transition matrix for a graph gives the probability of moving from one vertex to another if all edges from the vertex are equally likely to be taken.
- The steady states of a transition matrix give the proportion of time that would be spent at each vertex during a random walk around the graph.
- Kruskal's and Prim's algorithms are used to find the minimum spanning tree for a graph.
- The Chinese postman problem is to find the walk of least weight that goes along every edge at least once.
- In the Chinese postman problem for a graph with two odd vertices, the shortest route between the two odd vertices is found and indicated using multiple edges. The solution to the Chinese postman problem will be an Eulerian circuit around the graph formed.
- With four odd vertices the shortest total route between any two pairs of the odd vertices is found and indicated using multiple edges. The solution to the Chinese postman problem will be an Eulerian circuit around the graph formed.
- The classical travelling salesman problem is to find the Hamiltonian cycle of least weight in a weighted complete graph.
- The practical travelling salesman problem is to find the route of least weight around a graph which visits all the vertices at least once and returns to the starting vertex.
- A practical travelling salesman problem should be converted to the classical problem by completion of a table of least distances where necessary.
- The nearest neighbour algorithm is used to find an upper bound for the travelling salesman problem.
- The deleted vertex algorithm is used to find a lower bound for the travelling salesman problem.

Developing inquiry skills

Look back to the opening questions about the national park. What would be the shortest route for a visitor wanting to visit all of the viewpoints and return to A. Approximately how long would their journey be?

Chapter review

Click here for a mixed review exercise

1 **a** Explain why the graph shown has a Eulerian trail.

b Write down a possible Eulerian trail.

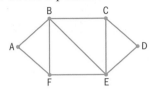

2 Use Kruskal's algorithm to find the minimum spanning tree for the graph shown. State the order in which the edges are added and the weight of the tree.

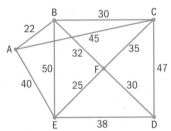

3 Solve the Chinese postman problem for the weighted graph shown, beginning at vertex A.

State which edges need to be repeated and the total weight of the route.

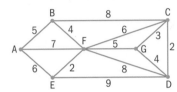

4 Consider the adjacency matrix **M** which represents the graph *G*.

$$\begin{array}{c} \quad A \ B \ C \ D \ E \\ \begin{array}{c} A \\ B \\ C \\ D \\ E \end{array} \begin{pmatrix} 0 & 1 & 1 & 2 & 0 \\ 1 & 0 & 2 & 0 & 0 \\ 1 & 2 & 0 & 1 & 0 \\ 2 & 0 & 1 & 0 & 1 \\ 0 & 0 & 0 & 1 & 0 \end{pmatrix} \end{array}$$

This question should be done **without** drawing the graph *G*.

a State whether *G* is:
  i directed   **ii** simple
  iii complete   **iv** a tree.
Justify your answers.

b State the degree of each of the vertices of *G*.

c Using your answer to part **b** state whether *G* has:
  i a Hamiltonian cycle
  ii an Eulerian circuit
  iii an Eulerian trail.
Justify your answers.

d By considering powers of **M** state whether it is possible to move between all vertices of *G* in two or fewer steps.
Justify your answer.

5 **a** Use Prim's algorithm to find the minimum spanning tree for the graph represented by the table below.
State the weight of the minimum spanning tree.

	A	B	C	D	E	F	G
A	0	20	10	30	15	11	15
B	20	0	8	22	27	13	9
C	10	8	0	24	16	10	12
D	30	22	24	0	29	13	18
E	15	27	16	29	0	16	14
F	11	13	10	13	16	0	25
G	15	9	12	18	14	25	0

Another vertex H is now added to the graph. H is connected to A by an edge of weight 9, to B by an edge of weight 12 and to C by an edge of weight 11.

b Find a lower bound for the travelling salesman problem for this extended graph.

6 The weights of the edges of a graph with vertices A, B, C, D and E are given in the following table.

	A	B	C	D	E
A	0	16	10	25	15
B	16	0	8	22	27
C	10	8	0	24	16
D	25	22	24	0	19
E	15	27	16	19	0

a **i** State whether or not the graph represented by the table is complete.

ii Draw the graph represented by the table.

iii Use the nearest neighbour algorithm, beginning at vertex A, to find an upper bound for the travelling salesman problem.

b **i** Use Kruskal's algorithm to find the minimum spanning tree for the subgraph obtained by removing vertex A from the graph and state the weight of this tree.

ii Hence find a lower bound for the travelling salesman problem.

7 The graph *G* is shown below.

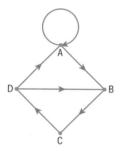

a State whether *G* is:

i directed   **ii** simple

iii strongly connected.

Justify your answers.

b For each vertex write down the in-degree and the out-degree.

c **i** State whether *G* has an Eulerian circuit.

ii Conjecture a necessary condition for a directed graph to have an Eulerian circuit.

iii Does *G* have an Eulerian trail? If so write down a possible trail.

iv Conjecture a necessary condition for a directed graph to have an Eulerian trail.

d Construct a transition matrix for *G*.

e Find the steady state probabilities and comment on your results.

8 Consider the weighted graph below.

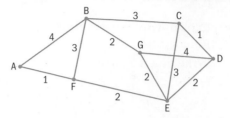

a Write down the four vertices of odd degree.

b Find a walk starting and ending at A, of minimum total weight, which includes every edge at least once, and state the weight of this walk.

Fully justify your answer.

c Find the minimum weight of a walk that includes every edge at least once if it is no longer necessary to start and finish at the same vertex.

State a possible starting and finishing vertex for this walk.

9 Let *G* be the weighted graph below.

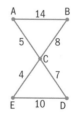

a Explain why *G* does not have a Hamiltonian cycle.

b Give an example of a Hamiltonian path in *G*.

c Construct a table of least distances for *G*.

d Use the nearest neighbour algorithm to find a Hamiltonian cycle on the complete graph represented by the table of least distances which begins and ends at vertex A.

e If this cycle was taken around *G*, state the number of times the cycle passes through vertex C.

Exam-style questions

10 P1: Consider the graph below.

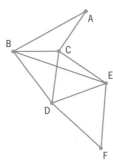

a State how you know a Eulerian circuit exists in the above graph. (1 mark)

b Write down one such Eulerian circuit. (2 marks)

11 P1: Use Prim's algorithm (starting at A) to determine a minimum spanning tree for the graph. State clearly in which order you are adding the edges. (3 marks)

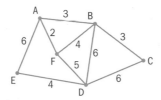

Determine the weight of the minimum spanning tree. (2 marks)

12 P1: The following graph shows seven points on a computer network, to be connected by electronic cable. The cost of connecting any two computers (in hundreds of pounds) is given by the number on each respective arc of the graph.

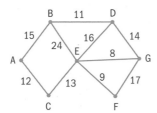

a By using Kruskal's algorithm, find the minimum spanning tree for the graph, stating the order in which you added the arcs. (2 marks)

b Draw the minimum spanning tree and hence find the least cost for connecting the computers. (4 marks)

13 P1: Consider the network.

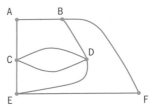

a Write down a Hamiltonian cycle, starting at the point F. (2 marks)

b Explain why it is not possible to construct a Eulerian circuit from this graph. (2 marks)

c Suggest which edge could be removed in order that it be impossible construct a Hamiltonian cycle from any point. Justify your answer. (2 marks)

14 P1: From the graph, write down all the odd vertices. (1 mark)

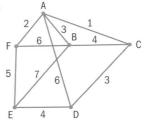

a Hence find a shortest route that starts and finishes at vertex A, travelling through every edge at least once. State also its weight. (6 marks)

15 P2: A network is represented by the following table.

	A	B	C	D	E
A	0	24	17	18	21
B	24	0	31	26	20
C	17	31	0	19	13
D	18	26	19	0	25
E	21	20	13	25	0

a Draw a weighted graph representing the network. (3 marks)

b Using Kruskal's algorithm, find a minimum spanning tree for the graph.

State clearly the order in which you add the edges. (2 marks)

c Hence find the weight of the minimum spanning tree. (2 marks)

16 P2: The following directed graph represents four islands served by a particular shipping company.

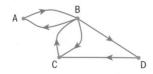

a Construct the adjacency matrix M for the shipping routes. (2 marks)

b i Find the matrix M^3.

ii Hence determine the number of ways it is possible to travel from $A \rightarrow C$ in exactly three journeys. (3 marks)

c i Find the matrix S_3, where $S_3 = \sum_{i=1}^{3} M^i$.

ii Hence find the number of ways it is possible to travel from $B \rightarrow C$ in fewer than four journeys.

iii List all such possible ways. (8 marks)

17 P2: The shipping company from question 8 decides to introduce an express route from $A \rightarrow D$ and vice versa.

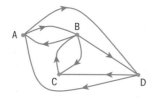

a Construct a transition matrix T for the new set of shipping routes. (3 marks)

b Show that a ship starting its journey from port B is just as likely to be stationed at any of the ports following three journeys. (3 marks)

c Find the steady state probabilities for the shipping network. (2 marks)

d Using your answer to part **c**, determine the best port for the shipping company to base its headquarters, justifying your answer. (2 marks)

18 P2: The graph shows seven schools, denoted by letters A, B, C, D, E, F, G.

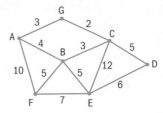

A school inspector starts from school A, and is required to visit each of the schools, returning to his starting point. The weights of each edge denote the travelling times for the inspector.

a Construct a table of least distances. (3 marks)

b By using the nearest neighbour algorithm, determine a best upper bound for the length of the journey. (3 marks)

c State the actual route taken by the inspector. (2 marks)

19 P2: Consider the graph below, where vertices A to E form a network of directed routes as shown.

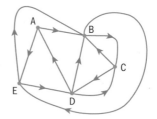

a Construct the transition matrix for this graph. (3 marks)

b If a "random walk" was undertaken starting at vertex A, determine average time per hour (to the nearest minute) spent at each vertex. (4 marks)

20 P2: Consider the following network, illustrating the possible routes available for a mouse trapped in a maze.

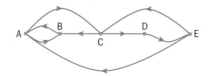

a Construct the adjacency matrix M for this network. (2 marks)

b i By evaluating the matrix M^7, show that there is only one journey in this network that can be done in exactly seven moves.

ii Describe the journey, listing (in order) the vertices visited. (6 marks)

21 P2: The diagram shows a network of cycle pathways joining seven points in a park, with the weights indicating the time of each journey (in minutes). Nasson aims to cycle along every pathway at least once in the shortest possible time. He starts from, and returns to, point A.

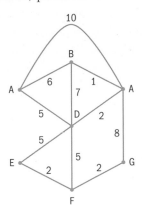

a State which pathways Nasson will need to cycle along twice, and find the total time that his journey will take. (7 marks)

b Hence, find a suitable route for Nasson to take. (2 marks)

c Instead of his original plan, Nasson decides to start at point F. He still needs to cycle every path in the least amount of time, but can finish at any other point.

Determine at which point Nasson should aim to finish, and justify your answer. (4 marks)

22 P2: Consider the following graph.

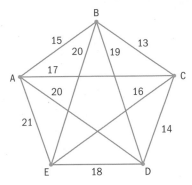

a By using the nearest neighbour algorithm, and starting at vertex A, determine an upper bound for the travelling salesman problem. State clearly the order in which you are taking the vertices. (3 marks)

b By deleting vertex A and using the deleted vertex algorithm, obtain a lower bound for the travelling salesman problem. (4 marks)

c Show that by deleting vertex B, the same lower bound will be found. (4 marks)

d Hence write down an inequality for the minimum length (l) of a tour. (2 marks)

e Write down a tour satisfying this inequality. (1 mark)

Click here for further exam practice

Geometry and trigonometry

Choosing the right path

Approaches to learning: Communication, Research, Reflection, Creative thinking
Exploration criteria: Presentation (A), Mathematical communication (B), Personal engagement (C), Reflection (D)
IB topic: Graph theory

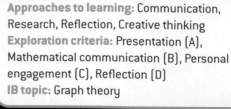

Minimum spanning trees

How many different spanning trees can you find for this graph?

What is the minimum length spanning tree?

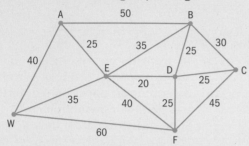

Hamiltonian paths and cycles (the travelling salesman)

Find the minimum length Hamiltonian cycle on this graph:

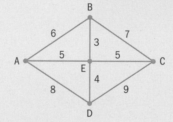

Eulerian trails (The Chinese postman)

Find the minimum length Eulerian circuit on this graph.

What if you did not need to return to the starting vertex?

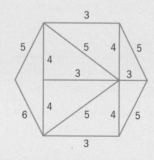

What real-life situations could you use these to solve?

In order to solve a real-life problem, you must:

- clearly define what it is that you want to find
- consider the method or algorithm you will follow to make this possible
- identify what the vertices and edges of the graph represent and find, record or collect the information required to put on this graph
- be able to draw a representation of the graph, perhaps using technology.

You might also:

- reflect on the accuracy and reliability of the values you have found and any assumptions or simplifications it has been necessary to make in order to collect them and finally answer the question
- consider what extensions you could solve based on what you have found out so far.

Your task

Choose one of these problems and think of a situation that is relevant to you that you could use this process to solve.

Based on this, try to give a brief answer to each of these questions:

- What real-life issue are you going to try to address?
- What is the **aim** of this exploration?
- What **personal** reason do you have for wanting to do this exploration?
- What **data** will you need to collect or find?
- What **research** will you need to do for this exploration?
- What **sources of information** will you use?
- What **definitions** will you need to give?
- What possible **representations** will you need to include?
- How will you **draw** these?
- What **technology** will you require?
- What **assumptions** or **simplifications** have you needed to make in this exploration?
- What possible **extensions** could there be to your exploration?
- Are there any **further information/comments** that may be relevant with regards to your exploration?

Extension

There are also other types of problems in Graph theory that have not been covered in this chapter. Here are two examples on vertex colouring and domination.

What real-life situations could you use these to solve?

Vertex colouring:

Find the chromatic number (the smallest number of colours needed to colour the vertices so that no two adjacent vertices are the same color) of this graph:

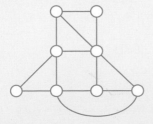

Domination:

Find the domination number (the size of a smallest **dominating set** which is a set of vertices of the graph such that all vertices not in the set are adjacent to a vertex in the set) of this graph:

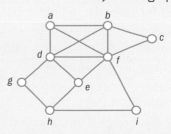

16 Exploration

All IB Diploma subjects have an Internal Assessment (IA). The IA in Mathematics is called an exploration. The exploration will be assessed internally by your teacher and externally moderated by the IB and counts for 20% of your final grade.

This chapter gives you advice on planning your exploration, as well as hints and tips to help you to achieve a good grade by making sure that your exploration satisfies the assessment criteria. There are also suggestions on choosing a topic and how to get started on your exploration.

About the exploration

The exploration is an opportunity for you to show that you can apply mathematics to an area that interests you. It is a piece of written work investigating an area of mathematics.

There are 30 hours in the syllabus for developing your mathematical toolkit and your exploration. The "toolkit" is the inquiry, investigative, problem solving and modelling skills you need to write a good exploration. You can build these skills throughout this book—in particular, in the Investigations, Developing Inquiry Skills and Modelling activities in each chapter.

You should expect to spend around 10–15 hours of class time on your exploration and up to 10 hours of your own time.

During **class time** you will:

- go through the assessment criteria with your teacher
- brainstorm to come up with suitable topics/titles
- look at previous explorations and the grading
- meet with your teacher to discuss your choice of topic and your progress.

During **your own time** you will:

- research the topic you have chosen, to make sure that it is appropriate for an exploration (if not, you will have to conduct further research to help you select a suitable topic)
- collect and organize your information/data and decide which mathematical processes to apply
- write your exploration
- submit a draft exploration to your teacher (your teacher will set a deadline for this)
- present your draft exploration to some of your peers, for their feedback.
- submit the final exploration (your teacher will set a deadline for this). If you do not submit an exploration then you receive a grade of "N" and will not receive your IB Diploma.

How the exploration is marked

After you have submitted the final version of your exploration your teacher will mark it. This is "internal assessment" (in school). Your teacher submits these marks to the IB, from which a random sample of explorations is selected automatically. Your teacher uploads these sample explorations to be marked by an external moderator. This external moderation of IA ensures that all teachers in all schools are marking students' work to the same standards.

To begin with, the external moderator will mark three of your school's explorations. If the moderator's mark is within 2 marks of your teacher's mark, then all your teacher's marks stay the same.

If the moderator's mark is more than 2 marks higher or lower than your teacher's mark, the external moderator will mark the remaining explorations in the sample. This may increase the mark if the teacher marked too harshly or decrease the mark if the teacher marked too leniently. The moderator sends a report to the school to explain the reason for any change in the marks.

Internal assessment criteria

Your exploration will be assessed by your teacher, against the criteria given below. The IB external moderator will use the same assessment criteria.

The final mark for each exploration is the sum of the scores for each criterion. The maximum possible final mark is 20. This is 20% of your final mark for Mathematics: applications and interpretation Higher level.

The criteria cover five areas, A to E

Criterion A	Presentation
Criterion B	Mathematical communication
Criterion C	Personal engagement
Criterion D	Reflection
Criterion E	Use of mathematics

Criterion A: Presentation

This criterion assesses the organization, coherence and conciseness of your exploration.

Achievement level	Descriptor
0	The exploration does not reach the standard described by the descriptors below.
1	The exploration has some coherence or some organization.
2	The exploration has some coherence and shows some organization.
3	The exploration is coherent and well organized.
4	The exploration is coherent, well organized and concise.

To get a good mark for Criterion A: Presentation

- A **well organized** exploration has:
  - a **rationale** which includes an explanation of why you chose this topic
  - an **introduction** in which you discuss the context of the exploration
  - a statement of the **aim** of the exploration, which should be clearly identifiable
  - a **conclusion**.

- A **coherent** exploration:
  - is logically developed and easy to follow
  - should "read well" and express ideas clearly
  - includes any graphs, tables and diagrams where they are needed—not attached as appendices to the document.

- A **concise** exploration:
  - focuses on the aim and avoids irrelevancies
  - achieves the aim you stated at the beginning
  - explains all stages in the exploration clearly and concisely.

- References must be cited where appropriate. Failure to do so could be considered academic malpractice.

> **IA tip**
>
> For more on citing references, academic honesty and malpractice, see pages 741 – 742.

Criterion B: Mathematical communication

This criterion assesses how you:

- use appropriate mathematical language (notation, symbols, terminology)
- define key terms, where required
- use multiple forms of mathematical representation, such as formulas, diagrams, tables, charts, graphs and models, where appropriate.

Achievement level	Descriptor
0	The exploration does not reach the standard described by the descriptors below.
1	There is some relevant mathematical communication which is partially appropriate.
2	The exploration contains some relevant, appropriate mathematical communication.
3	The mathematical communication is relevant, appropriate and is mostly consistent.
4	The mathematical communication is relevant, appropriate and consistent throughout.

> **IA tip**
>
> Only include forms of representation that are relevant to the topic, for example, don't draw a bar chart and pie chart for the same data. If you include a mathematical process or diagram without using or commenting on it, then it is irrelevant.

To get a good mark for Criterion B: Mathematical communication

- Use appropriate mathematical language and representation when communicating mathematical ideas, reasoning and findings.

- Choose and use appropriate mathematical and ICT tools such as graphic display calculators, screenshots, mathematical software, spreadsheets, databases, drawing and word-processing software, as appropriate, to enhance mathematical communication.

> **IA tip**
>
> Use technology to enhance the development of the exploration—for example, by reducing laborious and repetitive calculations.

- Define key terms that you use.
- Express results to an appropriate degree of accuracy.
- Label scales and axes clearly in graphs.
- Set out proofs clearly and logically.
- Define variables.
- Do not use calculator or computer notation.

Criterion C: Personal engagement

This criterion assesses how you engage with the exploration and make it your own.

Achievement level	Descriptor
0	The exploration does not reach the standard described by the descriptors below.
1	There is evidence of some personal engagement.
2	There is evidence of significant personal engagement.
3	There is evidence of outstanding personal engagement.

To get a good mark for Criterion C: Personal engagement

- Choose a topic for your exploration that you are interested in, as this makes it easier to display personal engagement
- Find a topic that interests you and ask yourself "What if...?"
- Demonstrate personal engagement by using some of these skills and practices from the mathematician's toolkit.
  - Creating mathematical models for real-life situations.
  - Designing and implementing surveys.
  - Running experiments to collect data.
  - Running simulations.
  - Thinking and working independently.
  - Thinking creatively.
  - Addressing your personal interests.
  - Presenting mathematical ideas in your own way.
  - Asking questions, making conjectures and investigating mathematical ideas.
  - Considering historical and global perspectives.
  - Exploring unfamiliar mathematics.

Criterion D: Reflection

This criterion assesses how you review, analyse and evaluate your exploration.

Achievement level	Descriptor
0	The exploration does not reach the standard described by the descriptors below.
1	There is evidence of limited reflection.
2	There is evidence of meaningful reflection.
3	There is substantial evidence of critical reflection.

IA tip

Students often copy their GDC display, which makes it unlikely they will reach the higher levels in this criterion. You need to express results in proper mathematical notation, for example, use 2^x and not $2^\wedge x$ use $\times$ not $*$ use 0.028 and not 2.8E-2

IA tip

Just showing personal interest in a topic is not enough to gain the top marks in this criterion. You need to write in your own voice and demonstrate your own experience with the mathematics in the topic.

To get a good mark for Criterion D: Reflection

- Include reflection in the conclusion to the exploration, but also throughout the exploration. Ask yourself "What next?"
- Show reflection in your exploration by:
  - discussing the implications of your results
  - considering the significance of your findings and results
  - stating possible limitations and/or extensions to your results
  - making links to different fields and/or areas of mathematics
  - considering the limitations of the methods you have used
  - explaining why you chose this method rather than another.

IA tip

Discussing your results without analysing them is not meaningful or critical reflection. You need to do more than just describe your results. Do they lead to further exploration?

Criterion E: Use of mathematics

This criterion assesses how you use mathematics in your exploration.

Achievement level	Descriptor
0	The exploration does not reach the standard described by the descriptors below.
1	Some relevant mathematics is used.
2	Some relevant mathematics is used. The mathematics explored is partially correct. Some knowledge and understanding are demonstrated.
3	Relevant mathematics commensurate with the level of the course is used. The mathematics explored is correct. Good knowledge and understanding are demonstrated.
4	Relevant mathematics commensurate with the level of the course is used. The mathematics explored is correct. Good knowledge and understanding are demonstrated.
5	Relevant mathematics commensurate with the level of the course is used. The mathematics explored is correct and demonstrates sophistication or rigour. Thorough knowledge and understanding are demonstrated.
6	Relevant mathematics commensurate with the level of the course is used. The mathematics explored is precise and demonstrates sophistication and rigour. Thorough knowledge and understanding are demonstrated.

To get a good mark for Criterion E: Use of mathematics

- Produce work that is commensurate with the level of the course you are studying. The mathematics you explore should either be part of the syllabus, at a similar level or beyond.
- If the level of mathematics is not commensurate with the level of the course you can only get a maximum of two marks for this criterion.
- Only use mathematics relevant to the topic of your exploration. Do not just do mathematics for the sake of it.
- Demonstrate that you fully understand the mathematics used in your exploration.

IA tip

Make sure the mathematics in your exploration is not only based on the prior learning for the syllabus. When you are deciding on a topic, consider what mathematics will be involved and whether it is commensurate with the level of the course.

- Justify **why** you are using a particular mathematical technique (do not just use it).
- Generalize and justify conclusions.
- Apply mathematics in different contexts where appropriate.
- Apply problem-solving techniques where appropriate.
- Recognize and explain patterns where appropriate.

- **Precise** mathematics is error-free and uses an appropriate level of accuracy at all times.
- Demonstrate **sophistication** of mathematics in your exploration.
  - Show that you understand and can use challenging mathematical concepts
  - Show that you can extend the applications of mathematics beyond those you learned in the classroom
  - look at a problem from different mathematical perspectives
  - identify underlying structures to link different areas of mathematics.

- Demonstrate **rigour** by using clear logic and language in your mathematical arguments and calculations.

> **IA tip**
>
> Each step in the mathematical development of the exploration needs to be clearly explained so that a peer can follow your working without stopping to think.

Academic honesty

This is very important in all your work. Your school will have an Academic Honesty Policy which you should be given to discuss in class, to make sure that you understand what malpractice is and the consequences of committing malpractice.

According to the IB Learner Profile for Integrity:

"We act with integrity and honesty, with a strong sense of fairness and justice, and with respect for the dignity and rights of people everywhere. We take responsibility for our actions and their consequences."

Academic Honesty means:
- that your work is authentic
- that your work is your own intellectual property
- that you conduct yourself properly during examinations
- that any work taken from another source is properly cited.

Authentic work:
- is work based on your own original ideas
- can draw on the work of others, but this must be fully acknowledged in footnotes and bibliography
- must use your own language and expression
- must acknowledge all sources fully and appropriately in a bibliography.

> **IA tip**
>
> Reference any photographs you use in your exploration, including to decorate the front page.

Malpractice

The IB Organization defines malpractice as "behaviour that results in, or may result in, the candidate or any other candidate gaining an unfair advantage in one or more assessment components."

Malpractice includes:

- plagiarism—copying from others' work, published or otherwise, whether intentional or not, without the proper acknowledgement
- collusion—working together with at least one other person in order to gain an undue advantage (this includes having someone else write your exploration)
- duplication of work—presenting the same work for different assessment components
- any other behaviour that gains an unfair advantage such as taking unauthorized materials into an examination room, stealing examination materials, disruptive behaviour during examinations, falsifying CAS records or impersonation.

Collaboration and collusion

It is important to understand the distinction between collaboration (which is allowed) and collusion (which is not).

Collaboration

In several subjects, including mathematics, you will be expected to participate in group work. It is important in everyday life that you are able to work well in a group situation. Working in a group entails talking to others and sharing ideas. Every member of the group is expected to participate equally and it is expected that all members of the group will benefit from this collaboration. However, the end result must be your own work, even if it is based on the same data as the rest of your group.

Collusion

This is when two or more people work together to intentionally deceive others. Collusion is a type of plagiarism. This could be working with someone else and presenting the work as your own or allowing a friend to copy your work.

References and acknowledging sources

The IB does not tell you which style of referencing you should use—this is left to your school.

[1]Words & Ideas. The Turnitin Blog. Top 15 misconceptions about Turnitin. Misconception 11: matched text is likely to be completely coincidental or common knowledge (posted by Katie P., March 09, 2010).

IA tip

Plagiarism detection software identifies text copied from online sources. The probability that a 16-word phrase match is "just a coincidence" is $\frac{1}{10^{12}}$.[1]

IA tip

Discussing individual exploration proposals with your peers or in class before submission is collaboration.

Individually collecting data and then pooling it to create a large data set is collaboration. If you use this data for your own calculations and write your own exploration, that is collaboration. If you write the exploration as a group, that is collusion.

IA tip

Be consistent and use the same style of referencing throughout your exploration.

The main reasons for citing references are:

- to acknowledge the work of others
- to allow your teacher and moderator to check your sources.

To refer to someone else's work:

- include a brief reference to the source in the main body of your exploration—either as part of the exploration or as a footnote on the appropriate page
- include a full reference in your bibliography.

The bibliography should include a list with full details of **all** the sources that you have used.

Choosing a topic

You need to choose a topic that interests you, as then you will enjoy working on the exploration and you will be able to demonstrate personal engagement by using your own voice and demonstrating your own experience.

Discuss the topic you choose with your teacher and your peers before you put too much time and effort into developing the exploration. Remember that the work does not need to go beyond the level of the course which you are taking, but you can choose a topic that is outside the syllabus and is at a commensurate level. You should avoid choosing topics that are too ambitious, or below the level of your course.

These questions may help you to find a topic for your exploration:

- What areas of the syllabus are you enjoying most?
- What areas of the syllabus are you performing best in?
- Would you prefer to work on purely analytical work or on modelling problems?
- Have you discovered, through reading or talking to peers on other mathematics courses, areas of mathematics that might be interesting to look into?
- What mathematics is important for the career that you eventually hope to follow?
- What are your special interests or hobbies? Where can mathematics be applied in this area?

One way of choosing a topic is to start with a general area of interest and create a mind map. This can lead to some interesting ideas on applications of mathematics to explore. The mind map on the following pages shows how the broad topic "Transport" can lead to suggestions for explorations into such diverse topics as baby carriage design, depletion of fossil fuels and queuing theory.

On page 744 there is an incomplete mind map for you to continue, either on your own or by working with other mathematics students.

> **IA tip**
>
> Cite references to others' work even if you paraphrase or rewrite the original text.
>
> You do not need to cite references to formulas taken from mathematics textbooks.

> **IA tip**
>
> You must include a brief reference in the exploration as well as in the bibliography. It is not sufficient just to include a reference in the bibliography.

> **IA tip**
>
> Your exploration should contain a substantial amount of mathematics at the level of your course, and should not just be descriptive. Although the history of mathematics can be very interesting it is not a good exploration topic.

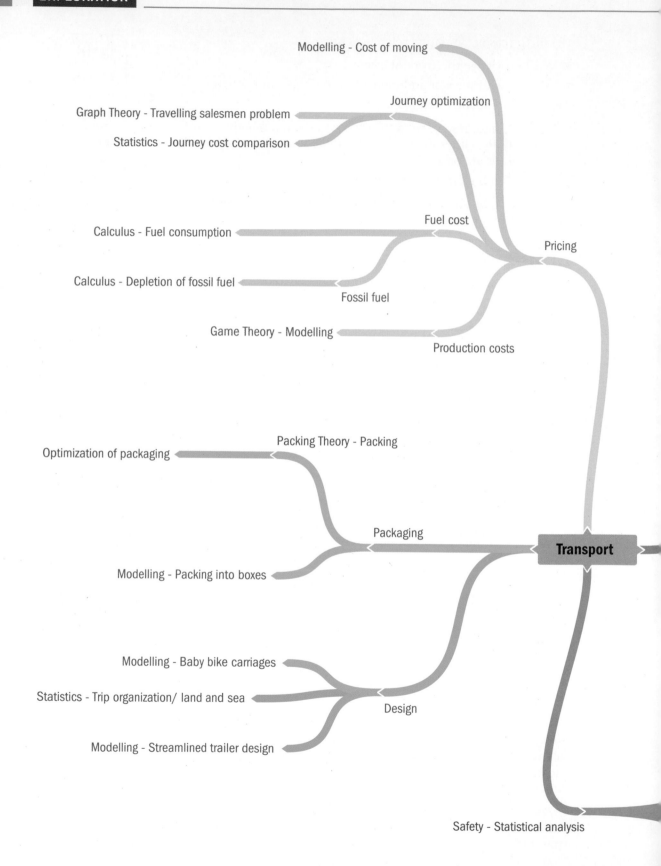

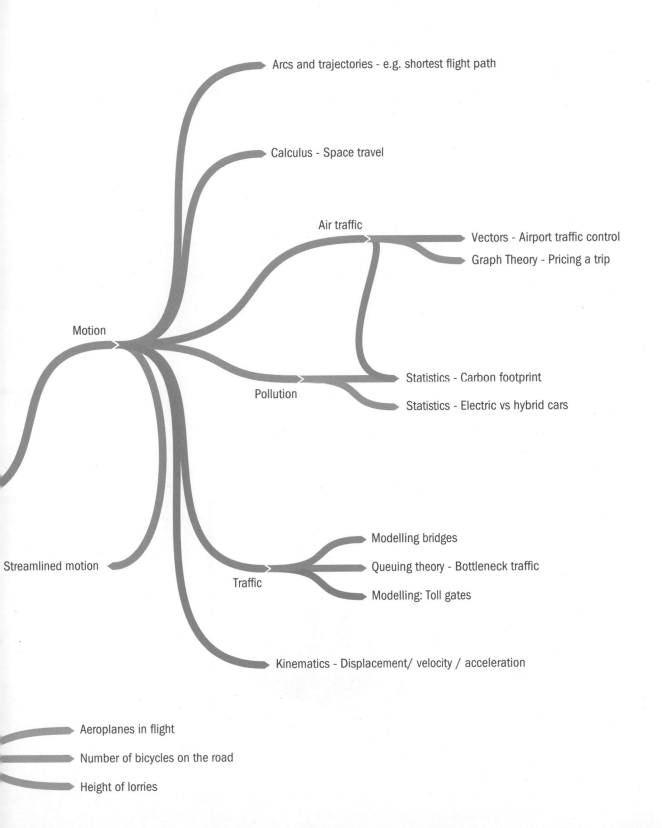

Arcs and trajectories - e.g. shortest flight path

Calculus - Space travel

Air traffic

Vectors - Airport traffic control

Graph Theory - Pricing a trip

Motion

Statistics - Carbon footprint

Pollution

Statistics - Electric vs hybrid cars

Streamlined motion

Modelling bridges

Queuing theory - Bottleneck traffic

Traffic

Modelling: Toll gates

Kinematics - Displacement/ velocity / acceleration

Aeroplanes in flight

Number of bicycles on the road

Height of lorries

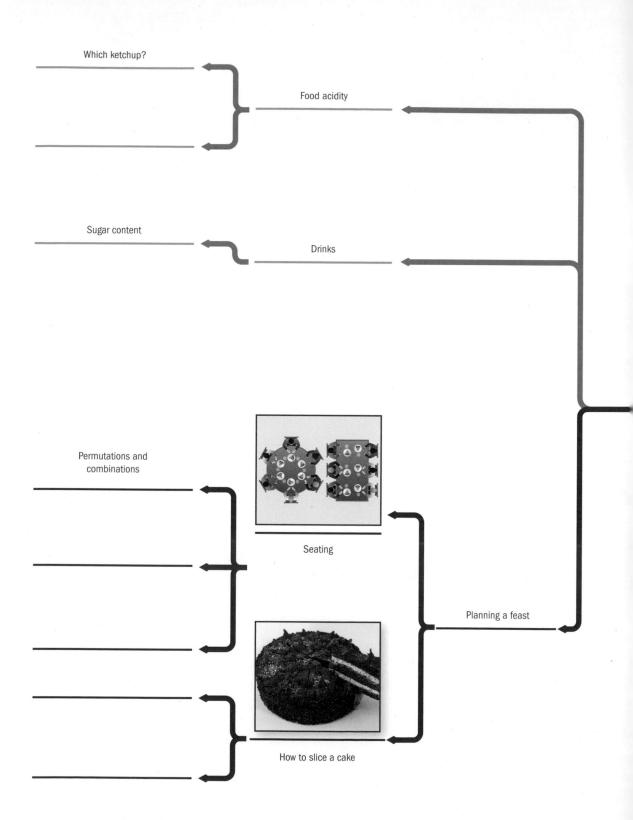

Which ketchup?

Food acidity

Sugar content

Drinks

Permutations and combinations

Seating

Planning a feast

How to slice a cake

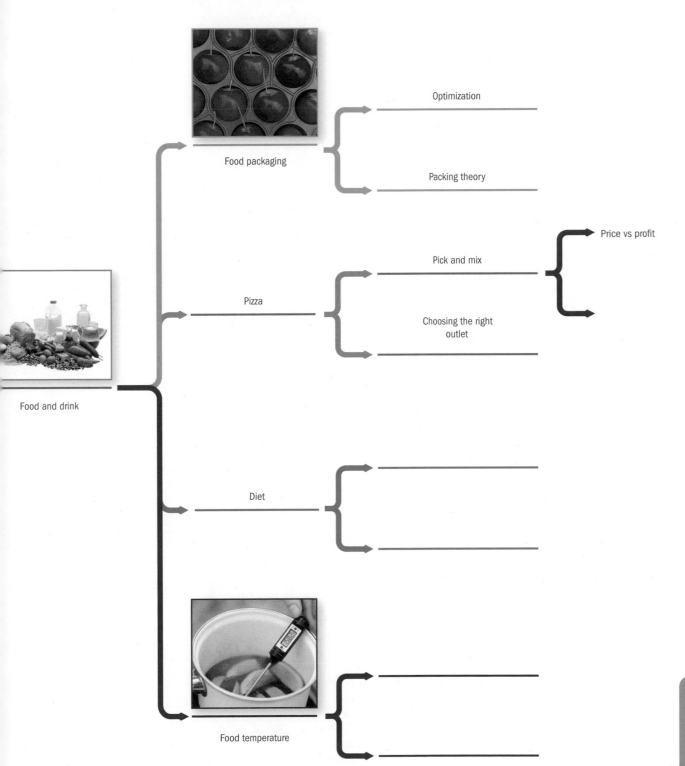

Food packaging

Optimization

Packing theory

Price vs profit

Pick and mix

Pizza

Choosing the right outlet

Food and drink

Diet

Food temperature

Research

Once you have chosen a topic, you will need to do some research. The purpose of this research is to help you determine how suitable your topic is.

- Don't rely on the Internet for all your research—you should also make use of books and academic publications.
- Plan your time wisely—make sure that you are organized.
- Don't put it off—start your research in good time.
- For Internet research: refine your topic so you know exactly what information you are looking for, and use multiple-word searches. It is very easy to spend hours on the Internet without finding any relevant information.
- Make sure that you keep a record of all the websites you use—this saves so much time afterwards. You will need to cite them as sources, and to include them in your bibliography.
- Make sure that the sources are reliable—who wrote the article? Are they qualified? Is the information accurate? Check the information against another source.
- Research in your own language if you find this easier.

These questions will help you to decide whether the topic you have chosen is suitable.

- What areas of mathematics are contained in the topic?
- Which of these areas are contained in the syllabus that you are following?
- Which of these areas are not in the syllabus that you are following but are contained in the other IB mathematics course?
- Which of these areas are in none of the IB mathematics courses? How accessible is this mathematics to you?
- Would you be able to understand the mathematics and write an exploration in such a way that a peer is able to understand it all?
- How can you demonstrate personal engagement in your topic?
- Will you manage to complete an exploration on this topic and meet all the top criterion descriptors within the recommended length of 12 to 20 pages (double spaced and font size 12)?

Writing an outline

Once you think you have a workable topic, write a brief outline including:

- Why you chose this topic.
- How your topic relates to mathematics.
- The mathematical areas in your topic, for example, algebra, geometry, calculus, etc.
- The key mathematical concepts covered in your topic, for example, modelling data, areas of irregular shapes, analysing data, etc.
- The mathematical skills you will use in the exploration, for example, integration by parts, working with complex numbers, using polar coordinates, etc.
- Any mathematics outside the syllabus that you need to learn.
- Technology you could use to develop your exploration.
- New key terms that you will need to define or explain.
- How you are going to demonstrate personal engagement.
- A list of any resources you have/ will use in the development of your exploration. If this list includes websites you should include the URL and the date when this was accessed.

Share this outline with your teacher and with your peers. They may ask questions that lead you to improve your outline.

IA tip

Try to avoid writing a research report in which you merely explain a well-known result that can easily be found online or in textbooks. Such explorations have little scope for meaningful and critical reflection and it may be difficult to demonstrate personal engagement

IA tip

Learning new mathematics is not enough to reach the top levels in Criterion C: Personal engagement.

IA tip

Popular topics such as the Monty Hall problem, the Birthday paradox, and so on are not likely to score well on all the criteria.

This template may help you write the outline for the exploration when presenting a formal proposal to your teacher.

Mathematics exploration outline

Topic:
Exploration title:
Exploration aim:
Exploration outline:
Resources used:
Personal engagement:

IA tip

As you write your exploration, remember to refer to the criteria below.

Writing your exploration

Now you should be ready to start writing your exploration in detail.

You could ask one of your classmates to read the exploration and give you feedback before you submit the draft to your teacher. If your exploration is related to another discipline, for example, Economics, it would be better if the peer reading your exploration is someone who does not study economics.

IA tip

Remember that your peers should be able to read and understand your work.

Mathematical exploration checklist

Work through this checklist to confirm that you have done everything that you can to make your exploration successful.

- ☐ Does your exploration have a title?
- ☐ Have you given a rationale for your choice of exploration?
- ☐ Have you ensured your exploration does not include any identifying features—for example, your name, candidate number, school name?
- ☐ Does your exploration start with an introduction?
- ☐ Have you clearly stated your aim?
- ☐ Does your exploration answer the stated aim?
- ☐ Have you used double line spacing and 12-point font?
- ☐ Is your exploration 12–20 pages long?
- ☐ Have you cut out anything that is irrelevant to your exploration?
- ☐ Have you checked that you have not repeated lots of calculations?
- ☐ Have you checked that tables only contain relevant information and are not too long?
- ☐ Is your exploration easy for a peer to read and understand?
- ☐ Is your exploration logically organized?
- ☐ Are all your graphs, tables and diagrams correctly labelled and titled?
- ☐ Are any graphs, tables and diagrams placed appropriately and not all attached at the end?
- ☐ Have you used appropriate mathematical language and representation (not computer notation, eg *, ^, etc.)?

- ☐ Have you used notation consistently through your exploration?
- ☐ Have you defined key terms (mathematical and subject specific) where necessary?
- ☐ Have you used appropriate technology?
- ☐ Have you used an appropriate degree of accuracy for your topic/exploration?
- ☐ Have you shown interest in the topic?
- ☐ Have you used original analysis for your exploration (eg simulation, modelling, surveys, experiments)?
- ☐ Have you expressed the mathematical ideas in your exploration in your own way (not just copy-and-pasted someone else's)?
- ☐ Does your exploration have a conclusion that refers back to the introduction and the aim?
- ☐ Do you discuss the implications and significance of your results?
- ☐ Do you state any possible limitations and/or extensions?
- ☐ Do you critically reflect on the processes you have used?
- ☐ Have you explored mathematics that is commensurate with the level of the course?
- ☐ Have you checked that your results are correct?
- ☐ Have you clearly demonstrated understanding of why you have used the mathematical processes you have used?
- ☐ Have you acknowledged direct quotes appropriately?
- ☐ Have you cited all references in a bibliography?
- ☐ Do you have an appendix if one is needed?

Paper 1

Time allowed: 2 hours

Answer all the questions.

All numerical answers must be given exactly or correct to three significant figures, unless otherwise stated in the question.

Answers should be supported by working and/or explanations. Where an answer is incorrect, some marks may be awarded for a correct method, provided this is shown clearly.

You need a graphic display calculator for this paper.

Short questions

1 A window-screen wiper blade on a car is of length 0.5 m. In its motion, it moves through an angle of $\frac{3\pi}{2}$ and back again.

   a Find the area of the window-screen that is wiped by the blade.   [2 marks]

   b There is an insect stuck on the blade at the far end. Find the distance that the insect travels as the blade moves through the angle of $\frac{3\pi}{2}$.   [2 marks]

     [Total 4 marks]

2 An explorer travels 5 km due South. He then travels 6 km on a bearing of 100°. He then wishes to go straight back to where he started from.

   a Calculate the distance he will have to travel.   [2 marks]

   b Find the bearing that he will have to travel on to return back to his starting point.   [4 marks]

     [Total 6 marks]

3 [Maximum marks: 6]

   Consider the relation $C = C(A)$ between the circumference of a circle C and its area A defined for $A \geq 0$.

   a Justify that

     i $C = C(A)$ is a function

     ii C has an inverse function C^{-1}.   [2 marks]

   b Sketch the graphs of $C(A)$ and $C^{-1}(A)$ on the same axes.   [2 marks]

   c Hence, find the area of a circle with circumference 25.   [2 marks]

4 [Maximum marks: 6]

A cup of hot chocolate is left on a counter for several hours. Initially its temperature was 86°C. After 30 minutes the temperature had already dropped to 28°C.

The temperature, $T\,°C$, of the hot chocolate is modelled by the function $T(t) = 22 + a2^{bt}$, where t is the number of hours that have elapsed since the hot chocolate was first left to stand.

a Find the value of

  i a

  ii b [4 marks]

b Write down the equation of the horizontal asymptote of the graph of T. [1 mark]

c State the meaning of the asymptote found in (b). [1 mark]

5 [Maximum marks: 5]

Kathy is collecting information for a statistics project. She asks a group of students that have pet dogs about the number of times that usually they walk the dog per day.

The data collected is shown in the following table.

Number of walks	1	2	3	4	5
Number of students	4	8	10	5	1

a State, with a reason, whether 'number of walks' is a discrete or continuous variable. [2 marks]

b For the students that Kathy surveyed, find

  a the modal number of dog walks per day [1 mark]

  b the mean number of dog walks per day. [2 marks]

6 [Maximum marks: 6]

Jasmine plays a computer game. In the game, she collects tokens of different colours. Each colour token gives the player a different number of points.

Jasmine records the relative frequencies of obtaining tokens of each colour. She uses this to estimate the probability of obtaining a token of a certain colour.

Colour	Red	Blue	Green	Yellow	Pink	Orange
Points	2	3	5	1	3	4
Estimate of probability	$\dfrac{1}{9}$	$\dfrac{1}{6}$	$\dfrac{1}{12}$	$\dfrac{2}{9}$	$\dfrac{1}{6}$	p

a Find the value of p. [2 marks]

b Find the expected score if Jasmine plays the game once. [2 marks]

Jasmine plays the game 2 times and adds the points together.

c Find the probability that Jasmine scores a total of 4 points. [2 marks]

7 [Maximum marks: 5]

Jeanny has 6 coloured pencils and 8 coloured pens in her colouring box. Every afternoon from Monday through to Friday, Jeanny returns from Kindergarten and picks a pen or pencil at random from this box. She then begins to draw with the object she picked.

a State the probability that, on any one day, Jeanny picks a pen. [1 mark]

b Find the probability that, in one week (Monday through to Friday), Jeanny picks a pen on

  i exactly two days. [2 marks]

  ii at least two days [2 marks]

8 [Maximum marks: 8]

Points A(2, 9), B(2, 3), C(8, 4), D(8, 7) and E(4, 6) represent wells in the Savannah National Park. These wells are shown in the coordinate axes below.

Horizontal scale: 1 unit represents 1 km.

Vertical scale: 1 unit represents 1 km.

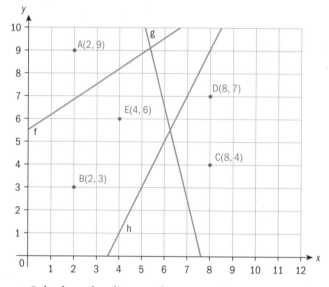

a Calculate the distance between the wells A and E. [2 marks]

Pablo, the Park Ranger draws three lines, f, g and h, around point E and obtains an incomplete Voronoi diagram around the point E.

b Find the equation of the line which would complete the Voronoi cell around point E. Give your answer in the form $ax + by + d = 0$ where $a, b, d \in \mathbb{Z}$. [5 marks]

c In the context of the question, explain the significance of the cell around point E. [1 mark]

9 In this question give all monetary answers to 2 decimal places.

Sarah borrows £10 000 from a bank that charges 4% compound interest per year.

  a If Sarah makes no repayments, calculate how much she will owe at the end of 5 complete years. [2 marks]

In the year in which the debt becomes more than £15 000, Sarah will pay the whole loan off with one repayment at the end of that complete year.

  b Calculate how many complete years it will take before Sarah pays the loan off.

  c Calculate how much Sarah has to pay back to the bank. [3 marks]

[Total 5 marks]

10 The random variable, X, represents the number of emails that Katherine receieves during a day. X satisfies a Poisson distribution with a mean of 30.

  a Find the probability that, on a particular day, she will receive less than 20 emails. [2 marks]

  b Find the probability that, on a particular day, she will receive more than 35 emails. [2 marks]

  c Find the probability that she will receive 200 emails or less in a 7-day week. [2 marks]

The number, R, of emails that Jane receives during a day satisfies a Poisson distribution with a mean of 20.

  d Find the probability that, on a particular day, the total number of emails received by both Katherine and Jane together is 50 or less. [2 marks]

[Total 8 marks]

11 The height of Gerry the giraffe is given by the equation $h(t) = \dfrac{6}{1 + 2e^{-0.4t}}$,

where h is measured in metres and t is the time in years since his birth.

  a Find Gerry's height when he was born. [2 marks]

  b State the height that Gerry approaches as he becomes incredibly old. [2 marks]

  c Find Gerry's height on his 4th birthday. [2 marks]

  d On Gerry's nth birthday, he is taller than 5 m for the first time on a birthday. Find the value of n. [2 marks]

[Total 8 marks]

12 The number of bacteria, n, in a jug of fruit juice can be modelled by $n = 10e^{\frac{t}{2}}$, where t is time measured in hours.

  a Write down the number of bacteria present initially. [1 mark]

  b Calculate the number of bacteria present after 6 hours. [2 marks]

If the number of bacteria exceeds 1000 the juice is no longer safe to drink.

c Calculate how long it takes before the juice is no longer safe to drink. Give your answer in hours and minutes correct to the nearest minute. [3 marks]

d Describe two limitations to this model. [2 marks]

[Total 8 marks]

13 The height above the ground, h cm, of the valve on a mountain bike wheel as the bike is being cycled is given by $h(t) = 35\sin(2\pi t) + 40$, where t is time measured in seconds.

a Write down the initial height of the valve. [1 mark]

b Find how long it takes for the wheel to make one complete revolution. [2 marks]

c State

i the maximum height that the valve reaches

ii the minimum height that the valve reaches. [2 marks]

d Find the height of the valve after 0.3 s. [1 mark]

e In the first second, calculate how long the valve is more than 60 cm above the ground. [3 marks]

[Total 9 marks]

14 The pressure P (measured in Pascals) and the volume V (measured in cm³) of a gas satisfy the differential equation $\dfrac{dP}{dV} = -\dfrac{P}{V}$.

a Solve the differential equation, simplifying the answer, given that if the pressure is 1000 Pascals then the volume is 200 cm³. [6 marks]

b Find the pressure required to compress the gas to a volume of 150 cm³. [2 marks]

[Total 8 marks]

15 Melchester Rovers football club have such an attacking style of play that they either win a match or lose it, but never draw. If they win a match, their confidence increases and the probability that they win their next match is 0.9. If they lose a match then their confidence decreases and the probability that they win their next match is only 0.3. Let $v_n = \begin{pmatrix} p_n \\ 1 - p_n \end{pmatrix}$ where p_n is the probability that they win their nth match.

a Find M, where M is the transition matrix definded by $v_{n+1} = Mv_n$. [2 marks]

b Sketch a labelled directed graph that represents the situation. [2 marks]

c As n tends to infinity v_n tends to a steady state of $V = \begin{pmatrix} r \\ 1 - r \end{pmatrix}$.

By solving a linear equation find r and V. [4 marks]

[Total 8 marks]

16 It is known that the IQs of "Grandmaster" chess players are normally distributed, with population mean of μ.

A sample of the IQs of ten Grandmasters were tested at a tournament. The sample mean $\bar{x}$ was 115 and the sample standard deviation s_n was 4.

  a Find the 90% confidence interval for μ, giving your answer to one decimal place. [3 marks]

  b State, with a reason, which distribution should have been used. [2 marks]

  [Total 5 marks]

17 The mass, m kg, of a swan is proportional to w^3, where w is its wingspan in metres.

  a State which of the following graphs would generate a straight line.

   i m plotted against w

   ii $\log m$ plotted against $\log w$

   iii $\log m$ plotted against w

   iv m plotted against $\log w$. [2 marks]

  b Justify your answer in (a), and state the gradient of whichever graphs generate a straight line. [3 marks]

  [Total 5 marks]

Paper 2

Time allowed: 2 hours

Answer all the questions.

All numerical answers must be given exactly or correct to three significant figures, unless otherwise stated in the question.

Answers should be supported by working and/or explanations. Where an answer is incorrect, some marks may be awarded for a correct method, provided this is shown clearly.

You need a graphic display calculator for this paper.

1 [Maximum mark: 19]

A company manufactures pencils. Before being sharpened, each pencil can be modelled by a cylinder of length 19.5 cm and diameter 6 mm.

The pencils are packaged in small, closed rectangular boxes. Each box is 19.7 cm long, 6.2 cm wide and 3.2 cm high. One pencil box is shown in the diagram below.

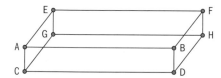

a Calculate

   i the surface area of the box in cm²

   ii the volume of the box in cm³. [3 marks]

b Determine the maximum number N of pencils that will fit in a single box. You must cleary justify your answer. [2 marks]

c Hence, calculate total volume occupied by the N pencils, and express it as a percentage of the volume of the box. [4 marks]

Each month, the company sells x thousand boxes of pencils.

It is known that $\dfrac{\mathrm{d}P}{\mathrm{d}x} = -x + 1200$, where P is the weekly profit (in euros) from the sale of x thousand boxes

d Find the number of boxes that should be sold each week to maximize the profit. [2 marks]

The profit from the sale of 3000 boxes is €1500.

e Find $P(x)$. [5 marks]

f Find the least number of boxes which must be sold each month in order to make a profit. [3 marks]

[Total marks 19]

2 The time, T, that competitors take to complete a 10 000 m race is normally distributed with mean $\mu = 50$ minutes and standard deviation $\sigma = 5$ minutes.

a Sketch a diagram to represent this information with the numbers 50 and 5 indicated on it. [3 marks]

b Find the probability that a random competitor takes between 45 and 55 minutes. [2 marks]

c Find the probability that a random competitor takes less than 40 minutes to complete the race. [2 marks]

d The fastest 75% of competitors receive a medal. Find the time that the race has to be completed under, in order for a competitor to receive a medal. [2 marks]

e Given that a competitor received a medal, find the probability that they finished the race in less than 40 minutes. [3 marks]

f If 10 000 competitors ran the race, estimate (to the nearest minute) how many competitors completed the race in less than 33 minutes. [2 marks]

[Total marks 14]

3 Eleven students, $A-K$, revised for and then took a maths exam. Let h represent the number of hours that each student spent revising, and let s represent the score (out of 100) that they gained. The data for each student is shown in the following table.

	A	B	C	D	E	F	G	H	I	J	K
h	10	9.5	9	8.5	8	7.5	7	6.5	6	5	0
s	100	91	93	90	80	85	79	70	69	60	65

a Identify any outliers in the values of h. Justify your answers. [4 marks]

b Calculate the Pearson product moment correlation coefficient, r, for this bivariate data. [2 marks]

c Write down the equation of the line of best fit of s on h. [2 marks]

d Hence estimate the score, to the nearest integer, of a twelfth student who spent 5.5 hours revising. [2 marks]

e Rank the students from 1 – 11 according to the number of hours they spent revising, h. Rank 1 should represent the most hours spent revising.

In a similar way, rank the students according to the test score, s, they obtained. Rank 1 should represent the highest test score.

Copy and complete the table below to show the rankings for each student.

	A	B	C	D	E	F	G	H	I	J	K
Hour rank	1	2	3								
Score rank	1	3	2								

[2 marks]

f Calculate the Spearman rank correlation coefficient, r_s, for this
data. [2 marks]

g Explain why $r_s > r$. [1 mark]

[Total marks 15]

4 [Maximum mark: 15]

The following graph shows the temperature in Algarve on a particular
day in winter.

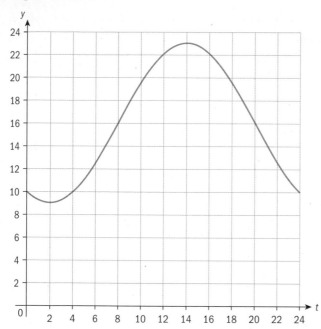

The temperature, y degrees Celsius, can be modelled by the curve
$y = a \sin(b(t - c)) + d$, $a, b, c, d \in \mathbb{R}^+$, for $0 \le t \le 24$ where t is the time in
hours after midnight. The maximum temperature of 23°C was
recorded at $t = 14$ hours, and the minimum temperature of 9°C was
recorded at $t = 2$ hours.

a Show that $a = -7$. [2 marks]

b Find the value of

   i b **ii** c **iii** d. [6 marks]

Using the temperature records for the in Algarve in August, it was
found that the temperature on a particular day in summer could be
modelled by the curve $y = -6 \sin(0.262(t + 1)) + 25$, for $0 \le t \le 24$
where t is the number of hours after midnight.

c In hours and minutes after midnight (correct to the nearest minute), find

   i the value of t when the temperature reaches its minimum

   ii the value of t when the temperature first drops below 21°C

   iii the length of time the temperature is below 21°C. [7 marks]

5 [Maximum mark: 12]

An drone's position is given by the coordinates (x, y, z), where x and y are the drone's displacement north and east of its lauching point at a deserted beach, and z is the height of the drone. All displacements are given in metres.

The drone travels with constant velocity $\begin{pmatrix} -5 \\ -10 \\ -1 \end{pmatrix}$ m s^{-1} and, at 1p.m.,

it is detected at a position 150 m north and 100 m east of the launching point, and at a height of 50 m. Let t be the time, in hours, after 1pm.

a Write down the equation for the position of the drone, relative to the launching point, at time t. [2 marks]

b Verify that if the drone continues to fly with constant velocity it will pass directly over a dog located at a point P, 100 m due north from the lauching point. State the height of the drone as it passes over point P, and the time at which it occurs. [4 marks]

At this moment, the drone's pilot adjusts the angle of descent so that the drone will travel in a straight line at a constant velocity and land at the point $(0,0,0)$ in 5 seconds.

c **i** Find the distance the drone has to travel from P its landing point.

   ii Determine the magnitude of the new velocity vector.

   iii Hence write down an equation for the new velocity vector of the drone. [6 marks]

6 [Maximum mark: 19]

Scientists have been collecting data about the migration habits of a particular species of birds. Annual censuses were conducted in two different regions, A and B, which are inhabited by these birds.

A steady pattern of of change has been observed in their movements: each year 40% of the birds move from location A to location B and 20% of the birds move from location B to location A.

Assume that there are no birds going to, or arriving from, any other locations.

a Write down a transition matrix **T** representing the movements of the birds between the two regions in a particular year. [2 marks]

b Find

   i the eigenvalues for the transition matrix **T**

   ii the eigenvectors for the transition matrix **T**. [6 marks]

c Hence find matrices **M** and **D** such that $\mathbf{T} = \mathbf{MDM}^{-1}$. [4 marks]

Initially location A had 4200 and location B had 6000 of these birds.

d Find an expression for the number of birds at

   i location A

   ii location B after n years. [4 marks]

e Hence write down the long-term number of birds that each location is expected to have. [1 mark]

f State two limitations of the model. [2 marks]

7 [Maximum mark: 16]

A law of cooling states that $\dfrac{dB}{dt} = -k\left(B^4 - R^4\right)$ where B is the temperature of a body and R the temperature of the room. In the model, B and R are measured in °C, t is the time in hours, and k is a constant.

Assume that the room temperature R is constant.

a Show that $\ln\dfrac{B+R}{B-R} + 2\arctan\dfrac{B}{R} - 4R^3kt = c$ is an implicit solution to the differential equation. [6 marks]

Consider the solution to the differential equation $\dfrac{dB}{dt} = -k\left(B^4 - R^4\right)$ that contains the point (0, 35) when $k = 0.00005$ and $R = 20$.

b i Use Euler's method with step $h = 0.1$ to approximate $B(0.5)$.

ii Find an implicit solution to the differential equation. [10 marks]

Paper 3

Answer all the questions.

All numerical answers must be given exactly or correct to three significant figures, unless otherwise stated in the question.

Answers should be supported by working and/or explanations. Where an answer is incorrect, some marks may be awarded for a correct method, provided this is shown clearly.

You need a graphic display calculator for this paper.

1 a For the following graphs, state the number of edges and the degree of each vertex. For (i), (ii) and (iii) give the degree of each vertex in a table of the form

vertex	a	b
Degree		

i

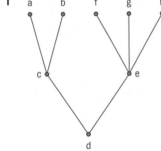

ii

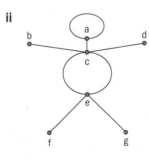

iii

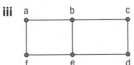

iv The complete graph K_n.

[8 marks]

761

b The Handshaking Lemma states that for any graph the sum of the degrees of the vertices is equal to twice the number of edges.

  i Verify that this rule is true for each of the four examples in (a).

  ii Explain why this rule must be true for any graph. [5 marks]

b A graph is called *planar* if it can be drawn on paper in 2-dimensions without any of the edges crossing (the edges can only touch at a vertex). Graphs (a) (i), (ii) and (iii) are all planar.

  i Draw K_3, the complete graph with 3 vertices, to show that it is planar.

  ii Draw K_4, the complete graph with 4 vertices, to show that it is planar.

The complete graph with 4 vertices models 4 houses with a cycle track from each house to every other house, where the cycle tracks do not cross (to avoid collisions). We will now consider the same problem with 5 houses. We want to find out if K_5 is planar.

A result has been proved that states that if a graph is planar, simple, and connected, then $e \leq 3v - 6$, for $v \geq 3$, where e is the number of edges and v is the number of vertices.

  iii Use this result to prove, by contradiction, that K_5 is not planar. [8 marks]

d Two newly built houses have to be connected to each of the utility services Gas, Water and Electricity. The houses are represented by vertices A and B, and the utility services by G, W and E. The connecting pipes will be represented by edges. The construction firm do not want any of the pipes to cross over each other.

  i Draw a graph of this situation that shows that the graph can be drawn in a planar fashion.

We will now consider the same situation but with three houses represented by A, B and C, each of which must be connected to Gas, Water and Electricity.

  ii Draw a graph of this situation, but do not attempt to draw it in a planar fashion.

  iii State how many vertices and edges this graph has.

Another result has been proved that states that if a graph is planar, simple and connected, and also contains no triangles (i.e. does not have K_3 as a subgraph), then $e \leq 2v - 4$, for $v \geq 3$, where e is the number of edges and v is the number of vertices.

  iv Use this result to prove, by contradiction, that the graph in (ii) cannot be planar. [9 marks]

[Total 30 marks]

2 In this question, you will perform various tests to determine what type of distribution certain random variables best fit.

100 observations of a discrete random variable X are taken and are displayed in the table below.

x	≤ 1	2	3	4	5	6	≥ 7
Observed frequency	8	16	18	20	17	12	8

a We will first test if this data fits the binomial $B(40, 0.1)$ distribution.

 i Write down the mean of the $B(40, 0.1)$ distribution.

100 values of a variable which fits a $B(40, 0.1)$ distribution are measured.

 ii Copy and complete the table below to show the expected frequencies when 100 values of a variable which fits the $B(40, 0.1)$ distribution are measured.

x	≤ 1	2	3	4	5	6	≥ 7
Expected frequency							

 iii Perform a χ^2 goodness of fit test at the 10% level to test the null hypothesis H_0: This data fits the $B(40, 0.1)$ distribution.

State the number of degrees of freedom, the p-value and the conclusion of the test. [8 marks]

b We will now test if this data fits the Poisson $Po(4)$ distribution.

 i Construct a table similar to that in part a (ii) to show the expected frequencies when 100 values of a variable which fits the $Po(4)$ distribution are measured.

 ii Perform a χ^2 goodness of fit test at the 10% level to test the null hypothesis H_0: This data fits the $Po(4)$ distribution.

State the number of degrees of freedom, the p-value and the conclusion of the test. [7 marks]

c Copy and complete the following conjecture by filling in the gaps.

For n large and p ____, the binomial distribution can be approximated by the _____ distribution with the same _____. [1 mark]

Another 100 observations of a different discrete random variable Y are measured and displayed in the table below.

y	$y < 15.5$	$15.5 < y < 18.5$	$18.5 < y < 21.5$	$21.5 < y < 24.5$	$24.5 < y$
Observed frequency	8	23	34	28	7

d We will first test if this data fits the binomial $B(40, 0.5)$ distribution.

 i Write down the mean and the variance of the $B(40, 0.5)$ distribution.

 ii If $Y \sim B(40, 0.5)$, calculate $P(Y = 22, 23 \text{ or } 24)$.

 iii Copy and complete the table below to show the expected frequencies when 100 values of a variable which fits the binomial distribution $B(40, 0.5)$ are measured.

y	$y < 15.5$	$15.5 < y < 18.5$	$18.5 < y < 21.5$	$21.5 < y < 24.5$	$24.5 < y$
Expected frequency	7.69	24.1	36.4		

iv Perform a χ^2 goodness of fit test at the 10% level to test the null hypothesis H_0: This new data fits the $B(40, 0.5)$ distribution.

State the number of degrees of freedom, the p-value and the conclusion of the test.

[7 marks]

e You will now test if this data fits the normal distribution $N(20, 10)$.

i If $Y \sim N(20, 10)$, calculate $P(21.5 < Y < 24.5)$.

ii Hence, Copy and complete the table below to show the expected frequencies when 100 values of a variable which fits the normal distribution $N(20, 10)$ are measured.

y	$y < 15.5$	$15.5 < y < 18.5$	$18.5 < y < 21.5$	$21.5 < y < 24.5$	$24.5 < y$
Expected frequency	7.73	24.1	36.5		

iii Perform a χ^2 goodness of fit test at the 10% level to test the null hypothesis H_0: This new data fits the $N(20, 10)$ distribution.

State the number of degrees of freedom, the p-value and the conclusion of the test.

[6 marks]

f Copy and complete the following conjecture by filling in the gaps.

For n _____ and p not close to 1 or 0, the binomial distribution can be approximated by the _____ distribution with the same _____ and _____, even though the binomial is a discrete distribution and the _____ is a _____ distribution.

[1 mark]

[Total 30 marks]

Answers Ⓢ

Chapter 1

Skills check

1 a i 0.69 **ii** 28.71
iii 77.98
b i 0.694 **ii** 28.7
iii 78.0

2 a $2^{-3} = \dfrac{1}{8}$ **b** $27^{\frac{1}{3}} = 3$

3 a $x^2 = 9^2 + 13^2 = 250, x = 5\sqrt{10}$
b $7^2 = x^2 + 5^2, x^2 = 24, x = 2\sqrt{6}$

Exercise 1A

1 i 7.3 m (accuracy of the least
accurate measurement)
ii 7.27 m

2 79 cm (to 2 s.f.)

Exercise 1B

1 a 23.5–24.5 mm
b 3.25–3.25 m
c 1.745–1.755 kg
d 1.395–1.405 g

2 a 0.09%
b 8847.5–8848.5 m

3 a 0.44 (2 s.f.)
b 2.7% (2 s.f.)
c Uncertainty much larger for
the measurements done by
group 1.

4 66×10^9 km (2 s.f.)

5 Max 0.35 min, 0.30

6 a Actual 10°C, approx 9°C
b 10%

7 a 7.20 m $\le r <$ 7.21 m (3 s.f.)
b 0.005 m

Exercise 1C

1 a i 9×10^4 **ii** 9.936×10
b i 10^{11} **ii** 5.068×10^{11}

2 a 9.4×10^{-5}
b 8.35×10^3
c 5.24×10^{-19}
d 3.87×10^{-7}

3 a i $\dfrac{15}{x^{\frac{1}{2}}}$ **ii** $15 \cdot x^{-\frac{1}{2}}$

b i 7^1 **ii** $1 \cdot 7^1$

c i $\dfrac{1}{2^{3+3t}}$
ii 2^{-3-3t}

d i $\dfrac{25}{3^{2x}}$ **ii** $25 \cdot 3^{-2x}$

4 a 240, 339, 480
b Rate of growth is
increasing. When $t = \dfrac{3}{2}$,
we have the number of
bacteria after one and a half
hours.

5 a $\dfrac{1600}{2^{\frac{t}{8}}}$ **b** 1100

6 0.24 mm

7 18.1

8 2×10^{-3}

Exercise 1D

1 a $\theta = 28.8°$, $v = 8$ cm, $w = 4$ cm
b $\theta = 56°$, $y = 18.2$ cm,
$x = 6.88$ cm
c $z = 5.7$ cm, $\alpha = 56°$, $\beta = 34°$

2 i 7.36 m
ii 4.25 m
iii 6.96 m

3 a

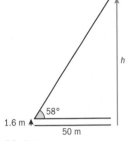

b 81.6 m

4 a

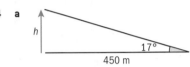

b 138 m

5 1.62 m

6 1300 m

7 45 km

8 a 1.20 m **b** 2.1%

Exercise 1E

1 a i

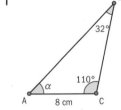

ii 1 possibility as we have all
3 angles and 1 side
iii $\alpha = 47°$, $AB = 14.8$ cm,
$BC = 10.7$ cm

b i

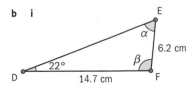

ii 2 possibilities, ambiguous
case of sine rule
iii $\alpha = 62.6°$ $\beta = 95.4°$
$DE = 16.5$ cm or $\alpha = 153°$
$\beta = 5°$ $DE = 1.44$ cm

c i

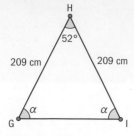

ii 1 possibility – properties of isosceles triangles

iii $\alpha = 64°$ $\beta = 52°$ $HI = 183$ cm

2 374 m

3 $PQ = 59$ m, $QT = 46$ m, $PT = 17$ m

4 381 km bearing 177°

5 382 m

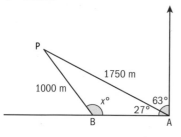

Exercise 1F

1 a 41.0°, 87.0°, 106 mm

b 66°, 17.2 cm, 17.2 cm

c 11.11 cm, 39°, 88°

d $x = 20°$, 16 m, 22 m

2 Kristian's method is correct; cannot use the cosine rule in this case because the angle given is not between the two sides given. Solve $\sin \hat{C} = 40 \times \dfrac{\sin 35°}{25}$,

$\hat{C} = 67°$, $\hat{B} = 78°$, $AC = \dfrac{25}{\sin 35°} \times \sin 78° = 43$ cm

3 32°, 97°, 51°

4 a 82.8°, 6 cm **b** 5 cm²

Exercise 1G

1 a i 6 cm **ii** 15 cm²

b i 3 cm **ii** 6 cm²

c i 23.8 cm **ii** 125 cm²

2 $l = 62.7$ cm

3 a 209 m

b 13 min

c 24 min

4 a 0.96π

b 24 cm

5 a 18 cm²

b 41 cm²

6 1.1 cm²

7 59.9 m²

Exercise 1H

1 a 35 000 cm³

b 1500 cm³

c 3150 cm³ (3 s.f.)

2 a 121 m³ **b** 1.13 m

3 a i 1.4×10^{-29} m³

ii 1.0868×10^{21} m³

iii 8.661×10^{35} m³

b The Earth compared to an atom

4 a 704 000 m³

b 3.15×10^9 kg

5 900 l

Exercise 1I

1 a 150 cm²

b 180 cm²

c 501 mm²

d 32 cm²

2 i 6.46 cm

ii 5.28 cm

iii 38 cm

3 a i $\dfrac{3}{r}$

ii 3.14×10^{-6} m

b i $\dfrac{6}{\left(\dfrac{4}{3}\pi\right)^{\frac{1}{3}} r}$

ii $\dfrac{42}{19} \times \dfrac{1}{\left(\dfrac{4}{19}\pi\right)^{\frac{1}{3}} r}$

iii Cube: 1.24, cylinder: 0.85

4 a 873 m²

b 27 **c** $432

5 19.60 cm²

6 a $V = 1400$ m³, $A = 750$ m² (2 s.f.)

b $V = 280$ cm³, $A = 240$ cm² (2 s.f.)

7 a $V = 396$ m³

b 37 l

8 $V = 213$ cm³, $A = 24$ cm²

Chapter review

1 a i 0.2 **ii** 0.154

b i 2.3 **ii** 2.30

c i 2.0 **ii** 1.99

d i 0.2 **ii** 0.248

e i 0.2 **ii** 0.248

2 a 5.6%

b Not enough time

3 $x = 1.15417$, 1.3×10^{-4}%

4 a Cosine rule gives the relation: $PR^2 - 2PQ \times PR \times \cos 31° + PQ^2 - QR^2 = 0$. Solve the quadratic equation to get $PR = 24.8$ cm.

b First, find the angle R: $\sin R = \dfrac{\sin 31°}{15} \times 13.4, R = 27°$, so $Q = 122°$. Apply the sine rule again to find $PR = \dfrac{15}{\sin 31°} \sin Q = 24.8$ cm.

5 Angle of elevation = 2.7°, angle of depression = 0.77°

6 a 52 670.25 m² ≤ A < 53 130.25 m²

b 6.38 ≤ R < 8.30

7 2.063×10^9 km

8 a Volume of the cone $V_1 = \dfrac{1}{3}\pi r^2 h$, volume of the modified cylinder $V_2 = \pi r^2 h - \dfrac{\alpha}{2} r^2 h$. For volumes to be equal, $\alpha = \dfrac{4}{3}\pi$.

b Lateral area of the modified cylinder is

$$\left(2\pi - \frac{4}{3}\pi + 2\right)rh = \left(\frac{2}{3}\pi + 2\right)rh.$$

Lateral area of the cone is $\dfrac{\pi r h}{\sin\theta}$. For them to be equal,

$$\sin\theta = \frac{\pi}{\left(\frac{2}{3}\pi + 2\right)}, \theta = 50^\circ.$$

9 **a** $BM = \dfrac{1}{2}EF = 115.178\,28$ m,

$VM = 186.472\,85$ m,

$\widehat{M} = 51.853\,975^\circ$,

$\widehat{V} = 38.146025$

b $BF = \sqrt{2}\,BM = 162.886\,68$ m,

$VF = 219.176\,09$ m,

$\widehat{F} = 41.997\,23^\circ$,

$\widehat{V} = 48.002\,77^\circ$.

c $VE = VF = 219.176\,09$ m,

$\widehat{E} = \widehat{F} = 58.297\,71^\circ$,

$\widehat{V} = 63.40458^\circ$,

$A = 21\,477.621$ m^2

d $VB^2 = 21\,506.008$ m^2
so percentage error

$$= \left|\frac{VB^2 - A}{VB^2}\right| \times 100\%$$

$$= 0.132\,365\,34\%.$$

10 **a** $t = \dfrac{\sqrt{5^2 + (12-d)^2}}{70} + \dfrac{d}{110}$

b $t = \dfrac{5}{\cos\theta} \times \dfrac{1}{70} + \dfrac{12 - 5\tan\theta}{110}$

Exam-style questions

11 **a** $\dfrac{5.5}{0.25}$ ohms $\leq R < \dfrac{6.5}{0.15}$ ohms,
22 ohms $\leq R < 43$ ohms

b 43%

12 **a** $12x^4$ **b** x^2 **c** $\dfrac{9y^2}{49x^6}$

13 **a** 1.12×10^{-27}

b $1 : 1840$

c 9.8%

14 675

15 **a** 209 cm^2

b 65.5 cm

16 22.5 cm

17 **a** 34°   **b** 64°

c 112°

d 1400 cm^3

e 840 cm^2

Chapter 2

Skills check

1 Mean = 19.2, median = 19, mode = 22

Exercise 2A

1 Student answers.

2 Use quota sampling; take n students' marks at random, from each of the five year groups

a

x	1	2	3	4	5	6	7	8	9	10	11	12	13	14	15	16
$f(x)$	10	8	16	13	21	9	10	9	5	4	4	3	3	2	1	2

b 24

c

x	1	2	3	4	5	6	7	8	9	10	11	12	13	14	15	16
Sample size	4	3	7	5	9	4	4	4	2	2	2	1	1	1	0	1

3 As different sectors of society are likely to vote differently, it is important to have those sectors represented proportionately. Strata might be income, age, gender, geographical region.

Exercise 2B

1 **a** Mean = 6.068, median = 5.2, mode = 7.5, 17.8 and 25.0 may be outliers

b Mean = 3.533, median = 3.6, mode = 2.5

c Mean = 64.65, median = 62, mode = 62

2 **a** Mean = 1.8, median = 1.5, mode = 6

b SD = 1.89, variance = 3.56

3 **a** Mean = 8.9444, median = 10, mode = 12, most appropriate = mode

b Standard deviation = 4.0958, average distance from mean = 4

c Range = 14, IQR = 6, data is mainly concentrated within middle range as the IQR is a lot smaller than the range.

4 **a** Basketball: mean = 200.8, standard deviation = 10.4575; Men: mean = 172.27, standard deviation = 10.2541

b On average basketball players are taller by approx. 28 cm; however, they vary in height by the same amount.

5

	Mean	Median	s_n	Q_1	Q_3
Boys	76.5	81	12.9	65	84
Girls	69.4	69	7.88	61	77

6 Answers will vary.

7 Mean = 60, standard deviation = 6

8 a Mrs Ginger: mean = 84, standard deviation = 16; Mr Ginger: mean = 80, standard deviation = 20, Miss Ginger: mean = 76, standard deviation = 24

b Matty: Mrs Ginger: 44, Mr Ginger: 30, Miss Ginger: 16

Zoe: Mrs Ginger: 70, Mr Ginger: 62.5, Miss Ginger: 55

Ans: Mrs Ginger: 92, Mr Ginger: 90, Miss Ginger: 88

c For all students, Mrs Ginger's methodology gives them the highest mark. For students with low marks, their marks are always relatively similar, for middling students, their marks can vary a bit, but for low-scoring students, the mark can vary widely. If a student had a mark of 6 or lower, their new mark would be negative with Miss Ginger's methodology.

Exercise 2C

1 a i $150 \leq n < 180$

ii 111.625

iii 119.29

Modal class indicates most common number of cars was between 150 and 180. Median suggests that middle value of number

of cars was 119 and the mean was 111. The mode is most appropriate here.

b i $50 \leq s < 55$

ii 54.4167

iii 53.913

Modal class indicates most common speed of cars was between 50 and 55. Median suggests that middle value of the number of cars was 53 and the mean was 54. All values here are similar; however, the most appropriate is the mean.

c i $7 \leq t < 8$ **ii** 5.8636

iii 5.9286

Mean and median very close, mode is higher (between 7 and 8). Median = best choice.

2 a $30 \leq c < 40$

b Mean = 34, median = £34.2857

c Standard deviation = £10.1158, the average amount of money spent more or less than the average amount was £10.11.

d Variance = 101.329, range = 50, IQR = 11.875; they assume the data is spread evenly within the classes.

3 a $180 \leq x < 190$

b Mean = 180.2, standard deviation = 10.9982, average distance from average height is approx. 11 cm

4 a Males: mean = 2546.3, standard deviation = 729.767 Females: mean = 2114.58, standard deviation = 635.257

b On average, men earned more than women and male income varied more than female income.

Exercise 2D

1

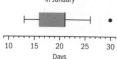

Days of precipitation in London in January

2 a

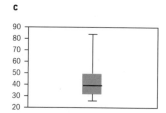

b Mean = 42.45, median = 39.5522, Q1 = 32.1875, Q3 = 49.7917, range = 70, at least 5 outliers, an estimated 7 outliers

c

3 a

Days of Sunshine in Helsinki

b The data is negatively skewed.

4 Students' own answers

Exercise 2E

1 a

Time, x (minutes)	Frequency	Cumulative frequency
$0 \le x < 2$	5	5
$2 \le x < 4$	11	16
$4 \le x < 6$	23	39
$6 \le x < 8$	31	70
$8 \le x < 10$	19	89
$10 \le x < 12$	8	97
$12 \le x < 14$	3	100

b

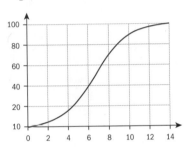

c Median = 6.7, IQR = 3.5

d 3.1

e 6

2 a

Number of words, x	Frequency	Cumulative frequency
$0 \le x < 4$	5	5
$4 \le x < 8$	32	37
$8 \le x < 12$	41	78
$12 \le x < 16$	28	106
$16 \le x < 20$	22	128
$20 \le x < 24$	12	140
$24 \le x < 28$	7	147
$28 \le x < 32$	3	150

b

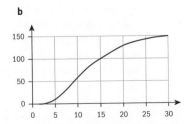

c Median = 11.5, IQR = 9

d There may or may not be outliers

e 22

f (assuming only one outlier):

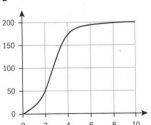

g Adults, because books more linguistically advanced than a children's book

3 a

Height, h (m)	Frequency	Cumulative frequency
$0 \le h < 1$	17	17
$1 \le h < 2$	35	52
$2 \le h < 3$	69	121
$3 \le h < 4$	51	172
$4 \le h < 6$	22	194
$6 \le h < 10$	6	200

b

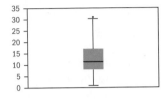

c 2.7 m

d IQR = 1.5

e 1.1 m

f 4.9 m

4

Lengths of Hawkmoth caterpillars

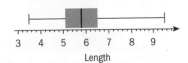

Length

5 a

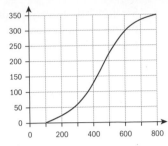

b Median = 450, IQR = 205

c No outliers

d

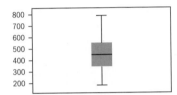

e 90

Exercise 2F

1 a

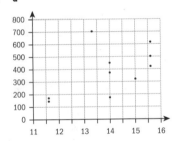

b Weak positive correlation

c A slight increase in price associated with an increase in screen size

2 a

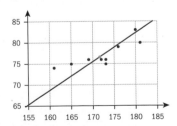

b Red dot in graph above

c See graph

d 75 kg

e $r = 0.9150$

f Strong positive correlation, means the taller the player, the heavier they are on average

g Causation: a taller person has more body mass and so weighs more

3 a

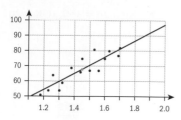

b Red dot in graph above

c See graph above

d 93%, not appropriate to use this as 1.9 is far outside the current data range

e $r = 0.884$

f Strong positive correlation

g Indicates taller people scored better on the vocabulary test – did not necessarily know better vocabulary

4 a

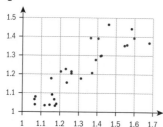

b $r = 0.8873$, strong positive correlation between price of unleaded and price of diesel

Chapter review

1 a Males: mean = 13.32, standard deviation = 3.374 Females: mean = 15.85, standard deviation = 4.228

On average, females are slower than males;

however, time taken varies more for women than men.

b Mean = 14.33, standard deviation = 3.9397

c Answers will vary

d Mean + 15.425, standard deviation = 3.6324

e Take every 2.5th element of the data, i.e. take alternately every 2 and 3 points. Mean = 14.975, standard deviation = 4.1018

f Answers will vary. Random sample of 24 males and 16 females: mean = 14.3, standard deviation = 4.1845; random sample: mean is larger and the standard deviation is smaller than that of the whole population; systematic sample: mean and standard deviation are larger than that of the whole population; stratified sample: mean is the same and the standard deviation is larger than that of the whole population.

2 b Mean   **c** Mode

d Mode

3 a $50 \leq l < 60$

b Median = 55, mean = 54.4167, standard deviation = 11.2765

c

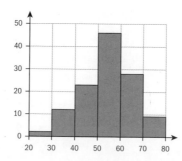

4 a $15\ 700

b $3249.62

c 8.33%

d i Misleading: makes it look like profit was multiple times higher each year

ii To make it seem profits are increasing more than they actually are

5 a Mean = 32.8, standard deviation = 7.5054

b Range = 25, IQR = 22

c 34, no outliers

d

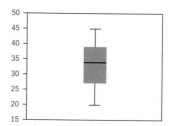

6 a Girls: mean = 16.24, median = 15, $Q_1 = 8$, $Q_3 = 24$, range = 25, no outliers

Boys: mean = 24.48, median = 22, $Q_1 = 15$, $Q_3 = 31$, range = 16, no outliers

b

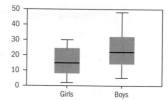

c Boys do more press ups on average and have a larger range, with a longer whisker in the top half of the boys, indicating that the data is more skewed.

7 a

Number of hours, x	Frequency	Cumulative frequency
$0 \leq x < 10$	8	8
$10 \leq x < 20$	16	24
$20 \leq x < 30$	41	65
$30 \leq x < 40$	54	119
$40 \leq x < 50$	36	155
$50 \leq x < 60$	22	177
$60 \leq x < 70$	17	194
$70 \leq x < 80$	6	200

b

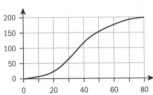

c Median = 36, IQR = 32

d

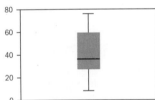

8 a Mean = 6.1326, standard deviation = 0.9213

b

Time (min), x	Frequency	Cumulative frequency
$3.5 \leq x < 4$	6	6
$4 \leq x < 4.5$	14	20
$4.5 \leq x < 5$	48	68
$5 \leq x < 5.5$	89	157
$5.5 \leq x < 6$	121	278
$6 \leq x < 6.5$	129	407
$6.5 \leq x < 7$	103	510
$7 \leq x < 7.5$	70	580
$7.5 \leq x < 8$	30	610
$8 \leq x < 8.5$	10	620
$8.5 \leq x < 9$	2	622

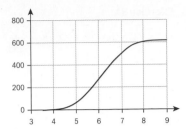

c i 6.1

ii $Q_1 = 5.5$, $Q_3 = 6.75$

iii 1.25 **iv** 7.1

d

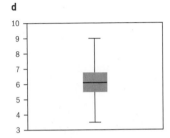

e There may be outliers at both ends of the data.

9 a

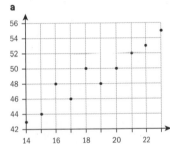

b Strong positive correlation

c It is likely that increasing the temperature increases the number of eggs as there is a strong positive correlation.

10 a

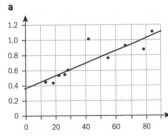

b (42, 1.02)

c (43.333, 0.698)

d See graph above

e $r = 0.9732$

f Very strong positive correlation

Exam-style questions

11 a 16 **b** 13.375

c 13.5 **d** 12

e 23.583

12 a Mean = 23.5833 °C

b Standard deviation = 3.3778 °C

c Mean = 22.8333 °C

d Standard deviation = 5.5202 °C

e The mean temperature in Tenerife (23.58 °C) is higher than that in Malta (22.83 °C) and the temperature in Malta varies more than in Tenerife as the standard deviation is larger (5.5202 °C and 3.3778 °C)

13 a 69 **b** 50 **c** 81

d 170 **e** 180

f

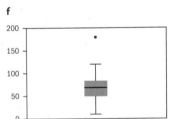

14 a

Height, $(x \text{ cm})$	Frequency
$20 \leq x < 25$	3
$25 \leq x < 30$	3
$30 \leq x < 35$	4
$35 \leq x < 40$	7
$40 \leq x < 45$	4
$45 \leq x < 50$	2
$50 \leq x < 55$	1

b 35.8333 **c** 63.89

d 7.9931

e On average, the plants in Eve's neighbour's garden are 3.73 cm shorter than in Eve's garden, whilst the plants in both gardens vary by a similar amount.

15 a

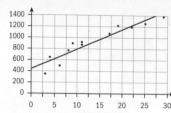

b (13.667, 926.667), line drawn on graph above

c $r = 0.9441$, close to one, indicating a strong positive correlation

d When temperature is higher, sales of ice cream are higher.

16 a 6920 kg

b 430 kg

17 a −0.7659

b

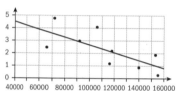

c (106 600, 2.49), it is extrapolating much further than the current data provided, there is no guarantee that the decrease in salary with distance is linear

Chapter 3

Skills check

1 $\sqrt{4^2 + 2^2} = 4.47$

2 $\left(\dfrac{1+5}{2}, \dfrac{2+4}{2}\right) = (3, 3)$

3 a $x = 7.66$, $y = 6.43$

b 33.7°

4 a i 43.3 km **ii** 25 km

b 240°

Exercise 3A

1 a i 5.10 **ii** 2.45

b i (1.5, −1.5)

ii (1, 3.5, −2.5)

2 a i 36.1 **ii** 19.4

b i (9, 0.5)

ii (−9.5, 9.5, −6)

3 a 8.54 km

b Two distances are 33.9 km and 42.2 km, so the tracking station will only be able to detect the first aircraft.

4 a A(250, 0, 0), B(250, 400, 0), C(0, 400, 60), D(0, 0, 60)

b M(125, 400, 30)

c 840 m

5 a 52 900 m² to 3 s.f.

b 2 430 000 m³ to 3 s.f.

c (218.5, −31, 117)

d 213 m

Exercise 3B

1 a $x = 2$ **b** $y = 6$

c (2, 6)

2 a $y = 3x + 5$

b $y = -0.2x + 0.4$

c $y = 4.5x + 5$

d $y = 2x + 1$

3 a $y = -4x + 17$

b $y = 5x - 11$

c $y = \dfrac{1}{3}x + 3$

4 a $y = -2x + 20$

b i (0, 20)

ii (22, −24)

c 49.2 km

Exercise 3C

1 a i $y - 9 = 2(x - 3)$

ii $y = 2x + 3$

iii $y - 2x - 3 = 0$

b i $y - 5 = \dfrac{1}{2}(x - 6)$

ii $y = \dfrac{1}{2}x + 2$

iii $2y - x - 4 = 0$

c i $y + 7 = -\dfrac{1}{3}(x - 6)$

ii $y = -\dfrac{1}{3}x - 5$

iii $3y + x + 15 = 0$

2 a i $y - 5 = 2(x - 2)$

ii $y = 2x + 1$

iii $-2x + y - 1 = 0$

b i $y - 4 = -2x - 0$

ii $y = -2x + 4$

iii $2x + y - 4 = 0$

c i $y - 6 = 3(x - 2)$

ii $y = 3x$

iii $3x + y = 0$

d i $y + 6 = -\dfrac{2}{3}(x + 2)$

ii $y = -\dfrac{2}{3}x - \dfrac{22}{3}$

iii $2x + 3y + 22 = 0$

3 a $\dfrac{2}{3}$ **b** $-\dfrac{4}{7}$ **c** $-\dfrac{a}{b}$

4 a $y = -1.5x + 6.5$

b $2y + 3x - 13 = 0$

c $\dfrac{1}{2} \times 6.5 \times \dfrac{13}{3} \approx 14.1 \text{m}^2$

Exercise 3D

1 a i $x = 7$, $y = 6$

ii $x = 0.5$, $y = 0.2$

iii $x = 3$, $y = 7$

iv $x = 1$, $y = -7$

b i $x = -8$, $y = 3$

ii $x = 2.6$, $y = -1.9$

2 a $\dfrac{1}{2} \times 50 - 100 = -75$

b (340, 70)

c **i** Distance of Alison from intersection is 481 m, distance of Bernard from intersection is 324 m, so Bernard arrives first.

    ii 174 seconds

3 **a** 25%

  b 15% (steeper going down)

  c **i** $y = 0.1x$

    ii $y = -0.15x + 0.3675$

  d 0.147 km or 147 m

  e 2.47 km

4 **a** Construct a right-angled triangle with two points on the line as the ends of the hypotenuse. The tangent of the angle is the opposite over the adjacent side in the triangle which is equivalent to the increase in the y values divided by the increase in the x values.

  b $y = 0.069\,927x + 55.55$

  c 55.55 m   **d** 94.4 m

Exercise 3E

1 **a** $\dfrac{1}{2}$ **b** -3

  c -2 **d** $\dfrac{7}{6}$

2 **a** Show $m_1 m_2 = -1$

  b $2x - y + 1 = 0$

  c $2x + 3y - 27 = 0$

3 **a** Any point away from the perpendicular will form the hypotenuse of triangle with the perpendicular distance as one of the sides which will necessarily be shorter than the hypotenuse.

  b $4x + 3y + 1 = 0$

  c $(-1, 1)$ **d** 10

4 **a** 5.83   **b** 4.43

5 Intersection of $y = 2.5x - 19.25$ and $y = x + 6$, $(16.8, 22.8)$

6 **a** Station should be built at $(11, 21)$

  b $(10, 43)$, 14.1 km

Exercise 3F

1 **a** Perpendicular bisectors are: $x = 2$, $x + 2y = 5.5$, $x - 2y = -1.5$

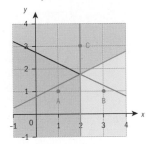

  b

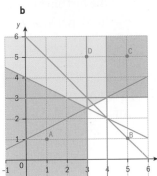

2 **a**

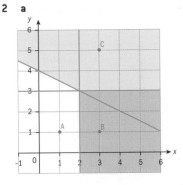

  b 21°C

3 **a** Perpendicular bisector: $x - 3y = -8$

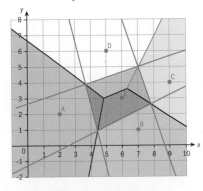

  b Perpendicular bisector: $x = 4$, $x - 2y = 3$

i 19 mm   **ii** 21 mm

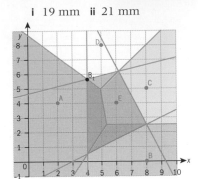

c **i** 11 mm   **ii** 12 mm

Exercise 3G

1 **a** The intersection of the perpendicular bisectors will be a vertex in the Voronoi diagram and hence the position of the solution to 'the toxic waste dump problem'.

  b $y = -5x + 21$ and $y = 2.5$

  c $(3.7, 2.5)$ **d** 2.75 km

2 **a** **i** $y = x - 10$

    ii $y = -2x + 140$

  b

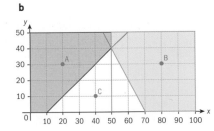

  c **i** 0.24   **ii** 0.34

  d **i** $(50, 40)$ **ii** 31.6 m

3 **a** $y - 4 = \dfrac{1}{2}(x - 2.5)$ or $y = \dfrac{1}{2}x + 2.75$

  b

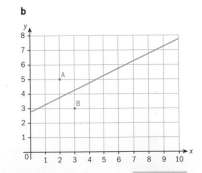

c

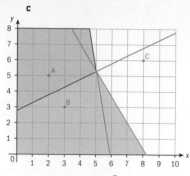

d i BD $y - 2 = \frac{5}{2}(x - 5.5)$ or

$y = \frac{5}{2}x - 11.75$ CD $y = 3.5$

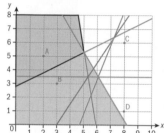

ii Because the perpendicular bisector of AD will always be outside the cell containing D (or, because either B or C are always closer than A to D). B and C are closer to D than they are to A.

iii

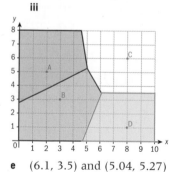

e (6.1, 3.5) and (5.04, 5.27)

f 28%   **g** (6.1, 3.5)

h

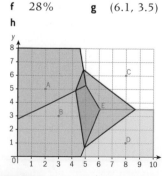

---

4 a

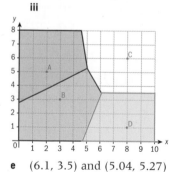

b (4.67, 4)

c i 213 000 miles² (to 3 s.f.)

ii 198 000 miles²

iii 150 000 miles²

iv 239 000 miles²

d So unable to support the other province

5 a i AB = 6, BC = 3, CD = 4, DA = 3.6055, total = 16.6 so 166 km

ii 0.289

b i Because (4, 3.5) is a vertex in the Voronoi diagram and so is an equal distance from three stations; B, C and D

ii 2.5

c i Median = 3.0, lower quartile = 2.7, upper quartile = 3.1, IQR = 0.4

ii

2.1 2.2 2.3 2.4 2.5 2.6 2.7 2.8 2.9 3 3.1 3.2 3.3 3.4

d The readings are all higher than the expected average except for one outlier so support claim.

Exercise 3H

1 a $\begin{pmatrix} 0 \\ -3 \end{pmatrix}$, $-3j$

b $\begin{pmatrix} -2 \\ -2 \end{pmatrix}$, $-2i - 2j$

c $\begin{pmatrix} 2 \\ 1 \end{pmatrix}$, $2i + j$

---

d $\begin{pmatrix} 1 \\ -3 \end{pmatrix}$, $i - 3j$

e $\begin{pmatrix} 2 \\ 0 \end{pmatrix}$, $2i$

2 a $\begin{pmatrix} -3 \\ 4 \end{pmatrix}$ **b** $7i + 4j$

c $\begin{pmatrix} -6 \\ 2 \end{pmatrix}$ **d** $5i - 2j$

3 a $\begin{pmatrix} 4 \\ 6 \end{pmatrix}$ **b** $\begin{pmatrix} 6 \\ 9 \end{pmatrix}$

c $\begin{pmatrix} 8 \\ 12 \end{pmatrix}$

Multiply each component in the vector by the scalar

d $3i + 4j = 3\begin{pmatrix} 1 \\ 0 \end{pmatrix} + 4\begin{pmatrix} 0 \\ 1 \end{pmatrix}$

$= \begin{pmatrix} 3 \\ 0 \end{pmatrix} + \begin{pmatrix} 0 \\ 4 \end{pmatrix} = \begin{pmatrix} 3 \\ 4 \end{pmatrix}$

4 a i $\begin{pmatrix} 1 \\ 2 \end{pmatrix} = \overrightarrow{AB}$

ii $\begin{pmatrix} -1 \\ -2 \end{pmatrix} = -\overrightarrow{AB}$

iii $\begin{pmatrix} 2 \\ 4 \end{pmatrix} = 2\overrightarrow{AB}$

iv $\begin{pmatrix} -\frac{1}{2} \\ -1 \end{pmatrix} = -\frac{1}{2}\overrightarrow{AB}$

b Parallel vectors are scalar multiples of each other

5 a, c, e, g

6 a i $p = -1, q = 2$

ii $p = 2, q = \frac{1}{2}$

b i $p = \frac{1}{7}$

ii $q = -3$

Exercise 3I

1 a i $\begin{pmatrix} 1 \\ 4 \end{pmatrix}$ **ii** $\begin{pmatrix} 1 \\ 1 \end{pmatrix}$

iii $\begin{pmatrix} -2 \\ 2 \end{pmatrix}$ **iv** $\begin{pmatrix} 2 \\ -2 \end{pmatrix}$

b **i** $\overrightarrow{BD} = \overrightarrow{BA} + \overrightarrow{AC} + \overrightarrow{CD}$

　　ii $\overrightarrow{BD} = -\overrightarrow{AB} + \overrightarrow{AC} + \overrightarrow{CD}$

　　iii $\overrightarrow{BD} = \begin{pmatrix} 1 \\ 2 \end{pmatrix}$ **iv** (3, 7)

2 **a** $\overrightarrow{AC} = \begin{pmatrix} 0 \\ 6 \end{pmatrix} \overrightarrow{CA} = \begin{pmatrix} 0 \\ -6 \end{pmatrix}$

　　b $\overrightarrow{DC} = \begin{pmatrix} -1 \\ 4 \end{pmatrix}$

3 **a** $\overrightarrow{AB} = \overrightarrow{DC} = \begin{pmatrix} 1 \\ 3 \end{pmatrix}$

　　b Parallelogram as two sides are equal length and parallel

　　c $\overrightarrow{BC}$ and $\overrightarrow{AD}$

4 **a** $\begin{pmatrix} 40 \\ -10 \end{pmatrix}$

　　b $\overrightarrow{CA} = \begin{pmatrix} -40 \\ 10 \end{pmatrix}$ **c** 41.2 km

5 **a** $13i + 11j$

　　b $-13i - 11j$

Exercise 3J

1 **a** **i** 5.66　　**ii** 45°

　　b **i** 2.24　　**ii** 297°

　　c **i** 19.3　　**ii** 21.3°

　　d **i** 8.06　　**ii** 7.1°

2 **a** $\begin{vmatrix} 48 \\ 20 \end{vmatrix} = \sqrt{48^2 + 20^2}$

　　　　$= \sqrt{2704} = \sqrt{16 \times 169}$

　　　　$= 4 \times \sqrt{169} = 4\sqrt{12^2 + 5^2}$

　　　　$= 4 \begin{vmatrix} 12 \\ 5 \end{vmatrix}$

　　b **i** 30　　**ii** 50　　**iii** 35

3 **a** $\frac{1}{5}\begin{pmatrix} 24 \\ 32 \end{pmatrix}$ **b** $\begin{pmatrix} 5 \\ 7 \end{pmatrix}$

　　c $\begin{pmatrix} 7 \\ 1 \end{pmatrix}$

4 **a** $\begin{pmatrix} 141.4 \\ 141.4 \end{pmatrix}, \begin{pmatrix} -175 \\ 0 \end{pmatrix}$

　　b 145 km

5 10.2 km, 260°

Exercise 3K

1 **a** 9　　**b** 3

　　c 15

　　d 35

2 $\begin{pmatrix} -12 \\ -9 \\ -6 \end{pmatrix}$

3 **a** To get from A to B, travel down the vector $\overrightarrow{AB} = b - a$ so to travel from A to the midpoint of [AB] travel down

　　$\overrightarrow{AM} = \frac{1}{2}\overrightarrow{AB} = \frac{1}{2}(b - a).$

　　Now $\overrightarrow{OM} = \overrightarrow{OA} + \overrightarrow{AM}$

　　　　　$= a + \frac{1}{2}(b - a)$

　　$\overrightarrow{OM} = \frac{1}{2}(a + b).$

　　b $\overrightarrow{PQ} = \begin{pmatrix} -2 \\ -3 \\ -1 \end{pmatrix}, \overrightarrow{QR} = \begin{pmatrix} 3 \\ 4 \\ -6 \end{pmatrix}$

　　c $\overrightarrow{PR} = \begin{pmatrix} 1 \\ 1 \\ -7 \end{pmatrix}$ **d** (4, 7, 0)

　　e $\begin{pmatrix} 0.5 \\ 0.5 \\ -3.5 \end{pmatrix}$ **f** $\begin{pmatrix} 2.5 \\ 3.5 \\ -2.5 \end{pmatrix}$

　　g Diagonals of a parallelogram bisect each other

Exercise 3L

1 **a** 40.7°　　**b** 156°

　　c 25.1°　　**d** 40.8°

　　e 0°　　**f** 180°

2 **a** **i** $\overrightarrow{AB}$ and $\overrightarrow{AC}$

　　　　ii $\overrightarrow{BC}$ and $\overrightarrow{BA}$

　　b $\angle A = 151.3°$ $\angle B = 20.1°$ $\angle C = 8.9°$

　　c BC = 7.14

3 **a** $p = \frac{1}{4}$

　　b $p = -1, 4$

4 **a** $k = -1, 2$

　　b When $k = -1$,

　　$AC = \sqrt{1^2 + 3^2} = \sqrt{10}.$

　　$BC = \sqrt{(-1)^2 + 0^2} = 1.$

　　Area of the triangle is $\frac{\sqrt{10}}{2}$.

　　When $k = 2$,

　　$AC = \sqrt{1^2 + (2 - 2)^2} = 1,$

　　$BC = \sqrt{(-1)^2 + (-1 + 2)^2} = \sqrt{2}.$

　　Area of the triangle $= \frac{\sqrt{2}}{2}$.

5 70.5°

Exercise 3M

1 **a** $\begin{pmatrix} 5 \\ -1 \\ -3 \end{pmatrix}$

　　b $a \cdot c = 2 \times 5 - 1 \times 1 - 3 \times 3$
　　　　　$= 10 - 1 - 9 = 0$
　　　$b \cdot c = 1 \times 5 - 1 \times -1 + 2 \times -3$
　　　　　$= 5 + 1 - 6 = 0$

2 **a** $\begin{pmatrix} 2 \\ 8 \\ 1 \end{pmatrix}$ **b** $\begin{pmatrix} -3 \\ 0 \\ 6 \end{pmatrix}$

　　c $2i - 3j + k$

　　d $9i + 4j + 7k$

3 **a** $\begin{pmatrix} -4 \\ 1 \\ -2 \end{pmatrix}$

　　b $\frac{1}{2}\sqrt{5} = 1.12$

4 $\frac{1}{2}\sqrt{42} = 3.24$

5 **a** (4, 3, −3)

　　b $8\sqrt{10} = 25.2$

　　c $\overrightarrow{AB} \cdot \overrightarrow{AD} = 0 \times 3 + 0 \times 1 + 8 \times 0$
　　　　　$= 0$

6 21.0 m²

7 27

Exercise 3N

1 a $r = \begin{pmatrix} 2 \\ 4 \end{pmatrix} + t\begin{pmatrix} -1 \\ -3 \end{pmatrix}$

b $r = \begin{pmatrix} 2 \\ 1 \\ -1 \end{pmatrix} + t\begin{pmatrix} 2 \\ 1 \\ 1 \end{pmatrix}$

2 a $a = 0.5, b = 2$

b $(0, -6, 3)$

3 a $s = 3, p = 4$

b i $t = -2$

ii $7\begin{pmatrix} 1 \\ 2 \\ -3 \end{pmatrix} = \begin{pmatrix} 7 \\ 14 \\ -21 \end{pmatrix}$

4 a $4 - t = 2 \Rightarrow t = 2, (4, -5, 1)$
$+ 2(-1, 3, 1) = (2, 1, 3)$
$4 + 2s = 2 \Rightarrow s = -1,$
$(4, 2, 0) - (2, 1, -3) =$
$(2, 1, 3)$

b $80.7°$

5 a The direction vectors are multiples of each other.

b $3 - t = 1 \Rightarrow t = 2, (3, 5, 2) +$
$2(-1, 2, 1) = (1, 9, 4)$
$3 + 2s = 1 \Rightarrow t = -1,$
$(3, 5, 2) - (2, -4, -2) =$
$(1, 9, 4)$

c The two lines are coincident (or the two equations are both for the same line).

6 a $3 + s = 1 \Rightarrow s = -2, (3, 1, 2)$
$- 2(1, 3, -2) = (1, -5, 6)$

b $\overrightarrow{AB} = \begin{pmatrix} 4 \\ 2 \\ 5 \end{pmatrix}, \overrightarrow{AB} \cdot \begin{pmatrix} 1 \\ 3 \\ -2 \end{pmatrix}$
$= 1 \times 4 + 2 \times 3 - 2 \times 5 = 0$

7 a $(2 + t, 3t, 1 + 2t)$

b $\begin{pmatrix} 1 + t \\ 3t - 2 \\ 3 + 2t \end{pmatrix}$ **c** $t = -\dfrac{1}{14}$

d $\left(\dfrac{27}{14}, -\dfrac{3}{14}, \dfrac{6}{7} \right)$

e 3.73

Exercise 3O

1 a i $i + 2j$ **ii** $\sqrt{5} = 2.24$

b i $\begin{pmatrix} -0.25 \\ 0.5 \end{pmatrix}$ **ii** 0.559

c i $-i + 2j + k$ **ii** $\sqrt{6} = 2.45$

d i $\begin{pmatrix} 0 \\ 1 \\ -1 \end{pmatrix}$ **ii** $\sqrt{2} = 1.41$

2 a $\begin{pmatrix} -10 \\ 0 \end{pmatrix}$ **b** $\begin{pmatrix} -4.5 \\ 6 \end{pmatrix}$

c $\begin{pmatrix} -2 \\ -8 \\ 16 \end{pmatrix}$ **d** $\begin{pmatrix} -3.54 \\ -3.54 \end{pmatrix}$

e $\begin{pmatrix} 9.64 \\ 11.5 \end{pmatrix}$ **f** $\begin{pmatrix} 10.4 \\ -6 \end{pmatrix}$

3 a 36.1 m

b $p = \begin{pmatrix} 20 \\ 30 \end{pmatrix} + \begin{pmatrix} -3 \\ -5 \end{pmatrix}t$ **c** 1.71 m

4 a $r = \begin{pmatrix} 3 \\ 1 \end{pmatrix} + \begin{pmatrix} 6 \\ -8 \end{pmatrix}t$

b $\begin{pmatrix} 27 \\ -31 \end{pmatrix}$ **c** 41.1 m

d 40 m

5 a $\begin{pmatrix} -2 \\ 9 \\ 5 \end{pmatrix}$

b i $r = \begin{pmatrix} -2 \\ 9 \\ 5 \end{pmatrix} + \begin{pmatrix} 1 \\ 4 \\ 0 \end{pmatrix}(t - 3)t,$
$t \geq 3$

ii $r = \begin{pmatrix} -2 \\ 9 \\ 5 \end{pmatrix} + \begin{pmatrix} 1 \\ 4 \\ 0 \end{pmatrix}t', t' \geq 0$

c i $\begin{pmatrix} 0 \\ 17 \\ 5 \end{pmatrix}$ **ii** 17.7

6 a At 12:00 the ships are in the same position $(-1, 14)$

b $\begin{pmatrix} 8 - 3t \\ -6 + 3t \end{pmatrix}$

c 2 km at 12:40

d 1.41 km at 12:20

7 a i $\begin{pmatrix} 3 \\ 1 \\ 1.5 \end{pmatrix}$ **ii** 1.5 m s⁻¹

b $\begin{pmatrix} 180 \\ 60 \\ 120 \end{pmatrix}$ **c** $r = \begin{pmatrix} 180 \\ 60 \\ 120 \end{pmatrix} + \begin{pmatrix} 3 \\ 1 \\ -0.6 \end{pmatrix}t'$

d 200 seconds **e** 822 m

8 a $\begin{pmatrix} 0 \\ -9 \end{pmatrix}$ **b** 22.4 km

c $\begin{pmatrix} 20 - 9t \\ 10 - 21t \end{pmatrix}$ **d** $t = 1, \begin{pmatrix} 9 \\ 17 \end{pmatrix}$

e $\begin{pmatrix} 20 \\ 6 \end{pmatrix}$ **f** $160.1°$

Chapter review

1 a 1.74 km **b** B

2 a $y = -0.4x + 5.4$

b $(1, 5)$

3 a $y = 5$ $x = 5$

b $3x + y = 20$

c

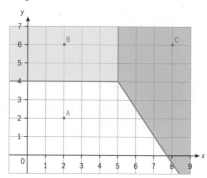

d $y = -2x + 2.5$

e

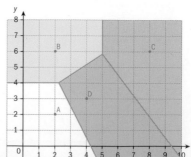

4 a $y = 8 - x$, $y = \frac{1}{2}x + \frac{7}{4}$

b (4.17, 3.83)

c 2.17 km

5 a $\begin{pmatrix} 5 \\ 6 \end{pmatrix}$ **b** $\begin{pmatrix} -3 \\ 0 \end{pmatrix}$

c 5 m min^{-1}

d 1.8 m when $t = 1.52$ min

6 a $2q + p = 0$

b $p = 0.5$, $q = 5$ **c** 40.2°

7 1.17

8 a $n = 24$

b $p = 82.5$, $q = -6.5$ and $u = 82.5$

9 a
$$r = \begin{pmatrix} 0 \\ 0 \\ 8.2 \end{pmatrix} + \frac{750\sqrt{2}}{2}t\begin{pmatrix} 1 \\ 1 \\ 0 \end{pmatrix} + t\begin{pmatrix} 0 \\ 0 \\ 2 \end{pmatrix}$$

b $r_{\text{B}} = \begin{pmatrix} 0 \\ 0 \\ 13.1 \end{pmatrix} + (t - 0.5)\begin{pmatrix} 400 \\ 692.8 \\ -1 \end{pmatrix}$

c 438 km

Exam-style questions

10 a (1, 5.5)

b -0.625

c i 1.6 **ii** $y = 1.6x + 3.9$

11 i Neither, gradients not the same and their product is not -1

ii Parallel, as both lines have a gradient of 3

iii Neither, gradients not the same and their product is not -1

iv Perpendicular, as product of gradients is -1

v Perpendicular, as product of gradients is -1

12 a 707 m **b** 1310 m

13 a $\begin{pmatrix} 1 \\ -1 \\ 0 \end{pmatrix}$ **b** $\frac{\sqrt{2}}{2}$

14 a -4.5 **b** $(-3.23, 1.85)$

15 a 126 **b** 8.37

c i (1.5, 2.5, 3) **ii** 64.6°

16 a (150, 70) **b** 99.0 km

17 a

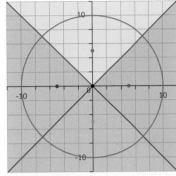

b 78.5 km

c

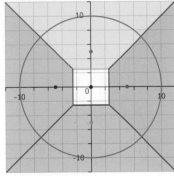

d 25 m²

e 72.3 m²

f 4

18 a $\begin{pmatrix} 200 \\ 240 \\ 5 \end{pmatrix}$

b The two flightpaths cross at $\begin{pmatrix} 150 \\ 180 \\ 4 \end{pmatrix}$

c The two aircraft do not collide as the first aircraft gets to the intersection point an hour before the second one does.

d 135 km

e 7.14 km, after 9 and a half hours

Chapter 4

Skills check

1 a $y = 0.25x + 1.75$

b $y = -3x - 4$

2 a $y = 23$

b $x = 4$

Exercise 4A

1 a Not a function, because one x-value will have multiple y-values.

b y is a function of x, each month has exactly one number of people with a birthday in it.

2 a Function: every element from first set maps onto only one element from second set

b Not a function: input 3 has two outputs

c Not a function: fails the vertical line test

d Function: passes the vertical line test

e Function

f Not a function: fails the vertical line test

3 a $R : x \rightarrow \frac{1}{x}$ **b** Yes

c $\frac{1}{2}$ **d** $a = \frac{1}{3}$

4 a -1 **b** $x = -4$

c $B = \{-1, 0, 1, 8, 27, 64\}$

d It is a function.

Exercise 4B

1 a i 5 **ii** -3

b i 0 **ii** 3

c $x > 3$

2 a i $f(2) = 10 - 4(2) = 2$

ii $f\left(-\frac{1}{2}\right) = 10 - 4\left(-\frac{1}{2}\right) = 12$

b $f(2.5) = 10 - 4(2.5) = 0$

c 4

3 a i 687 N **ii** 607 N

iii 88.4%. Jaime is 11.6% lighter on the space station.

b $h \approx 310$ km: gravity's force is 625 N at a height of 310 km above sea level.

c $F(653) = 170$

Exercise 4C

1 a On January 2nd last year the average temperature was 25°C.

b {1, 2, 3, ..., 31}

c Estimates should be close to $\{T \mid 20 \le T \le 30\}$

2 a i 5 **ii** −3

b $x = \dfrac{1}{2}$

c

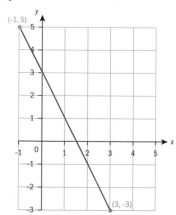

d $y \in [-3, 5]$ or $\{y \mid -3 \le y \le 5\}$

3 a Domain = {−5, −4, −3, −2, −1, 0, 1, 2}, range = {−2, 0, 2, 4, 6, 8}

b Domain = $\{x: -8 \le x \le 6\}$, range = $\{y: -4 \le y \le 3\}$

c Domain = $\{x: -7 < x \le 9\}$, range = $\{y: 0 < y \le 4\}$

d Domain = $\{x: -7 < x < 7\}$, range = $\{y: -4 \le y < 3\}$

4 a $\{p \mid p \ne -1\}$, $p \in \{3, 4, 5, 6, 7, 8\}$

b $w(3) = 12.75$ kg, $w(8) = 10.67$ kg

c $\{w \mid 10.67 \le w \le 12.75\}$

d 4–6

5 a $\{t \mid 0 \le t \le 5\}$

b $\{S \mid 1.2 \le t \le 3.9\}$

c $2.09 **d** 2018

e The researchers would be extrapolating far beyond the data set; also the values of the function become negative after 6 years.

6 a €12 031 **b** €9844

c $q = 3571$, it costs €20 000 to produce 3571 bottles

d

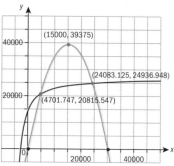

Break-even when $q = 4702$ and $q = 24\,083$

e Company makes a profit when $\{q: 4702 < q < 24083\}$

7 a $a = 9625$, $b = 5230$

b 2017 **c** 2066

Exercise 4D

1 a Linear, gradient zero

b Linear, gradient −2

c not linear

d Linear, gradient 5

2 a i independent = time parked (in hours), dependent = cost of parking (in $)

ii Linear, because there is a constant rate of change of $12.50 per hour

b i independent = time (in years), dependent = population (in number of fish)

ii Not linear, as a decline of 7% of the current population will not be a constant number of fish per year

c i independent = amount of purchase (euros), dependent = amount of tax (euros)

ii Linear, because constant rate of change of 0.22 euro tax per euro spent

d i independent = daily high temperature (°C), dependent = number of daily passes sold

ii Linear, rate of change between every two points in the table is constant and equivalent to a decrease of 8 passes per degree Celsius.

3 Not linear. The rate of change from 1 to 3 is $\dfrac{4}{2} = 2$. The rate of change from 5 to 8 is $\dfrac{4}{3} \ne 2$.

4 a US $30 **b** US $180

c 2.8 kg

5 a $d(t) = 13 - 0.065t$

b 9.1 km

c $d(t) = 0$ when $t = 200$; Ewout will take 200 minutes or approximately 3 and half hours to reach home.

6 a $S(t) = 64 - 1.35t$ **b** 2028

c Foot Talker grows at 2.5% of total sales per year, whereas Sneakies declines by 1.35% of total sales.

d $F(t) = 13 + 2.5t$

e 2031

7 a 120 m s^{-1} **b** 8 sec

c -15 m s^{-1}

d $v(t) = -15t + 120$

8 a $50m + c = 20$

b $80m + c = 35$

c $L = 0.5W - 5$

d 40 cm

Exercise 4E

1 a $c = \dfrac{1}{.21}a$ or $c = 4.67a$

b one AUD = 4.67 CNY

c 51 AUD

2 a $F(x) = 23.4\,x$

b $x = 3.42 \text{ m}$

c -35.1 N

Exercise 4F

1 a UK £1 = $1.33

b UK £75.19

c **i** $3.28 **ii** £75.19

iii UK £754.35

2 a Gradient: for each 1 euro that the price increases, the number of people willing to buy tickets deceases by 36. y-intercept: 5000 people will buy the tickets if they cost 0 euros.

b 2300

c $p = 138.89$; the price at which no one is willing to buy a ticket

d Domain $\{x\,|0 \le x \le 139\}$, range $\{y\,|0 \le y \le 5000\}$

e $86

3 a i 90.2% **ii** 89.3°C

b There is a constant rate of change between the two variables: cooking time and boiling point temperature.

c $T(B) = 5 + \dfrac{2}{5}(100 - B)$

d 24 min

e Domain: $B \in [40, 100]$, range $T \in [15, 39]$

4 a $x =$ number of regular dishes, $y =$ number of premium dishes: $3.5x + 6.50y = 25$

b (8.33, 0) and (0, 3.85) so Alfie can buy 714 g of just Pepperoni or 385 g of just Parma Ham

c Alfie should buy 180 g of Parma Ham and 380 g of Pepperoni

Exercise 4G

1 a

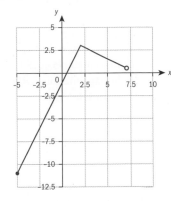

b i 1.15 **ii** -7.4

c $x = 1.5,\ x = 4$

d The pieces connect at $x = 2$; $2(2) - 1 = 3$ and $4 - \dfrac{1}{2}(2) = 3$. Outputs match.

e Domain: $x \in [-5, 7)$, Range $y \in [-11, 3]$ (highest point is at (2, 3)).

2 a

$$f(x) = \begin{cases} 130x & 0 \le x \le 5 \\ 650 & 5 \le x < 7 \\ 130x - 260 & 7 \le x \le 10 \end{cases}$$

b At $x = 5$, $130(5) = 650$, and at $x = 7$, $130(7) - 260 = 650$, pieces connect so f is continuous

c 5.84 min

3 a $C(d) = \begin{cases} 35 & 0 \le d \le 1 \\ 35 + 60(d - 1) & d > 1 \end{cases}$

b i $35

ii $95

c When more than 1.4 GB of data are used

d i 1.78 GBP

ii Switch, she will save $22.80

Exercise 4H

1 a $x = -\dfrac{1}{3}$ **b** $x = 8$

c $x = 2$ **d** $x = -6$

2 a Domain: $x \in (-6, 6]$, range: $y \in [2, 8)$

b $g(4) \approx -1$

3 1.27 (3 s.f.); a circle with circumference 8 units will have a radius of 1.27 units.

4 $c = 31$

Exercise 4I

1 a i

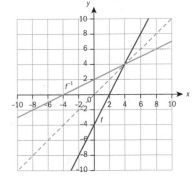

ii Domain: $x \in \mathbb{R}$, Range: $y \in \mathbb{R}$

iii $x = 4$

b i

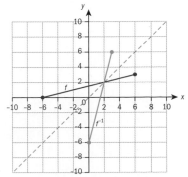

ii Domain: $\{x\,|0 \le x \le 3\}$, range $\{y\,|-6 \le y \le 6\}$ $x = 2$

c **i**

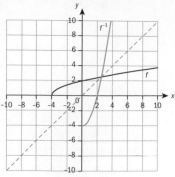

ii Domain: $\{x \mid x \geq 0\}$,
Range: $\{y \mid y \geq -4\}$

iii $x = 2.5$

2 **a**

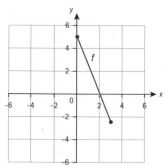

b $b = -2.5$

c

Function	Domain	Range
f	$0 \leq x \leq 3$	$-2.5 \leq y \leq 5$
f^{-1}	$-2.5 \leq x \leq 5$	$0 \leq y \leq 3$

d

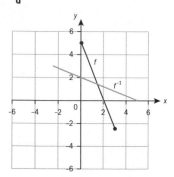

e $\left(\dfrac{10}{7}, \dfrac{10}{7}\right)$

3 **a** $d(x) = 90x + 630$

b $d^{-1}(x) = \dfrac{x}{90} - 7$

c **i** 8:47 am

ii 10:47 am

iii 16:33 or 4:33 pm

d **ii** is most reasonable as it is closest to the middle of the day.

Exercise 4J

1 **a** -1 **b** 10.5

c $29 - 8x$ **d** $\dfrac{27}{8}x$

2 **a** $c(t(x)) = 1.10x + 2$ and $t(c(x)) = 1.10x + 2.2$. These are not equal because they are linear functions with different y-intercepts.

b $t \circ c(x)$ provides a 0.20 euro larger tip, because $2.20 - 2.00 = 0.20$ and the rest of the two functions are equal.

3 Answers can vary, e.g.

a $g(x) = \dfrac{7}{3}x$ and $f(x) = x - 5$

b $g(x) = x - 2$ and $f(x) = 4x$

c $h(x) = 12 - 4x$, so one possibility is $g(x) = 4x$ and $f(x) = 12 - x$

4 **a** The company loses \$750 if it operates for exactly 4 hours a day.

b $350t - 2150$

c At least 7 hours each day

5 $C \circ F(x) = C\left(\dfrac{9}{5}x + 32\right)$

$= \dfrac{5}{9}\left(\dfrac{9}{5}x + 32\right) - 17.8$

$= x + 17.8 - 17.8$

$= x = i(x)$

Similarly, $F \circ C(x) = x$

6 $x = 1, -5$

Exercise 4K

1 **a** **i** 41.7, 50.3, 58.9

ii Yes, $d = 8.6$

b **i** $-83, -105, -127$

ii Yes, $d = -22$

c **i** 151, 196, 250

ii No, difference is not constant, it increases by 9 each time

d **i** 1.25, 0.625, 0.3125

ii No, the numbers are divided by 2 each time instead of being added or subtracted by a constant amount.

2 **a** 9.5, 12, 14.5. This is arithmetic; $a_1 = 9.5$, $d = 2.5$

b 2650, 300, -2050. This is arithmetic; $b_1 = 2650$, $d = -2350$

c 3, 10, 21. Not arithmetic; $21 - 10 \neq 10 - 3$

3 **a** $a_n = 5 + 4(n - 1)$ or $a_n = 1 + 4n$

b Not a term of the sequence

4 **a** 95 in second year, 105 in third

b 175 **c** 21 years

5 **a** $a_n = 2.6 + 1.22(n - 1)$

b $a_{28} = 35.54$ m

c Between 2064 and 2065

Exercise 4L

1 **a** $d = \dfrac{11}{6}$ **b** $\dfrac{47}{3}$

2 **a** $d = 2.5$ **b** $u_3 = 5$

3 **a** $d = -25$. The frog hops 25 cm closer to the finish line with each hop.

b $a_{10} = 750$ cm. After 10 hops, the frog is 750 cm from the finish line

c 40

d $a_n = -225$ when $n = 49$. The frog hops 49 times.

4 **a** $12 = u_1 + 2d$ and
$43.5 = u_1 + 9d$

b $u_1 = 3$, $d = 4.5$

c $u_{100} = 448.5$

5 **a** $3n + 19$ **b** 29

6 **a** $a_1 = 12$

b $a_3 = 12 + 2d$ and
$a_9 = 12 + 8d$

c $2(12 + 2d)$

d $d = 3$

e $a_n = 100$ has solution
$n = 30.3$, so Tyler should
use an object that is at
least 31 kg (!)

Exercise 4M

1 1350, $10\,593$

2 UK £17 142.86

3 4.6%

4 16th year

Exercise 4N

1 -450

2 3720

3 **a** 42 **b** $10\,794$

4 **a** $1 + 5 + 9 + \ldots + 37$

b $\sum_{i=1}^{10} 4i - 3$

c $S_{10} = 190$; $S_n = n(2n-1)$

d $n = 31.9$; it will take Janet
32 years to have a total of
2000 acres.

5 **a** $S_n = \dfrac{n}{2}\big(8 - 3(n-1)\big)$ or

$S_n = \dfrac{n}{2}(11 - 3n)$

b $S_{10} = -95$

c $n = 15$

6 **a** 8 km **b** 105 km

7 **a** $S_{29} = 1856$

b $d = 19$ will result in 6100
seats

Exercise 4O

1 Approximately 547 years old

2 -4.17% of GDP

Exercise 4P

1 **a** A linear regression is
appropriate because the
data displays a roughly
linear trend.

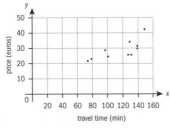

b $y = 0.16x + 9.84$

c $x = 120$, $y = 29.4$ euros

d 100 minutes by interpolation (within the
data set). Predicting for
10 minutes would be
extrapolation beyond the
data set.

2 **a** A linear regression is
appropriate because the
data displays a roughly
linear trend.

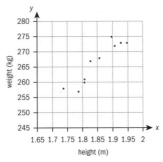

b $y = 93.7x + 92.8$

c $x = 1.8$, $y = 261$ kg

d A 1 cm increase in height
corresponds to a 0.937 kg
increase in weight.

3 **a** $f_1(x)$ is graph A because it
has the lower y-intercept
(8.11). $f_2(x)$ is Graph B.

b $SSR_1 = 0.576$, $SSR_2 = 0.614$
Since $f_1(x)$ has the smaller
sum of square residuals,
it is the least squares
regression equation.

Exercise 4Q

1 **a** The correlation coefficient
is weak, so prediction from
a linear regression will not
be accurate.

b The data does not display a
linear trend; it has a curved
trend. A linear regression is
not appropriate.

c A linear regression is
appropriate here, but
Kiernan is predicting the
independent variable
given as a value of the
dependent variable.
Only predictions of the
dependent variable are
valid.

d A linear regression is
appropriate here, but
Kiernan is extrapolating
beyond the data set ($x = 80$
is outside the data values).

2 **a** The graph displays a linear
trend.

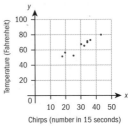

b $r = 0.951$; this is a strong
positive correlation

c Yes, it is a linear trend
with a strong correlation.

d **i** $T(c) = 1.14c + 30.3$

ii Invalid, can only use
this regression to predict
temperatures from
known chirp numbers.

iii $T(40) = 76\ °F$. Valid, because we are interpolating and have already checked that the linear regression is appropriate.

e Answers may vary. Rounding 14 seconds to 15, the Almanac's formula is $T_1(x) = x + 40$. The gradients of the two equations are similar, and the y-intercepts differ by 10 degrees. $T_1(40) = 80\ °F$, which is 4 degrees difference from the regression prediction.

3 a The data follows a linear trend, as evidenced by the scatter plot:

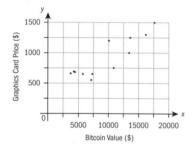

b $r = 0.884$; strong positive correlation

c Yes, linear trend with a strong correlation

d i $G(b) = 0.06b + 342$

   ii $G(12\,320) = \$1081.2$

e $m = 0.06$ means that for every dollar increase in Bitcoin value, graphics card prices increase by 6 cents.

Chapter review

1 a 500 hours

b $D: \{t \mid 0 \le t \le 500\}$, $R: \{A \mid 0 \le A \le 1350\}$

c

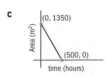

d $A(5) = 1336.5$; after 5 hours, 1336.5 m² of surface area remain to be cleaned.

2 a Function; not one-to-one

b Function; one-to-one (linear)

c Not a function: two cylinders with the same volume but different heights will have different radii.

3 a $x =$ babies per woman; $y =$ life expectancy; $y = -5.89x + 88.2$

b The scatter plot shows a linear relationship between the two variables; the correlation coefficient, $r = -0.726$, shows at least a moderately strong correlation.

c When $x = 2$, $y = 76.4$ years. Valid prediction because it is interpolation.

d $m = -5.89$; in the regression equation, an increase of 1 baby per woman corresponds to a decrease of 5.89 years of life expectancy.

4 a Graph 1, because it has a y-intercept of 0.

b Graph 1: gradient $\dfrac{1}{12}$; the plane uses 12 litres to travel 1 km Graph 2: gradient 0.08; the plane takes 8 minutes to travel 100 km

c $T\big(d(x)\big) = 20 + 0.08\left(\dfrac{1}{12}\right)x$
$= 20 + 0.0067x$;
$T(150\,000) = 1025$ min

5 a 61 months

b $k = \$111$

c 18 months

6 a $C(d) = 0.06d + 49$

b i Brussels: drive (costs €74.20); Hamburg: fly (drive costs €105.40); Paris: drive (costs €110.80)

   ii Approximately €335

7 €40 000 at 1.6% interest

8 a CA \$24 030.29

b $T(x) = \begin{cases} 0.15x & 0 \le x \le 46\,605 \\ 6990.85 + 0.205(x - 46\,605) & 46\,605 < x \le 93\,208 \\ 16\,544.37 + 0.26(x - 93\,208) & 93\,208 < x \le 144\,489 \end{cases}$

$29\,877.43 + 0.29\big(x - 144\,489\big)\ 144\,489 < x \le 205\,842$
$47\,669.80 + 0.33(x - 205\,842)\quad x > 205\,842$

c One payment: $T(162\,000) + T(122\,000) = 34\,955.62 + 24\,030.29$
$= 58\,985.91$

Two payments: $T(142\,000) \times 2 = (29\,230.29) \times 2$
$= 58\,460.58$ Ian should choose two payments; he will save \$525.33.

9 a $f^{-1}(x) = \begin{cases} 15 - 3x, & 4 \le x \le 7 \\ -\dfrac{1}{2}x + 5, & x < 4 \end{cases}$ domain: $\{x \mid x \le 7\}$, range: $\{y \mid y \ge -6\}$

b $f(x)$ is not one-to-one; for example, $f(0) = 5 = f(3.5)$. This can also be shown using the horizontal line test on the graph.

Exam-style questions

10 a i $m = \dfrac{4}{3}$, ii $c = 6\dfrac{2}{3}$

  b Positive

  c 126.67

  d 86.67

11 a 10 days

  b $\{C : 186.90 \le C \le 245.35\}$

12 a i $r = 0.849$

  ii Strong, positive correlation

  iii $y = 0.24 + 0.94x$

  b i $r = 0.26$

  ii Weak, positive correlation

  iii Data does not show a strong enough linear correlation for a linear regression line to be valid.

13 a $b = -\dfrac{5}{12}, a = 5$

  b $f^{-1}(x) = 12 - \dfrac{12}{5}x$

  c $3\dfrac{9}{17}$

  d $h^{-1}(x)$ is a reflection of $h(x)$ on line $y = x$ so they intersect when $h(x) = x$

14 a $a = 3, b = 0.5$

  b 27

15 a $\{f : f \in \mathbb{R}\}$

  b $\{gf : gf \ge 18\}$

  c $x = \pm\sqrt{3}$

  d $g(x) = 2x^2 + 96x + 1170$

Chapter 5

Skills check

1 a $\dfrac{1}{3}$ **b** $\dfrac{7}{12}$ **c** $\dfrac{5}{12}$

2 a $\dfrac{57}{116}$ **b** $\dfrac{3}{29}$ **c** $\dfrac{49}{58}$

Exercise 5A

1 $\dfrac{1}{3}$

2 a $\dfrac{17}{20}$ **b** $\dfrac{3}{5}$ **c** 1

  d $\dfrac{7}{20}$ **e** $\dfrac{2}{5}$ **f** $\dfrac{1}{5}$ **g** 0

3 a $\dfrac{73}{239}$ **b** $\dfrac{37}{136}$

4 a $\dfrac{1}{10\,000}$ **b** $\dfrac{99}{10\,000}$

  c $\dfrac{99}{10\,000}$ **d** $\dfrac{9987}{10\,000}$

5 $\dfrac{1}{4}$

6 1917.26

7 2

Exercise 5B

1 a $\dfrac{7}{20}$ **b** $\dfrac{1}{5}$ **c** $\dfrac{3}{20}$

  d $\dfrac{1}{3}$ **e** $\dfrac{4}{9}$ **f** $\dfrac{1}{2}$

2 a 5   **b** $\dfrac{41}{127}$

  c 3228

3 a 9   **b** $\dfrac{3}{4}$

4 P(A wins) $= \dfrac{2}{3}$, P(B wins) $= \dfrac{1}{3}$,

  P(C wins) $= \dfrac{2}{3}$, P(D wins) $= \dfrac{1}{3}$

5 P(A beats B) $=$ P(C beats D) $= \dfrac{2}{3}$

6 $\dfrac{4}{9}$

Exercise 5C

1 a Independent (I)

  b Neither (N)

  c N   **d** I

  e Mutually exclusive

  f N   **g** I

2 a Mutually exclusive as the areas shaded do not overlap.

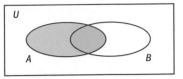

  b Using the Venn diagram from part **a**.

  c Using the Venn diagram from part **a**.

  d Independent as neither of the shaded sections for A or B' encloses the other.

3 a i $\left(\dfrac{1}{6}\right)^5$ ii $\left(\dfrac{1}{6}\right)^5$ iii $\left(\dfrac{1}{6}\right)^5$

  b $\dfrac{4651}{7776}$ **c** 1.286

  d $\dfrac{1}{1296}$ **e** 3888 throws

4 a 0.9   **b** 0.72   **c** 0.9

5 a $\dfrac{113}{512}$ **b** Yes

6 $\dfrac{8}{13}$

Exercise 5D

1 $\dfrac{115}{351}$ **2** $\dfrac{116}{175}$

3 a 0.915   **b** 0.3115

  c 170   **d** 0.6

4 0.4914   **5** 0.8

6 a 0.8831   **b** 23

Chapter review

1 0.6

2 a $\dfrac{5}{13}$ **b** No

3 a $1 - \left(\dfrac{5}{6}\right)^n$ **b** 30

4 a 0.8115   **b** 0.5525

  c 0.9025

5 a $\dfrac{5n+1}{2}$ **b** $\dfrac{n+1}{5n+1}$

6 9

7 a

		Chromosome inherited from mother	
		X	X
Chromosome inherited from father	X	X**X**	X**X**
	Y	**X**Y	XY

b There are two outcomes from a sample set of 4 which cause female characteristics to develop.

Exam-style questions

8 a $\dfrac{13}{40}$ **b** $\dfrac{7}{20}$

9 a 0.224 **b** 0.252

  c 0.32 **d** 0.964

10 a Let J be the event that Jake solves it and E be the event that Elisa solves it.

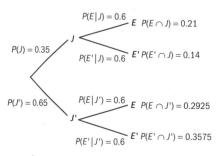

    $P(E|J) = 0.6$ E $P(E \cap J) = 0.21$

$P(J) = 0.35$

    $P(E'|J) = 0.6$ E' $P(E' \cap J) = 0.14$

$P(J') = 0.65$

    $P(E|J') = 0.6$ E $P(E \cap J') = 0.2925$

    $P(E'|J') = 0.6$ E' $P(E' \cap J') = 0.3575$

  b 0.6425 **c** 0.4179

11 a 0.4 **b** 0.6 **c** 0.75

12 a 9 **b** $\dfrac{23}{48}$

  c Because

$$P(\text{Europe}) \times P(\text{USA}) = \frac{32}{48} \times \frac{25}{48}$$
$$= \frac{25}{75} \neq \frac{9}{48}$$
$$= P(\text{both})$$

13 a $\dfrac{28}{50}$ **b** $\dfrac{7}{25}$ **c** $\dfrac{5}{11}$

  d 0 **e** $\dfrac{10}{17}$

14 a 0.15 **b** 0.65

  c 0.15 **d** 0.5

15 a Events B and C are not independent because C is a subset of B so if C occurs then B must also have occurred by definition, so $P(B \cap C) = P(C) \neq P(B) \times P(C)$

  b Events A and C are mutually exclusive as they do not overlap on the Venn diagram, meaning that it is not possible for them top both occur together.

  c If A and B are independent, then $P(A) \times P(B) = P(A \cap B)$:
$P(A) \times P(B) = 0.3 \times 0.28$
$= 0.084 \neq 0.12 = P(A \cap B)$
so not independent.

  d Events A' and C' are not mutually exclusive as they overlap on the Venn diagram, meaning that it is possible for them top both occur together.

  e 0.3

16 a $a = 0.72$, $c = 0.18$

  b $b = 0.08$, $d = 0.02$

  c 0.26 **d** 0.0889 **e** 0.1

  f **i** They are not mutually exclusive as they overlap on the Venn diagram, i.e. there are people who play both squash and tennis.

    ii Independent

Chapter 6

Skills check

1 $c = -3$

2 a $x = 3, x = -2$

  b $x = \dfrac{2}{3}, x = -1$

3 a $x = -4, x = 2$

  b $x = 4, x = 2$

Exercise 6A

1 a $x = -\dfrac{1}{2}$ **b** $x = 1$

  c $x = -4$ **d** $x = 3$

  e $x = 100$

2 a

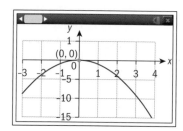

Range $-16 \le y \le 0$

b

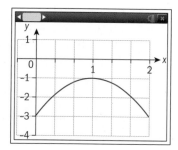

Range $-3 \le y \le -1$

c

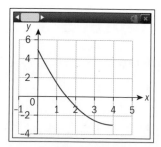

Range $-3 \le y \le 5$

d

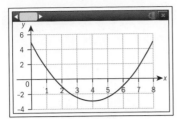

Range $-3 \le y \le 5$

e

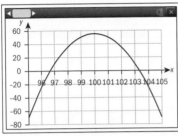

Range $-70 \le y \le 55$

f

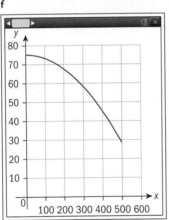

Range $28.5 \le y \le 75$

3 a $(-2.62, 0)$ and $(7.62, 0)$

b $(0, -8)$ **c** $x = 2.5$

d $(1.255, -9.88)$

4 a $5.05\,\text{m}$

b 31.75, ball travels $31.75\,\text{m}$ horizontally

c $(0, 1)$, Zander hits the ball when it is at a height of $1\,\text{m}$ above the ground

5 a $4.31\,\text{m}$ **b** $x = 7.5$

c $x = 16.79$, horizontal distance shot-put has travelled when it hits the floor

d $y = 1.5$, height of the shot-put when it leaves Omar's hand.

6 a $6\,\text{m}$

b $x = 10$

c $x = 0$ and $x = 20$; $x = 0$ is position of the ball when Ziyue kicks it, and $x = 20$ is the horizontal distance the ball has travelled when it hits the ground.

11 a

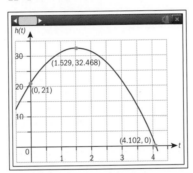

b $32.5\,\text{m}$ **c** $4.10\,\text{s}$

Exercise 6B

1 a $y = 50 - x$ **b** $A = 50x - x^2$

c

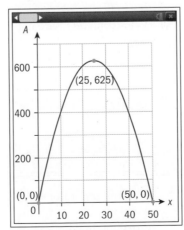

d $(0, 0)$ and $(50, 0)$

e $(0, 0)$ **f** $x = 25$

7 a $4.68\,\text{m}$

b $(8.59, 0)$ and $(29.8, 0)$, horizontal distance from the left hand side of the ramp as it passes through ground level.

8 a $8.01\,\text{m}$ **b** $4\,\text{s}$

9 a $96\,\text{m}$ **b** $164\,\text{m}$ **c** $174\,\text{m}$

10 a, b

n	1	2	3	4	5	6	7	8
$S_n = 15n - 2n^2$	13	22	27	28	25	18	7	-8

c 28 **d** 7

g $(25, 625)$

h $625\,\text{m}^2$, $x = 25\,\text{m}$ and $y = 25\,\text{m}$

2 a $y = 35 - x$

b $A = 35x - x^2$

c

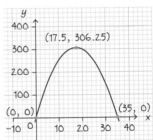

d $(0, 0)$ and $(35, 0)$

e These are the two values for the frame width which would give an area of zero. As such, these are the upper and lower limits for the width of the frame.

f $x = \dfrac{0 + 35}{2} = 17.5$, passes through the maximum point of the graph, so gives value of x which gives maximum area of the frame.

3 a (Profit) = (income) − (cost)

$$P(x) = \left(-0.12x^2 + 30x\right) - \left(0.1x^2 + 400\right)$$
$$= \left(-0.12 - 0.1\right)x^2 + 30x - 400$$
$$= -0.22x^2 + 30x - 400$$

b

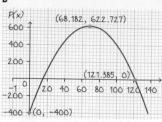

c The x-intercepts are the number of books which give a profit of €0.

d $x = 68.2$, since it is meaningless to produce 0.2 books, producing 68 books will maximise the profit.

4 a $a = 6$ and $d = 10 - 6 = 4$ so

$$S_n = \frac{n}{2}\big(2(6) + (n-1)(4)\big)$$

$$= \frac{n}{2}(12 + 4n - 4)$$

$$= 4n + 2n^2$$

b $2n^2 + 4n - 880 = 0$

c $n > 20$

5 After 2.6 s

6 a i $y = 6 - x$ **ii** $A = 6x - x^2$

iii

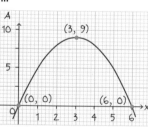

iv $9\,\text{m}^2$

b i $y = 12 - 2x$ **ii** $A = 12x - 2x^2$

iii

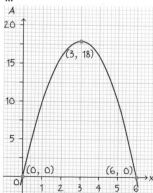

iv $18\,\text{m}^2$

c i $y = 12 - x$

ii $A = 12x - x^2$

iii

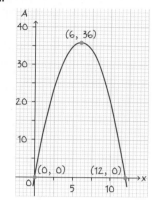

iv $36\,\text{m}^2$

v The design in part **c** will give the maximum area.

Exercise 6C

1 a $f^{-1}(x) = \sqrt{x - 4}$, domain $x \geq 4$, range $y \geq 0$

b $f^{-1}(x) = 1 + \sqrt{x + 2}$, domain $x \geq -2$, range $y \geq 1$

c $f^{-1}(x) = \sqrt{\dfrac{x}{2}} - 3$, domain $x \geq 0$, range $y \geq -3$

d $f^{-1}(x) = 2 + \sqrt{\dfrac{1-x}{3}}$, domain $x \geq 1$, range $y \geq 2$

2 a $R(p) = (175 - 3.5p)p$
$= 175p - 3.5p^2$

b $C(p) = 1750 - 17.5p$

c $P(p) = -3.5p^2 + 192.5p - 1750$

3 a

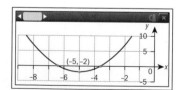

b $f(x)$ is not one-to-one if the domain is $x \in \mathbb{R}$. It fails the horizontal line test as it is symmetric about $x = -5$.

c $x \geq -5$

d

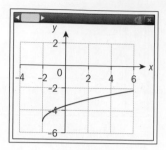

4

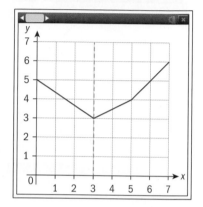

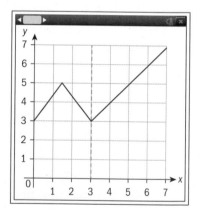

Exercise 6D

1 $y = x^2 + 3x - 4$

2 $y = -3x^2 + 3x + 6$

3 $y = 2x^2 - 7x - 4$

4 $y = 2x^2 - 12x + 22$

5 $y = -0.980x^2 - 9.80x - 12.5$

6 a Substituting $x = 3$ and $f(x) = -4$ into the function $f(x) = ax^2 + bx + c$ gives

$-4 = a \times 3^2 + b \times 3 + c$

$\Rightarrow 9a + 3b + c = -4$

b $9 = 4a - 2b + c$ and
$-30 = 25a + 5b + c$

c $a = -\dfrac{52}{35}, b = -\dfrac{39}{35}, c = \dfrac{89}{7}$

d

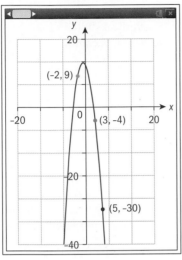

7 $y = -\dfrac{1}{48}x^2 + 192$

8 $y = -0.00915x^2 + 0.303x$

9 $f(x) = -0.12x^2 + 1.92x + 2$

Exercise 6E

1 **a, b**

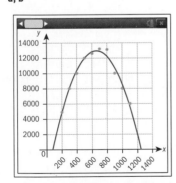

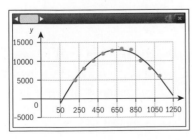

c $r = 0.988$ which is a very strong quadratic association, so equation $y = -0.0382x^2 + 50.5x - 3743$ is a good fit for this data.

d This equation only shows the association between the number of units sold and the profit. It is not linked to a particular period of the year, so could not be used to predict the company's profits at a particular time of year.

2 **a, b**

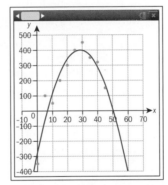

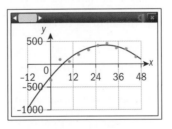

c $r = 0.954$ which is a very strong quadratic association, so equation $y = -0.835x^2 + 47.7x - 282$ is a good fit for this data.

d Week 52 lies outside the range of data given. Using this data to make a prediction for week 52 would be extrapolation, and therefore unreliable.

3 **a, b**

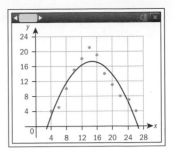

c 16.6 °C, since $r = 0.924$ suggests a very strong quadratic association, and because 17:00 is within the data range so is interpolation, this is likely to be a reliable estimate.

4 **a, b**

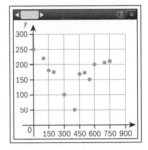

c A correlation coefficient of $r = 0.782$ suggests a strong quadratic association, and therefore Cindy can use this equation to accurately model the bridge.

d Since there is a strong correlation coefficient allowing Cindy to accurately use this equation to model the bridge, and also since 410 m is within the data range and is therefore interpolation, Cindy can use this equation to predict the height of the bridge at 410 m.

5 a

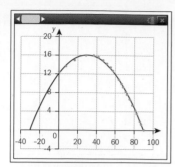

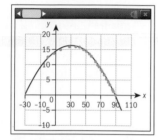

b 29.7°

c The coefficient of regression is 0.999, which indicates the data almost perfectly follows a quadratic model. Therefore, it is entirely appropriate to use the model function found in part **a**.

Exercise 6F

1 a $x^2 \to \left(\dfrac{x}{2}\right)^2 =$ horizontal stretch, scale factor 2,

$\left(\dfrac{x}{2}\right)^2 \to \left(\dfrac{x}{2}\right)^2 - 3 =$ vertical translation of 3 units down, with vector $\begin{pmatrix} 0 \\ -3 \end{pmatrix}$

b $2(x-3)^2 + 4 \to 2(x-3)^2$ = vertical translation down 4 units, with vector $\begin{pmatrix} 0 \\ -4 \end{pmatrix}$,

$2(x-3)^2 \to \dfrac{1}{2}\left[2(x-3)^2\right]$

$= (x-3)^2 =$ vertical stretch scale factor $\dfrac{1}{2}$,

$(x-3)^2 \to ((x-3)+3)^2 = x^2$
= horizontal translation 3 units to the left, vector $\begin{pmatrix} -3 \\ 0 \end{pmatrix}$

c $x^2 \to (x-1)^2$ is a horizontal translation 1 unit to the right, vector $\begin{pmatrix} 1 \\ 0 \end{pmatrix}$

$(x-1)^2 \to 4(x-1)^2$ is a vertical stretch, scale factor 4

$4(x-1)^2 \to 4(x-1)^2 + 2$ is a vertical translation of 2 units up, vector $\begin{pmatrix} 0 \\ 2 \end{pmatrix}$

d From part **b**, $2(x-3)^2 + 4 \to x^2 =$ is a vertical translation of 4 units down, with vector $\begin{pmatrix} 0 \\ -4 \end{pmatrix}$, followed by a vertical stretch scale factor $\dfrac{1}{2}$, followed by a horizontal translation 3 units to the left, with vector $\begin{pmatrix} -3 \\ 0 \end{pmatrix}$, $(x)^2 \to (x-2)^2$ is a translation 2 units to the right, with vector $\begin{pmatrix} 2 \\ 0 \end{pmatrix}$,

$(2-x)^2 \to -(2-x)^2$ is a reflection in the x-axis, $-(2-x)^2 \to 2-(2-x)^2$ = vertical translation of 2 units up, with vector $\begin{pmatrix} 0 \\ 2 \end{pmatrix}$

2 a $-2(x+3)^2$ **b** $\left(\dfrac{1}{2}x+1\right)^2$

c $\left(\dfrac{1}{2}x+2\right)^2$ **d** $(2-x)^2 + 1$

3 a $(1, 5)$

b $y(3) = 2(3-1)^2 + 5$
$= 2 \times 4 + 5 = 13$ so $(3, 13)$ lies on the curve.

c i $\left(\dfrac{1}{2}, 10\right)$ **ii** $(0, 26)$

d $y = 2(-(x)-1)^2 + 5$

---

e Horizontal translation 2 units right, curve becomes

$y = 2\left(-\left(x-\dfrac{3}{2}\right)-1\right)^2 + 5$

$= 2\left(\dfrac{1}{2}-x\right)^2 + 5$

Vertical stretch s.f. 2, curve becomes

$y = 4\left(\dfrac{1}{2}-x\right)^2 + 10$

4 a $x^2 \to (x-2)^2$ horizontal translation $\begin{pmatrix} 2 \\ 0 \end{pmatrix}$

$(x-2)^2 \to -(x-2)^2$ reflection in the x-axis

$-(x-2)^2 \to 5 - (x-2)^2$ vertical translation $\begin{pmatrix} 0 \\ 5 \end{pmatrix}$

b $h(x) = 13 - 2(x-1)^2$

5 a i

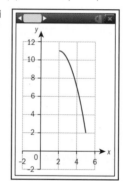

ii Range $2 \le y \le 11$

iii $x^2 \to (x-2)^2$ horizontal translation $\begin{pmatrix} 2 \\ 0 \end{pmatrix}$

$(x-2)^2 \to -(x-2)^2$ reflection in the x-axis

$-(x-2)^2 \to 11 - (x-2)^2$ vertical translation $\begin{pmatrix} 0 \\ 11 \end{pmatrix}$

b $g(x) = 5 - \dfrac{1}{2}(x-5)^2$

6 Need to reverse the transformations, in the reverse order in which they were applied.

Translation by $\begin{pmatrix} -2 \\ -5 \end{pmatrix}$ to take

$h(x) \to g(x)$

Translation $\begin{pmatrix} 0 \\ 15 \end{pmatrix}$ maps

$2(x+2)^2 - 15 \to 2(x+2)^2$

Stretch s.f. $\dfrac{1}{2}$ in y-direction

maps $2(x+2)^2 \to (x+2)^2$

Translation $\begin{pmatrix} 2 \\ 0 \end{pmatrix}$ maps

$(x+2)^2 \to ((x-2)+2)^2 = x^2$

7 a $x^2 \to (x-1)^2$ translation $\begin{pmatrix} 1 \\ 0 \end{pmatrix}$

$(x-1)^2 \to 3(x-1)^2$ vertical stretch s.f. 3

---

8 a $(t \circ f \circ r)(x) = t(-x)^2$ (reflection in the y-axis)

$= (-x)^2 + 1$ (translation $\begin{pmatrix} 0 \\ 1 \end{pmatrix}$)

b $(s \circ f \circ t)(x) = s(x+1)^2$ translation $\begin{pmatrix} -1 \\ 0 \end{pmatrix}$

$= 2(x+1)^2$ stretch s.f. 2 in y direction

c $(t \circ s \circ f)(x) = (t \circ s)x^2$

$= t(2x^2)$ stretch s.f. 2 in y direction

$= 2x^2 + 1$ translation $\begin{pmatrix} 0 \\ 1 \end{pmatrix}$

d $(f \circ s \circ r)(x) = ((s \circ r)(x))^2$

$= (s(-x))^2$ reflection in y-axis

$= (-2x)^2$ stretch s.f. $\dfrac{1}{2}$ in x-direction

e   Vertex of $f(x) = x^2$ is $(0, 0)$: part a: $(0, 0) \to (0, 0) \to (0, 1)$; part b: $(0, 0) \to (-1, 0) \to (-1, 0)$; part c: $(0, 0) \to (0, 0) \to (0, 1)$; part d: $(0, 0) \to (0, 0) \to (0, 0)$

---

9 a i $(4, 1)$

ii $(8, 1)$

b i $\left(\dfrac{1}{2}x - 3\right)^2$

ii $\left(\dfrac{1}{2}x - 3\right)^2$ These are the same equation.

$3(x-1)^2 \to 3(x-1)^2 + 2$

translation $\begin{pmatrix} 0 \\ 2 \end{pmatrix}$

b   Translation $\begin{pmatrix} 0 \\ -3 \end{pmatrix}$ maps

$3(x-1)^2 + 2 \to 3(x-1)^2 - 1$

Reflection in x-axis maps

$3(x-1)^2 - 1 \to -3(x-1)^2 + 1$

c $h(x) = -3(x-1)^2 + 1$

Exercise 6G

1

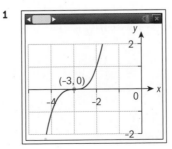

2

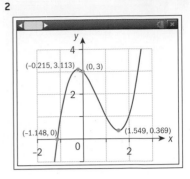

3

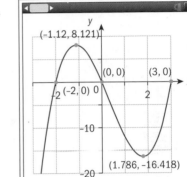

4

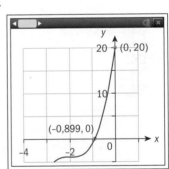

5

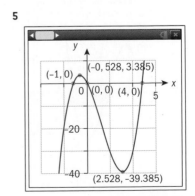

6 a

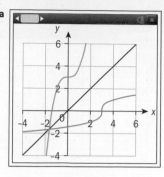

$$f^{-1}(x) = x^{\frac{1}{3}} - 3$$

b

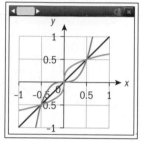

$$f^{-1}(x) = \left(\frac{1}{4}x\right)^{\frac{1}{3}}$$

c

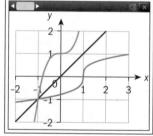

$$f^{-1}(x) = \left(\frac{x-1}{2}\right)^{\frac{1}{3}}$$

7

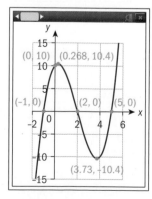

a (−1, 0), (0, 10), (2, 0) and (5, 0)

b (0.268, 10.4) and (3.73, −10.4)

c $f(-x) = -x^3 - 6x^2 - 3x + 10$

8 a High = 24.7 °C, low = 19.2 °C

b 20.7 °C

c 11.7 hours

d The function descends rapidly after $t = 24$, so is not a realistic model for the temperature when $t < 24$. As such, the model would not be helpful to predict the temperature at 01.00 on Wednesday.

9 a

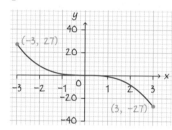

$$-27 \le f(x) \le 27$$

b

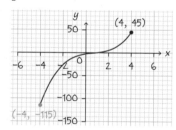

$$-115 \le f(x) \le 45$$

c

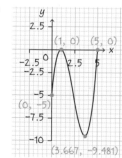

$$-9.48 \le f(x) \le 0$$

10 a Length = width = $(50 - 2x)$ cm, height = x cm

b Volume = $x(50 - 2x)^2$

c $0 < x < 25$

d

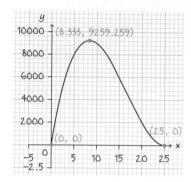

e Max volume = 9259 cm³ when $x = 8.33$ cm

11 a 31.2 °C

b Lowest max in October, highest max in April

c 20.45

d July

e July is midway between April and October. The max temperature in July is roughly equal to the mean max temperature of April and October suggesting the temperature falls uniformly between April and October.

12 a

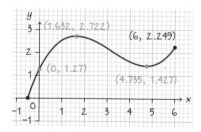

b $1.427 \le f(x) \le 2.722$.

c Length = 6, height = 1.295

13 a

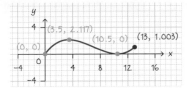

b 13 m

c 2.117 m

d The model function needs to be translated 24 units upwards, in the y-direction. This gives the function

$$y = \frac{1}{81}x^3 - \frac{7}{27}x^2 + \frac{49}{36}x + 24.$$

14 a

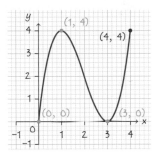

b $(0, 0)$

c Max at $(1, 4)$ and min at $(3, 0)$

d $0 \leq f(x) \leq 4$

e $g(x) = -f(x)$,

$h(x) = \frac{1}{2}f(x)$,

$j(x) = f(x) - 4$

f $(j \circ h \circ g \circ f)(x)$

$= (j \circ h)(-f(x))$

$= j\left(-\frac{1}{2}f(x)\right)$

$= -\frac{1}{2}f(x) - 4$

g $f(x) = -\frac{1}{2}x^3 + 3x^2 - \frac{9}{2}x - 4$,

$0 \leq x \leq 4$

h

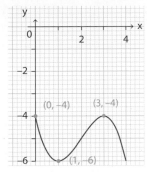

i A positive coefficient of x^3 means that the graph increases to a maximum first, descends to a minimum, and then goes off to infinity as x becomes large.

A negative coefficient of x^3 means that the graph decreases to a minimum first, ascends to a maximum, and then goes off to minus infinity as x becomes large.

j The constant term determines the value of the y-intercept.

15 a Function is one-to-one along its entire domain, so invertible for $x \in \mathbb{R}$

b Function is one-to-one for $x \geq 1.618$, so invertible for $x \geq 1.618$

c Function is one-to-one along its entire domain, so invertible for $x \in \mathbb{R}$

d Function is one-to-one along its entire domain, so invertible for $x \in \mathbb{R}$

16 7.85 cm, 24.3 cm and 44.3 cm

Exercise 6H

1 a $h(t) = 0.00758t^3 + 0.154t^2 - 1.662t + 6.227$

b 2.5 m

c $h(t) = 0.245t - 1.936t + 6.355$

d The cubic function is a better model, but only by a very small margin.

2 a

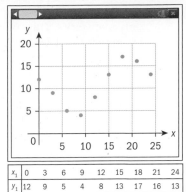

x_1	0	3	6	9	12	15	18	21	24
y_1	12	9	5	4	8	13	17	16	13

$T(t) = -0.00848t^3 + 0.335t^2 - 3.162t + 13.283$

b The shape of the points in the scatter diagram follows the general shape of a cubic, as it has both a minimum and a maximum point. The coefficient of regression is $R^2 = 0.915$ which is very strong, and confirms the observation.

c Using the model to approximate the temperature within the times recorded is interpolation, and the model would be valid for these times. Using the model to approximate the temperature for the next day is extrapolation, and the model might not be valid for these times.

3 a

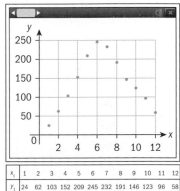

x_1	1	2	3	4	5	6	7	8	9	10	11	12
y_1	24	62	103	152	209	245	232	191	146	123	96	58

$y = 0.153x^3 - 9.15x^2 + 98.8x - 87.5$

b The scatterplot shows that the data appears to have only one vertex. This could mean that the data is in the shape of a parabola, in which case a best fit quadratic curve would be appropriate, or it could mean that a portion of a cubic curve might be best. The coefficient of regression for the quadratic curve is $R^2 = 0.909$, and for the cubic curve is $R^2 = 0.914$. This is marginally better, so use a best fit cubic curve.

c We do not know whether the data will continue to behave like this cubic function in the future, so the model is not useful in predicting the number of future cases.

4 a

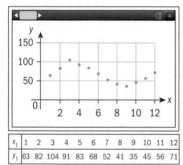

x_1	1	2	3	4	5	6	7	8	9	10	11	12
y_1	63	82	104	91	83	68	52	41	35	45	56	71

$y = 0.504x^3 - 9.57x^2 + 46.4x + 27.2$

b By observation, the shape of the points in the scatter diagram in part **a** follows the general shape of a cubic, as it has both a minimum and a maximum point.

c The coefficient of regression is $R^2 = 0.947$ which is very strong, and confirms our observation from **b**. A cubic model is appropriate.

5 a i $y = -2.71x^2 + 18.7x - 7.40$

 ii $R^2 = 0.902$

 iii $y = 0.5x^3 - 7.96x^2 + 34.5x - 20$

 iv $R^2 = 0.955$

b Cubic model

c A particle moving under gravity will always follow a parabolic path, so the quadratic function could be a better model.

6 a Max value is 0, at the two end points

b (0, 0)

7 a A quadratic model might be appropriate as the ball follows the general path of a parabola. However, it seems that the path is not quite symmetrical about the vertex (which a parabola is), so a quadratic model may not be appropriate.

b A cubic model does not need to be symmetric about a maximum point, so might be a better model.

c The theory does not take into account air resistance. When air resistance is considered, quadratic functions are not wholly appropriate.

8 a By plotting the points on a scatter diagram, it appears that the F-hole approximately follows the shape of a cubic curve, so could be modelled by a cubic equation.

b $y = -0.00716x^3 + 0.197x^2 - 1.69x + 8.97$, $0 \le x \le 16.5$

c The coefficient of determination is $R^2 = 0.991$ which is very strong, so this model is appropriate.

d

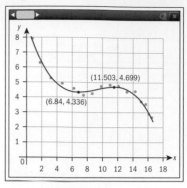

Best fit cubic curve gives minimum at (6.84, 4.34) and a maximum at (11.5, 4.70)

9 a 144 m **b** 5 m

c Roller coaster descends 139 m, so this is the greatest vertical descent

10 a

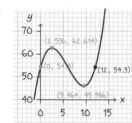

$0 \le x \le 12$

b 2.54 months

c $t = 9.46$ months

d Parts of August, September, October and November

Exercise 6I

1 a i $R = 2.1v$, $R = 1.05v^2$

 b Linear: $R(3.2) = 2.1 \times 3.2 = 6.72$, $R(4.0) = 2.1 \times 4.0 = 8.4$

 Quadratic: $R(3.2) = 1.05 \times 3.2^2 = 10.752$, $R(4.0) = 1.05 \times 4.0^2 = 16.8$

 c Linear model much more likely as the sum of squares of residuals is much smaller than for the quadratic model.

 d $R = 1.59v^{1.358}$

e Sum of squares of residuals is 0.809 which is much smaller than sum of squares of the linear model, so relationship between v and R is likely to be a power function.

2 a $d = kt^2$, $t = 2$,

$d = 9 \Rightarrow 9 = 4k \Rightarrow k = \dfrac{9}{4}$,

$d = \dfrac{9}{4}t^2$

b $d(5) = \dfrac{9}{4} \times 5^2 = 56.25$ m

c $26.01 = \dfrac{9}{4}t^2 \Rightarrow t$

$= \sqrt{\dfrac{4}{9} \times 26.01} = 3.4$ s

3 1570.83 g

4 a

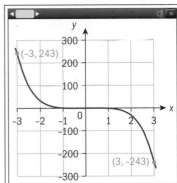

$-243 \le y \le 243$

b

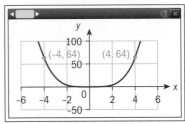

$0 \le y \le 64$

c

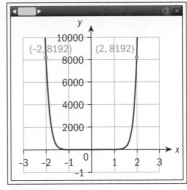

$0 \le y \le 8192$

5 a

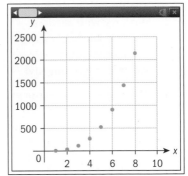

x_1	1	2	3	4	5	6	7	8
y_1	4.19	33.5	113	268	524	905	1440	2140

b $V = 4.19\,r^{3.00}$

c $R^2 = 1$ so the power model fits this data perfectly

d

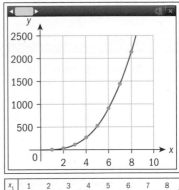

x_1	1	2	3	4	5	6	7	8
y_1	4.19	33.5	113	268	524	905	1440	2140

Power function is a perfect fit.

e 4190

f 4188.79

6 a $W = \dfrac{6875}{132}p^4$

b 173 827 kg

c 7.87 m

7 a $f^{-1}(x) = \sqrt{x}$, $x \ge 0$

b $f^{-1}(x) = \sqrt[3]{-x}$

c $f^{-1}(x) = \sqrt[5]{\dfrac{x}{2}}$

Exercise 6J

1 $V = 4$ Pa

2 8

3 a

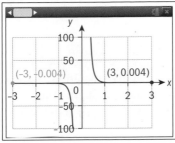

$-\infty < f(x) \le -0.004115$ and $0.004115 \le x < \infty$

b

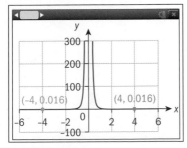

$0.016 \le g(x) < \infty$

c

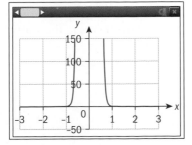

$\dfrac{1}{8192} \le f(x) < \infty$

4 a $\dfrac{1}{250}$ **b** 0.171 m

5 a

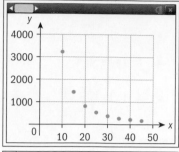

x_1	10	15	20	25	30	35	40	45
y_1	3232	1434	805	513	535	259	201	159

b Follows general shape of an inverse variation curve

c $I = \dfrac{261\,320}{x^{1.954}}$

d $R^2 = 0.975$ which is a very strong coefficient of determination, so the inverse variation function appears an appropriate model.

e

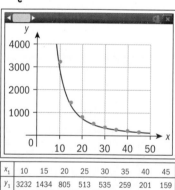

x_1	10	15	20	25	30	35	40	45
y_1	3232	1434	805	513	535	259	201	159

f 125 lux

6 a

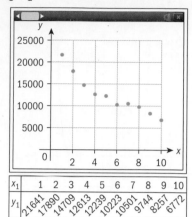

x_1	1	2	3	4	5	6	7	8	9	10
y_1	21641	17890	14709	12613	12239	10223	10501	9744	8257	6772

b The price of a car does not vary with age in a linear fashion. If it did, the value of the car would be worthless very quickly.

c The depreciation of the car is quite a lot in the early years, but levels off as the car gets older. An inverse variation function could model this.

d $P = 23688t^{-0.46253}$

e $R^2 = 0.939$ which is a very strong coefficient of determination, so the inverse variation function appears an appropriate model.

f

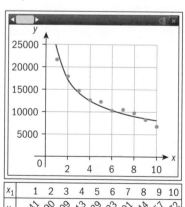

x_1	1	2	3	4	5	6	7	8	9	10
y_1	21641	17890	14709	12613	12239	10223	10501	9744	8257	6772

This model fits the general shape of the data well. There are a similar number of points above and below the curve.

g $4000 = 23\,688t^{-0.46253}$

Solving using GDC or logs $\Rightarrow t = 46.8$ years

7 a Invertible for $x \geq 0$

b Invertible for $x \in \mathbb{R}$

c Invertible for $x \geq 0$

8 a $f^{-1}(x) = -\dfrac{1}{x^{\frac{1}{4}}}$

b $f^{-1}(x) = \sqrt[3]{\dfrac{2}{x}}$

c $f^{-1}(x) = \dfrac{1}{\sqrt{x}}$

9 a $\dfrac{1}{x} \to \dfrac{1}{x-1}$, translation by vector $\begin{pmatrix} 1 \\ 0 \end{pmatrix}$

$\dfrac{1}{x-1} \to \dfrac{2}{x-1}$, stretch in y-direction s.f. = 2

$\dfrac{2}{x-1} \to -\dfrac{2}{x-1}$, reflection in x-axis

$-\dfrac{2}{x-1} \to 3 - \dfrac{2}{x-1}$, translation by vector $\begin{pmatrix} 0 \\ 3 \end{pmatrix}$

b $\dfrac{1}{x}$ has vertical asymptote at $x = 0$ as the function is not defined here

$\dfrac{1}{x}$ has horizontal asymptote at $y = 0$ as $\dfrac{1}{x} \to 0$ as $x \to \infty$

$3 - \dfrac{2}{x-1}$ has vertical asymptote at $x = 1$ as the function is not defined here

$3 - \dfrac{2}{x-1}$ has horizontal asymptote at $y = 3$ as $\dfrac{2}{x-1} \to 0$ as $x \to \infty$

c The same transformations which map f onto g also map the asymptotes of f onto the asymptotes of g.

10 $1 - \dfrac{2}{x-2} \to -\dfrac{2}{x-2}$

translation by vector $\begin{pmatrix} 0 \\ -1 \end{pmatrix}$

$-\dfrac{2}{x-2} \to \dfrac{2}{x-2}$ reflection in x-axis

$\dfrac{2}{x-2} \to \dfrac{1}{x-2}$ Stretch in y-direction s.f. $\dfrac{1}{2}$

$\dfrac{1}{x-2} \to \dfrac{1}{x}$ translation by vector $\begin{pmatrix} -2 \\ 0 \end{pmatrix}$

11 a i The shape of the demand curve resembles that of an inverse power law. As such, it must be true that $n < 0$.

ii As N gets large, this function suggests that a small percentage of the market might still buy the product, unlikely to be realistic when N is unreasonably large.

b $k = 57$, $n = -1.066$

Chapter review

1 a

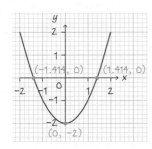

b

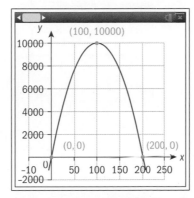

2 a $h = 200 - x$

b $A = 200x - x^2$

c

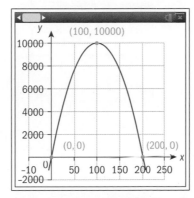

d $(0, 0)$ and $(200, 0)$, represent the limiting values of x for which the picture can be a rectangle.

3 a $(0, -7)$

b $(-7, 0)$ and $(1, 0)$

c $x = -3$

d $(-3, -16)$

4 a $(0, 1.9)$, stone is thrown from a height of $1.9\,\mathrm{m}$

b $10.025\,\mathrm{m}$

c $4\,\mathrm{s}$

5 a i $x = 2$ and $x = 4$

ii $x = 3$ **iii** $(3, -3)$

b i $x = -1$ and $x = 5$

ii $x = 2$ **iii** $(2, -36)$

6 a

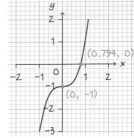

b

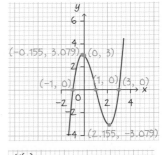

7 a

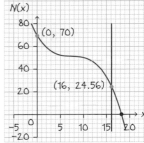

b 52.5 **c** 46.5

d $70, 2004$ **e** $25, 2017$

f 2001

8 a $m = 80t$ **b** 160 miles

c 3.75 hours

9 $(-3.41, -0.204)$ and $(1.91, 2.45)$

10

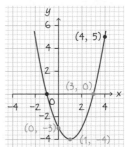

Minimum occurs at vertex, where $y = -4$, maximum value occurs at $x = 4$, and is $f(x) = 5$

11 a $a = \dfrac{205.701}{t^2}$

b 20.3 s

12 a 3

b $f(x) = -\dfrac{8}{9}x^2 + \dfrac{16}{3}x$

13 a $n = -4$, $k = 512$

b Same results as part **a**

14 $0.438 \leq x \leq 4.562$

15 a $BC = 60 - 2x$

b $A = 60x - 2x^2$

c

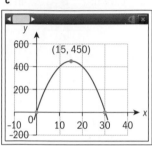

Max value of the area is $A = 450$ when $x = 15$.

16 a 12 m

b 17 m

c **i** $17 = -t^2 + 6t + 12$

ii $t = 1$ or 5

d **i** $x = 3$

ii 21 m

17

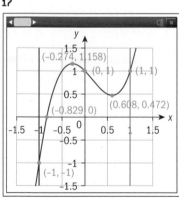

$-1 \leq y \leq 1.158$.

18 a 126 mm (3 s.f.)

b Greatest in December, lowest in February

c 230.31 mm

d October

e The mean rainfall occurs much nearer to December than to February. This suggests that the majority of the rainfall occurs towards the end of the year, confirmed by the shape of the curve, which is concave-up.

19 a

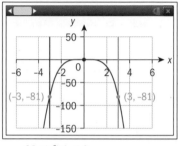

$-81 \leq f(x) \leq 0$

b

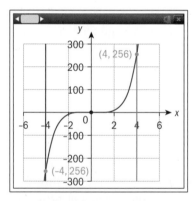

$-256 \leq g(x) \leq 256$

c

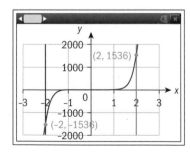

$-1536 \leq h(x) \leq 1536$

20 a $y = -0.00489x^3 + 29.6x^2 - 59\,561x + 40\,004\,542$

b Using this model to predict future gasoline prices would be extrapolation, so the model may not apply outside the given domain. However, this model does not suggest drastic changes over the 10 years after 2017, so it may well give a sensible estimate of gasoline prices, at least up to 2027.

c 31.35 Euros

21 a

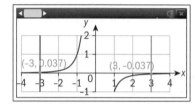

$-\infty < y \leq -0.037$ and $0.037 \leq y < \infty$

b

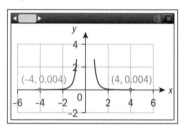

$0.004 \leq y < \infty$

c

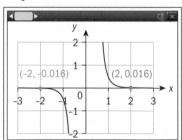

$-\infty < y \leq -0.016$ and $0.016 \leq y < \infty$

Exam-style questions

22 a $t = 10\text{s}$

  b Reaches max height at $t = 5\text{s}$

  c 126.7 m

  d The displacement-time graphs for Paul's bullet is a translation of Peter's graph by 0.1 m in the y-direction.

23 a $D = b^2 - 4ac = k^2 - 36$

    i $k = 6$ or $k = -6$

    ii $-6 < k < 6$

    iii $k < -6$ or $k > 6$

  b $D = b^2 - 4ac = k^2 + 36$, which is always positive, so there are always 2 roots.

24 a $(3, 7)$

  b Domain $x \geq 3$; Range $y \geq 7$

  c Domain $x \geq 7$; Range $y \geq 3$

25 a $(50, 12.5)$ **b** $(20, 26)$

  c $x > 73.4\text{m}$

26 a 7.07 s (3 s.f.)   **b** 12.8 m

  c $d = 5\text{m}$

27 1113 or 1311

28 a $k = -5$ **b** $l = 5$ or 1

  c $r = 3, s = 4$

  d $a < 0, b = 3, c = 4$

29 a $a = 9, b = -10, c = 11$

  b The point does not lie on the quadratic.

  c $p = 1, q = 2, r = 4, s = 3$

30 4 m

Chapter 7

Skills check

1 a x^6 **b** $\dfrac{b}{a}$

  c $\sqrt{x^3}$ **d** $\sqrt[6]{x}$

  e $\sqrt{x^5}$

2 a 0.72   **b** 10.8

  c 42

3 a $x = \{-1, 0, 1, 2\}$, $y = \{4, 1, -2, -5\}$

  b $f(12) = 1 - 3 \times 12 = -11$

  c

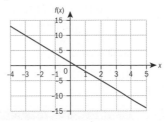

4 a 96   **b** 96   **c** 100

Exercise 7A

1 a $r = 2, u_7 = 320, u_n = 5 \times 2^{n-1}$

  b $r = -5, u_8 = -1\,171\,875$, $u_n = (-3)(-5)^{n-1}$

  c $r = \sqrt{3}, u_6 = 27\sqrt{2}$, $u_n = \sqrt{2} \times \left(\sqrt{3}\right)^{n-1}$

  d $r = \dfrac{2}{3}, u_4 = \dfrac{4}{9}, u_n = \left(\dfrac{2}{3}\right)^{n-2}$

  e $r = 10, u_{10} = 2 \times 10^9$, $u_n = 2 \times 10^{n-1}$

2 a $r = 2; u_n = 2 \times 2^{n-1}$

  b $r = 1.5, u_n = 32 \times 1.5^{n-1}$

  c $r = 3, u_n = 1 \times 3^{n-1}$

  d $r = \dfrac{2}{3}, u_n = \dfrac{1}{2} \times \dfrac{2}{3}^{n-1}$

  e $r = 3$ or $r = -3; u_n = -2 \times 3^{n-1}$

  f $r = 3\sqrt{\dfrac{245}{9}}; u_n = 13.5 \times 3\sqrt{\dfrac{245}{9}}^{n-1}$

3 a $r = \dfrac{10}{2} = 5$, so $u_3 = 2 \times 5^2 = 50$, so, geometric sequence

  b 31 250

  c 2.6×10^{255}; not a reasonable answer as the total population of the world is less than 10^{10} people.

Exercise 7B

1 a 223 000

  b 349 801

  c No, too fast. In just 4 years the population almost doubled!

2 $ 2.44

3 €33 079

4 a €10 222   **b** 8.59 years

5 a 1.125   **b** 0.27

  c 0.89   **d** 1.001

6 a 1.69 m   **b** 1.61 m

  c 1.77 m

7 a 15.43 billion

  b 4.73 billion

  c 35.54 billion

  d By 2029

  e 0.36%

Exercise 7C

1 a 7.53 cm   **b** 23.85 cm

2 a 12.3 million

  b 63.28 million

  c 350.89 million

  d 27 hours

3 a 1.062   **b** 3.29 billion

  c 193.5%

  d At least 10 years

  e It will soon reach scale of the population of the world, so it can no longer grow as fast.

4 a $r = 2$ **b** 768

  c 9   **d** 20

5 a 976 562

  b 479.275   **c** 3.55

6 a 0.998   **b** 30.1 s

  c Yes

Exercise 7D

1 a Series diverges

  b 2 000 000

  c Series diverges   **d** 1

2 a $r = \dfrac{6}{7}$ b 5

3 a $r = \dfrac{6}{7}$

b $u_1 = 4$

$u_2 = 4 \cdot \dfrac{5}{6} = \dfrac{10}{3}$

$u_3 = \dfrac{10}{3} \cdot \dfrac{5}{6} = \dfrac{25}{9}$

c $v_1 = 4^2 = 16$

$v_2 = \left(\dfrac{10}{3}\right)^2 = \dfrac{100}{9}$

$v_3 = \left(\dfrac{25}{9}\right)^2 = \dfrac{625}{81}$

d $r_{new} = \dfrac{\dfrac{100}{9}}{16} = \dfrac{25}{36}$

e $S_{\times(new)} = \dfrac{v_1}{1 - r_{new}}$

$= \dfrac{16}{1 - \dfrac{25}{36}} = \dfrac{576}{11}$

f $\dfrac{\dfrac{576}{11}}{24^2} = \dfrac{1}{11}$

4 a 1.5 m   b 1.125 m

c 0.834 75 m   d 0.75

e No   f 8 m

5 a 8π b 4π

c 12π d $\dfrac{\pi}{2}$

e 15.5π f 7

g 16π

6 a 0.792 m   b 7

c 5.07 m   d 9.09 m

Exercise 7E

1 Oswald

2 a 68 512 NIS

b 22.005 years

c 3.52%

3 a 5.1%   b 8

4 6

5 €6000

6 a 6.14%   b 6.17%

7 a 0.3%   b $20 060

8 a 0.6%   b $2012

Exercise 7F

1 a $111.02   b $5742.60

2 a AED 671.47

b AED 21 869.80

3 a TRY 951 026.40

b 542.5 months, or 45 years

4 a €178.12   b €2078.60

5 Yes

Exercise 7G

1 a i (0, 2)   ii $y = 1$

iii Increasing

b i (0, −3)   ii $y = -3$

iii Decreasing

Exercise 7H

1

	y-intercept	Horizontal asymptote	Growth or decay	Range
$f(x) = e^x + 3$	(0, 4)	$y = 3$	Growth	$[3, \infty)$
$f(x) = 2e^{-x} + 4$	(0, 6)	$y = 4$	Decay	$(-\infty, 4]$
$f(x) = 0.2e^{0.3x} - 2$	(0, 0)	$y = -2$	Growth	$[-2, \infty)$
$f(x) = 5 - 2e^{-3x}$	(0, 3)	$y = 5$	Decay	$(-\infty, 5)$

2 a

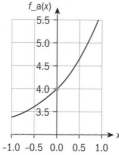

b

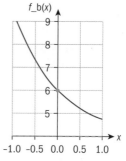

c

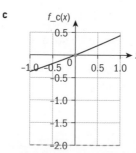

d

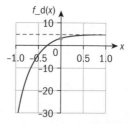

c i (0, 1)   ii $y = 0$

iii Increasing

d i (0, 3)   ii $y = 2$

iii Increasing

e i (0, −2) ii $y = -5$

iii Increasing

f i (0, 7)   ii $y = 3$

iii Decreasing

g i (0, 4)   ii $y = -1$

iii Increasing

h i (0, 1)   ii $y = -1$

iii Decreasing

2 a $2 \times 16^x + 5$ b $7 \times 8^x + 2$

3 a 22   b 6.6 hours

c $S_2(t) = 14 + 10 \times 1.2^{-t}$

d $S_3(t) = 12 + 10 \times 1.2^{-\frac{t}{2}}$

e $S_4(t) = 24 + 20 \times 1.2^{-t}$

3 **a** $T(0) = 80.4$

b It corresponds to the initial temperature at the moment it is removed from heat.

c Decay

d A hot cup of water will cool down and thus its temperature will fall.

e 24.5

f The temperature of the water will tend towards the temperature of the room it is in.

g $24.5 < T \le 80.4$ The initial temperature of 80.4 falls towards the temperature of the room, which is 24.5

h

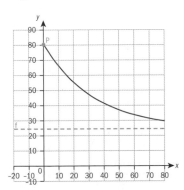

4 **a** 1.488

b $\dfrac{3}{2}$

Exercise 7I

1 **a** $k = 0.15$

b 64 825

c 63

2 **a** 952 kg

b 413.74 kg

c 2.079 min

d 6.908 min

3 **a** $y = -3$

b

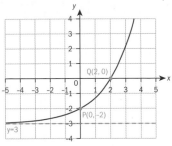

c $D_f: x \in , \mathbb{R}_f: y > -3$

4 **a** $a = 5000$ **b** 0.1

c 40

5 **a**

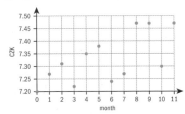

b It is an increasing set of points

c $CZK(t) = 4.08e^{0.004t} + 3.135$

d 0.446

e

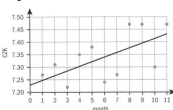

f 91 months, or 7.58 years

6 **a**

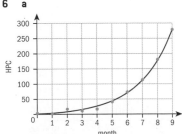

b Follows a geometric sequence with common ratio 2.

c $u_n = 200 \cdot 2^n$ **d** 566

e

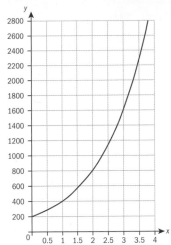

f The graph shows exponential growth. The domain is all the positive real numbers, whereas the range is $y \ge 200$.

7 **a** $k = 0.15$ **b** 64823

c 33

8 **a** $a = 5000$ **b** $b = -0.1$

c $T = 40$

9 **a** 1000 **b** $k = \dfrac{1}{2}$

c 16000 **d** $t = 10$

Exercise 7J

1 **a** 2 **b** −1 **c** 1 **d** −1

e 2 **f** $\dfrac{1}{2}$ **g** $-\dfrac{1}{2}$

2 **a** 1 **b** 2 **c** $\log(38)$

d 2 **e** $\ln(3)$

f $\ln(0.3)$ **g** 0

3 **a** $\log(x^2)$ **b** $\log \sqrt[3]{x}$

c $\log(x^3 y^2)$ **d** $\log\left(\dfrac{x}{y^3}\right)$

e $\ln(x^{-2})$ **f** $\log 100x$

g $\ln\left(\dfrac{x}{yz}\right)$

4 **a** $\ln\left(\dfrac{1}{2}\right)$ **b** $\dfrac{1}{2}e^4$

Exercise 7K

1 a i $\log(3)$

  ii $\log(75)$

  iii $\ln(5)$

  b i $\ln(5)$

  ii $\log(4)$

  iii $\ln\left(\dfrac{8}{3}\right)$

2 a $\log_a(c)$

  b $\ln\left(\dfrac{2}{b}\right)$

  c $\log\left(\dfrac{k}{2}\right)$

3 a x^3 **b** $\dfrac{x}{y}$

  c $\dfrac{x^2}{y}$ **d** $\dfrac{1}{x^2}$

4 a $2x+4$

  b Vertical asymptote at $x=-2$, $(-1, 0)$

  c

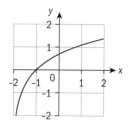

5 a $f^{-1}(x)=\log(x+3)$

  b Vertical asymptote: $x=-3$, $(-2, 0)$

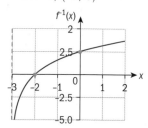

  c Domain: $x\in(-3, \infty)$, range: $y\in\mathbb{R}$.

6 a

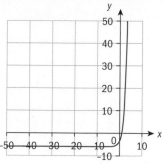

Horizontal asymptote: $y=-6$, $(\ln(3), 0)$

  b $f^{-1}(x)=\log\left(\dfrac{1}{2}(x+6)\right)$

  c Domain: $x\in(-6, \infty)$, range: $y\in\mathbb{R}$

Exercise 7L

1 a $B=1584.89$, $G=3\,981\,071$, G is 2511.88 times greater than B

  b From $A\to y=10^{1.7}=50.11$ to $J\to y=10^{10.1}=1.259\times10^{10}$

  c Yes

2 a

	GNI–Log float64	LE–Log float64
1	4.62408	1.90687
2	4.59406	1.90417
3	4.14551	1.8704
4	4.28623	1.88705
5	4.38525	1.89098
6	4.62634	1.90255
7	4.31869	1.88252
8	4.58546	1.90472
9	4.55206	1.91169
10	4.60173	1.9058
11	4.41647	1.9058
12	4.30664	1.87506
13	4.52153	1.90634
14	4.51468	1.91381
15	4.25091	1.87274
16	4.29425	1.87099
17	4.80895	1.91116
18	4.63609	1.90795
19	4.31133	1.88366
20	4.38881	1.90417
21	4.18013	1.87216
22	4.34694	1.88138
23	4.43072	1.90255
24	4.50051	1.91381
25	4.62531	1.91222
26	4.55558	1.9058

  b $y=0.079\log(x)+1.54$

  c $a=34.86$, $b=0.079$

  d In the power model we get $a=35.4$, $b=0.077$; they are pretty close

3 a $\ln(q)\in\{1.6, 3, 3.4, 3.69, 3.91\}$

  b

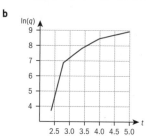

  c $\ln(a)=1.72$ $b=0.44$

  d $q(t)=5.61e^{0.44t}$

  e $5.38\,\text{min}$

4 a 1000

  b $\ln(S-c)=b\ln(n)+\ln(a)$

  c

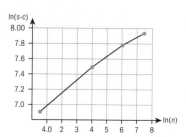

  d $\ln(a)=3.99$, $b=0.75$

  e $\ln(S-1000)=54.05\times n^{0.75}+1000$

  f \$6715.61

g For many shirts the behaviour may be different, as in the cases analysed for geometric series.

h **i** $x = n, y = S - c$

   ii $a = 55.2 \rightarrow \ln(a) = 4.01$, $b = 0.742$, similar to linear model

5 **a**

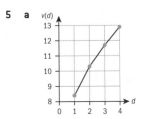

b $a = 4.5$ and $b = 12.9 - 2 \times 4.5 = 3.9$

Exercise 7M

1 **a**

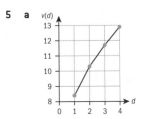

b When $t = 0 \rightarrow f(0) = \dfrac{100}{11} = 9.09\%$, the initial recorded percentage of people with access to the Internet. When $t \rightarrow \infty \rightarrow f(t) = \dfrac{100}{1} = 100\%$ we are getting asymptotically to a state where everyone will have Internet, at least according to this model.

c 4.6 years   **d** 99.9%

2 **a** 21400

   b 106934

   c 107000

3 **a** $L = 120 \times 10^6$, $C = 11\,999$, $k = 0.346$

   b 39898

   c 33.5 weeks

Chapter review

1 **a** 2.5

   b 1220.70

   c 2033.17

2 US $184.71

3 **a** 10%

   b 272 727 euros

   c 643 076 euros

4 **a** 11

   b 177 146

5 **a** UK £9652

   b UK £9787.13

6 **a** SGD 3453.80

   b 21.76 years

7 2.35%

8 US$73.67

9 115.36 euros

10 **a** 42 296

   b 6.116 years

11 **a** 95 °C

   b 32.95 °C

   c 7.46 minutes

   d 21 °C

12 **a** $y = 16$

   b (0, 20)

13 **a** 1101

   b 10.13, so after 11 days

14 **a** 1.37 m

   b 16.11, so 17 weeks

15 **a** $5 \times 2^n - 5$

   b $5 \times 4^n - 5$

16 $9905.5

Exam-style questions

17 **a** 0.1kg

   b 1.73 years (3 s.f.)

   c 5.76 years (3 s.f.)

18 **a** $\log xy = \log x + \log y = p + q$

   b $\log \dfrac{x}{y} = \log x - \log y = p - q$

c $\log \sqrt{x} = \dfrac{1}{2}\log x = \dfrac{1}{2}p$

d $\log x^2 y^5 = 2\log x + 5\log y$
$= 2p + 5q$

e $\log(x^y) = y\log x = 10^q p$

f $\log 0.01 x^3 = \log \dfrac{x^3}{100}$
$= \log x^3 - \log 10^2 = 3p - 2$

19 **a** $a = 6$, $b = 2$

   b 2.53 m (3 s.f.)

   c 19.5 years

20 **a** **i** 6000   **ii** 12000

   b 40000

   c $r = e^{-\left(\frac{\ln 2}{6000}\right)t}$

   d 0.315 (3 s.f.)

21 **a** $r = 3$, $a = 2$

   b **i** 4374   **ii** 6560

   c $n = 13$

22 **a** **i** $u_n = ar^{n-1}$

   ii $S_n = a\left(\dfrac{r^n - 1}{r - 1}\right)$

   b v_n is an arithmetic progression

   c $T_n = \dfrac{n}{2}\left(2\log a + (n-1)\log r\right)$

   d $T_n \neq \log S_n$

23 **a** $r = \dfrac{2}{3}$

   b $r = -\dfrac{1}{2}$

   c Sum to infinity cannot be equal to $\dfrac{1}{3}$ times the first term.

24 **a** £97.09

   b £74.41

   c £84.69

25 **a** Scheme 1

   b 1083.26 euros

   c No, scheme 1 is still better.

Chapter 8

Skills check

1 a, b

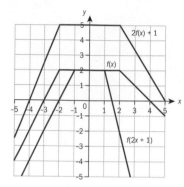

Exercise 8A

1 a $\dfrac{\pi}{6}$ **b** $\dfrac{11\pi}{12}$ **c** $\dfrac{3\pi}{2}$

 d $\dfrac{5\pi}{3}$ **e** $\dfrac{7\pi}{6}$

2 a $60°$ **b** $240°$ **c** $108°$

 d $540°$ **e** $57.3°$

3 a $14.66\,\text{m}$ **b** $51.31\,\text{m}^2$

 c $21.2\,\text{m}^2$ **d** $30.1\,\text{m}^2$

4 a $8.1\,\text{cm},\ 31.5\,\text{cm}^2$

 b $7\,\text{m},\ 30.1\,\text{m}^2$

 c $24\,\text{cm},\ 19.64\,\text{cm}^2$

5 a $56.4°$ **b** $4.41\,\text{m}^2$

6 a $11.08\,\text{cm}$ **b** $6.92\,\text{cm}^2$

7 7.36

Exercise 8B

1 a 0 **b** 1 **c** 0 **d** 0

 e -1 **f** -1 **g** -1 **h** 0

2 a i $x = \{10°,\ 170°,\ 370°,\ 530°\}$

 ii $x = \{17.5°,\ 162.5°,\ 376.5°,$
  $522.5°\}$

 iii $x = \{160°,\ 200°,\ 520°,\ 560°\}$

 b i $x = \left\{\dfrac{2\pi}{5}, \dfrac{3\pi}{5}, \dfrac{12\pi}{5}, \dfrac{13\pi}{5}\right\}$

 ii $x = \{0.3,\ 2.84,\ 6.58,\ 9.12\}$

 iii $x = \left\{\dfrac{\pi}{2}, \dfrac{3\pi}{2}, \dfrac{5\pi}{2}\right\}$

3 a i $(0.51, 0.49)$

 ii $(0.94, 0.81),\ (2.65, 0.47),$
  $(6.07, -0.21)$

 b Once the y-coordinate
 of points on the lines
 is greater than 1 or less
 than -1, the line will not
 intersect the curve again.

4 a On the unit circle the
 y-coordinate of one of the
 angles is the negative of the
 y-coordinate of the other
 angle.

 b i $30°$ **ii** $150°$

 c i Using the sine rule:

$$\frac{\sin(20)}{3} = \frac{\sin\left(B\hat{C}A\right)}{5}$$

$$\rightarrow \sin\left(B\hat{C}A\right) = \frac{5\sin\left(B\hat{C}A\right)}{3}$$

 ii $34.8°$ **iii** $145°$

 iv

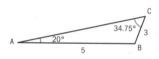

5 $4.72\,\text{cm}$ and $21.18\,\text{cm}$

6 a i $\dfrac{\sqrt{3}}{2}$ **ii** $\dfrac{1}{2}$

 iii $\dfrac{1}{2}$ **iv** $\dfrac{\sqrt{3}}{2}$

 b i $\dfrac{1}{2}$ **ii** $\dfrac{1}{2}$

 iii $\dfrac{\sqrt{3}}{2}$ **iv** $-\dfrac{\sqrt{3}}{2}$

7 a i $\dfrac{2\sqrt{2}}{3}$ **ii** $2\sqrt{2}$

 b i $\dfrac{1}{3}$ **ii** $-\dfrac{2\sqrt{2}}{3}$

8 a $\dfrac{1}{2}$

 b i $\dfrac{1}{\sqrt{5}}$ **ii** $\dfrac{2}{\sqrt{5}}$

 c $\sin x \le 0,\ \cos x \ge 0$, cannot both
 be 0, hence $2\sin x \ne \cos x$

Exercise 8C

1 a i 3 **ii** $y = 3$

 iii 2 **iv** $-\dfrac{3}{2}$

 b i 4 **ii** $y = 0$

 iii $\dfrac{2\pi}{3}$ **iv** 2

 c i 1 **ii** $y = -1$

 iii π **iv** -1.71

2 a $y = 2\sin\left(\dfrac{\pi}{2}x\right) + 1$

 b $y = 2.5\sin\left(\dfrac{\pi}{3}x\right) - 1$

3 a i $y = 4\sin\left(\dfrac{\pi}{2}(x - 0.5)\right) - 1$

 ii $y = 3\sin\left(\dfrac{\pi}{3}(x - 2)\right) + 2$

 b i $y = 4\cos\left(\dfrac{\pi}{2}(x - 1.5)\right) - 1$

 ii $y = 3\cos\left(\dfrac{\pi}{3}(x - 3.5)\right) + 2$

 c $\dfrac{1\pi}{2b}$

4 a To have a scale, to represent
 date as a single ordered
 number

 b Hour $+ \dfrac{1}{60}$ second

 c $f(t) = 1.5\sin(0.017t + 1.67) + 6.4$

 d Notice that 02-Feb-2019 is
 day 398 in our scale. Hence,
 $f(398) = 7.35 = 7{:}21$

 e Good fit, it cannot reproduce
 anomalies

5 a $b = 2513$

 b $0.001\,\text{s}$
 $S = 4\sin(800\pi(t - 0.001))$

c Looks like a sinewave which is on counterphase with roughly half the amplitude

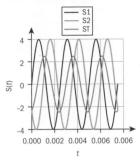

6 a

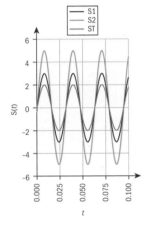

b max = 4.97 ≈ 5, min = −4.97 ≈ −5

c i 5   ii 200

d $S_T(t) = 5\sin(200(t - 0.0004)) + 0$

7 a $a = 1.65, d = 2.45$

b take the mean between the time difference on the highest and lowest tides to get the period:
$$P = \frac{1}{2}\big((15-15-3.033) + (21.32-8.9)\big) = 12.27.$$
Hence, $b = \frac{2\pi}{P} = 0.512$

c −0.034

d $f(t) = 1.54\sin(0.518(t - 0.03)) + 2.5$, similar to model by inspection of the table

e 1.4 m

Exercise 8D

1 a 1.71 or 0.29

b $x = 5$ or $x = -1$

c $1 \pm \frac{1}{2}i$ **d** $= \pm\sqrt{10}\,i$

2 a $-5 + 8i$ **b** $8 - i$

c $\frac{4+7i}{13}$ **d** $5 - 12i$

e $-2 - 2i$ **f** $\frac{-69+58i}{13}$

3 $2 \pm i$, hence, $x^2 - 4x + 5 = (x - (2 + i))(x - (2 - i))$

4 $p = -6, q = 10$

Exercise 8E

1 a $r = 8, \theta = 90°$

b $r = 7, \theta = 180°$

c $r = 12, \theta = 0°$

d $r = 5, \theta = 270°$

2 a 3.61, −0.983

b 5.39, 0.38

c 3.16, −0.322

d 4.47, 0.464

e 5.39, −1.19

f 3.16, −1.25

3 a $4\sqrt{2}\text{cis}\left(\frac{\pi}{4}\right)$ **b** $4\text{cis}\left(\frac{\pi}{3}\right)$

c $6\text{cis}\left(-\frac{\pi}{6}\right)$ **d** $2\text{cis}\left(\frac{\pi}{6}\right)$

e $5\sqrt{2}\text{cis}\left(\frac{\pi}{4}\right)$ **f** $14\text{cis}\left(-\frac{\pi}{3}\right)$

4 a $1.5 + 2.59i$ **b** $-2 + 3.46i$

c $-1.72 - i$ **d** $4.61 + 1.95i$

e $-0.776 + 2.27i$

f $3.14 - 2.14i$

Exercise 8F

1 a $a = 2\text{cis}\left(\frac{\pi}{3}\right)$, $b = \sqrt{2}\,\text{cis}\left(\frac{\pi}{4}\right)$,

$c = 2\text{cis}\left(-\frac{\pi}{6}\right)$

b i $2\sqrt{3} + 2i$ ii i   iii −4

    iv −4i   v $1 - i$

2 $n = \{5, 15, 25, 35, \cdots\}$

3 a $2\,e^{\frac{i\pi}{4}}$

b (3, 3) in the Argand diagram

c

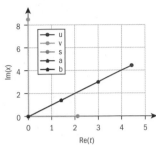

d u stays in the same line as a and b, v is a projection to the y-axis and s is a projection to the x-axis.

4 If $z = x + iy$, then $z* = x - iy$. Thus, $|z*| = |z| = r$ and
$$\arg(z^*) = \text{atan}\left(-\frac{y}{x}\right)$$
$$= -\text{atan}\left(\frac{y}{x}\right) = -\arg(z) = -\theta.$$
Hence $z* = re^{-i\theta}$.

5 $e^{i\pi} = \cos(\pi) + i\sin(\pi)$
$$= -1 \to e^{i\pi} + 1 = 0$$

6 a $\text{Re}(z) = \text{Im}(z)$

b i $t = 1$ ii $t = 2$

c Imaginary crossing: $z_I = 0 + i$, real crossing: $z_R = 2 + 0i$

d $z_1 = \left(1 + \frac{\theta}{\pi}\right)e^{i\theta}$,

$z_2 = \left(2 + \frac{\theta}{\pi}\right)e^{i\theta}$, $z_3 = \left(3 + \frac{\theta}{\pi}\right)e^{i\theta}$

e $|z_2| - |z_1| = 1$, $|z_3| - |z_2| = 1$, this relation will keep the same as the spiral is growing at a constant rate

Exercise 8G

1 Let the phase differences be $0°$ and $60°$.

$110\operatorname{cis}0° + 110°\operatorname{cis}60°$

$= 110 + 55 + 55\sqrt{3}\mathrm{i}$

$= 165 + 55\sqrt{3}\mathrm{i}$

$= 110\sqrt{3}\left(\dfrac{\sqrt{3}}{2} + \dfrac{1}{2}\mathrm{i}\right)$

$= 110\sqrt{3}\operatorname{cis}30°.$

So the voltage output will be $110\sqrt{3}$ V (with a phase shift of $30°$).

2 a Let the phase differences be $0°$, $120°$ and $-120°$.

$110\operatorname{cis}0° + 110\operatorname{cis}120°$

$+ 110\operatorname{cis}(-120°) =$

$110 - 55 + 55\sqrt{3}\mathrm{i}$

$-55 - 55\sqrt{3}\mathrm{i} = 0.$

b Connecting in reverse is equivalent to reflecting in the x-axis as all positive becomes negative and vice versa. That is the same as shifting by $180°$.

c Replacing $-120°$ with $60°$ gives

$110\operatorname{cis}0° + 110\operatorname{cis}120°$

$+ 110\operatorname{cis}60° = 110 - 55$

$+ 55\sqrt{3}\mathrm{i} + 55 + 55\sqrt{3}\mathrm{i}$

$= 110 + 110\sqrt{3}\mathrm{i} = 220\operatorname{cis}60$

3 15.09 V

4 3.61, 88.9°

5 a $g(t) - f(t) = 2.19\sin(0.0165t - 1.23) + 18.0 - 2.14\sin(0.0165t + 1.81) - 5.97$

$= 2.19\sin(0.0165t - 1.23) - 2.14\sin(0.0165t + 1.81) + 12.03 = 2.19\sin(0.0165t - 1.23) + 2.14\sin(0.0165t + 1.81 + \pi) + 12.03 = 2.19\sin(0.0165t - 1.23) + 2.14\sin(0.0165t + 4.95) + 12.03$

b Longest day is $12.03 + 4.32 = 16.35$ hours (or 16 hours 21 minutes) and the shortest day is $12.03 - 4.32 = 7.71$ hours (or 7 hours 43 minutes)

c The longest day occurs on day $172 = 21$ June. The shortest day occurs on day 363 which is 29 December.

Chapter review

1 R^2

2 a 1.14　　**b** 7

3 Perimeter $= 20$ cm, area $= 25$ cm²

4 $\dfrac{5\pi}{3}$

5 $z_1 = \sqrt{2}\operatorname{cis}\left(\dfrac{\pi}{4}\right)$, $z_2 = 2\operatorname{cis}\left(-\dfrac{\pi}{6}\right)$

a $2\sqrt{2}\operatorname{cis}\left(\dfrac{5\pi}{12}\right)$

b $\sqrt{2}\operatorname{cis}\left(\dfrac{\pi}{12}\right)$

c $16\sqrt{2}\operatorname{cis}\left(\dfrac{3\pi}{4}\right)$

6 $C = B + v_{\perp} = 1 - 2\mathrm{i}$, $D = A + v_{\perp} = 3 + 2\mathrm{i}$

7 a $|w| = \sqrt{8}$ and $\arg(w) = \dfrac{\pi}{4}$

b 64

8 $|z_2| = \sqrt{2}, |z_1| = 2\sqrt{2}$, $z_1 = 2\sqrt{2}\operatorname{cis}\left(\dfrac{\pi}{6}\right)$ and $z_2 = \sqrt{2}\operatorname{cis}\left(-\dfrac{\pi}{3}\right)$

9 $\dfrac{\sqrt{7}}{2}$

10 17.32 A

Exam-style questions

11 a $p = 3.5, q = 2, r = 3$

b $17.2° < x < 62.6°$ and $137.2° < x \leq 180°$

12 $32\sqrt{2} - 8$ cm

13 a

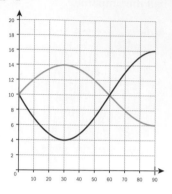

b $p = 10, q = 6, r = 3$

14 a 206 V

b 105.9°

15 a 12i

b $\dfrac{64}{27}\mathrm{i}$

c $-8 + 8\sqrt{3}\mathrm{i}$

16 0.872

Chapter 9

Skills check

1 $u_n = 18\left(-\dfrac{2}{3}\right)^{n-1}$

2 $S_{15} = 10.8\,(\text{to 3 s.f.})$

3 $S_{12} = 12\,(\text{to 3 s.f.})$

Exercise 9A

1 $a_{1,2} = -3$; $a_{2,3} = 6$; $b_{1,3} = 5$; $c_{2,2} = 0$; and $c_{3,1} = 1$

2 a 3×4

b $q_{2,4} = 100$; Manufacturer 4 produces 100 units of product 2.

c $T = \begin{bmatrix} 960 \\ 1200 \\ 990 \\ 335 \end{bmatrix}$

3 a $3W = \begin{bmatrix} 3 & -6 & 9 \\ 9 & 6 & -3 \end{bmatrix}$

a $R - W$ is undefined since dimensions of R are not equal to the dimensions of W.

b $4U + S = \begin{bmatrix} 35 & -14 & -7 \\ 28 & 29 & 1 \\ -9 & 10 & -2 \end{bmatrix}$

c $\dfrac{1}{3}T - \dfrac{1}{2}V = \begin{bmatrix} 0 & -3 \\ 4 & 8 \end{bmatrix}$

4 a $k = 0.075$

$T = \begin{bmatrix} 2433.75 \\ 1404.38 \\ 1813.12 \\ 1443.75 \end{bmatrix}$

b $C = 0.075P + P = 1.075P$

5 a i $\begin{bmatrix} -6 \\ 12 \end{bmatrix}$ **ii** $\begin{bmatrix} -1 \\ 2 \end{bmatrix}$ **iii** $\begin{bmatrix} 3 \\ -6 \end{bmatrix}$

b

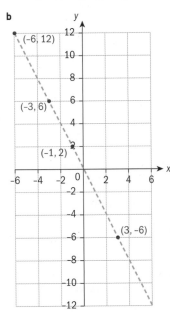

c The points described by kX lie along the line described by $y = -2x$

---

6 $\mu \begin{bmatrix} -9 & 12 \\ -6 & 3 \end{bmatrix} + \lambda \begin{bmatrix} 1 & -2 \\ 3 & -1 \end{bmatrix}$

$= \begin{bmatrix} -8 & 12 \\ -10 & 4 \end{bmatrix} \Leftrightarrow \begin{cases} -9\mu + \lambda = -8 \\ 12\mu - 2\lambda = 12 \\ -6\mu + 3\lambda = -10 \\ 3\mu - \lambda = 4 \end{cases}$

$\therefore \mu = \dfrac{2}{3}; \lambda = -2$

Exercise 9B

1 a $\begin{pmatrix} -4 & 1 \\ 13 & 16 \\ 5 & -3 \end{pmatrix}$ **b** $\begin{pmatrix} 3 \\ 18 \\ -7 \end{pmatrix}$

c $\begin{pmatrix} 18 & -23 \\ -13 & 17 \end{pmatrix}$

d Impossible **e** $\begin{pmatrix} -1 & -7 \\ 1 & 3 \end{pmatrix}$

2 $m = 2,\ n = 3$

3 $B = \begin{bmatrix} 1 \\ 1 \\ 1 \end{bmatrix}$

4 a $\begin{pmatrix} 1 & 0 & 0 \\ 0 & 1 & 0 \\ 0 & 0 & 1 \end{pmatrix}$ **b** $\begin{pmatrix} 1 & 0 \\ 0 & 1 \end{pmatrix}$

c Matrix A is not a square matrix, so its left and right multiplicative identities are not equal, i.e. a multiplicative identity does not exist.

5 a $R = \begin{pmatrix} 0.4 \\ 0.8 \\ 0.6 \end{pmatrix}$,

$N = AR = \begin{pmatrix} 45.0 \\ 36.8 \\ 94.8 \end{pmatrix}$

b $AC = \begin{pmatrix} 410 & 365 & 470 & 430 \\ 348 & 308 & 400 & 360 \\ 890 & 792 & 1020 & 928 \end{pmatrix}$,

entry $(AC)_{i,j}$ gives the total daily cost of removing all pollutants while producing the product i at the plant j.

Exercise 9C

1 a Not possible because the number of the columns of matrix A is not equal to the number of the rows of matrix B.

b $BA = \begin{pmatrix} -9 & 4 & 12 \\ 4 & -1 & -4 \end{pmatrix}$

c Not possible because A is not a square matrix.

d $B^2 = \begin{pmatrix} 11 & -8 \\ -4 & 3 \end{pmatrix}$

2 a $\begin{pmatrix} -11 & -13 \\ 18 & -9 \\ 5 & 50 \end{pmatrix}$

b Not possible because number of columns of matrix T is not equal to number of rows of matrix R.

c $\begin{pmatrix} -14 & -5 \\ 5 & 11 \end{pmatrix}$

d $\begin{pmatrix} -20 & 3 & 22 \\ 2 & 9 & -4 \end{pmatrix}$

e Not possible because the number of the columns of matrix $S - U$ is not equal to the number of the rows of matrix W.

3 $UR + R = \begin{pmatrix} 1 & -33 \\ -22 & -25 \\ 8 & 3 \end{pmatrix} + \begin{pmatrix} 0 & -1 \\ 3 & 7 \\ -5 & 4 \end{pmatrix}$

$= \begin{pmatrix} 1 & -34 \\ -19 & -18 \\ 3 & 7 \end{pmatrix}$

$(U + I)R = \begin{pmatrix} 5 & -3 & -2 \\ 5 & -3 & 2 \\ 0 & 1 & 0 \end{pmatrix} \times \begin{pmatrix} 0 & -1 \\ 3 & 7 \\ -5 & 4 \end{pmatrix}$

$= \begin{pmatrix} 1 & -34 \\ -19 & -18 \\ 3 & 7 \end{pmatrix}$

4 $(T+X)(T-X)=\begin{pmatrix} -48 & 32 \\ 77 & -35 \end{pmatrix}$,

$(T+X)^2=\begin{pmatrix} 64 & 0 \\ -105 & 49 \end{pmatrix}$

$(T+X)(T-X)=T^2-TX+XT-X^2$ and $(T+X)^2=(T+X)(T+X)$
$=T^2+TX+XT+X^2$ because matrix multiplication is not commutative and $TX \neq XT$.

5 $(SU)^2=\begin{pmatrix} 2 & 0 & -11 \\ 21 & -19 & -3 \\ -3 & 3 & 22 \end{pmatrix}^2 = \begin{pmatrix} 37 & -33 & -264 \\ -348 & 352 & -240 \\ -9 & 9 & 508 \end{pmatrix}$

$S^2U^2=\begin{pmatrix} -6 & -3 & 11 \\ 37 & -22 & -5 \\ -15 & 29 & -18 \end{pmatrix} \times \begin{pmatrix} 1 & -2 & -12 \\ 0 & 3 & -20 \\ 5 & -5 & 3 \end{pmatrix} = \begin{pmatrix} 49 & -52 & 165 \\ 12 & -115 & -19 \\ -105 & 207 & -454 \end{pmatrix}$

$(SU)^2=(SU) \times (SU)=SUSU \neq SSUU=S^2U^2$ because matrix multiplication is not commutative.

6 $2(RT)=2\begin{pmatrix} 1 & -3 \\ -4 & 27 \\ -9 & 2 \end{pmatrix} = \begin{pmatrix} 2 & -6 \\ -8 & 54 \\ -18 & 4 \end{pmatrix}$, $(2R)T=\begin{pmatrix} 0 & -2 \\ 6 & 14 \\ -10 & 8 \end{pmatrix}\begin{pmatrix} 1 & 2 \\ -1 & 3 \end{pmatrix} = \begin{pmatrix} 2 & -6 \\ -8 & 54 \\ -18 & 4 \end{pmatrix}$,

$R(2T)=\begin{pmatrix} 0 & -1 \\ 3 & 7 \\ -5 & 4 \end{pmatrix}\begin{pmatrix} 2 & 4 \\ -2 & 6 \end{pmatrix} = \begin{pmatrix} 2 & -6 \\ -8 & 54 \\ -18 & 4 \end{pmatrix}$.

Scalar multiplication is commutative with matrices.

7 a $AB=BA=\begin{pmatrix} 1 & 0 \\ 0 & 1 \end{pmatrix}$ **b** $(2AB)^{10}=2^{10}I_2=\begin{pmatrix} 1024 & 0 \\ 0 & 1024 \end{pmatrix}$.

8 a The conjecture is not true. Consider, for example,

matrices $A=\begin{pmatrix} -3 & 5 \\ 1 & -2 \end{pmatrix}$, $T=\begin{pmatrix} 1 & 2 \\ -1 & 3 \end{pmatrix}$ and $n=2$. Then,

$(AT)^2=\begin{pmatrix} -8 & 9 \\ 3 & -4 \end{pmatrix}^2=\begin{pmatrix} 91 & -108 \\ -36 & 43 \end{pmatrix}$,

but $A^2T^2=\begin{pmatrix} 14 & -25 \\ -5 & 9 \end{pmatrix}\begin{pmatrix} -1 & 8 \\ -4 & 7 \end{pmatrix}=\begin{pmatrix} 86 & -63 \\ -21 & 23 \end{pmatrix}$.

b The conjecture is true because of the scalar commutativity:
$(kA)^n=k^nA^n$

Exercise 9D

1 a $\begin{pmatrix} -2.5 & 2.0 \\ -1.5 & 1.0 \end{pmatrix}$

b $\begin{pmatrix} 0 & -1 \\ \frac{1}{3} & \frac{2}{3} \end{pmatrix}$

c $\begin{pmatrix} 2.4 & -1.6 \\ -1.6 & 2.4 \end{pmatrix}$

d $\begin{pmatrix} -\frac{4}{11} & \frac{16}{11} \\ \frac{15}{11} & -\frac{5}{11} \end{pmatrix}$

2 a $\begin{pmatrix} -2 & 1 & -4 \\ 1 & 0 & 2 \\ 1.5 & -0.5 & 2.5 \end{pmatrix}$

b $\begin{pmatrix} -\frac{20}{79} & -\frac{5}{158} & \frac{70}{79} \\ -\frac{52}{79} & \frac{33}{79} & \frac{24}{79} \\ -\frac{9}{79} & \frac{57}{158} & \frac{-8}{79} \end{pmatrix}$

c $\begin{pmatrix} \frac{24}{175} & \frac{54}{175} & \frac{6}{25} \\ -\frac{36}{25} & \frac{6}{25} & \frac{12}{25} \\ -\frac{12}{35} & -\frac{27}{35} & \frac{2}{5} \end{pmatrix}$

3 a $\begin{pmatrix} -12 \\ 30 \\ 4 \end{pmatrix}$ **b** $\begin{pmatrix} \frac{20}{11} \\ \frac{16}{11} \end{pmatrix}$

c $\begin{pmatrix} -\frac{91}{254} \\ -\frac{172}{127} \\ -\frac{456}{127} \\ \frac{447}{508} \end{pmatrix} \approx \begin{pmatrix} -0.36 \\ -1.35 \\ -3.59 \\ -0.88 \end{pmatrix}$

4 $W=\begin{pmatrix} 2 & 1 & 1 & 3 \\ 1 & 3 & 2 & 4 \\ 2 & 1 & 2 & 2 \\ 3 & 4 & 1 & 2 \end{pmatrix}$ $X=\begin{pmatrix} a \\ b \\ c \\ d \end{pmatrix}$,

$Z=\begin{pmatrix} 240 \\ 380 \\ 280 \\ 400 \end{pmatrix}$, $X=\begin{pmatrix} 36 \\ 48 \\ 60 \\ 20 \end{pmatrix}$

5

Machine	Product A	Product B	Product C	Product D
I	120	240	240	80
II	380	126	190	95
III	140	280	140	140
IV	133	100	400	200
Total	773	746	970	515

6 a Use the formula for the inverse of 2×2 square matrices:

$$(AB)^{-1} = \begin{pmatrix} 1 & 1 \\ -1 & -2 \end{pmatrix},$$

$$A^{-1}B^{-1} = \begin{pmatrix} -3 & 5 \\ -1 & 2 \end{pmatrix}$$

b

i $B^{-1}A^{-1} = \begin{pmatrix} 1 & 1 \\ -1 & -2 \end{pmatrix} = (AB)^{-1}$

ii e.g. $A = \begin{pmatrix} 1 & 2 \\ 3 & 4 \end{pmatrix}, B = \begin{pmatrix} 1 & 0 \\ 0 & 2 \end{pmatrix},$

$$B^{-1}A^{-1} = \begin{pmatrix} -2 & 1 \\ \dfrac{3}{4} & -\dfrac{1}{4} \end{pmatrix} = (AB)^{-1}$$

iii $(AB)(AB)^{-1} = I_2,$
$A^{-1}AB(AB)^{-1} = A^{-1},$
$B(AB)^{-1} = AA^{-1},$
$B^{-1}B\,(AB)^{-1} = B^{-1}A^{-1},$
$(AB)^{-1} = B^{-1}A^{-1}$

7 Mathematics is the music of reason.

Exercise 9E

1 a $\begin{pmatrix} 1 & 0 \\ 0 & -1 \end{pmatrix}$ **b** $\dfrac{1}{\sqrt{2}}\begin{pmatrix} 1 & -1 \\ 1 & 1 \end{pmatrix}$

c $\begin{pmatrix} 0 & 1 \\ -1 & 0 \end{pmatrix}$ **d** $\begin{pmatrix} 0 & -1 \\ -1 & 0 \end{pmatrix}$

e $\begin{pmatrix} 1 & 0 \\ 0 & 3 \end{pmatrix}$ **f** $\begin{pmatrix} 2 & 0 \\ 0 & 2 \end{pmatrix}$

g $\begin{pmatrix} -\dfrac{1}{2} & \dfrac{\sqrt{3}}{2} \\ \dfrac{\sqrt{3}}{2} & \dfrac{1}{2} \end{pmatrix}$

2 a $\begin{pmatrix} 4 & 0 \\ 0 & 4 \end{pmatrix}$ **b** $\begin{pmatrix} -1 & 0 \\ 0 & -1 \end{pmatrix}$

c $\begin{pmatrix} -4 & 0 \\ 0 & -4 \end{pmatrix}$, which is equal to the enlargement matrix with scale factor -4

3 a

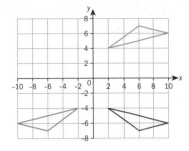

$$T = \begin{pmatrix} 1 & 0 \\ 0 & -1 \end{pmatrix},$$

$$TP = \begin{pmatrix} 2 & 6 & 10 \\ -4 & -7 & -6 \end{pmatrix}$$

4 a $\begin{pmatrix} \cos(2\alpha) & \sin(2\alpha) \\ \sin(2\alpha) & -\cos(2\alpha) \end{pmatrix}$

b $T^2 = \begin{pmatrix} \cos(2\alpha) & \sin(2\alpha) \\ \sin(2\alpha) & -\cos(2\alpha) \end{pmatrix}^2$

$$= \begin{pmatrix} \cos^2(2\alpha) + \sin^2(2\alpha) & 0 \\ 0 & \cos^2(2\alpha) + \sin^2(2\alpha) \end{pmatrix} = \begin{pmatrix} 1 & 0 \\ 0 & 1 \end{pmatrix}$$

5 a $\dfrac{1}{\sqrt{2}}\begin{pmatrix} 1 & 1 \\ -1 & 1 \end{pmatrix}$

b $R^8 = \begin{pmatrix} 1 & 0 \\ 0 & 1 \end{pmatrix}$, corresponds to rotation by 2π, i.e. the object stays the same

6 a 4 **b i** 72 **ii** 64

7 a If $T = \begin{pmatrix} \cos(2\alpha) & \sin(2\alpha) \\ \sin(2\alpha) & -\cos(2\alpha) \end{pmatrix}$, $\det T = -\cos^2(2\alpha) - \sin^2(2\alpha) = -1$.

New area gets multiplied by $|\det T| = 1$, i.e. does not change.

b If $T = \begin{pmatrix} \cos(\alpha) & -\sin(\alpha) \\ \sin(\alpha) & \cos(\alpha) \end{pmatrix}$, $\det T = \cos^2(2\alpha) + \sin^2(2\alpha) = 1$.

New area gets multiplied by $|\det T| = 1$, i.e. does not change.

8 a $\begin{pmatrix} 102 \\ 76 \end{pmatrix}$ **b** $\begin{pmatrix} -54 \\ 30 \end{pmatrix}$

b $T' = \begin{pmatrix} -1 & 0 \\ 0 & 1 \end{pmatrix},$

$$T'TP = \begin{pmatrix} -2 & -6 & -10 \\ -4 & -7 & -6 \end{pmatrix}$$

c Since $TT = \begin{pmatrix} 1 & 0 \\ 0 & 1 \end{pmatrix}$, reflecting the triangle ABC in x axis twice will result in the same triangle ABC.

d $T'T = \begin{pmatrix} -1 & 0 \\ 0 & -1 \end{pmatrix}$

= anticlockwise rotation by $180°$ as seen in the graph above.

9 a $\begin{pmatrix} -12 \\ 12 \end{pmatrix}$ **b** $(-12, 12)$

d $\begin{pmatrix} -1 & 0 \\ 0 & 1 \end{pmatrix}$ = reflection in y-axis

b $\begin{pmatrix} 1.9 & 0.5 \\ -1.0 & 3.9 \end{pmatrix}$

10 $\begin{pmatrix} 1 & -1 \\ 3 & -2 \end{pmatrix}$

e $\begin{pmatrix} 1 & 0 \\ 0 & -1 \end{pmatrix}$ = reflection in x-axis

c $\begin{pmatrix} -\dfrac{1}{2} & \dfrac{\sqrt{3}}{2} \\ \dfrac{\sqrt{3}}{2} & \dfrac{1}{2} \end{pmatrix} \begin{pmatrix} x \\ y \end{pmatrix} + \begin{pmatrix} -2-\sqrt{3} \\ 2\sqrt{3}-1 \end{pmatrix}$

11 a $R = \begin{pmatrix} 0 & 1 \\ -1 & 0 \end{pmatrix}, T = \begin{pmatrix} 0 & -1 \\ -1 & 0 \end{pmatrix}$

12 a $E = \begin{pmatrix} 0.5 & 0 \\ 0 & 0.5 \end{pmatrix}$

b $TR = \begin{pmatrix} 1 & 0 \\ 0 & -1 \end{pmatrix}$

b $E^n = \begin{pmatrix} 0.5^n & 0 \\ 0 & 0.5^n \end{pmatrix}$

c Triangle with vertices $(1, -1), (3, -1), (3, -3)$

5 a 7.75

b 7.75

c i $\dfrac{1}{4}$ **ii** $1.73 \left(\sqrt{3}\right)$

iii $\dfrac{\sqrt{3}\left(1-0.25^6\right)}{1-0.25} = 3.463$

13 a $\begin{pmatrix} -5.33 \\ 0.77 \end{pmatrix}$

b $\begin{pmatrix} \cos 20^\circ \cos 40^\circ - \sin 20^\circ \sin 40^\circ & -\cos 40^\circ \sin 20^\circ - \sin 40^\circ \cos 20^\circ \\ \sin 40^\circ \cos 20^\circ + \cos 40^\circ \sin 20^\circ & -\sin 40^\circ \sin 20^\circ + \cos 40^\circ \cos 20^\circ \end{pmatrix}$

c Rotation by $\alpha + \theta$ is given by the following matrix:

$$\begin{pmatrix} \cos(\alpha+\theta) & -\sin(\alpha+\theta) \\ \sin(\alpha+\theta) & \cos(\alpha+\theta) \end{pmatrix} = \begin{pmatrix} \cos\alpha & -\sin\alpha \\ \sin\alpha & \cos\alpha \end{pmatrix} \begin{pmatrix} \cos\theta & -\sin\theta \\ \sin\theta & \cos\theta \end{pmatrix}$$

$$= \begin{pmatrix} \cos\theta\cos\alpha - \sin\theta\sin\alpha & -\cos\alpha\sin\theta - \sin\alpha\cos\theta \\ \sin\alpha\cos\theta + \cos\alpha\sin\theta & -\sin\alpha\sin\theta + \cos\alpha\cos\theta \end{pmatrix}$$

Hence
$\cos(\alpha + \theta) = \cos\theta\cos\alpha - \sin\theta\sin\alpha$, $\sin(\alpha + \theta) = \sin\alpha\cos\theta + \cos\alpha\sin\theta$.

d $\begin{pmatrix} \dfrac{1}{2} & \dfrac{\sqrt{3}}{2} \\ -\dfrac{\sqrt{3}}{2} & \dfrac{1}{2} \end{pmatrix}$

e $\begin{pmatrix} \dfrac{1}{4} & \dfrac{\sqrt{3}}{4} \\ -\dfrac{\sqrt{3}}{4} & \dfrac{1}{4} \end{pmatrix}$

f $\begin{pmatrix} 0.004 & 0.008 & 0 \\ 0.007 & 0 & 0 \end{pmatrix}$

Exercise 9G

1 a

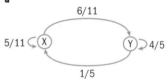

b

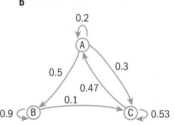

2 a $T = \begin{pmatrix} 0.75 & 0.2 \\ 0.25 & 0.8 \end{pmatrix}$

b $T^3 = \begin{pmatrix} 0.54 & 0.37 \\ 0.46 & 0.63 \end{pmatrix}$

Exercise 9F

1 a A'(18, 21), B'(−2, 12), C'(6, −18), D'(−14, −29)

b (3, 1)

2 a $\begin{pmatrix} 12 \\ 21 \end{pmatrix}$ **b** $\begin{pmatrix} 0 \\ 3 \end{pmatrix}$

c $\begin{pmatrix} -a \\ a \end{pmatrix}$ **d** $\begin{pmatrix} -\dfrac{a}{3} \\ \dfrac{a}{3} \end{pmatrix}$

3 a $T = \begin{pmatrix} 0 & -1 \\ 1 & 0 \end{pmatrix}\begin{pmatrix} 3 & 0 \\ 0 & 3 \end{pmatrix} = \begin{pmatrix} 0 & -3 \\ 3 & 0 \end{pmatrix}$,

$B = \begin{pmatrix} 2 \\ 3 \end{pmatrix}$

b $\begin{pmatrix} x'' \\ y'' \end{pmatrix} = \begin{pmatrix} -1 & 0 \\ 0 & -1 \end{pmatrix}\begin{pmatrix} x' \\ y' \end{pmatrix}$

$= \begin{pmatrix} 0 & 3 \\ -3 & 0 \end{pmatrix}\begin{pmatrix} x \\ y \end{pmatrix} - \begin{pmatrix} 2 \\ 3 \end{pmatrix}$,

i.e. $A = \begin{pmatrix} 0 & 3 \\ -3 & 0 \end{pmatrix}, c = -\begin{pmatrix} 2 \\ 3 \end{pmatrix}$

4 a i $\begin{pmatrix} 1 & 0 \\ 0 & -1 \end{pmatrix}$

ii $\begin{pmatrix} \cos 135^\circ & \sin 135^\circ \\ -\sin 135^\circ & \cos 135^\circ \end{pmatrix}$

iii $\begin{pmatrix} -\dfrac{1}{2} & \dfrac{\sqrt{3}}{2} \\ \dfrac{\sqrt{3}}{2} & \dfrac{1}{2} \end{pmatrix}$ **iv** $\begin{pmatrix} 2 & 0 \\ 0 & 4 \end{pmatrix}$

3 a $T = \begin{pmatrix} 0.65 & 0.26 & 0.05 \\ 0.25 & 0.7 & 0.05 \\ 0.10 & 0.04 & 0.90 \end{pmatrix}$

b 0.18

4 a $\begin{pmatrix} 0 & \frac{1}{4} & 0 \\ 1 & \frac{1}{2} & 1 \\ 0 & \frac{1}{4} & 0 \end{pmatrix}$

b $\begin{pmatrix} 0 & \frac{1}{9} & 0 & 0 \\ 1 & \frac{4}{9} & \frac{4}{9} & 0 \\ 0 & \frac{4}{9} & \frac{4}{9} & 1 \\ 0 & 0 & \frac{1}{9} & 0 \end{pmatrix}$

c Consider the general case nWm B with $m < n$ without loss of generality. Then, the transition matrix is of size $(m + 1) \times (m + 1)$. The element $T_{2,1} = 1$ and all the other entries in the first column are 0. The element $T_{m, m+1} = 1$ and all the other entries in the last column are 0. Then, to find the elements of the inner columns (elements $T_{j,j}$ $T_{j-1,j}$ $T_{j+1,j}$ all other elements in an inner column j are 0) consider having $j - 1$ blue coins in the box with n coins and $j - 1$ white coins in the box with m coins. Then, the probability of moving to the state with $j - 2$ blue coins in the box with n coins is $\dfrac{(j-1)^2}{nm}$ (this is element $T_{j-1, j}$). Similarly, the probability of moving to the state with j blue coins in the box with n coins is

$\dfrac{(n-j+1)(m-j+1)}{nm}$,

(this is element $T_{j+1, j}$). Finally, staying in the same state has probability

$1 - \dfrac{(j-1)^2}{nm} - \dfrac{(n-j+1)(m-j+1)}{nm}$

(this is element $T_{j, j}$). These formulae are valid for cases with $n = m$, too.

5 a $X = T^n B, T = \begin{pmatrix} 0.959 & 0.032 \\ 0.041 & 0.968 \end{pmatrix}$,

$B = \begin{pmatrix} 45520 \\ 38745 \end{pmatrix}, X = \begin{pmatrix} a \\ b \end{pmatrix}$,

where a, b is the number of people voting for candidates A and B respectively.

c Candidate A would win by 1360 votes, 1.62% of all votes

Exercise 9H

1 a $\begin{pmatrix} 0.45 & 0.45 \\ 0.55 & 0.55 \end{pmatrix}$

b $\begin{pmatrix} 0.14 & 0.14 & 0.14 \\ 0.51 & 0.51 & 0.51 \\ 0.35 & 0.35 & 0.35 \end{pmatrix}$

c $\begin{pmatrix} 0.35 & 0.35 & 0.35 & 0.35 \\ 0.10 & 0.10 & 0.10 & 0.10 \\ 0.25 & 0.25 & 0.25 & 0.25 \\ 0.29 & 0.29 & 0.29 & 0.29 \end{pmatrix}$

2 a $\begin{pmatrix} 0.32 \\ 0.27 \\ 0.41 \end{pmatrix}$

b $\begin{pmatrix} 0.32 & 0.32 & 0.32 \\ 0.27 & 0.27 & 0.27 \\ 0.41 & 0.41 & 0.41 \end{pmatrix}$

3 a $\begin{pmatrix} A \\ B \\ C \end{pmatrix} = T^2 \begin{pmatrix} 45 \\ 25 \\ 30 \end{pmatrix} = \begin{pmatrix} 34.6 \\ 36.5 \\ 28.9 \end{pmatrix}\%$

b $\begin{pmatrix} 0.2085 & 0.2085 & 0.2085 \\ 0.5787 & 0.5787 & 0.5787 \\ 0.2128 & 0.2128 & 0.2128 \end{pmatrix}$

c Convergence to the long-term matrix is slow even when the transition probabilities remain constant. Realistically, once the electricity providers notice the trend, they will respond to these changes quickly by changing the price or quality of their services in order to prevent customers from switching in which case the transition probabilities are unlikely to stay constant.

4 a Zeros signify that the cars that need minor or major repair will not be repaired. Fully broken-down cars will not be repaired to be functioning but still needing a repair, either.

b Check that all columns sum to 1

c $\begin{pmatrix} 388 \\ 70 \\ 28 \\ 39 \end{pmatrix}$

d The company should repair functioning cars which need a minor or major repair before they are fully broken down to reduce the number of broken-down cars.

Exercise 9I

1 a $\lambda^2 + 3\lambda + 2 = 0$
$\lambda = \{-2, -1\}$

b $\lambda^2 - 25 = 0$
$\lambda = \{\pm 5\}$

c $\lambda^2 - 3 = 0$
$\lambda = \{\pm\sqrt{3}\}$

2 No since $\lambda = -1$ is not a solution to the characteristic equation $\lambda^2 - 11\lambda + 18 = 0$

3 a $\lambda_1 = \lambda_2 = 1$; $X_1 = X_2 = \begin{pmatrix} 2 \\ 1 \end{pmatrix}$

b $(\lambda_1 = 7$ and $\lambda_2 = -2$

$X_1 = \begin{pmatrix} 4 \\ 5 \end{pmatrix}$ and $X_2 = \begin{pmatrix} 1 \\ -1 \end{pmatrix}$

c $\lambda_{1,2} = 1$, $\begin{pmatrix} 1 \\ 0 \end{pmatrix}$ and $\begin{pmatrix} 0 \\ 1 \end{pmatrix}$

d $\lambda_1 = -3$, $\lambda_2 = 3$, $\begin{pmatrix} 1 \\ 1 \end{pmatrix}$ and $\begin{pmatrix} 1 \\ -1 \end{pmatrix}$

e $\lambda_1 = 1$, $\lambda_2 = -0.3$, $\begin{pmatrix} 7 \\ 6 \end{pmatrix}$ and $\begin{pmatrix} 1 \\ -1 \end{pmatrix}$

4 a Find the eigenvalues from $\lambda^2 + (b - a - 1)\lambda + (a - b) = 0$, $\lambda_1 = 1$, $\lambda_2 = a - b$

b Then, $T\begin{pmatrix} x \\ y \end{pmatrix} = \begin{pmatrix} x \\ y \end{pmatrix}$

gives $y = \dfrac{1-a}{b}x$ and

$T\begin{pmatrix} x \\ y \end{pmatrix} = (a - b)\begin{pmatrix} x \\ y \end{pmatrix}$ gives

$y = -x$, so possible

eigenvectors are $\begin{pmatrix} b \\ 1 - a \end{pmatrix}$

and $\begin{pmatrix} 1 \\ -1 \end{pmatrix}$

Exercise 9J

1 $R = \begin{pmatrix} 1 & 1 \\ 1 & -2 \end{pmatrix}\begin{pmatrix} -1 & 0 \\ 0 & -4 \end{pmatrix}\begin{pmatrix} \frac{2}{3} & \frac{1}{3} \\ \frac{1}{3} & -\frac{1}{3} \end{pmatrix}$

2 a $\lambda_1 = 2$ and $X_1 = \begin{pmatrix} 5 \\ 2 \end{pmatrix}$;

$\lambda_2 = 1$ and $X_2 = \begin{pmatrix} 7 \\ 3 \end{pmatrix}$.

A is diagonalizable since the eigenvalues are distinct real values.

b $A = \begin{pmatrix} 7 & 5 \\ 3 & 2 \end{pmatrix}\begin{pmatrix} 1 & 0 \\ 0 & 2 \end{pmatrix}\begin{pmatrix} -2 & 5 \\ 3 & -7 \end{pmatrix}$

c $A^n = \begin{pmatrix} 15 \times 2^n - 14 & 35(1 - 2^n) \\ 6(2^n - 1) & 15 - 14 \times 2^n \end{pmatrix}$

d $A^4 = \begin{pmatrix} 226 & -525 \\ 90 & -209 \end{pmatrix}$

3 a $\lambda_1 = 1$ and $X_1 = \begin{pmatrix} 5 \\ 4 \end{pmatrix}$;

$\lambda_2 = -0.35$ and $X_2 = \begin{pmatrix} 1 \\ -1 \end{pmatrix}$

and therefore

$\begin{pmatrix} 5 & 1 \\ 4 & -1 \end{pmatrix}\begin{pmatrix} 1 & 0 \\ 0 & -0.35 \end{pmatrix}\begin{pmatrix} \frac{1}{9} & \frac{1}{9} \\ \frac{4}{9} & -\frac{5}{9} \end{pmatrix}$

b $\begin{pmatrix} 0.562 & 0.547 \\ 0.438 & 0.453 \end{pmatrix}$ (to 3sf)

c $T^n \to \begin{pmatrix} 0.56 & 0.56 \\ 0.44 & 0.44 \end{pmatrix}$ as $n \to \infty$

4 a $\begin{pmatrix} \frac{1}{4} & \frac{1}{3} \\ \frac{3}{4} & \frac{2}{3} \end{pmatrix}$

b $\begin{pmatrix} 3620 \\ 8080 \end{pmatrix}$ so more customers choose company S

c $\begin{pmatrix} 4 & 1 \\ 9 & -1 \end{pmatrix}\begin{pmatrix} 1 & 0 \\ 0 & -\frac{1}{12} \end{pmatrix}\begin{pmatrix} \frac{1}{13} & \frac{1}{13} \\ \frac{9}{13} & -\frac{4}{13} \end{pmatrix}$

d

$T^n = \begin{pmatrix} 4 & 1 \\ 9 & -1 \end{pmatrix}\begin{pmatrix} 1 & 0 \\ 0 & \left(-\frac{1}{12}\right)^n \end{pmatrix}\begin{pmatrix} \frac{1}{13} & \frac{1}{13} \\ \frac{9}{13} & -\frac{4}{13} \end{pmatrix}$

$= \frac{1}{13}\begin{pmatrix} 4 + 9p^n & 4 - 4p^n \\ 9 - 9p^n & 4p^n + 9 \end{pmatrix}$,

$p = -\frac{1}{12}$

e $\begin{pmatrix} 2900p^n + 3600 \\ 8100 - 2900p^n \end{pmatrix}$

f $\begin{pmatrix} \frac{2900}{12^2} + 3600 \\ 8100 - \frac{2900}{12^2} \end{pmatrix} = \begin{pmatrix} 3620 \\ 8080 \end{pmatrix}$

g 3600

Chapter review

1 a $\begin{pmatrix} -11 & 9 \\ -4 & -7 \end{pmatrix}$ **b** DNE

c $\begin{pmatrix} -4 & -2 & 7 \\ 5 & -20 & 10 \end{pmatrix}$

d $\begin{pmatrix} 4 & 7 & -11 \\ -1 & 4 & -9 \end{pmatrix}$

e $\begin{pmatrix} -6 & -1 & 3 \\ 0 & -3 & -2 \\ -7 & -11 & 13 \end{pmatrix}$

f $\begin{pmatrix} 8 & -20 \\ 10 & 17 \end{pmatrix}$ **g** $\begin{pmatrix} 0 \\ -4 \\ 8 \end{pmatrix}$

h $\begin{pmatrix} 2 & -1.5 \\ 1 & -0.5 \end{pmatrix}$ **i** $\begin{pmatrix} 47 \\ 74 \end{pmatrix}$

j $\begin{pmatrix} -3 & 3 \\ -2 & 2 \end{pmatrix}$

2 $a = 4$; $b = -\dfrac{1}{2}$

3 a $\begin{pmatrix} \frac{5}{3} & \frac{4}{3} \\ -2 & -\frac{2}{3} \end{pmatrix}$ **b** $\begin{pmatrix} -\frac{13}{5} & \frac{34}{5} \\ \frac{4}{5} & -\frac{8}{5} \end{pmatrix}$

c $\begin{pmatrix} 10 & 7 \\ 8 & 5.5 \end{pmatrix}$

4 a $\begin{pmatrix} \frac{3}{13} \\ -\frac{20}{13} \end{pmatrix}$ **b** $\begin{pmatrix} \frac{21}{19} \\ \frac{3}{19} \\ -\frac{21}{19} \end{pmatrix}$

c $\begin{pmatrix} -3 \\ -\frac{5}{2} \\ 2 \end{pmatrix}$

5 a $\begin{pmatrix} \dfrac{1}{2} & 0 \\ 0 & -\dfrac{1}{2} \end{pmatrix} X + \begin{pmatrix} -\dfrac{3}{2} \\ -\dfrac{5}{2} \end{pmatrix}$

   b P′(−3.5, −1.5), Q′(−2, −6), R′(2.5, −4.5) T′(1, 0)

   c $k = \dfrac{1}{4}$

6 a $\begin{pmatrix} 13 \\ 25 \end{pmatrix}$ b $\begin{pmatrix} 2 \\ 0 \end{pmatrix}$

   c $\begin{pmatrix} a & -1 \\ 7a & +2 \end{pmatrix}$

7 a i $\begin{pmatrix} \dfrac{\sqrt{2}}{4} & -\dfrac{\sqrt{2}}{4} \\ \dfrac{\sqrt{2}}{4} & \dfrac{\sqrt{2}}{4} \end{pmatrix}$

   ii $\begin{pmatrix} 0 & -\dfrac{1}{\sqrt{2}} & -\dfrac{1}{\sqrt{2}} \\ 0 & 0 & \dfrac{1}{\sqrt{2}} \end{pmatrix}$

   b i $\begin{pmatrix} \dfrac{\sqrt{2}}{4} & -\dfrac{\sqrt{2}}{4} \\ \dfrac{\sqrt{2}}{4} & \dfrac{\sqrt{2}}{4} \end{pmatrix}$

   ii $C_2 = \begin{pmatrix} 0 & -\dfrac{1}{4} \\ \dfrac{1}{4} & 0 \end{pmatrix}$,

   $C_3 = \begin{pmatrix} -\dfrac{1}{8\sqrt{2}} & -\dfrac{1}{8\sqrt{2}} \\ \dfrac{1}{8\sqrt{2}} & -\dfrac{1}{8\sqrt{2}} \end{pmatrix}$,

   $C_4 = \begin{pmatrix} -0.625 & 0 \\ 0 & -0.625 \end{pmatrix}$

   iii 26.7

8 a $\begin{pmatrix} 8 & 0 \\ 2 & -4 \end{pmatrix}$ b $\begin{pmatrix} -1 & -2 \\ 1 & -1 \end{pmatrix}$

   c $\begin{pmatrix} 10 & 4 \\ 5 & 6 \end{pmatrix}$ d $\begin{pmatrix} 43 & -4 \\ 6 & 19 \end{pmatrix}$

9 Find the determinant:
   $x(3 - x) - (-1) \times 4 = 0$,
   $-x^2 + 3x + 4 = 0$, $x = -1\ x = 4$.

10 a $\begin{pmatrix} 0 & -1 \\ 1 & 0 \end{pmatrix}$ b 6

11 a $A^2 - 10A + 21I$

   $= \begin{pmatrix} 19 & 10 \\ 30 & 39 \end{pmatrix} - \begin{pmatrix} 40 & 10 \\ 30 & 60 \end{pmatrix}$

   $+ \begin{pmatrix} 21 & 0 \\ 0 & 21 \end{pmatrix}$

   $= 0$

   b $A^3 = 79A - 210I$

   c $A^4 = 1000A - 1659I$

12 a

   $A^{-1} = \begin{pmatrix} 0.125 & -0.875 & 0.625 \\ 0.25 & 1.25 & -0.75 \\ -0.125 & -0.125 & 0.375 \end{pmatrix}$

   b $\begin{pmatrix} 0.75 & -0.875 & 0.75 \\ -0.5 & 1.25 & -0.5 \\ 0.25 & -0.125 & 0.25 \end{pmatrix}$

13 a $A = \begin{pmatrix} 5 & 0 & 3 \\ 1 & -2 & 5 \\ 0 & 3 & 7 \end{pmatrix}$,

   $X = \begin{pmatrix} x \\ y \\ z \end{pmatrix}, B = \begin{pmatrix} 23 \\ 23 \\ 122 \end{pmatrix}$

   b $\begin{pmatrix} \dfrac{29}{136} & -\dfrac{9}{136} & -\dfrac{3}{68} \\ \dfrac{7}{136} & -\dfrac{25}{136} & \dfrac{11}{68} \\ -\dfrac{3}{136} & \dfrac{15}{136} & \dfrac{5}{68} \end{pmatrix}$

   c $X = A^{-1}B = \begin{pmatrix} -2 \\ 15 \\ 11 \end{pmatrix}$

14 180

15 a $\lambda_1 = 2, \lambda_2 = 6, \begin{pmatrix} 1 \\ 1 \end{pmatrix}$ and $\begin{pmatrix} 1 \\ -1 \end{pmatrix}$

   b $D = \begin{pmatrix} 2 & 0 \\ 0 & 6 \end{pmatrix}, P = \begin{pmatrix} 1 & 1 \\ 1 & -1 \end{pmatrix}$

   c $A^n = \dfrac{1}{2}\begin{pmatrix} 2^n + 6^n & 2^n - 6^n \\ 2^n - 6^n & 2^n + 6^n \end{pmatrix}$

Chapter 10

Skills check

1 $y = -\dfrac{1}{2}x + \dfrac{11}{2}5$

2 a x^{-5} b x^{-1} c $3x^{-\frac{1}{2}}$

3 −20 (1, 12)

Exercise 10A

1 $f'(x) = 4$ **6** $f'(x) = 2x - 3$
2 $f'(x) = 0$ **7** $f'(x) = 4x$
3 $f'(x) = 3$ **8** $f'(x) = 4x^3$
4 $f'(x) = 0$ **9** $f'(x) = -\dfrac{1}{x^2}$
5 $f'(x) = m$ **10** $f'(x) = anx^{n-1}$

Exercise 10B

1 a 0   b 4   c 12
   d 17   e 103   f 150

2 a $\dfrac{1}{3}$ b 1   c 10
   d −14   e −1

3 a $\dfrac{ds}{dt} = 4 + \dfrac{4}{t^{\frac{3}{2}}}, 4\dfrac{1}{16}$

   b $\dfrac{dv}{dt} = 3t^{-\frac{1}{4}} + 4t^{-\frac{5}{4}}, \dfrac{52}{32}$

4 a i $\dfrac{dy}{dx} = 12x + 5$

ii $12x > -5, x > -\dfrac{5}{12}$

b i $f'(x) = 8x^3 + 16x - 10$

ii $x > 0.544$

c i $g'(x) = 3x^2 + 6x - 9$

ii $x < -3$ and $x > 1$

5 a $2\pi r$ **b** 4π

6 a $-0.102c + 5.6$

b When $c = 20$, $\dfrac{dP}{dc} = 3.56$,

when $c = 60$, $\dfrac{dP}{dc} = -0.52$

c When derivative is positive, increasing the number of cupcakes sold increases profit, but when derivative is negative, increasing the number of cupcakes sold decreases the profit.

7 a $10 - 10t$ **b** Speed

c $f'(0.5) = 5, f'(1.5) = 1-5$, positive value represents the bungee jumper going downwards while negative value represents the bungee jumper going upwards.

d $f(2) = 0$, but $f'(2) = -10$, model suggests correctly that bungee jumper ends at starting point, but it also predicts a large upwards speed at the end of the jump.

8 $A = -1, B = \dfrac{1}{3}$

9 7.5

Exercise 10C

1 $y = 12x - 22$

2 $y = 1$

3 $y = -\dfrac{1}{2}x + \dfrac{9}{2}$

4 a Tangent: $z = 26x - 43$,

normal: $w = -\dfrac{1}{26}x + 9\dfrac{1}{13}$

b Tangent: $z = x - 9$, normal: $w = -x + 27$

5 $w = -\dfrac{1}{4}(x - 2) + 4$ and

$z = \dfrac{1}{4}(x + 2) + 4$, meet at $x = 0$

6 $a = 1, b = 9$

7 $k = 1, b = 5$

8 $a = 2, b = -5$

Exercise 10D

1 a $\dfrac{3}{4}$ **b** 2.0986

2 a -0.786 max, 2.12 min

b 0 max, 2 min

c No stationary points

3 a $x = \dfrac{1}{2}$, minimum

b $x = -2$ is a maximum and $x = 2$ is a minimum

c $x = -\dfrac{1}{2}$ is a maximum and

$x = \dfrac{1}{2}$ is a minimum

4 a i $P(5) = 4.67$

ii €52 000

iii €46 700

b Strategy **ii**

5 Maximum $y = 3.92$ at $x = 5.15$

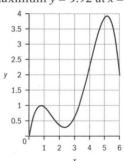

6 0.693

Exercise 10E

1 a $l = 50 - x$

b Area $A = x \times l = x(50 - x)$ **m²**

c $50 - 2x$

d Maximum when $\dfrac{dA}{dx} = 0$,

$x = 25, l = 25, A = 25 \times 25$
$= 625$ **m²**

2 a The base of the cylinder is a disc of area $A_b = \pi r^2$, and

the volume of a cylinder is then $V = Ah = \pi r^2 h$.

b $h = \dfrac{400}{\pi r^2}$

c $A = \pi r^2 + 2\pi r\, h$

d $A = \pi r^2 + 2\pi r \times \dfrac{400}{\pi r^2}$

$= \pi r^2 + \dfrac{800}{r}$

e

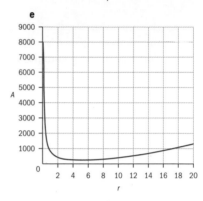

f $A = 238.53$ at $r = 5.03$

3 $h = \dfrac{2500}{\pi r} - r, r \approx 16.3\,\text{cm}$,

$V = \dfrac{250\,000}{3\sqrt{3\pi}} \approx 27145$

4 a $V = 6\pi r^2 - \dfrac{1}{3}\pi r^3$,

$\dfrac{dV}{dr} = 12\pi r - \pi r^2 = \pi r(12 - r)$

b $r = 12, V(12) = 288\pi$ but e.g. $V(18) = 0$, so maximum point

5 a Height of box $h = x$, width $w = 20 - 2x$, length $l = 24 - 2x$. Hence, volume is $V = hwl = x(20 - 2x)(24 - 2x) = 4x^3 - 88x^2 + 480x$

b $12x^2 - 176x + 480$

c 3.62, 11.05

d At end points, $V(0) = 0$, $V(10) = 0$

e $V(3.62) = 774.165\,\text{cm}^3$

6 a Profit = demand × (price − cost), so

$P = \dfrac{100}{x^2}(x - 0.75) = \dfrac{100}{x} - \dfrac{75}{x^2}$

b $\dfrac{dP}{dx} = -\dfrac{100}{x^2} + \dfrac{150}{x^3}$

c $-100x + 150 = 0 \Rightarrow x = 1.5$

d $x = 1 \Rightarrow \dfrac{dP}{dx} = 50$

$x = 2 \Rightarrow \dfrac{dP}{dx} = -6.25$,
gradient goes from positive to negative, hence a maximum

7 a From the Pythagoras theorem, $x^2 + y^2 = 6^2$.
The area of the rectangle is
$A = 2x \times 2y = 4x\sqrt{36 - x^2}$ as required.

b $\dfrac{dA}{dx} = 4\sqrt{36 - x^2} - \dfrac{4x^2}{\sqrt{36 - x^2}}$

$= 0, 36 - 2x^2 = 0,$

$x = 3\sqrt{2}, A = 72$

8 a $A = 2\pi \times 8\sin\theta \times 2 \times 8 \times \cos\theta \text{ cm}^2$
$= 256\pi \sin\theta\cos\theta \text{ cm}^2$

b $A = 128\pi \sin 2\theta, \dfrac{dA}{d\theta}$
$= 256\pi \cos 2\theta = 0$
when $\theta = \dfrac{\pi}{4}. A\left(\dfrac{\pi}{4}\right) = 128\pi$

Exercise 10F

1 a i $= u^3, u = x^2 + 4y$

ii $\dfrac{dy}{du} = 3u^2 = 3\left(x^2 + 4\right)$

b i $y = u^2, u = 5x - 7$

ii $\dfrac{dy}{du} = 2u = 10x - 14$

c i $y = 2u^4, u = x^3 - 3x^2$

ii $\dfrac{dy}{du} = 8u^3 = 8\left(x^3 - 3x^2\right)^3$

d i $y = u^{\frac{1}{2}}, u = 4x - 5$

ii $\dfrac{dy}{du} = \dfrac{1}{2}u^{-\frac{1}{2}} = \dfrac{1}{2}\left(4x - 5\right)^{-\frac{1}{2}}$

e i $y = u^{-2}, u = x^2 + 1$

ii $\dfrac{dy}{du} = -2u^{-3} = -2\left(x^2 + 1\right)^{-3}$

f i $y = 2u^{-\frac{1}{2}}, u = 5x - 2$

ii $\dfrac{dy}{du} = -u^{-\frac{3}{2}} = -\left(5x - 2\right)^{-\frac{3}{2}}$

2 a $f'(x) = 6x^5 + 12x^3 + 6x$

b $g'(x) = \dfrac{10}{\left(5x + 2\right)^{\frac{2}{3}}}$

c $h(x) = \dfrac{3\left(\sqrt{x} - x\right)^2}{2\sqrt{x}}$

d $s'(t) = 12\left(t^3 - 2t\right)$

e $v'(t) = -\dfrac{20}{\left(5t - 1\right)^2}$

f $a'(t) = \dfrac{3\left(2 - \dfrac{1}{t}\right)^2}{t^2}$

3 a 1   **b** -4

Exercise 10G

1 a $2x(3x + 1)$

b $3x^2 + 4x + 3$ (this has imaginary roots)

c $(x + 1)(5x^3 + 3x^2 - 2)$

d $(t - 4)^4(-14t^2 + 16t - 15)$

e $\dfrac{4(x - 1)\left(x^2 + x + 1\right)}{x^2}$

f $2(2t + 1)^3(t + 1)(t^2 - t + 1)$
$(t^3 + 3t^2 + 4)$

2 a $4x^2 + 2 + \dfrac{4}{x}$

b $\dfrac{x^2 - 2x - 1}{x^2 + 1}$

c $\dfrac{x + 2}{(x + 1)^{\frac{3}{2}}}$

d $\dfrac{4}{(2t + 1)^2}$

e $\dfrac{2x^3 + 3x^2 + 1}{(x + 1)^2}$

f $-\dfrac{4}{3t^{\frac{2}{3}}\left(t^{\frac{1}{3}} - 4\right)^2}$

3 a $2(x^2 + 1)^2x(4x^2 + 1)$

b $-\dfrac{8}{(2x + 3)^2}$ **c** $\dfrac{x + 1}{(2x + 1)^{\frac{3}{2}}}$

d $\dfrac{12(t - 1)}{\sqrt{2t - 3}}$ **e** $\dfrac{3 + 2x}{(3 - 2x)^3}$

f $\dfrac{4(t + 1)\left(4t^2 - 9t - 3\right)}{2t - 3}$

4 a $(2x - 1)(6x - 1)$

b i $y = 5x - 4$

ii $y = -\dfrac{1}{5}x + \dfrac{6}{5}$

c 2.6

5 a $y = -1.5x + 5$

b $\left(-\dfrac{7}{3}, 8.5\right)$

6 $\dfrac{dy}{dx} = -u\dfrac{dv}{dx}\dfrac{1}{v^2} + \dfrac{du}{dx}\dfrac{1}{v}$

$= \dfrac{v\dfrac{du}{dx} - u\dfrac{dv}{dx}}{v^2}$

Exercise 10H

1 a $4\cos x$ **b** $-2\sin x - 2x$

c $\dfrac{5}{\cos^2 x}$ **d** $-8\sin 4t$

e $5\cos 5x + 12x^2$

f $3\cos 3t + 6\sin 2t - 2t$

2 a $x\cos x + \sin x$ **b** $\cos 2x$

c $\dfrac{2x^2}{\cos^2 x} + 4x\tan x$

d $\dfrac{t\cos t - \sin t}{t^2}$

e $-\dfrac{1}{\sin^2 x}$

f $4\cos t - \dfrac{2}{\cos t} + 2\sin t\tan t$

3 a $2x\cos x^2$ **b** $6\sin 3x$

c $\dfrac{3}{\cos^2(3x - 1)}$ **d** $2\sin t\cos t$

e $-9\cos^2 x\sin x$ **f** $8\cos 8t$

g $3\sin 6x$

h $-\sin t + 3\cos^2 t\sin t$

4 a $A = 2xy = 10.2x\cos\dfrac{\pi}{10}x$

b

$$-1.02\pi\, x\sin\frac{\pi}{10}x+10.2\cos\frac{\pi}{10}x$$

c $A(2.74)=18.22$

Exercise 10I

1 a $\dfrac{2x}{x^2+1}$

b $xe^x+e^x=e^x(1+x)$

c $4xe^{2x^2}$ **d** $t(1+2\ln t)$

e $4e^2x(x+1)$ **f** $\dfrac{1-\ln t}{t^2}$

g $\dfrac{6t^2}{t^2-2}$ **h** $\dfrac{2e^{4x}}{x^2}(4x-1)$

i $e^{3t^2}\left(1+6t^2\right)$

2 a $\dfrac{5}{x}$ **b** $\dfrac{8}{2x+3}$

c $\dfrac{1}{x}+\dfrac{2}{x-3}$ **d** $\dfrac{2}{2x+1}-\dfrac{1}{x}$

e $2x$ **f** $\dfrac{2}{x}-\dfrac{6}{2x+1}$

3 a $(\ln ax)'=\dfrac{1}{x}$

b $(\ln ax)'=\dfrac{1}{ax}\times a=\dfrac{1}{x}$

4 a i $f'(x)=20\cos\ln x\times\dfrac{1}{x}$

    ii $x=0.175$

b i $f'(x)=\dfrac{1}{\cos x+2}\times(-\sin x)$

    ii $x=\pi$

c i $f'(x)=2\cos x\,e^{2\sin x}$

    ii $2\cos x=1,\ x=\dfrac{\pi}{3}$

5 a $x=-2.5,\ y=2e^{-5}$

b $y=2e^{-5}$

Exercise 10J

1 a $-x\sin x+2\cos x$

b $\dfrac{12}{(x-3)^4}$ **c** $\dfrac{2}{t}$

2 a $x=0$ is a maximum,

$x=\left(\dfrac{6}{5}\right)^{\frac{1}{3}}$ is a minimum

b Inflection point occurs

when $x=0.3^{\frac{1}{3}}$

c $x\in\left(0.3^{\frac{1}{3}},\infty\right)$

3 a $e^x\left(\dfrac{1}{x}-\dfrac{2}{x^2}+\dfrac{2}{x^3}\right)$

b At $x=1$,

$\dfrac{dy}{dx}=0,\dfrac{d^2y}{dx^2}=e>0$, so it is

a minimum point

c Points of inflection would

occur if $\dfrac{d^2y}{dx^2}=0$, i.e. if

$\left(\dfrac{1}{x}-\dfrac{2}{x^2}+\dfrac{2}{x^3}\right)=0$,

$x^2-2x+2=0$.

The discriminant is

$4-4\times2=-4<0$ so there

are no real roots of this

equation and hence no

points of inflection exist.

4 a $f'(x)=\dfrac{x-3-x}{(x-3)^2}$

$=-\dfrac{3}{(x-3)^2}<0$

for all values of x

b $f''(x)=\dfrac{6}{(x-3)^3}<0$

for $x<3$, $f''(x)>0$ for $x>3$

($f''(x)$ is infinite at $x=3$),

so $f''(x)$ never vanishes.

5 a i $x=-\dfrac{1}{4}$, minimum

    ii $\left(-\dfrac{1}{4}-2\right)(-3-9)$

    iii $x=2,\dfrac{1}{2}$

    iv Concave down for

$x\in\left(\dfrac{1}{2},2\right)$ and concave

up otherwise

b i $x=\dfrac{3\pi}{4}$ is a minimum,

$x=\dfrac{7\pi}{4}$ is a maximum

    ii $e^{-x}2\sin x$

    iii $x=0,\ \pi,\ 2\pi$

    iv Concave up for $x\in(0,\pi)$

and concave down for

$x\in(\pi,2\pi)$

c i $x=\dfrac{3}{2}$ is a maximum

    ii $e^{-2x}2x(2x^2-6x+3)$

    iii $x=0,\dfrac{1}{2}\left(3\pm\sqrt3\right)$

    iv Concave up for

$x\in\left(0,\dfrac{1}{2}\left(3-\sqrt3\right)\right)\cup\left(\dfrac{1}{2}\left(3+\sqrt3\right),\infty\right)$

and concave down for

$x\in(-\infty,0)\cup\left(\dfrac{1}{2}\left(3-\sqrt3\right),\dfrac{1}{2}\left(3+\sqrt3\right)\right)$

6 a i $p'(t)=\dfrac{80e^{-2t}}{\left(1+4e^{-2t}\right)^2}$

    ii Both numerator and

denominator are

positive for $t\geq0$ hence

the population is always

increasing.

b i $p''(t)=\dfrac{160e^{-2t}\left(4e^{-2t}-1\right)}{\left(1+4e^{-2t}\right)^3}$

    ii $\ln2$ or 0.693

    iii This is the point at

which the rate of

population growth has

reached is maximum.

c i $p(\ln2)=5$

    ii This is the half the

carrying capacity of the

population.

Exercise 10K

1 a 2 **b** 4

2 a $\dfrac{1}{3}$

b Velocity $=-11$,

acceleration $=-14$

c Increasing

d $t = 2$

e i $t = \dfrac{2}{3}$

  ii Point of inflexion.

3 $a \approx -33.54$

4 a $v(t) = y'(t) = -0.4t + 2$

  b i $v(0) = 2$ **ii** 6 m

  iii -2.19

5 a i 1.31   **ii** $t \approx 3.37$

  b $s'(t) = 0.4(1 + e^{-0.5t})$

  c $s'(0) = 0.8$

  d As $t \to \infty$, $s'(t) \to 0.4$

  e The marble is first moving within 1% of its terminal velocity when $e^{-0.5t} = 0.01$, $t = -2\log 0.01 = \log 100^2$ ≈ 9.21

6 a $t \approx 65.04$

  b $v(t) = 3 + \dfrac{2}{2t + 1}$

  c i $v(0) = 3 + 2 = 5\,\text{m s}^{-1}$

  ii $v(65.04) = 3.02\,\text{m s}^{-1}$

  d $a(t) = v(t)$

  $= -\dfrac{4}{(2t + 1)^2} < 0\,\forall\,t$

7 a

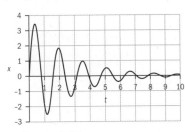

  b $t = 2.84$

  c $\dot{x}(t) = 4e^{-0.4t}(-0.4\sin 4t + 4\cos 4t)$

  d i $t = \dfrac{n\pi}{4}$

  ii -11.69

8 1.11

Exercise 10L

1 a $\pi r^2 \dfrac{dh}{dt}$ **b** $2\pi r \dfrac{dr}{dt} h$

2 $\dfrac{8}{3}\,\text{m}^2\text{s}^{-1}$

3 $0.75\,\text{rad s}^{-1}$

4 $8\,\text{cm min}^{-1}$

5 $1.15\,\text{cm}^2\text{s}^{-1}$

6 a

$f(x) = \dfrac{\cos x}{\sin x}$,

$f'(x) = \dfrac{-\sin x \times \sin x - \cos x \times \cos x}{\sin^2 x}$

$= -\dfrac{1}{\sin^2 x}$

  b $87.01\,\text{m s}^{-1}$

Chapter review

1 a 33.5

  b $(65\,536, -1\,048\,580)$

  c -60

2 a $f'(x) = -2\sin x + 2\cos x$

  b $f'(x) = \dfrac{1}{\cos^2 x \tan x}$

  $= \dfrac{2}{\sin 2x}$

  c $\dfrac{dy}{dx} = \dfrac{-\sin^2 x - \cos^2 x}{\sin^2 x}$

  $= -\dfrac{1}{\sin^2 x}$

  d $\dfrac{dy}{dx} = 2xe^{2x} + e^{2x}$

3 a $f'(x) = -\dfrac{24}{x^3} + \dfrac{3}{2\sqrt{x}}$,

  $f''(x) = \dfrac{72}{x^4} - \dfrac{3}{4}x^{-\frac{3}{2}}$

  b $f'(x) = 6x - 10$, $f''(x) = 6$

  c $\dfrac{dy}{dx} = -\dfrac{1}{x^2} + \dfrac{24}{x^3}$,

  $\dfrac{d^2y}{dx^2} = \dfrac{2}{x^3} - \dfrac{72}{x^4}$

  d $\dfrac{dy}{dx} = \dfrac{x^2 - 24x}{(x - 12)^2}$,

  $\dfrac{d^2y}{dx^2} = \dfrac{288}{(x - 12)^3}$

4 $\dfrac{dy}{dx} = \dfrac{2e^{2x}}{(e^{2x} + 1)^2}$

Since e^{2x} is always greater than zero so is the gradient.

5 $\left(-\dfrac{14}{3}, \dfrac{22}{3}\right)$

  a $(1, -7)$ **b** $\dfrac{d^2y}{dx^2} = \dfrac{7}{2x^{\frac{3}{2}}}$

  c When $x = 1$ $\dfrac{d^2y}{dx^2} = \dfrac{7}{2} > 0$ hence a minimum

6 a $(x(64 - x))$

  b 32   **c** $1024\,\text{m}^2$

7 a Right as v is positive

  b i To the right when $0 < t < 7$, $t > 10$.

  ii To the left when $7 < t < 10$. It depends on the sign of v.

  c Positive as the graph of v has a positive gradient.

  [0, 4]: v is initially 2 but accelerates at $0.5\,\text{m s}^{-2}$

  [4, 6]: constant velocity of $4\,\text{m s}^{-1}$

  [6, 8.5]: slowing down at a decreasing rate until 7 seconds whenstarts moving to the left and reaches a maximum speed of $2.2\,\text{m s}^{-1}$at $t = 8.5$s

  d [8.5, 10]: slowing down until at 10 seconds it has a velocity of 0

  e $t = 7$ because it begins to travel to the left at 7 seconds and stays travelling to the left until 10 seconds.

8 $x = 9.5$. The point of inflexion is $(14.5, 35)$

9 $\dfrac{6}{\sqrt{17}}$

Exam-style questions

10 $y = \dfrac{x}{2} + 1$

11 a $\left(1, \dfrac{25}{6}\right)$ and $\left(\dfrac{3}{2}, -\dfrac{145\,833}{100\,000}\right)$

  b he gradient is negative between $x = \dfrac{1}{4}\left(7 \pm \sqrt{33}\right)$

12 a The height of the box is $h = x$, the width is $w = 30 - 2x$ and the length is $l = 40 - 2x$. Hence, the volume is $V = hwl = x(30 - 2x)(40 - 2x) = 4x^3 - 140x^2 + 1200x$.

b $\dfrac{\mathrm{d}V}{\mathrm{d}x} = 12x^2 - 280x + 1200$

c $\dfrac{\mathrm{d}V}{\mathrm{d}x} = 0$ for
$12x^2 - 280x + 1200 = 0,$
$x^2 - \dfrac{70}{3}x + 100 = 0$

d Range $x \in (0, 15)$,
$V(5.66) = 3032.3$.

13 a $f'(x) = \dfrac{-2x^4 - 2x}{\left(2x^3 - 1\right)^2}$

b $y = -4x + 5$

c $x = 0, x = -1$

d $f(x)$ is increasing for positive gradient, this happens for $x \in (-1, 0)$

14 $\dfrac{3}{20\pi}$

15 a 1.53

b $\dfrac{\mathrm{d}x}{\mathrm{d}t} = -\dfrac{5}{(t-5)^2} + \dfrac{2}{1+t} = 0,$
stationary at
$t = \dfrac{1}{4}\left(25 - \sqrt{256}\right)$

16 a First, find that
$$\frac{\mathrm{d}x}{\mathrm{d}t} = \mathrm{e}^{-2t}\left(-2\cos\sqrt{12}t - \sqrt{12}\sin\sqrt{12}t\right),$$
$$\frac{\mathrm{d}^2 x}{\mathrm{d}t^2} = \mathrm{e}^{-2t}\left(4\cos\sqrt{12}t + 2\sqrt{12}\sin\sqrt{12}t + 2\sqrt{12}\sin\sqrt{12}t - 12\cos\sqrt{12}t\right)$$
$$= \mathrm{e}^{-2t}\left(-8\cos\sqrt{12}t + 4\sqrt{12}\sin\sqrt{12}t\right).$$

Substitute into the given equation:
$$\mathrm{e}^{-2t}\left(-8\cos\sqrt{12}t + 4\sqrt{12}\sin\sqrt{12}t - 4\sqrt{12}\sin\sqrt{12}t - 8\cos\sqrt{12}t + 16\cos\sqrt{12}t\right)$$
$$= 0.$$

b

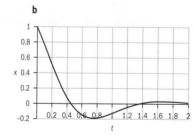

c $t = 0.75$

d 0.64

Chapter 11

Skills check

1 $\dfrac{1}{2} \times 1.8(3.2 + 4.8) = 7.2$ cm^2

2 a $\dfrac{\mathrm{d}y}{\mathrm{d}x} = 9x^2 - x^{-\frac{1}{2}} - 8x^{-3}$ or
$\dfrac{\mathrm{d}y}{\mathrm{d}x} = 9x^2 - \dfrac{1}{\sqrt{x}} - \dfrac{8}{x^3}$

b $f'(x) = -5\sin 5x + 2\sin x \cos x$

c $\dfrac{\mathrm{d}s}{\mathrm{d}t} = \dfrac{1}{t} - 4t\mathrm{e}^{t^2}$

1 a i $y = \sqrt{9 - x^2}, 0 \le x \le 3$

   ii $\displaystyle\int_0^3 \sqrt{9 - x^2}\,\mathrm{d}x$

b

x	0	0.5	1.0	1.5	2.0	2.5	3.0
y	3	2.958	2.828	2.598	2.2361	1.658	0

c i 6.139   **ii** 7.639

d 6.889   **e** 3%

2 a

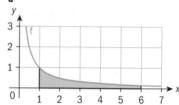

b $\displaystyle\int_1^6 \frac{1}{x}\,\mathrm{d}x$

c i 1.45   **ii** $2.28\dot{3}$

d $\dfrac{29}{20} < \displaystyle\int_1^6 \frac{1}{x}\,\mathrm{d}x < \dfrac{137}{60}$

1 a i $\displaystyle\int_2^4 x^2\,\mathrm{d}x$ **ii** $\dfrac{56}{3}$

b i $\displaystyle\int_{-1}^1 2^x\,\mathrm{d}x$ **ii** 22.4

c i $\displaystyle\int_{-1}^1 \frac{1}{1+x^2}\,\mathrm{d}x$ **ii** 1.57

d i $\displaystyle\int_{0.5}^3 \frac{1}{x}\,\mathrm{d}x$ **ii** 1.79

e i $\displaystyle\int_0^1 -(x-3)(x+2)\,\mathrm{d}x$

   ii $\dfrac{37}{6}$

f i $\displaystyle\int_{-2}^0 -(x-3)(x+2)\,\mathrm{d}x$ or
$\displaystyle\int_0^3 -(x-3)(x+2)\,\mathrm{d}x$

   ii $\dfrac{22}{3}$ or 13.5

g i $\displaystyle\int_{-2}^3 -(x-3)(x+2)\,\mathrm{d}x$

   ii $\dfrac{125}{6}$

h i $\int_{-2}^{4.5} -x^2 + 2x + 15\,dx$

ii 80.71

i i $\int_{-\sqrt{17}}^{\sqrt{17}} -x^2 + 2x + 15\,dx$

ii 58.33

j i $\int_{-1}^{\ln(3)} 3 - e^x\,dx$

ii 3.66

k i $\int_{-2-5^{\frac{1}{3}}}^{0} (x+2)^3 + 5\,dx$

ii 20.41

2 a −2, 2 **b** (0, 4)

c 20 **d** 5.33

e 20.41

3 3

4 −0.8169

Exercise 11C

1 a

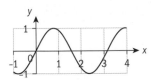

b i 0.230 **ii** 0.807

iii 1.64

2 a

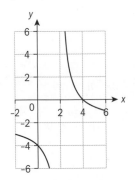

b The interval [0, 3] contains a discontinuity

c i 0.773 **ii** 1.23

d 2.00

Exercise 11D

1 55

2 18

3 9.85

4 11.553

5 a 5.19 **b** 15

c 12.21 **d** 35

6 a $\frac{1}{2} \times 2\left(4 + 5 + 2(6 + 5.5 + 6.2)\right)$
$= 44.4$

b $\frac{1}{2} \times 2\left(4 + 5 + 2(3 + 2.2 + 3.4)\right)$
$= 26.2$

c $44.4 - 26.2 = 18.2 \text{ km}^2$

7 a

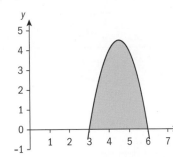

b i $\int_{3}^{6} -2(x-3)(x-6)\,dx$

ii 9

c 8.75 **d** 2.78%

8 a

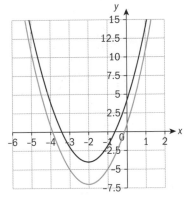

b i $\int_{0}^{2} (1 + e^x)\,dx$ **ii** 8.389

c 8.474 **d** 1.01%

9 26.5

10 a 51.8 **b** 52.3

c 0.96%

Exercise 11E

1 a $10x + c$ **b** $0.2x^3 + c$

c $\frac{x^6}{6} + c$ **d** $7x - x^2 + c$

e $x + x^2 + c$

f $5x + \frac{x^2}{2} - \frac{1}{9}x^3 + c$

g $-\frac{x^2}{2} - \frac{x^3}{4} + 0.5x + c$

h $x - \frac{x^2}{2} + \frac{x^4}{8} + c$

i $\frac{x^3}{3} - \frac{x^2}{4} + 4x + c$

2 a $2x - \frac{1}{3}$

b $\frac{x^3}{3} - \frac{x^2}{6} + 4x + c$

3 a $\frac{1}{2}t^2 - t^3 + c$

b $t^4 - 1.5t^2 + t + c$

4 a

b i $f(-2) = -7$
ii $f(-2) = -4$

5 a $-2\cos x + c$ **b** $4\sin x + c$

c $-\frac{1}{3}\cos x + c$ **d** $3\tan|x| + c$

6 a $2e^x + c$ **b** $3e^x + \ln x + c$

c $4\ln|x| - 3e^x + c$

7 a $\frac{2}{3}e^{3x} + c$ **b** $-\frac{2}{5}\cos 5t + c$

c $4x + \frac{2}{3}e^{-3x} + c$

d $\frac{1}{2}\sin 2t + \frac{1}{3}\cos 3t + c$

8 a $\sqrt{5}\times\dfrac{2}{3}t^{\frac{3}{2}}+c$ **b** $3\pi x^{\frac{1}{3}}+c$

c $\dfrac{1}{4}a^4-a^3+2a+c$

d $2x^{\frac{1}{2}}+c$

e $\dfrac{1}{2}x^3+2x+3\ln|x|+c$

f $\dfrac{1}{2}e^{2x}-\dfrac{3}{4}\cos 4x+c$

g $\dfrac{2}{9}x^{\frac{3}{2}}-\dfrac{1}{12}\sin 4x+c$

9 a i $\dfrac{dy}{dx}=-\dfrac{\cos x}{\sin^2 x}$

ii $c-\dfrac{1}{\sin x}$

b i $\dfrac{dy}{dx}=\dfrac{2}{\sqrt{4x-1}}$

ii $\dfrac{1}{2}\sqrt{4x-1}+c$

10 $y=\dfrac{x^2}{2}+\dfrac{x^3}{15}+2x+c$

11 $f(x)=3x-\dfrac{x^2}{2}+c1$

12 $y=\dfrac{1}{2}\sin 2x-\cos 2x+4.5$

13 $y=2e^{4x}+x^3+x+2$

Exercise 11F

1 a $\dfrac{1}{12}(4x-1)^3+c$

b $-\dfrac{1}{4x-1}+c$

c $\dfrac{1}{2}\sqrt{4x-1}+c$

d $\dfrac{3}{4}\ln|4x-1|+c$

2 a $4x^2+12x+c$

b $e^{1+x^2}+c$

c $2\tan(4+2x)+c$

d $\dfrac{1}{2}\ln|2x+3|+c$

e $2\sin(x^2+2)+c$

f $\dfrac{1}{3}\sin^3 x+c$

3 $y=\dfrac{1}{2}+\ln|x+2|+3$

4 a $\dfrac{1}{3}e^{\sin 3x}+c$

b $\dfrac{1}{12}\left(x^2-6x+4\right)^6+c$

5 a $-\ln|\cos x|+c$

b $y=-\ln|\cos x|+2x+c,\ c=4$

6 a $\dfrac{y^2}{9}+\dfrac{x^2}{4}=1$

b $x=0,\ y=\pm 3$

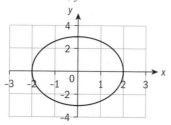

c 18.85

d 6π

7 a $C(n)=2\ln(n^2+1)+1.5$

b 9.3

c As n increases, the cost is growing slower and slower, and the shape of the curve becomes more and more logarithmic.

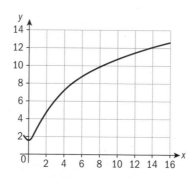

8 a $R(t)=\dfrac{3}{5\left(1+12e^{-0.5t}\right)}+c$

b 9.6 hours

c 75%

9 a $0<t<5$

b
$$T(t)=\dfrac{5}{2}\left(\ln\left(2t^2+1\right)+240\cos\left(\dfrac{t}{120}\right)\right)-575$$

c $t=5,\ T(5)=34\,\text{m}^3$

Exercise 11G

1 a $\dfrac{1}{2}\left(e^2+1\right)$

b $2\ln 2$

c $\dfrac{1}{3}\left(\sqrt{11^3}-8\right)$

2 $\displaystyle\int_1^4\dfrac{x}{x^2+2}\,dx=\int_3^{18}\dfrac{du}{2u}=\left[\dfrac{1}{2}\ln|u|\right]_3^{18}$
$$=\dfrac{1}{2}\ln 6,$$

where $u=x^2+2$

3 $\displaystyle\int_{\frac{\pi}{6}}^{\frac{\pi}{4}}\cos 2x\,dx=\left[\dfrac{1}{2}\sin 2x\right]_{\frac{\pi}{6}}^{\frac{\pi}{4}}$
$$=\dfrac{1}{2}\left(1-\dfrac{\sqrt{3}}{2}\right)$$

4 Energy
$$E=\int_0^{t_1}\dfrac{4t}{t^2+2}\,dt=2\int_2^{t_1^2+2}\dfrac{du}{u}=2\ln\dfrac{t_1^2+2}{2}$$

5 27.27

Exercise 11H

1 a -1.875 **b** $\dfrac{81}{4}$ **c** 1.15

d $\dfrac{32}{3}$ **e** 4.24 **f** 5.52

2 3.296

3 4

4 a $a=4,\ b=\dfrac{\pi}{5}$

b $y=4\sin\dfrac{\pi}{5}x-1$

c $V=69\,\text{m}^3$

5 a i $p_a = \frac{1}{2}\ln(a+1)$

ii $A_1 = \frac{a}{2} - \frac{1}{2}\ln(a+1)$

b 0

Exercise 11I

1 a $\frac{\pi}{3}$ **b** $\frac{\pi}{5}$ **c** $\frac{\pi}{7}$

d $\frac{\pi}{2}(e^2 - 1)$

2 a $\frac{\pi}{3}$ **b** $\frac{\pi}{2}$ **c** $\frac{3\pi}{5}$

b $\pi(e - 2)$

3 a $\frac{300}{10000}x^3 - \frac{x^5}{50000} + c$

b $1018\,\text{mm}^3$ **c** £580

4 a i $V = \int_0^3 \pi\left(4 - \frac{4}{3}x\right)^2 dx$

ii $V = \int_0^4 \pi\left(3 - \frac{3}{4}y\right)^2 dy$

b i 16π

ii 12π

5 a Hany's model is best. 279 units^3

b i 110 inches^3

ii 1803 cm^3

6 a i

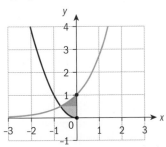

ii $V = \int_{-0.70}^0 \pi\left(e^{2x} - x^4\right)dx$

iii 1.1

b i

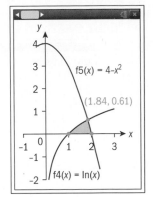

ii Volume $= \pi\int_1^{1.84}\left(\ln(x)\right)^2 dx$
$+ \pi\int_{1.84}^2\left(4 - x^2\right)^2 dx$

iii 0.46

7 a

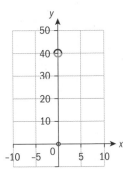

b The shape is a torus.

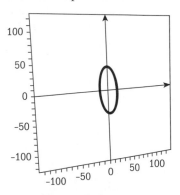

c Volume $=$
$\pi\int_{-2}^2\left(40 + \sqrt{4 - x^2}\right)^2$
$-\left(40 - \sqrt{4 - x^2}\right)^2 dx$
$= 3158$ cubic units

8 Consider triangles CAD and DAB. $AC = AB = r$, $CD = DB$ and AD is common. Hence the triangles are congruent.

Hence, $\angle ADB = \angle ADC = \frac{\pi}{2}$.

9 a 358 m

b $2.7 \times 10^6\,\text{m}^3$

Exercise 11J

1 a $v(t) = -\frac{3}{t+1} + 3$,
$d(t) = 3\left(t - \ln(1+t)\right)$

b 20 s

2 a i $a(t) = 3e^{2\sin 3t}(2\cos^2 3t - \sin 3t)$

ii $t = 0.3$

b $s(t) = \frac{1}{6}(e^{2\sin 3t} - 1)$

c $s_{max} - \frac{1}{6}(e^2 - 1)$

3 a 1 **b** $k < \frac{1}{8}$

4 a Velocity of the projectile $v(t) = \int g\,dt = gt + v_0$, height of the projectile $s(t) = \int v(t)\,dt = \frac{1}{2}gt^2 + v_0 t + y_0$.

b $s(t_0) = y_0 - \frac{v_0^2}{2g}$

c $s(t_0) = 4913\,\text{m} > 4\,\text{km}$, so rocket will reach the target height

Exercise 11K

1 a $-21.3\,°\text{C}$ **b** $76.8\,°\text{C}$

2 a

Particle	Distance travelled	Displacement
A	50 m	50 m
B	25 m	25 m
C	25 m	0 m
D	25 m	25 m

3

	a	b
Sketch	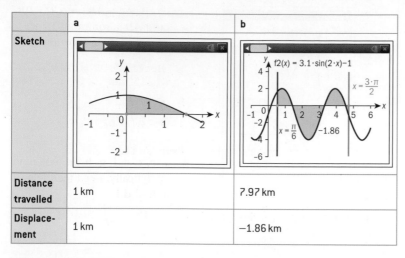	
Distance travelled	1 km	7.97 km
Displacement	1 km	−1.86 km

	c	d
	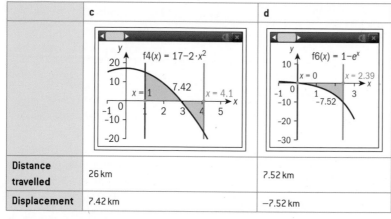	
Distance travelled	26 km	7.52 km
Displacement	7.42 km	−7.52 km

4 a i 20 m   **ii** 33.3 m

  b 16.45 seconds

5 a −0.015 cm

  b 6.53 cm

6 a i

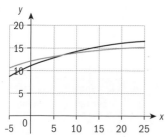

  ii 6.49 seconds

  b 917.5 m above the ground.

7 $a = \dfrac{2}{\pi}\,\text{mJ s}^{-1}$

8 $0.19\,\text{s}^{-1}$

9 a April

  b i −13.6   **ii** −5.72

  c −9.65

Exercise 11L

1 $y^4 = 2e^{\frac{1}{8}x^2}$

2 $y = 3|x^2 - 1|$

3 a $\dfrac{dM}{dt} = -kM,$

  separable equation:

  $\displaystyle\int \frac{1}{M}\,dM = \int -k\,dt,\ \ln M$
  $= -kt + c,\ M = Ae^{-kt}$

  b $k = \dfrac{1}{2}\ln 2$

4 a $\dfrac{dy}{dx} = -\dfrac{x}{\sqrt{4 - x^2}}$

  b $-\dfrac{x}{\sqrt{4 - x^2}} = -\dfrac{x}{\sqrt{4 - x^2}}$

  c $y = \pm\sqrt{c - x^2}$

5 a $y = -\ln(-c - e^x)$

  b $\dfrac{1}{2}y^2 + \ln y = x + \sin x + c$

6 a $y = \dfrac{1}{2}\left(x^{\frac{3}{2}} + 7\right)^{\frac{2}{3}}$

  b $\dfrac{1}{2}y^2 = x^2 - \cos x + \dfrac{3}{2}$

  c $y = x$

7 a Initially when the difference between the temperature of the coffee and the ambient temperature is greatest.

  b 75 °C

  c $T = 24 + 51e^{-kt}$

  d $e^{-kt} > 0$

8 a 6.561×10^{151}

  b 0.611 hours

9 a $N = N_0 e^{-kt}$ When
  $t = T\ N = \dfrac{N_0}{2}$ Hence
  $\dfrac{1}{2} = e^{-kT} \Rightarrow k = -\dfrac{1}{T}\ln\dfrac{1}{2} = \dfrac{\ln 2}{T}$

  b 3.90 g

10 a The amount of water leaving the tank every second is $Av = A\sqrt{2gh}$. Hence, rate of change of the total volume of water in the tank is $\dfrac{dV}{dt} = -A\sqrt{2gh}.$

  b i Since $V = \pi r^2 h, \dfrac{dV}{dt} = -A\sqrt{\dfrac{2gV}{\pi r^2}} = -k\sqrt{V}$

  ii $k = A\sqrt{\dfrac{2g}{\pi r^2}}$

  c $t = \dfrac{2\sqrt{V_0}}{k}$

Exercise 11M

1 a

x \ y	1	2	3
1	2	3	4
2	5	6	7
3	10	11	12

b

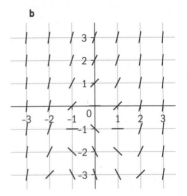

c

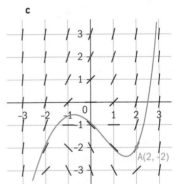

$A(2, -2)$

2 a III **b** I **c** IV **d** II

3 a i Along the lines

$$x + y = \pm\frac{\pi}{2}.$$

ii Along the lines

$$x - y = \pm\frac{\pi}{2}$$

b i IB   **ii** A

4 a, b

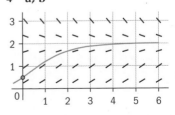

c $2\,\text{cm}^3$

d Maximal size of the tumour agrees with the fact that it grows in the environment where the availability of nutrients is limited.

Exercise 11N

1 4.25

2 −0.71

3 0.274

4 a 0.53

b $y(1.5) = 0.54$, error = 1.9%

5 a 3.99

b $y(1.3) = 4.04$, error = 1.2%

6 a $b = 2, a = 4$

b

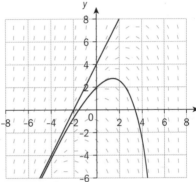

c $N_0 = 4$

d $N = 6$

e 4 more meerkats

f 195

Chapter review

1 a For $t \in (0, 30)$, drone moves in positive direction with constant velocity $v = 40$

For $t \in (30, 60)$, drone moves in positive direction with decreasing speed, i.e. with acceleration $v = -\frac{4}{3}$

For $t \in (0, 30)$, drone moves in negative direction with increasing speed, i.e. with acceleration $v = -\frac{4}{3}$

For $t \in (75, 90)$, drone moves in negative direction with constant velocity $v = -20$

b $30 < t < 75$ **c** $30 < t < 60$

d 2250 km **e** 2250 km

2 a 46.7 m **b** 10 seconds

c 30.6 s

3 933.5 m

4 **a, b, c, e, f, g, h** can be found analytically; need technology to find **d, i**.

5 a $\dfrac{\mathrm{d}P}{\mathrm{d}t} = -aP$

b $P = 600\,000\mathrm{e}^{\left(\frac{1}{4}\ln\left(\frac{5}{6}\right)\right)t}$

c 20.1 years

6 a Hemisphere

b $\pi\displaystyle\int_0^r \left(r^2 - x^2\right)^2 \mathrm{d}x$

c $V = 2\displaystyle\int_0^r \pi\left(r^2 - x^2\right)\mathrm{d}x$
$= 2\pi\left(r^3 - \dfrac{1}{3}r^3\right) = \dfrac{4}{3}\pi r^3$

7 a 3.6, 4.39, 5.45

b $3\mathrm{e}^{x^2+2x}$, −0.10103, −0.27, −0.54

8 a $\dfrac{\mathrm{d}V}{\mathrm{d}t} = -k\sqrt{h}$

b $k\sqrt{h} = \dfrac{4\pi}{25}\dfrac{\mathrm{d}h}{\mathrm{d}t}$

c 50 minutes

9 a $11\,\text{m}^2$

b $352\,000\,\text{m}^3$

Exam-style questions

10 a 0.347

b $\dfrac{1}{2}\ln\left(x^2 + 4\right) + c$

c $\dfrac{\ln 2}{2}$

11 **a** $\frac{1}{3}x^3 + \frac{3}{2}x^2 + x + c$

b $-\cos x + \frac{1}{2}\sin 2x + c$

c $e^x - e^{-x} + c$

d $\frac{1}{21}(3x+1)^7 + c$

e $\frac{1}{2}x^2 + x + c$

12 $65 \times 10^4 \, \text{m}^2$

13 **a** $122.98 \, \text{m}^2$

b $124.42 \, \text{m}^2$

c 1.2%

d Approximating the area using trapezium leaves small area above the trapezium and below the actual curve which is not taken into account while finding the area. Hence, the estimate is smaller than the true value.

14 7.42

15 **a** $v(t) = 20(1 - e^{-0.2t})$

b $(t) = 20t + 100(e^{-0.2t} - 1)$

c $v(t) \to 20$ as $t \to \infty$

d $d(60) = 1100 \, \text{m}$

16 **a**

x	y
1.25	2.50
1.50	3.28
1.75	4.51
2.00	6.49

b $y = e^{\frac{1}{2}x^2 - \frac{1}{2} + \ln 2}$

c $2e^{\frac{3}{2}}$

d 28%

17 **a** $2x\sin x + x^2\cos x$

b $4\sin x + 3x^2\sin x + c$

18 **a** **i** Isocline with $k = 4$

ii Not an isocline, $\frac{dy}{dx}$ changes with x

iii Isocline with $k = 1$

iv Not an isocline because

$\frac{dy}{dx} = \frac{2x^2 + 2x + 1}{2x^2 + 2x} \neq \text{const}$

v Isocline with $k = -1$

b Turning point occurs when $\frac{dy}{dx} = 0$. This is impossible for $x \neq 0$, $y \neq 0$.

Chapter 12

Skills check

1 **a** $\int 6e^{3x} - \frac{1}{e^{2x}}\, dx = 2e^{3x} + \frac{1}{2e^{2x}} + c$

b $\int 3\cos(6x) - 4\sin(2x)\, dx$

$= \frac{1}{2}\sin(6x) + 2\cos(2x) + c$

2 **a** $87.2°$

b $\begin{pmatrix} 2 \\ 3 \\ 2 \end{pmatrix} \times \begin{pmatrix} -2 \\ 2 \\ 3 \end{pmatrix} = \begin{pmatrix} 5 \\ -10 \\ 10 \end{pmatrix}$

3 $\lambda = 4, -3$. For $\lambda = 4$ eigenvectors are multiples of $\begin{pmatrix} 1 \\ 1 \end{pmatrix}$. For $\lambda = -3$ eigenvectors are multiples of $\begin{pmatrix} -2 \\ 5 \end{pmatrix}$.

Exercise 12A

1 **a** $6.71 \, \text{N}, 26.6°$

b $5 \, \text{N}, 126.9°$

2 **a** $\begin{pmatrix} 4.95 \\ 4.95 \end{pmatrix} \text{m s}^{-1}$

b $\begin{pmatrix} 10.4 \\ -6 \end{pmatrix} \text{m s}^{-1}$

3 $6.08 \, \text{m s}^{-1}, 350.54°$ clockwise

4 **a** Perpendicular to the force F and displacement r

b $5 \, \text{N m}$

5 **a** Resistance force $= \begin{pmatrix} -70 \\ 0 \end{pmatrix} \text{N}$,

force from the first dog $= \begin{pmatrix} 147.72 \\ 26.05 \end{pmatrix} \text{N}$, force from

second dog $= \begin{pmatrix} 0.97D \\ -0.26D \end{pmatrix} \text{N}$

b $\begin{pmatrix} 77.72 + 0.97D \\ 26.05 - 0.26D \end{pmatrix} \text{N}$

c $100.19 \, \text{N}$

d $2.91 \, \text{m s}^{-2}$

Exercise 12B

1 **a** 3.13 and 2.68

b -0.333 and 5.37

2 **a** $38.3 \, \text{N}$

b $0.255 \, \text{m s}^{-2}$

3 **a** $\begin{pmatrix} 6 \\ 8 \end{pmatrix}$

b $9.90 \, \text{km h}^{-1}$

4 **a** $b_i = a + (b_i \cdot n)n$

b $b_r = b_i - 2kn = b_i - 2(b_i \cdot n)n$

c $\begin{pmatrix} 4 \\ 1 \\ 0 \end{pmatrix}$

Exercise 12C

1 **a** $\begin{pmatrix} 2 \\ 0 \end{pmatrix} \text{m}$

b $\begin{pmatrix} 4 \\ -1 \end{pmatrix} \text{m s}^{-1}, 4.12 \, \text{m s}^{-1}$

c $a = \begin{pmatrix} 0 \\ 6 \end{pmatrix} \text{m s}^{-2}, 6 \, \text{m s}^{-2}$,

$126.9°$

2 **a** $r = (2t^2 - t + 2)i +$
$(-1 + 5t - t^2)j$

    b $9.43\,\text{m}$

3 **a** $v = \begin{pmatrix} 2t + 2 \\ t + 3 \end{pmatrix}\text{m s}^{-1}$

    b $r = \begin{pmatrix} t^2 + 2t + 4 \\ \dfrac{1}{2}t^2 + 3t - 1 \end{pmatrix}\text{m}$

4 **a** $t = 0.5$

    b $76.0°$

    c $r = (t^2 - t + 2)i + (t^3 - 3)j$

    d $t = 2.61$

5 **a** $v = \begin{pmatrix} 3t^2 + 4 \\ 2t + 12 \end{pmatrix}\text{m s}^{-1}$

    b $t = 2\,\text{s}$

6 **a** $r = \begin{pmatrix} 2t^2 - 2.5t + 2 \\ t^3 \end{pmatrix}\text{m}$

    b $v = \begin{pmatrix} 6 \\ 4t - 8 \end{pmatrix}\text{m s}^{-1}$

    c $t = 4\,\text{s}$

7 $4\,\text{km h}^{-1}$, $t = 1.5\,\text{h}$

Exercise 12D

1 **a** $\begin{pmatrix} 0 \\ -9.8 \end{pmatrix}\text{m s}^{-2}$

    b $v = \begin{pmatrix} 5 \\ 2 - 9.8t \end{pmatrix}\text{m s}^{-1}$

      ii $r = \begin{pmatrix} 5t \\ 2t - 4.9t^2 + 1.5 \end{pmatrix}\text{m}$

    c $0.793\,\text{s}$, $3.97\,\text{m}$

2 **a** $v = 4i + (2 - gt)j\,\text{m s}^{-1}$

    b $r = (4t)i + \left(2t - \dfrac{g}{2}t^2\right)j\,\text{m}$

    c $3.40\,\text{s}$

    d $13.6\,\text{m}$

3 **a** $\begin{pmatrix} 12.7 \\ 7.35 \end{pmatrix}\text{m s}^{-1}$

    b $v = \begin{pmatrix} 12.7 \\ 7.35 - 9.8t \end{pmatrix}\text{m s}^{-1}$

    c $0.75\,\text{s}$

    d $r = \begin{pmatrix} 12.7t \\ 7.35t - 4.9t^2 \end{pmatrix}$

    e $2.75\,\text{m}$

    f $19.1\,\text{mg}$

    g $12.7\,\text{m s}^{-1}$

4 $58.9\,\text{m s}^{-1}$

5 **a** $\begin{pmatrix} 5\sqrt{2} \\ 5\sqrt{2} - gt \end{pmatrix}\text{m s}^{-1}$

    b $1.69\,\text{m}$

    c $11.5\,\text{m}$

6 **a** $\begin{pmatrix} 25\sqrt{3} \\ 25 \end{pmatrix}\text{m s}^{-1}$

    b $\begin{pmatrix} 25\sqrt{3}t \\ 25t - \dfrac{g}{2}t^2 \end{pmatrix}\text{m}$

    c $3.11\,\text{s}$

    d $5.18\,\text{s}$, $224\,\text{m}$

Exercise 12E

1 **a** $a = \begin{pmatrix} 4e^{2t} \\ 2e^{2t} \end{pmatrix}$

    b $r = \begin{pmatrix} e^{2t} - 1 \\ \dfrac{1}{2}e^{2t} + 2t - \dfrac{1}{2} \end{pmatrix}$

2 $\begin{pmatrix} 2.5e^{2t} - 0.5t^2 - 5t - 2.5 \\ e^{2t} + t^2 - 2t - 1 \end{pmatrix}$

3 **a** $r = \begin{pmatrix} -2\cos 2t \\ -2\sin 2t \end{pmatrix}$

    b 2

    c Circle of radius 2 with a centre $(0, 0)$

    d $k = -4$

4 **a** $v = \begin{pmatrix} 2e^{2t} \\ 6e^{2t} \end{pmatrix}$

    b $a = \begin{pmatrix} 4e^{2t} \\ 12e^{2t} \end{pmatrix}$

    c $k = 4$

5 **a** e^{-t}

    b Spiral into the point $\begin{pmatrix} 2 \\ 5 \end{pmatrix}$

    c
$$v = \frac{dr}{dt} = \begin{pmatrix} -4e^{-t}\sin 4t - e^{-t}\cos 4t \\ 4e^{-t}\cos 4t - e^{-t}\sin 4t \end{pmatrix}$$

via the chain and product rules.
Write $s = \sin 4t$, $c = \cos 4t$ to simplify the notation. The speed is
$$|v| = e^{-t}\left|\begin{pmatrix} -4s - c \\ 4c - s \end{pmatrix}\right|$$
$$= e^{-t}\sqrt{(-4s - c)^2 + (4c - s)^2}$$
$$= e^{-t}\sqrt{16s^2 + 8sc + c^2 + 16c^2 - 8sc + s^2}$$
$$= e^{-t}\sqrt{17s^2 + 17c^2} = e^{-t}\sqrt{17}.$$

    d $0.693\,\text{s}$

6 **a** $r = \begin{pmatrix} 4\sin\left(\dfrac{\pi}{3}t\right) \\ -4\cos\left(\dfrac{\pi}{3}t\right) \end{pmatrix}$

    b $r = \begin{pmatrix} 4\sin\left(\dfrac{\pi}{3}t\right) + 5 \\ -4\cos\left(\dfrac{\pi}{3}t\right) + 4 \end{pmatrix}$

    c $v = \begin{pmatrix} \dfrac{4\pi}{3}\cos\left(\dfrac{\pi}{3}t\right) \\ \dfrac{4\pi}{3}\sin\left(\dfrac{\pi}{3}t\right) \end{pmatrix}$

Exercise 12F

1 **a** **i** $x = 2e^{4t}\begin{pmatrix} 1 \\ 1 \end{pmatrix} + 4e^{-3t}\begin{pmatrix} -2 \\ 5 \end{pmatrix}$

      ii $x = 2e^{t}\begin{pmatrix} -2 \\ 5 \end{pmatrix} + e^{3t}\begin{pmatrix} 1 \\ 1 \end{pmatrix}$

      iii $x = 3e^{-3t}\begin{pmatrix} 2 \\ -1 \end{pmatrix} - 4e^{-4t}\begin{pmatrix} 1 \\ -1 \end{pmatrix}$

      iv $x = 3e^{-5t}\begin{pmatrix} -1 \\ 3 \end{pmatrix} + 2e^{2t}\begin{pmatrix} 2 \\ 1 \end{pmatrix}$

b **i** $y = x$, $y = -\dfrac{5}{2}x$

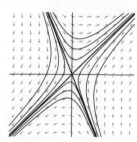

ii $y = x$, $y = 0$

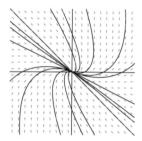

iii $y = -x$, $y = -\dfrac{1}{2}x$

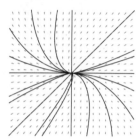

iv $y = -3x$, $y = \dfrac{1}{2}x$

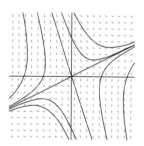

2 **a** D **b** A
c C **d** B

3 **a** $x = Ae^{-t}\begin{pmatrix} -3 \\ 1 \end{pmatrix} + Be^{5t}\begin{pmatrix} 1 \\ 1 \end{pmatrix}$

b Asymptotes are $y = x$ and $y = -3x$. Asymptotic behaviour: $\begin{pmatrix} 0 \\ 0 \end{pmatrix}$ is an equilibrium point, trajectories on the line $y = -3x$ stay on that line and move away from $\begin{pmatrix} 0 \\ 0 \end{pmatrix}$ and all other trajectories move away from $\begin{pmatrix} 0 \\ 0 \end{pmatrix}$ and towards the line $y = x$.

$x = 2e^{-t}\begin{pmatrix} -3 \\ 1 \end{pmatrix} - 3e^{5t}\begin{pmatrix} 1 \\ 1 \end{pmatrix}$

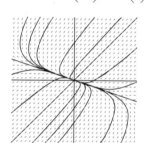

4 **a**
$x = Ae^{-1.45t}\begin{pmatrix} 1 \\ -4.45 \end{pmatrix} + Be^{3.45t}\begin{pmatrix} 1 \\ 0.449 \end{pmatrix}$

b The asymptotes are $y = -4.45x$ and $y = 0.449x$. Asymptotic behaviour: $\begin{pmatrix} 0 \\ 0 \end{pmatrix}$ is an equilibrium point, trajectories on the line $y = -4.45x$ stay on that line and move towards $\begin{pmatrix} 0 \\ 0 \end{pmatrix}$ and all other trajectories move away from $\begin{pmatrix} 0 \\ 0 \end{pmatrix}$ and towards the line $y = 0.449x$.

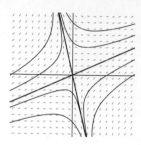

c $x = -0.112e^{-1.45t}\begin{pmatrix} 1 \\ -4.45 \end{pmatrix}$
$+ 1.11e^{3}.45t\begin{pmatrix} 1 \\ 0.449 \end{pmatrix}$

5 **a** When the initial conditions are $x = 0$, $y = 0$, then $\dfrac{dx}{dt} = \dfrac{dy}{dt} = 0$ so trajectory remains at $\begin{pmatrix} 0 \\ 0 \end{pmatrix}$.

b The condition needed is that $\boldsymbol{M}$ has two distinct real eigenvalues.

c False, this is a sufficient condition for a saddle point instead. We need every point near the equilibrium to tend towards it and not just some of them.

6 **a**

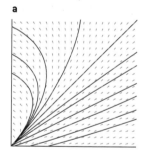

b **i** $\dfrac{dx}{dy} = 0$, $\dfrac{dy}{dt} = 0.1y$,
$y = Be^{0.1t}$ and $x = 0$

ii $\dfrac{dx}{dt} = 0.4x$, $\dfrac{dy}{dt} = 0$,
$x = Ae^{0.4t}$ and $y = 0$

c **i** 2:1 **ii** 2:1
iii 0:1 **iv** 1:1

Exercise 12G

1 **a** **i** $\lambda = \pm i$ **ii** $\frac{1}{2}$

iii

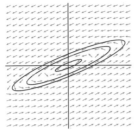

b **i** $1 \pm 2\sqrt{2}i$ **ii** -4

iii

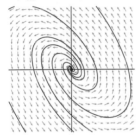

c **i** $\lambda = 0.2 \pm i$ **ii** 5

iii

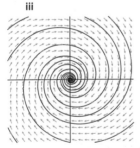

d **i** $\lambda = 1 \pm 5i$ **ii** -5

iii

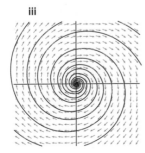

e **i** $\lambda = \pm 3\sqrt{3}$ **ii** $\frac{4}{3}$

iii

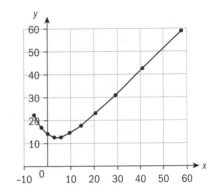

2 **a** $M = \begin{pmatrix} 2 & 1 \\ -1 & 2 \end{pmatrix}$.

$|M - \lambda I| = \begin{vmatrix} 2 - \lambda & 1 \\ -1 & 2 - \lambda \end{vmatrix}$
$= (\lambda - 2)^2 + 1,$

so $\lambda = 2 \pm i$. The real part is positive, so the satellite spirals away from the Earth at $\begin{pmatrix} 0 \\ 0 \end{pmatrix}$ as claimed.

b

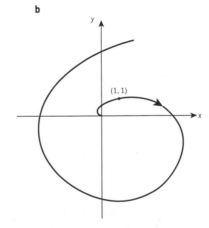

Exercise 12H

1 **a** **i** The formulae from the Euler method are
$x_{n+1} = 1.2x_n + 0.2y_n,$
$y_{n+1} = 0.5x_n + 0.9y_n$

n	x_n	y_n
0	−6	22
1	−2.8	16.8
2	0	13.72
3	2.744	12.348
4	5.7624	12.4852

n	x_n	y_n
5	9.41192	14.11788
6	14.11788	17.41205
7	20.42387	22.72979
8	29.0546	30.66874
9	40.99926	42.12917
10	57.62495	58.41588

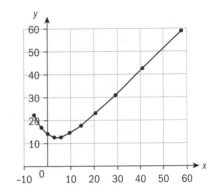

$\frac{y_{10}}{x_{10}} = 1.01$ and when $t = 1$, $x = 108.8$, $y = 110.2$. The Euler method severely underestimates the values of x and y.

ii The formulae from the Euler method are
$x_{n+1} = 1.1x_n + 0.2y_n,$
$y_{n+1} = 1.3y_n$

n	x_n	y_n
0	3	1
1	3.5	1.3
2	4.11	1.69
3	4.859	2.197
4	5.7843	2.8561
5	6.93395	3.71293
6	8.369931	4.826809
7	10.17229	6.274852
8	12.44448	8.157307
9	15.32039	10.6045
10	18.97333	13.78585

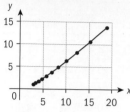

$\frac{y_{10}}{x_{10}} = 0.73$ and when $t = 1$, $x = 25.52$, $y = 20.09$. The Euler method underestimates the values of x and y and also has a slow rate of convergence of $\frac{y_n}{x_n}$ to 1.

iii The formulae from the Euler method are
$$x_{n+1} = 0.8x_n + 0.2y_n,$$
$$y_{n+1} = -0.1x_n + 0.95$$

n	x_n	y_n
0	2	1
1	1.8	0.3
2	1.5	−0.03
3	1.194	−0.165
4	0.9222	−0.2019
5	0.69738	−0.19317
6	0.51927	−0.16632
7	0.382151	−0.13509
8	0.278703	−0.10576
9	0.201811	−0.08075
10	0.145299	−0.06056

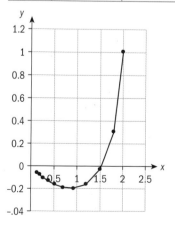

$\frac{y_{10}}{x_{10}} = -0.42$ and when $t = 1$, $x = 0.23$, $y = -0.08$. The Euler is misestimating the values of x and y, although the ratio of $x : y$ is closer to the limiting value of $-\frac{1}{2}$ than for the exact values.

iv The formulae from the Euler method are
$$x_{n+1} = 1.1x_n + 0.2y_n,$$
$$y_{n+1} = 0.3x_n + 0.6y_n$$

n	x_n	y_n
0	1	11
1	3.3	6.9
2	5.01	5.13
3	6.537	4.581
4	8.1069	4.7097
5	9.85953	5.25789
6	11.89706	6.112593
7	14.30929	7.236674
8	17.18755	8.63479
9	20.63326	10.33714
10	24.76402	12.39226

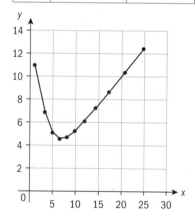

$\frac{y_{10}}{x_{10}} = 0.5004$ and when $t = 1$, $x = 29.54$, $y = 14.84$. The Euler method has some imprecision with the exact values of x, y, although the ratio

converges to the limit of $\frac{1}{2}$ much, much faster than for the exact data.

2 a The formulae from the Euler method are
$$x_{n+1} = x_n(0.9 + 0.2y_n),$$
$$y_{n+1} = y_n(1.2 - 0.1x_n)$$

n	x_n	y_n
0	1	1
1	1.1	1.1
2	1.232	1.199
3	1.404234	1.291083
4	1.626407	1.368002
5	1.908751	1.419109
6	2.259622	1.432058
7	2.680842	1.394879
8	3.160647	1.29991
9	3.666294	1.149036
10	4.142205	0.957573

b The formulae from the Euler method are
$$x_{n+1} = x_n(1 + 0.2x_n - 0.1y_n),$$
$$y_{n+1} = y_n(1 + 0.2x_n - 0.1y_n)$$

n	x_n	y_n
0	1	1
1	1.1	1.1
2	1.221	1.221
3	1.370084	1.370084
4	1.557797	1.557797
5	1.80047	1.80047
6	2.12464	2.12464
7	2.576049	2.576049
8	3.239652	3.239652
9	4.289186	4.289186
10	6.128898	6.128898

3 a The formulae from the Euler method are

$t_{n+1} = t_n + 0.1,$

$x_{n+1} = x_n + 0.1\left(-2t_n x_n + y_n^2\right),$

$y_{n+1} = y_n + 0.1(-3x_n^2 + 3t_n y_n)$

n	t_n	x_n	y_n
0	0	−1	2
1	0.1	0.2	1.7
2	0.2	1.063	1.739
3	0.3	1.927716	1.504349
4	0.4	2.490973	0.524914
5	0.5	2.374356	−1.27358

b The formulae from the Euler method are

$t_{n+1} = t_n + 0.1,$

$x_{n+1} = x_n + 0.1\left(2t_n x_n + y_n\right),$

$y_{n+1} = y_n + 0.1(-3x_n^2 + t_n y_n)$

n	t_n	x_n	y_n
0	0	0	1
1	0.1	0.1	1
2	0.2	0.202	1.007
3	0.3	0.31078	1.014899
4	0.4	0.430917	1.016371
5	0.5	0.567027	1.001319

Exercise 12I

1 a (0, 0) and (1, 2)

b If $P = 0$ then $\dfrac{dP}{dt} = 0$

so $P = 0$ forever and

$\dfrac{dQ}{dt} = Q \Rightarrow Q = Ae^t$

c If $Q = 0$ then $\dfrac{dQ}{dt} = 0$

so $Q = 0$ forever and

$\dfrac{dP}{dt} = -2P \Rightarrow P = Be^{-2t}$

d Approximately 1042 prey and 998 predators

2 a 833 rabbits and 50 foxes

b Both populations are initially decreasing.

c i 50 foxes

ii 833 rabbits

d The computer generated phase plane sketch shows that the population of both rabbits and foxes decreases until we reach 50 foxes, and then the rabbit population starts to increase, followed by the fox population until the fox population recovers to 50. After this, the rabbit population decreases again until we return to the starting populations, and the cycle repeats.

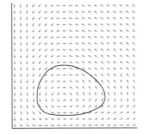

3 a X goes extinct

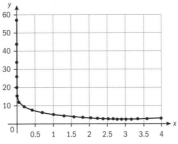

b i $\dfrac{dy}{dt} = 3y$

ii $y = Ae^{3t}$

c When $x = 0$, $\dfrac{dy}{dt} = 0$ and

so $\dfrac{dy}{dx}$ is ill-defined, so the y-axis is an asymptote.

When $y = 0$, $\dfrac{dy}{dt} = 0$ and so

$\dfrac{dy}{dx} = 0$, so the x-axis is an asymptote.

d i $\dfrac{dy}{dt} = \left(3 - x\right)y < 0$

so y decreases and

$\dfrac{dy}{dt} = \left(2 - y\right)x < 0$ so for

a while x decreases also. Thus Y decreases for a while.

ii $\dfrac{dx}{dt} = \left(2 - y\right)x < 0$

so x decreases,

$\dfrac{dy}{dt} = \left(3 - x\right)y > 0$

so y is increasing. Thus X is always decreasing.

e (0, 0) and (3, 2)

f

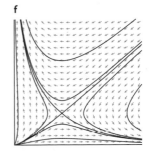

Exercise 12J

1 a $x = 2e^{2t}$

b $x = 4e^{4t} - e^{-t}$

c i

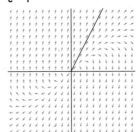

ii

2 **a** $\dot{x} = y$, $\dot{y} = -2x - 3y + 6t + 4$

   b $x = 6.78$

   c $x = 5.854$ when $t = 1.6$

   d $\dfrac{dx}{dt} = 3$; $x = -2 + 3t$

3 **a**

$$\frac{dx}{dt} = y, \frac{dy}{dt} = -2x - 3y + 5\cos(5t)$$

   b x decays in bursts, and then has approximate oscillatory behaviour around 0.

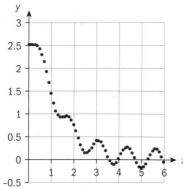

Chapter review

1 **a** $x = Ae^{-3t}\begin{pmatrix}1\\-3\end{pmatrix} + Be^{2t}\begin{pmatrix}1\\2\end{pmatrix}$

   b There is exactly one asymptote, $y = 2x$. $y = -3x$ is not an asymptote.

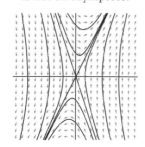

2 **b** $t = 1.5\,\text{s}$

   c Speed $= 2.73\,\text{cm}\,\text{s}^{-1}$

3 **a** $r = \begin{pmatrix}\frac{4}{3}t^{\frac{3}{2}} + t\\ t^2\end{pmatrix}$

   b 2.54

4 **a** (0, 0), (1, 0) and (2, 2)

   b **i** 20 lions, 2023 zebra

      ii 18 lions, 1670 zebra

   c converging to (2, 2) or 20 lions, 2000 zebra. The population will eventually be stable in the absence of any external factors.

5 **a** 49 J

   b $W = \boldsymbol{F} \cdot \overrightarrow{AB} = |\boldsymbol{F}| \times |\overrightarrow{AB}| \cos\theta$
$$= |\boldsymbol{F}| \times |\overrightarrow{AB}| \cos 0 = |\boldsymbol{F}| \times |\overrightarrow{AB}|$$

   c 6 810 000 J or 6810 kJ (to 3 s.f.)

6 **a** $\begin{pmatrix}141\\0\\78\end{pmatrix}$ kN

   b $\begin{pmatrix}4.7\\0\\2.6\end{pmatrix}$ m s^{-2}

   c **i** $r = \begin{pmatrix}2.35t^2 + 55t\\0\\1.3t\end{pmatrix}$

      ii $r = \begin{pmatrix}11760\\0\\4680\end{pmatrix}$ m

7 **a** 20 cm   **b** m

   c $\dot{x} = \begin{pmatrix}-1.26\sin 6.28t\\1.26\cos 6.28t\end{pmatrix}$ m s^{-1}

   d $1.26\,\text{m}\,\text{s}^{-1}$

8 **a** $r_A = \begin{pmatrix}5t\\3t - t^2\end{pmatrix}$, $r_B = \begin{pmatrix}17 - 4t\\5t - t^2\end{pmatrix}$

   b $r_A - r_B = \begin{pmatrix}9t - 17\\-2t\end{pmatrix}$

   c 3.69

   d $a = 13$, $b = 4$

   e 17.1°

9 31.2°   58.8°

Exam-style questions

10 **a** **i** $\boldsymbol{v}(t) = \begin{pmatrix}\frac{t^2}{2}\\4t\end{pmatrix}$

      ii $\boldsymbol{s}(t) = \begin{pmatrix}\frac{t^3}{6}\\2t^2\end{pmatrix}$

   b **i** $\boldsymbol{v}(6) = \begin{pmatrix}18\\24\end{pmatrix}$

      ii $\boldsymbol{s}(6) = \begin{pmatrix}36\\72\end{pmatrix}$

11 **a** 26.4 N   **b** 4.8 N

   c $-15.84i - 21.12j$ N

12 **a** **i** $x = Ae5t + Be-2t$,
      $\dot{x} = 5Ae5t - 2Be-2t$ and
      $\ddot{x} = 25Ae5t + 4Be-2t$.
      Now $\ddot{x} - 3\dot{x} - 10x$
      $= 25Ae5t + 4Be-2t$
      $- 15Ae5t + 6Be-2t -$
      $10Ae5t - 10Be-2t = 0$.

      ii $x = 2e^{5t} - 2e^{-2t}$

   b **i** $x = A + Be^{-3t}$,
      $\dot{x} = -3Be^{-3t}$ and
      $\ddot{x} = 9Be^{-3t}$. Now
      $\ddot{x} + 3\dot{x} = 9Be^{-3t} - 9Be^{-3t}$
      $= 0$.

      ii $x = 3 - 3e^{-3t}$

      iii $x(t) \to 3$ as $t \to \infty$ since $e^{-3t} \to 0$ as $t \to \infty$.

13 **a** $x = 4e^{-t}\begin{pmatrix}1\\1\end{pmatrix} + 2e^{2t}\begin{pmatrix}1\\0\end{pmatrix}$

   b 160, 000 Homosapiens and 15, 000 Neanderthals.

   c **i** $x \approx 2e^{2t}$ as $t \to \infty$

      ii Dies out

14 **a** $a = \begin{pmatrix}315\pi^2 \sin 3\pi t\\-315\pi^2 \cos 3\pi t\end{pmatrix}$ cm s^{-2}

   b $s = \begin{pmatrix}-35\sin 3\pi t\\35\cos 3\pi t + 40\end{pmatrix}$ cm

   c $\begin{pmatrix}-35\\75\end{pmatrix}$ cm and $\begin{pmatrix}35\\75\end{pmatrix}$ cm

   d 90

15 a Both eigenvalues are positive so the solutions move away from 0

b Both eigenvalues are negative and the solutions move towards 0

c Eigenvalues are $2 \pm i$, real part is positive so solutions spiral away from the origin

d Eigenvalues are $-2 \pm i$, real part is negative so solutions spiral towards the origin

16 a $(0, 0)$ and $(2, 1)$

b Euler's method gives
$x_{n+1} = x_n(1.25 - 0.25y_n)$
and $y_{n+1} = y_n(0.5 + 0.25x_n)$
with initial conditions
$x_0 = 1$ and $y_0 = 0.5$.
Tabulating the results below we get approximately 3716 lemmings and 31 owls:

n	x_n	y_n
0	1	0.5
1	1.125	0.375
2	1.300781	0.292969
3	1.530704	0.241756
4	1.820866	0.213393
5	2.178943	0.203836
6	2.612642	0.212955
7	3.126708	0.245571
8	3.716428	0.314743

c It is to 3 decimal places for x and seems a reasonable level of accuracy. However, Euler's method with step size $t = 0.25$ does lead to an unphysical negative value of x_{15}, and is somewhat suspect.

17 Let θ be the angle between a and b, and n a unit vector perpendicular to both a and b, so that $|n| = 1$. We have $a \cdot b = |a||b|\cos\theta$ and $a \times b = |a||b|\sin\theta n$.

Therefore
$$\left(\frac{a \cdot b}{|b|}\right)^2 + \left(\frac{|a \times b|}{|b|}\right)^2$$
$$= (|a|\cos\theta)^2 + (|a|\sin\theta|n|)^2$$
$$= |a|^2\left(\cos^2\theta + \sin^2\theta\right) = |a|^2$$
as claimed.

18 We have
$$\frac{dx}{dt} = 0x + 1y, \frac{dy}{dt} = -cx - by.$$
In the usual notation
$M = \begin{pmatrix} 0 & 1 \\ -c & -b \end{pmatrix}$. Now
$$|M - \lambda I| = \begin{vmatrix} -\lambda & 1 \\ -c & -b - \lambda \end{vmatrix}$$
$$= \lambda^2 + b\lambda + c.$$

Write λ_1 and λ_2 for the roots $\dfrac{-b + \sqrt{b^2 - 4c}}{2}$ and $\dfrac{-b - \sqrt{b^2 - 4c}}{2}$ respectively.

Two eigenvectors that correspond to each eigenvalue are $\begin{pmatrix} 1 \\ \lambda_1 \end{pmatrix}$ and $\begin{pmatrix} 1 \\ \lambda_2 \end{pmatrix}$ respectively, since λ_1 and λ_2 are both roots of the quadratic $\lambda^2 + b\lambda + c = 0$. Then
$$x = Ae^{\lambda_1 t}\begin{pmatrix} 1 \\ \lambda_1 \end{pmatrix} + Be^{\lambda_2 t}\begin{pmatrix} 1 \\ \lambda_2 \end{pmatrix},$$
so that $x = Ae^{\lambda_1 t} + Be^{\lambda_2 t}$ as claimed.

Chapter 13

Skills check

1 2.5 **2** $x \approx 1.39119$

Exercise 13A

1 None of the tables can represent a discrete probability distribution because

a the sums of probabilities is greater than 1;

b -0.2 is not a probability;

c Discrete probability distribution

2 a $P(A = 12) = 0.11$ **b** 0.14 **c** 0.59

d 0.41 **e** 0.281 **f** 7.78

3 a $P(B = 1) = 0.001$, $P(B = 2) = 0.00009999$, $P(B = 3) = 0.0000998$

b To win on your b-th crisp packet, you need to have had $(b-1)$ losses and then a win on the b-th try, so $P(B = b) = P(\text{lose})^{b-1} \times P(\text{win}) = 0.0001 \times (0.9999)^{b-1}$

c $b \in \mathbb{Z}^+$ **d** 0.00099955

4 a

c	1	2	3	4	5
$P(C = c)$	0.07	0.02	0.17	0.46	0.28

b 3.86

5 a

d	1	2	3	4	6	8	9	12	16
$P(D = d)$	$\dfrac{1}{16}$	$\dfrac{1}{8}$	$\dfrac{1}{8}$	$\dfrac{3}{16}$	$\dfrac{1}{8}$	$\dfrac{1}{8}$	$\dfrac{1}{16}$	$\dfrac{1}{8}$	$\dfrac{1}{16}$

b $\dfrac{2}{5}$

6 a $E(M) = \dfrac{3y + 32}{8}$ **b** $y = 8$

7 a

f	0	1	2
$P(F = f)$	$\dfrac{2}{7}$	$\dfrac{4}{7}$	$\dfrac{1}{7}$

b $\dfrac{6}{7}$

8 a i $f(g) = \dfrac{10 - g}{45}$

ii $E(G) = \dfrac{11}{3}$

b $f(g) = 0.2 \times 0.8^{g-1}$

c $E(G) = 5$

9 a

$$P(B \geq x + y \mid B \geq x) = \frac{P(B \geq x + y)}{P(B \geq x)}$$

$$= \frac{1 - P(B \leq x + y - 1)}{1 - P(B \leq x - 1)}$$

$$= \frac{1 - \left(1 - (1-p)^{x+y-1}\right)}{1 - \left(1 - (1-p)^{x-1}\right)}$$

$$= (^1 = 1 - F(y) = P(B \geq y + 1)$$

b $P(B \geq 15 | B \geq 10) = P(B \geq 6)$ means that the process has no "memory". The probability of finding a golden ticket after at least 15 trails given that no golden ticket was found after at least 10 has the same probability as starting over. The same logic works for $P(B \geq 6 | B \geq 1) = P(B \geq 6)$.

Exercise 13B

1 a 0.0535 **b** 0.991

c 0.809 **d** 0.558

e 0.983

f Not independent

2 0.773

3 a $n = 13$, Var $(Y) = 3.12$

b $p = 0.2$ or 0.8

4 a 0.00163

b 0.6785

---

5 a $A \sim B(25, 0.2)$ **b** 0.617

c 0.220 **d** 0.234

e 5. This is the number of correct answers Alex would expect to have if he guesses every question.

f 0.383 **g** 0

h 0.212

6 a $T \sim B(538, 0.91)$

b 9.21×10^{-23}. The probability that all 538 passengers turn up in time to make the flight is negligible.

c 0.000672. It is highly likely that there will be empty seats on the flight.

d $n = 551$

e $n = 591$

f 0.0573; 0.468; it is very

7 a 0.00000750.

b 0.00000750

8 a 0.0504 **b** 1

c 0.00142

9 a 2.25 **b** 1.56

Exercise 13D

1 a 0.5 **b** 0.16 **c** 0.16

d 0.819 **e** 0.00135 **f** 0.857

2 a 0.483 **b** 0.184

c 0.0829 **d** 0.525 **e** 0.887

---

likely that the plane will be overbooked.

7 $p = 0.5$

8 a

Number of 1s thrown	Frequency observed	Frequency expected if fair
0	79	102.4
1	83	76.8
2	9	19.2
3	29	1.6

$O \sim B(3, 0.2)$

b There are significant differences between what is observed from the experiment and what is expected if the dice were fair.

Exercise 13C

1 a 0.0390 **b** 0.414 **c** 0.727 **d** 0.259 **e** 0.184

2 1.20

3 2.99 and 0.179. In both cases, $P(Y = 1)$ is an unlikely event.

4 27 **5** £20420

6

Number of calls	0	1	2	3	4	5 or more
Observed Number of hours	15	30	28	14	7	8
Expected number of hours	14.9	28.7	27.6	17.7	8.48	3.26

This appears to be modelled well by the Poisson distribution except for the frequencies for 5 or more.

3 404

4 0.767

5 a 0.756

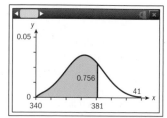

b 384

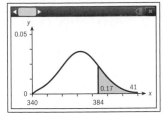

6 a 0.212 **b** 0.959

c 0.0446 **d** 446

7 a 0.170 **b** 21.6

c 15 145

8 35 minutes

9 a Route A is on average shorter, but has more variability so a greater risk of taking longer than route B. Route B takes on average longer but has less variability so the average time is more reliable to predict.

b Route A

c i 0.113 **ii** 0.759

iii 0.101

Exercise 13E

1 a $\dfrac{5}{3}$ **b** $\dfrac{7}{4}$

2 a 2.6 **b** 6.22

3 a 17.02 **b** 31.14

c 2.43 **d** 3.6

e 11.82 **f** 7.0771

4 $a = 1.29, b = -0.07689$

5 $a = 0.165, b = 0.496$

6 $a = 1.29, b = -0.143$

7 a

t	1	2
$\text{P}(T=t)$	$\dfrac{1}{3}$	$\dfrac{2}{3}$

t	3	4	5
$\text{P}(T=t)$	$\dfrac{1}{4}$	$\dfrac{1}{4}$	$\dfrac{1}{2}$

b i $\text{E}(T) = \dfrac{5}{3}$ **ii** $\text{E}(H) = \dfrac{17}{4}$

c $\text{E}(S) = \dfrac{71}{12}$

d

s	4	5	6	7
$\text{P}(S=s)$	$\dfrac{1}{12}$	$\dfrac{1}{4}$	$\dfrac{1}{3}$	$\dfrac{1}{3}$

8 In the first game,

$$\text{E}(Z_1 + Z_2) = \text{E}(Z_1) + \text{E}(Z_2) = \frac{17}{2}$$

and $\text{Var}(Z_1 + Z_2)$

$$= \text{Var}(Z_1) + \text{Var}(Z_2) = \frac{11}{8}.$$

In the second game,

$$\text{E}(2Z) = 2\text{E}(Z) = \frac{17}{2} \text{ and}$$

$$\text{Var}(2Z) = 4\text{Var}(Z) = \frac{11}{4}.$$

Chapter review

1 a $p = 0.25, q = -0.1$ **b** 0.5

2 a

t	4	5	6	7	8	9	10
$\text{P}(T=t)$	$\dfrac{1}{36}$	$\dfrac{4}{36}$	$\dfrac{8}{36}$	$\dfrac{10}{36}$	$\dfrac{8}{36}$	$\dfrac{4}{36}$	$\dfrac{1}{36}$

b 18

3 a 16

b i 0.0309 **ii** 0.03465

iii 0.996 **iv** 0.00617

4 a 0.123 **b** 0.210

c 0.0281

5 a 0.325 **b** 14.8 **c** 81.0

d 0.756 **e** 325

6 a 0.998 **b** 0.000 0313

7 793

8 a C does not follow the Poisson distribution since $\text{E}(C) \neq \text{Var}(C)$, D does not follow the Poisson distribution since its domain does not include values less than 9, E does follow the Poisson distribution and F does not follow the Poisson

Hence Zeinab is correct – since the variances differ, so do the distributions. Also, each game has a different set of outcomes.

Exercise 13F

1 0.7275 **2** 0.1943

3 0.0639 **4** 0.334

5 a 0.5 **b** 0.5

6 a 0.000 878 **b** 0.387 **c** 6

7 0.186

8 Argentina: 0.0161, Egypt 0.000 178

9 25

distribution since $\text{E}(F) \neq \text{Var}(F)$.

b 14 batteries should be in stock

c 2.2888

9 a $\text{E}(T) = 12.04$, $\text{Var}(T) = 16.9$

b 0.8496 **c** 66

Exam-style questions

10 a i 0.15 **ii** 0.4

b 2

11 a 0.1755 **b** 0.4405

c 0.5898 **d** 0.4557

e i 23 **ii** 61

f Does not satisfy Poisson distribution as $\text{E}(Z) = \text{Var}(Z)$

12 a 0.2503 **b** 0.7224

c 19

13 a i 0.6827 **ii** 0.9545

b i 1.6449 **ii** 1.96

14 a 0.8321 **b** 0.1336

15 a 10.57% **b** 0.4575

16 a 6

b Mode occurs at $n = \mu$

17 a i $\dfrac{1}{4}$ **ii** $\dfrac{3}{16}$

b i $\dfrac{1}{4}$ **ii** $\dfrac{3}{1600}$

c 0.1020 **d** 0.1020

e i $T \sim B\left(100, \dfrac{1}{4}\right)$

ii 0.1038

18 a $\dfrac{5}{6}$

b i $\dfrac{5}{3}$ **ii** $\dfrac{5}{9}$

c i $\dfrac{20}{3}$ **ii** $\dfrac{80}{9}$

d i 5 **ii** $\dfrac{5}{3}$

e i $\dfrac{13}{18}$

ii Not true because
$\dfrac{13}{18} \neq \dfrac{1}{\frac{5}{3}} = \dfrac{3}{5}$

Chapter 14

Skills check

1 $P(S) = \dfrac{n(\{1,4\})}{n(\{1,2,3,4,5,6\})} = \dfrac{1}{3}$,

$P(E) = \dfrac{n(\{2,4,6\})}{n(\{1,2,3,4,5,6\})} = \dfrac{1}{2}$,

$P(E \cap S) = \dfrac{n(\{4\})}{n(\{1,2,3,4,5,6\})} = \dfrac{1}{6}$

$= \dfrac{1}{3} \times \dfrac{1}{2} = P(S) \times P(E)$
so independent

2 0.6306 **3** $r_s = 0.7719$

Exercise 14A

1 a 1 **b** 0.99

c −1 **d** 0

2 a $r_S = -0.9636$

b 0.8929

3 a Not appropriate as the plot indicates that the relationship is not linear.

b −0.9605

c Indicates a strong inverse relationship between velocity and force. From the scatter graph we can see that the result is valid, though the actual relationship between the data is lost and when the values for force are very close for high velocities small changes could affect the value of r_s.

4 a $r = 0.6699$, indicates students who do better in Maths tend to do better in English

b −0.942

c Strong inverse relationship between velocity and force.

d From the scatter graph we can see that the result is valid, though the actual relationship between the data is lost and when the values for force are very close for high velocities small changes could affect the value of r_S.

5 a Because the ranks are given rather than quantifiable data

b −0.8857, generally the more expensive ones are preferred

6 a i $r = 0.9462$

ii $r = 0.6021$

b i $r_s = 0.6242$

ii $r_s = 0.4833$

c Spearman's correlation coefficient is affected less than the PMCC by an outlier.

Exercise 14B

1 a $P(X \geq 6) = 0.0386$, $0.0386 < 0.05$, significant so reject H_0

b $P(X \leq 6) = 0.250$, $0.250 > 0.10$, not significant so no reason to reject H_0

c $P(X \geq 9) = 0.149$, $0.149 > 0.10$, not significant so no reason to reject H_0

2 a $H_0: p = 0.6$ $H_1: p < 0.6$

b Critical region is $X \leq 13$

c $13 < 14$, not in the critical region so not significant, therefore no reason to reject H_0.

3 a $X \geq 4$

b Binomial may not be appropriate as tripping on one fence may mean tripping on others more (i.e. not independent)

4 $H_0: p = 0.3$ $H_1: p > 0.3$
Let X be the number of objects remembered $P(X \geq 8) = 0.2277$, not significant so no reason to reject H_0

5 $P(X \geq 2) = 0.0815$, $0.0815 > 0.05$. The result is not significant at the 5% level so there is not sufficient evidence to reject H_0

Exercise 14C

1 a $P(X \leq 5) = 0.276$, $0.276 > 0.05$ not significant so no evidence to reject H_0

b $P(X \geq 10) = 0.0772$, $0.0772 > 0.05$ not significant so no evidence to reject H_0

c $P(X \geq 23) = 0.00588$, $0.00588 < 0.01$, significant so reject H_0

2 $H_0: \lambda = 3.6$, $H_1: \lambda < 3.6$;
$P(X \leq 2) = 0.303$; $0.303 > 0.05$,
not significant so no evidence
to reject H_0 that the mean is
still 1.8 times per week.

3 **a** $H_0: \lambda = 11.0$, $H_1: \lambda < 11.0$

b $X \leq 5$, 3.75%

c A constant rate is
assumed for the Poisson
distribution: this may not
be appropriate as different
games will be different, so
the rate is likely to vary.

4 **a** $H_0: \lambda = 4.0$, $H_1: \lambda > 4.0$; Let
X be the number of cases
of infection. Critical region
is $X \geq 9$.

b Need to assume that
the infections occur
independently

Exercise 14D

1 **a** **i** 0.961

ii p-value $= 0.1789 > 0.1$
so there is insufficient
evidence to reject the
null hypothesis $\rho = 0$

b **i** 0.7246

ii p-value $= 0.103 > 0.1$
so there is insufficient
evidence to reject the
null hypothesis $\rho = 0$

c **i** 0.718

ii p-value $= 0.0860 < 0.1$
so we reject the null
hypothesis that there is
no correlation between
the two variables.

iii $y = 42.8 + 0.521x$

2 **a** $r = -0.901$

b **i** $H_0:\rho = 0$ and $H_1:\rho < 0$;
p-value $= 0.00112$
< 0.05. The result is
highly significant and
so the null hypothesis
is rejected and the
alternative that there is
a negative correlation

between price and
number of sales is
accepted.

ii $s = 20.2 - 2.76p$

iii \$8.19

c

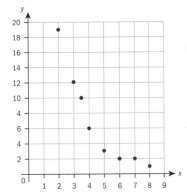

Relationship is not linear
so an exponential or power
regression might be more
appropriate.

3 **a** $r = 0.8683$, highly
significant so reason to
reject the null hypothesis

b $x = 77.7334 + 3.9522y$

c € 192.35

d 35 °C is outside the domain
of the data provided, so
not suitable to extrapolate

Exercise 14E

1 **a** $0.08281 < 0.025$, not
significant so no reason to
reject H_0

b $0.01511 < 0.025$,
significant so reject H_0

c $0.2061 < 0.05$, not
significant so no reason to
reject H_0

2 **a** The sample size is large
enough for the central
limit theorem to apply.

b $H_0: \mu = 24$, $H_1: \mu < 24$

c p-value $= 0.0139 < 0.05$
significant, so reject H_0
that the average coverage
of the paint is 24 m².

d Critical region is
$\bar{X} \leq 23.4766$, confirming
the result of the test

3 **a** $H_0: \mu = 8.3$, $H_1: \mu > 8.3$

b 8.56

c $\bar{X} \sim N(8.3, 0.882)$

d 0.391

e $0.391 > 0.05$ and 0.01 so
the result is not significant
even at the 10% level so
insufficient evidence to reject
the null hypothesis that the
mean time between buses is
8.3 minutes.

f p-value $= 0.391$

g $\bar{X} < 6.46$, $\bar{X} > 9.8448$

Exercise 14F

1 **a** p-value $= 0.100 > 0.05$ not
significant, so do not reject H_0

b p-value $= 0.42104 > 0.025$
not significant, so do not
reject H_0

c p-value $= 0.0239 < 0.05$
significant, so reject H_0

2 **a** p-value $= 0.0288 > 0.05$ not
significant, so do not reject H_0

b p-value $= 0.0331 > 0.025$ not
significant, so do not reject H_0

c p-value $= 0.0476 < 0.05$
significant, reject H_0

3 **a** The sample size is large
enough for the central limit
theorem to apply.

b $H_0: \mu = 28.2$, $H_1: \mu > 28.2$

c p-value $= 0.233 > 0.05$ not
significant, so insufficient
evidence to reject H_0

4 **a** $H_0: \mu = 83$, $H_1: \mu > 38$

b **i** 86.0 **ii** 3.41 **iii** 3.81

c $0.0765 > 0.05$, not
significant so insufficient
evidence to reject the null
hypothesis

Exercise 14G

1 a (10.4, 14.4)

   b (61.9, 62.7)

   c (4.58, 8.02)

   d (2.10, 2.50)

   e (4.47, 4.73)

2 a (10.24, 14.28)

   b (−7.85, 6.89)

3 a i (19.76, 22.64)

      ii (20.30, 22.10)

      iii (20.67, 21.73)

      iv (20.83, 21.57)

   b The larger the sample the smaller the width of the confidence interval.

4 a (11.57, 15.23)

   b The population can be modelled by a normal distribution.

   c 15.3 is outside the range for the confidence interval so is unlikely to be the population mean.

Exercise 14H

1 p-value = 0.251; 0.251 > 0.10, not significant, do not reject the null hypothesis. There is no difference in the weights of the apples.

2 p-value = 0.005 39; 0.005 39 < 0.01, significant, so reject the null hypothesis. Those using the new remedy do lose more weight.

Exercise 14I

1 $\chi^2 = 9.5218 > 9.210$, significant so reject H_0

2 a H_0: GPA is independent of number of hours on social media, H_1: GPA is not independent of number of hours on social media

   b 31.2

3 a Let μ_D be the mean difference. $H_0: \mu_D = 0$ $H_1: \mu_D < 0$

p-value = 0.000127 < 0.05 so the result is significant and the drug has a positive effect.

   b $H_0: \mu_D = 0.7$ $H_1: \mu_D < 0.7$; p-value = 0.0285 > 0.05 so the result is significant and there evidence that the drug has a positive effect.

   c i Yes because there is some good evidence the drug is working

      ii Larger sample, group chosen to eliminate other factors e.g. age, gender.

Exercise 14J

1 0.008 56 < 0.01, significant so reject the null hypothesis that favourite chocolate and gender are independent.

2 a H_0: GPA is independent of number of hours on social media.
H_1: GPA is not independent of number of hours on social media.

   b $\dfrac{85}{270} \times \dfrac{99}{270} \times 270$
$= 31.166\ldots \approx 31.2$

   c Degrees of freedom $(3 - 1) \times (3 - 1) = 2 \times 2 = 4$

   d $\chi^2 = 78.5167$, $P(\chi^2_4 > 78.5167) = 3.33 \times 10^{-16}$

   e 78.5167 > 7.779. Significant so reject the null hypothesis that GPA is independent of number of hours on social media.

3 H_0: number of people walking their dog is independent of the time of day.

H_1: number of people walking their dog is not independent of the time of day.

Either: The χ^2 test statistic = 5.30; 5.30 < 9.488 so the result is not significant so no reason to reject the null hypothesis or: the p-value = 0.257; 0.257 > 0.05

so the result is not significant so no reason to reject the null hypothesis

4 a H_0: the type of degree that a person has is independent of their annual salary
H_1: the type of degree that a person has is not independent of their annual salary.

   b BA earning less than $60 000

   c Combine the first and second row to contain salaries < $120 000

   d p-value = 0.00403

   e 0.00403 < 0.01 The result is significant so reject the null hypothesis that type of degree and salary are independent.

Exercise 14K

1 a

Colour	Frequency
Yellow	120
Orange	120
Red	120
Purple	120
Green	120

   b 4

   c H_0: the colours follow a uniform distribution; H_1: the colours do not follow a uniform distribution; $\chi^2_{calc} = 10.45$ 10.45 > 9.488; The result is significant so reject the null hypothesis that the distribution is normal.

2 a All are 50

   b H_0: the last number follows a uniform distribution; H_1: the last number does not follow a uniform distribution. $\chi^2 = 9.08$, $P(\chi^9 > \chi^2) = 0.4299 \nless 0.1$ not significant so no reason to reject the null hypothesis that the last number on the lottery tickets follows a normal distribution.

3 a

Expected frequency	6.8	68.92	148.56	68.92	6.8

b H_0: the grades fit a normal distribution with mean of 65% and standard deviation of 7.5%. H_1: the grades do not fit a normal distribution with mean of 65% and standard deviation of 7.5%. The p-value = 0.947; 0.947 > 0.10 so the result is not significant and hence there is no reason to reject the null hypothesis that the exam results follow the given distribution.

4 a 21.6, 59.6, 87.6, 59.6, 21.6

b H_0: the heights fit a $N(250, 11^2)$ distribution. H_1: the heights do not fit a $N(250, 11^2)$ distribution. p-value = 0.0906; 0.0906 > 0.05 not significant so no reason to reject the null hypothesis that the sample of elephants was taking from a population whose heights are fit a $N(250, 11^2)$ distribution.

5 a H_0: the scores are normally distributed with mean of 100 and standard deviation of 10. H_1: the scores are not normally distributed with mean of 100 and standard deviation of 10.

b Because if the expected values for the scores outside the range of the observed data are not zero then this would contribute to the test statistic.

c

Score, x	Probability	Expected score
$x < 90$	0.1586	31.7
$90 \le x < 100$	0.3414	68.3
$100 \le x < 110$	0.3414	68.3
$110 \le x < 120$	0.1358	27.2
$120 \le x < 130$	0.0214	4.28
$130 \le x$	0.00140	0.28

d

Score, x	Probability	Expected score
$x < 90$	0.1586	31.7
$90 \le x < 100$	0.3414	68.3
$100 \le x < 110$	0.3414	68.3
$110 \le x$	0.1586	31.7

e 3

f $\chi^2_{calc} = 54.8$ and p-value = 7.61×10^{-12}

58.4 > 6.251 so result is significant and the null hypothesis that the IQs of the students have been taken from this distribution should be rejected.

g **i** Mean is 105.9, standard deviation is 11.7554

ii The data is fairly symmetrical and most of the data is within two standard deviations of the mean which indicates a normal distribution is possible. The high value of the chi-squared statistic is probably due more to the mean and the standard deviation being quite far from those being tested.

iii Redo the test with a different mean and standard deviation.

Exercise 14L

1 a i 0.694, 0.278, 0.0278

ii 173.61, 69.45, 6.95

b H_0: the number of 6s fits a $B\left(2, \dfrac{1}{6}\right)$ distribution (or the dice are fair

H_1: the dice are not fair; $\chi^2 = 28.1 > 5.991$. 28.1 > 5.991, result is significant so there is strong evidence to reject the null hypothesis

2 a

Goals	0	1	2	3	4	5	≥ 6
Probability	0.0907	0.218	0.261	0.209	0.125	0.0602	0.0357
Expected frequency	4.53	10.89	13.07	10.45	6.27	3.01	1.78

b H_0: The number of goals in a football match follows a Poisson distribution with a mean of 2.4.
H_1: The number of goals in a football match does not follow a Poisson distribution with a mean of 2.4. Join together the final three columns to get:

Goals	≥ 4
Probability	0.2213
Expected frequency	11.06

4 degrees of freedom, p-value = 0.770. 0.770 > 0.10, the result is not significant and so there is insufficient evidence to reject the null hypothesis that the sample is taken from a population which follows a Po(2.4) distribution.

3 a 0.0156, 0.1406, 0.4219, 0.4219

b H_0: The number of seeds germinating fit a $B(3.0.75)$ distribution.

H_1: The number of seeds germinating does not fit a $B(3.0.75)$ distribution.

c

Number of seeds germinating	0	1	2	3
Expected frequency	0.78	7.03	21.1	21.1

d 2 as two columns need to be combined to give probability 0.1562 and expected frequency 7.81

e p-value $= 0.01472 < 0.05$ The result is significant so reject the null hypothesis that the seeds fit a $B(3.0.75)$ distribution.

4 a

Number of people	Observed frequency	Expected frequency
0	5	0.90
1	7	3.78
2	6	7.94
3	7	11.11
4	8	11.67
5	6	9.80
6	4	6.86
7	8	4.12
≥ 8	9	3.84

Combine the first three and last two columns.

Number of people	Probability	Expected frequency
≥ 2	0.2103	12.62
3	7	11.11
4	8	11.67
5	6	9.80
6	4	6.86
≥ 7	0.1325	7.95

p-value $= 0.00306 < 0.05$, significant so reject the null hypothesis that the number of people joining the queue follows a $Po(4.2)$ distribution.

b i Mean $= 4.23$, variance 6.81

ii The parameter for the Poisson is the mean and the mean of the sample is close to the mean for the distribution. For the Poisson distribution the mean and variance are close together, that is not the case in the sample which indicates the distribution is not Poisson.

5 a $B(5, 0.25)$

b 118.65, 197.75, 131.85, 43.95, 7.3, 0.5

c H_0: The students are guessing randomly. H_1: The students are not guessing randomly. Combine 4 and 5 to get 0.0157, 7.85. There are 4 degrees of freedom. p-value $= 0.05177 > 0.05$ not significant so insufficient evidence to reject the null hypothesis that the students are guessing randomly.

Exercise 14M

1 a Standard deviation $= 121$

b

Lifespan, h hours	Expected frequency
$h < 1000$	19.7
$1000 \leq h < 1100$	62.0
$1100 \leq h < 1200$	118.3
$1200 \leq h < 1300$	118.3
$1300 \leq h < 1400$	62.0
$1400 \leq h$	19.7

c 4

d H_0: The lifespan of lightbulbs follows an $N(1200, 121^2)$ distribution.

H_1: The lifespan of lightbulbs does not follow an $N(1200, 121^2)$ distribution.

p-value $= 5.83 \times 10^{-7} < 0.05$ This result is significant and so we reject the null hypothesis

2 a $\bar{x} = 1.5319$, $p = 0.5106$

b H_0: The number of boys in a family has a $B(3, 0.5106)$ distribution.

H_1: The number of boys in a family does not have a $B(3, 0.5106)$ distribution.

Expected values:

Number of boys	Expected frequency
0	11.02
1	34.39
2	35.98
3	12.51

Degrees of freedom $= 2$, p-value $= 0.05715. > 0.01$ The result is not significant and so there is not sufficient evidence to reject the null hypothesis

3 a $\bar{x} = 2.85$

b H_0: The number of fish caught has a $Po(2.85)$ distribution.

H_1: The number of fish caught does not have a $Po(2.85)$ distribution.

Expected values:

Number of fish	Expected frequency
≤ 1	17.8
2	18.8
3	17.9
4	12.7
5	7.3
≥ 6	5.6

Degrees of freedom = 4, p-value = 0.677 > 0.05. The result is not significant so no reason to reject the null hypothesis

4 **a** $\bar{x} = 52.6$, $s_{n-1} = 5.15$

b H_0: The weights of the children have an N(52.6, 5.15^2) distribution

H_1: The weights of the children do not have a N(52.6, 5.15^2) distribution.

Expected values:

Weight, w kg	Expected frequency
$w < 45$	14.12
$45 \leq w < 50$	47.58
$50 \leq w < 55$	74.54
$55 \leq w < 60$	48.84
$60 \leq w$	14.92

Degrees of freedom = 2, p-value = 0.000 051 7 < 0.05. The result is significant so the sample is very unlikely to have come from a population with a normal distribution.

c The data has two peaks, which suggests two populations, it is possible that the sample included a mixture of boys and girls.

5 **a** B(50, p)

b $\bar{x} = 1.9 \Rightarrow p = 0.03167$

c H_0: The sample is from a B(50, 0.03167) population

H_1: The sample is not from a B(50, 0.03167) population

Expected values

Number of prizes	Expected frequency
0	12.01
1	19.63
2	15.73
≥ 3	12.63

Degrees of freedom = 3, p-value = 0.0470 < 0.05

The result is significant so reason to reject the null hypothesis

6 **a** H_0: The sample is from a Po(2.0).

H_1: The sample is not from a Po(2.0) population.

Expected values:

Number of calls / 5 minute	Expected frequency
0	8.1
1	16.2
2	16.2
3	10.8
≥ 4	8.6

Degrees of freedom = 4, p-value = 0.01329 < 0.05 significant, so reject the null hypothesis that the data follows a Po(2) distribution.

b $\bar{x} = 2.57$; H_0: The sample is from a Po(2.57). H_1: The sample is not from a Po(2.57) population.

Expected values:

Number of calls / 5 minute	Expected frequency
0	4.6
1	11.8
2	15.2
3	13.0
4	8.3
≥ 5	7.1

Degrees of freedom = 4, p-value = 0.333 > 0.05, hence the result is not significant and there is no reason to reject the null hypothesis.

Exercise 14N

1 **a** The first data shows random error and the second shows systematic error.

b The second data would have a correlation of 1, the first data would be close to but not equal to 1.

c A high correlation normally means a line of regression is useful. In this case the systematic error has resulted in a perfect correlation but the line of regression would be increasingly inaccurate as x increases.

2 **a** $P(\chi_2^2 > 7.0142)$
$= 0.0300 < 0.05$
so significant and the two factors are not independent.

b $\binom{10}{2} = 45$ **c**   0.9006

d Need to know if there are other reasons to suspect the two attributes given in part a were not independent. If there are no other reasons, need to do further tests as not enough evidence otherwise.

3 **a** **i** Taking a random or stratified sample sample. If measuring which school is better it is important the sample is representative of the school.

ii The samples from the two schools should be as equal as possible between girls and boys, so the improvement is due to the teaching method and not to the gender of the student.

iii A sample of girls should be compared with a

sample of boys in each of the schools. The samples could also be pooled so a mixture of boys / girls from both schools. But to avoid the results being affected by teaching methods there should be equal numbers of boys and girls from each of the schools.

b A t-test on the difference between the average improvement in each school to see if there is a significant difference. Assume the populations are normally distributed or the sample size is large enough for the central limit theorem to apply.

4 a Good points include – the census contains details of most of the population, it will be relatively cheap and easy to collect, because it contains other information focused sampling could take place if required.

Bad points include – the data is 6 years out of date, it records who is living in the house on that day so if taken in the holidays might include a lot of students who do not normally live at home.

b i $P(140 \leq X \leq 160)$
$= P(X \leq 160) - P(X \leq 139)$
$= 0.648$

ii 1.00

The survey is almost certain to find the correct proportion to within 0.05, but there is a about a 0.35 chance it will not be within 0.1. If this level of accuracy is

needed more households will need to be surveyed.

c 'Do you have any children who have left school? If so how many live at home and how many live away from home? (A single question such as 'Do you have any children who are still living at home?' is ambiguous as it is answered 'no' both by those with no children and by those with children who are not living at home).

5 a The method of obtaining the sample, to ensure it is appropriate (the two groups are as uniform as possible) and unbiased. The size of the sample to ensure a t-test can be performed (greater than 30).

b Let X be the number of significant results in the 6 tests. $X \sim B(8, 0.05)$. The probability of at least one significant result by chance is $P(X \geq 1) = 1 - P(X = 0) = 0.337$.

Exercise 140

1 a i Two outcomes, each trial independent and identical.

ii Events are independent and occur at a uniform average rate during the period of interest.

iii Data comes from a normal population or the sample size is large

b Chi-squared goodness of fit test

2 a The test involves the sum of Poisson distributions (as total infected equals the sum of those infected by

the individuals with the infection), this assumes the numbers of infections passed on by each of those infected is independent of the others. This is unlikely as they will be moving in close proximity and so may be meeting the same people. A Poisson distribution assumes a uniform rate. This is unlikely, as the days progress more people become infected so the numbers who are susceptible goes down and the rate will decrease. The numbers infected by an individual might not be independent, contact with one person might make contact with a second more likely, for example if a patient is receiving treatment or has plenty of visitors.

b A chi-squared goodness of fit. A significant result might be because the distribution is not Poisson or because the rate of reaction is not r.

3 a Chi-squared or test for $\rho = 0$

b Chi-squared, as we do not know if distance or weekly allowance are normally distributed. If it is suspected they might be normally distributed a test should be done to see.

c The distances and allowances need to be categorised into groups so that the expected values all greater than 5.

4 a Difficult to find parallel forms for questions about food. Test–retest will also indicate any change over time as well as considering the reliability of the data.

b 0.907, which indicates the survey is reliable as a source of information.

c Test 1 quartiles 4.5 and 5.5, median 4.9
Test 2 quartiles 5.2 and 5.7, median 5.5

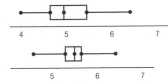

d Boxplots indicate there has been an improvement as the median and lower quartile have improved considerably not much change for upper quartile and maximum score.

e Box plots are reasonably symmetrical so no reason to assume not normal, so reasonable to use the t-test.

H_0: There has been no improvement in the average score awarded to the canteen.

H_1: There has been an improvement.

p-value = 0.00528 < 0.05 so the result is significant at 5% level so significant evidence to say the canteen has improved.

5 a p-value = 0.008783 < 0.05, significant so very strong evidence to reject H_0

b Male/female mix implies that heights are not likely to have been normal.

Females on average shorter than males so extra factor in that has not been tested for. The positive relationship between height and salary might be a reflection on women getting paid less than men. Better to have all female or all male group and alter hypothesis accordingly.

c Group the sample into salary bands and use a χ^2 test for independence between gender and salary.

Exercise 14P

1 a 0.608 **b** 0.281

2 a i 0.0435 **ii** 0.792
b i 0.0386 **ii** 0.9351

3 a i 0.0458 **ii** 0.9245
b i 0.0421 **ii** 0.377

4 a Critical regions $\bar{X} < 48.3$, $\bar{X} > 53.68$

b
$P\left(48.3 < \bar{X} < 53.7 \,\middle|\, \mu = 51.5\right)$
$= 0.9346$

5 a $\bar{X} > 53.121$ **b** 0.322
c Increase the sample size, (or increase the significance level of the test)

6 a H_0: number of people with a car follows a $B(50, 0.3)$ distribution

b Let X be the number of people in the sample who own a car. $X \geq 21$

c i 0.561 **ii** 0.101

7 a The hours chosen for the sample need to be independent. If they were adjacent to each other an event such as a large car crash might cause several of the hours to be larger than usual.

b H_0: $\mu = 82$, H_1: $\mu < 82$

c The mean of the sample is less than 7.5 but the average number of patients has not dropped from 8.2, and so the phone line is continued unnecessarily.
$P(X \leq 75 | \mu = 82) = 0.239$

d $P(X \geq 76 | \mu = 78) = 0.605$. This is the probability of discontinuing the phone line even though it has had a positive effect. This might be justified if it is felt that the reduction is too small to cover the extra costs involved.

8 a H_0: $\mu = 1.2$, H_1: $\mu \neq 1.2$
b 0.05

c Critical regions are $\bar{X} < 1.1562$ and $\bar{X} > 1.2438$,
$P\left(1.1562 < \bar{X} < 1.2438 \,\middle|\, \mu = 1.17\right)$
$= 0.731$

Exercise 14Q

1 a Under the null hypothesis that the shapes are guessed randomly, the probability of 3 correct is $0.2^3 = 0.008$.

b The probability he is quoting is the probability of not getting all three cards right if guessing randomly, not the probability he is not just guessing randomly.

c Other evidence would also have to be taken into account, including how many previous tests this person had taken and the results of those, what other evidence is there for the existence of ESP. The evidence from the test does indicate that he was unlikely to be guessing randomly, but all the alternatives, including the possibility of tricks need to be considered, and the likelihood of each compared.

d

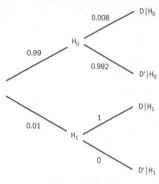

e **i** $P(D) = 0.99 \times 0.008 + 0.01 \times 1 = 0.01792$

ii $P(H_1|D) = \dfrac{P(H_1)P(D|H_1)}{P(D)}$

$= \dfrac{0.01 \times 1}{0.01792}$

$= 0.558$

f **i** The researchers believe that the probability of ESP existing is 0.01

ii $P(D) = 0.999 \times 0.008 + 0.001 \times 1 = 0.008992$

$P(H_1|D) = \dfrac{P(H_1)P(D|H_1)}{P(D)}$

$= \dfrac{0.001 \times 1}{0.008992}$

$= 0.111$

2 **a** **i** Let X be the number of patients in the sample with the infection $X \sim$ B(100, 0.01) $P(X \geq 3) = 1 - P(X \leq 2) = 0.07937$

ii No, more information is needed.

b **i** 0.583

ii The probability of bad practice is just under 60%. Though not significant, further checks might be advisable.

3 **a** $\overline{X} > 4.71$ **b** 0.361

c 0.1089 **d** 0.413

Chapter review

1 **a** −0.9525

b The value is strong and negative – so, the taller the person is the less time they take to run the 100 metres.

2 **a** H_0: The colour of the eggs is independent from the type of hen.
H_1: The colour of the eggs is not independent from the type of hen.

b $\dfrac{30 \times 42}{90} = 14$

c 2

d $\chi^2 = 21.7$, p-value $= 0.0000194$

e $21.7 > 5.991$ or $0.0000194 < 0.05$ so reject the null hypothesis. The colour of the eggs is not independent from the type of hen.

3 **a** Probability of tossing a tail $= \dfrac{1}{2}$, so the probability of tossing 2 tails is $\dfrac{1}{2} \times \dfrac{1}{2} = \dfrac{1}{4}$, $60 \times \dfrac{1}{4} = 15$

b

Number of tails	0	1	2
Frequency	15	30	15

c 2

d H_0: The data fits a binomial distribution.
H_1: The data does not fit a binomial distribution.
$\chi^2 = 1.2$ or p-value $= 0.549$

e $0.1.2 < 5.991$ or $0.549 > 0.05$, so not significant and no reason to reject the null hypothesis that the data fits a binomial distribution.

4 **a** H_0: $\mu_1 = \mu_2$ H_1: $\mu_1 \neq \mu_2$

b two-tailed

c p-value $= 0.3391 > 0.05$, not significant so no reason to reject the null hypothesis that there is no difference between the two groups.

5 **a** (1.3733, 1.741)

b (21.611, 22.589)

6 H_0: $\lambda = 15.0$, H_1: $\lambda > 15.0$; $P(X \geq 19) = 0.181$. $0.181 > 0.05$ not significant so insufficient evidence to reject H_0 that the number of hurricanes is still 7.5 on average.

7 **a** $B(42, 0.82)$ Just two possible outcomes and recovery of patients is likely to be independent of all other patients.

b H_0: $p = 0.82$, H_1: $p < 0.82$

c $X \leq 29$ **d** 2.93%

8 **a** **i** 0.05 **ii** 0, 01

b **i** Critical region $\overline{X} > 32.47$. Probability of a type II error $= 0.623$

ii Critical region $\overline{X} > 33.49$. Probability of a type II error $= 0.840$

c **i** Decrease **ii** Increase

iii Decrease

9 **a** Test–retest means the same test is given to the same people after a period of time. If the test is reliable there should be a good correlation between the two sets of results.

b $r = 0.968$ which indicates that the test is very reliable.

c Let μ_D be average difference between the scores on the first and second tests. $H_0: \mu_D = 0$, $H_1: \mu_D \neq 0$.

p-value = 0.133

Not significant at 10% so no reason to reject H_0 that there has been no increase in the overall level of satisfaction.

Assumptions: The differences can be modelled by a normal distribution and the responses of those surveyed were independent of each other.

Exam-style questions

10 a 0.0626   **b** 0

11 a H_0: favourite TV channel is independent of age, H_1: favourite TV channel isn't independent of age, Degrees of freedom = 4, $P(\chi_4^2 > 21.2774) = 0.000279 < 0.01$, significant so reject the null hypothesis. Favourite TV channel is not independent of age.

b Values are valid as they are all > 5

Expected	Alpha	Beta	Peppa
Up to 5 years old	$\dfrac{60}{200} \times \dfrac{40}{200} \times 20 = 12$	$\dfrac{60}{200} \times \dfrac{70}{200} \times 20 = 21$	$\dfrac{60}{200} \times \dfrac{90}{200} \times 20 = 27$
Between 6 and 10 years	$\dfrac{70}{200} \times \dfrac{40}{200} \times 20 = 14$	$\dfrac{70}{200} \times \dfrac{70}{200} \times 20 = 24.5$	$\dfrac{70}{200} \times \dfrac{90}{200} \times 20 = 31.5$
Between 11 and 15 years	$\dfrac{70}{200} \times \dfrac{40}{200} \times 20 = 14$	$\dfrac{70}{200} \times \dfrac{70}{200} \times 20 = 24.5$	$\dfrac{70}{200} \times \dfrac{90}{200} \times 20 = 31.5$

12 a i 173.75   **ii** 177.8

b 2-sample t-test since variance is unknown

$H_0: \mu_{Welsh} = \mu_{Scottish}$
$H_1: \mu_{Welsh} < \mu_{Scottish}$
$p = 0.0214$

0.0214 < 0.05 so we reject the null hypothesis and conclude that there is sufficient evidence at the 5% level to conclude that Welsh policemen are shorter than Scottish policemen.

c 0.0214 > 0.01 so at the 1% level we would accept H_0.

13 One tailed test. $H_0: \lambda = 20.0$, $H_1: \lambda < 20.0$, assume H_0 is true, then

$$P(X \leq 100) = \sum_{i=0}^{100} \frac{120^i e^{-120}}{i!},$$
$$= 0.0347 < 0.05$$

significant so sufficient evidence to reject H_0, suggesting that Narcissus is exaggerating.

14 a If X has a mean of μ and a standard deviation of σ then the mean of a sample that is sufficiently large (> 30), has distribution $X \sim N\left(\mu, \dfrac{\sigma^2}{n}\right)$

b (4.804, 5.1960)

c 97

15 A paired t-test is used because we wish to directly compare measurements associated with the same cars. Let μ_D be average difference between the scores on the first and second tests.

Differences	0.2	0	0.4	-0.1	0.6	0	0.2	0.1	−0.1	0.3

$H_0: \mu_D = 0$, $H_1: \mu_D > 0$

$$\bar{d} = \frac{0.2 + 0 + 0.4 + \cdots + 0.1 + (-0.1) + 0.3}{10} = 0.16$$

$$s_n = \sqrt{\frac{0.2^2 + 0^2 + 0.4^2 + \cdots + 0.1^2 + (-0.1)^2 + 0.3^2}{10} - 0.16^2} = 0.2154,$$

$$T = \frac{\bar{d}}{s_n \div \sqrt{n-1}} = \frac{0.16}{0.2154 \div \sqrt{9}} = 2.2284$$

$P(t_9 > T) = 0.0264 < 0.05$, significant at 5% so evidence to reject H_0 that front wheels wear at the same rate as the rear wheels.

16 p-value is 0.7996 $\not< 0.05$ so not significant, so not enough evidence to reject the null hypothesis that there is a linear relationship between a female's height and the number of pets she owns.

17 Use a Chi squared goodness of fit test. H_0: toys appear in the colour ratio 3:4:2:1, H_1: toys don't appear in the distribution stated. Degrees of freedom = 3 because once you know three of the probabilities, you know the fourth by definition.

Colour	Blue	Pink	Purple	Green
Observed	32	37	23	8
Expected	30	40	20	10

$$X^2 = \frac{(32-30)^2}{30} + \cdots + \frac{(8-10)^2}{10}$$
$$= 1.2083$$

$$P(\chi_3^2 > 1.2083) = 0.7510$$

$0.7510 \not< 0.05$. Not significant so do not reject the null hypothesis. The colour of the toys follows the stated distribution

Chapter 15

Skills check

1 a $\begin{pmatrix} -1 & -2 & -1 \\ 3 & -1 & 3 \\ -3 & 1 & 4 \end{pmatrix}$

b $\begin{pmatrix} -2 & 3 & -9 \\ -15 & -2 & 6 \\ -6 & 9 & 22 \end{pmatrix}$

2 a $3y = 2x$ Combine with $x + y = 1$ to give $x = 0.6$ and $y = 0.4$

b As an example $P^{10} = \begin{pmatrix} 0.6004 & 0.5994 \\ 0.3996 & 0.4006 \end{pmatrix}$

c 0.4

Exercise 15A

1 All except **c**

2 a

	A	B	C	D	E
A		1	1	1	
B	1			1	
C	1	1			1
D	1		1		1
E					1

b

	P	Q	R	S	T
P		1	1		
Q	1			1	1	1
R	1	1			
S		1			2
T		1		2	

3 a

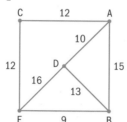

b

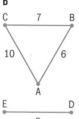

4 a

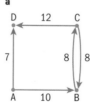

b

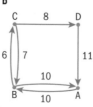

5 a

b

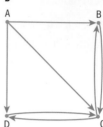

6 a Sheffield to Manchester is 38 miles, Sheffield to Nottingham is 39 miles

b One route from Manchester to Nottingham will be via Sheffield = 77 miles, a route via any town more than 77 miles from Manchester will necessarily be longer.

c

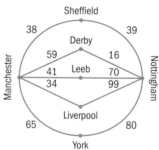

d $38 + 59 + 16 + 39 = 152$ miles

Exercise 15B

1 a and **c** are undirected, **b** and **d** are directed.

2 a i

	A	B	C	D
A		1		
B	1			1
C	1			1
D			1	

ii

	A	B	C	D
A				
B	8			
C	9			4
D		7	5	

b i Strongly connected

  ii Connected but not strongly connected

3 a i

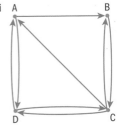

  ii A in-degree 2 out degree 2; B in-degree 2-out degree 1; C in-degree 2 out-degree 3; D in-degree 2 out-degree 2

b i

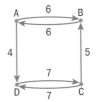

  ii A in-degree 1 out-degree 2; B in-degree 2 out-degree 1; C in-degree 1 out-degree 2; D in-degree 2 out-degree 1

4 A in-degree 1 out-degree 3; B in-degree 2 out-degree 1; C in-degree 2 out-degree 2; D in-degree 2 out-degree 2; E in-degree 3 out-degree 2

5 a

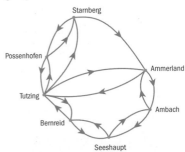

b It is easier to see which towns are connected, and the routes between the towns

c Starnberg and Tutzing and Starnberg and Ammerland

d Starnberg, Ammerland, Ambach

Starnberg Possenhofen, Tutzing, Ammerland, Ambach

Starnberg Possenhofen, Tutzing, Bernreid, Seeshaupt, Ambach

Starnberg Ammerland, Tutzing, Bernreid, Seeshaupt, Ambach

e All, except Starnberg Ammerland, Tutzing, Bernreid, Seeshaupt, Ambach

Exercise 15C

1 a

$$\begin{array}{c} \\ A \\ B \\ C \\ D \end{array} \begin{array}{cccc} A & B & C & D \\ \begin{pmatrix} 0 & 1 & 0 & 1 \\ 1 & 0 & 1 & 1 \\ 0 & 1 & 0 & 1 \\ 1 & 1 & 1 & 0 \end{pmatrix} \end{array}$$

b

$$\begin{array}{c} \\ A \\ B \\ C \\ D \end{array} \begin{array}{cccc} A & B & C & D \\ \begin{pmatrix} 0 & 1 & 0 & 0 \\ 0 & 0 & 0 & 1 \\ 0 & 1 & 0 & 0 \\ 1 & 0 & 1 & 0 \end{pmatrix} \end{array}$$

c

$$\begin{array}{c} \\ A \\ B \\ C \\ D \\ E \end{array} \begin{array}{ccccc} A & B & C & D & E \\ \begin{pmatrix} 0 & 1 & 0 & 0 & 1 \\ 1 & 0 & 1 & 1 & 1 \\ 0 & 1 & 0 & 1 & 0 \\ 0 & 1 & 1 & 0 & 1 \\ 1 & 1 & 0 & 1 & 0 \end{pmatrix} \end{array}$$

d

$$\begin{array}{c} \\ A \\ B \\ C \\ D \\ E \\ F \end{array} \begin{array}{cccccc} A & B & C & D & E & F \\ \begin{pmatrix} 0 & 1 & 0 & 0 & 1 & 0 \\ 0 & 0 & 1 & 0 & 0 & 0 \\ 0 & 0 & 1 & 1 & 0 & 0 \\ 0 & 1 & 0 & 0 & 0 & 0 \\ 1 & 0 & 0 & 1 & 0 & 1 \\ 0 & 0 & 0 & 0 & 0 & 0 \end{pmatrix} \end{array}$$

2 The adjacency matrix consists only of zeros and ones and has zeros on the diagonal.

3 a Sum of entries in either row or column headed by that vertex

  b i Sum of elements in the column headed by that vertex

   ii Sum of elements in the row headed by that vertex

4 a i Everyone knows their own name

   ii It is possible for someone to know the name of someone else without them knowing their name.

  b i 3 **ii** 3

   iii C **iv** E

  c D

Exercise 15D

1 a i 2 ABDA, ADBA

   ii 5 CBAD, CDBD, CDAD, CDCD, CBCD

  b i 1 ABD **ii** 0

  c i 2 ABEA, AEBA

   ii 5 CBED, CBCD, CDCD, CDBD, CDED

  d i 0 **ii** 1 CCCD

2 DA entry in M^2 is 0

3 a i $M^2 = \begin{pmatrix} 2 & 1 & 1 & 1 \\ 1 & 2 & 1 & 1 \\ 1 & 1 & 3 & 0 \\ 1 & 1 & 0 & 1 \end{pmatrix}$

$M^3 = \begin{pmatrix} 2 & 3 & 4 & 1 \\ 3 & 2 & 4 & 1 \\ 4 & 4 & 2 & 3 \\ 1 & 1 & 3 & 0 \end{pmatrix}$

  ii 1

  iii $S_3 = \begin{pmatrix} 4 & 5 & 6 & 2 \\ 5 & 4 & 6 & 2 \\ 6 & 6 & 5 & 4 \\ 2 & 2 & 4 & 1 \end{pmatrix} = 6$

iv S_1 contains 0s but S_2 does not, so diameter is 2

b i
$$M^2 = \begin{pmatrix} 1 & 0 & 1 & 0 & 0 \\ 0 & 2 & 0 & 1 & 1 \\ 1 & 0 & 3 & 1 & 1 \\ 0 & 1 & 1 & 2 & 1 \\ 0 & 1 & 1 & 1 & 2 \end{pmatrix}$$

$$M^3 = \begin{pmatrix} 0 & 2 & 0 & 1 & 1 \\ 2 & 0 & 4 & 1 & 1 \\ 0 & 4 & 2 & 4 & 4 \\ 1 & 1 & 4 & 2 & 3 \\ 1 & 1 & 4 & 3 & 2 \end{pmatrix}$$

ii 1   **iii** 1

iv S_1 and S_2 contains 0s but S_3 does not, so diameter is 3.

4 a 5

b Castlebay, Lochboisdale and Tobermory

c
$$S_5 = \begin{pmatrix} 57 & 2 & 56 & 20 & 10 & 47 & 58 \\ 2 & 3 & 6 & 4 & 8 & 2 & 2 \\ 56 & 6 & 43 & 28 & 8 & 36 & 56 \\ 20 & 4 & 28 & 11 & 14 & 18 & 20 \\ 10 & 8 & 8 & 14 & 7 & 4 & 10 \\ 47 & 2 & 36 & 18 & 4 & 32 & 47 \\ 58 & 2 & 56 & 20 & 10 & 47 & 57 \end{pmatrix}$$

the largest number of trips needed to get between any two of the ports is 5. S_4 has a zero element at Eigg-Tiree intersection, so this is the route that takes five trips.

5 a
$$M = \begin{pmatrix} 0 & 1 & 0 & 1 & 0 & 0 & 0 & 0 \\ 1 & 0 & 1 & 0 & 0 & 0 & 0 & 0 \\ 1 & 1 & 0 & 1 & 1 & 0 & 0 & 0 \\ 0 & 0 & 1 & 0 & 0 & 1 & 0 \\ 0 & 0 & 1 & 0 & 0 & 0 & 1 \\ 0 & 0 & 0 & 1 & 0 & 0 & 1 \\ 0 & 0 & 0 & 0 & 1 & 1 & 0 \end{pmatrix}$$

Town order is Starnberg, Possenhofen, Tutzing, Ammerland, Bernried, Ambach, Seeshaupt

b Starnberg to Bernreid
Starnberg to Seeshaupt
Possenhofen to Seeshaupt
Possenhofen to Ambach
Seeshaupt to Starnberg
Seeshaupt to Possenhofen
Ambach to Starnberg
Ambach to Possenhofen

Exercise 15E

1 a i
$$\begin{pmatrix} 0 & \frac{1}{3} & 0 & \frac{1}{3} \\ \frac{1}{2} & 0 & \frac{1}{2} & \frac{1}{3} \\ 0 & \frac{1}{3} & 0 & \frac{1}{3} \\ \frac{1}{2} & \frac{1}{3} & \frac{1}{2} & 0 \end{pmatrix}$$

ii
$$\begin{pmatrix} 0.2 \\ 0.3 \\ 0.2 \\ 0.3 \end{pmatrix}$$

b i
$$\begin{pmatrix} \frac{1}{2} & \frac{1}{2} & 0 & \frac{1}{2} \\ \frac{1}{2} & 0 & 1 & 0 \\ 0 & 0 & 0 & \frac{1}{2} \\ 0 & \frac{1}{2} & 0 & 0 \end{pmatrix}$$

ii
$$\begin{pmatrix} \frac{6}{13} \\ \frac{4}{13} \\ \frac{1}{13} \\ \frac{2}{13} \end{pmatrix} = \begin{pmatrix} 0.462 \\ 0.308 \\ 0.0769 \\ 0.154 \end{pmatrix}$$

2 a

b
$$\begin{pmatrix} 0 & \frac{1}{3} & 0 & 0 & \frac{1}{3} & 0 \\ \frac{1}{2} & 0 & \frac{1}{2} & \frac{1}{4} & 0 & 0 \\ 0 & \frac{1}{3} & 0 & \frac{1}{4} & 0 & 0 \\ 0 & \frac{1}{3} & \frac{1}{2} & 0 & \frac{1}{3} & \frac{1}{2} \\ \frac{1}{2} & 0 & 0 & \frac{1}{4} & 0 & \frac{1}{2} \\ 0 & 0 & 0 & \frac{1}{4} & \frac{1}{3} & 0 \end{pmatrix}$$

c 0.222

d i B and E   **ii** 18.75%

3 a $T = \begin{pmatrix} 0 & 0.5 & 0.5 & 0 \\ 1 & 0 & 0.5 & 0.5 \\ 0 & 0 & 0 & 0.5 \\ 0 & 0.5 & 0 & 0 \end{pmatrix}$

b
$$T^3 = \begin{pmatrix} 0 & 0.5 & 0.25 & 0.125 \\ 0.75 & 0.125 & 0.375 & 0.625 \\ 0.25 & 0 & 0.125 & 0.125 \\ 0 & 0.375 & 0.25 & 0.125 \end{pmatrix}$$

Hence not possible to go from B to C in 3 steps or from A to A and A to D.

c i $A\left(\frac{5}{19}\right)$, $B\left(\frac{8}{19}\right)$, $C\left(\frac{2}{19}\right)$, $D\left(\frac{4}{19}\right)$

ii $\frac{8}{19}$

d B, A, D, C

4 a

b It would only be possible if George ended on Frances' page, otherwise he would need to visit Dawn's page twice. This is not possible as you cannot pass through all the other pages and end at Dawn's page without repeating some pages.

c Yes, if you begin on Frances' page; Frances, Dawn, Emil, Antoine, Bella and Charles

d
$$\begin{pmatrix} 0 & \frac{1}{2} & \frac{1}{3} & 0 & \frac{1}{2} & 0 \\ \frac{1}{3} & 0 & \frac{1}{3} & 0 & 0 & 0 \\ \frac{1}{3} & \frac{1}{2} & 0 & 0 & 0 & 0 \\ 0 & 0 & \frac{1}{3} & 0 & \frac{1}{2} & 1 \\ \frac{1}{3} & 0 & 0 & \frac{1}{2} & 0 & 0 \\ 0 & 0 & 0 & \frac{1}{2} & 0 & 0 \end{pmatrix}$$

e $\dfrac{85}{648} \approx 0.131$

f $\dfrac{1}{3} \times \dfrac{1}{2} \times \dfrac{1}{3} \times \dfrac{1}{2} \times \dfrac{1}{2} = \dfrac{1}{72}$

g i Most likely to visit Dawn's page

   ii Least likely to visit Belle's page

5 a Because two states are absorbing states and the probability of entering each of them will depend on the starting position.

b 1   c 3

d
$$\begin{pmatrix} 1 & \frac{1}{2} & 0 & 0 & 0 & 0 \\ 0 & 0 & \frac{1}{3} & 0 & 0 & 1 \\ 0 & 0 & 0 & \frac{1}{3} & 0 & 0 \\ 0 & 0 & \frac{1}{3} & 0 & 0 & 0 \\ 0 & 0 & 0 & \frac{1}{3} & 1 & 0 \\ 0 & \frac{1}{2} & \frac{1}{3} & \frac{1}{3} & 0 & 0 \end{pmatrix}$$

e 0.125

Exercise 15F

1 a Minimum weight is 35, AF, FE, FD, DC, AB

b Minimum weight is 67, AB, AF, FE, ED, DC, DG

c Minimum weight is 23, AF, FC, CB, CD, FE

d Minimum weight is 39, AB, BF, FE, BG, FC, CD (or FC, CD, BG)

2 a Minimum weight is 35, EF, FD, DC, FA, AB

b Minimum weight is 67, CD, AB (or GD), GD (or AB), AF, FE, ED

c Minimum weight is 23, BC, AF, FC (or CD), CD (or FC), FE

d Minimum weight is 39, EF, CD (or FB), FB, (or CD), CF (or BG), AB, BG

3 You begin with a single vertex. Every time you add a new vertex to the tree you also add an edge. You need to add $v - 1$ vertices and so the spanning tree will have $v - 1$ edges.

4 a AE, CD, ED (or CB), CB (or ED), AF; $380,000

b i Begin by connecting B and D and apply the algorithm from this point.

   ii BD, DC, DE, EA, AF; $400 000

5 a 75

b 17

c Because it is difficult to check whether adding an edge will form a cycle.

6 a 63

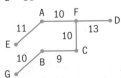

b 10

7 a i

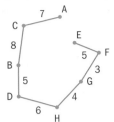

   ii 38

b i 47   ii 41

Exercise 15G

1 a A route is ABFCFEFGBCDEGA, repeated edges CF and EF, weight 103

b A route is ABCDEFBFDBA, repeated edges AB and BF, weight 340

c A route is ABCDEFBECEFA, repeated edges CE and EF (or CB and BF) weight 66

2 a There are two vertices of odd degree

b i $160 + \dfrac{30}{3} = 170$ minutes, GF and FE

   ii because this could be shown on a graph by having two edges between each vertex, and hence every vertex would have an even degree. Any route which traverses each edge of the graph twice e.g. ABCDEFGABGBFBCF CECDEFGA

3 a $59

b The cost will go down as all vertices now have even degree and so no routes need be repeated. There is an additional cost of $7 but a saving of $9. Total cost is $57.

Exercise 15H

1 a HB 4 FD 5; HF 6 BD 5; HD 6 BF 7; repeat edges HB, DI and IF

b BC 8 FE 11; BF 13 CE 13; BE 21 CF 7; repeat edges BC and FE

2 a IF 100 DC 70; ID 110 CF 90; IC 110 DF 70; need to repeat IH, HF, DG, GC; Possible route AIHFHIBHGFE DGCDGCBA, length 650 + 170 = 820

b Either I and C or I and F

3 a Odd vertices are A, B, D and H; AB 38 DH 49; AD 43 BH 73; AH 35 BD 88; need to repeat AB, DG and GH. A possible route is ABCDGABDGFDEFHGHA. Weight is 526 + 38 + 49 = 613 m.

b He would have to repeat BD which is 88 m. Previously he has had to repeat AB and DH which total 87 m

c As he needs to return to A the best place to be picked up is at B so he will only need to repeat DH, so length of repeated roads will be 49 m.

Exercise 15I

1 a i

	A	B	C	D	E
A	0	9	14	8	10
B	9	0	7	4	7
C	14	7	0	6	9
D	8	4	6	0	3
E	10	7	9	3	0

ii Nearest neighbour algorithm gives ADEBCA, actual route is ADEDBCDA, weight = 39

b i

	A	B	C	D	E	F
A	0	6	7	12	10	4
B	6	0	3	8	11	8
C	7	3	0	5	8	5
D	12	8	5	0	7	10
E	10	11	8	7	0	6
F	4	8	5	10	6	0

ii Nearest neighbour algorithm gives AFCBDEA, actual route is AFCBCDEFA, weight = 37

c i

	A	B	C	D	E	F
A	0	6	6	5	4	9
B	6	0	4	6	9	8
C	6	4	0	2	5	4
D	5	6	2	0	3	6
E	4	9	5	3	0	5
F	9	8	4	6	5	0

ii Hamiltonian cycle AEDCBFA or AEDCBFA, routes AEDCB**CFE**A 30 or AEDCF**C**BA 27, weights 30 or 27, 27 is the better upper bound

d i

	A	B	C	D	E
A	0	40	45	25	10
B	40	0	25	15	30
C	45	25	0	20	35
D	25	15	20	0	15
E	10	30	35	15	0

ii Hamiltonian cycle AEDBCA, route AEDBC**DE**A, weight 110

2 a Because it does not follow the triangle inequality the upper bound produced by the NNA is far higher than the solution to the TSP.

b Once the algorithm reaches E it is not possible to directly reach another vertex that has not already been passed.

Exercise 15J

1 a i 30

ii Deleting D gives a lower bound of 32

iii The solution to the TSP is between 30 and 39

b i 29

ii Deleting D or E will give a lower bound of 30, deleting C will give a lower bound of 31

iii Solution to the TSP is between 30 or 31 and 37

c i 22

ii Deleting B will give a lower bound of 23, and deleting C gives a lower bound of 24

iii Solution to the TSP is between 23 or 24 and 27

d i 85

ii Deleting D gives a lower bound of 95

iii Solution to the TSP is between 95 and 110

2 a Lower bound is 115

b

	A	B	C	D	E
A	0	35	20	25	10
B	35	0	25	35	15
C	20	25	0	30	10
D	25	35	30	0	20
E	10	15	10	20	0

c AEC**EB**EDA 105

d Lower than lower bound; because shortest route between adjacent vertices is not always the direct route (the triangle inequality does not hold on the graph)

3 52 hours

4 a ADBCEA upper bound = 23 min

b Deleting A or E gives a lower bound of 21 minutes

c The minimum weight of two of the edges adjacent to C is 9 and the minimum weight of the two edges adjacent to E is 11. This adds up to 20. Five edges are needed for a cycle and as the smallest is 3 then the solution to the TSP must be at least 23.

d Start at A and move to the nearest vertex which has not already been visited but not B. When all other vertices have been visited go to B then to A. An alternative is to go to B first and then use the NNA as usual. The route would then be the reverse of the one obtained.

Chapter review

1 a There are two odd vertices, C and F

b e.g. CDECBEFBAF

2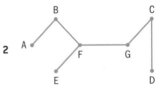

Order of edge selection: EF(CD), CD(EF), CG, BF, FG(AB), AB(FG); total weight 21

3 Possible route ABCDEAEDFEB-FCA. Repeat AE and ED. Total weight 472

4 a i No, it is not symmetric

ii No, it contains multiple edges

iii No, for example, there is no edge between A and E

iv No, it contains a circuit, for example BCB

b A4, B3, C4, D4, E1

c i No, it has a vertex of degree 1

ii No, not all vertices are even

iii Yes, it has 2 odd vertices

d No, there is no walk of length 1 or length 2 between B and E. The matrix $M + M^2$ has zero entries for these values.

5 a Total weight 65

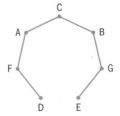

b $65 + 9 + 11 = 85$

6 a i The graph is complete.

ii

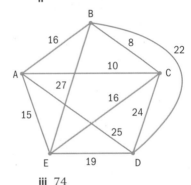

iii 74

b i Weight is 43

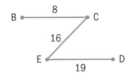

ii 68

7 a i Yes, as the edges are directed.

ii No, as it contains a loop.

iii Yes, as it contains a circuit that includes all the vertices.

b

	A	B	C	D
In-degree	2	2	1	1
Out-degree	2	1	1	2

c i No

ii For each vertex the in-degree must equal the out-degree

iii Yes, DAABCDB

iv All vertices must have in-degree equal to out-degree except for one vertex which has an out-degree one more than its in-degree and another vertex which has an in-degree one more than its out-degree.

d

$$\begin{array}{c} \\ A \\ B \\ C \\ D \end{array} \begin{array}{cccc} A & B & C & D \end{array}$$

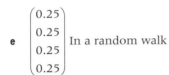

e $\begin{pmatrix} 0.25 \\ 0.25 \\ 0.25 \\ 0.25 \end{pmatrix}$ In a random walk

approximately equal amounts of time will be spent at each vertex.

8 a C, D, F, G

b CD and FG $1 + 4 = 5$; CF and DG $5 + 4 = 9$; CG and DF $5 + 4 = 8$; possible walk is ABCDCEDGEFEGBFA; weight is 32

c 28: begin at F and end at G, or begin at G and end at F

9 a The cycle would have to pass through vertex C twice to return to the starting point.

b For example ABCDE

c

	A	B	C	D	E
A	-	13	5	12	9
B	13	-	8	22	12
C	5	8	-	7	16
D	12	15	7	-	10
E	9	12	16	10	-

d ACDEBA **e** 3

10 a Every vertex is of even order.

b One possibility is ACEFDEBDCBA

11 a AF, AB, BC, DF, DE; 17

b Algorithm attempts to find the 'optimum choice' at each stage

12 a EG, EF, BD, AC, CE, DG

b £6700

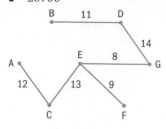

13 a E.g. FEDBAC

b For a Eulerian circuit, all vertices must be even, and there are two odd vertices here (B and E).

c BF, EF, AB or AC: This would then leave a vertex of degree 1, so no Hamiltonian cycle would be possible.

14 Weight of route is 48. One possible route is AFACABFEBCDEDA

15 a

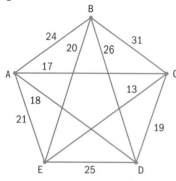

b CE, AC, AD, BE **c** 68

16 a $M = \begin{pmatrix} 0 & 1 & 0 & 0 \\ 1 & 0 & 1 & 1 \\ 0 & 1 & 0 & 0 \\ 0 & 0 & 1 & 0 \end{pmatrix}$

b i $M^3 = \begin{pmatrix} 0 & 2 & 1 & 0 \\ 2 & 1 & 2 & 2 \\ 0 & 2 & 1 & 0 \\ 1 & 0 & 1 & 1 \end{pmatrix}$

ii 1

c i $= \begin{pmatrix} 1 & 3 & 2 & 1 \\ 3 & 3 & 4 & 3 \\ 1 & 3 & 2 & 1 \\ 1 & 1 & 2 & 1 \end{pmatrix}$

ii 4

iii $B \to C$, $B \to D \to C$, $B \to A \to B \to C$, $B \to C \to B \to C$

17 a $T = \begin{pmatrix} 0 & \frac{1}{3} & 0 & \frac{1}{2} \\ \frac{1}{2} & 0 & 1 & 0 \\ 0 & \frac{1}{3} & 0 & \frac{1}{2} \\ \frac{1}{2} & \frac{1}{3} & 0 & 0 \end{pmatrix}$

b $T^3 = \begin{pmatrix} \frac{1}{12} & \frac{1}{4} & \frac{1}{6} & \frac{3}{8} \\ \frac{5}{8} & \frac{1}{4} & \frac{1}{2} & 0 \\ \frac{1}{12} & \frac{1}{4} & \frac{1}{6} & \frac{3}{8} \\ \frac{5}{24} & \frac{1}{4} & \frac{1}{6} & \frac{1}{4} \end{pmatrix}$

c $\begin{pmatrix} 0.222 \\ 0.333 \\ 0.222 \\ 0.222 \end{pmatrix}$

d After a large amount of time, a ship is more likely to be based at port B, hence it would likely make the best place for the company's headquarters.

18 a

	A	B	C	D	E	F	G
A	0	4	5	10	9	9	3
B	4	0	3	8	5	5	5
C	5	3	0	5	8	8	2
D	10	8	5	0	6	13	7
E	6	5	8	6	0	7	10
F	9	5	8	13	7	0	10
G	3	5	2	7	10	10	0

b AGCBFEDA

c AGCBFEDCGA

19 a $\begin{pmatrix} 0 & 0 & 0 & \frac{1}{3} & 0 \\ \frac{1}{2} & 0 & \frac{1}{2} & \frac{1}{3} & \frac{1}{2} \\ 0 & \frac{1}{2} & 0 & \frac{1}{3} & 0 \\ 0 & 0 & \frac{1}{2} & 0 & \frac{1}{2} \\ \frac{1}{2} & \frac{1}{2} & 0 & 0 & 0 \end{pmatrix}$

b A = 4 min, B = 19 min, C = 13 min, D = 13 min, E = 11 min

20 a $M = \begin{pmatrix} 0 & 1 & 1 & 0 & 0 \\ 1 & 0 & 0 & 0 & 0 \\ 0 & 1 & 0 & 1 & 0 \\ 0 & 0 & 0 & 0 & 1 \\ 1 & 0 & 1 & 0 & 0 \end{pmatrix}$

b i $M^7 = \begin{pmatrix} 6 & 8 & 7 & 3 & 2 \\ 5 & 4 & 3 & 2 & 2 \\ 5 & 9 & 5 & 5 & 1 \\ 5 & 6 & 3 & 3 & 3 \\ 9 & 8 & 8 & 3 & 3 \end{pmatrix}$

Therefore the required journey is from C to E since there is only one element of '1' here.

ii CBABACDE

21 a AB, DF; Weight of route = 64

b One possible route is ACBABDCGFDFEDA

c If Nasson starts at F, the only possible routes that need to be repeated will either be AB (= 6), BD (= BC + CD = 3) or AD (= 5). BD is the shortest, so this should be repeated. Therefore, given Nasson starts at F, he should finish at A.

22 a Order is ABCDEA. Upper bound is 81.

b By deleting A, Kruskal gives MST for the remainder as BC, CD, CE; weight = 43, lower bound = 75

c By deleting B, Kruskal gives MST for the remainder as CD, CE, CA; weight 47. Lower bound is therefore 47 + (13 + 15) = 75.

d $75 \le L \le 81$

e E.g. tour for original upper bound: ABCDEA

Index